Essentials of
Oceanography

Essentials of
Oceanography

TENTH EDITION

Alan P. Trujillo

DISTINGUISHED TEACHING PROFESSOR
PALOMAR COLLEGE

Harold V. Thurman

PROFESSOR EMERITUS
MT. SAN ANTONIO COLLEGE

PHI Learning Private Limited

New Delhi-110001
2012

This Indian Reprint—₹ 895.00
(Original U.S. Edition—₹ 6953.00)

ESSENTIALS OF OCEANOGRAPHY, 10th ed.
by Alan P. Trujillo and Harold V. Thurman

Original edition, entitled *Essentials of Oceanography, 10th ed.* by Alan P. Trujillo and Harold V. Thurman, published by Pearson Education, Inc., publishing as Pearson Prentice Hall.

ISBN-978-81-203-4414-3

Cover Photograph: *estockphoto, Egypt, Red Sea, Manta Ray*

Indian edition published by PHI Learning Private Limited.

This edition is manufactured in India, and is authorized for sale in India, Pakistan, Sri Lanka, Bhutan, Bangladesh, Nepal and the Maldives only.

Published by Asoke K. Ghosh, PHI Learning Private Limited, M-97, Connaught Circus, New Delhi-110001 and Printed by Replika Press Pvt. Ltd., EPIP, Kundli, Haryana-131028.

To my loyal and faithful companion
Hawthorn
—Al Trujillo

For Deb and Bill
—Hal Thurman

ABOUT THE AUTHORS

ALAN P. TRUJILLO Al Trujillo is a professor in the Earth, Space, and Aviation Sciences Department at Palomar College in San Marcos, California. He received his bachelor's degree in geology from the University of California at Davis and his master's degree in geology from Northern Arizona University, afterwards working for several years in industry as a developmental geologist, hydrogeologist, and computer specialist. Al began teaching at Palomar in 1990. In 1997, he was awarded Palomar's Distinguished Faculty Award for Excellence in Teaching and in 2005 he received Palomar's Faculty Research Award. He has co-authored *Introductory Oceanography* with Hal Thurman and is a contributing author for the textbooks *Earth* and *Earth Science*. In addition to writing and teaching, Al works as a naturalist and lecturer aboard natural history expedition vessels in Alaska and the Sea of Cortez/Baja California. His research interests include beach processes, sea cliff erosion, and computer applications in oceanography. As a hobby, he collects sand and is a member of the International Sand Collectors Society; he also serves as the organization's Oceanography Division Advisor. Al and his wife, Sandy, have two children, Karl and Eva.

HAROLD V. THURMAN Hal Thurman retired in May 1994, after 24 years of teaching in the Earth Sciences Department at Mt. San Antonio College in Walnut, California. Interest in geology led to a bachelor's degree from Oklahoma A&M University, followed by seven years working as a petroleum geologist, mainly in the Gulf of Mexico, where his interest in the oceans developed. He earned a master's degree from California State University at Los Angeles and then joined the Earth Sciences faculty at Mt. San Antonio College. Other books that Hal has co-authored include *Introductory Oceanography* with Alan Trujillo as well as a marine biology textbook. He has also written articles on the Pacific, Atlantic, Indian, and Arctic Oceans for the 1994 edition of *World Book Encyclopedia* and served as a consultant on the National Geographic publication *Realms of the Sea*. He still enjoys going to sea on vacations with his wife, Iantha.

BRIEF CONTENTS

CONTENTS

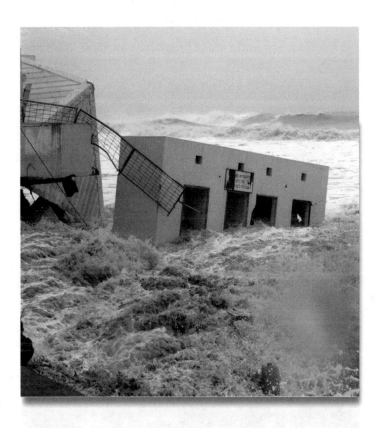

10 THE COAST: BEACHES AND SHORELINE PROCESSES 284

11 THE COASTAL OCEAN 312

12 MARINE LIFE AND THE MARINE ENVIRONMENT 344

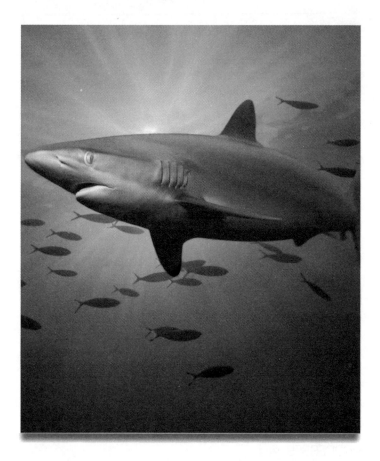

PREFACE

"The sea, once it casts its spell, holds one in its net of wonder forever."

—*Jacques-Yves Cousteau,
oceanographer, underwater videographer,
and explorer (circa 1963)*

To the Student

Welcome! You're about to embark on a journey that is far from ordinary. Over the course of this term, you will discover the central role the oceans play in the vast global system of which you are a part.

This book's content was carefully developed to provide a foundation in science by examining the vast body of oceanic knowledge. This knowledge includes information from a variety of scientific disciplines—geology, chemistry, physics, and biology—as they relate to the oceans. However, no formal background in any of these disciplines is required to successfully master the subject matter contained within this book. Our desire is to have you take away from your oceanography course much more than just a collection of facts. Instead, we want you to develop a fundamental understanding of how the oceans work or why the oceans behave the way that they do.

This book is intended to help you in your quest to know more about the oceans. Taken as a whole, the components of the ocean—its sea floor, chemical constituents, physical components, and life forms—comprise one of Earth's largest interacting, interrelated, and interdependent systems. Because humans are beginning to impact Earth systems, it is important to understand not only how the oceans operate, but also how the oceans interact with Earth's other systems (such as its atmosphere, biosphere, and hydrosphere) as part of a larger picture. Thus, this book uses a systems approach to highlight the interdisciplinary relationships among oceanographic phenomena and how those phenomena affect other Earth systems.

To that end—and to help you make the most of your study time—we focused the presentation in this book by organizing the material around three essential components:

1. **Concepts:** General ideas derived or inferred from specific instances or occurrences (for instance, the concept of density can be used to explain why the oceans are layered).

2. **Processes:** Actions or occurrences that bring about a result (for instance, the process of waves breaking at an angle to the shore results in the movement of sediment along the shoreline).

3. **Principles:** Rules or laws concerning the functioning of natural phenomena or mechanical processes (for instance, the principle of sea floor spreading suggests that the geographic positions of the continents have changed through time).

Interwoven within these concepts, processes, and principles are hundreds of photographs, illustrations, real-world examples, and applications that make the material relevant and accessible (and maybe sometimes even *entertaining*) by bringing the science to life.

Ultimately, it is our hope that by understanding how the oceans work, you will develop a new awareness and appreciation of all aspects of the marine environment and its role in Earth systems. To this end, the book has been written for you, the student of the oceans. So enjoy and immerse yourself! You're in for an exciting ride.

Al Trujillo
Harold Thurman

To the Instructor

The tenth edition of *Essentials of Oceanography* is designed to accompany an introductory college-level course in oceanography taught to students with no formal background in mathematics or science. As in previous editions, the goal of this edition of the textbook is to clearly present the relationships of scientific principles to ocean phenomena in an engaging and meaningful way.

This edition has greatly benefited from being thoroughly reviewed by hundreds of students who made numerous suggestions for improvement. A few comments by former students about the book include, *"I really enjoyed the textbook we read as part of the class. As a student, I found it not only easier to read but also a lot more informative than other textbooks. The authors of the book seemed to have a lot more human qualities about them than the authors of other textbooks I've read. This makes reading* Essentials of Oceanography *entertaining at times."* and *"What I really liked about the book is that it's a welcoming textbook—open and airy. You could almost read it at bedtime like a story because of all the interesting pictures."*

This edition has been reviewed in detail by a host of instructors from leading institutions across the country. As one reviewer of the ninth edition remarked, *"The textbook does an outstanding job of distilling down complicated topics in astronomy, geology, chemistry, and physics, all of which are incorporated in the field of oceanography, that are easily understandable by students taking an introductory course in the subject. Even for those who do not have a strong science background, the plentiful figures present each topic very clearly."*

The 16-chapter format of this textbook is designed for easy coverage of the material in a 15- or 16-week semester. For courses taught on a 10-week quarter system, instructors may need to select those chapters that cover the topics and concepts of primary relevance to their course. Chapters are self-contained and can thus be covered in any order. Following the introductory chapter (Chapter 1, which covers the general geography of the oceans; a historical perspective of oceanography; the reasoning behind the scientific method; and a discussion of the origin of Earth, the atmosphere, the oceans, and life itself), the four major academic disciplines of oceanography are represented in the following chapters:

- Geological oceanography (Chapters 2, 3, 4, and parts of Chapters 10 and 11)
- Chemical oceanography (Chapter 5 and part of Chapter 11)
- Physical oceanography (Chapters 6-9 and parts of Chapters 10 and 11)
- Biological oceanography (Chapters 12–15)

One of the most significant additions to the book is a new interdisciplinary chapter "The Oceans and Climate Change" (Chapter 16), which focuses on the important environmental issue of human-caused global climate change and its impact on the ocean.

We strongly believe that oceanography is at its best when it links together several scientific disciplines and shows how they are interrelated in the oceans. Therefore, this interdisciplinary approach is a key element of every chapter.

What's New in This Edition?

Changes in this edition are designed to increase the readability, relevance, and appeal of this book. Major changes include the following:

- The new chapter "The Oceans and Climate Change" (Chapter 16), which includes content that was previously included in Chapters 5, 6, 7, and 10; in addition, it presents some of the latest scientific findings about human-caused climate change and its impact on the ocean
- Incorporation of comments from hundreds of students who thoroughly reviewed and edited the previous edition in small focus group discussions and one-on-one meetings with author Al Trujillo
- A new feature called "Chapter at a Glance" at the beginning of each chapter that focuses attention on the most important concepts covered within each chapter
- The geoscience animations library, which is a suite of 45 state-of-the-art computer animations that have been created by Al Trujillo and a panel of geoscience educators to help students visualize some of the most challenging oceanographic concepts
- Addition of seven new oceanographic animations that have been specifically designed for this edition
- Inclusion of new Web Videos, which are an extensive suite of hand-selected short video clips available online that show oceanographic processes in action
- Addition of Encounter Earth activities that illustrate interesting oceanographic features with interactive online maps
- Updating of information throughout the text to include some of the most recent developments in oceanography, such as recent satellite missions and deep-ocean observations

- Greater emphasis on the ocean's role in Earth systems
- Feature boxes—several of them new—reorganized around the following four themes:

  - HISTORICAL FEATURES: These boxes focus on historical developments in oceanography that tie into chapter topics.
  - RESEARCH METHODS IN OCEANOGRAPHY: These boxes highlight how oceanographic knowledge is obtained.
  - OCEANS AND PEOPLE: These boxes illustrate the interaction of humans and the ocean environment.
  - FOCUS ON THE ENVIRONMENT: These boxes emphasize environmental issues, which are an increasingly important component of the book.

- Addition of several new tables that better organize and summarize important data
- New Web boxes and Web tables on the Online Study Guide that contain some of the existing boxes and summary tables from the previous edition to reduce the length of the book
- Addition of an extensive array of updated photos and illustrations to improve the illustration package and make the figures more consistent throughout
- Standardization of all graphs throughout the text to make the data easier to read and understand
- Thoroughly reviewed and edited text in all chapters, in a continued effort to refine the style and clarity of the writing
- A detailed list of specific chapter-by-chapter changes is available at http://daphne.palomar.edu/atrujillo.

In addition, this edition continues to offer some of the previous edition's most popular features, including the following:

- Extensive rigor and depth of material
- "Students Sometimes Ask . . ." questions, which contain actual student questions along with the authors' answers
- Use of the international metric system (Système International [SI] units), with comparable English system units in parentheses
- Explanation of word etymons (*etumon* = sense of a word) as new terms are introduced, in an effort to demystify scientific terms by showing what the terms actually mean
- Use of **bold print** on key terms, which are defined when they are introduced and are included in the glossary
- "Key Concept" statements that denote important concepts as they are discussed in each chapter
- A "Chapter in Review" summary at the end of each chapter
- End-of-chapter "Review Questions" and "Critical Thinking Exercises" to help students test their knowledge
- An Online Study Guide (http://www.mygeoscienceplace .com) that features chapter-specific learning objectives, online quizzes including critical thinking exercises, animations, Web videos, and relevant Internet links

The New Instructional Package
For the Student

- The student-friendly **Premium Online Study Guide with eText** (http://www.mygeoscienceplace.com), which is designed to function as a study tool, a one-stop source for additional oceanographic resources including visualizations, and a launching pad for further exploration. Content for the site was written by author Al Trujillo and is tied, chapter-by-chapter, to the text.

  - *To help students understand difficult concepts:* The site contains **student animations**—a suite of 45 animations that aid in visualizing complex oceanographic concepts and processes. These animations have been specifically crafted by a team of geoscience educators to aid student learning by allowing the user to control the action. For example, students can fully examine how an animation develops by replaying it, controlling its pace, and stopping and starting the animation anywhere in its sequence. In order to facilitate effective study, Al Trujillo has written accompanying narrations for each animation.

  - *To aid in reviewing the text material:* The site contains several **self-testing modules**, including multiple choice and true/false, multiple answer, and image-labeling exercises. Answers, once submitted, are automatically graded for instant feedback.

  - *To encourage and enable further exploration:* Every chapter contains both **general and chapter-specific annotated links** to some of the best oceanography sites on the World Wide Web. Students can also subscribe to **RSS feeds** to stay up-to-date on oceanographic discoveries. **Web videos** contain some of the best short video clips of oceanographic processes in action.

For the Instructor

- **Instructor Manual with Test Bank** The Instructor Manual contains learning objectives, chapter outlines, answers to end-of-chapter questions, and suggested short demonstrations to spice up your lectures. The Test Bank incorporates art and averages 75 multiple-choice, true/false, short-answer, and critical-thinking questions per chapter.

- **Instructor Resource Center (IRC) on DVD** The IRC puts all of your lecture resources in one easy-to-reach place:

  - *Animations:* An extensive collection of 45 animations—7 of them new—from the Prentice Hall Geoscience Animation Library can be shown in class to help students understand some of the most difficult-to-visualize topics of oceanography. These animations are provided both as Flash files and preloaded into PowerPoint slides.

  - *PowerPoint presentations:* The IRC makes available three PowerPoint files for each chapter. Cut down on your preparation time, no matter what your lecture needs:
    1. **Exclusively art:** This file provides all the photos, art, and tables from the text, in order, loaded into Power-Point slides.
    2. **Lecture outline:** This file averages 35 slides per chapter and includes customizable lecture outlines with supporting art.
    3. **Classroom Response System (CRS) questions:** Authored for use in conjunction with classroom response systems, this PowerPoint allows you to electronically poll your class for responses to questions, pop quizzes, attendance, and more.

  - *Transparency acetates:* Provided electronically, every table and most of the illustrations in this edition are available to be printed out as full-color, projection-enhanced transparencies.

  - *TestGen:* You can use this electronic version of the TestBank to build and customize your tests. You can create multiple versions, add or edit questions, and add illustrations; this powerful software easily addresses your customization needs.

Acknowledgments

We are indebted to many individuals for their helpful comments and suggestions during the revision of this book. Al Trujillo is indebted to his colleagues at Palomar Community College for their keen interest in the project, for allowing him to use some of their creative ideas in the book, and for continuing to provide valuable feedback. They are simply the finest colleagues imaginable. A particularly big thank you goes to Patty Deen for her continuing support and for recognizing the contribution the book makes to the Oceanography Program at Palomar.

Adam Petrusek of Charles University, Prague, Czech Republic, deserves special recognition for his many suggestions for improving the text. Adam translated a previous edition of the textbook into Czech, and in the process, he thoroughly reviewed every part of it.

Many people were instrumental in helping the text evolve from its manuscript stage. My chief liaison at Pearson Education, Geoscience Editor-in-Chief Nicole Folchetti, expertly guided the project and helped overcome several hurdles in order to get the book published. Copy Editor Kitty Wilson did a superb job of editing the manuscript, in many cases catching obscure errors that had persisted throughout several previous editions. Assistant Editor Sean Hale kept the book on track by making sure deadlines were met along the way. Media Producers Angela Bernhardt and Lee Ann Doctor provided key initiative and support in the creation of the electronic supplements that accompany this book, including the newly revised Online Study Guide and all of its outstanding features. Some of these new features include the Web videos, which were researched by Mike Lubby, and the Encounter Earth links, which were coordinated by Crissy Dudonis. New photos were found by Photo Researcher Roman Barnes, and the entire photo program was overseen by Science Photo Programs Manager Travis Amos. The Australian animations studio Cadre demonstrated rare patience and creativity while updating existing animations and creating new ones. The Pearson art studios did a beautiful job of modernizing many of the figures to make them more consistent throughout. The artful design of the text, including text wrapping and image placement, was developed by Art Director Mark Ong and Prentice Hall's design department. Last but not least, Production Editor Karpagam Jagadeesan deserves special recognition for her encouragement all the way from India during the many long hours of turning the manuscript into the book you see today.

Al Trujillo would also like to thank his students, whose questions provided the material for the "Students Sometimes Ask . . ." sections and whose continued input has proved invaluable for improving the text. Because scientists (and all good teachers) are always experimenting, thanks also for allowing yourselves to be a captive audience with which to conduct my experiments.

Al Trujillo also thanks his patient and understanding family for putting up with his absence during the long hours of preparing "The Book." Finally, appreciation is extended to the chocolate manufacturers Hershey, See's, and Ghirardelli for providing inspiration. A heartfelt thanks to all of you!

Many other individuals (including several anonymous reviewers) have provided valuable technical reviews for this and previous works. The following reviewers are gratefully acknowledged:

Patty Anderson, *Scripps Institution of Oceanography*
William Balsam, *University of Texas at Arlington*
Tsing Bardin, *City College of San Francisco*
Steven Benham, *Pacific Lutheran University*
Lori Bettison-Varga, *College of Wooster*
Thomas Bianchi, *Tulane University*
David Black, *University of Akron*
Mark Boryta, *Consumnes River College*
Laurie Brown, *University of Massachusetts*
Kathleen Browne, *Rider University*
Nancy Bushell, *Kauai Community College*
Mark Chiappone, *Miami-Dade College-Homestead Campus*
Chris Cirmo, *State University of New York, Cortland*
G. Kent Colbath, *Cerritos Community College*
Thomas Cramer, *Brookdale Community College*
Richard Crooker, *Kutztown University*
Cynthia Cudaback, *North Carolina State University*
Warren Currie, *Ohio University*
Hans Dam, *University of Connecticut*
Dan Deocampo, *California State University, Sacramento*
Richard Dixon, *Texas State University*
Holly Dodson, *Sierra College*
Joachim Dorsch, *St. Louis Community College*
Wallace Drexler, *Shippensburg University*
Walter Dudley, *University of Hawaii*
Iver Duedall, *Florida Institute of Technology*
Charles Ebert, *State University of New York, Buffalo*
Jiasong Fang, *Hawaii Pacific University*
Kenneth Finger, *Irvine Valley College*
Dave Gosse, *University of Virginia*
Gary Griggs, *University of California, Santa Cruz*
Joseph Holliday, *El Camino Community College*
Mary Anne Holmes, *University of Nebraska, Lincoln*
Timothy Horner, *California State University, Sacramento*
Ron Johnson, *Old Dominion University*
Eryn Klosko, *State University of New York, Westchester Community College*
M. John Kocurko, *Midwestern State University*
Lawrence Krissek, *Ohio State University*
Gary Lash, *State University of New York, Fredonia*
Richard Laws, *University of North Carolina*

Richard Little, *Greenfield Community College*
Stephen Macko, *University of Virginia, Charlottesville*
Chris Marone, *Pennsylvania State University*
Matthew McMackin, *San Jose State University*
James McWhorter, *Miami-Dade Community College*
Gregory Mead, *University of Florida*
Keith Meldahl, *MiraCosta College*
Nancy Mesner, *Utah State University*
Chris Metzler, *MiraCosta College*
Johnnie Moore, *University of Montana*
P. Graham Mortyn, *California State University, Fresno*
Andrew Muller, *Millersville University*
Andrew Muller, *Utah State University*
Jay Muza, *Florida Atlantic University*
Jennifer Nelson, *Indiana University–Purdue University at Indianapolis*
Jim Noyes, *El Camino Community College*
Sarah O'Malley, *Maine Maritime Academy*
B. L. Oostdam, *Millersville University*
William Orr, *University of Oregon*
Donald Palmer, *Kent State University*
Curt Peterson, *Portland State University*
Edward Ponto, *Onondaga Community College*
Donald Reed, *San Jose State University*
Randal Reed, *Shasta College*
M. Hassan Rezaie Boroon, *California State University, Los Angeles*
Cathryn Rhodes, *University of California, Davis*
James Rine, *University of South Carolina*
Felix Rizk, *Manatee Community College*
Angel Rodriguez, *Broward Community College*
Beth Simmons, *Metropolitan State College of Denver*
Jill Singer, *State University of New York, Buffalo*
Arthur Snoke, *Virginia Polytechnic Institute*
Pamela Stephens, *Midwestern State University*
Dean Stockwell, *University of Alaska, Fairbanks*
Lenore Tedesco, *Indiana University–Purdue University at Indianapolis*
Craig Tobias, *University of North Carolina, Wilmington*
M. Craig VanBoskirk, *Florida Community College at Jacksonville*
Bess Ward, *Princeton University*
Jackie Watkins, *Midwestern State University*
Arthur Wegweiser, *Edinboro University of Pennsylvania*
Katryn Wiese, *City College of San Francisco*
John Wormuth, *Texas A&M University*
Memorie Yasuda, *Scripps Institution of Oceanography*

Although this book has benefited from careful review by many individuals, the accuracy of the information rests with the authors. If you find errors or have comments about the text, please contact us.

Al Trujillo
  Department of Earth, Space, & Aviation Sciences
  Palomar College
  1140 W. Mission Rd.
  San Marcos, CA 92069
  atrujillo@palomar.edu
  Web: http://daphne.palomar.edu/atrujillo

Hal Thurman
  17580 SE 88th Covington Circle
  The Villages, FL 32162
  ilhvt@thevillages.net

"Oceanography is not so much a science as a collection of scientists who find common cause in trying to understand the complex nature of the ocean. In the vast salty seas that encompass the earth, there is plenty of room for persons trained in physics, chemistry, biology, and engineering to practice their specialties. Thus, an oceanographer is any scientifically trained person who spends much of his [or her] career on ocean problems."

— Willard Bascom, Oceanographer and Explorer (1980)

INTRODUCTION

Welcome to a book about the oceans. As you read this book, we hope that it elicits a sense of wonder and a spirit of curiosity about our watery planet. The ocean represents many different things to different people. To some, it is a wilderness of beauty and tranquility, a refuge from hectic civilized lives. Others see it as a vast recreational area that inspires either rest or physical challenge. To others, it is a mysterious place that is full of unknown wonders. And to others, it is a place of employment unmatched by any on land. To be sure, its splendor has inspired artists, writers, and poets for centuries. Whatever your view, we hope that understanding the way the oceans work will increase your appreciation of the marine environment. Above all, take time to admire the oceans.

Essentials of Oceanography was first written to help students develop *an awareness about the marine environment*—that is, develop an appreciation for the oceans by learning about oceanic processes (how the oceans behave) and their interrelationships (how physical entities are related to one another in the oceans). In this tenth edition, our goal is the same: to give the reader the scientific background to understand the basic principles underlying oceanic phenomena. In this way, one can then make informed decisions about the oceans in the years to come. We hope that some of you will be inspired so much by the oceans that you will continue to study them formally or informally in the future. (For those who may be considering a life-long career in oceanography, see Appendix V, "Careers in Oceanography," for some tips and practical advice.)

I.1 What Is Oceanography?

Oceanography (*ocean* = the marine environment, *graphy* = the name of a descriptive science) is literally the description of the marine environment. Although the term was first coined in the 1870s at the beginning of scientific exploration of the oceans, this definition does not fully portray the extent of what oceanography encompasses: Oceanography is much more than just *describing* marine phenomena. Oceanography could be more accurately called the scientific study of all aspects of the marine environment. Hence, the field of study called oceanography could (and maybe *should*) be called oceanology (*ocean* = the marine environment, *ology* = the study of). However, the science of studying the oceans has traditionally been called oceanography. It is also called *marine science* and includes the study of the water of the ocean, the life within it, and the (not so) solid Earth beneath it.

Since prehistoric time, people have used the oceans as a means of transportation and as a source of food. However, the importance of ocean processes has been studied technically only since the 1930s. The impetus for these studies began with the search for offshore petroleum and expanded with the emphasis on ocean warfare during World War II. In fact, it was during World War II that the great expansion in oceanography, which continues today, began. The realization by governments of the

Chocolate chip sea stars (*Protoreaster nodosus*) extend along a shallow sandy bank. Sea stars belong to the class Asteroidea, which includes various organisms that have five-part symmetry. Sea stars crawl across the bottom using hundreds of small tube feet called podia that line the underside of each appendage.

importance of marine problems and their readiness to make money available for research, the growth in the number of ocean scientists at work, and the increasing sophistication of scientific equipment have made it feasible to study the ocean on a scale and to a degree of complexity never before attempted nor even possible. Historically, those who make their living fishing in the ocean go where the physical processes of the oceans offer good fishing. But how marine life interrelates with ocean geology, chemistry, and physics to create good fishing grounds has been more or less a mystery until only recently when scientists in these disciplines began to investigate the oceans with new technology. Along with these expanded studies came the realization of how much of an impact humans are beginning to have on the ocean. As a result, much recent research has been concerned with documenting human impacts on the ocean.

Oceanography is typically divided into different academic disciplines (or subfields) of study. The four main disciplines of oceanography that are covered in this book are as follows:

- **Geological oceanography**, which is the study of the structure of the sea floor and how the sea floor has changed through time; the creation of sea floor features; and the history of sediments deposited on it.
- **Chemical oceanography**, which is the study of the chemical composition and properties of seawater; how to extract certain chemicals from seawater; and the effects of pollutants.
- **Physical oceanography**, which is the study of waves, tides, and currents; the ocean–atmosphere relationship that influences weather and climate; and the transmission of light and sound in the oceans.
- **Biological oceanography**, which is the study of the various oceanic life forms and their relationships to one another; adaptations to the marine environment; and developing sustainable methods of harvesting seafood.

Other disciplines include ocean engineering, marine archaeology, and marine policy. Since the study of oceanography often examines in detail all the different disciplines of oceanography, it is frequently described as being an *interdisciplinary* science, or one covering all the disciplines of science as they apply to the oceans (Figure I.1). The content of this book includes the broad range of interdisciplinary science topics that comprises the field of oceanography. In essence, this is a book about *all* aspects of the oceans.

FIGURE I.1 A Venn diagram showing the interdisciplinary nature of oceanography.

I.2   How Are Earth's Oceans Unique?

The oceans are the largest and most prominent feature on Earth. In fact, they are the single most defining feature of our planet. As viewed from space, our planet is a beautiful blue, white, and brown globe (see the chapter-opening photo in Chapter 1). It is our oceans of liquid water that set us apart in the solar system. No other body in the solar system has a confirmed ocean; however, recent satellite missions have revealed a spidery network of fluid-filled cracks on Jupiter's moon Europa (Figure I.2), which almost certainly betrays the presence of an ocean of liquid water beneath its icy surface. Another of Jupiter's moons, Callisto, may also have a liquid ocean beneath its cold, icy crust. Yet another tantalizing possibility for a nearby world with an ocean beneath its icy surface is Saturn's tiny moon Enceladus, which displays geysers of water vapor and ice that have recently been analyzed and, remarkably, contain salt. And evidence continues to mount that

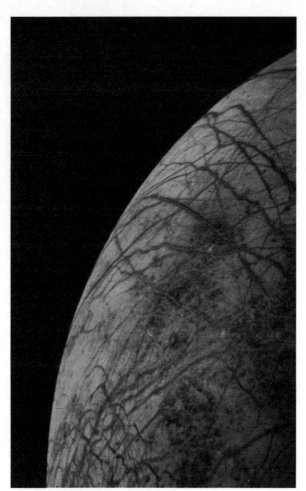

FIGURE I.2 Jupiter's moon Europa. Europa's network of dark fluid-filled cracks suggests the presence of an ocean beneath its icy surface. If the presence of an ocean is confirmed, Europa would become the only other body in the solar system besides Earth that has an ocean of liquid water.

Saturn's giant moon Titan with its thick obscuring atmosphere may possess seas of liquid hydrocarbons. Currently, there is much debate in the United States as to which of these moons is the best target to send a follow-up space mission for the detection of life outside Earth. Still, the fact that our planet has so much water, *and in the liquid form*, is unique in the solar system.

The oceans determine where our continents end and have thus shaped political boundaries and human history. The oceans conceal many features; in fact, the majority of Earth's geographic features are on the ocean floor. Remarkably, there was once more known about the surface of the moon than about the floor of the oceans! Fortunately, our knowledge of both has increased dramatically over the past few decades.

The oceans influence climate and weather all over the globe—even in continental areas far from any ocean—through an intricate pattern of currents and heating/cooling mechanisms that scientists are only now beginning to understand. The oceans are also the lungs of the planet, taking carbon dioxide gas (CO_2) out of the atmosphere and replacing it with oxygen gas (O_2). Some scientists have estimated that the oceans supply as much as 70% of the oxygen humans breathe.

The oceans are essential to all life and are in large part responsible for the development of life on Earth, providing a stable environment in which life could evolve over millions of years. Today, the oceans contain the greatest number of living things on the planet, from microscopic bacteria and algae to the largest life form alive today (the blue whale). Interestingly, water is the major component of nearly every life form on Earth, and our own body fluid chemistry is remarkably similar to the chemistry of seawater.

The oceans hold many secrets waiting to be discovered, and new discoveries about the oceans are made nearly every day. The oceans are a source of food, minerals, and energy that remains largely untapped. More than half of the world population lives in coastal areas near the oceans, taking advantage of the mild climate, an inexpensive form of transportation, and vast recreational opportunities. Unfortunately, the oceans are also the dumping ground for many of society's wastes. In fact, the oceans are currently showing alarming strains caused by pollution, overfishing, invasive species, and climate change, among other things.

I.3 What Is Rational Use of Technology?

Many stresses have been put on the oceans by an ever-increasing human population. For instance, population studies reveal that more than 50% of world population—some 3.2 billion people—live along the coastline, and more than 80% of all Americans live within an hour's drive from an ocean or the Great Lakes. In the future, these figures are expected to increase. In the United States, for example, 8 of the 10 largest cities are in coastal environments, and 3600 people move to the coast every day. By 2025, as much as 75% of the global population is expected to live at the coast. Clearly, coastal regions are desirable places to live (Figure I.3).

Human migration to the coasts will further mar fragile coastal ocean ecosystems. Specifically, the surge in coastal population has resulted in increasing amounts of industrial waste and sewage disposal at sea, large volumes of polluted runoff, and increasing use of seawater for human benefit (for example, using seawater as a coolant in coastal power plants). Coastal habitats have also come under intense pressure as more development has occurred, resulting in coastal wetlands being filled in even though they are vital to the cleansing of runoff waters, and their diversity and high productivity support coastal fisheries. In addition, all this development and its ecological impacts will pose immense challenges for coastal communities, including increased demands on energy, infrastructure, and the supply of freshwater.

Although it may seem as if humans have severely and irreversibly damaged the oceans, our impact has mostly been felt in coastal areas. The world's oceans are a vast habitat that has not yet been lethally damaged. Humans have been able to inflict only minor damage here and there along the margins of the oceans. However, as our technology makes us more powerful, the threat of irreversible harm becomes greater. For instance, in the open ocean (those areas far from shore), deep-ocean mining and nuclear waste disposal have been proposed. How do we as a society deal with these increased demands on the marine environment? How do we regulate the ocean's use? One of the first steps is to understand how the oceans work and, at the same time, increase our understanding of how human actions affect the oceans.

If used wisely, our technology can actually reduce the threat of irreversible harm. Which path will we take? We all need to carefully evaluate our own actions and the effects those actions have on the environment. In addition, we need to make conscientious decisions about those we elect to public office. Some of you may even have direct responsibility for initiating legislation that affects our environment. It is our hope that you, as a student of the marine environment, will gain enough knowledge while studying oceanography to help your community (and perhaps even your nation) make rational use of technology in the oceans.

> *"Our environment, our health, our economic prospect, our national defense, the foods we eat and the air we breathe— even our genetic future—will depend upon how wisely we apply the technologies that become available. And to do this we need a population of scientists, but also of citizens, of workers, of administrators, of policy makers . . . who can grasp the scientific way of thinking."*
>
> — *Leon Lederman, Nobel Prize–winning physicist, testifying before the U.S. Congress (2000)*

FIGURE I.3 Dubai's artificial islands as seen from space: The Palms and The World. This series of artificial islands that jut audaciously into the Persian Gulf off Dubai, United Arab Emirates, was created specifically for coastal housing tracts and other buildings. The structures are visible from space and resemble the shape of palm trees and, when completed, a globe of the world. Although the artificial islands have been dubbed the Eighth Wonder of the World and have doubled Dubai's shoreline, they have also disrupted its coastal ecosystem. The larger palm island (*lower left*) is about 10 kilometers (6 miles) wide. North is toward the top of the image.

The blue marble next generation.
This composite image of satellite data shows Earth's interrelated atmosphere, oceans, and land—including human presence. Its various layers include the land surface, sea ice, ocean, cloud cover, city lights, and the hazy edge of Earth's atmosphere.

"When you're circling the Earth every 90 minutes, what becomes clearest is that it's mostly water; the continents look like they're floating objects."

— *Loren Shriver,*
NASA astronaut (2008)

1

INTRODUCTION TO PLANET "EARTH"

It seems perplexing that our planet is called "Earth" when 70.8% of its surface is covered by oceans. Many early human cultures that lived near the Mediterranean (*medi* = middle, *terra* = land) Sea envisioned the world as being composed of large landmasses surrounded by marginal bodies of water (Figure 1.1). How surprised they must have been when they ventured into the larger oceans of the world. Our planet is misnamed "Earth" because we live on the land portion of the planet. If we were marine animals, our planet would probably be called "Ocean," "Water," "Hydro," "Aqua," or even "Oceanus" to indicate the prominence of Earth's oceans.

1.1 How Many Oceans Exist on Earth?

A world map (Figure 1.2) shows how extensive our oceans really are. Notice that *the oceans dominate the surface area of the globe*. For those people who have traveled by boat across an ocean (or even flown across one in an airplane), the one thing that immediately strikes them is that the oceans are enormous. Notice, also, that *the oceans are interconnected* and form a single continuous body of seawater, which is why the oceans are commonly referred to as a "world ocean" (singular, not plural). For instance, a vessel at sea can travel from one ocean to another, whereas it is impossible to travel on land from one continent to most others without crossing an ocean. In addition, the oceans contain 97.2% of all the water on or near Earth's surface, so *the volume of the oceans is immense*.

The Four Principal Oceans, Plus One

Our world ocean can be divided into four principal oceans (plus an additional ocean), based on the shape of the ocean basins and the positions of the continents (Figure 1.2).

PACIFIC OCEAN The **Pacific Ocean** is the world's largest ocean, covering more than half of the ocean surface area on Earth (Figure 1.3b). The Pacific Ocean is the single largest geographic feature on the planet, spanning more than one-third of Earth's entire surface. The Pacific Ocean is so large that *all* of the continents could fit into the space occupied by it—with room left over! Although the Pacific Ocean is also the deepest ocean in the world (Figure 1.3c), it contains many small tropical islands. It was named in 1520 by explorer Ferdinand Magellan's party in honor of the fine weather they encountered while crossing into the Pacific (*paci* = peace) Ocean.

ATLANTIC OCEAN The **Atlantic Ocean** is about half the size of the Pacific Ocean and is not quite as deep (Figure 1.3). It separates the Old World (Europe, Asia, and Africa) from the New World (North and South America). The Atlantic Ocean was named after Atlas, who was one of the Titans in Greek mythology.

INDIAN OCEAN   The **Indian Ocean** is slightly smaller than the Atlantic Ocean and has about the same average depth (Figure 1.3). It is mostly in the Southern Hemisphere (south of the equator, or below 0 degrees latitude in Figure 1.2). The Indian Ocean was named for its proximity to the subcontinent of India.

ARCTIC OCEAN   The **Arctic Ocean** is about 7% the size of the Pacific Ocean and is only a little more than one-quarter as deep as the rest of the oceans (Figure 1.3). Although it has a permanent layer of sea ice at the surface, the ice is only a few meters thick. The Arctic Ocean was named after its location in the Arctic region, which exists beneath the northern constellation Ursa Major, otherwise known as the Big Dipper, or the Bear (*arktos* = bear).

SOUTHERN OCEAN, OR ANTARCTIC OCEAN   Oceanographers recognize an additional ocean near the continent of Antarctica in the Southern Hemisphere (Figure 1.2). Defined by the meeting of currents near Antarctica called the Antarctic Convergence, the **Southern Ocean**, or **Antarctic Ocean**, is really the portions of the Pacific, Atlantic, and Indian Oceans south of about 50 degrees south latitude. This ocean was named for its location in the Southern Hemisphere.

Oceans versus Seas: What Are the Seven Seas?

What is the difference between a sea and an ocean? In common use, the terms "sea" and "ocean" are often used interchangeably. For instance, a *sea* star lives in the *ocean*; the *ocean* is full of *sea*water; *sea* ice forms in the *ocean*; and one might stroll the *sea*shore while living in *ocean*-front property. Technically, however, a *sea* is defined as follows:

- Smaller and shallower than an ocean (this is why the Arctic Ocean might be more appropriately considered a sea)

FIGURE 1.1 An early map of the world. The world according to the Greek Herodotus in 450 B.C., showing the prominence of the Mediterranean Sea surrounded by the continents of Europe, Libya (Africa), and Asia. Seas are labeled "mare" and are shown as a band of water encircling the land.

FIGURE 1.2 Earth's oceans. Map showing the four principal oceans, plus the Southern or Antarctic Ocean. Dark blue shading represents shallow areas.

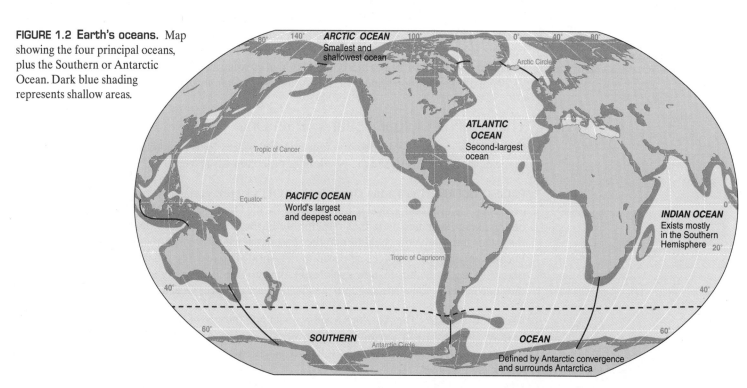

- Composed of salt water (although some inland "seas," such as the Caspian Sea in Asia, are actually large lakes with relatively high salinity)
- Somewhat enclosed by land (but some seas, such as the Sargasso Sea in the Atlantic Ocean, are defined by strong ocean currents rather than by land)
- Directly connected to the world ocean

"Sailing the seven seas" is a familiar phrase in literature and song, but are there really seven seas? To the ancients, the term "seven" often meant "many," and before the 15th century, Europeans considered the main seas of the world to be:

1. The Red Sea
2. The Mediterranean Sea
3. The Persian Gulf
4. The Black Sea
5. The Adriatic Sea
6. The Caspian Sea
7. The Indian Ocean

Today, the world ocean is generally divided into the four principal oceans (plus one). If the oceans are counted as seas and the Pacific and Atlantic Oceans are arbitrarily split at the equator, a more modern count of the seven "seas" includes: (1) the North Pacific, (2) the South Pacific, (3) the North Atlantic, (4) the South Atlantic, (5) the Indian, (6) the Arctic, and (7) the Southern or Antarctic.

COMPARING THE OCEANS TO THE CONTINENTS   Figure 1.3d shows that the average depth of the world's oceans is 3729 meters[1] (12,234 feet). This means that there must be some extremely deep areas in the ocean to offset the shallow areas close to shore. Figure 1.3d also shows that the deepest depth in the oceans (the Challenger Deep region of the Mariana Trench, which is near Guam) is a staggering 11,022 meters (36,161 feet) below sea level.

How do the continents compare to the oceans? Figure 1.3d shows that the average height of the continents is only 840 meters (2756 feet), illustrating that the average height of the land is not very far above sea level. The highest mountain in the world (the mountain with the greatest height above sea level) is Mount Everest in the Himalaya Mountains of Asia, at 8850 meters (29,035 feet). Even so, Mount Everest is a full 2172 meters (7126 feet) shorter than the Mariana Trench is deep. The mountain with the *greatest total height* from base to top is Mauna Kea on the island of Hawaii in the United States. It measures 4206 meters (13,800 feet) above sea level and 5426 meters (17,800 feet) from sea level down to its base, for a total height of 9632 meters (31,601 feet). The total height of Mauna Kea is 782 meters (2566 feet) higher than Mount Everest, but it is still 1390 meters (4560 feet) shorter than the Mariana Trench is deep. In essence, no mountain on Earth is taller than the Mariana Trench is deep.

(a) Earth's Surface

Land 29.2%   Ocean 70.8%

(b) Relative Ocean Size

Atlantic 26.0%
Pacific 50.1%
Indian 20.5%
Arctic 3.4%

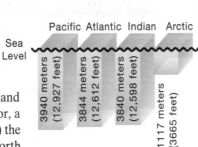

(c) Average Ocean Depth

Pacific Atlantic Indian Arctic

Sea Level

3940 meters (12,927 feet)
3844 meters (12,612 feet)
3840 meters (12,598 feet)
1117 meters (3665 feet)

(d) Comparing Oceans to Land

Sea Level

Deepest area of ocean = Mariana Trench 11,022 meters (36,161 feet)
Average depth 3729 meters (12,234 feet) of oceans
Average height of land 840 meters (2756 feet)
Tallest mountain = Mt. Everest 8850 meters (29,035 feet)

FIGURE 1.3 Ocean size and depth. (a) Relative proportions of land and ocean on Earth's surface. **(b)** Relative size of the four principal oceans. **(c)** Average ocean depth. **(d)** Comparing average and maximum depth of the oceans to average and maximum height of land.

KEY CONCEPT
The deepest part of the ocean is the Mariana Trench in the Pacific Ocean. It is 11,022 meters (36,161 feet) deep and was visited by humans in 1960, in a specially designed deep-diving bathysphere.

---

[1]Throughout this book, metric measurements are used (and the corresponding English measurements follow in parentheses). See Appendix I, "Metric and English Units Compared," for conversion factors between the two systems of units.

FIGURE 1.4 The U.S. Navy's bathyscaphe *Trieste*. The *Trieste* suspended on a crane before its record-setting deep dive in 1960. The 1.8-meter (6-foot) diameter diving chamber (round ball below the float) accommodated two people and had steel walls 7.6 centimeters (3 inches) thick.

STUDENTS SOMETIMES ASK...

Have humans ever explored the deepest ocean trenches? Could anything live there?

Humans have indeed visited the deepest part of the oceans—where there is crushing high pressure, complete darkness, and near-freezing water temperatures—half a century ago! In January 1960, U.S. Navy Lt. Don Walsh and explorer Jacques Piccard descended to the bottom of the Challenger Deep region of the Mariana Trench in the *Trieste*, a deep diving bathyscaphe (*bathos* = depth, *scaphe* = a small ship) (Figure 1.4). At 9906 meters (32,500 feet), the men heard a loud cracking sound that shook the cabin. They were unable to see that a 7.6-centimeter (3-inch) Plexiglas viewing port had cracked (miraculously, it held for the rest of the dive). More than five hours after leaving the surface, they reached the bottom, at 10,912 meters (35,800 feet)—a record depth of human descent that has not been broken since. They did see some life forms that are adapted to life in the deep: a small flatfish, a shrimp, and some jellyfish. Other notable voyages to the deep ocean in submersibles are discussed in Box 1.1.

1.2 How Was Early Exploration of the Oceans Achieved?

In spite of the ocean's huge extent over the surface area of Earth, it has not prevented humans from exploring its furthest reaches. Since early times, humans have developed technology that has allowed civilizations to travel across large stretches of open ocean. Today, we can cross even the Pacific Ocean in less than a day by airplane. Even so, much of the deep ocean remains out of reach and woefully unexplored. In fact, the surface of the Moon has been mapped more accurately than most parts of the sea floor. Yet satellites at great distances above Earth are being used to gain knowledge about our watery home.

Early History

Humankind probably first viewed the oceans as a source of food. Archeological evidence suggests that when boat technology was developed about 40,000 years ago, people probably traveled the oceans. Most likely, their vessels were built to move upon the ocean's surface and transport oceangoing people to new fishing grounds. The oceans also provided an inexpensive and efficient way to move large and heavy objects, facilitating trade and interaction between cultures.

PACIFIC NAVIGATORS The peopling of the Pacific Islands (Oceania) is somewhat perplexing because there is no evidence that people actually evolved on these islands. Their presence required travel over hundreds or even thousands of kilometers of open ocean from the continents (probably in small vessels of that time—double canoes, outrigger canoes, or balsa rafts) as well as remarkable navigation skills (Box 1.2). The islands in the Pacific Ocean are widely scattered, so it is likely that only a fortunate few of the voyagers made landfall and that many others perished during voyages. Figure 1.5 shows the three major inhabited island regions in the Pacific Ocean: Micronesia (*micro* = small, *nesia* = islands), Melanesia (*mela* = black, *nesia* = islands), and Polynesia (*poly* = many, *nesia* = islands), which covers the largest area.

VOYAGES TO INNER SPACE: VISITING THE DEEP-OCEAN FLOOR IN SUBMERSIBLES

For as long as people have been harvesting the bounty of the oceans and traveling across it in vessels, they have dreamed of plumbing the mysterious depths of the deep ocean, an area known as "inner space." However, the inaccessibility of the deep ocean and its harsh conditions have limited human exploration. One way to explore the deep ocean is in vessels called *submersibles* that can transport surface conditions to the intense pressure at depth.

History credits *Alexander the Great* with the first descent in a sealed waterproof container; this reportedly took place in 332 B.C. Unfortunately, there is no record of what Alexander's submersible looked like. Much later, the *submarine*, which can submerge, propel itself underwater, and surface under its own power, was developed. Because submarines are difficult to detect, they can be used to sink enemy ships. The earliest report of a submarine used in warfare is from the early 16th century, when Greenlanders used sealskins to waterproof a three-person, oar-powered submarine, which was used to drill holes in the sides of Norwegian ships.

In 1934, reaching even deeper depths for scientific exploration was the goal for naturalist **William Beebe** and his engineer-associate **Otis Barton**. They used a submersible called a *bathysphere* (*bathos* = depth, *sphere* = ball) to observe marine life in the clear waters off Bermuda. The bathysphere (Figure 1A)—a heavy steel ball with small windows—was suspended from a ship and lowered to a then-record depth of 923 meters (3028 feet), allowing the first descriptions of the deep. Prior to this historic dive, the farthest down a living human had descended was 160 meters (525 feet)!

In 1964, the research submersible *Alvin* (Figure 1B) from Woods Hole Oceanographic Institution began to explore the deep ocean. At 7.6 meters (25 feet) long, *Alvin* can carry a crew of one pilot and two scientists to a depth of 4000 meters (13,120 feet) and maneuver independently along the sea floor. *Alvin* has completed 4500 dives and transported more than 12,000 people into the deep for study and retrieval of samples. Under the direction of famed oceanographer **Robert Ballard**, some notable accomplishments of *Alvin* include discovering unique life forms along hydrothermal vents (sea floor hot springs) in 1977 and locating the sunken wreck of the RMS *Titanic* in 1985 (see Web Box 6.1). In 2009, a major makeover was undertaken to update *Alvin*'s components and substantially increase its diving range. Currently, the deepest-diving manned submersible is *Shinkai 6500*, a Japanese research vessel that can dive to 6500 meters (21,320 feet).

FIGURE 1A William Beebe and his bathysphere. In 1934, William Beebe (*exiting the bathysphere*) and Otis Barton (*standing at left, not wearing a hat*) descended to a record depth of 923 meters (3028 feet) in this steel bathysphere, which weighed 2268 kilograms (5000 pounds). To combat the high pressure at depth, the bathysphere had walls that were 0.5 meter (1.5 feet) thick and small windows made of fused quartz.

FIGURE 1B The deep-diving submersible *Alvin*. Since it was commissioned in 1964, the research submersible *Alvin* from Woods Hole Oceanographic Institution has safely carried thousands of scientists to the sea floor and back.

HOW DO SAILORS KNOW WHERE THEY ARE AT SEA?: FROM STICK CHARTS TO SATELLITES

How do you know where you are in the ocean, without roads, signposts, or any land in sight? How do you determine the distance to a destination? How do you find your way back to a good fishing spot or where you have discovered sunken treasure? Sailors have relied on a variety of navigation tools to help answer questions such as these by locating where they are at sea.

Some of the first navigators were the Polynesians. Remarkably, the Polynesians were able to successfully navigate to small islands located at great distances across the Pacific Ocean. These early navigators must have been very aware of the marine environment and been able to read subtle differences in the ocean and sky. The tools they used to help them navigate between islands included the Sun and Moon, the nighttime stars, the behavior of marine organisms, various ocean properties, and an ingenious device called a *stick chart* (Figure 1C). These stick charts accurately depicted the consistent pattern of ocean waves. By orienting their vessels relative to this regular ocean wave direction, sailors could successfully navigate at sea.

FIGURE 1C Navigational stick chart. This bamboo stick chart of Micronesia's Marshall Islands shows islands (represented by shells at the junctions of the sticks), regular ocean wave direction (represented by the straight strips), and waves that bend around islands (represented by the curved strips). Similar stick charts were used by early Polynesian navigators.

The bent wave directions let them know when they were getting close to an island—even one that was located beyond the horizon.

The importance of knowing where you are at sea is illustrated by a tragic incident in 1707, when a British battle fleet was more than 160 kilometers (100 miles) off course and ran aground in the Isles of Scilly near England, with the loss of four ships and nearly 2000 men. **Latitude** (location north or south) was relatively easy to determine at sea by measuring the position of the Sun and stars using a device called a *sextant* (*sextant* = sixth, in reference to the instru-

ment's arc, which is one-sixth of a circle) (Figure 1D). The accident occurred because the ship's crew had no way of keeping track of their **longitude** (location east or west; see Appendix III, "Latitude and Longitude on Earth"). To determine longitude, which is a function of time, it was necessary to know the time difference between a reference meridian and when the Sun was directly overhead of a ship at sea (noon local time). The pendulum-driven clocks in use in the early 1700s, however, would not work for long on a rocking ship at sea. In 1714, the British Parliament offered a £20,000 prize (about $20 million today) for developing a device that would

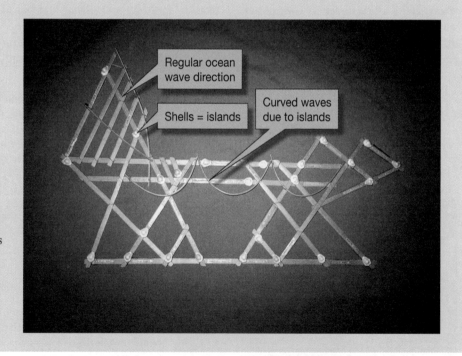

Regular ocean wave direction

Shells = islands

Curved waves due to islands

No written records of Pacific human history exist before the arrival of Europeans in the 16th century. Nevertheless, the movement of Asian peoples into Micronesia and Melanesia is easy to imagine because distances between islands are relatively short. In Polynesia, however, large distances separate island groups, which must have presented great challenges to ocean voyagers. Easter Island, for example, at the southeastern corner of the triangular-shaped Polynesian islands region, is more than 1600 kilometers (1000 miles) from Pitcairn Island, the next nearest island. Clearly, a voyage to the Hawaiian Islands must have been one of work well enough at sea to determine longitude within half a degree or 30 nautical miles (34.5 statute miles) after a voyage to the West Indies.

A cabinetmaker in Lincolnshire, England, named **John Harrison** began working in 1728 on such a timepiece, which was dubbed the *chronometer* (*chrono* = time, *meter* = measure) Harrison's first chronometer, H-1, was successfully tested in 1736, but he received only £500 of the prize because the device was deemed too complex, costly, and fragile. Eventually, his more compact fourth version, H-4—which resembles an oversized pocket watch (Figure 1E)—was tested during a trans-Atlantic voyage in 1761. Upon reaching Jamaica, it was so accurate that it had lost only *five seconds* of time, a longitude error of only 0.02 degree, or 1.2 nautical miles (1.4 statute miles)! Although Harrison's chronometer greatly exceeded the requirements of the government, the committee in charge of the prize withheld payment, mostly because the astronomers on the board wanted the solution to come from measurement of the stars. Because the committee refused to award him the prize without further proof, a second sea trial was conducted in 1764, which confirmed his success. Harrison was reluctantly granted £10,000. Only when King George III intervened in 1773 did Harrison finally receive the remaining prize money and recognition for his life work—at age 80.

Today, navigating at sea relies on the *Global Positioning System (GPS)*, which was initiated in the 1970s by the U.S. Department of Defense. Initially designed for military purposes but now available for a variety of civilian uses, GPS relies on a system of 24 satellites that send continuous radio signals to the surface. Position is determined by very accurate measurement of the time of travel of radio signals from at least four of the satellites to receivers on board a ship (or on land). Thus, a vessel can determine its exact latitude and longitude to within a few meters—a small fraction of the length of most ships. Navigators from days gone by would be amazed at how quickly and accurately a vessel's location can be determined, but they might say that it has taken all the adventure out of navigating at sea.

FIGURE 1D **Using a handheld sextant.** This sextant is similar to the ones used by early navigators to determine latitude.

FIGURE 1E **John Harrison and his chronometer H-4.** Painting (circa 1735) of John Harrison holding his chronometer H-4, which was his life's work. The timepiece H-4 proved to be a vital technological breakthrough that allowed the determination of longitude at sea and won Harrison the prize for solving the longitude problem.

the most difficult because Hawaii is more than 3000 kilometers (2000 miles) from the nearest inhabited islands, the Marquesas Islands (Figure 1.5).

Archeological evidence suggests that humans from New Guinea may have occupied New Ireland as early as 4000 or 5000 B.C. However, there is little evidence of human travel farther into the Pacific Ocean before 1100 B.C. By then, the *Lapita*, a group of early people who are thought to have come from island Southeast Asia and produced a distinctive type of pottery, had traveled on to Fiji, Tonga, and Samoa (Figure 1.5, *yellow arrow*). From there, Polynesians sailed on to the Marquesas (about 30 B.C.), which appear to have been the starting point for voyages to the far reaches of the island Pacific (Figure 1.5, *green arrows*), including the Hawaiian Islands (about 300 A.D.) and New Zealand (about 800 A.D.). Surprisingly, new genetic research suggests that Polynesians populated Easter Island relatively recently, about 1200 A.D.

Despite the obvious Polynesian backgrounds of the Hawaiians, the Maori of New Zealand, and the Easter Islanders, an adventurous biologist/anthropologist named **Thor Heyerdahl** proposed that voyagers from South America may have reached islands of the South Pacific before the coming of the Polynesians. To prove his point, in 1947 he sailed the *Kon Tiki*—a balsa raft designed like those that were used by South American navigators at the time of European discovery—from South America to the Tuamotu Islands, a journey of more than 11,300 kilometers (7000 miles) (Figure 1.5, *red arrow*). Although the remarkable voyage of the *Kon Tiki* demonstrates that early South Americans could have traveled to Polynesia just as easily as early Asian cultures, anthropologists can find no evidence of such a migration. Further, comparative DNA studies show a strong genetic relationship between the peoples of Easter Island and Polynesia, but none between these groups and natives in coastal North or South America.

FIGURE 1.5 The peopling of the Pacific islands.
The major island groups of the Pacific Ocean are Micronesia (*brown shading*), Melanesia (*red shading*), and Polynesia (*green shading*). The "Lapita people" present in New Ireland 5000-4000 B.C. can be traced to Fiji, Tonga, and Samoa by 1100 B.C. (*yellow arrow*). Green arrows show the peopling of distant islands throughout Polynesia. The route of Thor Heyerdahl's balsa raft *Kon Tiki* is also shown (*red arrow*).

EUROPEAN NAVIGATORS The first humans from the Western Hemisphere known to have developed the art of navigation were the **Phoenicians**, who lived at the eastern end of the Mediterranean Sea, in the present-day area of Egypt, Syria, Lebanon, and Israel. As early as 2000 B.C., they investigated the Mediterranean Sea, the Red Sea, and the Indian Ocean. The first recorded circumnavigation of Africa, in 590 B.C., was made by the Phoenicians, who had also sailed as far north as the British Isles.

The Greek astronomer-geographer **Pytheas** sailed northward in 325 B.C. using a simple yet elegant method for determining latitude (one's position north or south) in the Northern Hemisphere. His method involved measuring the angle between an observer's line of sight to the North Star and line of sight to the northern horizon.[2] Despite Pytheas's method for determining latitude, it was still impossible to accurately determine longitude (one's position east or west).

One of the key repositories of scientific knowledge at the time was the **Library of Alexandria** in Alexandria, Egypt, which was founded in the 3rd century B.C. by *Alexander the Great*. It housed an impressive collection of written knowledge that attracted scientists, poets, philosophers, artists, and writers who studied and researched there. The Library of Alexandria soon became the intellectual capital of the world, featuring history's greatest accumulation of ancient writings.

As long ago as 450 B.C., Greek scholars became convinced that Earth was round using lines of evidence such as the way ships disappeared beyond the horizon and the shadows of Earth that appeared during eclipses of the Moon. This inspired the Greek **Eratosthenes** (pronounced "AIR-uh-TOS-thuh-neez")

---

[2]Pytheas's method of determining latitude is featured in Appendix III, "Latitude and Longitude on Earth."

(276–192 B.C.), the second librarian at the Library of Alexandria, to cleverly use the shadow of a stick in a hole in the ground and elementary geometry to determine Earth's circumference. His value of 40,000 kilometers (24,840 miles) compares well with the true value of 40,032 kilometers (24,875 miles) known today.

An Egyptian-Greek named **Claudius Ptolemy** (c. 85 A.D.–c. 165 A.D.) produced a map of the world in about 150 A.D. that represented the extent of Roman knowledge at that time. The map included the continents of Europe, Asia, and Africa, as did earlier Greek maps, but it also included vertical lines of longitude and horizontal lines of latitude, which had been developed by Alexandrian scholars. Moreover, Ptolemy showed the known seas to be surrounded by land, much of which was as yet unknown and proved to be a great enticement to explorers.

Ptolemy also introduced an (erroneous) update to Eratosthenes's surprisingly accurate estimate of Earth's circumference. Unfortunately, Ptolemy wrongly depended on flawed calculations and an overestimation of the size of Asia, so he determined Earth's circumference to be 29,000 kilometers (18,000 miles), which is about 28% too small. Remarkably, nearly 1500 years later, Ptolemy's error caused explorer Christopher Columbus to believe he had encountered parts of Asia rather than a new world.

The Middle Ages

After the destruction of the Library of Alexandria in 415 A.D. (in which all of its contents were burned) and the fall of the Roman Empire in 476 A.D., the achievements of the Phoenicians, Greeks, and Romans were mostly lost. Some of the knowledge, however, was retained by the *Arabs*, who controlled northern Africa and Spain. The Arabs used this knowledge to become the dominant navigators in the Mediterranean Sea area and to trade extensively with East Africa, India, and southeast Asia. The Arabs were able to trade across the Indian Ocean because they had learned how to take advantage of the seasonal patterns of monsoon winds. During the summer, when monsoon winds blow from the southwest, ships laden with goods would leave the Arabian ports and sail eastward across the Indian Ocean. During the winter, when the trade winds blow from the northeast, ships would return west.[3]

Meanwhile, in the rest of southern and eastern Europe, Christianity was on the rise. Scientific inquiry counter to religious teachings was actively suppressed and the knowledge gained by previous civilizations was either lost or ignored. As a result, the Western concept of world geography degenerated considerably during these so-called *Dark Ages*. For example, one notion envisioned the world as a disk with Jerusalem at the center.

In northern Europe, the **Vikings** of Scandinavia, who had excellent ships and good navigation skills, actively explored the Atlantic Ocean (Figure 1.6). Late in the 10th century, aided by a period of worldwide climatic warming, the Vikings colonized Iceland. In about 981, **Erik "the Red" Thorvaldson** sailed westward from Iceland and discovered Greenland. He may also have traveled further westward to Baffin Island. He returned to Iceland and led the first wave of Viking colonists to Greenland in 985. **Bjarni Herjolfsson** sailed from Iceland to join the colonists, but he sailed too far southwest and is thought to be the first Viking to have seen what is now called Newfoundland. Bjarni did not land but instead returned to the new colony at Greenland. **Leif Eriksson**, son of Erik the Red, became intrigued by Bjarni's stories about the new land Bjarni had seen. In 995, Leif bought Bjarni's ship and set out from Greenland for the land that Bjarni had seen to the southwest. Leif spent the winter in that portion of North America and named the land *Vinland* (now Newfoundland, Canada) after the grapes that were found there. Climatic cooling and inappropriate farming practices for the region

FIGURE 1.6 Viking colonies in the North Atlantic. Map showing the routes and dates of Viking explorations and the locations of the colonies that were established in Iceland, Greenland, and parts of North America.

---

[3]More details about Indian Ocean monsoons can be found in Chapter 7, "Ocean Circulation."

caused these Viking colonies in Greenland and Vinland to struggle and die out by about 1450.

The Age of Discovery in Europe

The 30-year period from 1492 to 1522 is known as the **Age of Discovery**. During this time, Europeans explored the continents of North and South America and the globe was circumnavigated for the first time. As a result, Europeans learned the true extent of the world's oceans and that human populations existed elsewhere on newly "discovered" continents and islands with cultures vastly different from those familiar to European voyagers.

Why was there such an increase in ocean exploration during the Age of Discovery? One reason was that Sultan Mohammed II had captured Constantinople (the capital of eastern Christendom) in 1453, a conquest that isolated Mediterranean port cities from the riches of India, Asia, and the East Indies (modern-day Indonesia). As a result, the Western world had to search for new Eastern trade routes by sea.

The Portuguese, under the leadership of **Prince Henry the Navigator** (1392–1460), led a renewed effort to explore outside Europe. The prince established a marine institution at Sagres to improve Portuguese sailing skills. The treacherous journey around the tip of Africa was a great obstacle to an alternative trade route. Cape Agulhas (at the southern tip of Africa) was first rounded by **Bartholomeu Diaz** in 1486. He was followed in 1498 by **Vasco da Gama**, who continued around the tip of Africa to India, thus establishing a new Eastern trade route to Asia.

Meanwhile, the Italian navigator and explorer **Christopher Columbus** was financed by Spanish monarchs to find a new route to the East Indies across the Atlantic Ocean. During Columbus's first voyage in 1492, he sailed west from Spain and made landfall after a two-month journey (Figure 1.7). Columbus believed that he had arrived in the East Indies somewhere near India, but Earth's circumference had been substantially underestimated, so he was unaware that he had actually arrived in uncharted territory in the Caribbean. Upon his return to Spain and the announcement of his discovery, additional voyages were

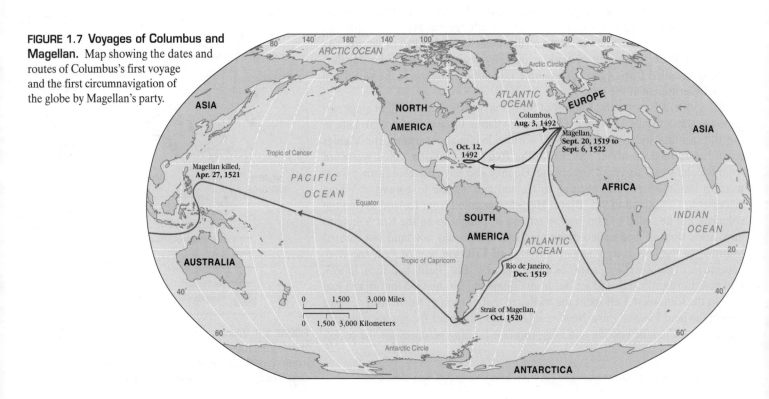

FIGURE 1.7 Voyages of Columbus and Magellan. Map showing the dates and routes of Columbus's first voyage and the first circumnavigation of the globe by Magellan's party.

planned. During the next 10 years, Columbus made three more trips across the Atlantic.

Even though Christopher Columbus is widely credited with discovering North America, he never actually set foot on the continent.[4] Still, his journeys inspired other navigators to explore the "New World." For example, in 1497, only five years after Columbus's first voyage, Englishman **John Cabot** landed somewhere on the northeast coast of North America. Later, Europeans first saw the Pacific Ocean in 1513, when **Vasco Núñez de Balboa** attempted a land crossing of the Isthmus of Panama and sighted a large ocean to the west from atop a mountain.

The culmination of the Age of Discovery was a remarkable circumnavigation of the globe initiated by **Ferdinand Magellan** (Figure 1.7). Magellan left Spain in September 1519, with five ships and 280 sailors. He crossed the Atlantic Ocean, sailed down the eastern coast of South America, and traveled through a passage to the Pacific Ocean at 52 degrees south latitude, now named the Strait of Magellan in his honor. After landing in the Philippines on March 15, 1521, Magellan was killed in a fight with the inhabitants of these islands. **Juan Sebastian del Caño** completed the circumnavigation by taking the last of the ships, the *Victoria*, across the Indian Ocean, around Africa, and back to Spain in 1522. After three years, just one ship and 18 men completed the voyage.

Following these voyages, the Spanish initiated many others to take gold from the Aztec and Inca cultures in Mexico and South America. The English and Dutch, meanwhile, used smaller, more maneuverable ships to rob the gold from bulky Spanish galleons, which resulted in many confrontations at sea. The maritime dominance of Spain ended when the English defeated the Spanish Armada in 1588. With control of the seas, the English thus became the dominant world power—a status they retained until early in the 20th century.

The Beginning of Voyaging for Science

The English realized that increasing their scientific knowledge of the oceans would help maintain their maritime superiority. For this reason, Captain **James Cook** (1728–1779), an English navigator and prolific explorer (Figure 1.8), undertook three voyages of scientific discovery with the ships *Endeavour*, *Resolution*, and *Adventure* between 1768 and 1779. He searched for the continent Terra Australis ("Southern Land," or Antarctica) and concluded that it lay beneath or beyond the extensive ice fields of the southern oceans, if it existed at all. Cook also mapped many previously unknown islands, including the South Georgia, South Sandwich, and Hawaiian islands. During his last voyage, Cook searched for the fabled "northwest passage" from the Pacific Ocean to the Atlantic Ocean and stopped in Hawaii, where he was killed in a skirmish with native Hawaiians.

Cook's expeditions added greatly to the scientific knowledge of the oceans. He determined the outline of the Pacific Ocean and was the first person known to cross the Antarctic Circle in his search for Antarctica. Cook initiated systematic sampling of subsurface water temperatures, measuring winds and currents, taking *soundings* (which are depth measurements that, at the time, were taken by lowering a long rope with a weight on the end to the sea floor), and collecting data on coral reefs. Cook also discovered that a shipboard diet containing the German staple sauerkraut prevented his crew from contracting scurvy, a disease that incapacitated sailors. Scurvy is caused by a vitamin C deficiency and the cabbage used to make sauerkraut contains large quantities of vitamin C. Prior to Cook's discovery about preventing scurvy, the malady claimed more lives than all other types of deaths at sea, including contagious disease, gunfire, and shipwreck. In addition, by proving the value of John Harrison's chronometer as a means of determining

---

[4]For more information about the voyages of Columbus, see Box 6.1 in Chapter 6, "Air-Sea Interaction."

FIGURE 1.8 Captain James Cook (1728–1779) and his voyages of exploration. Routes taken by Captain James Cook (*inset*) on his three scientific voyages, which initiated scientific exploration of the oceans. Cook was killed in 1779 in Hawaii during his third voyage.

Cook's first voyage 1768–71
Cook's second voyage 1772–75
Cook's third voyage 1776–80

longitude (see Box 1.2), Cook made possible the first accurate maps of Earth's surface, some of which are still in use today.

History of Oceanography . . . To Be Continued

Much has changed from the early days of studying the oceans. Today, oceanographers use many high-technology tools, such as state-of-the-art research vessels that routinely use sonar to map the sea floor, remotely operated data collection devices, robotics, sea floor observation networks, sophisticated computer models, and Earth-orbiting satellites. Many of these tools are featured throughout this book. Further, additional events in the history of oceanography can be found as historical feature boxes in subsequent chapters. These boxed features are identified by the "Historical Feature" theme and introduce an important historical event that is related to the subject of that particular chapter.

KEY CONCEPT

The ocean's large size did not prohibit early explorers from venturing into all parts of the ocean for discovery, trade, or conquest. Voyaging for science began relatively recently.

1.3 What Is the Nature of Scientific Inquiry?

In modern society, scientific studies are increasingly used to substantiate the need for action. However, there is often little understanding of how science operates. For instance, how certain are we about a particular scientific theory? How are facts different from theories?

The overall goal of science is to discover underlying patterns in the natural world and then to use this knowledge to make predictions about what should or should not be expected to happen given a certain set of circumstances. Scientists develop explanations about the causes and effects of various natural phenomena (such as why Earth has seasons or what the structure of matter is). This work is based on an assumption that all natural phenomena are controlled by understandable physical processes and the same physical processes operating today have been operating throughout time. Consequently, science has demonstrated remarkable power in allowing scientists to describe the natural world accurately, to identify the underlying causes of natural phenomena, and to better predict future events that rely on natural processes.

Science supports the explanation of the natural world that best explains all available observations. Scientific inquiry is formalized into what is called the **scientific method**, which is used to formulate scientific theories (Figure 1.9).

Observations

The scientific method begins with *observations*, which are occurrences we can measure with our senses. They are things we can manipulate, see, touch, hear, taste, or smell, often by experimenting with them directly or by using sophisticated tools (such as a microscope or telescope) to sense them. If an observation is repeatedly confirmed—that is, made so many times that it is assumed to be completely valid—then it can be called a *scientific fact*.

Hypothesis

As observations are being made, the human mind attempts to sort out the observations in a way that reveals some underlying order or pattern in the objects or phenomena being observed. This sorting process—which involves a lot of trial and error—seems to be driven by a fundamental human urge to make sense of our world. This is how **hypotheses** (*hypo* = under, *thesis* = an arranging) are made. A hypothesis is sometimes labeled as an informed or educated guess, but it is more than that. A hypothesis is a tentative, testable statement about the general nature of the phenomena observed. In other words, a hypothesis is an initial idea of how or why things happen in nature.

Suppose we want to understand why whales *breach* (that is, why whales sometimes leap entirely out of water). After scientists observe breaching many times, they can organize their observations into a hypothesis. For instance, one hypothesis is that a breaching whale is trying to dislodge parasites from its body. Scientists often have multiple working hypotheses (for example, whales may use breaching to communicate with other whales). If a hypothesis cannot be tested, it is not scientifically useful, no matter how interesting it might seem.

Testing

Hypotheses are used to predict certain occurrences that lead to further research and the refinement of those hypotheses. For instance, the hypothesis that a breaching whale is trying to dislodge its parasites suggests that breaching whales have more parasites than whales that don't breach. Analyzing the number of parasites on breaching versus nonbreaching whales would either support that hypothesis or cause it to be recycled and modified. If observations clearly suggest that the hypothesis is incorrect (the hypothesis is *falsified*), then it must be dropped and other alternative explanations of the facts must be considered.

In science, the validity of any explanation is determined by its coherence with observations in the natural world and its ability to predict further observations. Only after much testing and experimentation—usually done by many experimenters using a wide variety of repeatable tests—does a hypothesis gain validity where it can be advanced to the next step.

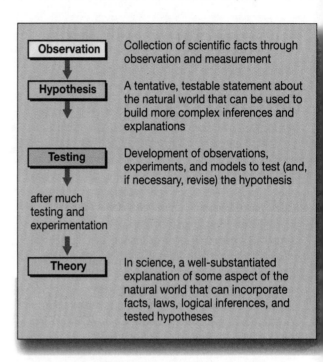

FIGURE 1.9 The scientific method. A flow diagram showing the main steps in the scientific method, along with definitions of terms. In actuality, the process of science is often less formally conducted than is implied in this figure.

Theory

If a hypothesis has been strengthened by additional observations and if it is successful in predicting additional phenomena, then it can be advanced to what is called a **theory** (*theoria* = a looking at) A theory is a well-substantiated explanation of some aspect of the natural world that can incorporate facts, laws (descriptive generalizations about the behavior of an aspect of the natural world), logical inferences, and tested hypotheses. A theory is not a guess or a hunch. Rather, it is an understanding that develops from extensive observation, experimentation, and creative reflection.

In science, theories are formalized only after many years of testing and verifying predictions. Thus, scientific theories are those that have been rigorously scrutinized to the point where most scientists agree that they are the best explanation of certain observable facts. Examples of prominent, well-accepted theories that are held with a very high degree of confidence include biology's theory of evolution (which is discussed later in this chapter) and geology's theory of plate tectonics (which will be covered in the next chapter).

Theories and the Truth

We've seen how the scientific method is used to develop theories, but does science ever arrive at the undisputed "truth"? Science never reaches an absolute truth because we can never be certain that we have all the observations, especially considering that new technology will be available in the future to examine phenomena in different ways. New observations are always possible, so the nature of scientific truth is subject to change. Therefore, it is more accurate to say that science arrives at that which is *probably* true, based on the available observations.

It is not a downfall of science that scientific ideas are modified as more observations are collected. In fact, the opposite is true. Science is a process that depends on reexamining ideas as new observations are made. Thus, science progresses when new observations yield new hypotheses and modification of theories. As a result, science is littered with hypotheses that have been abandoned in favor of later explanations that fit new observations. One of the best known is the idea that Earth was at the center of the universe, a proposal that was supported by the apparent daily motion of the Sun, Moon, and stars around Earth.

The statements of science should never be accepted as the "final truth." Over time, however, they generally form a sequence of increasingly more accurate statements. Theories are the endpoints in science and do not turn into facts through accumulation of evidence. Nevertheless, the data can become so convincing that the accuracy of a theory is no longer questioned. For instance, the *heliocentric* (*helios* = sun, *centric* = center) *theory* of our solar system states that Earth revolves around the Sun rather than vice versa. Such concepts are supported by such abundant observational and experimental evidence that they are no longer questioned in science.

Is there really such a formal method to science as the scientific method suggests? Actually, the work of scientists is much less formal and is not always done in a clearly logical and systematic manner. Like detectives analyzing a crime scene, scientists use ingenuity and serendipity, visualize models, and sometimes follow hunches in order to unravel the mysteries of nature.

1.4 How Were Earth and the Solar System Created?

Earth is the third of eight major planets[5] in our **solar system** that revolve around the Sun (Figure 1.10). Evidence suggests that the Sun and the rest of the solar system formed about 5 billion years ago from a huge cloud of gas and space dust

[5]Pluto, which used to be considered the ninth planet in our solar system, was reclassified by the International Astronomical Union as a "dwarf planet" in 2006, along with other similar bodies.

(a)

(b)

FIGURE 1.10 The solar system. **(a)** Schematic view of the planets and other features of the solar system. **(b)** Relative sizes of the Sun and the eight major planets. Distance not to scale.

called a **nebula** (*nebula* = a cloud) Astronomers base this hypothesis on the orderly nature of our solar system and the consistent age of meteorites (pieces of the early solar system). Using sophisticated telescopes, astronomers have also been able to observe distant nebula in various stages of formation (Figure 1.11). In addition, more than 300 planets have been discovered outside our solar system—including one that is about the size of Earth—by detecting the telltale wobble of distant stars.

The Nebular Hypothesis

According to the **nebular hypothesis** (Figure 1.12), all bodies in the solar system formed from an enormous cloud composed mostly of hydrogen and helium, with only a small percentage of heavier elements. As this huge accumulation of gas and dust revolved around its center, the Sun began to form as magnetic fields and turbulence worked with the force of gravity to concentrate particles. In its early stages, the diameter of the Sun may have equaled or exceeded the diameter of our entire planetary system today.

As the nebular matter that formed the Sun contracted, small amounts of it were left behind in eddies, which are similar to small whirlpools in a stream. The material in these eddies was the beginning of the **protoplanets** (*proto* = original, *planetes* = wanderer) and their orbiting satellites, which later consolidated into the present planets and their moons.

Protoearth

Protoearth looked very different from Earth today. Its size was larger than today's Earth, and there were neither oceans nor any life on the planet. In addition, the structure of the deep Protoearth is thought to have been *homogenous* (*homo* = alike, *genous* = producing), which means that it had a uniform composition

FIGURE 1.11 The Ghost Head Nebula. NASA's Hubble Space Telescope image of the Ghost Head Nebula (NGC 2080), which is a site of active star formation.

throughout. The structure of Protoearth changed, however, when its heavier constituents migrated toward the center to form a heavy core.

During this early stage of formation, many meteorites from space bombarded Protoearth (Figure 1.13). In fact, a leading theory states that the Moon was born in the aftermath of a titanic collision between a Mars-size planet named *Theia* and the Protoearth. While most of Theia was swallowed up and incorporated into the magma ocean it created on impact, the collision also flung a small world's worth of vaporized and molten rock into orbit. Over time, this debris coalesced into a sphere and created Earth's orbiting companion, the Moon.

During this early formation of the protoplanets and their satellites, the Sun condensed into such a hot, concentrated mass that forces within its interior began releasing energy through a process known as a **fusion** (*fusus* = melted) **reaction**. A fusion reaction occurs when temperatures reach tens of millions of degrees and hydrogen **atoms** (*a* = not, *tomos* = cut) combine to form helium atoms, releasing large amounts of energy.[6] Not only does the Sun emit light, but it also emits *ionized* (electrically charged) particles that make up the *solar wind*. During the early stages of creation of the solar system, this solar wind blew away the nebular gas that remained from the formation of the planets and their satellites.

Meanwhile, the protoplanets closest to the Sun (including Earth) were heated so intensely by solar radiation that their initial atmospheres (mostly hydrogen and helium) boiled away. In addition, the combination of ionized solar particles and internal warming of these protoplanets caused them to

The Nebular Hypothesis of Solar System Formation

FIGURE 1.12 The nebular hypothesis of solar system formation. **(a)** A huge cloud of dust and gases (a nebula) contracts. **(b)** Most of the material is gravitationally swept toward the center, producing the Sun, while the remainder flattens into a disk. **(c)** Small eddies are created by the circular motion. **(d)** In time, most of the remaining debris forms the planets and their moons.

---

[6]Fusion in stars also combines higher elements to form even higher elements, such as carbon. As a result, all matter—even the matter that comprises our bodies—originated as stardust long ago.

FIGURE 1.13 Protoearth. An artist's conception of what Earth looked like early in its development.

drastically shrink in size. As the protoplanets continued to contract, heat was produced deep within their cores from the spontaneous disintegration of atoms, called *radioactivity* (*radio* = ray, *acti* = to cause).

Density and Density Stratification

Density, which is an extremely important physical property of matter, is defined as mass per unit volume. In common terms, an easy way to think about density is that it is a measure of *how heavy something is for its size*. For instance, an object that has a low density is light for its size (like a dry sponge, foam packing, or a surfboard). Conversely, an object that has a high density is heavy for its size (like cement, most metals, or a large container full of water). Note that density has nothing to do with the *thickness* of an object; some objects (like a stack of foam packing) can be thick but have low density. In reality, density is related to molecular packing, with higher packing of molecules into a certain space resulting in higher density. As we'll see, the density of Earth's layers dramatically affects their positions within Earth. In subsequent chapters, we'll also explore how the density of air masses affects their properties and how the density of water masses influences their position and movement.

The release of internal heat was so intense that Earth's surface became molten. Once Earth became a ball of hot liquid rock, the elements were able to segregate according to their densities in a process called **density stratification** (*strati* = a layer, *fication* = making), which occurs because of *gravitational separation*. The highest-density materials (primarily iron and nickel) concentrated in the core, whereas progressively lower-density components (primarily rocky material) formed concentric spheres around the core. If you've ever noticed how oil-and-vinegar salad dressing settles out into a lower-density top layer (the oil) and a higher-density bottom layer (the vinegar), then you've seen how density stratification causes separate layers to form.

Earth's Internal Structure

As a result of density stratification, Earth became a layered sphere based on density, with the highest-density material found near the center of Earth and the lowest-density material located near the surface. Let's examine Earth's internal structure and the characteristics of its layers.

CHEMICAL COMPOSITION VERSUS PHYSICAL PROPERTIES   The cross-sectional view of Earth in Figure 1.14 shows that Earth's inner structure can be subdivided according to its chemical composition (the chemical makeup of Earth materials) or its physical properties (how the rocks respond to increased temperature and pressure at depth).

CHEMICAL COMPOSITION   Based on chemical composition, Earth consists of three layers: the **crust**, the **mantle**, and the **core** (Figure 1.14). If Earth were reduced to the size of an apple, then the crust would be its thin skin. It extends

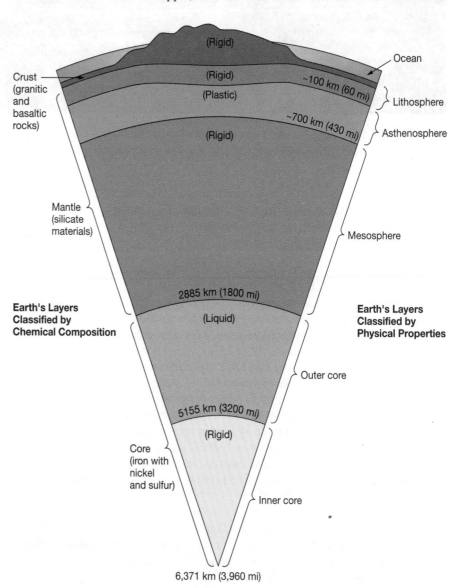

FIGURE 1.14 Comparison of Earth's chemical composition and physical properties. A cross-sectional view of Earth, showing Earth's layers classified by chemical composition along the left side of the diagram. For comparison, Earth's layers classified by physical properties are shown along the right side of the diagram.

from the surface to an average depth of about 30 kilometers (20 miles). The crust is composed of relatively low-density rock, consisting mostly of various *silicate minerals* (common rock-forming minerals with silicon and oxygen). There are two types of crust, oceanic and continental, which will be discussed in the next section.

Immediately below the crust is the mantle. It occupies the largest volume of the three layers and extends to a depth of about 2885 kilometers (1800 miles). The mantle is composed of relatively high-density iron and magnesium silicate rock.

Beneath the mantle is the core. It forms a large mass from 2885 kilometers (1800 miles) to the center of Earth at 6371 kilometers (3960 miles). The core is composed of even higher-density metal (mostly iron and nickel).

PHYSICAL PROPERTIES   Based on physical properties, Earth is composed of five layers (Figure 1.14): the **inner core**, the **outer core**, the **mesosphere** (*mesos* = middle, *sphere* = ball), the **asthenosphere** (*asthenos* = weak, *sphere* = ball), and the **lithosphere** (*lithos* = rock, *sphere* = ball).

The lithosphere is Earth's cool, rigid, outermost layer. It extends from the surface to an average depth of about 100 kilometers (62 miles) and includes the crust plus the topmost portion of the mantle. The lithosphere is *brittle* (*brytten* = to shatter), meaning that it will fracture when force is applied to it. As will be discussed in Chapter 2, "Plate Tectonics and the Ocean Floor," the plates involved in plate tectonic motion are the plates of the lithosphere.

Beneath the lithosphere is the asthenosphere. The asthenosphere is *plastic* (*plasticus* = molded), meaning that it will flow when a gradual force is applied to it. It extends from about 100 kilometers (62 miles) to 700 kilometers (430 miles) below the surface, which is the base of the upper mantle. At these depths, it is hot enough to partially melt portions of most rocks.

Beneath the asthenosphere is the mesosphere. The mesosphere extends to a depth of about 2885 kilometers (1800 miles), which corresponds to the middle and lower mantle. Although the asthenosphere deforms plastically, the mesosphere is rigid, most likely due to the increased pressure at these depths.

Beneath the mesosphere is the core. The core consists of the outer core, which is liquid and capable of flowing, and the inner core, which is rigid and does not flow. Again, the increased pressure at the center of Earth keeps the inner core from flowing.

NEAR THE SURFACE   The top portion of Figure 1.16 shows an enlargement of Earth's layers closest to the surface.

Lithosphere   The lithosphere is a relatively cool, rigid shell that includes all the crust and the topmost part of the mantle. In essence, the topmost part of the mantle is attached to the crust and the two act as a single unit, approximately 100 kilometers (62 miles) thick. The expanded view in Figure 1.16 shows that the crust portion of the lithosphere is further subdivided into oceanic crust and continental crust, which are compared in Table 1.1.

Oceanic versus Continental Crust   **Oceanic crust** underlies the ocean basins and is composed of the igneous rock **basalt**, which is dark colored and has a relatively high density of about 3.0 grams per cubic centimeter.[7] The average thickness of the oceanic crust is only about 8 kilometers (5 miles). Basalt originates as molten magma beneath Earth's crust (typically from the mantle), some of which comes to the surface during underwater sea floor eruptions.

Continental crust is composed mostly of the lower-density and lighter-colored igneous rock **granite**.[8] It has a density of about 2.7 grams per cubic centimeter. The

---

[7]Water has a density of 1.0 grams per cubic centimeter. Thus, basalt with a density of 3.0 grams per cubic centimeter is three times denser than water.

[8]At the surface, continental crust is often covered by a relatively thin layer of surface sediments. Below these, granite can be found.

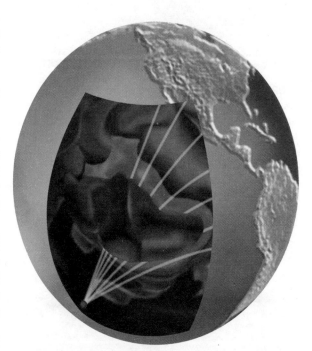

FIGURE 1.15 Determining the internal structure of Earth. When an earthquake occurs (*red dot*), it sends seismic waves through Earth's interior, which is shown diagrammatically. Detection of these seismic waves around the globe reveals information about the structure, composition, and properties of the deep Earth.

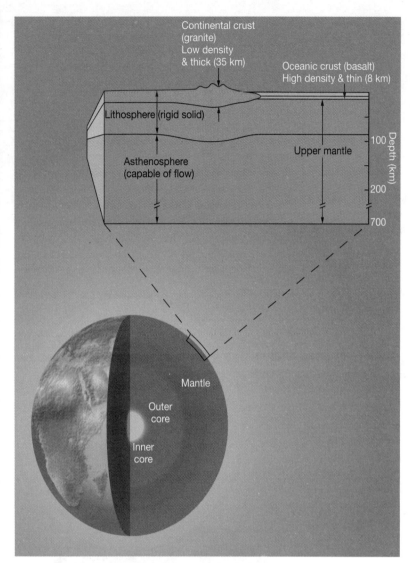

FIGURE 1.16 Internal structure of Earth.
Enlargement (*top*) shows that the rigid lithosphere includes the crust (either continental or oceanic) plus the topmost part of the mantle to a depth of about 100 kilometers (60 miles). Beneath the lithosphere, the plastic asthenosphere extends to a depth of 700 kilometers (430 miles).

average thickness of the continental crust is about 35 kilometers (22 miles) but may reach a maximum of 60 kilometers (37 miles) beneath the highest mountain ranges. Most granite originates beneath the surface as molten magma that cools and hardens within Earth's crust. No matter which type of crust is at the surface, it is all part of the lithosphere.

Asthenosphere The asthenosphere is a relatively hot, plastic region beneath the lithosphere. It extends from the base of the lithosphere to a depth of about 700 kilometers (430 miles) and is entirely contained within the upper mantle. The asthenosphere can deform without fracturing if a force is applied slowly. This means that it has the ability to flow but has high **viscosity** (*viscosus* = sticky). Viscosity is a measure of a substance's resistance to flow.[9] Studies indicate that the high-viscosity asthenosphere is flowing slowly through time; this has important implications for the movement of lithospheric plates.

ISOSTATIC ADJUSTMENT Isostatic (*iso* = equal, *stasis* = standing) **adjustment**—the vertical movement of crust—is the result of the buoyancy of Earth's lithosphere as it floats on the denser, plasticlike asthenosphere below. Figure 1.17, which shows a container ship floating in water, provides an example of isostatic adjustment. It shows that an empty ship floats high in the water. Once the ship is loaded with cargo, though, the ship undergoes isostatic adjustment and floats lower in the water (but hopefully won't sink!). When the cargo is unloaded, the ship isostatically adjusts itself and floats higher again.

Similarly, both continental and oceanic crust float on the denser mantle beneath. Oceanic crust is denser than continental crust, however, so oceanic crust floats lower in the mantle because of isostatic adjustment. Oceanic crust is also thin, which creates low areas for the oceans to occupy. Areas where the continental crust is thickest (such as large mountain ranges on the continents) float higher than continental crust of normal thickness, also because of isostatic

FIGURE 1.17 A container ship experiences isostatic adjustment. A ship will ride higher in water when it is empty and will ride lower in water when it is loaded with cargo, illustrating the principle of isostatic adjustment.

TABLE 1.1	COMPARING OCEANIC AND CONTINENTAL CRUST	
	Oceanic crust	**Continental crust**
Main rock type	Basalt (dark-colored igneous rock)	Granite (light-colored igneous rock)
Density (grams per cubic centimeter)	3.0	2.7
Average thickness	8 kilometers (5 miles)	35 kilometers (22 miles)

[9]Substances that have high viscosity (a high resistance to flow) include toothpaste, honey, tar, and Silly Putty; a common substance that has low viscosity is water. A substance's viscosity often changes with temperature. For instance, as honey is heated, it flows more easily.

adjustment. These mountains are similar to the top of a floating iceberg—they float high because there is a very thick mass of crustal material beneath them, plunged deeper into the asthenosphere. Thus, tall mountain ranges on Earth are composed of a great thickness of crustal material that in essence keeps them buoyed up.

Areas that are exposed to an increased or decreased load experience isostatic adjustment. For instance, during the most recent ice age (which occurred during the Pleistocene Epoch between about 1.8 million and 10,000 years ago), massive ice sheets alternately covered and exposed northern regions such as Scandinavia and northern Canada. The additional weight of ice several kilometers thick caused these areas to isostatically adjust themselves lower in the mantle. Since the end of the ice age, the reduced load on these areas caused by the melting of ice caused these areas to rise and experience **isostatic rebound**, which continues today. The rate at which isostatic rebound occurs gives scientists important information about the properties of the upper mantle.

Further, isostatic adjustment provides additional evidence for the movement of Earth's tectonic plates. Because continents isostatically adjust themselves by moving *vertically*, then they must not be firmly fixed in one position on Earth. If this is true, the plates that contain these continents should certainly be able to move *horizontally* across Earth's surface. This idea will be explored in more detail in the next chapter.

1.5 How Were Earth's Atmosphere and Oceans Created?

The creation of Earth's atmosphere is related to the creation of the oceans; both are a direct result of density stratification.

Origin of Earth's Atmosphere

Where did the atmosphere come from? As previously mentioned, Earth's initial atmosphere consisted of leftover gases from the nebula, but those particles were blown out to space by the Sun's solar wind. After that, a second atmosphere was most likely expelled from inside Earth by a process called **outgassing**. During the period of density stratification, the lowest-density material contained within Earth was composed of various gases. These gases rose to the surface and were expelled to form Earth's early atmosphere.

What was the composition of these atmospheric gases? They are believed to have been similar to the gases emitted from volcanoes, geysers, and hot springs today: mostly water vapor (steam), with small amounts of carbon dioxide, hydrogen, and other gases. The composition of this early atmosphere was not, however, the same composition as today's atmosphere. The composition of the atmosphere changed over time because of the influence of life (as will be discussed shortly) and possibly because of changes in the mixing of material in the mantle.

Origin of Earth's Oceans

Where did the oceans come from? Their origin is directly linked to the origin of the atmosphere. Figure 1.18 shows that as Earth cooled, the water vapor released to the atmosphere during outgassing condensed and fell to Earth. Evidence suggests that by at least 4 billion years ago, most of the water vapor from outgassing had accumulated to form the first permanent oceans on Earth.

THE DEVELOPMENT OF OCEAN SALINITY   The relentless rainfall that landed on Earth's rocky surface dissolved many elements and compounds and carried them into the newly forming oceans. Even though Earth's oceans have existed since early in the formation of the planet, its chemical composition must have

FIGURE 1.18 Formation of Earth's oceans. Early in Earth's history, widespread volcanic activity released large amounts of water vapor (H_2O vapor) and smaller quantities of other gases. As Earth cooled, the water vapor **(a)** condensed into clouds and **(b)** fell to Earth's surface, where it accumulated to form the oceans **(c)**.

Have the oceans always been salty? Are the oceans growing more or less salty through time?

It is likely that the oceans have always been salty because wherever water comes in contact with the rocks of Earth's crust, some of the minerals dissolve. This is the source of salts in the oceans, whether from stream runoff or dissolving directly from the sea floor. Today, new minerals are forming on the sea floor at the same rate as dissolved materials are added. Thus, the salt content of the ocean is in a "steady state," meaning that it is not increasing or decreasing.

Interestingly, these questions can also be answered by studying the proportion of water vapor to chloride ion, Cl^-, in ancient marine rocks. Chloride ion is important because it forms part of the most common salts in the ocean (for example, sodium chloride, potassium chloride, and magnesium chloride). Also, chloride ion is produced by outgassing, like the water vapor that formed the oceans. Currently, there is no indication that the ratio of water vapor to chloride ion has fluctuated throughout geologic time, so it can be reasonably concluded that the oceans' salinity has been relatively constant through time.

KEY CONCEPT
Originally, Earth had no oceans. The oceans (and atmosphere) came from inside Earth as a result of outgassing and were present by at least 4 billion years ago.

changed. This is because the high carbon dioxide and sulfur dioxide content in the early atmosphere would have created a very acidic rain, capable of dissolving greater amounts of minerals in the crust than occurs today. In addition, volcanic gases such as chlorine became dissolved in the atmosphere. As rain fell and washed to the ocean, it carried some of these dissolved compounds, which accumulated in the newly forming oceans.[10] Eventually, a balance between inputs and outputs was reached, producing an ocean with a chemical composition similar to today's oceans. Further aspects of the oceans' salinity are explored in Chapter 5, "Water and Seawater."

1.6 Did Life Begin in the Oceans?

The fundamental question of how life began on Earth has puzzled humankind since ancient times and has recently received a great amount of scientific study. The evidence required to understand our planet's prebiotic environment and the events that led to first living systems is scant and difficult to decipher. Still, the inventory of current views on life's origin reveals a broad assortment of opposing positions. One recent hypothesis is that the organic building blocks of life may have arrived embedded in meteors, comets, or cosmic dust. Alternatively, life may have originated around hydrothermal vents—hot springs—on the deep-ocean floor. Yet another idea is that life originated in certain minerals that acted as chemical catalysts within rocks deep below Earth's surface.

According to the fossil record on Earth, the earliest known life forms were primitive bacteria that lived in sea floor rocks about 3.5 billion years ago. Unfortunately, Earth's geologic record for these early times is so sparse and the rocks so deformed by Earth processes that the rocks no longer reveal life's precursor molecules. In addition, there is no direct evidence of Earth's environmental conditions (such as its temperature, ocean acidity, or the exact composition of the atmosphere) at the time of life's origin. Still, it is clear that the basic building blocks for the development of life were available from materials already present on the early Earth. And the oceans were the most likely place for these materials to interact and produce life.

The Importance of Oxygen to Life

Oxygen, which comprises almost 21% of Earth's present atmosphere, is essential to human life for two reasons. First, our bodies need oxygen to "burn" (*oxidize*) food, releasing energy to our cells. Second, oxygen in the upper atmosphere in the form of *ozone* (*ozone* = to smell[11]) protects the surface of Earth from most of the Sun's harmful ultraviolet radiation (which is why the atmospheric ozone hole over Antarctica has generated such concern).

Evidence suggests that Earth's early atmosphere (the product of outgassing) was different from Earth's initial hydrogen–helium atmosphere and different from the mostly nitrogen–oxygen atmosphere of today. The early atmosphere probably contained large percentages of water vapor and carbon dioxide and smaller percentages of hydrogen, methane, and ammonia but very little free oxygen (oxygen that is not chemically bound to other atoms). Why was there so little free oxygen in the early atmosphere? Oxygen may well have been outgassed, but oxygen and iron have a strong affinity for each other.[12] As a result, iron in Earth's early crust would have reacted with the outgassed oxygen immediately, removing it from the atmosphere.

Without oxygen in Earth's early atmosphere, moreover, there would have been no ozone layer to block most of the Sun's ultraviolet radiation. The lack of a

---

[10]Note that some of these dissolved components were removed or modified by chemical reactions between ocean water and rocks on the sea floor.

[11]Ozone gets its name because of its pungent, irritating odor.

[12]As an example of the strong affinity of iron and oxygen, consider how common rust—a compound of iron and oxygen—is on Earth's surface.

protective ozone layer may, in fact, have played a crucial role in several of life's most important developmental milestones.

Stanley Miller's Experiment

In 1952, a 22-year-old graduate student of chemist Harold Urey at the University of Chicago named **Stanley Miller** (Figure 1.19b) conducted a laboratory experiment that had profound implications about the development of life on Earth. In Miller's experiment, he exposed a mixture of carbon dioxide, methane, ammonia, hydrogen, and water (the components of the early atmosphere and ocean) to ultraviolet light (from the Sun) and an electrical spark (to imitate lightning) (Figure 1.19a). By the end of the first day, the mixture turned pink and after a week it was a deep, muddy brown, indicating the formation of a large assortment of organic molecules including amino acids, which are the basic components of life, and other biologically significant compounds.

Miller's now-famous laboratory experiment of a simulated primitive Earth in a bottle—which has been duplicated and confirmed numerous times since—demonstrated that vast amounts of organic molecules could have been produced in Earth's early oceans, often called a "prebiotic soup." This "prebiotic soup," perhaps spiced by extraterrestrial molecules aboard comets, meteorites, or interplanetary dust, was fueled by raw materials from volcanoes, certain minerals in sea floor rocks, and undersea hydrothermal vents. On the early Earth, the mixture was energized by lightning, cosmic rays, and the planet's own internal heat, and is thought to have created life's precursor molecules about 4 billion years ago.

Exactly how these simple organic compounds in the "prebiotic soup" assembled themselves into more complex molecules—such as proteins and DNA—and then into the first living entities remains one of the most tantalizing questions in science. Recent research suggests that with the vast array of organic compounds available in the "prebiotic soup," several kinds of chemical reactions led to increasingly more elaborate molecular complexes. Among these complexes, some began to carry out functions associated with the basic molecules of life. As the products of one generation became the building blocks for another, complex molecules, or polymers, emerged over many generations that could store and transfer information. Such genetic polymers ultimately became encapsulated within cell-like membranes that were also present in Earth's primitive broth. The resulting cell-like complexes thereby housed self-replicating molecules capable of multiplying—and

STUDENTS SOMETIMES ASK...

You mentioned that the oceans came from inside Earth. However, I've heard that the oceans came from outer space as icy comets. Which one is true?

Comets, being about half water, were once widely held to be the source of Earth's oceans. During Earth's early development, space debris left over from the origin of the solar system bombarded the young planet, and there could have been plenty of water supplied to Earth. However, spectral analyses of the chemical composition of three comets—Halley, Hyakutake, and Hale-Bopp—during near-Earth passes they made in 1986, 1996, and 1997, respectively, revealed a crucial chemical difference between the hydrogen in comet ice and that in Earth's water. If comets supplied large quantities of water to Earth, much of Earth's water would still exhibit the telltale type of hydrogen identified in comets. Instead, this type of hydrogen is exceedingly rare in water on Earth. Assuming that the compositions of these three comets are representative of all comets, it seems unlikely that comets supplied much water to Earth.

FIGURE 1.19 Creation of organic molecules.
(a) Laboratory apparatus used by Stanley Miller to simulate the conditions of the early atmosphere and the oceans. The experiment produced various organic molecules and suggests that the basic components of life were created in a "prebiotic soup" in the oceans. **(b)** Stanley Miller in 1999, with his famous apparatus in the foreground.

THE VOYAGE OF HMS *BEAGLE*: HOW IT SHAPED CHARLES DARWIN'S THINKING ABOUT THE THEORY OF EVOLUTION

Nothing in biology makes sense except in the light of evolution.
    —*Geneticist Theodosius Dobzhansky (1973)*

In the early 19th century, the English naturalist **Charles Darwin** (1809–1882) proposed the *theory of evolution* by natural selection, which explains how biologic processes operating in nature produce the many diverse and remarkable species on Earth. Many of the observations upon which he based the theory were made aboard the vessel HMS *Beagle* during its famous expedition from 1831 to 1836 that circumnavigated the globe (Figure 1F).

Darwin became interested in natural history during his student days at Cambridge University, where he was studying to become a minister. Because of the influence of John Henslow, a professor of botany, he was selected to serve as an unpaid naturalist on the HMS *Beagle*. The *Beagle* sailed from Devonport, England, on December 27, 1831, under the command of Captain Robert Fitzroy. The major objective of the voyage was to complete a survey of the coast of Patagonia (Argentina) and Tierra del Fuego and to make chronometric measurements. The voyage allowed the 22-year-old Darwin—who was often seasick—to disembark at various locations and study local plants and animals. What particularly influenced his thinking about evolution were the discovery of fossils in South America and the identification of 14 closely related species of finches in the Galápagos Islands. These finches differ greatly in the configuration of their beaks (Figure 1F, *left inset*), which are suited to their diverse feeding habitats. After his return to England, he noted the adaptations of finches and other organisms living in different habitats and concluded that all organisms change slowly over time as a product of their environment.

Darwin recognized the similarities between birds and mammals and reasoned that they must have evolved from reptiles. Patiently making observations over many years, he also noted the similar skeletal framework of species such as bats, horses, giraffes, elephants, porpoises, and humans, which led him to establish relationships between various groups. Darwin suggested that the differences between species were the result of adaptation over time to different environments and modes of existence.

In 1858, Darwin hastily published a summary of his ideas about natural selection because fellow naturalist *Alfred Russel Wallace*, working half a world away in what is now Indonesia, had independently discovered the same idea. A year later, Darwin published his remarkable masterwork *On the Origin of Species by Means of Natural Selection* (Figure 1F, *right inset*), in which he provided extensive and compelling evidence that all living beings—including humans—have evolved from a common ancestor. At the time, Darwin's ideas were highly controversial because they stood in stark conflict with what most people believed about the origin of humans. Darwin also produced important publications on subjects as diverse as barnacle biology, carnivorous plants, and the formation of coral reefs.

Over 150 years later, Darwin's theory of evolution is still considered a landmark influence in the scientific understanding of the underlying biologic processes operating in nature. Evolution is now as well established by argument and evidence and reproducible experiment as any truth in science and as well established a theory as any in the history of science. Discoveries made since Darwin's time—including genetics and the structure of DNA—confirm how the process of evolution works. In fact, most of Darwin's ideas

KEY CONCEPT
Organic molecules were produced in a simulation of Earth's early atmosphere and ocean, suggesting that life most likely originated in the oceans.

hence evolving—genetic information. Many specialists consider this emergence of genetic replication to be the true origin of life.

Evolution and Natural Selection

Every living organism that inhabits Earth today is the result of **evolution** by the process of **natural selection** that has been occurring since life first existed on Earth. The theory of evolution states that groups of organisms adapt and change with the passage of time, causing descendants to differ morphologically and physiologically from their ancestors (Box 1.3). Certain advantageous traits are naturally selected and passed on from one generation to the next. Evolution is the process by which various **species** (*species* = a kind) have been able to inhabit increasingly numerous environments on Earth.

As we shall see, when species adapt to Earth's various environments, they can also modify the environments in which they live. This modification can be localized or nearly global in scale. For example, when plants emerged from the oceans

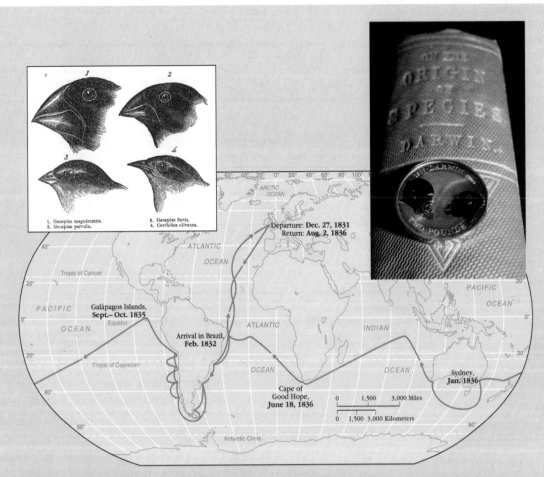

FIGURE 1F Charles Darwin: Galápagos finches, route of the HMS *Beagle*, and the *Origin of Species*. Map showing the route of the HMS *Beagle*, beak differences in Galápagos finches (*left inset*) that greatly influenced Charles Darwin, and the new British two-pound coin commemorating Darwin and his masterwork *On the Origin of Species* (*right inset*).

have been so thoroughly accepted by scientists that they are now the underpinnings of the modern study of biology. That's why the name *Darwin* is synony-mous with evolution. In 2009, to commemorate Darwin's birth and his accomplishments, the Church of England even issued this formal apology to Darwin: "The Church of England owes you an apology for misunderstanding you and, by getting our first reaction wrong, encouraging others to misunderstand you still."

and inhabited the land, they changed Earth from a harsh and bleak landscape as barren as the Moon to one that is green and lush.

Plants and Animals Evolve

The very earliest forms of life were probably **heterotrophs** (*hetero* = different, *trophos* = nourishment). Heterotrophs require an external food supply, which was abundantly available in the form of nonliving organic matter in the ocean around them. **Autotrophs** (*auto* = self, *trophos* = nourishment), which can manufacture their own food supply, evolved later. The first autotrophs were probably similar to present-day **anaerobic** (*an* = without, *aero* = air) bacteria, which live without atmospheric oxygen. They may have been able to derive energy from inorganic compounds at deep-water hydrothermal vents using a process called **chemosynthesis** (*chemo* = chemistry, *syn* = with, *thesis* = an arranging).[13] In fact,

---

[13]More details about chemosynthesis are discussed in Chapter 15, "Animals of the Benthic Environment."

FIGURE 1.20 Photosynthesis (*top*), respiration (*middle*), and representative reactions viewed chemically (*bottom*). The process of photosynthesis, which is accomplished by plants, is represented in the upper panel. The second panel shows respiration, which is done by animals. Both processes are shown chemically in the third panel.

the recent detection of microbes deep within the ocean crust as well as the discovery of 3.2-billion-year-old microfossils of bacteria from deep-water marine rocks support the idea of life's origin on the deep-ocean floor in the absence of light.

PHOTOSYNTHESIS AND RESPIRATION Eventually, more complex single-celled autotrophs evolved. They developed a green pigment called **chlorophyll** (*chloro* = green, *phyll* = leaf), which captures the Sun's energy through cellular **photosynthesis** (*photo* = light, *syn* = with, *thesis* = an arranging). In photosynthesis (Figure 1.20, *top*), plant cells capture light energy and store it as sugars. In cellular **respiration** (*respirare* = to breathe) (Figure 1.20, *middle*), sugars are oxidized with oxygen, releasing stored energy that is used as a source of energy by the organism that consumes the plant to carry on various life processes.

Not only are photosynthesis and respiration chemically opposite processes, they are also complementary because the products of photosynthesis (sugars and oxygen) are used during respiration and the products of respiration (water and carbon dioxide) are used in photosynthesis (Figure 1.20, *bottom*). Thus, autotrophs (algae and plants) and heterotrophs (most bacteria and animals) have developed a mutual need for each other.

The oldest fossilized remains of organisms are primitive photosynthetic bacteria recovered from rocks formed on the sea floor about 3.5 billion years ago. However, the oldest rocks containing iron oxide (rust)—an indicator of an oxygen-rich atmosphere—did not appear until about 2.4 billion years ago. Thus, photosynthetic organisms needed about a billion years to develop and begin producing abundant free oxygen in the atmosphere. At the same time, when a large amount of oxygen-rich (ferric) iron sank to the base of the mantle, it may have been heated by the core, risen as a plume to the ocean floor, and begun releasing large amounts of oxygen through outgassing about 2.5 billion years ago.

THE GREAT OXIDATION EVENT/OXYGEN CRISIS Based on the chemical makeup of certain rocks, Earth's atmosphere became oxygen rich about 2.45 billion years ago—called the *great oxidation event*—and fundamentally changed Earth's ability to support life. Particularly for anaerobic bacteria, which had grown successfully in an oxygen-free world, all this oxygen was nothing short of a catastrophe! This is because the increased atmospheric oxygen caused the ozone concentration in the upper atmosphere to build up, thereby shielding Earth's surface from ultraviolet

FIGURE 1.21 The effect of plants on Earth's environment. As microscopic photosynthetic cells (*inset*) became established in the ocean, Earth's atmosphere was enriched in oxygen and depleted of carbon dioxide. As organisms died and accumulated on the ocean floor, some of their remains were converted to oil and gas. The same process occurred on land, sometimes producing coal.

radiation—and effectively eliminating anaerobic bacteria's food supply of organic molecules (recall that Stanley Miller's experiment created organic molecules but needed ultraviolet light). In addition, oxygen (particularly in the presence of light) is highly reactive with organic matter. When anaerobic bacteria are exposed to oxygen and light, they are killed instantaneously. By 1.8 billion years ago, the atmosphere's oxygen content had increased to such a high level that it began causing the extinction of many anaerobic organisms. Nonetheless, descendants of such bacteria survive on Earth today in isolated microenvironments that are dark and free of oxygen, such as deep in soil or rocks, in garbage, and inside other organisms.

Although oxygen is very reactive with organic matter and can even be toxic, it also yields nearly 20 times more energy than anaerobic respiration—a fact that some organisms exploited. For example, blue-green algae, which are also known as *cyanobacteria* (*kuanos* = dark blue), adapted to and thrived in this new oxygen-rich environment. In doing so, they altered the composition of the atmosphere.

CHANGES TO EARTH'S ATMOSPHERE Remarkably, the development and successful evolution of photosynthetic organisms are greatly responsible for the world as we know it today (Figure 1.21). By the trillions, these microscopic organisms transformed the planet by capturing the energy of the Sun to make food and releasing oxygen as a waste product. By this process, these organisms reduced the high amount of carbon dioxide in the early atmosphere and gradually replaced it with free oxygen. This created a third and final atmosphere on Earth: one that is oxygen rich (about 21% today). Little by little, these tiny organisms turned the atmosphere into breathable air, opening the way to the diversity of life that followed.

The graph in Figure 1.22 shows how the concentration of atmospheric oxygen has varied during the past 600 million years. When atmospheric oxygen concentrations are high, organisms thrive and rapid speciation occurs. At such times in the past, insects grew to gargantuan proportions, reptiles took to the air, and the forerunners of mammals developed a warm-blooded metabolism. More oxygen was dissolved in the oceans, too, and so marine biodiversity increased. At other times when atmospheric oxygen concentrations fell precipitously, biodiversity

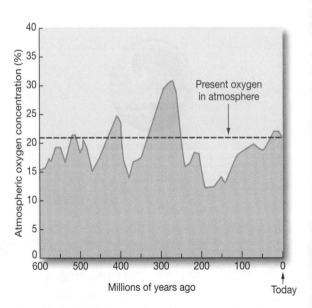

FIGURE 1.22 Atmospheric oxygen concentration. Graph showing how the concentration of oxygen in the atmosphere has varied during the past 600 million years. Today's oxygen level is about 21%. Low oxygen levels are closely associated with major extinction events whereas high oxygen levels are associated with rapid speciation, including species gigantism.

was smothered. In fact, some of the planet's worst mass extinctions are associated with sudden drops in atmospheric oxygen.

The remains of ancient plants and animals buried in oxygen-free environments have become the oil, natural gas, and coal deposits of today. These deposits, which are called *fossil fuels*, provide more than 90% of the energy humans consume to power modern society. In essence, humans depend not only on the food energy stored in today's plants but also on the energy stored in plants during the geologic past—in the form of fossil fuels.

Because of increased burning of fossil fuels for home heating, industry, power generation, and transportation during the industrial age, the atmospheric concentration of carbon dioxide and other gases that help warm the atmosphere has increased, too. Scientists predict that these human emissions will increase global warming and cause serious environmental problems in the not-too-distant future. This phenomenon, referred to as the atmosphere's *enhanced greenhouse effect*, is discussed in Chapter 16, "The Oceans and Climate Change."

1.7 How Old Is Earth?

How can Earth scientists tell how old a rock is? It can be a difficult task to tell if a rock is thousands, millions, or even billions of years old—unless the rock contains telltale fossils. Fortunately, Earth scientists can determine how old most rocks are by using the radioactive materials contained within rocks. In essence, this technique involves reading a rock's internal "rock clock."

Radiometric Age Dating

Most rocks on Earth (as well as those from outer space) contain small amounts of radioactive materials such as uranium, thorium, and potassium. These radioactive materials spontaneously break apart or decay into atoms of other elements. Radioactive materials have a characteristic **half-life**, which is the time required for one-half of the atoms in a sample to decay to other atoms. The older the rock is, the more radioactive material will have been converted to decay product. Analytical instruments can accurately measure the amount of radioactive material and the amount of resulting decay product in rocks. By comparing these two quantities, the age of the rock can thus be determined. Such dating is referred to as **radiometric** (*radio* = radioactivity, *metri* = measure) **age dating** and is an extremely powerful tool for determining the age of rocks.

Figure 1.23 shows an example of how radiometric age dating works. It shows how uranium 235 decays into lead 207 at a rate of which one-half of the atoms turn into lead every 704 million years. By counting the number of each type of atom in a rock sample, one can tell how long it has been decaying (as long as the sample does not gain or lose atoms). Using uranium and other radioactive

Radioactive Decay

Uranium 235 atoms	1,000,000	500,000	250,000	125,000	62,500	31,250	15,625
Lead 207 atoms	0	500,000	750,000	875,000	937,500	968,750	984,375
Half-life (figures rounded for clarity)	**Zero** 4.2 billion years ago	**One** 3.5 billion years ago	**Two** 2.8 billion years ago	**Three** 2.1 billion years ago	**Four** 1.4 billion years ago	**Five** 700 million years ago	**Six** Today

FIGURE 1.23 Radiometric age dating. During one half-life, half of all radioactive uranium 235 atoms decay into lead 207. With each successive half-life, half of the remaining radioactive uranium atoms convert to lead. By counting the number of each type of atom in a rock sample, the rock's age can be determined.

elements and applying this same technique, hundreds of thousands of rock samples have been age dated from around the world.

The Geologic Time Scale

The ages of rocks on Earth are shown in the **geologic time scale** (Figure 1.24; see Web Box 1.2), which lists the names of the geologic time periods as well as important advances in the development of life forms on Earth. Initially, the divisions

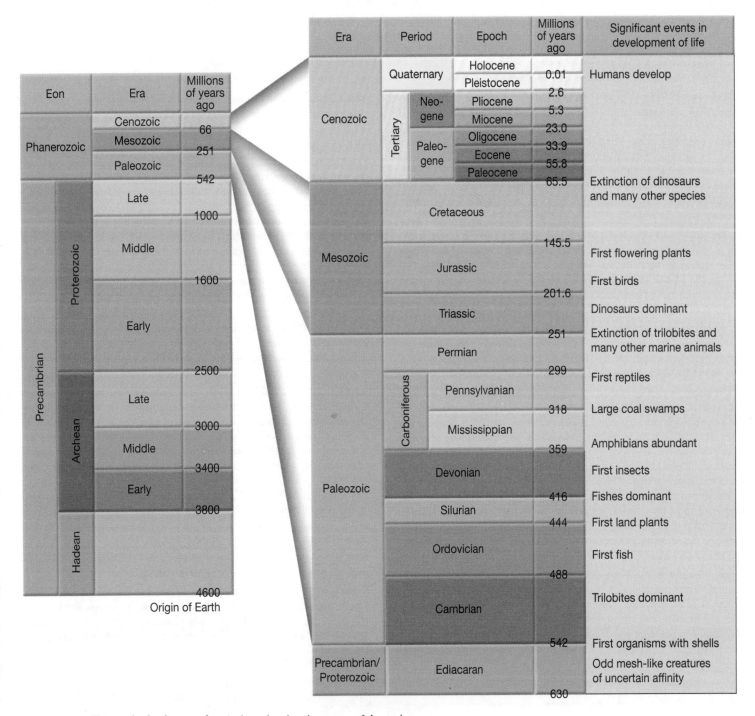

FIGURE 1.24 The geologic time scale. A chart showing the names of the various periods of geologic time, from the origin of the Earth (*bottom*) to today (*top*); the most recent 630 million years is enlarged at the right. Numbers on the time scale represent time in millions of years before the present; significant advances in the development of plants and animals on Earth are also shown.

between geologic periods were based on major extinction episodes as recorded in the fossil record. As radiometric age dates became available, they were also included on the geologic time scale. The oldest-known rocks on Earth, for example, are about 4.3 billion years old, and the oldest-known crystals within rocks have been dated at up to 4.4 billion years old.[14] In all, the time scale indicates that Earth is 4.6 billion years old, but few rocks survived its molten youth, a time when Earth was being bombarded by meteorites.

[14]Recent research suggests that crystals this old imply that significant continental crust must have formed on Earth early on, perhaps by nearly 4.5 billion years ago.

Chapter in Review

• *Water covers 70.8% of Earth's surface.* The world ocean is a *single interconnected body of water*, which is large in size and volume. It can be divided into *four principal oceans* (the Pacific, Atlantic, Indian, and Arctic Oceans), plus an additional ocean (the Southern or Antarctic Ocean). Even though there is a technical distinction between a sea and an ocean, the two terms are used interchangeably. In comparing the oceans to the continents, it is apparent that *the average land surface does not rise very far above sea level* and that *there is not a mountain on Earth that is as tall as the ocean is deep.*

• In the Pacific, *people who populated the Pacific Islands may have been the first great navigators.* In the Western world, the *Phoenicians* were making remarkable voyages as well. Later the *Greeks, Romans,* and *Arabs* made significant contributions and advanced oceanographic knowledge. During the Middle Ages, the *Vikings* colonized Iceland and Greenland and made voyages to North America.

• The *Age of Discovery* in Europe renewed the Western world's interest in exploring the unknown. It began with the voyage of *Christopher Columbus* in 1492 and ended in 1522 with the first circumnavigation of Earth by a voyage initiated by *Ferdinand Magellan. Captain James Cook* was one of the first to explore the ocean for scientific purposes.

• The *scientific method* is used to understand the occurrence of physical events or phenomena and can be stated as *science supports explanation of the natural world that best explains all available observations.* Steps in the scientific method include making *observations* and establishing *scientific facts*; forming one or more *hypotheses* (a tentative, testable statement about the general nature of the phenomena observed); extensive *testing* and *modification of hypotheses*; and, finally, developing a *theory* (a well-substantiated explanation of some aspect of the natural world that can incorporate facts, laws, logical inferences, and tested hypotheses). Science never arrives at the absolute "truth"; rather, *science arrives at what is probably true* based on the available observations and can *continually change because of new observations.*

• Our *solar system,* consisting of *the Sun and eight major planets,* probably formed from a *huge cloud of gas and space dust* called a *nebula.* According to the *nebular hypothesis,* the nebular matter contracted to form the Sun, and the planets were formed from eddies of material that remained. The Sun, composed of hydrogen and helium, was massive enough and concentrated enough to emit *large amounts of energy* from fusion. The Sun also emitted *ionized particles that swept away any nebular gas* that remained from the formation of the planets and their satellites.

• *Protoearth,* more massive and larger than Earth today, *was molten and homogenous.* The *initial atmosphere,* composed mostly of hydrogen and helium, *was later driven off into space* by intense solar radiation. Protoearth began a period of rearrangement called *density stratification* and formed a *layered internal structure based on density,* resulting in the development of the *crust, mantle,* and *core.* Studies of Earth's internal structure indicate that brittle plates of the *lithosphere* are riding on a plastic, high-viscosity *asthenosphere.* Near the surface, the lithosphere is composed of *continental* and *oceanic crust.* Continental crust consists mostly of granite and oceanic crust consists mostly of basalt. *Continental crust is lower in density, lighter in color, and thicker than oceanic crust.* Both types float isostatically on the denser mantle below.

• *Outgassing produced an early atmosphere* rich in water vapor and carbon dioxide. Once Earth's surface cooled sufficiently, the *water vapor condensed and accumulated to give Earth its oceans.* Rainfall on the surface dissolved compounds that, when carried to the ocean, *made it salty.*

• *Life is thought to have begun in the oceans. Stanley Miller's experiment* showed that ultraviolet radiation from the Sun and hydrogen, carbon dioxide, methane, ammonia, and inorganic molecules from the oceans may have combined to produce *organic molecules such as amino acids.* Certain combinations of these molecules eventually produced *heterotrophic organisms* (which cannot make their own food) that were probably similar to present-day anaerobic bacteria. Eventually, *autotrophs evolved* that had the ability to make their own food through *chemosynthesis.* Later, some cells developed *chlorophyll,* which made *photosynthesis* possible and led to the *development of plants.*

• *Photosynthetic organisms altered the environment* by extracting carbon dioxide from the atmosphere and also by releasing free oxygen, thereby creating today's *oxygen-rich atmosphere.* Eventually, both *plants and animals evolved* into forms that could survive on land.

• *Radiometric age dating* is used to determine the age of most rocks. Information from extinctions of organisms and from age dating rocks comprises the *geologic time scale,* which indicates that Earth has experienced a long history of changes since *its origin 4.6 billion years ago.*

Key Terms

Key People

Ballard, Robert (p. 7)	Cabot, John (p. 13)	Darwin, Charles (p. 26)	Eratosthenes (p. 10)
Barton, Otis (p. 7)	Columbus, Christopher (p. 12)	de Balboa, Vasco Núñez (p. 13)	Eriksson, Leif (p. 11)
Beebe, William (p. 7)	Cook, James (p. 13)	del Caño, Juan Sebastian (p. 13)	Harrison, John (p. 9)
	da Gama, Vasco (p. 12)	Diaz, Bartholomeu (p. 12)	Herjolfsson, Bjarni (p. 11)

Heyerdahl, Thor (p. 10)
Magellan, Ferdinand (p. 13)
Miller, Stanley (p. 25)
Phoenicians (p. 10)
Prince Henry the Navigator (p. 12)
Ptolemy, Claudius (p. 11)
Pytheas (p. 10)
Thorvaldson, Erik "the Red" (p. 11)
Vikings (p. 11)

Key Places and Things
Age of Discovery (p. 12)
Anaerobic (p. 27)
Antarctic Ocean (p. 4)
Arctic Ocean (p. 4)
Asthenosphere (p. 21)

Atlantic Ocean (p. 3)
Atom (p. 18)
Autotroph (p. 27)
Basalt (p. 21)
Chemosynthesis (p. 27)
Chlorophyll (p. 28)
Continental crust (p. 21)
Core (p. 20)
Crust (p. 20)
Density (p. 19)
Density stratification (p. 19)
Evolution (p. 26)
Fusion reaction (p. 18)
Geologic time scale (p. 31)
Granite (p. 21)
Half-life (p. 30)

Heterotroph (p. 27)
Hypothesis (p. 15)
Indian Ocean (p. 4)
Inner core (p. 21)
Isostatic adjustment (p. 22)
Isostatic rebound (p. 23)
Kon Tiki (p. 10)
Latitude (p. 8)
Library of Alexandria (p. 10)
Lithosphere (p. 21)
Longitude (p. 8)
Mantle (p. 20)
Mesosphere (p. 21)
Natural selection (p. 26)
Nebula (p. 17)
Nebular hypothesis (p. 17)

Oceanic crust (p. 21)
Outer core (p. 21)
Outgassing (p. 23)
Pacific Ocean (p. 3)
Photosynthesis (p. 28)
Protoearth (p. 17)
Protoplanet (p. 17)
Radiometric age dating (p. 30)
Respiration (p. 28)
Scientific method (p. 15)
Solar system (p. 16)
Southern Ocean (p. 4)
Species (p. 26)
Theory (p. 16)
Viscosity (p. 22)

Review Questions

1. How did the view of the ocean by early Mediterranean cultures influence the naming of planet "Earth"?

2. What is the difference between an ocean and a sea? Name the seven seas (both ancient and modern versions).

3. While the Arabs dominated the Mediterranean region during the Middle Ages, what were the most significant ocean-related events taking place in northern Europe?

4. Describe the important events in oceanography that occurred during the Age of Discovery in Europe.

5. List some of the major achievements of Captain James Cook.

6. Discuss the origin of the solar system using the nebular hypothesis.

7. How was Protoearth different from Earth today?

8. What is density stratification, and how did it change Protoearth?

9. Discuss how the chemical composition of Earth's interior differs from its physical properties. Include specific examples.

10. What are some differences between the lithosphere and the asthenosphere?

11. What is the origin of Earth's oceans, and how is it related to the origin of Earth's atmosphere?

12. Have the oceans always been salty? Why or why not?

13. How does the presence of oxygen in our atmosphere help reduce the amount of ultraviolet radiation that reaches Earth's surface?

14. What was Stanley Miller's experiment, and what did it help demonstrate?

15. Earth has had three atmospheres (initial, early, and present). Describe the composition and origin of each one.

16. Describe how the half-life of radioactive materials can be used to determine the age of a rock through radiometric age dating.

Critical Thinking Exercises

1. Describe the development of navigation techniques that have enabled sailors to navigate in the open ocean far from land.

2. Using a diagram, illustrate the method used by Pytheas to determine latitude in the Northern Hemisphere.

3. What is the difference between a fact and a theory? Can either (or both) be revised?

4. Briefly comment on the phrase "scientific certainty." Is it an oxymoron (a combination of contradictory words), or are scientific theories considered to be the absolute truth?

5. Construct a representation of the geologic time scale, using an appropriate quantity of any substance (other than dollar bills or toilet paper). Be sure to indicate some of the major changes that have occurred on Earth since its origin.

Oceanography on the Web

Visit the *Essentials of Oceanography* Online Study Guide for Internet resources, including chapter-specific quizzes to test your understanding and Web links to further your exploration of the topics in this chapter.

The *Essentials of Oceanography* Online Study Guide is at http://www.mygeoscienceplace.com/.

Tall mountains created by tectonic uplift.
Tall coastal mountains such as these in Glacier Bay National Park in southeast Alaska have been uplifted by plate tectonic processes, creating a large amount of relief. Some of the uplifted rocks here have come from distant areas and include parts of the sea floor.

"It is just as if we were to refit the torn pieces of a newspaper by matching their edges and then check whether the lines of print run smoothly across. If they do, there is nothing left but to conclude that the pieces were in fact joined in this way."

— *Alfred Wegener,*
The Origins of Continents and Oceans (1929)

2 PLATE TECTONICS AND THE OCEAN FLOOR

Each year at various locations around the globe, several thousand earthquakes and dozens of volcanic eruptions occur, both of which indicate how remarkably dynamic our planet is. These events have occurred throughout history, constantly changing the surface of our planet, yet only a few decades ago most scientists believed the continents were stationary over geologic time. Since that time, a bold new theory has been advanced that helps explain surface features and phenomena on Earth, including:

• The worldwide locations of volcanoes, faults, earthquakes, and mountain building
• Why mountains on Earth haven't been eroded away
• The origin of most landforms and ocean floor features
• How the continents and ocean floor formed and why they are different
• The continuing development of Earth's surface
• The distribution of past and present life on Earth

This revolutionary new theory is called **plate tectonics** (*plate* = plates of the lithosphere; *tekton* = to build), or "the new global geology." According to the theory of plate tectonics, the outermost portion of Earth is composed of a patchwork of thin, rigid plates[1] that move horizontally with respect to one another, like icebergs floating on water. As a result, the continents are mobile and move about on Earth's surface, controlled by forces deep within Earth.

The interaction of these plates as they move builds features of Earth's crust (such as mountain belts, volcanoes, and ocean basins). For example, the tallest mountain range on Earth is the Himalaya Mountains that extend through India, Nepal, and Bhutan. This mountain range contains rocks that were deposited millions of years ago in a shallow sea, providing testimony of the power and persistence of plate tectonic activity.

In this chapter, we'll examine the early ideas about the movement of plates, the evidence for those ideas, and how they led to the theory of plate tectonics. Then we'll explore features of plate boundaries and some applications of plate tectonics, including what our planet may look like in the future.

2.1 What Evidence Supports Continental Drift?

Alfred Wegener (Figure 2.1), a German meteorologist and geophysicist, was the first to advance the idea of mobile continents in 1912. He envisioned that the continents were slowly drifting across the globe and called his idea **continental drift**. Let's examine the evidence that Wegener compiled that led him to formulate the idea of drifting continents.

---

[1]These thin, rigid plates are pieces of the *lithosphere* that comprise Earth's outermost portion and contain oceanic and/or continental crust, as described in Chapter 1.

Fit of the Continents

The idea that continents—particularly South America and Africa—fit together like pieces of a jigsaw puzzle originated with the development of reasonably accurate world maps. As far back as 1620, Sir Francis Bacon wrote about how the continents appeared to fit together. However, little significance was given to this idea until 1912, when Wegener used the shapes of matching shorelines on different continents as a supporting piece of evidence for continental drift.

Wegener suggested that during the geologic past, the continents collided to form a large landmass, which he named **Pangaea** (*pan* = all, *gaea* = Earth) (Figure 2.2). Further, a huge ocean, called **Panthalassa** (*pan* = all, *thalassa* = sea) surrounded Pangaea. Panthalassa included several smaller seas, including the **Tethys** (*Tethys* = a Greek sea goddess) **Sea**. Wegener's evidence indicated that as Pangaea began to split apart, the various continental masses started to drift toward their present geographic positions.

Wegener's attempt at matching shorelines revealed considerable areas of crustal overlap and large gaps. Some of the differences could be explained by material deposited by rivers or eroded from coastlines. What Wegener didn't know at the time was that the shallow parts of the ocean floor close to shore are underlain by materials similar to those beneath continents. In the early 1960s, Sir Edward Bullard and two associates used a computer program to fit the continents together (Figure 2.3). Instead of using the shorelines of the continents as Wegener had done, Bullard achieved the best fit (for example, with minimal overlaps or gaps) by using a depth of 2000 meters (6560 feet) below sea level. This depth corresponds to halfway between the shoreline and the deep-ocean basins; as such, it represents the true edge of the continents. By using this depth, the continents fit together remarkably well.

Matching Sequences of Rocks and Mountain Chains

If the continents were once together, as Wegener had hypothesized, then evidence should appear in rock sequences that were originally continuous but are now separated by large distances. To test the idea of drifting continents, geologists began comparing the rocks along the edges of continents with rocks found in adjacent positions on matching continents. They wanted to see if the rocks had similar types, ages, and structural styles (the type and degree of deformation). In some areas younger rocks had been deposited during the millions of years since the continents separated, covering the rocks that held the key to the past history of the continents. In other areas, the rocks had been eroded away. Nevertheless, in many other areas, the key rocks were present.

Moreover, these studies showed that many rock sequences from one continent were identical to rock sequences on an adjacent continent—although the two were separated by an ocean. In addition, mountain ranges that terminated abruptly at the edge of a continent continued on another continent across an ocean basin, with identical rock sequences, ages, and structural styles. Figure 2.4 shows, for example, how similar rocks from the Appalachian Mountains in North America match up with identical rocks from the British Isles and the Caledonian Mountains in Europe.

Wegener noted the similarities in rock sequences on both sides of the Atlantic and used the information as a supporting piece of evidence for continental drift. He suggested that mountains such as those seen on opposite sides of the Atlantic formed during the collision when Pangaea was formed. Later, when the continents split apart,

FIGURE 2.1 Alfred Wegener, circa 1912–1913. Alfred Wegener (1880–1930), shown here in his research station in Greenland, was one of the first scientists to suggest that continents are mobile.

once-continuous mountain ranges were separated. Confirmation of this idea exists in a similar match with mountains extending from South America through Antarctica and across Australia.

Glacial Ages and Other Climate Evidence

Wegener also noticed the occurrence of past glacial activity in areas now tropical and suggested that it, too, provided supporting evidence for drifting continents. Currently, the only places in the world where thick continental *ice sheets* occur are in the polar regions of Greenland and Antarctica. However, evidence of ancient glaciation is found in the lower latitude regions of South America, Africa, India, and Australia.

These deposits, which have been dated at 300 million years old, indicate one of two possibilities: (1) There was a worldwide **ice age**, and even tropical areas were covered by thick ice, or (2) some continents that are now in tropical areas were once located much closer to one of the poles. It is unlikely that the entire world was covered by ice 300 million years ago because coal deposits from the same geologic age now present in North America and Europe originated as vast semitropical swamps. Thus, a reasonable conclusion is that some of the continents must have been closer to the poles than they are today.

Another type of glacial evidence indicates that certain continents have moved from more polar regions during the past 300 million years. When glaciers flow, they move and abrade the underlying rocks, leaving grooves that indicate the direction of flow. The arrows in Figure 2.5a show how the glaciers would have flowed away from the South Pole on Pangaea 300 million years ago. The direction of flow is consistent with the grooves found on many continents today (Figure 2.5b), providing additional evidence for drifting continents.

Many examples of plant and animal fossils indicate very different climates than today. Two such examples are fossil palm trees in Arctic Spitsbergen and coal deposits in Antarctica. Earth's past environments can be interpreted from these rocks because plants and animals need specific environmental conditions in which to live. Corals, for example, generally need seawater above 18 degrees centigrade (°C) or 64 degrees Fahrenheit (°F) in order to survive. When fossil corals are found in areas that are cold today, two explanations seem most plausible: (1) Worldwide climate has changed dramatically; or (2) the rocks have moved from their original location.

Latitude (distance north or south of the equator), more than anything else, determines climate. Moreover, there is no evidence to suggest that Earth's axis of rotation has changed significantly throughout its history, so the climate at any particular latitude must not have changed significantly either. Thus, fossils that come from climates that seem out of place today must have moved from their original location through the movement of the continents as Wegener proposed.

Distribution of Organisms

To add credibility to his argument for the existence of the supercontinent of Pangaea, Wegener cited documented cases of several fossil organisms found on different landmasses that could not have crossed the vast oceans presently separating the continents. For example, the fossil remains of ***Mesosaurus*** (*meso* = middle, *saurus* = lizard), an extinct, presumably aquatic reptile that lived about 250 million years ago, are located only in eastern South America and western Africa (Figure 2.6). If *Mesosaurus* had been strong enough to swim across an ocean, why aren't its remains more widely distributed?

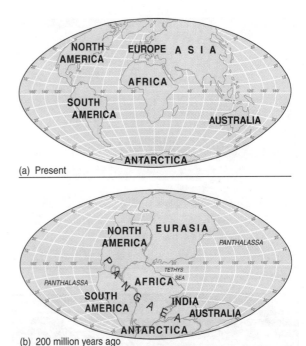

(a) Present

(b) 200 million years ago

FIGURE 2.2 Reconstruction of Pangaea. The positions of the continents about 200 million years ago, showing the supercontinent of Pangaea and the single large ocean, Panthalassa.

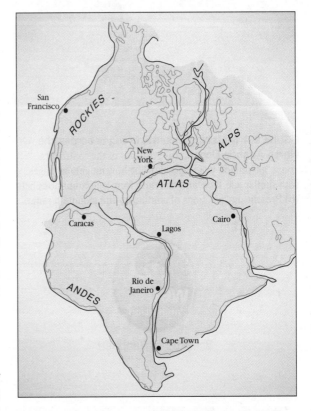

FIGURE 2.3 An early computer fit of the continents. Map showing the 1960s fit of the continents using a depth of 2000 meters (6560 feet) (black lines), which is the true edge of the ocean basin. The results indicate a remarkable match, with few overlaps and minimal gaps. Note that the present-day shorelines of the continents are shown with blue lines.

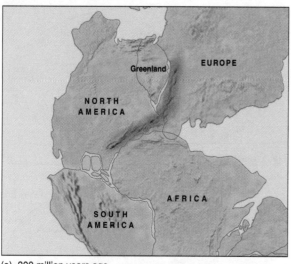

(a) 300 million years ago

(b) Today

FIGURE 2.4 Matching mountain ranges across the North Atlantic Ocean. (a) Positions of the continents about 300 million years ago, showing how mountain ranges with similar age, type, and structure form one continuous belt. (b) Present-day positions of continents and mountain ranges.

Breakup of Pangaea

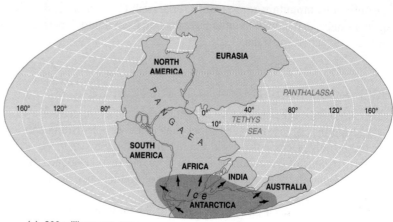

(a) 300 million years ago

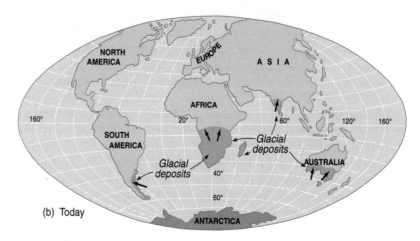

(b) Today

FIGURE 2.5 Ice age on Pangaea. (a) Reconstruction of the supercontinent Pangaea, showing the area covered by glacial ice about 300 million years ago. Arrows indicate direction of ice flow. (b) The positions of the continents today.

Wegener's idea of continental drift provided an elegant solution to this problem. He suggested that the continents were closer together in the geologic past, so *Mesosaurus* didn't have to be a good swimmer to leave remains on two different continents. Later, after *Mesosaurus* became extinct, the continents moved to their present-day positions, and a large ocean now separates the once-connected landmasses. Other examples of similar fossils on different continents include those of plants, which would have had a difficult time traversing a large ocean.

Before continental drift, several ideas were proposed to help explain the curious pattern of these fossils, such as the existence of island stepping stones or a land bridge. It was even suggested that at least one pair of land-dwelling *Mesosaurus* survived the arduous journey across several thousand kilometers of open ocean by rafting on floating logs. However, there is no evidence to support the idea of island stepping stones or a land bridge and the idea of *Mesosaurus* rafting across an ocean seems implausible.

Wegener also cited the distribution of present-day organisms as evidence to support the concept of drifting continents. For example, modern organisms with similar ancestries clearly had to evolve in isolation during the last few million years. Most obvious of these are the Australian marsupials (such as the kangaroos, koalas, and wombats), which have a distinct similarity to the marsupial opossums found in the Americas.

Objections to the Continental Drift Model

Wegener first published his ideas in *The Origins of Continents and Oceans* in 1915, but the book did not attract much attention until it was translated into English, French, Spanish, and Russian in 1924. From that point until his death in 1930,[2] his drift hypothesis received much hostile criticism—and sometimes open ridicule—from the scientific community because of the mechanism he proposed for the movement of the continents. Wegener suggested the continents plowed through the ocean basins to reach their present-day positions and that the leading edges of the continents deformed into mountain ridges because of the drag imposed by ocean rocks. Further, the driving mechanism he proposed was a combination of the gravitational attraction of Earth's equatorial bulge and tidal forces from the Sun and Moon.

Scientists rejected the idea as too fantastic and contrary to the laws of physics. Debate over the mechanism of drift concentrated on the long-term behavior of the substrate and the forces that could move continents laterally. Material strength calculations, for example, showed that ocean rock was too strong for continental rock to plow through it. Further, analysis of gravitational and tidal forces indicated that they were too small to move the great continental landmasses. Even without an acceptable mechanism, many geologists who studied rocks in South America and Africa accepted continental drift because it was consistent with the rock record. North American geologists—most of whom were unfamiliar with these Southern Hemisphere rock sequences—remained highly skeptical.

As compelling as his evidence may seem today, Wegener was unable to convince the scientific community as a whole of the validity of his ideas. Although his hypothesis was correct in principle, it contained several incorrect details, such as the driving mechanism for continental motion and how continents move across ocean basins. In order for any scientific viewpoint to gain wide acceptance, it must explain all available observations and have supporting evidence from a wide variety of scientific fields. This supporting evidence would not come until more details of the nature of the ocean floor were revealed, which, along with new technology that enabled scientists to determine the original positions of rocks on Earth, provided additional observations in support of drifting continents.

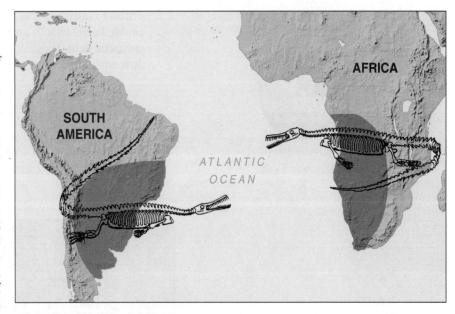

FIGURE 2.6 Fossils of *Mesosaurus*. Fossils of the aquatic reptile *Mesosaurus*, which lived about 250 million years ago, are found only in South America and Africa. The limited distribution of *Mesosaurus* fossils suggest that these two continents were once joined.

> **KEY CONCEPT**
> Alfred Wegener used a variety of interdisciplinary information from land to support continental drift. However, he did not have a suitable mechanism or any information about the sea floor.

2.2 What Evidence Supports Plate Tectonics?

Very little new information about Wegener's continental drift hypothesis was introduced between the time of Wegener's death in 1930 and the early 1950s. However, studies of the sea floor using sonar that were initiated during World War II and continued after the war provided critical evidence in support of

---

[2]Wegener perished in 1930, during an expedition in Greenland while collecting data to help support his idea of continental drift.

Flipping of Earth's
Magnetic Field

drifting continents. In addition, technology unavailable in Wegener's time enabled scientists to analyze the way rocks retained the signature of Earth's **magnetic field**. These developments caused scientists to reexamine continental drift and advance it into the more encompassing theory of plate tectonics.

Earth's Magnetic Field and Paleomagnetism

Earth's magnetic field is shown in Figure 2.7. The invisible lines of magnetic force that originate within Earth and travel out into space resemble the magnetic field produced by a large bar magnet.[3] Similar to Earth's magnetic

(a)

(b)

(c)

FIGURE 2.7 Earth's magnetic field. (a) Earth's magnetic field generates invisible lines of magnetic force similar to a large bar magnet. Note that magnetic north and true north are not in exactly the same location. **(b)** Earth's magnetic field causes a dip needle to align parallel to the lines of magnetic force and change orientation with increasing latitude. Consequently, an approximation of latitude can be determined based on the dip angle. **(c)** Map showing the location of Earth's north magnetic pole since 1831, and where it is projected to be in the future.

---

[3]The properties of a magnetic field can be explored easily enough with a bar magnet and some iron particles. Place the iron particles on a table and place a bar magnet nearby. Depending on the strength of the magnet, you should get a pattern resembling that in Figure 2.7a.

field, the ends of a bar magnet have opposite polarities (labeled either + and − or N for north and S for south) that cause magnetic objects to align parallel to its magnetic field. In addition, notice in Figures 2.7b and 2.7c that Earth's geographic North Pole (the rotational axis) and Earth's magnetic north pole (magnetic north) do not coincide.

ROCKS AFFECTED BY EARTH'S MAGNETIC FIELD   *Igneous* (*igne* = fire, *ous* = full of) *rocks* solidify from molten *magma* (*magma* = a mass) either underground or after volcanic eruptions at the surface that produce *lava* (*lavare* = to wash). Nearly all igneous rocks contain **magnetite**, a naturally magnetic iron mineral. Particles of magnetite in magma align themselves with Earth's magnetic field because magma and lava are fluid. Once molten material cools and solidifies, internal magnetite particles are frozen into position, thereby recording the angle of Earth's magnetic field at that place and time. In essence, grains of magnetite serve as tiny compass needles that record the strength and orientation of Earth's magnetic field. Unless the rock is heated to the temperature where magnetite grains are again mobile, these magnetite grains contain information about the magnetic field where the rock originated, regardless of where the rock subsequently moves.

Magnetite is also deposited in sediments. As long as the sediment is surrounded by water, the magnetite particles can align themselves with Earth's magnetic field. After sediment is buried and solidifies into *sedimentary* (*sedimentum* = settling) *rock*, the particles are no longer able to realign themselves if they are subsequently moved. Thus, magnetite grains in sedimentary rocks also contain information about the magnetic field where the rock originated. Although other rock types have been used successfully to reveal information about Earth's ancient magnetic field, the most reliable ones are igneous rocks that have high concentrations of magnetite such as *basalt*, which is the rock type that comprises oceanic crust.

PALEOMAGNETISM   The study of Earth's ancient magnetic field is called **paleomagnetism** (*paleo* = ancient). The scientists who study paleomagnetism analyze magnetite particles in rocks to determine not only their north–south direction but also their angle relative to Earth's surface. The degree to which a magnetite particle points into Earth is called its **magnetic dip**, or *magnetic inclination*.

Magnetic dip is directly related to latitude. Figure 2.7b shows that a dip needle does not dip at all at Earth's magnetic equator. Instead, the needle lies horizontal to Earth's surface. At Earth's magnetic north pole, however, a dip needle points straight into the surface. A dip needle at Earth's magnetic south pole is also vertical to the surface, but it points out instead of in. Thus, magnetic dip increases with increasing latitude, from 0 degrees at the magnetic equator to 90 degrees at the magnetic poles. Because magnetic dip is retained in magnetically oriented rocks, measuring the dip angle reveals the latitude at which the rock initially formed. Done with care, paleomagnetism is an extremely powerful tool for interpreting where rocks first formed. Based on paleomagnetic studies, convincing arguments could finally be made that the continents had drifted relative to one another.

APPARENT POLAR WANDERING   When magnetic dip data for rocks on the continents were used to determine the apparent position of the magnetic north pole over time, it appeared that the magnetic pole was wandering or moving through time. For example, Figure 2.8a shows the magnetic **polar wandering curves** for North America and Eurasia. Both curves have a similar shape but, for all rocks older than about 70 million years, the pole determined from North

---

STUDENTS SOMETIMES ASK...

What causes Earth's magnetic field?

Studies of Earth's magnetic field and research in the field of magnetodynamics suggest that convective movement of fluids in Earth's liquid iron–nickel outer core is the cause of Earth's magnetic field. The most widely accepted view is that Earth's magnetic field is created by strong electrical currents generated by a dynamo process resulting from the flow of molten iron in Earth's outer core. Earth's magnetic field is so complex that it has only recently been successfully modeled using some of the world's most powerful computers. Interestingly, the Sun and most other planets (and even some planets' moons) also exhibit magnetic fields.

FIGURE 2.8 Apparent polar wandering paths. (a) The apparent magnetic polar wandering paths for North America and Eurasia (*red* and *blue curves*, respectively) resulted in a dilemma because they were not in alignment. **(b)** The positions of the magnetic polar wandering paths more closely coincide when the landmasses are assembled.

(a)   (b)

American rocks lies to the west of that determined from Eurasian rocks. There can be only one north magnetic pole at any given time, however, and it is unlikely that its position has changed very much through time because it always nearly coincides with Earth's rotational axis. This discrepancy implies that the magnetic pole remained stationary while North America and Eurasia moved relative to the pole and relative to each other. Figure 2.8b shows that when the continents are moved into the positions they occupied when they were part of Pangaea, the two wandering curves match up, providing strong evidence that the continents have moved throughout geologic time.

MAGNETIC POLARITY REVERSALS   Magnetic compasses on Earth today follow lines of magnetic force and point toward magnetic north. It turns out, however, that the **polarity** (the directional orientation of the magnetic field) has reversed itself periodically throughout geologic time. In essence, the north and south magnetic poles switch. Figure 2.9 shows how ancient rocks have recorded the switching of earth's magnetic polarity through time.

Paleomagnetic studies reveal that about 170 major reversals have occurred in the past 76 million years. The pattern of switching of Earth's magnetic field is highly irregular but occurs about every 250,000 years or so. On average, it takes several hundred to several thousand years for a change in polarity to occur; it is identified in rock sequences by a gradual decrease in the intensity of the magnetic field of one polarity, followed by a gradual increase in the intensity of the magnetic field of opposite polarity.

Earth's magnetic north pole—which does not coincide with the geographic North Pole—was discovered at Canada's Cape Adelaide in 1831; since that time, it's been migrating northwest by about 50 kilometers (30 miles) each year (Figure 2.7c). At this rate, Earth's magnetic pole will pass within 400 kilometers (250 miles) of the geographic North Pole in 2018 and will be in Siberia by 2050. In addition, evidence suggests that Earth's magnetic field has also been weakening during the past 2000 years, which may be an indication that Earth's current "normal" polarity may reverse itself. In fact, the last major reversal of Earth's magnetic poles occurred 780,000 years ago, which suggests that the next one is overdue.

PALEOMAGNETISM AND THE OCEAN FLOOR   Paleomagnetism had certainly proved its usefulness on land, but, up until the mid-1950s, it had only been conducted on continental rocks. Would the ocean floor also show variations in magnetic polarity? To test this idea, the U.S. Coast and Geodetic Survey in

STUDENTS SOMETIMES ASK...

What changes to Earth's environment would occur when the magnetic poles reverse?

During a reversal, compasses would likely show incorrect directions, and people could have difficulty navigating. The same goes for those fish, birds, and mammals that sense the magnetic field during migrations (see Box 2.1). The decrease in strength also reduces the protection that the magnetic field provides against cosmic rays and particles coming from the Sun, and this could disrupt low-Earth-orbiting satellites as well as some communication and power grid systems. Also, the aurora, which is a phenomenon of light in the sky known as the Northern Lights, might be visible at much lower latitudes. On the bright side, we know that life on Earth has successfully survived previous magnetic reversals, so reversals might not be as dangerous as they are sometimes portrayed (such as in the 2003 science fiction film *The Core*, which is full of scientific inaccuracies).

DO SEA TURTLES (AND OTHER ANIMALS) USE EARTH'S MAGNETIC FIELD FOR NAVIGATION?

Sea turtles travel great distances across the open ocean so they can lay their eggs on the island where they themselves were hatched. Interestingly, this behavior of migrating to remote, isolated islands thousands of kilometers from the closest continent may have gradually evolved as ocean basins widened due to plate movement, separating the turtles' feeding and breeding grounds. How do the turtles know where an island is located, and how do they navigate at sea during their long voyage?

Radio tagging of green sea turtles (*Chelonia mydas*; Figure 2A) indicates that during their migration, they often travel in an essentially straight-line path to reach their destination. One hypothesis suggests that, like the Polynesian navigators (see Box 1.2), sea turtles use wave direction to help them steer. However, studies of their migration route reveal that green sea turtles continue along a straight-line path that is independent of wave direction.

Research in *magnetoreception*, which is the study of an animal's ability to sense magnetic fields, suggests that sea turtles may use Earth's magnetic field for navigation. For instance, turtles can distinguish between different magnetic inclination angles, which in effect would allow them to sense latitude. Sea turtles can also distinguish magnetic field intensity, which gives a rough indication of longitude. By sensing these two magnetic field properties, a sea turtle could determine its position at sea and relocate to a tiny island thousands of kilometers away. Like any good navigator, sea turtles may also use other tools, such as olfactory (scent) clues, Sun angles, local landmarks, and oceanographic phenomena.

Other animals may also use magnetic properties to navigate. For example, some whales and dolphins may detect and follow the magnetic stripes on the sea floor during their movements, which may help to explain why whales sometimes beach themselves. In addition, certain bacteria use the magnetic mineral magnetite to align themselves parallel to Earth's magnetic field. Subsequently, magnetite has been found in many other organisms that have a "homing" ability, including fish, honeybees, birds, turtles, lobsters, cows, and even humans. What remains unclear is how these animals detect—and potentially use—Earth's magnetic field. Recent findings by a research team studying rainbow trout have traced magnetically receptive fibers of nerves back to the brain, more closely linking a magnetic sense with an organism's sensory system.

Do humans have an innate ability to use Earth's magnetic field for navigation? Studies conducted on humans indicate that the majority of people can identify north after being blindfolded and disoriented. Interestingly, many people point *south* instead of north, but this direction is along the lines of magnetic force. Similarly, migratory animals that rely on magnetism for navigation will not be confused by a reversal in Earth's magnetic field and will still be able to get to where they need to go. Exactly how organisms navigate with their magnetic sense seems likely to remain one of the most puzzling questions in sensory biology.

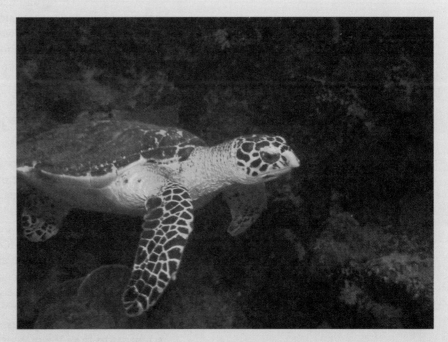

FIGURE 2A Green sea turtle. Green sea turtles (*Chelonia mydas*) get their name from the green-colored fat tissue in their bodies. They are listed as a threatened species and are protected by international law.

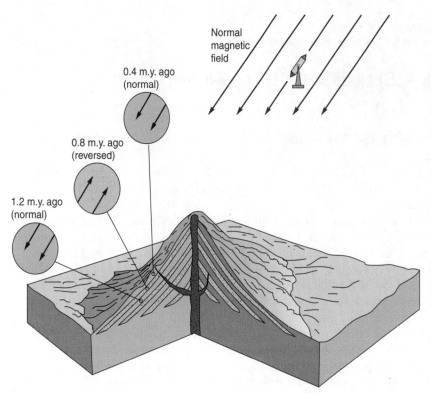

Normal magnetic field

0.4 m.y. ago (normal)

0.8 m.y. ago (reversed)

1.2 m.y. ago (normal)

FIGURE 2.9 Paleomagnetism preserved in rocks. The switching of Earth's magnetic polarity through time is preserved in rocks such as these lava flows.

conjunction with scientists from Scripps Institution of Oceanography undertook an extensive deep-water mapping program off Oregon and Washington in 1955. Using a sensitive instrument called a *magnetometer* (*magneto* = magnetism, *meter* = measure), which is towed behind a research vessel, the scientists spent several weeks at sea moving back and forth in a regularly spaced pattern, measuring Earth's magnetic field and how it was affected by the magnetic properties of rocks on the ocean floor.

When the scientists analyzed their data, they found that the entire surveyed area had a pattern of north–south stripes in a surprisingly regular and alternating pattern of above-average and below-average magnetism. What was even more surprising was that the pattern appeared to be symmetrical with respect to a long mountain range that was fortuitously in the middle of their survey area.

Detailed paleomagnetism studies of this and other areas of the sea floor confirmed a similar pattern of alternating stripes of above-average and below-average magnetism. These stripes are called **magnetic anomalies** (*a* = without, *nomo* = law; an anomaly is a departure from normal conditions). The ocean floor had embedded in it a regular pattern of alternating magnetic stripes unlike anywhere on land.

Researchers had a difficult time explaining why the ocean floor had such a regular pattern of magnetic anomalies. Nor could they explain how the sequence on one side of the underwater mountain range matched the sequence on the opposite side—in essence, they were a mirror image of each other. To understand how this pattern could have formed, more information was needed about ocean floor features and their origin.

Sea Floor Spreading and Features of the Ocean Basins

Geologist **Harry Hess** (1906–1969), when he was a U.S. Navy captain in World War II, developed the habit of leaving his depth recorder on at all times while his ship was traveling at sea. After the war, compilation of these and many other depth records showed extensive mountain ridges near the centers of ocean basins and extremely deep, narrow trenches at the edges of ocean basins. In 1962, Hess published *History of Ocean Basins*, which contained the idea of **sea floor spreading** and the associated circular movement of rock material in the **mantle**—**convection** (*con* = with, *vect* = carried) **cells**—as the driving mechanism (Figure 2.10). He suggested that new ocean crust was created at the ridges, split apart, moved away from the ridges, and later disappeared back into the deep Earth at trenches. Mindful of the resistance of North American scientists to the idea of continental drift, Hess referred to his own work as "geopoetry."

As it turns out, Hess's initial ideas about sea floor spreading have been confirmed. The **mid-ocean ridge** (Figure 2.10) is a continuous underwater mountain range that winds through every ocean basin in the world and resembles the seam on a baseball. It is entirely volcanic in origin, wraps one-and-a-half times around the globe, and rises more than 2.5 kilometers (1.5 miles) above the surrounding deep-ocean floor. It even rises above sea level in places such as Iceland. New ocean floor forms at the crest, or axis, of the mid-ocean ridge. By the process of

Volcanic arc — Subduction at trench — Sea floor spreading at mid-ocean ridge — Subduction at trench — Volcanic arc

Ocean

Subduction zone

Subduction zone

Hot molten rock to surface

Convection cell

Convection cell

Mantle

FIGURE 2.10 Processes of plate tectonics. Hot molten rock comes to the surface at the mid-ocean ridge and moves outward by the process of sea floor spreading. Eventually, sea floor is destroyed at the trenches, where the process of subduction occurs. Convection of material in the mantle produces convection cells.

web animation

Sea Floor Spreading and Plate Boundaries

sea floor spreading, new ocean floor is split in two and carried away from the axis, replaced by the upwelling of volcanic material that fills the void with new strips of sea floor. Sea floor spreading occurs along the axis of the mid-ocean ridge, which is referred to as a **spreading center**. One way to think of the mid-ocean ridge is as a zipper that is being pulled apart. Thus, Earth's zipper (the mid-ocean ridge) is becoming unzipped!

At the same time, ocean floor is being destroyed at deep **ocean trenches**. Trenches are the deepest parts of the ocean floor and resemble a narrow crease or trough (Figure 2.10). Some of the largest earthquakes in the world occur near these trenches; they are caused by a plate that bends downward and slowly plunges back into Earth's interior. This process is called **subduction** (*sub* = under, *duc* = lead), and the sloping area from the trench along the downward-moving plate is called a **subduction zone**.

In 1963, geologists **Frederick Vine** and **Drummond Matthews** of Cambridge University combined the seemingly unrelated pattern of magnetic sea floor stripes with the process of sea floor spreading to explain the perplexing pattern of alternating and symmetric magnetic stripes on the sea floor (Figure 2.11). Vine and Matthews interpreted the pattern of above-average and below-average magnetic polarity episodes embedded in sea floor rocks to be caused by Earth's magnetic field alternating between "normal" polarity (similar to today's magnetic pole position in the north) and "reversed" polarity (with the magnetic pole to the south). They proposed that the pattern could be created when newly formed rocks at the mid-ocean ridge are magnetized with whichever polarity exists on Earth during their formation. As those rocks are slowly moved away from the crest of the mid-ocean ridge, they maintain their original polarity and subsequent rocks record the periodic switches of Earth's magnetic polarity. The result is an alternating pattern of magnetic polarity stripes that are symmetric with respect to the mid-ocean ridge.

The pattern of alternating reversals of Earth's magnetic field as recorded in the sea floor was the most convincing piece of evidence set forth to support the concept of sea floor spreading—and, as a result, continental drift. However, the continents weren't plowing through the ocean basins as Wegener had envisioned. Instead, the ocean floor was a conveyer belt that was being

FIGURE 2.11 Magnetic evidence of sea floor spreading. As new basalt is added to the ocean floor at mid-ocean ridges, it is magnetized according to Earth's existing magnetic field. This produces a pattern of normal and reversed magnetic polarity "stripes" that are identical on either side of the mid-ocean ridge.

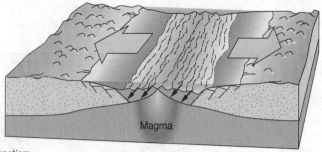

(a) Period of normal magnetism

Sea Floor Spreading and Rock Magnetism

(b) Period of reverse magnetism

(c) Period of normal magnetism

KEY CONCEPT

The plate tectonic model states that new sea floor is created at the mid-ocean ridge, where it moves outward by the process of sea floor spreading and is destroyed by subduction into ocean trenches.

continuously formed at the mid-ocean ridge and destroyed at the trenches, with the continents just passively riding along on the conveyer. By the late 1960s, most geologists had changed their stand on continental drift in light of this new evidence.

Other Evidence from the Ocean Basins

Even though the tide of scientific opinion had indeed switched to favor a mobile Earth, additional evidence from the ocean floor would further support the ideas of continental drift and sea floor spreading.

AGE OF THE OCEAN FLOOR   In the late 1960s, an ambitious deep-sea drilling program was initiated to test the existence of sea floor spreading. One of the program's primary missions was to drill into and collect ocean floor rocks for radiometric age dating. If sea floor spreading does indeed occur, then the youngest sea floor rocks would be atop the mid-ocean ridge and the ages of rocks would increase on either side of the ridge in a symmetric pattern.

The map in Figure 2.12, showing the age of the ocean floor beneath deep-sea deposits, is based on the pattern of magnetic stripes verified with thousands of radiometrically age-dated samples. It shows the ocean floor is youngest along the mid-ocean ridge, where new ocean floor is created, and the age of rocks increases

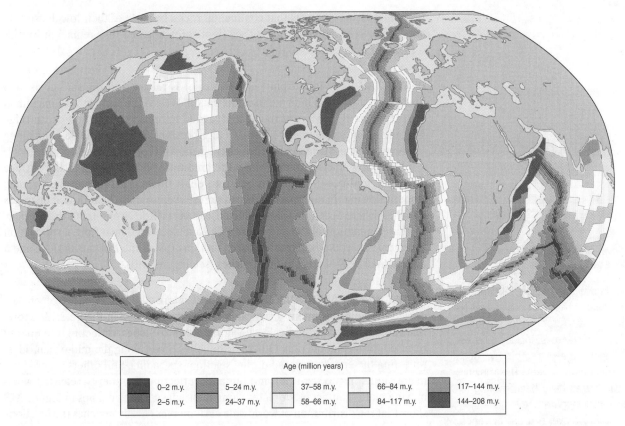

Age (million years)

0–2 m.y.	5–24 m.y.	37–58 m.y.
2–5 m.y.	24–37 m.y.	58–66 m.y.

66–84 m.y.	117–144 m.y.
84–117 m.y.	144–208 m.y.

FIGURE 2.12 Age of the ocean crust beneath deep-sea deposits. The youngest rocks (*bright red areas*) are found along the mid-ocean ridge. Farther away from the mid-ocean ridge, the rocks increase linearly in age in either direction. Ages shown are in millions of years before present.

with increasing distance in either direction away from the axis of the ridge. The symmetric pattern of ocean floor ages confirms that the process of sea floor spreading must indeed be occurring.

The Atlantic Ocean has the simplest and most symmetric pattern of age distribution in Figure 2.12. The pattern results from the newly formed Mid-Atlantic Ridge that rifted Pangaea apart. The Pacific Ocean has the least symmetric pattern because many subduction zones surround it. For example, ocean floor east of the East Pacific Rise that is older than 40 million years old has already been subducted. The ocean floor in the northwestern Pacific, about 180 million years old, has not yet been subducted. A portion of the East Pacific Rise has even disappeared under North America. The age bands in the Pacific Ocean are wider than those in the Atlantic and Indian Oceans, which suggests the rate of sea floor spreading is greatest in the Pacific Ocean.

Recall from Chapter 1 that the ocean is at least 4 billion years old. However, the oldest ocean floor is only 180 million years old (or 0.18 billion years old), and the majority of the ocean floor is not even half that old (see Figure 2.12). How could the ocean floor be so incredibly young while the oceans themselves are so phenomenally old? According to plate tectonic theory, new ocean floor is created at the mid-ocean ridge by sea floor spreading and moves off the ridge to eventually be subducted and remelted in the mantle. In this way, the ocean floor keeps regenerating itself. The floor beneath the oceans today is not the same one that existed beneath the oceans 4 billion years ago.

If the rocks that comprise the ocean floor are so young, why are continental rocks so old? Based on radiometric age dating, the oldest rocks on land are about 4 billion years old. Many other continental rocks approach this age, implying that the same processes that constantly renew the sea floor do not operate on land.

Rather, evidence suggests that continental rocks, because of their low density, do not get recycled by the process of sea floor spreading and thus remain at Earth's surface for long periods of time.

HEAT FLOW   The heat from Earth's interior is released to the surface as **heat flow**. Current models indicate that this heat moves to the surface with magma in convective motion. Most of the heat is carried to regions of the mid-ocean ridge spreading centers (see Figure 2.10). Cooler portions of the mantle descend along subduction zones to complete each circular-moving convection cell.

Heat flow measurements show the amount of heat flowing to the surface along the mid-ocean ridge can be up to eight times greater than the average amount flowing to other parts of Earth's crust. Additionally, heat flow at deep-sea trenches, where ocean floor is subducted, can be as little as one-tenth the average. Increased heat flow at the mid-ocean ridge and decreased heat flow at subduction zones is what would be expected based on thin crust at the mid-ocean ridge and a double thickness of crust at the trenches (see Figure 2.10).

WORLDWIDE EARTHQUAKES   *Earthquakes* are sudden releases of energy caused by fault movement or volcanic eruptions. The map in Figure 2.13a shows that most large earthquakes occur along ocean trenches, reflecting the energy released during subduction. Other earthquakes occur along the mid-ocean ridge, reflecting the energy released during sea floor spreading. Still others occur along major faults in the sea floor and on land, reflecting the energy released when moving plates contact other plates along their edges. The two maps in Figure 2.13 show that the distribution of worldwide earthquakes closely matches the locations of plate boundaries.

The Acceptance of a Theory

The accumulation of lines of evidence such as those mentioned in this section, along with many other lines of evidence in support of moving continents, has convinced scientists of the validity of continental drift. Since the late 1960s, the concepts of continental drift and sea floor spreading have been united into a much more encompassing theory known as plate tectonics, which describes the movement of the outermost portion of Earth and the resulting creation of continental and sea floor features. These tectonic plates are pieces of the **lithosphere** (*lithos* = rock, *sphere* = ball) that float on the more fluid **asthenosphere** (*asthenos* = weak, *sphere* = ball) below.[4]

Although several mechanisms have been proposed for the force or forces responsible for driving this motion, none of them are able to explain all aspects of plate motion. However, recent research based on a simple model of lithosphere and mantle interactions suggests that two major tectonic forces may act in unison on the leading edges of subducting plates (slabs) to generate the observed plate movements: (1) *slab pull*, which is generated by a subducting plate that pulls the rest of the plate behind it, and (2) *slab suction*, which is created as a subducting plate drags against the viscous mantle and causes the mantle to flow in toward the subduction zone, thereby sucking in nearby plates much in the same way pulling a plug from a bathtub draws floating objects toward it. If this model is true, then the unequal distribution of heat within Earth, which was thought to be the underlying driving force for plate movement, may not be nearly as important as a driving mechanism.

Since the acceptance of the theory of plate tectonics, much research has focused on understanding various features associated with plate boundaries.

[4]See Chapter 1 for a discussion of properties of the lithosphere and asthenosphere.

Relationship Between Plate
Boundaries and Features

FIGURE 2.13 Earthquakes and lithospheric plates. (a) Distribution of earthquakes with magnitudes equal to or greater than $M_w = 5.0$ for the period 1980–1990. (b) Plate boundaries define the major lithospheric plates (*shaded*), with arrows indicating the direction of motion and numbers representing the rate of motion in centimeters per year. Notice how closely the pattern of major earthquakes follows plate boundaries.

2.3 What Features Occur at Plate Boundaries?

Plate boundaries—where plates interact with each other—are associated with a great deal of tectonic activity, such as mountain building, volcanic activity, and earthquakes. In fact, the first clues to the locations of plate boundaries were the dramatic tectonic events that occur there. For example, Figure 2.13 shows the close correspondence between worldwide earthquakes and plate boundaries. Further, Figure 2.13b shows that Earth's surface is composed of seven major plates along with many smaller ones. Close examination of Figure 2.13b shows that the boundaries of plates do not always follow coastlines and, as a consequence, nearly all plates contain both oceanic and continental crust.[5] Notice also that about 90% of plate boundaries occur on the sea floor.

There are three types of plate boundaries, as shown in Figure 2.14. **Divergent** (*di* = apart, *vergere* = to incline) **boundaries** are found along oceanic ridges where new lithosphere is being added. **Convergent** (*con* = together, *vergere* = to incline) **boundaries** are found where plates are moving together and one plate subducts beneath the other. **Transform** (*trans* = across, *form* = shape) **boundaries** are found where lithospheric plates slowly grind past one another. Table 2.1 summarizes characteristics, tectonic processes, features, and examples of these plate boundaries.

Motion at Plate
Boundaries

FIGURE 2.14 The three types of plate boundaries. **(a)** Divergent, where plates move away from each other. **(b)** Convergent, where plates approach each other. **(c)** Transform, where plates slide past each other.

---

[5]For a review of the differences between (basaltic) oceanic and (granitic) continental crust, see Chapter 1.

| TABLE 2.1 | | CHARACTERISTICS, TECTONIC PROCESSES, FEATURES, AND EXAMPLES OF PLATE BOUNDARIES | | | | | |

Plate boundary	Plate movement	Crust types	Sea floor created or destroyed?	Tectonic process	Sea floor feature(s)	Geographic examples
Divergent plate boundaries	Apart ← →	Ocean–ocean	New sea floor is created	Sea floor spreading	Mid-ocean ridge; volcanoes; young lava flows	Mid-Atlantic Ridge, East Pacific Rise
		Continent–continent	As a continent splits apart, new sea floor is created	Continental rifting	Rift valley; volcanoes; young lava flows	East Africa Rift Valleys, Red Sea, Gulf of California
Convergent plate boundaries	Together → ←	Ocean–continent	Old sea floor is destroyed	Subduction	Trench; volcanic arc on land	Andes Mountains, Cascade Mountains
		Ocean–ocean	Old sea floor is destroyed	Subduction	Trench; volcanic arc as islands	Aleutian Islands, Mariana Islands
		Continent–continent	N/A	Collision	Tall mountains	Himalaya Mountains, Alps
Transform plate boundaries	Past each other → —— ←	Oceanic	N/A	Transform faulting	Fault	Mendocino Fault, Eltanin Fault (between mid-ocean ridges)
		Continental	N/A	Transform Faulting	Fault	San Andreas Fault, Alpine Fault (New Zealand)

Divergent Boundary Features

Divergent plate boundaries occur where two plates move apart, such as along the crest of the mid-ocean ridge where sea floor spreading creates new oceanic lithosphere (Figure 2.15). A common feature along the crest of the mid-ocean ridge is a **rift valley**, which is a central downdropped linear depression (Figure 2.16). Pull-apart faults located along the central rift valley show that the plates are *continuously being pulled apart* rather than being pushed apart by the upwelling of material beneath the mid-ocean ridge. Upwelling of magma beneath the mid-ocean ridge is simply filling in the void left by the separating plates of lithosphere. In the process, sea floor spreading produces about 20 cubic kilometers (4.8 cubic miles) of new ocean crust worldwide each year.

Figure 2.17 shows how the development of a mid-ocean ridge creates an ocean basin. Initially, molten material rises to the surface, causing upwarping and thinning of the crust. Volcanic activity produces vast quantities of high-density basaltic rock. As the plates begin to move apart, a linear rift valley is formed and volcanism continues. Further splitting apart of the land—a process called **rifting**—and more spreading cause the area to drop below sea level. When this occurs, the rift valley eventually floods with seawater and a young linear sea is formed. After millions of years of sea floor spreading, a full-fledged ocean basin is created with a mid-ocean ridge in the middle of the two landmasses.

Two different stages of ocean basin development are shown in the map of East Africa in Figure 2.18. First, the rift valleys are actively pulled apart and are at the rift valley stage of formation. Second, the Red Sea is at the linear sea stage. It has rifted apart so far that the land has dropped below sea level. The Gulf of California in Mexico is another linear sea. The Gulf of California and the Red Sea are two of the youngest seas in the world, having been created only a few million years ago. If plate motions continue rifting the plates apart in these areas, they will eventually become large oceans.

OCEANIC RISES VERSUS OCEANIC RIDGES   The rate at which the sea floor spreads apart varies along the mid-ocean ridge and dramatically affects its appearance. Faster spreading, for instance, produces broader and less rugged segments of the global mid-ocean ridge system. This is because fast-spreading segments of the mid-ocean ridge produce vast amounts of rock, which move away from the spreading center at a rapid rate and consequently undergo less thermal contraction and subsidence than slower-spreading segments do. In addition, central rift valleys on slow-spreading segments tend to be larger and better developed.

FIGURE 2.15 Divergent boundary at the Mid-Atlantic Ridge. Most divergent plate boundaries occur along the crest of the mid-ocean ridge, where sea floor spreading creates new oceanic lithosphere.

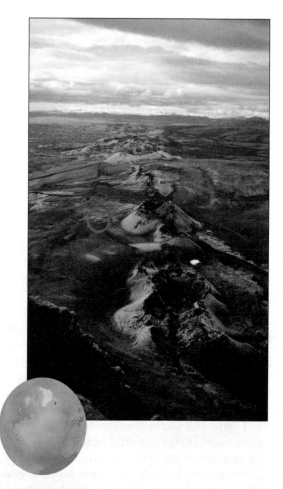

FIGURE 2.16 Rift valley in Iceland. View along a rift valley looking south from Laki volcano in Iceland, which sits atop the Mid-Atlantic Ridge. The rift valley is marked by the linear row of volcanoes extending from the bottom of the photo to the horizon that are split in half. Note the bus (*red circle*) for scale.

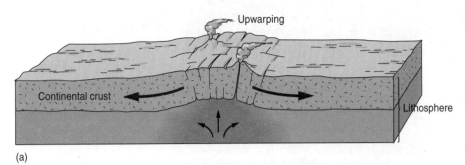

Upwarping

Continental crust

Lithosphere

(a)

Rift valley

(b)

Linear sea

(c)

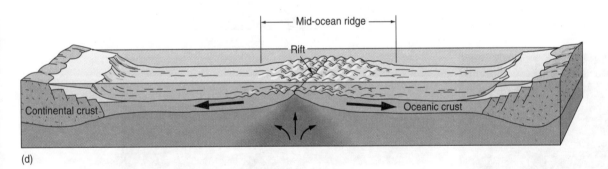

Mid-ocean ridge

Rift

Continental crust

Oceanic crust

(d)

FIGURE 2.17 Formation of an ocean basin by sea floor spreading. Sequence of events in the formation of an ocean basin: **(a)** A shallow heat source develops under a continent, causing initial upwarping and volcanic activity; **(b)** movement apart creates a rift valley; **(c)** with increased spreading, a linear sea is formed; **(d)** after millions of years, a full-fledged ocean basin is created, separating continental pieces that were once connected.

Formation of an Ocean Basin by Sea Floor Spreading

The gently sloping and fast-spreading parts of the mid-ocean ridge are called **oceanic rises**. For example, the **East Pacific Rise** (Figure 2.19, *bottom*) between the Pacific and Nazca Plates is a broad, low, gentle swelling of the sea floor with a small, indistinct central rift valley and has a spreading rate as high as 16.5 centimeters (6.5 inches) per year.[6] Conversely, steeper-sloping and slower-spreading areas of the mid-ocean ridge are called **oceanic ridges**. For instance, the **Mid-Atlantic Ridge** (Figure 2.19, *top*) between the South American and African Plates is a tall, steep, rugged oceanic ridge that has an average spreading rate of 2.5 centimeters (1 inch) per year and stands as much as 3000 meters (10,000 feet) above the surrounding sea floor. Its prominent central rift valley is as much as 32 kilometers (20 miles) wide and averages 2 kilometers (1.2 miles) deep.

Recently, a new class of spreading centers called *ultra-slow spreading centers* has also been recognized. These spreading centers, which were discovered along

[6]The spreading rate is the total widening rate of an ocean basin resulting from motion of *both* plates away from a spreading center.

(a)

(b)   (c)

FIGURE 2.18 East African rift valleys and associated features. **(a)** Parts of east Africa are splitting apart (*arrows*), creating a series of linear downdropped rift valleys (*red lines*) along with prominent volcanoes (*triangles*). Similarly, the Red Sea and Gulf of Aden have split apart so far they are now below sea level. The mid-ocean ridge in the Indian Ocean has experienced similar stages of development. **(b)** Land elevation perspective view looking southwest along part of the East African Rift in Tanzania, showing the downdropped Lake Eyasi and numerous volcanic peaks and craters of the Crater Highlands. Color indicates elevation, where green is lower elevation and brown/white is higher. **(c)** Photo of a rift that formed in 2005 after seismic activity and a volcanic eruption of Mount Dabbahu in Ethiopia's Afar triangle, Africa; note people at left for scale.

the Southwest Indian and Arctic segments of the mid-ocean ridge, are characterized by spreading rates less than 2 centimeters (0.8 inch) per year, a deep rift valley, and volcanoes that occur only at widely spaced intervals. The ultra-slow ridges are spreading so slowly, in fact, that Earth's mantle itself is exposed on the ocean floor in great slabs of rock between these volcanoes.

EARTHQUAKES ASSOCIATED WITH DIVERGENT BOUNDARIES   The amount of energy released by earthquakes along divergent plate boundaries is closely related to the spreading rate. The faster the sea floor spreads, the less energy is released in each earthquake. Earthquake intensity is usually measured on a scale called the **seismic moment magnitude**, which reflects the energy released to create very long-period seismic waves. Because it more adequately represents larger magnitude earthquakes, the moment magnitude scale is increasingly used instead of the well-known *Richter scale* and is represented by the symbol M_w. Earthquakes in the rift valley of the slow-spreading Mid-Atlantic Ridge reach a maximum magnitude of about $M_w = 6.0$ whereas those occurring along the axis of the fast-spreading East Pacific Rise seldom exceed $M_w = 4.5$.[7]

Convergent Boundary Features

Convergent boundaries—where two plates move together and collide—result in the destruction of ocean crust as one plate plunges below the other and is remelted in the mantle. One feature associated with a convergent plate boundary is a deep-ocean trench, which is a deep and narrow depression on the sea floor that marks the beginning of the subduction zone. Another feature is an arc-shaped row of highly active and explosively erupting volcanoes called a **volcanic arc** that parallels the trench and occurs above the subduction zone. Volcanic arcs are formed by the downgoing plate in the subduction zone heating up and releasing superheated gases—mostly water—that cause the overlying mantle to partially melt. This molten rock, which is more buoyant than the rock around it, slowly rises up to the surface and feeds the active volcanoes.

Figure 2.20 shows the three subtypes of convergent boundaries that result from interactions between the two different types of crust (oceanic and continental).

OCEANIC–CONTINENTAL CONVERGENCE   When an oceanic plate and a continental plate converge, the denser oceanic plate is subducted (Figure 2.20a). The oceanic plate becomes heated as it is subducted into the asthenosphere and releases superheated gases that partially melt the overlying mantle, which rises to

Mid–Atlantic Ridge

East Pacific Rise

FIGURE 2.19 Comparing oceanic rises and ridges. Perspective views of the ocean floor based on satellite bathymetry showing differences between oceanic rises and ridges. The fast-spreading East Pacific Rise (*left*) is a broad, low, gentle swelling of the mid-ocean ridge that lacks a prominent rift valley. The slow-spreading Mid-Atlantic Ridge (*above*) is a tall, steep, rugged portion of the mid-ocean ridge with a prominent central rift valley.

---

[7]Note that each one-unit increase of earthquake magnitude represents an increase of energy release of about 30 times.

(a) Ocean–Continent Collision

Oceanic crust
Trench
Continental arc
Lithosphere
Asthenosphere
Continental crust
Lithosphere
Partial melting

Oceanic crust
Trench
Island arc
Lithosphere
Continental crust
Lithosphere
Partial melting
Asthenosphere

(b) Ocean–Ocean Collision

Mountain range
Continental crust
Continental crust
Lithosphere
Asthenosphere
Lithosphere
Oceanic crust

(c) Continent–Continent Collision

FIGURE 2.20 The three subtypes of convergent plate boundaries and their associated features. (a) Oceanic–continental convergence, where denser oceanic crust subducts and a continental arc is created. (b) Oceanic–oceanic convergence, where the older, denser sea floor subducts and an oceanic island arc is created. (c) Continental–continental convergence, where continental crust is too low in density to subduct. Instead, a tall uplifted mountain range is created.

the surface through the overriding continental plate. The rising basalt-rich magma mixes with the *granite* of the continental crust, producing lava in volcanic eruptions at the surface that is intermediate in composition between basalt and granite. One type of volcanic rock with this composition is called *andesite*, named after the Andes Mountains of South America because it is so common there. Because andesite magma is more viscous than basalt magma and contains such high gas content, andesitic volcanic eruptions are usually quite explosive and have historically been very destructive. The result of this volcanic activity on the continent above the subduction zone produces a type of volcanic arc called a **continental arc**. Continental arcs are created by andesitic volcanic eruptions and by the folding and uplifting associated with plate collision.

If the spreading center producing the subducting plate is far enough from the subduction zone, an oceanic trench becomes well developed along the margin of the continent. The Peru–Chile Trench is an example, and the Andes Mountains are the associated continental arc produced by partially melting the mantle above the subducting plate. If the spreading center producing the subducting plate is close to the subduction zone, however, the trench is not nearly as well developed. This is the case where the Juan de Fuca Plate subducts beneath the North American Plate off the coasts of Washington and Oregon to produce the Cascade Mountains continental arc (Figure 2.21). Here, the Juan de Fuca Ridge is so close to the North American Plate that the subducting lithosphere is less than 10 million years old and has not cooled enough to become very deep. In addition, the large amount of sediment carried to the ocean by the Columbia River has filled most of the trench with sediment. Many of the Cascade volcanoes of this continental arc have been active within the last 100 years. Most recently, Mount St. Helens erupted in May 1980, killing 62 people. Box 2.2 presents information about a new high-tech sea floor observatory on the Juan de Fuca Plate.

OCEANIC–OCEANIC CONVERGENCE When two oceanic plates converge, the denser oceanic plate is subducted (Figure 2.20b). Typically, the older oceanic plate is denser because it has had more time to cool and contract. This type of convergence produces the deepest trenches in the world, such as the Mariana Trench in the western Pacific Ocean. Similar to oceanic–continental convergence, the subducting oceanic plate becomes heated, releases superheated gases, and partially melts the overlying mantle. This buoyant molten material rises to the surface and fuels the active volcanoes, which occur as an arc-shaped row of volcanic islands that is a type of volcanic arc called an **island arc**. The molten material is mostly basaltic because there is no mixing with granitic rocks from the continents, and the eruptions are not nearly as destructive. Examples of island arc/trench systems are the West Indies's Leeward and Windward Islands/Puerto Rico Trench in the Caribbean Sea and the Aleutian Islands/Aleutian Trench in the North Pacific Ocean.

CONTINENTAL–CONTINENTAL CONVERGENCE When two continental plates converge, which one is subducted? you might expect that the older of the two (which is most likely the denser one) will be subducted. Continental lithosphere

FIGURE 2.21 Convergent tectonic activity produces the Cascade Mountains.
(a) Tectonic features of the Cascade Mountain Range and vicinity. **(b)** The volcanoes of the Cascade Mountains are created by the subduction of the Juan de Fuca Plate beneath the North American Plate. **(c)** The eruption of Mount St. Helens in 1980.

forms differently than oceanic lithosphere, however, and old continental lithosphere is no denser than young continental lithosphere. It turns out that neither subducts because both are too low in density to be pulled very far down into the mantle. Instead, a tall uplifted mountain range is created by the collision of the two plates (Figure 2.20c). These mountains are composed of folded and deformed sedimentary rocks originally deposited on the sea floor that previously separated the two continental plates. the oceanic crust itself may subduct beneath such mountains. A prime example of continental–continental convergence is the collision of India with Asia (Figure 2.22). It began 45 million years ago and has created the Himalaya mountains, presently the tallest mountains on Earth.

EARTHQUAKES ASSOCIATED WITH CONVERGENT BOUNDARIES Both spreading centers and trench systems are characterized by earthquakes, but in different ways. Spreading centers have shallow earthquakes, usually less than 10 kilometers (6 miles) deep. Earthquakes in the trenches, on the other hand, vary from near the surface down to 670 kilometers (415 miles) deep, which are the deepest earthquakes in the world. These earthquakes are clustered in a band about 20 kilometers (12.5 miles) thick that closely corresponds to the location of the subduction zone. In fact, the subducting plate in a convergent plate boundary

web *animation*

Collapse of Mount
St. Helens

THE NEPTUNE PROJECT: AN INTERACTIVE SEA FLOOR OBSERVATORY

The earth, ocean, and planetary sciences are shifting from an intermittent expeditionary mode of identifying "what's out there" to a sustained, on-site presence that enables scientists to explore natural systems in real-time. This shift arises in part from the rapidly expanding developments in the computational, robotic, communications, and sensor industries and in part from a growing awareness of the complexity and interactive dynamics of many natural systems over long time spans. Several countries are engaged in developing remote-controlled observatories to monitor the sea floor and its adjacent components. One of the most elaborate is the North–East Pacific Time-series Undersea Networked Experiments, or **NEPTUNE**, which is also the name of Roman mythology's god of the sea.

The NEPTUNE project is a multinational partnership between the University of Washington in Seattle and the University of Victoria, Canada, aimed at establishing a cutting-edge sea floor observatory system designed to monitor tectonic activity along the Juan de Fuca tectonic plate in the northeast Pacific Ocean (Figure 2B). To accomplish its goals, the project seeks to establish a network of fiber-optic/power cables that will encircle and cross the Juan de Fuca Plate. Between 30 and 50 experimental sites will be established at nodes along the cables. These sites will be instrumented to interact with various geological, physical, chemical, and biological phenomena. Sensor networks will monitor activity between nodes and will include multipurpose robotic underwater vehicles that will reside at depth, recharge at nodes, and respond to events such as submarine volcanic eruptions. The network will provide real-time information and command-and-control capabilities to shore-based users via the Internet (http://www.neptune.washington.edu/).

NEPTUNE, which is expected to be fully operational in 2012, will enable regional-scale, long-term, real-time observations and experiments within the ocean, on the sea floor, and beneath the sea floor. The network will be a resource for the scientific and educational communities, much as a research vessel is an observational platform open to a wide range of users. For the first time, researchers, as well as decision makers and shore-based learners of all ages, will be able to participate in detailed studies and experiments on a wide area of sea floor and ocean for decades rather than just hours or days. With an anticipated life span of 30 years, the network will provide unprecedented interdisciplinary measurements of oceanic variables.

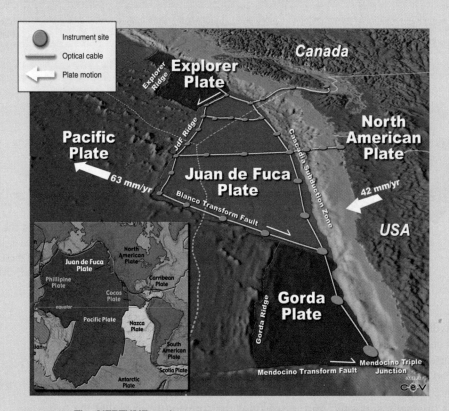

FIGURE 2B The NEPTUNE project. NEPTUNE's 2500-kilometer (1550-mile) network of fiber-optic/power cables (*yellow lines*) will encircle and cross the Juan de Fuca Plate to allow long-term observation of ocean variables. Between 15 and 20 instrument sites (*green dots*) will be established at nodes along the cables and will be instrumented to measure various physical, chemical, and biological properties. Note that plates are shaded in different colors in the figure; arrows represent plate motions.

can be traced below the surface by examining the pattern of successively deeper earthquakes extending from the trench.

Many factors combine to produce large earthquakes at convergent boundaries. The forces involved in convergent-plate boundary collisions are enormous. Huge lithospheric slabs of rock are relentlessly pushing against each other, and the

(a) 45 million years ago

(b) Today

(c)

FIGURE 2.22 The collision of India with Asia. (a) Sea floor spreading along the mid-ocean ridge south of India caused the collision of India with Asia, which began about 45 million years ago. **(b)** The collision closed the shallow sea between India and Asia, crumpled the two continents together, and is responsible for the continued uplift of the Himalaya Mountains. **(c)** View of Ladakh, India, with the snow-capped Himalaya Mountains in the background.

subducting plate must actually bend as it dives below the surface. In addition, thick crust associated with convergent boundaries tends to store more energy than the thinner crust at divergent boundaries. Also, mineral structure changes occur at the higher pressures encountered deep below the surface, which are thought to produce changes in volume that lead to some of the most powerful earthquakes in the world. In fact, the largest earthquake ever recorded was the 1960 Chilean earthquake near the Peru–Chile Trench, which had a magnitude of $M_w = 9.5$!

Convergent Margins:
India-Asia Collision

Transform Boundary Features

A global sea floor map (such as the one inside the front cover of this book) shows that the mid-ocean ridge is offset by many large features oriented perpendicular (at right angles) to the crest of the ridge. What causes these offsets? They are formed because spreading at a mid-ocean ridge only occurs perpendicular to the axis of a ridge and all parts of a plate must move together. As a result, offsets are oriented perpendicular to the ridge and parallel to each other to accommodate spreading of a linear ridge system on a spherical Earth. In addition, the offsets allow different segments of the mid-ocean ridge to spread apart at different rates. These offsets—called **transform faults**—give the mid-ocean ridge a zigzag appearance. There are thousands of these transform faults, some large and some small, which dissect the global mid-ocean ridge.

OCEANIC VERSUS CONTINENTAL TRANSFORM FAULTS   There are two types of transform faults. The first and most common type occurs wholly on the ocean floor and is called an **oceanic transform fault**. The second type cuts across a continent and is called a **continental transform fault**. Regardless of type, though, transform faults *always* occur between two segments of a mid-ocean ridge, as shown in Figure 2.23.

EARTHQUAKES ASSOCIATED WITH TRANSFORM BOUNDARIES   The movement of one plate past another—a process called **transform faulting**—produces shallow but often strong earthquakes in the lithosphere. Magnitudes of $M_w = 7.0$ have been recorded along some oceanic transform faults. One of the best studied faults in the world is California's **San Andreas Fault**, a continental transform fault that runs from the Gulf of California past San Francisco and beyond into northern California. Because the San Andreas Fault cuts through continental crust, which is much thicker than oceanic crust, earthquakes are considerably larger than those produced by oceanic transform faults, sometimes up to $M_w = 8.5$.

Because California experiences large periodic earthquakes, many people are mistakenly concerned that it will "fall off into the ocean" during a large earthquake along the San Andreas Fault. These earthquakes occur as the Pacific Plate continues to move to the northwest past the North American Plate at a rate of about 5 centimeters (2 inches) a year. At this rate, Los Angeles (on the Pacific Plate) will be adjacent to San Francisco (on the North American Plate) in about 18.5 million years—a length of time for about 1 million generations of people to live their lives. Although California will never fall into the ocean, people living near this fault should be very aware they are likely to experience a large earthquake within their lifetime.

> **KEY CONCEPT**
> The three main types of plate boundaries are divergent (plates moving apart such as at the mid-ocean ridge), convergent (plates moving together such as at an ocean trench), and transform (plates sliding past each other such as at a transform fault).

2.4 Testing the Model: What Are Some Applications of Plate Tectonics?

One of the strengths of plate tectonic theory is how it unifies so many seemingly separate events into a single consistent model. Let's look at a few examples that illustrate how plate tectonic processes can be used to explain the origin of features that, up until the acceptance of plate tectonics, were difficult to explain.

Hotspots and Mantle Plumes

Although the theory of plate tectonics helped explain the origin of many features near plate boundaries, it did not seem to explain the origin of *intraplate* (*intra* = within, *plate* = plate of the lithosphere) *features* that are far from any

Tectonic Settings of
Volcanic Activity

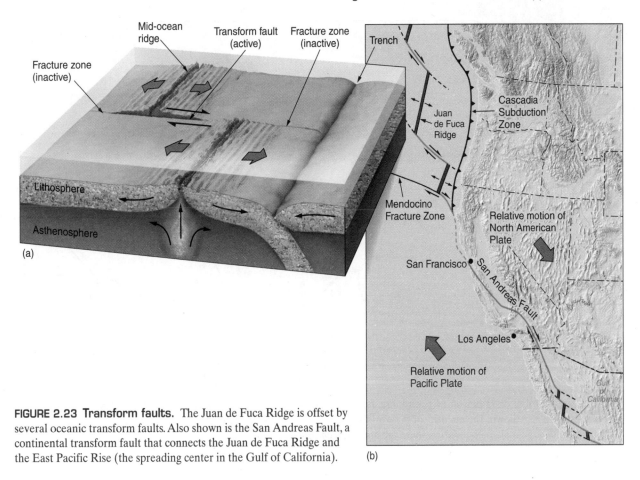

FIGURE 2.23 Transform faults. The Juan de Fuca Ridge is offset by several oceanic transform faults. Also shown is the San Andreas Fault, a continental transform fault that connects the Juan de Fuca Ridge and the East Pacific Rise (the spreading center in the Gulf of California).

plate boundary. For instance, how can plate tectonics explain volcanic islands near the middle of a plate? Areas of intense volcanic activity that remain in more or less the same location over long periods of geologic time and are unrelated to plate boundaries are called **hotspots**.[8] For example, the continuing volcanism in Yellowstone National Park and Hawaii are caused by hotspots.

Why is there so much volcanic activity at hotspots? The plate tectonic model infers that hotspot volcanism is caused by the presence of **mantle plumes** (*pluma* = a soft feather), which are columnar areas of hot molten rock that arise from deep within the mantle. Mantle plumes are most likely related to the positions of convection cells in the mantle. There appear to be several types of mantle plumes: Some come from the core–mantle boundary, while others have a shallower source. Recent research reveals that the core–mantle boundary is not a simple smooth dividing zone but has many regional variations, which has implications for the development of mantle plumes. Currently, there is vigorous scientific debate regarding mantle plumes and volcanism at hotspots, mainly because the seismic data to support or disprove the plume model have so far been inconclusive.[9] In fact, new studies suggest that hotspots are neither deep phenomenon nor fixed in position over geologic time as assumed in the standard plume model.

Worldwide, more than 100 hotspots have been active within the past 10 million years. Figure 2.24 shows the global distribution of prominent hotspots today. In

---

[8]Note that a hotspot is different from either a volcanic arc or a mid-ocean ridge (both of which are related to plate boundaries), even though all are marked by a high degree of volcanic activity.

[9]For more information about this debate, see http://mantleplumes.org/.

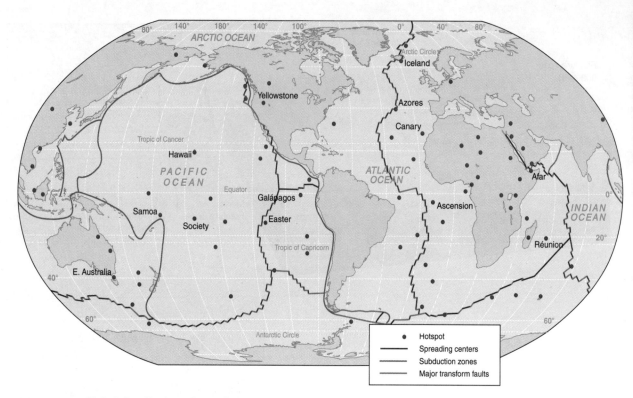

FIGURE 2.24 Global distribution of prominent hotspots. Prominent hotspots are shown by red dots; the locations of plate boundaries are also shown. The majority of the world's hotspots are not associated with plate boundaries; those that are tend to occur along divergent plate boundaries where the lithosphere is thin.

general, hotspots do not coincide with plate boundaries. Notable exceptions are those that are near divergent boundaries where the lithosphere is thin, such as at the Galápagos Islands and Iceland. In fact, Iceland straddles the Mid-Atlantic Ridge (a divergent plate boundary). It is also directly over a 150-kilometer- (93-mile)-wide mantle plume, which accounts for its remarkable amount of volcanic activity—so much that it has caused Iceland to be one of the few areas of the global mid-ocean ridge that rise high above sea level.

Throughout the Pacific Plate, many island chains are oriented in a northwestward-southeastward direction. The most intensely studied of these is the **Hawaiian Islands–Emperor Seamount Chain** in the northern Pacific Ocean (Figure 2.25). What created this chain of more than 100 intraplate volcanoes that stretch over 5800 kilometers (3000 miles)? Further, what caused the prominent bend in the overall direction that occurs in the middle of the chain?

To help answer these questions, examine the ages of the volcanoes in the chain. Every volcano in the chain has long since become extinct, except the volcano Kilauea on the island of Hawaii, which is the southeasternmost island of the chain. The age of volcanoes progressively increases northwestward from Hawaii (Figure 2.25). To the northwest, the volcanoes increase in age past Suiko Seamount (65 million years old) to Detroit Seamount (81 million years old) near the Aleutian Trench.

These age relationships suggest that the Pacific Plate has steadily moved northwestward while the underlying mantle plume remained relatively stationary. The resulting Hawaiian hotspot created each of the volcanoes in the chain. As the plate moved, it carried the active volcano off the hotspot and a new volcano began forming, younger in age than the previous one. A chain of extinct volcanoes that is progressively older as one travels away from a hotspot is called a **nematath** (*nema* = thread, *tath* = dung or manure), or a *hotspot track*. Evidence suggests

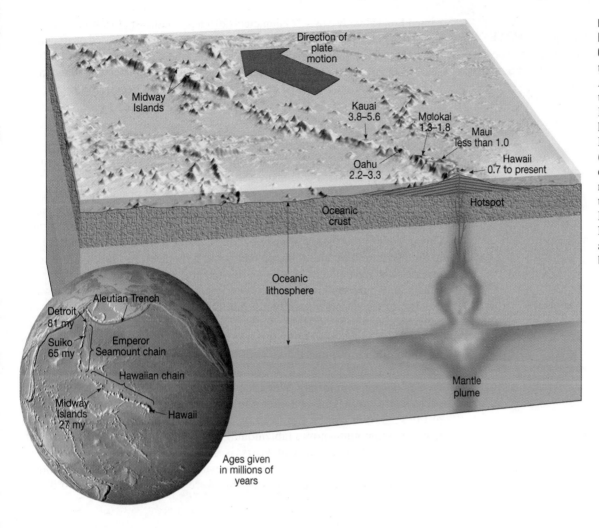

FIGURE 2.25 Hawaiian Islands–Emperor Seamount Chain. The chain of volcanoes that extends from Hawaii to the Aleutian Trench results from the movement of the Pacific Plate over the Hawaiian hotspot. The sharp bend in the Hawaiian–Emperor chain (*globe*) was created by a combination of the changing motion of the Pacific Plate and the slow movement of the Hawaiian hotspot itself. Numbers represent radiometric age dates in millions of years before present.

that about 47 million years ago, the Pacific Plate shifted from a northerly to a northwesterly direction. This change in plate motion can account for the bend (large elbow) in Figure 2.25 about halfway through the chain, separating the Hawaiian Islands from the Emperor Seamounts. If this is true, then other hotspot tracks throughout the Pacific Plate should show a similar bend at roughly the same time, but most do not.

Recent research that may help resolve this disparity indicates that hotspots do not remain completely stationary. In fact, several studies have shown that most hotspots move at less than 1 centimeter (0.4 inch) per year but some like Hawaii may have moved faster in the geologic past. Even if Hawaii's hotspot had moved faster in the past, it did not do so in a way that would have created the sharp bend in the Hawaiian–Emperor track seen in Figure 2.25. Moreover, recent plate reconstructions suggest that the observed bend in the Hawaiian–Emperor chain was created by a combination of the changing motion of the Pacific Plate (mainly as a result of changes in plate motions near Australia and Antarctica) and the slow movement of the Hawaiian hotspot itself. Other hotspot tracks may have been at least partially created by motion of their hotspots as well. Remarkably, hotspots appear to be moving in the exact opposite direction of plates, so hotspots may still be useful for tracking plate motions.

In the future, what will become of Hawaii—the island that currently resides on the hotspot? Based on the hotspot model, the island will be carried to the northwest off the hotspot, become inactive, and eventually be subducted into the Aleutian Trench, like all the rest of the volcanoes in the chain to the north of it. In turn, other volcanoes will build up over the hotspot. In fact, a 3500-meter (11,500-foot) volcano

KEY CONCEPT
Mantle plumes create hotspots at the surface,
which produce volcanic chains called nemataths that
record the motion of plates.

named **Loihi** already exists 32 kilometers (20 miles) southeast of Hawaii. Still 1 kilometer (0.6 mile) below sea level, Loihi is volcanically active and, based on its current rate of activity, it should reach the surface sometime between 30,000 and 100,000 years from now. As it builds above sea level, it will become the newest island in the long chain of volcanoes created by the Hawaiian hotspot.

Seamounts and Tablemounts

Many areas of the ocean floor (most notably on the Pacific Plate) contain tall volcanic peaks that resemble many volcanoes on land. These large volcanoes are called **seamounts** if they are cone-shaped on top, like an upside-down ice cream cone. Some volcanoes are flat on top—unlike anything on land—and are called **tablemounts**, or **guyots**, after Princeton University's first geology professor, Arnold Guyot.[10] Until the theory of plate tectonics, it was unclear how the differences between seamounts and tablemounts could have been produced. The theory explains why tablemounts are flat on top and also explains why the tops of some tablemounts have shallow-water deposits despite being located in very deep water.

The origin of many seamounts and tablemounts is related to the volcanic activity occurring at hotspots; others are related to processes occurring at the mid-ocean ridge (Figure 2.26). Because of sea floor spreading, active volcanoes (seamounts) occur along the crest of the mid-ocean ridge. Some may be built up so high they rise above sea level and become islands, at which point wave erosion becomes important. When sea floor spreading has moved the seamount off its source of magma (whether it is a mid-ocean ridge or a hotspot), the top of the seamount can be flattened by waves in just a few million years. This flattened seamount—now a tablemount—continues to be carried away from its source and, after millions of years, is submerged deeper into the ocean. Frequently, tops of tablemounts contain evidence of shallow-water conditions (such as ancient coral reef deposits) that were carried with them into deeper water.

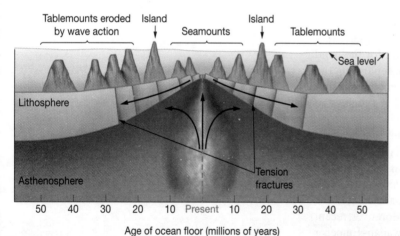

FIGURE 2.26 **Formation of seamounts and tablemounts at a mid-ocean ridge.** Seamounts are tall volcanoes formed at volcanic centers such as the mid-ocean ridge. If they are tall enough to reach the surface, their tops are eroded flat by wave activity and become tablemounts. Through sea floor spreading, seamounts and tablemounts are transported into deeper water, sometimes carrying with them evidence of their tops once reaching shallow water.

Coral Reef Development

On his voyage aboard the HMS *Beagle*, the famous naturalist **Charles Darwin**[11] noticed a progression of stages in **coral reef** development. He hypothesized that the origin of coral reefs depended on the subsidence (sinking) of volcanic islands (Figure 2.27) and published the concept in *The Structure and Distribution of Coral Reefs* in 1842. What Darwin's hypothesis lacked was a mechanism for how volcanic islands subside. Much later, advances in plate tectonic theory and samples of the deep structure of coral reefs provided evidence to help support Darwin's hypothesis.

Reef-building corals are colonial animals that live in shallow, warm, tropical seawater and produce a hard skeleton of limestone. Once corals are established in an area that has the conditions necessary for their growth, they continue to grow upward layer by layer with each new generation attached to the skeletons of its predecessors. Over millions of years, a thick sequence of coral reef deposits may develop if conditions remain favorable.

---

[10]Guyot is pronounced "GEE-oh," with a hard *g*, as in "give."

[11]For more information about Charles Darwin and the voyage of HMS *Beagle*, see Box 1.3 in Chapter 1.

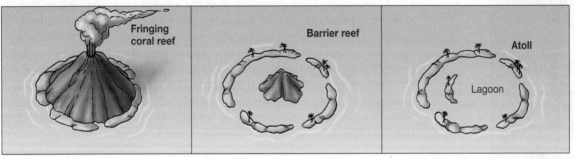

FIGURE 2.27 Stages of development in coral reefs. Cross-sectional view (*above*) and map view (*below*) of **(a)** a fringing reef, **(b)** a barrier reef, and **(c)** an atoll. With the right conditions for coral growth, coral reefs change through time from fringing reef to barrier reef to atoll.

The three stages of development in coral reefs are called fringing, barrier, and atoll. **Fringing reefs** (Figure 2.27a) initially develop along the margin of a landmass (an island or a continent) where the temperature, salinity, and turbidity (cloudiness) of the water are suitable for reef-building corals. Often, fringing reefs are associated with active volcanoes whose lava flows run down the flanks of the volcano and kill the coral. Thus, these fringing reefs are not very thick or well developed. Because of the close proximity of the landmass to the reef, runoff from the landmass can carry so much sediment that the reef is buried. The amount of living coral in a fringing reef at any given time is relatively small, with the greatest concentration in areas protected from sediment and salinity changes. If sea level does not rise or the land does not subside, the process stops at the fringing reef stage.

The **barrier reef** stage follows the fringing reef stage. Barrier reefs are linear or circular reefs separated from the landmass by a well-developed lagoon (Figure 2.27b). As the landmass subsides, the reef maintains its position close to sea level by growing upward. Studies of reef growth rates indicate most have grown 3 to 5 meters (10 to 16 feet) per 1000 years during the recent geologic past. Evidence suggests that some fast-growing reefs in the Caribbean have grown more than 10 meters (33 feet) per 1000 years. Note that if the landmass subsides at a rate faster than coral can grow upward, the coral reef will be submerged in water too deep for it to live.

The largest reef system in the world is Australia's **Great Barrier Reef**, a series of more than 3000 individual reefs collectively in the barrier reef stage of development, home to hundreds of coral species and thousands of other reef-dwelling organisms. The Great Barrier Reef lies 40 kilometers (25 miles) or more offshore, averages 150 kilometers (90 miles) in width, and extends for more than 2000 kilometers (1200 miles) along Australia's shallow northeastern coast. The effects of the Indian–Australian plate moving north toward the equator from colder Antarctic waters are clearly visible in the age and structure of the Great Barrier Reef (Figure 2.28). It is oldest (around 25 million years old) and thickest at its northern end because the northern part of

web animation

Formation of Seamounts/ Tablemounts and Stages of Coral Reef Development

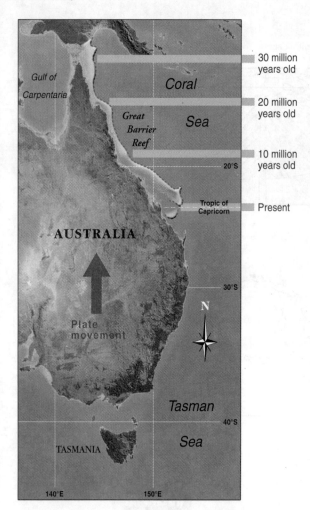

FIGURE 2.28 **Australia's Great Barrier Reef records plate movement.** About 30 million years ago, the Great Barrier Reef began to develop as northern Australia moved into tropical waters that allowed coral growth.

> **KEY CONCEPT**
> Many independent lines of evidence, such as the detection of plate motion by satellites, provide strong support for the theory of plate tectonics.

Australia reached water warm enough to grow coral before the southern parts did. In other areas of the Pacific, Indian, and Atlantic Oceans, smaller barrier reefs are found around the tall volcanic peaks that form tropical islands.

The **atoll** (*atar* = crowded together) stage (Figure 2.27c) comes after the barrier reef stage. As a barrier reef around a volcano continues to subside, coral builds up toward the surface. After millions of years, the volcano becomes completely submerged, but the coral reef continues to grow. If the rate of subsidence is slow enough for the coral to keep up, a circular reef called an atoll is formed. The atoll encloses a lagoon usually not more than 30 to 50 meters (100 to 165 feet) deep. The reef generally has many channels that allow circulation between the lagoon and the open ocean. Buildups of crushed-coral debris often form narrow islands that encircle the central lagoon (Figure 2.29) and are large enough to allow human habitation.

Alternatively, a new theory has been put forward to explain the origin of coral atolls. The theory suggests that glacial cycles cause sea level to fluctuate, leading to episodes of reef exposure and dissolution when global sea level is lower during ice ages, alternating with coral reef submergence and deposition when sea level is higher during interglacial stages. Instead of the slow growth of ring-shaped coral above a sinking volcanic island, this alternating cycle may be responsible for the formation of coral atolls. More about sea level change is discussed in Chapter 10, "The Coast: Beaches and Shoreline Processes," and Chapter 16, "The Oceans and Climate Change."

Detecting Plate Motion with Satellites

Since the late 1970s, orbiting satellites have allowed the accurate positioning of locations on Earth. (This technique is also used for navigation by ships at sea; see Box 1.2.) If the plates are moving, satellite positioning should show this movement over time. The map in Figure 2.30 shows locations that have been measured in this manner and confirms that locations on Earth are indeed moving in good agreement with the direction and rate of motion predicted by plate tectonics. Successful prediction that locations on Earth are moving with respect to one another very strongly supports plate tectonic theory.

2.5 How Has Earth Changed in the Past, and How Will It Look in the Future?

One of the most powerful features of any scientific theory is its ability to predict occurrences. Let's examine how plate tectonics can be used to predict the locations of the continents and oceans in the past, as well as the implications it has for their future configurations on Earth.

The Past: Paleogeography

The study of historical changes of continental shapes and positions is called **paleogeography** (*paleo* = ancient, *geo* = earth, *graphy* = the name of a descriptive science). As a result of paleogeographic changes, the size and shape of ocean basins have changed as well.

Figure 2.31 is a series of world maps showing the paleogeographic reconstructions of Earth at 60-million-year intervals. At 540 million years ago, many of the present-day continents are barely recognizable. North America was on the equator and rotated 90 degrees clockwise. Antarctica was on the equator and was connected to many other continents.

Between 540 and 300 million years ago, the continents began to come together to form Pangaea. Notice that Alaska had not yet formed. Continents are thought to add material through the process of **continental accretion** (*ad* = toward, *crescere* = to grow). Like adding layers onto a snowball, bits and pieces of continents, islands, and volcanoes are added to the edges of continents and create larger landmasses.

From 180 million years ago to the present, Pangaea separated and the continents moved toward their present-day positions. North America and South America rifted away from Europe and Africa to produce the Atlantic Ocean. In the Southern Hemisphere, South America and a continent composed of India, Australia, and Antarctica began to separate from Africa.

By 120 million years ago, there was a clear separation between South America and Africa, and India had moved northward, away from the Australia–Antarctica mass, which began moving toward the South Pole. As the Atlantic Ocean continued to open, India moved rapidly northward and collided with Asia about 45 million years ago. Australia had also begun a rapid journey to the north since separating from Antarctica.

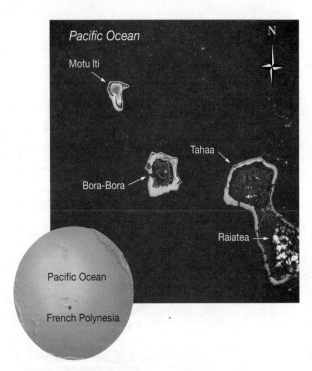

FIGURE 2.29 Barrier reefs and atoll. A portion of the Society Islands (French Polynesia) in the Pacific Ocean as photographed from the space shuttle. From lower right, the islands of Raiatea, Tahaa, and Bora-Bora are in the barrier reef stage of development, while Motu Iti is an atoll.

FIGURE 2.30 Satellite positioning of locations on Earth. Arrows show direction of motion based on satellite measurement of positions on Earth. Rate of plate motion in millimeters per year is indicated with different colored arrows (*see legend*). Plate boundaries are shown with black lines and are dashed where uncertain or diffuse.

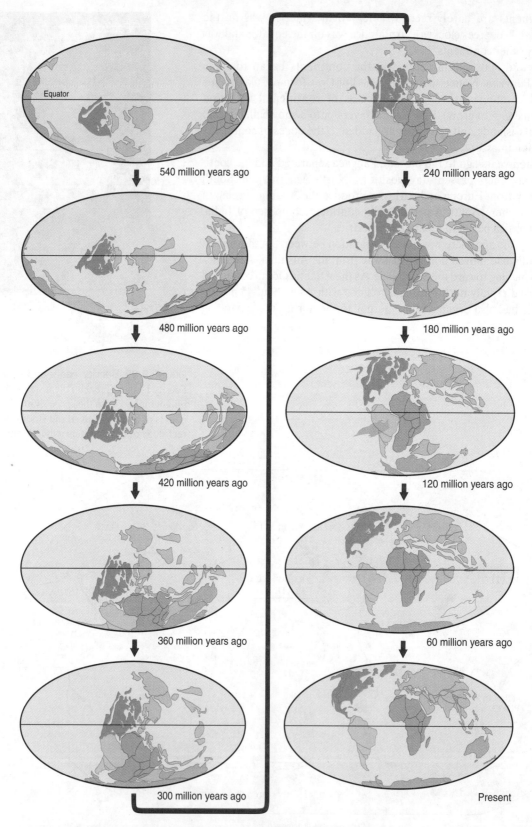

FIGURE 2.31 Paleogeographic reconstructions of Earth. The positions of the continents at 60-million-year intervals.

One major outcome of global plate tectonic events over the past 180 million years has been the creation of the Atlantic Ocean, which continues to grow as the sea floor spreads along the Mid-Atlantic Ridge. At the same time, the Pacific Ocean continues to shrink due to subduction along the many trenches that surround it and continental plates that bear in from both the east and west.

The Future: Some Bold Predictions

Using plate tectonics, a prediction of the future positions of features on Earth can be made based on the assumption that the rate and direction of plate motion will remain the same. Although these assumptions may not be entirely valid, they do provide a framework for the prediction of the positions of continents and other Earth features in the future.

Figure 2.32 is a map of what the world may look like 50 million years from now, showing many notable differences compared to today. For instance, the east African rift valleys may enlarge to form a new linear sea and the Red Sea may be greatly enlarged from rifting there. India may continue to plow into Asia, further uplifting the Himalaya Mountains. As Australia moves north toward Asia, it may use New Guinea like a snowplow to accrete various islands. North America and South America may continue to move west, enlarging the Atlantic Ocean and decreasing the size of the Pacific Ocean. The land bridge of Central America may no longer connect North and South America; this would dramatically alter ocean circulation. Finally, the thin sliver of land that lies west of the San Andreas Fault may become an island in the North Pacific, soon to be accreted onto southern Alaska.

STUDENTS SOMETIMES ASK...

Will the continents come back together and form a single landmass anytime soon?

Yes, it is very likely that the continents will come back together, but not anytime soon. Because all the continents are on the same planetary body, a continent can travel only so far before it collides with other continents. Recent research suggests that the continents may form a supercontinent once every 500 million years or so. It has been 200 million years since Pangaea split up, so we have only about 300 million years to establish world peace!

KEY CONCEPT

The geographic positions of the continents and ocean basins are not fixed in time or place. Rather, they have changed in the past and will continue to change in the future.

web animation

Plate Motions Through Time

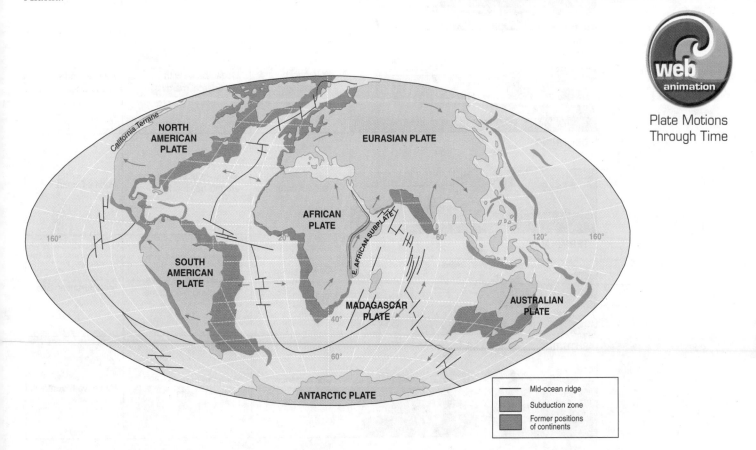

FIGURE 2.32 The world as it may look 50 million years from now. Purple shadows indicate the present-day positions of continents and tan shading indicates positions of the continents in 50 million years. Green arrows indicate direction of plate motion.

Terrane Formation

2.6 Plate Tectonics ... To Be Continued

Since its inception by Alfred Wegener nearly 100 years ago, plate tectonics has been supported by a wealth of scientific evidence—some of which has been presented in this chapter. Although there are still details to be worked out (such as the exact driving mechanism), it has been universally accepted by Earth scientists today because it helps explain so many observations about our planet. Further, it has led to predictive models that have been used to successfully understand Earth behavior. One such example is the **Wilson cycle** (Figure 2.33),

Stage, showing cross-sectional view	Motion	Physiography	Example
EMBRYONIC	Uplift	Complex system of linear rift valleys on continent	East African rift valleys
JUVENILE	Divergence (spreading)	Narrow seas with matching coasts	Red Sea
MATURE	Divergence (spreading)	Ocean basin with continental margins	Atlantic and Arctic Oceans
DECLINING	Convergence (subduction)	Island arcs and trenches around basin edge	Pacific Ocean
TERMINAL	Convergence (collision) and uplift	Narrow, irregular seas with young mountains	Mediterranean Sea
SUTURING	Convergence and uplift	Young to mature mountain belts	Himalaya Mountains

FIGURE 2.33 The Wilson cycle of ocean basin evolution. The Wilson cycle depicts the stages of ocean basin development, from the initial embryonic stage of formation to the destruction of the basin as continental masses collide and undergo suturing.

named in honor of geophysicist *John Tuzo Wilson*, for his contribution to the early ideas of plate tectonics. The Wilson cycle uses plate tectonic processes to show the distinctive life cycle of ocean basins during their formation, growth, and destruction over many millions of years.

In the embryonic stage of the Wilson cycle, a heat source beneath the lithosphere creates uplift and begins to split a continent apart. The juvenile stage is characterized by further spreading, downdropping, and the formation of a narrow, linear sea. The mature stage is where an ocean basin is fully developed, with a mid-ocean ridge that runs down the middle of the ocean basin. Eventually, a subduction zone occurs along the continental margin and the plates come back together, producing the declining stage where the ocean basin shrinks. The terminal stage occurs when the plates come back together, creating a progressively narrower ocean. Finally, in the suturing stage, the ocean disappears, the continents collide, and tall uplifted mountains are created. Over time as the uplifted mountains erode, the stage is set to repeat the cycle again.

Not only is plate tectonic activity primarily responsible for the creation of landforms, but it also plays a prominent role in the development of ocean floor features—which is the topic of the next chapter. Armed with the knowledge of plate tectonic processes you've gained from this chapter, understanding the history and development of ocean floor features in various marine provinces will be a much simpler task.

Chapter in Review

• According to the theory of plate tectonics, *the outermost portion of Earth is composed of a patchwork of thin, rigid lithospheric plates that move horizontally* with respect to one another. The idea began as a hypothesis called continental drift proposed by *Alfred Wegener* at the start of the 20th century. He suggested that *about 200 million years ago, all the continents were combined* into one large continent (*Pangaea*) surrounded by a single large ocean (*Panthalassa*).

• *Many lines of evidence were used to support the idea of continental drift,* including the similar shape of nearby continents, matching sequences of rocks and mountain chains, glacial ages and other climate evidence, and the distribution of fossil and present-day organisms. Although this evidence suggested that continents have drifted, other incorrect assumptions about the mechanism involved caused many geologists and geophysicists to discount this hypothesis throughout the first half of the 20th century.

• *More convincing evidence for drifting continents was introduced in the 1960s, when paleomagnetism*—the study of Earth's ancient magnetic field—*was developed* and the significance of features of the ocean floor became better known. The paleomagnetism of the ocean floor is permanently recorded in oceanic crust and reveals stripes of normal and reverse magnetic polarity in a symmetric pattern relative to the mid-ocean ridge.

• *Harry Hess advanced the idea of sea floor spreading. New sea floor is created at the crest of the mid-ocean ridge* and moves apart in opposite directions and is *eventually destroyed by subduction into an ocean trench*. This helps explain the pattern of magnetic stripes on the sea floor and why sea floor rocks increase linearly in age in either direction from the axis of the mid-ocean ridge. Other supporting evidence for plate tectonics includes oceanic heat flow measurements and the pattern of worldwide earthquakes. The combination of evidence *convinced geologists* of Earth's dynamic nature and helped advance the idea of continental drift into the more encompassing plate tectonic theory.

• *As new crust is added to the lithosphere at the mid-ocean ridge* (*divergent boundaries* where plates move apart), the opposite ends of the *plates are subducted into the mantle at ocean trenches* or beneath continental mountain ranges such as the Himalayas (*convergent boundaries* where plates come together). Additionally, oceanic ridges and rises are offset and *plates slide past one another along transform faults* (*transform boundaries* where plates slowly grind past one another).

• *Tests of the plate tectonic model indicate that many features and phenomena provide support for shifting plates*. These include mantle plumes and their associated hotspots that record the motion of plates past them, the origin of flat-topped tablemounts, stages of coral reef development, and the detection of plate motion by accurate positioning of locations on Earth using satellites.

• *The positions of various sea floor and continental features have changed in the past, continue to change today, and will look very different in the future.*

Key Terms

Asthenosphere (p. 48)
Atoll (p. 66)
Barrier reef (p. 65)
Continental accretion (p. 67)
Continental arc (p. 56)
Continental drift (p. 35)
Continental transform fault (p. 60)
Convection cell (p. 44)
Convergent boundary (p. 50)
Coral reef (p. 64)
Darwin, Charles (p. 64)
Divergent boundary (p. 50)
East Pacific Rise (p. 53)
Fringing reef (p. 65)
Great Barrier Reef (p. 65)
Guyot (p. 64)
Hawaiian Islands–Emperor
 Seamount Chain (p. 62)

Heat flow (p. 48)
Hess, Harry (p. 44)
Hotspot (p. 61)
Ice age (p. 37)
Island arc (p. 56)
Lithosphere (p. 48)
Loihi (p. 64)
Magnetic anomaly (p. 44)
Magnetic dip (p. 41)
Magnetic field (p. 40)
Magnetite (p. 41)
Mantle (p. 44)
Mantle plume (p. 61)
Matthews, Drummond (p. 45)
Mesosaurus (p. 37)
Mid-Atlantic Ridge (p. 53)
Mid-ocean ridge (p. 44)

Nematath (p. 62)
NEPTUNE (p. 58)
Ocean trench (p. 45)
Oceanic ridge (p. 53)
Oceanic rise (p. 53)
Oceanic transform fault (p. 60)
Paleogeography (p. 66)
Paleomagnetism (p. 41)
Pangaea (p. 36)
Panthalassa (p. 36)
Plate tectonics (p. 35)
Polar wandering curve (p. 41)
Polarity (p. 42)
Rift valley (p. 51)
Rifting (p. 51)
San Andreas Fault (p. 60)
Sea floor spreading (p. 44)

Seamount (p. 64)
Seismic moment magnitude(M_w)
 (p. 55)
Spreading center (p. 45)
Subduction (p. 45)
Subduction zone (p. 45)
Tablemount (p. 64)
Tethys Sea (p. 36)
Transform boundary (p. 50)
Transform fault (p. 60)
Transform faulting (p. 60)
Vine, Frederick (p. 45)
Volcanic arc (p. 55)
Wegener, Alfred (p. 35)
Wilson cycle (p. 70)

Review Questions

1. When did the supercontinent of Pangaea exist? What was the ocean that surrounded the supercontinent called?

2. Cite the lines of evidence Alfred Wegener used to support his idea of continental drift. Why did scientists doubt that continents drifted?

3. Describe Earth's magnetic field, including how it has changed through time.

4. Describe how sea turtles use Earth's magnetic field for navigation.

5. Why was the pattern of alternating reversals of Earth's magnetic field as recorded in sea floor rocks such an important piece of evidence for advancing the theory of plate tectonics?

6. Describe sea floor spreading and why it was an important piece of evidence in support of plate tectonics.

7. Describe the general relationships that exist among distance from the spreading centers, heat flow, age of the ocean crustal rock, and ocean depth.

8. Why does a map of worldwide earthquakes closely match the locations of worldwide plate boundaries?

9. Most lithospheric plates contain both oceanic- and continental-type crust. Use plate boundaries to explain why this is true.

10. Describe the differences between oceanic ridges and oceanic rises. Include in your answer why these differences exist.

11. Describe the difference in earthquake magnitudes that occur between the three types of plate boundaries, and include why these differences occur.

12. How can plate tectonics be used to help explain the difference between a seamount and a tablemount?

13. How is the age distribution pattern of the Hawaiian Islands–Emperor Seamount Chain explained by the position of the Hawaiian hotspot? What could have caused the curious bend in the chain?

14. What are differences between a mid-ocean ridge and a hotspot?

15. Using the paleogeographic reconstructions shown in Figure 2.31, determine when the following events first appear in the geologic record:

    a. North America lies on the equator.

    b. The continents come together as Pangaea.

    c. The North Atlantic Ocean opens.

    d. India separates from Antarctica.

Critical Thinking Exercises

1. If you could travel back in time with three illustrations from this chapter to help Alfred Wegener convince the scientists of his day that continental drift does exist, what would they be and why?

2. List and describe the three types of plate boundaries. Include in your discussion any sea floor features that are related to these plate boundaries and include a real-world example of each. Construct a map view and cross section showing each of the three boundary types and direction of plate movement.

3. Convergent boundaries can be divided into three types, based on the type of crust contained on the two colliding plates. Compare and contrast the different types of convergent boundaries that result from these collisions.

4. Describe the differences in origin between the Aleutian Islands and the Hawaiian Islands. Provide evidence to support your explanation.

5. Assume that you travel at the same rate as a fast-moving continent—at a rate of 10 centimeters (2.5 inches) per year. Calculate how long it would take you to travel from your present location to a nearby large city. Also, calculate how long it would take you to travel across the United States from the East Coast to the West Coast.

Oceanography on the Web

Visit the *Essentials of Oceanography* Online Study Guide for Internet resources, including chapter-specific quizzes to test your understanding and Web links to further your exploration of the topics in this chapter.

The *Essentials of Oceanography* Online Study Guide is at http://www.mygeoscienceplace.com/.

The North Atlantic Sea Floor
The sea floor has many interesting features, some of which are completely different from those on land. Recent improvements in technology have aided exploration of the sea floor and given scientists the ability to create high-resolution maps like this one, which shows deep areas in dark blue and shallow areas in yellow-green; high elevations on land are shown in pink.

"Could the waters of the Atlantic be drawn off so as to expose to view this great sea-gash which separates the continents, and extends from the Arctic to the Antarctic, it would present a scene most rugged, grand, and imposing."

— *Matthew Fontaine Maury (1854),*
the "father of oceanography," commenting about the Mid-Atlantic Ridge

3 MARINE PROVINCES

CHAPTER AT A GLANCE

■ Echo-sounding from ships is used to determine the shape of the sea floor. More recently, data from satellites are also used to map sea floor features.

■ Most continental margins include a shelf, slope, and rise; the deep-ocean floor is dominated by volcanic features and the mid-ocean ridge; ocean trenches are the deepest parts of the sea floor.

■ Most ocean floor features are originated by plate tectonic processes.

What does the shape of the ocean floor look like? Over a century and a half ago, most scientists believed that the ocean floor was completely flat and carpeted with a thick layer of muddy sediment containing little of scientific interest. Further, it was believed that the deepest parts were somewhere in the middle of the ocean basins. However, as more and more vessels crisscrossed the seas to map the ocean floor and to lay transoceanic cables, scientists found the terrain of the sea floor was highly varied and included deep troughs, ancient volcanoes, submarine canyons, and great mountain chains. It was unlike anything on land and, as it turns out, some of the deepest parts of the oceans are actually very close to land!

As marine geologists and oceanographers began to analyze the features of the ocean floor, they realized that certain features had profound implications not only for the history of the ocean floor, but also for the history of Earth. How could all these remarkable features have formed, and how can their origin be explained? Over long periods of time, the shape of the ocean basins has changed as continents have ponderously migrated across Earth's surface in response to forces within Earth's interior. The ocean basins as they presently exist reflect the processes of plate tectonics (the topic of the previous chapter), which help explain the origin of sea floor features.

3.1 What Techniques Are Used to Determine Ocean Bathymetry?

Bathymetry (*bathos* = depth, *metry* = measurement) is the measurement of ocean depths and the charting of the shape, or *topography* (*topos* = place, *graphy* = description of) of the ocean floor. Determining bathymetry involves measuring the vertical distance from the ocean surface down to the mountains, valleys, and plains of the sea floor.

Soundings

The first recorded attempt to measure the ocean's depth was conducted in the Mediterranean Sea in about 85 B.C. by a Greek named Posidonius. His mission was to answer an age-old question: How deep is the ocean? Posidonius's crew made a **sounding**[1] by letting out nearly 2 kilometers

---

[1] A *sounding* refers to a probe of the environment for scientific observation and was borrowed from atmospheric scientists, who released probes called soundings into the atmosphere. Ironically, the term does not actually refer to sound; the use of sound to measure ocean depths came later.

(1.2 miles) of line before the heavy weight on the end of the line touched bottom. Sounding lines were used for the next 2000 years by voyagers who used them to probe the ocean's depths. The standard unit of ocean depth is the **fathom** (*fathme* = outstretched arms[2]), which is equal to 1.8 meters (6 feet).

The first systematic bathymetric measurements of the oceans were made in 1872 aboard the HMS *Challenger*, during its historic three-and-a-half-year voyage.[3] Every so often, *Challenger*'s crew stopped and measured the depth, along with many other ocean properties. These measurements indicated that the deep-ocean floor was not flat but had significant *relief* (variations in elevation), just as dry land does. However, determining bathymetry by making occasional soundings rarely gives a complete picture of the ocean floor. For instance, imagine trying to determine what the surface features on land look like while flying in a blimp at an altitude of several kilometers on a foggy night, using only a long weighted rope to determine your height above the surface. This is similar to how bathymetric measurements were collected from ships using sounding lines.

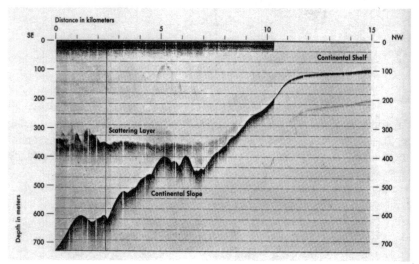

FIGURE 3.1 An echo sounder record. An echo sounder record of the East Coast U.S. offshore region shows the provinces of the sea floor. Vertical exaggeration (the amount of expansion of the vertical scale) is 12 times. The scattering layer probably represents a concentration of marine organisms.

Sonar and Echolocation

Echo Soundings

The presence of mid-ocean undersea mountains had long been known, but recognition of their full extent into a connected worldwide system had to await the invention and use of the **echo sounder**, or *fathometer*, in the early 1900s. An echo sounder sends a sound signal (called a **ping**) from the ship downward into the ocean, where it produces echoes when it bounces off any density difference, such as marine organisms or the ocean floor (Figure 3.1). Water is a good transmitter of sound, so the time it takes for the echoes to return[4] is used to determine the depth and corresponding shape of the ocean floor. In 1925, for example, the German vessel *Meteor* used echo sounding to identify the underwater mountain range running through the center of the South Atlantic Ocean.

Echo sounding, however, lacks detail and often gives an inaccurate view of the relief of the sea floor. For instance, the sound beam emitted from a ship 4000 meters (13,100 feet) above the ocean floor widens to a diameter of about 4600 meters (15,000 feet) at the bottom. Consequently, the first echoes to return from the bottom are usually from the closest (highest) peak within this broad area. Nonetheless, most of our knowledge of ocean bathymetry has been provided by the echo sounder.

Because sound from echo sounders bounces off any density difference, it was discovered that echo sounders could detect and track submarines. During World War II, antisubmarine warfare inspired many improvements in the technology of "seeing" into the ocean using sound.

During and after World War II, there was great improvement in sonar technology. For example, the **precision depth recorder (PDR)**, which was developed in the 1950s, uses a focused high-frequency sound beam to measure depths to a resolution of about 1 meter (3.3 feet). Throughout the 1960s, PDRs were used

---

[2]This term is derived from the method used to bring depth sounding lines back on board a vessel by hand. While hauling in the line, workers counted the number of arm-lengths collected. By measuring the length of the person's outstretched arms, the amount of line taken in could be calculated. Much later, the distance of 1 fathom was standardized to equal exactly 6 feet.

[3]For more information about the accomplishments of the *Challenger* expedition, see Box 5.2.

[4]This technique uses the speed of sound in seawater, which varies with salinity, pressure, and temperature but averages about 1507 meters (4945 feet) per second.

extensively and provided a reasonably good representation of the ocean floor. From thousands of research vessel tracks, the first reliable global maps of sea floor bathymetry were produced. These maps helped confirm the ideas of sea floor spreading and plate tectonics.

Modern *acoustic* (*akouein* = to hear) instruments that use sound to map the sea floor include *multibeam echo sounders* (which use multiple frequencies of sound simultaneously) and side-scan **sonar** (an acronym for *so*und *na*vigation *a*nd *r*anging). **Seabeam**—the first multibeam echo sounder—made it possible for a survey ship to map the features of the ocean floor along a strip up to 60 kilometers (37 miles) wide. Multibeam systems use sound emitters directed away from both sides of a survey ship, with receivers permanently mounted on the ship's hull. Multibeam instruments emit multiple beams of sound waves, which are reflected off the ocean floor. As the sound waves bounce back with different strengths and timing, computers analyze these differences to determine the depth and shape of the sea floor, and whether the bottom is rock, sand, or mud (Figure 3.2). In this way, multibeam surveying provides incredibly detailed imagery of the seabed. Because its beams of sound spread out with depth, multibeam systems have resolution limitations in deep water.

In deep water or where a detailed survey is required, side-scan sonar can provide enhanced views of the sea floor. Side-scan sonar systems such as **Sea MARC** (*Sea M*apping *a*nd *R*emote *C*haracterization) and **GLORIA** (*G*eological *Long-Range Inclined Acoustical* instrument) can be towed behind a survey ship to produce a detailed strip map of ocean floor bathymetry (Figure 3.3). To maximize its

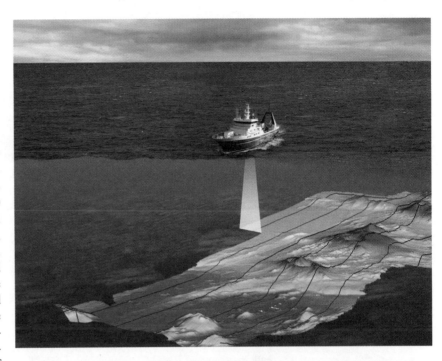

FIGURE 3.2 Multibeam sonar. An artist's depiction of how a survey vessel uses multibeam sonar to map the ocean floor. Hull-mounted multibeam instruments emit multiple beams of sound waves, which are reflected off the ocean floor. Receivers collect data that allow oceanographers to determine the depth, shape, and even composition of the sea floor. As a ship travels back and forth throughout an area, it can produce a detailed image of sea floor bathymetry.

FIGURE 3.3 Side-scanning sonar. The side-scan sonar system GLORIA (*left*) is towed behind a survey ship and can map a strip of ocean floor (a swath) with a gap in data directly below the instrument. Side-scan sonar image of a volcano (*right*) with a summit crater about 2 kilometers (1.2 miles) in diameter in the Pacific Ocean. The black stripe through the middle of the image is the data gap.

3.1   RESEARCH METHODS IN OCEANOGRAPHY

SEA FLOOR MAPPING FROM SPACE

Recently, satellite measurements of the ocean surface have been used to make maps of the sea floor. How does a satellite—which orbits at a great distance above the planet and can view only the ocean's *surface*—obtain a picture of the sea *floor*?

The answer lies in the fact that sea floor features directly influence Earth's gravitational field. Deep areas such as trenches correspond to a lower gravitational attraction, and large undersea objects such as seamounts exert an extra gravitational pull. These differences affect sea level, causing the ocean surface to bulge outward and sink inward mimicking the relief of the ocean floor. A 2000-meter (6500-foot)-high seamount, for example, exerts a small but measurable gravitational pull on the water around it, creating a bulge 2 meters (7 feet) high on the ocean surface. These irregularities are easily detectable by satellites, which use microwave beams to measure sea level to within 4 centimeters (1.5 inches) accuracy. After corrections are made for waves, tides, currents, and atmospheric effects, the resulting pattern of dips and bulges at the ocean

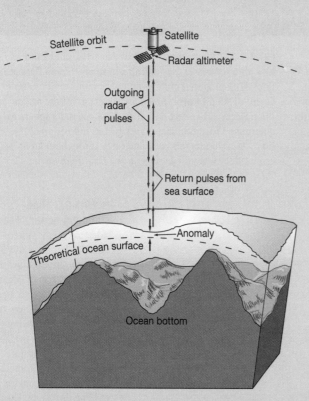

FIGURE 3A **Satellite measurements of the ocean surface.** A satellite measures the variation of ocean surface elevation, which is caused by gravitational attraction and mimics the shape of the sea floor. The sea surface *anomaly* is the difference between the measured and theoretical ocean surface.

FIGURE 3B **Comparing bathymetric maps of the sea floor.** Both bathymetric maps show the same portion of the Brazil Basin in the South Atlantic Ocean. *Top:* A map made using conventional echo sounder records from ships (ship tracks shown by thin lines). *Bottom:* A map from satellite data made using measurements of the ocean surface.

WEB VIDEO

The Ocean Floor
Seascape

resolution, a side-scan instrument can be towed behind a ship on a cable so that it "flies" just above the ocean floor.

Although multibeam and side-scan sonar produce very detailed bathymetric maps, mapping the sea floor by ship is an expensive and time-consuming process. A research vessel must tediously travel back and forth throughout an area (a process called "mowing the lawn") to produce an accurate map of bathymetric surface can be used to indirectly reveal ocean floor bathymetry (Figure 3A). For example, Figure 3B compares two different maps of the same area: one based on bathymetric data from ships (*top*) and the other based on satellite measurements (*bottom*), which shows much higher resolution of sea floor features.

Data from the European Space Agency's ERS-1 satellite and from Geosat, a U.S. Navy satellite, were collected during the 1980s. When this infor-

mation was recently declassified, Walter Smith of the National Oceanic and Atmospheric Administration and David Sandwell of Scripps Institution of Oceanography began producing sea floor maps based on the shape of the sea surface. What is unique about these researchers' maps is that they provide a view of Earth similar to being able to drain the oceans and view the ocean floor directly. Their map of ocean surface gravity (Figure 3C) uses depth soundings

to calibrate the gravity measurements. Although gravity is not exactly bathymetry, this new map of the ocean floor clearly delineates many ocean floor features, such as the mid-ocean ridge, trenches, seamounts, and nemataths (island chains). In addition, this new mapping technique has revealed sea floor bathymetry in areas where research vessels have not conducted surveys.

FIGURE 3C Global sea surface elevation map from satellite data. A map showing the satellite-derived global gravity field, which, when adjusted using measured depths, closely corresponds to ocean depth. Purple indicates deep water; the mid-ocean ridge (intermediate water depths) is mostly light green and yellow; pink indicates shallowest water. The map also shows land surface elevations, with dark green color indicating low elevations and white color indicating high elevations.

features (see Figure 3.2). Unfortunately, only a small percentage of the ocean floor has been mapped in this way. An Earth-orbiting satellite, on the other hand, can observe large areas of the ocean at one time. Consequently, satellites are increasingly used to determine ocean properties. Remarkably, technology exists to allow the ocean floor to be mapped by an orbiting satellite (Box 3.1). Recent U.S. oceanographic satellite missions and their objectives are listed in Web Table 3.1.

KEY CONCEPT
Sending pings of sound into the ocean (echo sounding) is a commonly-used technique to determine ocean bathymetry. More recently, satellites are being used to map sea floor features.

FIGURE 3.4 Seismic profiling. **(a)** An air gun explosion emits low frequency sounds (*1*) that can penetrate bottom sediments and rock layers. The sound reflects off the boundaries between these layers (*2*) and returns to the receiver (*3*). **(b)** *Top*: Seismic reflection profile of the western Mediterranean, showing the location of *JOIDES Resolution* Drill Site 977. *Bottom*: An interpretation of the same seismic profile showing faults (*black lines*). M = M-reflector, which was created during the drying up of the Mediterranean Sea approximately 5.5 million years ago.

Seismic Reflection Profiles

Oceanographers who want to know about ocean structure beneath the sea floor use strong low-frequency sounds produced by explosions or air guns, as shown in Figure 3.4. These sounds penetrate beneath the sea floor and reflect off the boundaries between different rock or sediment layers, producing **seismic reflection profiles**, which have applications in mineral and petroleum exploration.

3.2 What Does Earth's Hypsographic Curve Reveal?

Figure 3.5 illustrates Earth's **hypsographic** (*hypos* = height, *graphic* = drawn) **curve**, which shows the relationship between the height of the land and the depth of the oceans. The bar graph (Figure 3.5, *left side*) gives the percentage of Earth's surface area at various ranges of elevation and depth. The cumulative curve (Figure 3.5, *right side*) gives the percentage of surface area from the highest peaks to the deepest depths of the oceans. Together, they show that 70.8% of Earth's surface is covered by oceans and that the average depth of the ocean is 3729 meters (12,234 feet) while the average height of the land is only 840 meters (2756 feet). The difference, recalling our discussion of isostasy in Chapter 1, results from the greater density and lesser thickness of oceanic crust as compared to continental crust.

The cumulative hypsographic curve (Figure 3.5, *right side*) shows five differently sloped segments. On land, the first steep segment of the curve represents tall mountains, while the gentle slope represents low coastal plains (and continues just offshore, representing the shallow parts of the continental margin). The first slope below sea level represents steep areas of the continental margins and also includes the mountainous mid-ocean ridge. Further offshore, the longest, flattest part of the whole curve represents the deep-ocean basins, followed by the last steep part, which represents ocean trenches.

The shape of the hypsographic curve can be used to support the existence of plate tectonics on Earth. Specifically, the two flat areas and three sloped areas of the curve show that there is a very uneven distribution of area at different depths and elevations. If there were no active mechanism involved in creating such features on Earth, the bar graph portions would all be about the same length and the cumulative curve would be a straight line. Instead, the variations in the curve suggest that plate tectonics is actively working to modify Earth's surface. The flat portions of the curve represent various intraplate elevations both on land and underwater while the slopes of the curve represent mountains, continental slopes, the mid-ocean ridge, and deep-ocean trenches, all of which are created by plate tectonic processes. Interestingly, hypsographic curves constructed for other planets and moons using satellite data have been used to determine if plate tectonics is actively modifying the surface of these worlds.

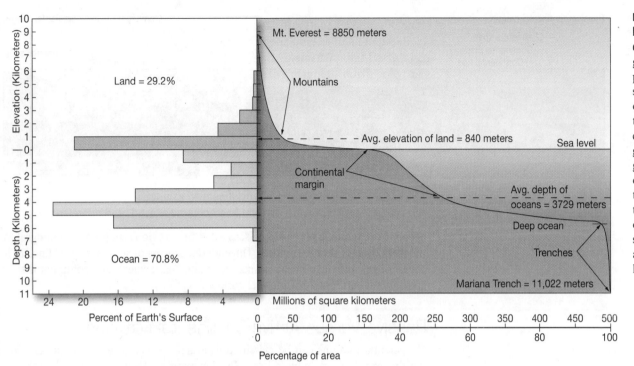

FIGURE 3.5 Earth's hypsographic curve. The bar graph (*left*) gives the percentage of Earth's surface area at various ranges of elevation and depth. The cumulative hypsographic curve (*right*) gives the percentage of surface area from the highest peaks to the deepest depths of the oceans. Also shown are the average ocean depth and land elevation.

3.3 What Features Exist on Continental Margins?

The ocean floor can be divided into three major provinces (Figure 3.6): (1) **continental margins**, which are shallow-water areas close to continents, (2) **deep-ocean basins**, which are deep-water areas farther from land, and (3) the **mid-ocean ridge**, which is composed of shallower areas near the middle of an

FIGURE 3.6 Major regions of the North Atlantic Ocean floor. Map view below and profile view above, showing that the ocean floor can be divided into three major provinces: continental margins, deep-ocean basins, and the mid-ocean ridge.

FIGURE 3.7 Passive and active continental margins. Cross-sectional view of typical features across an ocean basin, including a passive continental margin (*left*) and a convergent active continental margin (*right*). Vertical exaggeration is 10 times.

Passive continental margin

Convergent active continental margin

Continental shelf
Continental slope
Continental rise
Sea level
Rift valley
Continental slope
Continental shelf
Abyssal plain
4 kilometers
Seamounts
Ocean trench
Mid-ocean ridge
Ocean trench

50 kilometers   Vertical exaggeration = $\dfrac{\text{horizontal scale}}{\text{vertical scale}} = \dfrac{50}{5} = 10\times$

ocean. Plate tectonic processes (discussed in the previous chapters) are integral to the formation of these provinces. Through the process of sea floor spreading, mid-ocean ridges and deep-ocean basins are created. Elsewhere, as a continent is split apart, new continental margins are formed.

Passive Versus Active Continental Margins

Continental margins can be classified as either passive or active, depending on their proximity to plate boundaries. **Passive margins** (Figure 3.7, *left side*) are embedded within the interior of lithospheric plates and are therefore not in close proximity to any plate boundary. Thus, passive margins usually lack major tectonic activity (such as large earthquakes, eruptive volcanoes, and mountain building).

The East Coast of the United States, where there is no plate boundary, is an example of a passive continental margin. Passive margins are usually produced by rifting of continental landmasses and continued sea floor spreading over geologic time. Features of passive continental margins include the continental shelf, the continental slope, and the continental rise that extends toward the deep-ocean basins (Figures 3.7 and 3.8).

Active margins (Figure 3.7, *right side*) are associated with lithospheric plate boundaries and are marked by a high degree of tectonic activity. Two types of active margins exist. **Convergent active margins** are associated with oceanic–continental convergent plate boundaries. From the land to the ocean, features include an onshore arc-shaped row of active volcanoes, then a narrow shelf, a steep slope, and an offshore trench that delineates the plate boundary. Western South America, where the Nazca Plate is being subducted beneath the South American Plate, is an example of a convergent active margin. **Transform active margins** are less common and are associated with transform plate boundaries. At these locations, offshore faults usually parallel the main transform plate boundary fault and create linear islands, banks (shallowly submerged areas), and deep basins close to shore. Coastal California along the San Andreas Fault is an example of a transform active margin.

KEY CONCEPT

Passive continental margins lack a plate boundary and have different features than active continental margins, which include a plate boundary (either convergent or transform).

Continental Shelf

The **continental shelf** is defined as a generally flat zone extending from the shore beneath the ocean surface to a point at which a marked increase in slope angle occurs, called the **shelf break** (Figure 3.8). It is usually flat and relatively featureless because of marine sediment deposits but can contain coastal islands, reefs, and raised banks. The underlying rock is granitic continental crust, so the continental shelf is geologically part of the continent. Accurate sea floor mapping is essential for determining the extent of the continental shelf, which has come into question recently in the Arctic Ocean. The general bathymetry of the continental shelf can usually be predicted by examining the topography of the adjacent land.

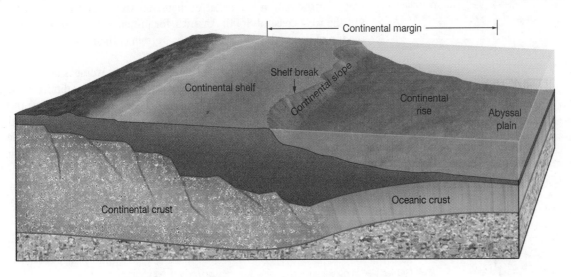

FIGURE 3.8 Features of a passive continental margin. Schematic view showing the main features of a passive continental margin.

With few exceptions, the coastal topography extends beyond the shore and onto the continental shelf.

The average width of the continental shelf is about 70 kilometers (43 miles), but it varies from a few tens of meters to 1500 kilometers (930 miles). The broadest shelves occur off the northern coasts of Siberia and North America in the Arctic Ocean. The average depth at which the shelf break occurs is about 135 meters (443 feet). Around the continent of Antarctica, however, the shelf break occurs at 350 meters (2200 feet). The average slope of the continental shelf is only about a tenth of a degree, which is similar to the slope given to a large parking lot for drainage purposes.

Sea level has fluctuated over the history of Earth, causing the shoreline to migrate back and forth across the continental shelf. When colder climates prevailed during the most recent ice age, for example, more of Earth's water was frozen as glaciers on land, so sea level was lower than it is today. During that time, more of the continental shelf was exposed.

The type of continental margin will determine the shape and features associated with the continental shelf. For example, the east coast of South America has a broader continental shelf than its west coast. The east coast is a passive margin, which typically has a wider shelf. In contrast, the convergent active margin present along the west coast of South America is characterized by a narrow continental shelf and a shelf break close to shore. For transform active margins such as along California, the presence of offshore faults produces a continental shelf that is not flat. Rather, it is marked by a high degree of relief (islands, shallow banks, and deep basins) called a **continental borderland** (Figure 3.9).

FIGURE 3.9 Continental borderland. A continental borderland, like the one offshore Southern California, consists of a series of islands, shallow banks, and deep basins. It is a result of its proximity to the San Andreas Fault, a major transform plate boundary.

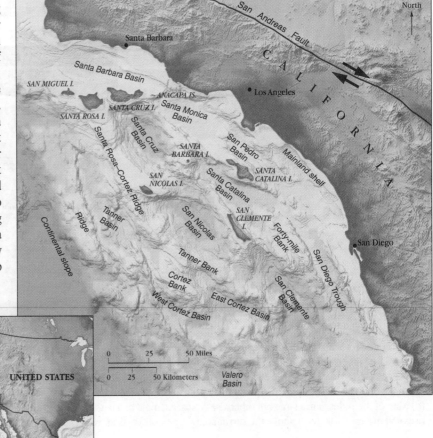

Continental Slope

The **continental slope**, which lies beyond the shelf break, is where the deep-ocean basins begin. Total relief in this region is similar to that found in mountain ranges on the continents. The break at the top of the slope may be from 1 to 5 kilometers (0.6 to 3 miles) above the deep-ocean

Graded bedding sequences

basin at its base. Along convergent active margins where the slope descends into submarine trenches, even greater vertical relief is measured. Off the west coast of South America, for instance, the total relief from the top of the Andes Mountains to the bottom of the Peru–Chile Trench is about 15 kilometers (9.3 miles).

Worldwide, the slope of the continental slopes averages about 4 degrees but varies from 1 to 25 degrees.[5] A study that compared different continental slopes in the United States revealed that the average slope is just over 2 degrees. Around the margin of the Pacific Ocean, the continental slopes average more than 5 degrees because of the presence of convergent active margins that drop directly into deep offshore trenches. The Atlantic and Indian Oceans, on the other hand, contain many passive margins, which lack plate boundaries. Thus, the amount of relief is lower and slopes in these oceans average about 3 degrees.

Submarine Canyons and Turbidity Currents

The continental slope—and, to a lesser extent, the continental shelf—exhibit **submarine canyons**, which are narrow but deep submarine valleys that are V-shaped in profile view and have branches or tributaries with steep to overhanging walls (Figure 3.10). They resemble canyons formed on land that are carved by rivers and can be quite large. In fact, the Monterey Canyon off California is comparable in size to Arizona's Grand Canyon (Figure 3.11).

How are submarine canyons formed? Initially it was thought submarine canyons were ancient

FIGURE 3.10 Submarine canyons, turbidity currents, and deep-sea fans. **(a)** Turbidity currents move downslope, eroding the continental margin to enlarge submarine canyons. Deep-sea fans are composed of turbidite deposits, which consist of sequences of graded bedding (*inset*). **(b)** A diver descends into La Jolla Submarine Canyon, offshore California. **(c)** Outcrop of layered turbidite deposits that have been tilted and uplifted onto land in California. Each light-colored layer is sandstone that marks the coarser bottom of a graded bedding sequence. **(d)** Map of the Indus Fan, a large but otherwise typical example of a passive margin fan. **(e)** Sonar perspective view of southeast Alaska's Chatham Fan, which rises 450 meters (1500 feet) above the surrounding sea floor. Vertical exaggeration is 20 times; view looking northeast.

[5]For comparison, the windshield of an aerodynamically designed car has a slope of about 25 degrees.

river valleys created by the erosive power of rivers when sea level was lower and the continental shelf was exposed. Although some canyons are directly offshore from where rivers enter the sea, the majority of them are not. Many, in fact, are confined exclusively to the continental slope. In addition, submarine canyons continue to the base of the continental slope, which averages some 3500 meters (11,500 feet) below sea level. There is no evidence, however, that sea level has ever been lowered by that much.

Side-scan sonar surveys along the Atlantic coast indicate that the continental slope is dominated by submarine canyons from Hudson Canyon near New York City to Baltimore Canyon in Maryland. Canyons confined to the continental slope are straighter and have steeper canyon floor gradients than those that extend into the continental shelf. These characteristics suggest the canyons are created on the continental slope by some marine process and enlarge into the continental shelf through time.

Both indirect and direct observation of the erosive power of **turbidity** (*turbidus* = disordered) **currents** (Box 3.2) has suggested that they are responsible for carving submarine canyons. Turbidity currents are underwater avalanches of muddy water mixed with rocks and other debris. The sediment portion of turbidity currents comes from sea floor materials that move across the continental shelf into the head of a submarine canyon and accumulate there, setting the stage for initiation of a turbidity current. Trigger mechanisms for turbidity currents include shaking by an earthquake, the oversteepening of sediment that accumulates on the shelf, hurricanes passing over the area, and the rapid input of sediment from flood waters. Once a turbidity current is set in motion, the dense mixture of water and debris moves rapidly downslope under the force of gravity and carves the canyon as it goes, resembling a flash flood on land. Turbidity currents are strong enough to transport huge rocks down submarine canyons and do a considerable amount of erosion over time.

Continental Rise

The **continental rise** is a transition zone between the continental margin and the deep-ocean floor comprised of a huge submerged pile of debris. Where did all this debris come from, and how did it get there?

The existence of turbidity currents suggests that the material transported by these currents is responsible for the creation of continental rises. When a turbidity current moves through and erodes a submarine canyon, it exits through the mouth of the canyon. The slope angle decreases and the turbidity current slows, causing suspended material to settle out in a distinctive type of layering called **graded bedding** that *grades in size upward* (Figure 3.10a, *inset*). As the energy of the turbidity current dissipates, larger pieces settle first, then progressively smaller pieces settle, and eventually even very fine pieces settle out, which may occur weeks or months later.

An individual turbidity current deposits one graded bedding sequence. The next turbidity current may partially erode the previous deposit and then deposit another graded bedding sequence on top of the previous one. After some time, a thick sequence of graded bedding deposits can develop one on top of another. These stacks of graded bedding are called **turbidite deposits** (Figure 3.10c), of which the continental rise is composed.

As viewed from above, the deposits at the mouths of submarine canyons are fan, lobate, or apron shaped (Figure 3.10a and 3.10e). Consequently, these deposits are called **deep-sea fans**, or **submarine fans**. Deep-sea fans create the continental rise when they merge together along the base of the continental slope. Along convergent active margins, however, the steep continental slope leads directly into a deep-ocean trench. Sediment from turbidity currents accumulates in the trench and there is no continental rise.

(a)

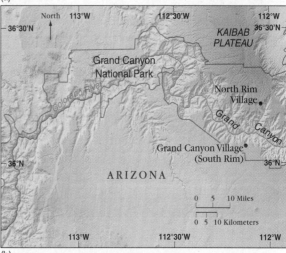

(b)

FIGURE 3.11 Comparison of the Monterey Submarine Canyon and Arizona's Grand Canyon. In these same-scale maps, it can be seen that the Monterey Submarine Canyon **(a)** is comparable to Arizona's Grand Canyon **(b)** in terms of length, depth, width, and steepness.

KEY CONCEPT
Turbidity currents are underwater avalanches of muddy water mixed with sediment that move down the continental slope and are responsible for carving submarine canyons.

Turbidity Currents and Graded Bedding

WEB VIDEO
Turbidity Current Flume Experiment

3.2 RESEARCH METHODS IN OCEANOGRAPHY

A GRAND "BREAK": EVIDENCE FOR TURBIDITY CURRENTS

How do earthquakes and telephone cables help explain how turbidity currents move across the ocean floor and carve submarine canyons? In 1929, the $M_w = 7.2$ Grand Banks earthquake in the North Atlantic Ocean severed some of the trans-Atlantic telegraph cables that lay across the sea floor south of Newfoundland near the earthquake epicenter (Figure 3D). At first, it was assumed that sea floor movement caused all these breaks. However, analysis of the data revealed that the cables closest to the earthquake broke simultaneously with the earthquake, but cables that crossed the slope and deeper ocean floor at greater distances from the earthquake were broken progressively

later in time. It seemed unusual that certain cables were affected by the failure of the slope due to ground shaking but others were broken several minutes later.

The mystery was solved several years later, when reanalysis of the event suggested that the earthquake triggered a major submarine landslide and initiated a turbidity current, which moved down the slope and was responsible for the successive cable breaks. How fast do turbidity currents move? By studying the pattern of broken cables, scientists determined that the turbidity current in this case reached speeds of about 80 kilometers (50 miles) per hour on the steep portions of the continental slope and about 24 kilo-

meters (15 miles) per hour on the more gently sloping continental rise. The study showed that turbidity currents can reach high speeds and are strong enough to break underwater cables, suggesting that they must be powerful enough to erode submarine canyons.

Further evidence of turbidity currents comes from several sonar studies that have documented turbidity currents. For instance, a study of Rupert Inlet in British Columbia, Canada, monitored turbidity currents moving through an underwater channel. These studies indicate that submarine canyons are carved by turbidity currents over long periods of time, just as canyons on land are carved by running water.

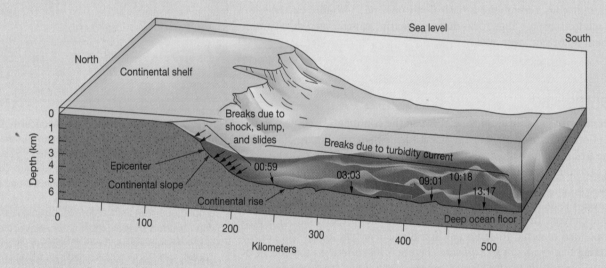

FIGURE 3D Grand Banks earthquake. Diagrammatic view of the sea floor showing the sequence of events for the 1929 Grand Banks earthquake. The epicenter is the point on Earth's surface directly above the earthquake. The arrows point to cable breaks; the numbers show times of breaks in hours and minutes after the earthquake. Vertical scale is greatly exaggerated.

One of the largest deep-sea fans in the world is the Indus Fan, a passive margin fan that extends 1800 kilometers (1100 miles) south of Pakistan (Figure 3.10d). The Indus River carries extensive amounts of sediment from the Himalaya Mountains to the coast. This sediment eventually makes its way down the submarine canyon and builds the fan, which, in some areas, has sediment that is more than 10 kilometers (6.2 miles) thick. The Indus Fan has a main submarine canyon channel extending seaward onto the fan but soon divides into several branching distributary channels. These distributary channels are similar to those found on deltas, which form at the mouths of streams. On the lower fan, the surface has a very low slope, and the flow is no longer confined to channels, so it spreads out and forms layers of fine sediment across the fan surface. The Indus Fan has so much sediment, in fact, that it partially buries an active mid-ocean ridge, the Carlsberg Ridge!

3.4 What Features Exist in the Deep-Ocean Basins?

The deep-ocean floor lies beyond the continental margin province (the shelf, slope, and the rise) and contains a variety of features.

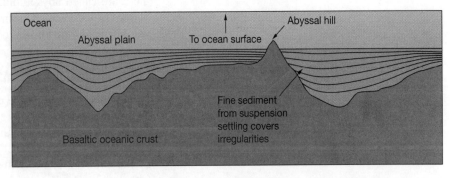

FIGURE 3.12 **Abyssal plain formed by suspension set-tling.** Seismic cross section (*above*) and matching drawing (*below*) for a portion of the deep Madeira Abyssal Plain in the eastern Atlantic Ocean, showing the irregular volcanic terrain buried by sediments.

Abyssal Plains

Extending from the base of the continental rise into the deep-ocean basins are flat depositional surfaces with slopes of less than a fraction of a degree that cover extensive portions of the deep-ocean basins. These **abyssal** (*a* = without, *byssus* = bottom) **plains** average between 4500 meters (15,000 feet) and 6000 meters (20,000 feet) deep. They are not literally bottomless, but they are some of the deepest (and flattest) regions on Earth.

Abyssal plains are formed by fine particles of sediment slowly drifting onto the deep-ocean floor. Over millions of years, a thick blanket of sediment is produced by **suspension settling** as fine particles (analogous to "marine dust") accumulate on the ocean floor. With enough time, these deposits cover most irregularities of the deep ocean, as shown in Figure 3.12. In addition, sediment traveling in turbidity currents from land adds to the sediment load.

The type of continental margin determines the distribution of abyssal plains. For instance, few abyssal plains are located in the Pacific Ocean; instead, most occur in the Atlantic and Indian Oceans. The deep-ocean trenches found on the convergent active margins of the Pacific Ocean prevent sediment from moving past the continental slope. In essence, the trenches act like a gutter that traps sediment transported off the land by turbidity currents. On the passive margins of the Atlantic and Indian Oceans, however, turbidity currents travel directly down the continental margin and deposit sediment on the abyssal plains. In addition, the distance from the continental margin to the floor of the deep-ocean basins in the Pacific Ocean is so great that most of the suspended sediment settles out before it reaches these distant regions. Conversely, the smaller size of the Atlantic and Indian Oceans does not prevent suspended sediment from reaching their deep-ocean basins.

Volcanic Peaks of the Abyssal Plains

Poking through the sediment cover of the abyssal plains are a variety of volcanic peaks, which extend to various elevations above the ocean floor. Some extend above sea level to form islands while others are just below the surface (see Web Box 3.2). Those that are below sea level but rise more than 1 kilometer (0.6 mile) above the deep-ocean floor and have a pointy top like an upside-down ice cream cone are called **seamounts**. Worldwide, there are more than 50,000 known seamounts, and scientists estimate that seamounts could number as high as 200,000. On the other hand, if a volcano has a flattened top, it is called a

tablemount, or *guyot*. The origin of seamounts and tablemounts was discussed as a piece of supporting evidence for plate tectonics in Chapter 2 (refer to Figure 2.26).

Volcanic features on the ocean floor that are less than 1000 meters (0.6 mile) tall—the minimum height of a seamount—are called **abyssal hills**, or **seaknolls**. Abyssal hills are one of the most abundant features on the planet (several hundred thousand have been identified) and cover a large percentage of the entire ocean basin floor. Many are gently rounded in shape, and they have an average height of about 200 meters (650 feet). Most abyssal hills are created by stretching of crust during the creation of new sea floor at the mid-ocean ridge.

In the Atlantic and Pacific Oceans, many abyssal hills are found buried beneath abyssal plain sediment. In the Pacific Ocean, the abundance of active margins traps land-derived sediment and so the rate of sediment deposition is lower. Consequently, extensive regions dominated by abyssal hills have resulted; these are called **abyssal hill provinces**. The evidence of volcanic activity on the bottom of the Pacific Ocean is particularly widespread. In fact, more than 20,000 volcanic peaks are known to exist on the Pacific sea floor.

Ocean Trenches and Volcanic Arcs

Along passive margins, the continental rise commonly occurs at the base of the continental slope and merges smoothly into the abyssal plain. In convergent active margins, however, the slope descends into a long, narrow, steep-sided **ocean trench**. Ocean trenches are deep linear scars in the ocean floor, caused by the collision of two plates along convergent plate margins (as discussed in Chapter 2). The landward side of the trench rises as a **volcanic arc** that may produce islands (such as the islands of Japan, an **island arc**) or a volcanic mountain range along the margin of a continent (such as the Andes Mountains, a **continental arc**).

The deepest portions of the world's oceans are found in these trenches. In fact, the deepest point on Earth's surface—11,022 meters (36,161 feet)—is found in the Challenger Deep area of the Mariana Trench. The majority of ocean trenches are found along the margins of the Pacific Ocean (Figure 3.13), while only a few exist in the Atlantic and Indian Oceans.

THE PACIFIC RING OF FIRE   The **Pacific Ring of Fire** occurs along the margins of the Pacific Ocean. It has the majority of Earth's active volcanoes and large earthquakes because of the prevalence of convergent plate boundaries along the Pacific Rim. A part of the Pacific Ring of Fire is South America's western coast, including the Andes Mountains and the associated Peru–Chile Trench. Figure 3.14 shows a cross-sectional view of this area and illustrates the tremendous amount of relief at convergent plate boundaries where deep-ocean trenches are associated with tall volcanic arcs.

> **KEY CONCEPT**
> Deep-ocean trenches and volcanic arcs are a result of the collision of two plates at convergent plate boundaries and mostly occur along the margins of the Pacific Ocean (Pacific Ring of Fire).

3.5 What Features Exist Along the Mid-Ocean Ridge?

The global mid-ocean ridge is a continuous, fractured-looking mountain ridge that extends through all the ocean basins. The portion of the mid-ocean ridge found in the North Atlantic Ocean is called the Mid-Atlantic Ridge (Figure 3.15), which dwarfs all mountain ranges on land. As discussed in Chapter 2, the mid-ocean ridge results from sea floor spreading along divergent plate boundaries. The enormous mid-ocean ridge forms Earth's longest mountain chain, extending across some 75,000 kilometers (46,600 miles) of the deep-ocean basin. The width of the mid-ocean ridge averages about 1000 kilometers (620 miles). The mid-ocean ridge is a topographically high feature, extending an average of 2.5 kilometers (1.5 miles)

Selected Pacific Ocean Trenches

Name	Depth (km)	Width (km)	Length (km)
Middle America	6.7	40	2800
Aleutian	7.7	50	3700
Peru-Chile	8.0	100	5900
Kermadec-Tonga	10.0	50	2900
Kuril	10.5	120	2200
Mariana	11.0	70	2550

Atlantic Ocean Trenches

Name	Depth (km)	Width (km)	Length (km)
South Sandwich	8.4	90	1450
Puerto Rico	8.4	120	1550

FIGURE 3.13 Location and dimensions of ocean trenches. The majority of ocean trenches are along the margins of the Pacific Ocean where plates are being subducted. Most of the world's large earthquakes (due to subduction) and active volcanoes (as volcanic arcs) occur around the Pacific Rim, which is why the area is also called the Pacific Ring of Fire.

Indian Ocean Trenches

Name	Depth (km)	Width (km)	Length (km)
Java (Sunda)	7.5	80	4500

FIGURE 3.14 Profile across the Peru–Chile Trench and the Andes Mountains. Over a distance of 200 kilometers (125 miles), there is a change in elevation of more than 14,900 meters (49,000 feet) from the Peru–Chile Trench to the Andes Mountains. This dramatic relief is a result of plate interactions at a convergent active margin, producing a deep-ocean trench and associated continental volcanic arc. Vertical scale is exaggerated 10 times.

above the surrounding sea floor. The mid-ocean ridge contains only a few scattered islands, such as Iceland and the Azores, where it peeks above sea level. Remarkably, the mid-ocean ridge covers 23% of Earth's surface.

The mid-ocean ridge is entirely volcanic and is composed of basaltic lavas characteristic of the oceanic crust. Along most of its crest is a central downdropped **rift valley** created by sea floor spreading (rifting) where two plates diverge (see, for example, Figure 2.15 and Figure 2.16). Along the Mid-Atlantic Ridge, for example, is a central rift valley that is as much as 30 kilometers (20 miles) wide and 3 kilometers (2 miles) deep. Here, molten rock presses upward toward the sea floor, setting off earthquakes, creating jets of superheated seawater, and eventually solidifying to form new oceanic crust. Cracks called *fissures* (*fissus* = split) and faults are commonly observed in the central rift valley. Swarms of small earthquakes occur along the central rift valley caused by the injection of magma into the sea floor or rifting along faults.

Segments of the mid-ocean ridge called **oceanic ridges** have a prominent rift valley and steep, rugged slopes, and **oceanic rises** have slopes that are gentler and less rugged. As explained

FIGURE 3.15 Floor of the North Atlantic Ocean. The global mid-ocean ridge cuts through the center of the Atlantic Ocean, where it is called the Mid-Atlantic Ridge.

WEB VIDEO

Formation of Pillow Lava

in Chapter 2, the differences in overall shape are caused by the fact that oceanic ridges (such as the Mid-Atlantic Ridge) spread more slowly than oceanic rises (such as the East Pacific Rise).

Volcanic Features

Volcanic features associated with the mid-ocean ridge include tall volcanoes called *seamounts*[6] (Figure 3.16a) and recent underwater lava flows. When hot basaltic lava spills onto the sea floor, it is exposed to cold seawater that chills the margins of the lava. This creates **pillow lavas** or **pillow basalts**, which are smooth, rounded lobes of rock that resemble a stack of bed pillows (Figure 3.16b and 3.16c).

Although most people are usually not aware of it, frequent volcanic activity is common along the mid-ocean ridge. In fact, 80% of Earth's volcanic activity takes place on the sea floor, and every year about 12 cubic kilometers (3 cubic miles) of molten rock erupts underwater. The amount of erupted lava along the mid-ocean ridge is large enough to fill an Olympic-sized swimming pool every three seconds! Bathymetric studies along the Juan de Fuca Ridge off Washington and Oregon, for example, revealed that 50 million cubic meters (1800 million cubic feet) of new lava were released sometime between 1981 and 1987. Subsequent surveys of the area indicated many changes along the mid-ocean ridge, including new volcanic features, recent lava flows, and depth changes of up to 37 meters (121 feet). Interest in the continuing volcanic activity along the Juan de Fuca Ridge has led to the development of a permanent sea floor observation system there (see Box 2.2). Other parts of the mid-ocean ridge, such as East Pacific Rise, also experience frequent volcanic activity (Box 3.3).

Hydrothermal Vents

Other features in the central rift valley include **hydrothermal** (*hydro* = water, *thermo* = heat) **vents**. Hydrothermal vents are sea floor hot springs created when cold seawater seeps down along cracks and fractures in the ocean crust and approaches an underground magma chamber (Figure 3.17). The water picks up heat

STUDENTS SOMETIMES ASK...

What effect does all this volcanic activity along the mid-ocean ridge have at the ocean's surface?

Sometimes an underwater volcanic eruption is large enough to create what is called a *megaplume* of warm, mineral-rich water that is lower in density than the surrounding seawater and thus rises to the surface. Remarkably, a few research vessels have reported experiencing the effects of a megaplume at the surface while directly above an erupting sea floor volcano! Researchers on board describe bubbles of gas and steam at the surface, a marked increase in water temperature, and the presence of enough volcanic material to turn the water cloudy. In terms of warming the ocean, the heat released into the ocean at mid-ocean ridges is probably not very significant, mostly because the ocean is so good at absorbing and redistributing heat.

STUDENTS SOMETIMES ASK...

Has anyone seen pillow lava forming?

Amazingly, yes! In the 1960s, an underwater film crew ventured to Hawaii during an eruption of the volcano Kilauea, where lava spilled into the sea. They braved high water temperatures and risked being burned on the red-hot lava but filmed some incredible footage. Underwater, the formation of pillow lava occurs where a tube emits molten lava directly into the ocean. When hot lava comes into contact with cold seawater, it forms the characteristic smooth and rounded margins of pillow basalt. The divers also experimented with a hammer on newly formed pillows and were able to initiate new lava outpourings.

---

[6]In a number of cases, researchers have discovered seamounts that initially formed along the crest of the mid-ocean ridge and have been split in two as the plates spread apart.

and dissolved substances and then works its way back toward the surface through a complex plumbing system, exiting through the sea floor. The temperature of the water that rushes out of a particular hydrothermal vent determines its appearance:

- **Warm-water vents** have water temperatures below 30°C (86°F) and generally emit water that is clear in color.
- **White smokers** have water temperatures from 30° to 350°C (86° to 662°F) and emit water that is white because of the presence of various light-colored compounds, including barium sulfide.
- **Black smokers** have water temperatures above 350°C (662°F) and emit water that is black because of the presence of dark-colored **metal sulfides**, including iron, nickel, copper, and zinc.

(a)

> ### STUDENTS SOMETIMES ASK...
>
> *If black smokers are so hot, why isn't there steam coming out of them instead of hot water?*
>
> Indeed, black smokers emit water that can be up to four times the boiling point of water at the ocean's surface and hot enough to melt lead. However, the depth where black smokers are found results in much higher pressure than at the surface. At these higher pressures, water has a much higher boiling point. Thus, water from hydrothermal vents remains in the liquid state instead of turning into water vapor (steam).

Many black smokers spew out of chimney-like structures (Figure 3.17b) that can be up to 60 meters (200 feet) high and were named for their resemblance to factory smokestacks belching clouds of smoke. The dissolved metal particles often come out of solution, or **precipitate**,[7] when the hot water mixes with cold seawater, creating coatings of mineral deposits on nearby rocks. Chemical analyses of these deposits reveal that they are composed of various metal sulfides and sometimes even silver and gold.

(b)

In addition, most hydrothermal vents foster unusual deep-ocean ecosystems that include organisms such as giant tubeworms, large clams, beds of mussels, and many other creatures—most of which were new to science when they were first encountered. These organisms are able to survive in the absence of sunlight because the vents discharge hydrogen sulfide gas, which is metabolized by archaeons[8] and bacteria and provides a food source for other organisms in the community. Recent studies of active hydrothermal vent fields indicate that vents have short life spans of only a few years to several decades, which has important implications for the organisms that depend on hydrothermal vents. The interesting associations of these organisms are discussed in Chapter 15, "Animals of the Benthic Environment."

Fracture Zones and Transform Faults

The mid-ocean ridge is cut by a number of **transform faults**, which offset spreading zones. Oriented perpendicular to the spreading zones, transform faults give the mid-ocean ridge the zigzag appearance seen in Figure 3.15. As described in Chapter 2, transform faults occur to accommodate spreading of a linear ridge system on a spherical Earth and because different segments of the mid-ocean ridge spread apart at different rates.

(c)

FIGURE 3.16 Mid-ocean ridge volcanoes and pillow lava. **(a)** False-color perspective view based on sonar mapping of a portion of the East Pacific Rise (*center*) showing volcanic seamount (*left*). The depth, in meters, is indicated by the color scale along the left margin; vertical exaggeration is six times. **(b)** Recently formed pillow lava along the East Pacific Rise. Photo shows an area of the sea floor about 3 meters (10 feet) across that also displays ripple marks from deep-ocean currents. **(c)** Pillow lava that was once on the sea floor but has since been uplifted onto land at Port San Luis, California. Maximum width of an individual pillow is 1 meter (3 feet).

---

[7]A *chemical precipitate* is formed whenever dissolved materials change from existing in the dissolved state to existing in the solid state.

[8]Archaeons are microscopic bacteria-like organisms—a newly discovered domain of life.

3.3   RESEARCH METHODS IN OCEANOGRAPHY

RECOVERING OCEANOGRAPHIC EQUIPMENT STUCK IN LAVA

Although the mid-ocean ridge is one of the most active features on the planet and experiences an abundance of volcanic activity, nobody has ever directly observed an undersea volcanic eruption there. However, a team of oceanographers on a research cruise to the East Pacific Rise in 2006 came close to this remarkable feat.

The story starts a year earlier, when scientists deployed 12 ocean-bottom seismometers (OBSs) over a few square kilometers of sea floor along an unusually active portion of the East Pacific Rise that is about 725 kilometers (450 miles) south of Acapulco, Mexico, and 2.5 kilometers (1.6 miles) deep. The OBSs—each about the size and weight of a small refrigerator—are designed to stay on the sea floor for up to a year and collect seismic data. Researchers returned in 2006, thinking that they would simply recover the instruments and send down others. When the research vessel sent a sonar signal to the OBSs to release their weights and use their floats to return to the surface, only four came bobbing up. That's when the scientists suspected that a volcanic eruption had occurred. Three other OBSs responded to the signal but did not come to the surface, and five other instruments were not heard from, presumably because they were buried in lava.

Two months later, scientists returned with a camera-equipped sled that is towed behind a ship and were able to locate the three OBSs embedded in recent lava. Although they tried to nudge and pry them loose with the sled, the OBSs were thoroughly stuck. Wanting to retrieve the stuck OBSs with the hope that they had recorded data while riding out an active sea floor lava flow, the scientists had to wait until a year later, when the tethered robotic vehicle *Jason* was sent down to try to free the instruments. Using *Jason*'s video camera and its mechanical arms controlled remotely from a command center on the ship, the crew was able to pry away large chunks of lava that locked the instruments in place. After much yanking, two of the OBSs finally broke free and rose to the surface, with help from attached floats. Although the researchers attempted to free the third OBS, it was never recovered because it was stuck too tightly in lava.

The recovered OBS instruments—although badly scorched from the hot lava (Figure 3E)—had usable data that have given researchers new information about the volcanic processes that occur at the mid-ocean ridge. This and other evidence suggests that the fresh lava had erupted for six hours straight, heating and darkening the water above it and spreading along the ridge for more than 16 kilometers (10 miles). The researchers consider themselves lucky to have fortuitously caught Earth's crust in the very act of ripping itself apart, documenting swarms of undersea earthquakes and culminating in a volcanic eruption that buried their instruments in lava.

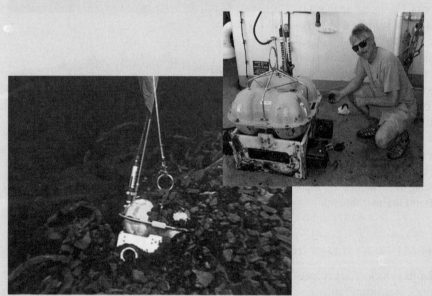

FIGURE 3E   An ocean-bottom seismometer (OBS) stuck in lava. A 2006 sea floor eruption along the East Pacific Rise trapped this and several other OBS instruments in lava. The yellow plastic covering protects glass ball floats that are normally used to raise the instrument to the surface; additional attached floats are shown above the OBS. Scientists freed the device by using a robotic vehicle to remove chunks of lava that were embedded into the instrument and singed its outer casing. Inset (*right*) shows marine geologist Dan Fornari prying off chunks of recently erupted sea floor lava from the recovered instrument.

WEB VIDEO
Recovering Oceanographic
Equipment Stuck in Lava

KEY CONCEPT

The mid-ocean ridge is created by plate divergence and typically includes a central rift valley, faults and fissures, seamounts, pillow basalts, hydrothermal vents, and metal sulfide deposits.

On the Pacific Ocean sea floor, where scars are less rapidly covered by sediment than in other ocean basins, transform faults are prominently displayed (Figure 3.18). Here, they extend for thousands of kilometers away from the mid-ocean ridge and have widths of up to 200 kilometers (120 miles). These extensions, however, are not transform faults. Instead, they are **fracture zones**.

What is the difference between a transform fault and a fracture zone? Figure 3.19 shows that both run along the same long linear zone of weakness in

(a)

FIGURE 3.17 Hydrothermal vents.
(a) Diagram showing hydrothermal circulation along the mid-ocean ridge and the creation of black smokers. Photo (*inset*) shows a close-up view of a black smoker along the East Pacific Rise. (b) Black smoker chimney and fissure at Susu north active site, Manus Basin, western Pacific Ocean. Chimney is about 3 meters (10 feet) tall.

WEB VIDEO

Black Smoker Venting Fluid

KEY CONCEPT
Transform faults are plate boundaries that occur *between* offset segments of the mid-ocean ridge, while fracture zones are intraplate features that occur *beyond* the offset segments of the mid-ocean ridge.

(b)

Earth's crust. In fact, by following the same zone of weakness from one end to the other, it changes from a fracture zone to a transform fault and back again to a fracture zone. A transform fault is a seismically active area that offsets the axis of a mid-ocean ridge. A fracture zone, on the other hand, is a seismically inactive area that shows evidence of past transform fault activity. A helpful way to visualize the difference is that transform faults occur *between* offset segments of the mid-ocean ridge, while fracture zones occur *beyond* the offset segments of the mid-ocean ridge.

The relative direction of plate motion across transform faults and fracture zones further differentiates these two features. Across a transform fault, two lithospheric plates are moving in opposite directions. Across a fracture zone (which occurs entirely within a plate), there is no relative motion because the parts of the lithospheric plate cut by a fracture zone are moving in the same direction (Figure 3.19). Transform faults are actual plate boundaries, whereas fracture zones are not. Rather, fracture zones are ancient, inactive fault scars embedded within a plate.

In addition, earthquake activity is different in transform faults and fracture zones. Earthquakes shallower than 10 kilometers (6 miles) are common when plates move in opposite directions along transform faults. Along fracture zones, where plate motion is in the same direction, seismic activity is almost completely absent.

FIGURE 3.18 The Eltanin Fracture Zone. Enlargement of the Eltanin Fracture Zone in the South Pacific Ocean, showing its relationship to the East Pacific Rise. The Eltanin Fracture Zone is actually both a fracture zone and a transform fault; the name was given to it before the modern understanding of plate tectonic processes.

web animation

Transform Faults

FIGURE 3.19 Transform faults and fracture zones. Transform faults are active transform plate boundaries that occur *between* the segments of the mid-ocean ridge. Fracture zones are inactive intraplate features that occur *beyond* the segments of the mid-ocean ridge.

Table 3.1 summarizes the differences between transform faults and fracture zones.

Oceanic Islands

Some of the most interesting features of ocean basins are islands, which are unusually tall features that reach from the sea floor all the way above sea level. There are three basic types of oceanic islands: (1) islands associated with volcanic activity along the mid-ocean ridge (such as Ascension Island along the Mid-Atlantic Ridge); (2) islands associated with hotspots (such as the Hawaiian Islands in the Pacific Ocean); and (3) islands that are island arcs and associated with convergent plate boundaries (such as the Aleutian Islands in the Pacific Ocean). Note that all three types are volcanic in origin. In addition, there is a fourth type of island: islands that are parts of continents (such as the British Isles off Europe), but these occur close to shore and thus do not occur in the deep ocean.

TABLE 3.1	COMPARISON BETWEEN TRANSFORM FAULTS AND FRACTURE ZONES	
	Transform faults	**Fracture zones**
Plate boundary?	Yes—a transform plate boundary	No—an intraplate feature
Relative movement across feature	Movement in opposite directions ← ——— →	Movement in the same direction ← ——— ←
Earthquakes?	Many	Few
Relationship to mid-ocean ridge	Occur *between* offset mid-ocean ridge segments	Occur *beyond* offset mid-ocean ridge segments
Geographic examples	San Andreas Fault, Alpine Fault, Dead Sea Fault	Mendocino Fracture Zone, Molokai Fracture Zone

Chapter in Review

• *Bathymetry is the measurement of ocean depths and the charting of ocean floor topography.* The varied bathymetry of the ocean floor was first determined using *soundings* to measure water depth. Later, the development of the *echo sounder* gave ocean scientists a more detailed representation of the sea floor. Today, much of our knowledge of the ocean floor has been obtained using various *multibeam echo sounders* or *side-scan sonar instruments* (to make detailed bathymetric maps of a small area of the ocean floor); *satellite measurement* of the ocean surface (to produce maps of the world ocean floor); and *seismic reflection profiles* (to examine Earth structure beneath the sea floor).

• *Earth's hypsographic curve* shows the amount of Earth's surface area at different elevations and depths. *The distribution of area is uneven* with respect to height above or below sea level. The shape of the curve also *reflects the existence of plate tectonic processes.*

• *Continental margins can be either passive* (not associated with any plate boundaries) *or active* (associated with convergent or transform plate boundaries). Extending from the shoreline is the generally shallow, low relief, and gently sloping *continental shelf*, which can contain various features such as coastal islands, reefs, and banks. The boundary between the continental slope and the continental shelf is marked by an increase in slope that occurs at the *shelf break*. Cutting deep into the slopes are *submarine canyons*, which resemble canyons on land but are created by erosive turbidity currents. *Turbidity currents* deposit their sediment load at the base of the continental slope, creating deep-sea fans that merge to produce a gently sloping continental rise. The deposits from turbidity currents (called *turbidite deposits*) have characteristic sequences of graded bedding. Active margins have similar features although they are modified by their associated plate boundary.

• The *continental rises* gradually become flat, extensive, deep-ocean *abyssal plains*, which form by *suspension settling* of fine sediment. Poking through the sediment cover of the abyssal plains are numerous *volcanic peaks*, including volcanic islands, seamounts, tablemounts, and abyssal hills. In the Pacific Ocean, where sedimentation rates are low, abyssal plains are not extensively developed, and abyssal hill provinces cover broad expanses of ocean floor.

Along the margins of many continents—especially those around the Pacific Ring of Fire—are deep linear scars called ocean trenches that are associated with convergent plate boundaries and volcanic arcs.

• The *mid-ocean ridge is a continuous mountain range* that winds through all ocean basins and is entirely *volcanic in origin*. Common features associated with the mid-ocean ridge include a *central rift valley, faults and fissures, seamounts, pillow basalts, hydrothermal vents, deposits of metal sulfides,* and *unusual life forms*. Segments of the mid-ocean ridge are either *oceanic ridges* if steep with rugged slopes (indicative of slow sea floor spreading) or *oceanic rises* if sloped gently and less rugged (indicative of fast spreading).

• *Long linear zones of weakness—fracture zones and transform faults—cut* across vast distances of ocean floor and *offset the axes of the mid-ocean ridge*. Fracture zones and transform faults are differentiated from one another based on the direction of movement across the feature. *Fracture zones* (an intraplate feature) *have movement in the same direction*, while *transform faults* (a transform plate boundary) *have movement in opposite directions*.

Key Terms

Abyssal hill (p. 88)
Abyssal hill province (p. 88)
Abyssal plain (p. 87)
Active margin (p. 82)
Bathymetry (p. 75)
Black smoker (p. 91)
Continental arc (p. 88)
Continental borderland (p. 83)
Continental margin (p. 81)
Continental rise (p. 85)
Continental shelf (p. 82)
Continental slope (p. 83)
Convergent active margin (p. 82)
Deep-ocean basin (p. 81)

Deep-sea fan (p. 85)
Echo sounder (p. 76)
Fathom (p. 76)
Fracture zone (p. 92)
GLORIA (p. 77)
Graded bedding (p. 85)
Hydrothermal vent (p. 90)
Hypsographic curve (p. 80)
Island arc (p. 88)
Metal sulfide (p. 91)
Mid-ocean ridge (p. 81)
Ocean trench (p. 88)
Oceanic ridge (p. 89)
Oceanic rise (p. 89)

Pacific Ring of Fire (p. 88)
Passive margin (p. 82)
Pillow basalt (p. 90)
Pillow lava (p. 90)
Ping (p. 76)
Precipitate (p. 91)
Precision depth recorder (PDR) (p. 76)
Rift valley (p. 89)
Seabeam (p. 77)
Seaknoll (p. 88)
Sea MARC (p. 77)
Seamount (p. 87)
Seismic reflection profile (p. 80)

Shelf break (p. 82
Sonar (p. 77)
Sounding (p. 75)
Submarine canyon (p. 84)
Submarine fan (p. 85)
Suspension settling (p. 87)
Tablemount (p. 88)
Transform active margin (p. 82)
Transform fault (p. 91)
Turbidite deposit (p. 85)
Turbidity current (p. 85)
Volcanic arc (p. 88)
Warm-water vent (p. 91)
White smoker (p. 91)

Review Questions

1. What is bathymetry?

2. Discuss the development of bathymetric techniques, indicating significant advancements in technology.

3. Describe differences between passive and active continental margins. Be sure to include how these features relate to plate tectonics and include an example of each type of margin.

4. Describe the major features of a passive continental margin: continental shelf, continental slope, continental rise, submarine canyon, and deep-sea fans.

5. Explain how submarine canyons are created.

6. What are some differences between a submarine canyon and an ocean trench?

7. Explain what graded bedding is and how it forms.

8. Describe the process by which abyssal plains are created.

9. Discuss the origin of the various volcanic peaks of the abyssal plains: seamounts, tablemounts, and abyssal hills.

10. Describe characteristics and features of the mid-ocean ridge, including the difference between oceanic ridges and oceanic rises.

11. List and describe the different types of hydrothermal vents.

12. What kinds of unusual life can be found associated with hydrothermal vents? How do these organisms survive?

13. Describe the origin of the three basic types of oceanic islands.

Critical Thinking Exercises

1. Describe what is shown by a hypsographic curve and explain why its shape reflects the presence of active tectonic processes on Earth.

2. In which ocean basin are most ocean trenches found? Use plate tectonic processes to help explain why.

3. Use pictures and words to describe differences between fracture zones and transform faults.

Oceanography on the Web

Visit the *Essentials of Oceanography* Online Study Guide for Internet resources, including chapter-specific quizzes to test your understanding and Web links to further your exploration of the topics in this chapter.

The *Essentials of Oceanography* Online Study Guide is at http://www.mygeoscienceplace.com/.

Microscopic view of arranged diatoms.
The objects in this photomicrograph are diatoms, which are microscopic marine algae that exist in incredible abundance in the ocean. This image shows various species of diatoms magnified several hundred times and was made by carefully arranging them under a microscope.

"When I think of the floor of the deep sea, the single, overwhelming fact that possesses my imagination is the accumulation of sediments. I see always the steady, unremitting, downward drift of materials from above, flake upon flake, layer upon layer. . . . For the sediments are the materials of the most stupendous snowfall the Earth has ever seen."

—*Rachel Carson,*
The Sea Around Us (1956)

4 MARINE SEDIMENTS

Why are **sediments** (*sedimentum* = settling) interesting to oceanographers? Although ocean sediments are little more than eroded particles and fragments of dirt, dust, and other debris that have settled out of the water and accumulated on the ocean floor (Figure 4.1), they reveal much about Earth's history. For example, sediments provide clues to past climates, movements of the ocean floor, ocean circulation patterns, and nutrient supplies for marine organisms. By examining cylindrical **cores** of sediment collected from the sea floor and interpreting them (Figure 4.2), oceanographers can ascertain the timing of major extinctions, global climate change, and the movement of plates. In fact, most of what is known of Earth's past geology, climate, and biology has been learned through studying ancient marine sediments.

Over time, sediments can become *lithified* (*lithos* = stone, *fic* = making)—turned to rock—and form *sedimentary rock*. More than half of the rocks exposed on the continents are sedimentary rocks deposited in ancient ocean environments and uplifted onto land by plate tectonic processes. Perhaps surprisingly, even the tallest mountains on the continents—far from any ocean—contain telltale marine fossils, which indicate that these rocks originated on the ocean floor in the geologic past. For example, the summit of the world's tallest mountain (Mount Everest in the Himalaya Mountains) consists of limestone, which is a type of rock that originated as sea floor deposits.

Particles of sediment come from worn pieces of rocks, as well as living organisms, minerals dissolved in water, and outer space. Clues to sediment origin are found in its mineral composition and its **texture** (the size and shape of its particles).

This chapter is organized around Table 4.1, which shows the classification of marine sediments according to type, composition, sources, and main locations found. The chapter begins with a brief discussion about what sediments reveal about Earth history and how sediments are collected. As you work through the remainder of this chapter, note that each of the four main types of sediment are discussed (Table 4.1, *first column*). Then, within each type of sediment, the composition (Table 4.1, *second column*), origin (*third column*), and distribution (*fourth column*) are examined. Finally, the chapter concludes with a discussion of the resources that sediments provide.

4.1 Why Are Marine Sediments Important?

Marine sediments provide a wealth of information about past conditions on Earth; in fact, sediments of the deep-ocean floor represent one of the few complete and undisturbed records of Earth history over the past several hundred million years. As sediment accumulates on the ocean floor, it preserves materials that existed in the overlying water column. By carefully analyzing these materials, Earth

TABLE 4.1	CLASSIFICATION OF MARINE SEDIMENTS

Type	Composition			Sources		Main locations found
Lithogenous	Continental margin	Rock fragments		Rivers; coastal erosion; landslides		Continental shelf
		Quartz sand		Glaciers		Continental shelf in high latitudes
		Quartz silt		Turbidity currents		Continental slope and rise; ocean basin margins
		Clay				
	Oceanic	Quartz silt		Wind-blown dust; rivers		Deep-ocean basins
		Clay				
		Volcanic ash		Volcanic eruptions		
Biogenous	Calcium carbonate ($CaCO_3$)	Calcareous ooze (microscopic)	Warm surface water	Coccolithophores (algae); Foraminifers (protozoans)		Low-latitude regions; sea floor above CCD; along mid-ocean ridges and the tops of volcanic peaks
		Shell coral fragments (macroscopic)		Macroscopic shell-producing organisms		Continental shelf; beaches
				Coral reefs		Shallow low-latitude regions
	Silica ($SiO_2 \cdot nH_2O$)	Siliceous ooze	Cold surface water	Diatoms (algae); Radiolarians (protozoans)		High-latitude regions; sea floor below CCD; upwelling areas where cold, deep water rises to the surface, especially that caused by surface current divergence near the equator
Hydrogenous	Manganese nodules (manganese, iron, copper, nickel, cobalt)			Precipitation of dissolved materials directly from seawater due to chemical reactions		Abyssal plain
	Phosphorite (phosphorous)					Continental shelf
	Oolites ($CaCO_3$)					Shallow shelf in low-latitude regions
	Metal sulfides (iron, nickel, copper, zinc, silver)					Hydrothermal vents at mid-ocean ridges
	Evaporites (gypsum, halite, other salts)					Shallow restricted basins where evaporation is high in low-latitude regions
Cosmogenous	Iron–nickel spherules Tektites (silica glass)			Space dust		In very small proportions mixed with all types of sediment and in all marine environments
	Iron–nickel meteorites			Meteors		Localized near meteor impact structures

FIGURE 4.1 **Oceanic sediment.** View of the deep-ocean floor from a submersible. Most of the deep-ocean floor is covered with particles of material that have settled out through the water.

FIGURE 4.2 **Examining deep-ocean sediment cores.** Long cylinders of sediment and rock called cores are cut in half and examined, revealing interesting aspects of Earth history.

scientists can infer past conditions such as sea surface temperature, nutrient supply, abundance of marine life, atmospheric winds, ocean current patterns, volcanic eruptions, major extinction events, changes in Earth's climate, and the movement of tectonic plates. The study of how the ocean, atmosphere, and land have interacted to produce changes in ocean chemistry, circulation, biology, and climate is called **paleoceanography** (*paleo* = ancient, *ocean* = the marine environment, *graphy* = the name of a descriptive science), which relies on sea floor sediments to gain insight into these past changes.

Recent paleoceanographic studies, for example, have linked changes in deep-ocean circulation with rapid climate change. In the North Atlantic Ocean, cold, relatively salty water sinks and forms a body of water called *North Atlantic Deep Water*. Water in this deep current circulates through the global ocean, driving deep-ocean circulation and global heat transport and, thus, impacting global climate. Widely viewed as one of the most climatically sensitive regions on Earth, North Atlantic sea floor sediments from the past several million years have revealed that the region has experienced abrupt changes to its ocean-atmosphere system, triggered by fluctuations of fresh water from melting glaciers. Understanding the timing, mechanisms, and causes of this abrupt climate change is one of the major challenges facing paleoceanography today.

Collecting sediments suitable for analysis from the deep ocean is an arduous process. During early exploration of the oceans, a bucket-like device called a *dredge* was used to scoop up sediment from the deep-ocean floor for analysis. This technique, however, was limited to gathering samples from just the surface of the ocean floor. Later, the *gravity corer*—a hollow steel tube with a heavy weight on top—was thrust into the sea floor to collect the first *cores* (cylinders of sediment and rock). Although the gravity corer could sample below the surface, its depth of penetration was limited. Today, specially designed ships perform **rotary drilling** to collect cores from the deep ocean (Box 4.1).

KEY CONCEPT
Marine sediments accumulate on the ocean floor and contain a record of recent Earth history, including past environmental conditions.

WEB VIDEO
The Ocean Floor Seascape

WEB VIDEO
Rotary Drilling

COLLECTING THE HISTORICAL RECORD OF THE DEEP-OCEAN FLOOR

In 1963, the U.S. National Science Foundation funded a program that borrowed drilling technology from the offshore oil industry to obtain long sections of core from deep below the surface of the ocean floor. The program united four leading oceanographic institutions (Scripps Institution of Oceanography in California; Rosenstiel School of Atmospheric and Oceanic Studies at the University of Miami, Florida; Lamont-Doherty Earth Observatory of Columbia University in New York; and the Woods Hole Oceanographic Institution in Massachusetts) to form the *Joint Oceanographic Institutions for Deep Earth Sampling (JOIDES)*. The oceanography departments of several other leading universities later joined JOIDES.

The first phase of the **Deep Sea Drilling Project (DSDP)** was initiated in 1968 when the specially designed drill ship *Glomar Challenger* was launched. It had a tall drilling rig resembling a steel tower. Cores could be collected by drilling into the ocean floor in water up to 6000 meters (3.7 miles) deep. From the initial cores collected, scientists confirmed the existence of sea floor spreading by documenting that (1) the age of the ocean floor increased progressively with distance from the mid-ocean ridge; (2) sediment thickness increased progressively with distance from the mid-ocean ridge; and (3) Earth's magnetic field polarity reversals were recorded in ocean floor rocks.

Although the oceanographic research program was initially financed by the U.S. government, it became international in 1975, when West Germany, France, Japan, the United Kingdom, and the Soviet Union also provided financial and scientific support. In 1983, the Deep Sea Drilling Project became the **Ocean Drilling Program (ODP)**, with 20 participating countries under the supervision of Texas A&M University and a broader objective of drilling the thick sediment layers near the continental margins.

In 1985, the *Glomar Challenger* was decommissioned and replaced by the drill ship **JOIDES Resolution** (Figure 4A). The new ship also has a tall metal drilling rig to conduct *rotary drilling*. The drill pipe is in individual sections of 9.5 meters (31 feet), and sections can be screwed together to make a single string of pipe up to 8200 meters (27,000 feet) long (Figure 4B). The drill bit, located at the end of the pipe string, rotates as it is pressed against the ocean bottom and can drill up to 2100 meters (6900 feet) below the sea floor. Like twirling a soda straw into a layer cake, the drilling operation crushes the rock around the outside and retains a cylinder of rock (a *core sample*) on the inside of the hollow pipe. Cores can then be raised to the surface from inside the pipe and are analyzed with state-of-the-art laboratory facilities on board the *Resolution*. Worldwide, more than 2000 holes have been drilled into the sea floor using this method, allowing the collection of cores that provide scientists with valuable information about Earth history as recorded in sea floor sediments.

In 2003, the ODP was replaced by the **Integrated Ocean Drilling Program (IODP)**, whose main participants are Japan, the United States, and the European Union. This new international effort will not rely on just one drill ship, but will use multiple vessels for exploration. One of the new vessels that began operations in 2007 is a state-of-the-art drill ship named *Chikyu* (which means "Planet Earth" in Japanese) that can drill up to 7000 meters (23,000 feet) below the sea floor, with plans to upgrade the vessel with new drilling technology to allow it to drill even deeper, perhaps as deep as through Earth's crust into the mantle. The program's primary objective is to collect cores that will allow scientists to better understand Earth history and Earth system processes, including the properties of the deep crust, climate change patterns, earthquake mechanisms, and the microbiology of the deep-ocean floor.

FIGURE 4B Rotary drilling from the *JOIDES Resolution*.

FIGURE 4A The drill ship *JOIDES Resolution*.

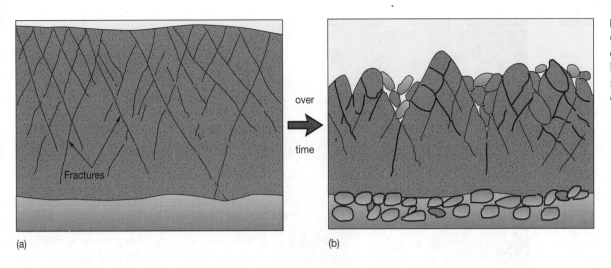

FIGURE 4.3 Weathering.
Over time, weathering
occurs along fractures and
breaks rock into smaller
fragments, which are much
easier to transport.

4.2 What Is Lithogenous Sediment?

Lithogenous (*lithos* = stone, *generare* = to produce) **sediment** is derived from
preexisting rock material that originates on the continents or islands from erosion, volcanic eruptions, or blown dust. Note that lithogenous sediment is sometimes referred to as **terrigenous** (*terra* = land, *generare* = to produce) **sediment**.

Origin of Lithogenous Sediment

Lithogenous sediment begins as rocks on continents or islands. Over time,
weathering agents such as water, temperature extremes, and chemical effects
break rocks into smaller pieces, as shown in Figure 4.3. When rocks are in smaller
pieces, they can be more easily **eroded** (picked up) and transported. This eroded
material is the basic component of which all lithogenous sediment is composed.

Eroded material from the continents is carried to the oceans by streams,
wind, glaciers, and gravity (Figure 4.4). Each year, stream flow alone carries about
20 billion metric tons (22 billion short tons) of sediment to Earth's continental
margins; almost 40% is provided by runoff from Asia.

Transported sediment can be deposited in many environments, including bays
or lagoons near the ocean, as deltas at the mouths of rivers, along beaches at the
shoreline, or further offshore across the continental margin. It can also be carried
beyond the continental margin to the deep-ocean basin by turbidity currents, as
discussed in Chapter 3.

The greatest quantity of lithogenous material is found around the margins of
the continents, where it is constantly moved by high-energy currents along the
shoreline and in deeper turbidity currents. Lower-energy currents distribute finer
components that settle out onto the deep-ocean basins. Microscopic particles
from wind-blown dust or volcanic eruptions can even be carried far out over the
open ocean by prevailing winds. These particles either settle into fine layers as the
velocity of the wind decreases or disperse into the ocean when they serve as nuclei around which raindrops and snowflakes form.

Composition of Lithogenous Sediment

The composition of lithogenous sediment reflects the material from which it was
derived. All rocks are composed of discrete crystals of naturally occurring compounds called *minerals*. One of the most abundant, chemically stable, and durable
minerals in Earth's crust is **quartz**, composed of silicon and oxygen in the form of
SiO_2—the same composition as ordinary glass. Quartz is a major component of
most rocks. Because quartz is resistant to abrasion, it can be transported long

FIGURE 4.4 Sediment transporting media. Transporting media include **(a)** streams (Po River, Italy, which displays a prominent delta and a visible sediment plume in the water); **(b)** wind (dust storm, Australia); **(c)** glaciers (Riggs Glacier, Glacier Bay National Park, Alaska, which displays a dark stripe of sediment along its length called a medial moraine); **(d)** gravity, which creates landslides (Del Mar, California).

(a)

(b)

(c)

(d)

distances and deposited far from its source area. The majority of lithogenous deposits—such as beach sands—are composed primarily of quartz (Figure 4.5).

A large percentage of lithogenous particles that find their way into deep-ocean sediments far from continents are transported by prevailing winds that remove small particles from the continents' subtropical desert regions. The map in Figure 4.6 shows a close relationship between the location of microscopic fragments of lithogenous quartz in the surface sediments of the ocean floor and the strong prevailing winds in the desert regions of Africa, Asia, and Australia. Satellite observations of dust storms (Figure 4.6, *inset*) confirm this relationship. Sediment is not the only item transported by wind. In fact, there has been recent documentation of the transportation of a variety of airborne substances—including viruses, pollutants, and even living insects—from Africa all the way across the Atlantic Ocean to North America.

Sediment Texture

One of the most important properties of lithogenous sediment is its texture, including its **grain size**.[1] The **Wentworth scale of grain size** (Table 4.2) indicates that particles can be classified as boulders (largest), cobbles, pebbles, granules, sand, silt, or clay (smallest). Sediment size is proportional to the energy needed to lay down a deposit. Deposits laid down where wave action is strong (areas of high energy) may be composed primarily of larger particles—cobbles and boulders. Fine-grained particles, on the other hand, are deposited where the energy level is low and the current speed is minimal. When clay-sized particles—many of which are flat—are deposited, they tend to stick together by cohesive forces. Consequently, higher-energy conditions than what would be expected based on grain size alone are required to erode and transport clays. In general, however, lithogenous sediment tends to become finer with increasing distance from shore. This relationship is mostly because high-energy transporting media predominate close to shore and lower-energy conditions exist in the deep-ocean basins.

The texture of lithogenous sediment also depends on its **sorting**. Sorting is a measure of the uniformity of grain sizes and indicates the selectivity of the transportation process. For example, sediments composed of particles that are primarily the same size are well sorted—such as in coastal sand dunes, where winds can only pick up a certain size particle. Poorly sorted deposits, on the other hand, contain a variety of different sized particles and indicate a transportation process capable of picking up clay- to boulder-sized particles. An example of poorly sorted sediment is that which is carried by a glacier and left behind when the glacier melts.

Distribution of Lithogenous Sediment

Marine sedimentary deposits can be categorized as either neritic or pelagic. **Neritic** (*neritos* = of the coast) **deposits** are found on continental shelves and in shallow water near islands; these deposits are generally coarse grained. Alternatively, **pelagic** (*pelagios* = of the sea) **deposits** are found in the deep-ocean basins and are typically fine grained. Moreover, lithogenous sediment in the ocean is ubiquitous: At least a small percentage of lithogenous sediment is found nearly everywhere on the ocean floor.

NERITIC DEPOSITS Lithogenous sediment dominates most neritic deposits. Lithogenous sediment is derived from rocks on nearby landmasses, consists of coarse-grained deposits, and accumulates rapidly on the continental shelf, slope, and rise. Examples of lithogenous neritic deposits include beach deposits, continental shelf deposits, turbidite deposits, and glacial deposits.

Beach Deposits Beaches are made of whatever materials are locally available. Beach materials are composed mostly of quartz-rich sand that is washed down to the coast by rivers but can also be composed of a wide variety of sizes and

FIGURE 4.5 Lithogenous beach sand. Lithogenous beach sand is composed mostly of particles of white quartz, plus small amounts of other minerals. This sand, from North Beach, Hampton, New Hampshire, is magnified approximately 23 times.

---

[1]Sediment grains are also known as particles, fragments, or clasts.

FIGURE 4.6 Lithogenous quartz in surface sediments of the world's oceans and transport by wind. High concentrations of microscopic lithogenous quartz in deep-sea sediment (*map below*) match prevailing winds from land (*green arrows*). SeaStar SeaWiFS satellite photo (*inset above*) on February 26, 2000, shows a wind storm that has blown dust from the Sahara Desert off the northwest coast of Africa. Some of this dust is transported across the Atlantic Ocean to South America, the Caribbean, and North America.

compositions. This material is transported by waves that crash against the shoreline, especially during storms.

Continental Shelf Deposits At the end of the last ice age (about 18,000 years ago), glaciers melted and sea level rose. As a result, many rivers of the world today deposit their sediment in drowned river mouths rather than carry it onto the continental shelf as they did during the geologic past. In many areas, the sediments that cover the continental shelf—called *relict* (*relict* = left behind) *sediments*—were deposited from 3000 to 7000 years ago and have not yet been covered by more recent deposits. These sediments presently cover about 70% of the world's continental shelves. In other areas, deposits of sand ridges on the

TABLE **4.2**	WENTWORTH SCALE OF GRAIN SIZE FOR SEDIMENTS				
Size range (millimeters)	Particle name		Grain size	Example	Energy of the depositional environment
Above 256	Boulder	↑	Coarse-grained	Coarse material found in streambeds near the source areas of rivers	High energy
64 to 256	Cobble	Gravel			
4 to 64	Pebble				
2 to 4	Granule	↓			
1/16 to 2	Sand			Beach sand	
1/256 to 1/16	Silt			Feels gritty in teeth	
1/4096 to 1/256	Clay		Fine-grained	Microscopic; feels sticky	Low energy

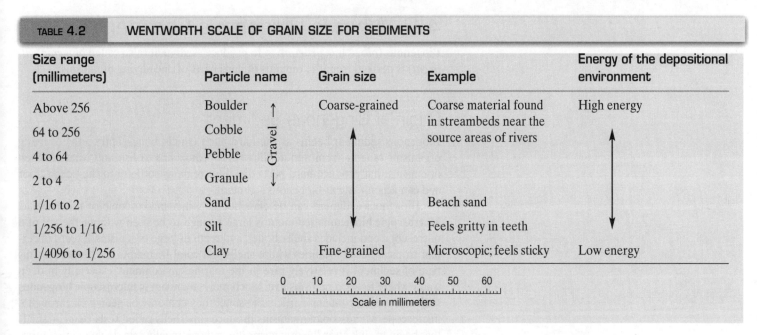

0   10   20   30   40   50   60
Scale in millimeters

continental shelves appear to have been formed more recently than the most recent ice age and at present water depths.

Turbidite Deposits   As discussed in Chapter 3, **turbidity currents** are underwater avalanches that periodically move down the continental slopes and carve submarine canyons. Turbidity currents also carry vast amounts of neritic material. This material spreads out as deep-sea fans, comprises the continental rise, and gradually thins toward the abyssal plains. These deposits are called **turbidite deposits** and are composed of characteristic layering called *graded bedding* (see Figure 3.10).

Glacial Deposits   Poorly sorted deposits containing particles ranging from boulders to clays may be found in the high-latitude[2] portions of the continental shelf. These **glacial deposits** were laid down during the most recent ice age by glaciers that covered the continental shelf and eventually melted. Glacial deposits are currently forming around the continent of Antarctica and around Greenland by **ice rafting**. In this process, rock particles trapped in glacial ice are carried out to sea by icebergs that break away from coastal glaciers. As the icebergs melt, lithogenous particles of many sizes are released and settle onto the ocean floor.

PELAGIC DEPOSITS   Turbidite deposits of neritic sediment on the continental rise can spill over into the deep-ocean basin. However, most pelagic deposits are composed of fine-grained material that accumulates slowly on the deep-ocean floor. Pelagic lithogenous sediment includes particles that have come from volcanic eruptions, windblown dust, and fine material that is carried by deep-ocean currents.

Abyssal Clay   **Abyssal clay** is composed of at least 70% (by weight) fine, clay-sized particles from the continents. Even though they are far from land, deep abyssal plains contain thick sequences of abyssal clay deposits composed of particles transported great distances by winds or ocean currents and deposited on the deep-ocean floor. Because abyssal clays contain oxidized iron, they are commonly red-brown or buff in color and are sometimes referred to as **red clays**. The predominance of abyssal clay on abyssal plains is caused not by an abundance of clay settling on the ocean floor but by the absence of other material that would otherwise dilute it.

> **KEY CONCEPT**
> Lithogenous sediment is produced from preexisting rock material, is found on most parts of the ocean floor, and can occur as thick deposits close to land.

---

[2]High-latitude regions are those far from the equator (either north or south); low latitudes are areas close to the equator.

4.3 What Is Biogenous Sediment?

Biogenous (*bio* = life, *generare* = to produce) **sediment** (also called *biogenic sediment*) is derived from the remains of hard parts of once-living organisms.

Origin of Biogenous Sediment

Biogenous sediment begins as the hard parts (shells, bones, and teeth) of living organisms ranging from minute algae and protozoans to fish and whales. When organisms that produce hard parts die, their remains settle onto the ocean floor and can accumulate as biogenous sediment.

Biogenous sediment can be classified as either macroscopic or microscopic. **Macroscopic biogenous sediment** is large enough to be seen without the aid of a microscope and includes shells, bones, and teeth of large organisms. Except in certain tropical beach localities where shells and coral fragments are numerous, this type of sediment is relatively rare in the marine environment, especially in deep water where fewer organisms live. Much more abundant is **microscopic biogenous sediment**, which contains particles so small they can only be seen well through a microscope. Microscopic organisms produce tiny shells called **tests** (*testa* = shell) that begin to sink after the organisms die and continually rain down in great numbers onto the ocean floor. These microscopic tests can accumulate on the deep-ocean floor and form deposits called **ooze** (*wose* = juice). As its name implies, ooze resembles very fine-grained, mushy material.[3] Technically, biogenous ooze must contain at least 30% biogenous test material by weight. What comprises the other part— up to 70% of an ooze? Commonly, it is fine-grained lithogenous clay that is deposited along with biogenous tests in the deep ocean. By volume, much more microscopic ooze than macroscopic biogenous sediment exists on the ocean floor.

The organisms that contribute to biogenous sediment are chiefly **algae** (*alga* = seaweed) and **protozoans** (*proto* = first, *zoa* = animal). Algae are primarily aquatic, eukaryotic,[4] photosynthetic organisms, ranging in size from microscopic single cells to large organisms like giant kelp. Protozoans are any of a large group of single-celled, eukaryotic, usually microscopic organisms that are generally not photosynthetic.

Composition of Biogenous Sediment

The two most common chemical compounds in biogenous sediment are **calcium carbonate** ($CaCO_3$, which forms the mineral **calcite**) and **silica** (SiO_2) Often, the silica is chemically combined with water to produce $SiO_2 \cdot nH_2O$, the hydrated form of silica, which is called *opal*.

SILICA Most of the silica in biogenous ooze comes from microscopic algae called **diatoms** (*diatoma* = cut in half) and protozoans called **radiolarians** (*radio* = a spoke or ray).

Because diatoms photosynthesize, they need strong sunlight and are found only within the upper, sunlit surface waters of the ocean. Most diatoms are free-floating, or **planktonic** (*planktos* = wandering). The living organism builds a glass greenhouse out of silica as a protective covering and lives inside. Most species have two parts to their test that fit together like a petri dish or pillbox (Figure 4.7a). The tiny tests are perforated with small holes in intricate patterns to allow nutrients to

---

[3]Ooze has the consistency of toothpaste mixed about half and half with water. As a way to remember this term, imagine walking barefoot across the deep-ocean floor and having the fine sediment there *ooze* between your toes.

[4]Eukaryotic (*eu* = good, *karyo* = the nucleus) cells contain a distinct membrane-bound nucleus.

pass in and waste products to pass out. Where diatoms are abundant at the ocean surface, thick deposits of diatom-rich ooze can accumulate below on the ocean floor. When this ooze lithifies, it becomes **diatomaceous earth**,[5] a light-weight white rock composed of diatom tests and clay (Box 4.2).

Radiolarians are microscopic single-celled proto-zoans, most of which are also planktonic. As their name implies, they often have long spikes or rays of silica pro-truding from their siliceous shell (Figure 4.7b). They do not photosynthesize but rely on external food sources such as bacteria and other plankton. Radiolarians typi-cally display well-developed symmetry, which is why they have been described as the "living snowflakes of the sea."

The accumulation of siliceous tests of diatoms, radio-larians, and other silica-secreting organisms produces **siliceous ooze** (Figure 4.7c).

CALCIUM CARBONATE Two significant sources of calcium carbonate biogenous ooze are the **foraminifers** (*foramen* = an opening)—close relatives of radiolarians—and microscopic algae called **coccolithophores** (*coccus* = berry, *lithos* = stone, *phorid* = carrying).

Coccolithophores are single-celled algae, most of which are planktonic. Coccolithophores produce thin plates or shields made of calcium carbonate, 20 or 30 of which overlap to produce a spherical test (Figure 4.8a). Like diatoms, coccolithophores photosynthesize, so they need sunlight to live. Coccolithophores are about 10 to 100 times smaller than most diatoms (Figure 4.8b), which is why coccolithophores are often called **nannoplankton** (*nanno* = dwarf, *planktos* = wandering).

When the organism dies, the individual plates (called **coccoliths**) disaggregate and can accumulate on the ocean floor as coccolith-rich ooze. When this ooze lithifies over time, it forms a white deposit called **chalk**, which is used for a variety of purposes (including writing on chalk-boards). The White Cliffs of southern England are com-posed of hardened, coccolith-rich calcium carbonate ooze, which was deposited on the ocean floor and has been up-lifted onto land (Figure 4.9). Deposits of chalk the same age as the White Cliffs are so common throughout Europe, North America, Australia, and the Middle East that the geologic period in which these deposits formed is named the Cretaceous (*creta* = chalk) Period.

Foraminifers are single-celled protozoans, many of which are planktonic, ranging in size from microscopic to macroscopic. They do not photosynthesize, so they must ingest other organisms for food. Foraminifers produce a hard calcium carbonate test in which the organism lives (Figure 4.8c). Most foraminifers pro-duce a segmented or chambered test, and all tests have a prominent opening in one end. Although very small in size, the tests of foraminifers resemble the large shells that one might find at a beach.

Deposits comprised primarily of tests of foraminifers, coccoliths, and other calcareous-secreting organisms are called **calcareous ooze** (Figure 4.8d).

(a)

(b)

(c)

FIGURE 4.7 Microscopic siliceous tests. Scanning electron micrographs: **(a)** Diatom (length = 30 micrometers, equal to 30 millionths of a meter), show-ing how the two parts of the diatom's test fit together; **(b)** radiolarian (length = 100 micrometers) and **(c)** siliceous ooze, showing mostly fragments of diatom tests (magnified 250 times).

WEB VIDEO

Microscopic Marine Organisms

---

[5]Diatomaceous earth is also called diatomite, tripolite, or kieselguhr.

DIATOMS: THE MOST IMPORTANT THINGS YOU HAVE (PROBABLY) NEVER HEARD OF

Few objects are more beautiful than the minute siliceous cases of the diatomaceae: were these created that they might be examined and admired under the higher powers of the microscope?
— Charles Darwin (1872)

Diatoms are microscopic single-celled photosynthetic organisms. Each one lives inside a protective silica test, most of which contain two halves that fit together like a shoebox and its lid. First described with the aid of a microscope in 1702, their tests are exquisitely ornamented with holes, ribs, and radiating spines unique to individual species. The fossil record indicates that diatoms have been on Earth since the Jurassic Period (180 million years ago), and at least 70,000 species of diatoms have been identified.

Diatoms live for a few days to as much as a week, can reproduce sexually or asexually, and occur individually or linked together into long communities. They are found in great abundance floating in the ocean and in certain freshwater lakes but can also be found in many diverse environments, such as on the undersides of polar ice, on the skins of whales, in soil, in thermal springs, and even on brick walls.

When marine diatoms die, their tests rain down and accumulate on the sea floor as siliceous ooze. Hardened deposits of siliceous ooze, called *diatomaceous earth*, can be as much as 900 meters (3000 feet) thick. Diatomaceous earth consists of billions of minute silica tests and has many unusual properties: It is lightweight, has an inert chemical composition, is resistant to high temperatures, and has excellent filtering properties. Diatomaceous earth is used to produce a variety of common products (Figure 4C). The main uses of diatomaceous earth include

- filters (for refining sugar, separating impurities from wine, straining yeast from beer, and filtering swimming pool water)
- mild abrasives (in toothpaste, facial scrubs, matches, and household cleaning and polishing compounds)
- absorbents (for chemical spills, in cat litter, and as a soil conditioner)
- chemical carriers (in pharmaceuticals, paint, and even dynamite)

Other products from diatomaceous earth include optical-quality glass (because of the pure silica content of diatoms) and space shuttle tiles (because they are lightweight and provide good insulation). It is also used as an additive in concrete, a filler in tires, an anticaking agent, a natural pesticide, and is even used as a building stone in the construction of houses.

Further, the vast majority of oxygen that all animals breathe is a by-product of photosynthesis by diatoms. In addition, each living diatom contains a tiny droplet of oil. When diatoms die, their tests containing droplets of oil accumulate on the sea floor and are the beginnings of petroleum deposits, such as those found offshore California.

Given their many practical applications, it is difficult to imagine how different our lives would be without diatoms!

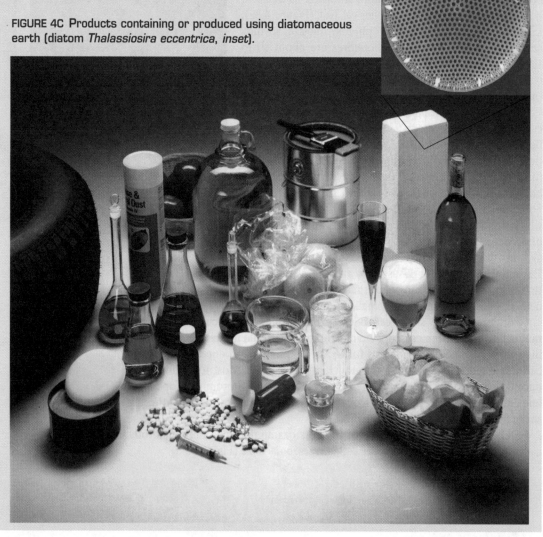

FIGURE 4C Products containing or produced using diatomaceous earth (diatom *Thalassiosira eccentrica*, inset).

(a)

(b)

(c)

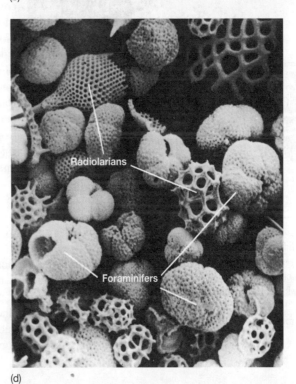

Radiolarians

Foraminifers

(d)

FIGURE 4.8 Microscopic calcareous tests. Scanning electron micrographs: **(a)** Coccolithophores (diameter of individual coccolithophores = 20 micrometers, equal to 20 millionths of a meter); **(b)** diatom (siliceous) and coccoliths (diameter of diatom = 70 micrometers); **(c)** foraminifers (most species 400 micrometers in diameter); and **(d)** calcareous ooze, which also includes some siliceous radiolarian tests (magnified 160 times).

Distribution of Biogenous Sediment

Biogenous sediment is one of the most common types of pelagic deposits. The distribution of biogenous sediment on the ocean floor depends on three fundamental processes: (1) productivity, (2) destruction, and (3) dilution.

Productivity is the number of organisms present in the surface water above the ocean floor. Surface waters with high biologic productivity contain many living and reproducing organisms—conditions that are likely to produce biogenous sediments. Conversely, surface waters with low biologic productivity contain too few organisms to produce biogenous oozes on the ocean floor.

Destruction occurs when skeletal remains (tests) dissolve in seawater at depth. In some cases, biogenous sediment dissolves before ever reaching the sea floor; in other cases, it is dissolved before it has a chance to accumulate into deposits on the sea floor.

Dilution occurs when the deposition of other sediments decreases the percentage of the biogenous sediment found in marine deposits. For example, other types of sediments can dilute biogenous test material below the 30% necessary to

WEB VIDEO

Microscopic Marine Organisms

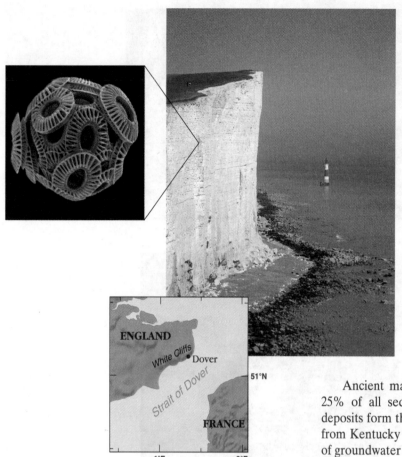

FIGURE 4.9 The White Cliffs of southern England. The White Cliffs near Dover in southern England are composed of chalk, which is hardened coccolith-rich calcareous ooze. Inset shows a colored image of the coccolithophore *Emiliana huxleyi* (diameter = 20 micrometers, equal to 20 millionths of a meter).

classify it as ooze. Dilution occurs most often because of the abundance of coarse-grained lithogenous material in neritic environments, so biogenous oozes are uncommon along continental margins.

NERITIC DEPOSITS Although neritic deposits are dominated by lithogenous sediment, both microscopic and macroscopic biogenous material may be incorporated into lithogenous sediment in neritic deposits. In addition, biogenous carbonate deposits are common in some areas.

Carbonate Deposits **Carbonate** minerals are those that contain CO_3 in their chemical formula—such as calcium carbonate, $CaCO_3$. Rocks from the marine environment composed primarily of calcium carbonate are called **limestones**. Most limestones contain fossil marine shells, suggesting a biogenous origin, while others appear to have formed directly from seawater without the help of any marine organism. Modern environments where calcium carbonate is currently forming (such as in the Bahama Banks, Australia's Great Barrier Reef, and the Persian Gulf) suggest that these carbonate deposits occurred in shallow, warm-water shelves and around tropical islands as coral reefs and beaches.

Ancient marine carbonate deposits constitute 2% of Earth's crust and 25% of all sedimentary rocks on Earth. In fact, these marine limestone deposits form the underlying bedrock of Florida and many midwestern states, from Kentucky to Michigan and from Pennsylvania to Colorado. Percolation of groundwater through these deposits has dissolved the limestone to produce sinkholes and, in some cases, spectacular caverns.

Stromatolites **Stromatolites** are lobate structures consisting of fine layers of carbonate that form in specific warm, shallow-water environments such as the high salinity tidal pools in shark bay, western Australia (Figure 4.10). Cyanobacteria[6] produce these deposits by trapping fine sediment in mucous mats. Other types of algae produce long filaments that bind carbonate particles together. As layer upon layer of these algae colonize the surface, a bulbous structure

FIGURE 4.10
Stromatolites. (a) Shark Bay stromatolites, which form in high-salinity tidal pools and reach a maximum height of about 1 meter (3.3 feet). **(b)** Diagrammatic cross section through a stromatolite, showing internal fine layering.

(a)

(b)

[6]Cyanobacteria (*kuanos* = dark blue) are simple, ancient creatures whose ancestry can be traced back to some of the first photosynthetic organisms.

is formed. In the geologic past—particularly from about 1 to 3 billion years ago—conditions were ideal for the development of stromatolites, so stromatolitic structures hundreds of meters high can be found in rocks from these ages.

PELAGIC DEPOSITS Microscopic biogenous sediment (ooze) is common on the deep-ocean floor because there is so little lithogenous sediment deposited at great distances from the continents that could dilute the biogenous material.

Siliceous Ooze Siliceous ooze contains at least 30% of the hard remains of silica-secreting organisms. When the siliceous ooze consists mostly of diatoms, it is called *diatomaceous ooze*. When it consists mostly of radiolarians, it is called *radiolarian ooze*. When it consists mostly of single-celled silicoflagellates—another type of protozoan—it is called *silicoflagellate ooze*.

The ocean is undersaturated with silica at all depths, so the destruction of siliceous biogenous particles by dissolving in seawater occurs continuously and slowly at all depths. How can siliceous ooze accumulate on the ocean floor if it is being dissolved? One way is to accumulate the siliceous tests faster than seawater can dissolve them. For instance, many tests sinking at the same time will create a deposit of siliceous ooze on the sea floor below (Figure 4.11).[7] Once buried beneath other siliceous tests, they are no longer exposed to the dissolving effects of seawater. Thus, siliceous ooze is commonly found in areas below surface waters with high biologic productivity of silica-secreting organisms.

Calcareous Ooze and the CCD Calcareous ooze contains at least 30% of the hard remains of calcareous-secreting organisms. When it consists mostly of coccolithophores, it is called *coccolith ooze*. When it consists mostly of foraminifers, it is called *foraminifer ooze*. One of the most common types of foraminifer ooze is *Globigerina ooze*, named for a foraminifer that is especially widespread in the Atlantic and South Pacific oceans. Other calcareous oozes include *pteropod oozes* and *ostracod oozes*.

The destruction of calcium carbonate varies with depth. At the warmer surface and in the shallow parts of the ocean, seawater is generally saturated with calcium carbonate, so calcite does not dissolve. In the deep ocean, however, the colder water contains greater amounts of carbon dioxide, which forms carbonic acid and causes calcareous material to dissolve. The higher pressure at depth also helps speed the dissolution of calcium carbonate.

The depth in the ocean at which the pressure is high enough and the amount of carbon dioxide in deep-ocean waters is great enough to begin dissolving calcium carbonate is called the **lysocline** (*lusis* = a loosening, *cline* = slope). Below the lysocline, calcium carbonate dissolves at an increasing rate with increasing depth until the **calcite compensation depth (CCD)**[8] is reached (Figure 4.12).

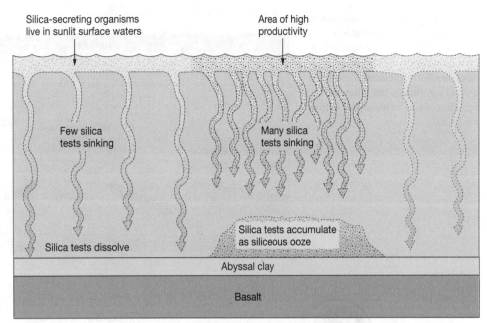

FIGURE 4.11 Accumulation of siliceous ooze. Siliceous ooze accumulates on the ocean floor beneath areas of high productivity, where the rate of accumulation of siliceous tests is greater than the rate at which silica is being dissolved.

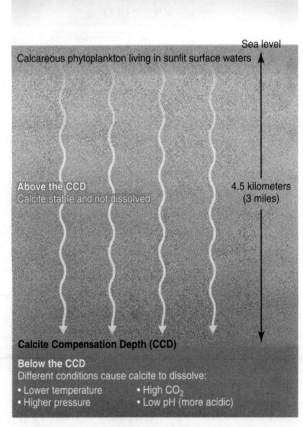

FIGURE 4.12 Characteristics of water above and below the calcite compensation depth (CCD). Schematic diagram showing the calcite compensation depth (CCD). Above the CCD, calcite is stable and does not dissolve; below the CCD, ocean conditions cause calcite to dissolve rapidly.

---

[7]An analogy to this is trying to get a layer of sugar to form on the bottom of a cup of hot coffee. If a few grains of sugar are slowly dropped into the cup, a layer of sugar won't accumulate. If a whole bowl full of sugar is dumped into the coffee, however, a thick layer of sugar will form on the bottom of the cup.

[8]Because the mineral calcite is composed of calcium carbonate, the calcite compensation depth is also known as the calcium carbonate compensation depth, or the carbonate compensation depth. All go by the handy abbreviation CCD.

FIGURE 4.13 Sea floor spreading and sediment accumulation. Relationships among carbonate compensation depth, the mid-ocean ridge, sea floor spreading, productivity, and destruction that allow calcareous ooze to be preserved below the CCD.

How Calcareous Ooze
Can Be Found
Beneath the CCD

KEY CONCEPT

Biogenous sediment is produced from the hard remains of once-living organisms. Microscopic biogenous sediment is especially widespread and forms deposits of ooze on the ocean floor.

STUDENTS SOMETIMES ASK ...

I've been to Hawaii and seen a black sand beach. Because it forms by lava flowing into the ocean that is broken up by waves, is it hydrogenous sediment?

No. Many active volcanoes in the world have black sand beaches that are created when waves break apart dark-colored volcanic rock. The material that produces the black sand is derived from a continent or an island, so it is considered lithogenous sediment. Even though molten lava sometimes flows into the ocean, the resulting black sand could never be considered hydrogenous sediment because the lava was never *dissolved* in water.

At the CCD and greater depths, sediment does not usually contain much calcite because it readily dissolves; even the thick tests of foraminifers dissolve within a day or two. The CCD, on average, is 4500 meters (15,000 feet) below sea level, but, depending on the chemistry of the deep ocean, may be as deep as 6000 meters (20,000 feet) in portions of the Atlantic Ocean, or as shallow as 3500 meters (11,500 feet) in the Pacific Ocean. The depth of the lysocline also varies from ocean to ocean but averages about 4000 meters (13,100 feet).

Because of the CCD, modern carbonate oozes are generally rare below 5000 meters (16,400 feet). Still, buried deposits of ancient calcareous ooze are found beneath the CCD. How can calcareous ooze exist below the CCD? The necessary conditions are shown in Figure 4.13. The mid-ocean ridge is a topographically high feature that rises above the sea floor. It often pokes up above the CCD, even though the surrounding deep-ocean floor is below the CCD. Thus, calcareous ooze deposited on top of the mid-ocean ridge will not be dissolved. Sea floor spreading causes the newly created sea floor and the calcareous sediment on top of it to move into deeper water away from the ridge, eventually being transported below the CCD. This calcareous sediment will dissolve below the CCD unless it is covered by a deposit that is unaffected by the CCD (such as siliceous ooze or abyssal clay).

The map in Figure 4.14 shows the percentage (by weight) of calcium carbonate in the modern surface sediments of the ocean basins. High concentrations of calcareous ooze (sometimes exceeding 80%) are found along segments of the mid-ocean ridge, but little is found in deep-ocean basins below the CCD. For example, in the northern Pacific Ocean—one of the deepest parts of the world ocean—there is very little calcium carbonate in the sediment. Calcium carbonate is also rare in sediments accumulating beneath cold, high-latitude waters where calcareous-secreting organisms are relatively uncommon.

Table 4.3 compares the environmental conditions that can be inferred from siliceous and calcareous oozes. It shows that siliceous ooze typically forms below cool surface water regions, including areas of **upwelling** where deep-ocean water comes to the surface and supplies nutrients that stimulate high rates of biological productivity. Calcareous ooze, on the other hand, is found on the shallower areas of the ocean floor beneath warmer surface water.

4.4 What Is Hydrogenous Sediment?

Hydrogenous (*hydro* = water, *generare* = to produce) **sediment** is derived from the dissolved material in water.

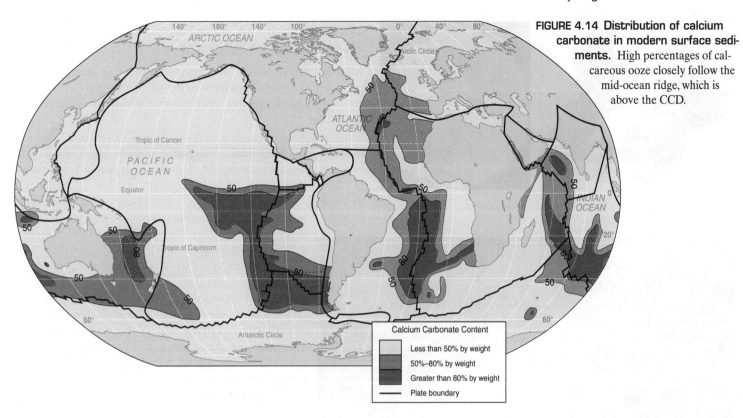

FIGURE 4.14 Distribution of calcium carbonate in modern surface sediments. High percentages of calcareous ooze closely follow the mid-ocean ridge, which is above the CCD.

Origin of Hydrogenous Sediment

Seawater contains many dissolved materials. Chemical reactions within seawater cause certain minerals to come out of solution, or **precipitate** (change from the dissolved to the solid state). Precipitation usually occurs when there is a *change in conditions*, such as a change in temperature or pressure or the addition of chemically active fluids. To make rock candy, for instance, a pan of water is heated and sugar is added. When the water is hot and the sugar dissolved, the pan is removed from the heat and the sugar water is allowed to cool. The *change in temperature* causes the sugar to become oversaturated, which causes it to precipitate. As the water cools, the sugar precipitates on anything that is put in the pan, such as pieces of string or kitchen utensils.

TABLE **4.3**	COMPARISON OF ENVIRONMENTS INTERPRETED FROM DEPOSITS OF SILICEOUS AND CALCAREOUS OOZE IN SURFACE SEDIMENTS	
	Siliceous ooze	**Calcareous ooze**
Surface water temperature above sea floor deposits	Cool	Warm
Main location found	Sea floor beneath cool surface water in high latitudes	Sea floor beneath warm surface water in low latitudes
Other factors	Upwelling brings deep, cold, nutrient-rich water to the surface	Calcareous ooze dissolves below the CCD
Other locations found	Sea floor beneath areas of upwelling, including along the equator	Sea floor beneath warm surface water in low latitudes along the mid-ocean ridge

(a)

(b)

FIGURE 4.15 Manganese nodules. (a) Manganese nodules including some that are cut in half, revealing their central nucleation object and layered internal structure. **(b)** A portion of the South Pacific Ocean floor about 4 meters (13 feet) across showing an abundance of manganese nodules.

Composition and Distribution of Hydrogenous Sediment

Although hydrogenous sediments represent a relatively small portion of the overall sediment in the ocean, they have many different compositions and are distributed in diverse environments of deposition.

MANGANESE NODULES **Manganese nodules** are rounded, hard lumps of manganese, iron, and other metals typically 5 centimeters (2 inches) in diameter up to a maximum of about 20 centimeters (8 inches). When cut in half, they often reveal a layered structure formed by precipitation around a central nucleation object (Figure 4.15a). The nucleation object may be a piece of lithogenous sediment, coral, volcanic rock, a fish bone, or a shark's tooth. Manganese nodules are found on the deep-ocean floor at concentrations of about 100 nodules per square meter (square yard). In some areas, they occur in even greater abundance (Figure 4.15b), resembling a scattered field of baseball-sized nodules. The formation of manganese nodules requires extremely low rates of lithogenous or biogenous input so that the nodules are not buried.

The major components of these nodules are manganese dioxide (around 30% by weight) and iron oxide (around 20%). The element manganese is important for making high-strength steel alloys. Other accessory metals present in manganese nodules include copper (used in electrical wiring, in pipes, and to make brass and bronze), nickel (used to make stainless steel), and cobalt (used as an alloy with iron to make strong magnets and steel tools). Although the concentration of these accessory metals is usually less than 1%, they can exceed 2% by weight, which may make them attractive exploration targets in the future.

The origin of manganese nodules has puzzled oceanographers since manganese nodules were first discovered in 1872 during the voyage of HMS *Challenger*.[9] If manganese nodules are truly hydrogenous and precipitate from seawater, then how can they have such high concentrations of manganese (which occurs in seawater at concentrations often too small to measure accurately)? Furthermore, why are the nodules on *top* of ocean floor sediment and not buried by the constant rain of sedimentary particles?

Unfortunately, nobody has definitive answers to these questions. Perhaps the creation of manganese nodules is the result of one of the slowest chemical reactions known—on average, they grow at a rate of about 5 millimeters (0.2 inch) per *million years*. Recent research suggests that the formation of manganese nodules may be aided by bacteria and an as-yet-unidentified marine organism that intermittently lifts and rotates them. Other studies reveal that the nodules don't form continuously over time but in spurts that are related to specific conditions such as a low sedimentation rate of lithogenous clay and strong deep-water currents. Remarkably, the larger the nodules are, the faster they grow. The origin of manganese nodules is widely considered the most interesting unresolved problem in marine chemistry.

PHOSPHATES Phosphorus-bearing compounds (**phosphates**) occur abundantly as coatings on rocks and as nodules on the continental shelf and on banks at

---

[9]For more information about the accomplishments of the *Challenger* expedition, see Box 5.2.

depths shallower than 1000 meters (3300 feet). Concentrations of phosphates in such deposits commonly reach 30% by weight and indicate abundant biological activity in surface water above where they accumulate. Because phosphates are valuable as fertilizers, ancient marine phosphate deposits that have been uplifted onto land are extensively mined to supply agricultural needs.

CARBONATES   The two most important carbonate minerals in marine sediment are **aragonite** and calcite. Both are composed of calcium carbonate ($CaCO_3$) but aragonite has a different crystalline structure that is less stable and changes into calcite over time.

As previously discussed, most carbonate deposits are biogenous in origin. However, hydrogenous carbonate deposits can precipitate directly from seawater in tropical climates to form aragonite crystals less than 2 millimeters (0.08 inch) long. In addition, **oolites** (*oo* = egg, *lithos* = rock) are small calcite spheres 2 millimeters (0.08 inch) or less in diameter that have layers like an onion and form in some shallow tropical waters where concentrations of $CaCO_3$ are high. Oolites are thought to precipitate around a nucleus and grow larger as they roll back and forth on beaches by wave action, but some evidence suggests that a type of algae may aid their formation.

METAL SULFIDES   Deposits of **metal sulfides** are associated with hydrothermal vents and black smokers along the mid-ocean ridge. These deposits contain iron, nickel, copper, zinc, silver, and other metals in varying proportions. Transported away from the mid-ocean ridge by sea floor spreading, these deposits can be found throughout the ocean floor and can even be uplifted onto continents.

EVAPORITES   **Evaporite minerals** form where there is restricted open ocean circulation and where evaporation rates are high, such as in the Mediterranean Sea (see Web Box 4.1). As water evaporates from these areas, the remaining seawater becomes saturated with dissolved minerals, which then begin to precipitate. Heavier than seawater, they sink to the bottom or form a white crust of evaporite minerals around the edges of these areas (Figure 4.16). Collectively termed "salts," some evaporite minerals, such as *halite* (common table salt, NaCl), taste salty, and some, such as the calcium sulfate minerals *anhydrite* ($CaSO_4$) and *gypsum* ($CaSO_4 \cdot H_2O$) do not.

FIGURE 4.16 Evaporative salts.   Due to a high evaporation rate, salts (white material) precipitate onto the floor of Death Valley, California.

> **KEY CONCEPT**
> Hydrogenous sediment is produced when dissolved materials precipitate out of solution, producing a variety of materials found in local concentrations on the ocean floor.

4.5 What Is Cosmogenous Sediment?

Cosmogenous (*cosmos* = universe, *generare* = to produce) **sediment** is derived from extraterrestrial sources.

Origin, Composition, and Distribution of Cosmogenous Sediment

Forming an insignificant portion of the overall sediment on the ocean floor, cosmogenous sediment consists of two main types: microscopic **spherules** and macroscopic **meteor** debris.

FIGURE 4.17 Microscopic cosmogenous spherule. Scanning electron micrograph of an iron-rich spherule of cosmic dust. Bar scale of 75 micrometers is equal to 75 millionths of a meter.

Microscopic spherules are small globular masses. Some spherules are composed of silicate rock material and show evidence of being formed by extraterrestrial impact events on Earth or other planets that eject small molten pieces of crust into space. These **tektites** (*tektos* = molten) then rain down on Earth and can form *tektite fields*. Other spherules are composed mostly of iron and nickel (Figure 4.17) that form in the asteroid belt between the orbits of Mars and Jupiter and are produced when asteroids collide. This material constantly rains down on Earth as a general component of *space dust* or *micrometeorites* that float harmlessly through the atmosphere. Although about 90% of micrometeorites are destroyed by frictional heating as they enter the atmosphere, it has been estimated that as much as 300,000 metric tons (330,000 short tons) of space dust reach Earth's surface each year, which equates to about 10 kilograms (22 pounds) every second of every day! The iron-rich space dust that lands in the oceans often dissolves in seawater. Glassy tektites, however, do not dissolve as easily and sometimes comprise minute proportions of various marine sediments.

Macroscopic meteor debris is rare on Earth but can be found associated with meteor impact sites. Evidence suggests that throughout time meteors have collided with Earth at great speeds and that some larger ones have released energy equivalent to the explosion of multiple large nuclear bombs. To date, nearly 200 meteorite impact structures have been identified on Earth, most of them on land but new ones are being discovered on the ocean floor (Box 4.3). The debris from meteors—called **meteorite** material—settles out around the impact site and is either composed of silicate rock material (called *chondrites*) or iron and nickel (called *irons*).

STUDENTS SOMETIMES ASK...

How are scientists able to identify cosmogenous sediment? I mean, how can they tell that it's extraterrestrial?

Cosmogenous sediment can be differentiated from other sediment types primarily by its structure but also by its composition. Cosmogenous sediment can be either silicate rock or rich in iron—both of which are common compositions of lithogenous sediment. However, glassy fragments indicative of melting (called *tektites*) are uniquely cosmogenous, as are iron-rich spherules (see Figure 4.17). Compositionally, cosmogenous particles from outer space typically contain more nickel than those that originate in other ways; most of the nickel in Earth's crust has sunk below the surface during density stratification early in Earth's history.

4.6 What Mixtures of Sediment Exist?

Lithogenous and biogenous sediment rarely occur as absolutely pure deposits that do not contain other types of sediment. For instance,

- Most calcareous oozes contain some siliceous material, and vice versa (see, for example, Figure 4.8d).
- The abundance of clay-sized lithogenous particles throughout the world and the ease with which they are transported by winds and currents means that these particles are incorporated into every sediment type.
- The composition of biogenous ooze includes up to 70% fine-grained lithogenous clays.
- Most lithogenous sediment contains small percentages of biogenous particles.
- There are many types of hydrogenous sediment.
- Tiny amounts of cosmogenous sediment are mixed in with all other sediment types.

Deposits of sediment on the ocean floor are usually a mixture of different sediment types. Figure 4.18 shows the distribution of sediment across a passive continental margin and illustrates how mixtures can occur. Typically, however, one type of sediment dominates, which allows the deposit to be classified as primarily lithogenous, biogenous, hydrogenous, or cosmogenous.

4.7 A Summary: How Are Pelagic and Neritic Deposits Distributed?

Neritic (nearshore) deposits cover about one-quarter of the ocean floor while pelagic (deep-ocean basin) deposits cover the other three-quarters.

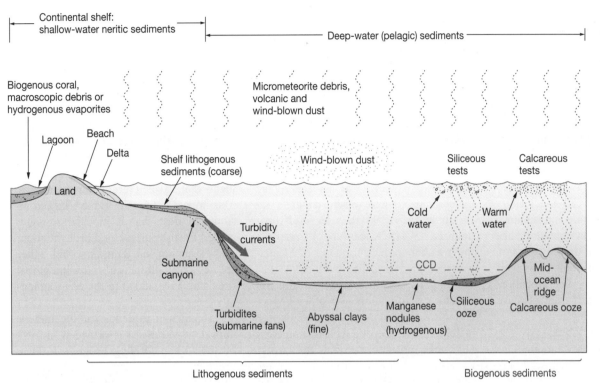

Continental shelf:
shallow-water neritic sediments

Deep-water (pelagic) sediments

Biogenous coral,
macroscopic debris or
hydrogenous evaporites

Micrometeorite debris,
volcanic and
wind-blown dust

Lagoon   Beach
          Delta

Shelf lithogenous
sediments (coarse)

Wind-blown dust

Siliceous
tests

Calcareous
tests

Land

Cold
water

Warm
water

Turbidity
currents

Submarine
canyon

CCD

Mid-
ocean
ridge

Turbidites
(submarine fans)

Abyssal clays
(fine)

Manganese
nodules
(hydrogenous)

Siliceous
ooze

Calcareous ooze

Lithogenous sediments

Biogenous sediments

FIGURE 4.18 Distribution of sediment across a passive continental margin. Schematic cross-sectional view of various sediment types and their distribution across an idealized passive margin.

Neritic Deposits

The map in Figure 4.19 shows the distribution of neritic and pelagic deposits in the world's oceans. Coarse-grained lithogenous neritic deposits dominate continental margin areas (*dark brown shading*), which is not surprising because lithogenous sediment is derived from nearby continents. Although neritic deposits

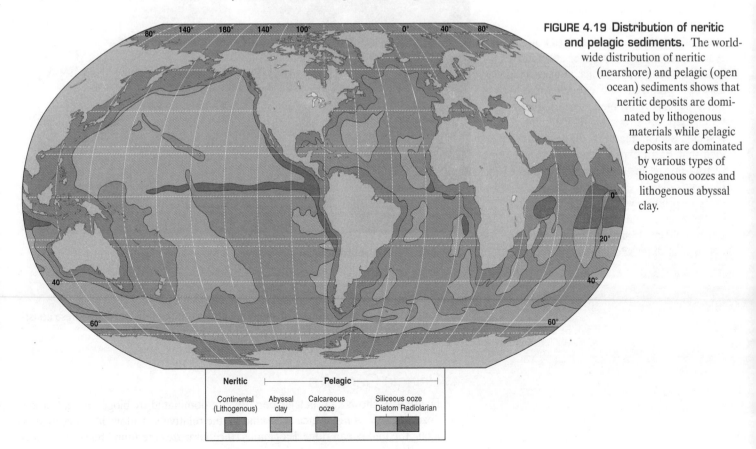

FIGURE 4.19 Distribution of neritic and pelagic sediments. The worldwide distribution of neritic (nearshore) and pelagic (open ocean) sediments shows that neritic deposits are dominated by lithogenous materials while pelagic deposits are dominated by various types of biogenous oozes and lithogenous abyssal clay.

Neritic	Pelagic		
Continental (Lithogenous)	Abyssal clay	Calcareous ooze	Siliceous ooze Diatom Radiolarian

4.3   RESEARCH METHODS IN OCEANOGRAPHY

WHEN THE DINOSAURS DIED: THE CRETACEOUS–TERTIARY (K–T) EVENT

The extinction of the dinosaurs—and two-thirds of all plant and animal species on Earth (including many marine species)—occurred about 66 million years ago. This extinction marks the boundary between the Cretaceous (K) and Tertiary (T) Periods of geologic time and is known as the **K–T event**. Did slow climate change lead to the extinction of these organisms, or was it a catastrophic event? Was their demise related to disease, diet, predation, or volcanic activity? Earth scientists have long sought clues to this mystery.

In 1980, geologist Walter Alvarez, his father, Nobel Physics Laureate Luis Alvarez, and two nuclear chemists, Frank Asaro and Helen Michel, reported that deposits collected in northern Italy from the K–T boundary contained a clay layer with high proportions of the metallic element iridium (Ir). Iridium is rare in rocks from Earth but occurs in greater concentration in meteorites. Therefore, layers of sediment that contain unusually high concentrations of iridium suggest that the material may be of extraterrestrial origin. Additionally, the clay layer contained shocked quartz grains, which indicate that an event occurred with enough force to fracture and partially melt pieces of quartz. Other deposits from the K–T boundary revealed similar features, supporting the idea that Earth experienced an extraterrestrial impact at the same time that the dinosaurs died.

One problem with the impact hypothesis, however, is that volcanic eruptions on Earth could create similar clay deposits enriched in iridium and containing shocked quartz. In fact, large outpourings of basaltic volcanic rock in India (called the Deccan Traps) and other locations had occurred at about the same time as the dinosaur extinction. Also, if there was a catastrophic meteor impact, where was the crater?

In the early 1990s the *Chicxulub* (pronounced "SCHICK-sue-lube") *Crater* off the Yucatán coast in the Gulf of Mexico was identified as a likely candidate because of its structure, age, and size. Its structure is comparable to other impact craters in the solar system, and its age matches the K–T event. At 190 kilometers (120 miles) in diameter, it is the largest impact crater on Earth. To create a crater this large, a 10-kilometer (6-mile)-wide meteoroid composed of rock and/or ice traveling at speeds up to 72,000 kilometers (45,000 miles) per hour must have slammed into Earth (Figure 4D). The impact probably bared the sea floor in the area and created huge waves—estimated to be more than 900 meters (3000 feet) high—that traveled throughout the oceans. This impact is thought to have kicked up so much dust that it blocked sunlight, chilled Earth's surface, and brought about the extinction of dinosaurs and other species. In addition, acid rains and global fires may have added to the environmental disaster.

Supporting evidence for the meteor impact hypothesis was provided in 1997 by the Ocean Drilling Program (ODP). Previous drilling close to the impact site did not reveal any K–T deposits. Evidently, the impact and resulting huge waves had stripped the ocean floor of its sediment. However, at 1600 kilometers

FIGURE 4D The K–T meteorite impact event.

usually contain biogenous, hydrogenous, and cosmogenous particles, these constitute only a minor percentage of the total sediment mass.

Pelagic Deposits

Figure 4.19 shows that pelagic deposits are dominated by biogenous calcareous oozes (*blue shading*), which are found on the relatively shallow deep-ocean areas along the mid-ocean ridge. Biogenous siliceous oozes are found beneath areas of

(1000 miles) from the impact site, some of the telltale sediments were preserved on the sea floor. Drilling into the continental margin off Florida into an underwater peninsula called the Blake Nose, the ODP scientific party recovered cores from the K–T boundary that contain a complete record of the impact (Figure 4E).

The cores reveal that before the impact, the layers of Cretaceous-age sediment are filled with abundant fossils of calcareous coccoliths and foraminifers and show signs of underwater landslide activity— perhaps the effect of an impact-triggered earthquake. Above this calcareous ooze is a 20-centimeter (8-inch) thick layer of rubble containing evidence of an impact: spherules, tektites, shocked quartz from hard-hit terrestrial rock—even a 2-centimeter (1-inch) piece of reef rock from the Yucatán peninsula! This layer is also rich in iridium, just like other K–T boundary sequences. Atop this layer is a thick, gray clay deposit containing meteor debris and severely reduced numbers of coccoliths and foraminifers. Life in the ocean apparently recovered slowly, taking at least 5000 years before sediment teeming with new Tertiary-age microorganisms began to be deposited.

Convincing evidence of the K–T impact from this and other cores along with the observation of Comet Shoemaker-Levy's 1994 spectacular collision with Jupiter suggests that Earth has experienced many such extraterrestrial impacts over geologic time. In fact, nearly 200 impact craters have been identified on Earth so far. Statistics show that an impact the size of the K–T event should occur on Earth about once every 100 million years, severely affecting life on Earth as it did the dinosaurs. Nevertheless, their extinction made it possible for mammals to eventually rise to the position of dominance they hold on Earth today.

FIGURE 4E K–T boundary meteorite impact core.

unusually high biologic productivity such as the North Pacific, Antarctic (*light green shading*, where diatomaceous ooze occurs), and the equatorial Pacific (*dark green shading*, where radiolarian ooze occurs). Fine lithogenous pelagic deposits of abyssal clays (*light brown shading*) are common in deeper areas of the ocean basins. Hydrogenous and cosmogenous sediment comprise only a small proportion of pelagic deposits in the ocean.

Figure 4.20 shows the proportion of each ocean floor that is covered by pelagic calcareous ooze, siliceous ooze, or abyssal clay. Calcareous oozes

FIGURE 4.20 Pelagic sediment types within each major ocean basin. World map and accompanying pie charts showing the relative amount of deep-ocean floor covered by each of the three pelagic sediment types: calcareous ooze, siliceous ooze, and abyssal clay. Pie chart for the world ocean (*below*) combines all three ocean basins.

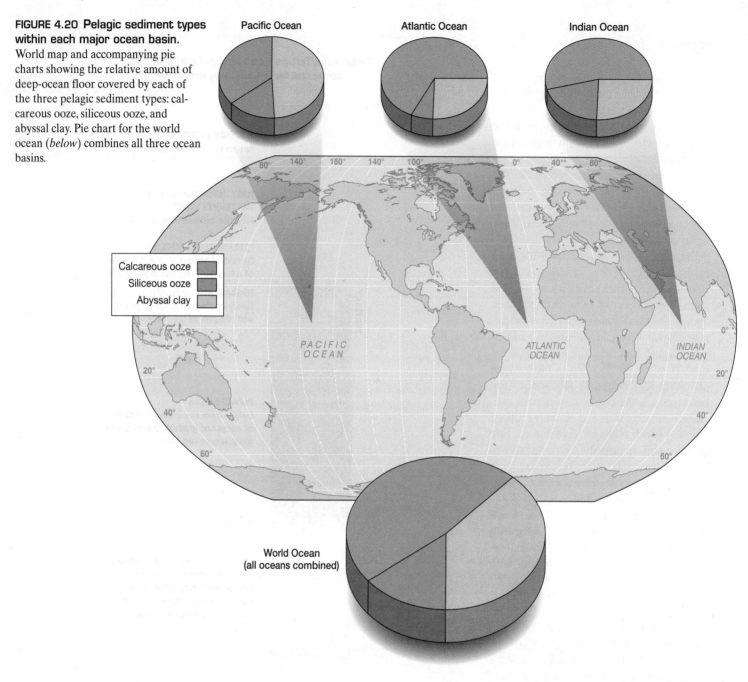

Calcareous ooze
Siliceous ooze
Abyssal clay

World Ocean
(all oceans combined)

predominate, covering almost 48% of the world's deep-ocean floor. Abyssal clay covers 38% and siliceous oozes 14% of the world ocean floor area. The graph also shows that the amount of ocean basin floor covered by calcareous ooze decreases in deeper basins because they generally lie beneath the CCD. The dominant oceanic sediment in the deepest basin—the Pacific—is abyssal clay (see also Figure 4.19). Calcareous ooze is the most widely deposited sediment in the shallower Atlantic and Indian Oceans. Siliceous oozes cover a smaller percentage of the ocean bottom in all the oceans because regions of high productivity of siliceous-secreting organisms are generally restricted to the equatorial region (for radiolarians) and high latitudes (for diatoms). Table 4.4 shows the average rates of deposition of selected marine sediments in neritic and pelagic deposits.

TABLE 4.4	AVERAGE RATES OF DEPOSITION OF SELECTED MARINE SEDIMENTS	
Type of sediment/deposit	Average rate of deposition (per 1000 years)	Thickness of deposit after 1000 years equivalent to . . .
Coarse lithogenous sediment, neritic deposit	1 meter (3.3 feet)	A meter stick
Biogenous ooze, pelagic deposit	1 centimeter (0.4 inch)	The diameter of a dime
Abyssal clay, pelagic deposit	1 millimeter (0.04 inch)	The thickness of a dime
Manganese nodule, pelagic deposit	0.001 millimeter (0.00004 inch)	A microscopic dust particle

How Sea Floor Sediments Represent Surface Conditions

Microscopic biogenous tests should take from 10 to 50 years to sink from the ocean surface where the organisms lived to the abyssal depths where biogenous ooze accumulates. During this time, even a sluggish horizontal ocean current of only 0.05 kilometer (0.03 mile) per hour could carry tests as much as 22,000 kilometers (13,700 miles) before they settled onto the deep-ocean floor. Why, then, do biogenous tests on the deep-ocean floor closely reflect the population of organisms living in the surface water directly above? Remarkably, about 99% of the particles that fall to the ocean floor do so as part of *fecal pellets*, which are produced by tiny animals that eat algae and protozoans living in the water column, digest their tissues, and excrete their hard parts. These pellets are full of the remains of algae and protozoans from the surface waters (Figure 4.21) and, though still small, are large enough to sink to the deep-ocean floor in only 10 to 15 days.

Worldwide Thickness of Marine Sediments

Figure 4.22 is a map of marine sediment thickness. The map shows that areas of thick sediment accumulation occur on the continental shelves and rises, especially near the mouths of major rivers. The reason sediments in these locations are so

FIGURE 4.21 Fecal pellet. A 200-micrometer (0.008-inch)-long fecal pellet, which is large enough to sink rapidly from the surface to the ocean floor. Close-up of the surface of a fecal pellet (*inset*) shows the remains of coccoliths and other debris.

FIGURE 4.22 Marine sediment thickness. Map showing the thickness of sediments in the oceans and marginal seas. Thickness shown in meters; dark blue color represents thinnest sediments and red represents thickest sediment accumulations. White color indicates no available data.

Thickness in Meters

Are there any areas of the ocean floor where no sediment is being deposited?

Various types of sediment accumulate on nearly all areas of the ocean floor in the same way dust accumulates in all parts of your home (which is why marine sediment is often referred to as "marine dust"). Even the deep-ocean floor far from land receives small amounts of windblown material, microscopic biogenous particles, and space dust. There are some places in the ocean, however, where very little sediment accumulates. A few such places include the South Pacific Bare Zone east of New Zealand, which has a combination of factors that limit sediment accumulation; along the continental slope, where there is active erosion by turbidity and other deep-ocean currents; and along the mid-ocean ridge, where the age of the sea floor is so young (because of sea floor spreading) and the rates of sediment accumulation far from land are so slow that there hasn't been enough time for sediments to accumulate.

thick is because they are close to major sources of lithogenous sediment. Conversely, areas where marine sediments are thinnest are where the ocean floor is young, such as along the crest of the mid-ocean ridge. Since sediments accumulate slowly in the deep ocean and the sea floor is continually being created here, there hasn't been enough time for much sediment to accumulate. However, as the sea floor moves away from the mid-ocean ridge, it gets progressively older and carries a thicker pile of sediments.

4.8 What Resources Do Ocean Sediments Provide?

The sea floor is rich in potential mineral and organic resources. Much of these resources, however, are not easily accessible, so their recovery involves technological challenges and high cost. Nevertheless, let's examine some of the most appealing exploration targets.

Energy Resources

The main energy resources associated with marine sediments are *petroleum* and *gas hydrates*.

PETROLEUM The ancient remains of microscopic organisms, buried within marine sediments before they could decompose, are the source of today's **petroleum** (oil and natural gas) deposits. Of the nonliving resources extracted from the oceans, more than 95% of the economic value is in petroleum products.

The percentage of world oil produced from offshore regions has increased from small amounts in the 1930s to more than 30% today. Most of this increase results from continuing technological advancements employed by offshore drilling platforms (Figure 4.23). Major offshore reserves exist in the Persian Gulf, in the Gulf of Mexico, off Southern California, in the North Sea, and in the East Indies. Additional reserves are probably located off the north coast of Alaska and in the Canadian Arctic, Asian seas, Africa, and Brazil. With almost no likelihood of finding major new reserves on land, future offshore petroleum exploration will continue to be intense, especially in deeper waters of the continental margins. However, a major drawback to offshore petroleum exploration is the inevitable oil spills caused by inadvertent leaks or blowouts during the drilling process.

GAS HYDRATES **Gas hydrates**, which are also known as *clathrates* (*clathri* = a lattice) are unusually compact chemical structures made of water and natural gas. They form only when high pressures squeeze chilled water and gas molecules into an icelike solid. Although hydrates can contain a variety of gases—including carbon dioxide, hydrogen sulfide, and larger hydrocarbons such as ethane and propane—**methane hydrates** are by far the most common hydrates in nature. Gas hydrates occur beneath Arctic permafrost areas on land and under the ocean floor, where they were discovered in 1976.

In deep-ocean sediments, where pressures are high and temperatures are low, water and natural gas combine in such a way that the gas is trapped inside a lattice-like cage of water molecules. Vessels that have drilled into gas hydrates have retrieved cores of mud mixed with chunks or layers of gas hydrates that fizzle and decompose quickly when they are exposed to the relatively warm, low-pressure conditions at the ocean surface. Gas hydrates resemble chunks of ice but ignite when lit by a flame because methane and other flammable gases are released as gas hydrates vaporize (Figure 4.24).

Most oceanic gas hydrates are created when bacteria break down organic matter trapped in sea floor sediments, producing methane gas with minor amounts

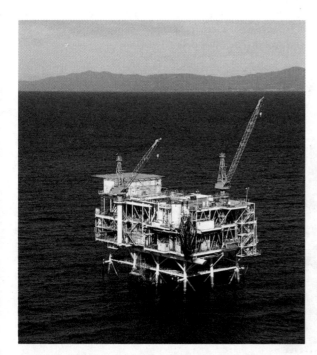

FIGURE 4.23 Offshore oil drilling platform. Constructed on tall stilts, drilling platforms are important for extracting petroleum reserves from beneath the continental shelves.

of ethane and propane. These gases can be incorporated into gas hydrates under high-pressure and low-temperature conditions. Most ocean floor areas below 525 meters (1720 feet) provide these conditions, but gas hydrates seem to be confined to continental margin areas, where high productivity surface waters enrich ocean floor sediments below with organic matter.

Studies of the deep-ocean floor reveal that at least 50 sites worldwide may contain extensive gas hydrate deposits. Research suggests that at various times in the geologic past, changes in sea level or sea floor instability have released large quantities of methane, which oxidizes and produces carbon dioxide. The release of methane from the sea floor can affect global climate as methane and carbon dioxide—important greenhouse gases—increase in the atmosphere. In fact, recent analysis of sea floor sediments off Norway suggests an abrupt increase in global temperature about 55 million years ago was driven by an explosive release of gas hydrates from the sea floor. Sudden releases of methane hydrates have also been linked to underwater slope failure, which can cause *seismic sea waves* or *tsunami* (see Chapter 8, "Waves and Water Dynamics"). In addition, methane seeps support a rich community of organisms, many of which are species new to science.

Some estimates indicate that as much as 20 quadrillion cubic meters (700 quadrillion cubic feet) of methane are locked up in sediments containing gas hydrates. This is equivalent to about *twice* as much carbon as Earth's coal, oil, and conventional gas reserves combined (Figure 4.25), so gas hydrates may potentially be the world's largest source of usable energy. One of the major drawbacks in exploiting reserves of gas hydrate is that they rapidly decompose at surface temperatures and pressures. Another problem is that they are typically spread too thinly within the sea floor for economical recovery. Nonetheless, a Japanese research team is currently evaluating the economic potential of methane hydrates found in the Nankai Trough off Japan and could begin producing methane as early as 2016.

Other Resources

Other resources associated with marine sediments include *sand and gravel*, *evaporative salts*, *phosphorite*, and *manganese nodules and crusts*.

SAND AND GRAVEL   The offshore sand and gravel industry is second in economic value only to the petroleum industry. Sand and gravel, which includes rock fragments that are washed out to sea and shells of marine organisms, is mined by offshore barges using a suction dredge. This material is primarily used as aggregate in concrete, as a fill material in grading projects, and on recreational beaches.

Offshore deposits are a major source of sand and gravel in New England, New York, and throughout the Gulf Coast. Many European countries, Iceland, Israel, and Lebanon also depend heavily on such deposits.

Some offshore sand and gravel deposits are rich in valuable minerals. Gem-quality diamonds, for example, are recovered from gravel deposits on the continental shelf offshore of South Africa and Australia, where waves rework them during low stands of the sea. Sediments rich in tin have been mined offshore of southeast Asia from Thailand to Indonesia. Platinum and gold have been found in deposits offshore of gold mining areas throughout the world, and some Florida beach sands are rich in titanium. The largest unexplored potential for metallic minerals in offshore sand deposits may exist along the west coast of South America, where rivers have transported Andean metallic minerals.

EVAPORATIVE SALTS   When seawater evaporates, the salts increase in concentration until they can no longer remain dissolved, so they precipitate out of solution and form **salt deposits** (Figure 4.26). The most economically useful salts are *gypsum* and *halite*. Gypsum is used in plaster of Paris to make casts and molds and is the main component in gypsum board (wallboard or sheet rock).

STUDENTS SOMETIMES ASK...

When will we run out of oil?

Not any time soon. However, from an economic perspective, when the world runs completely out of oil—a finite resource—is not as relevant as when production begins to taper off. When this happens, we will run out of the *abundant* and *cheap* oil on which all industrialized nations depend. Several oil-producing countries are already past the peak of their production—including the United States and Canada, which topped out in 1972. Current estimates indicate that sometime between now and 2040, more than half of all known and likely-to-be-discovered oil will be gone. After that, it will be increasingly more costly to produce oil, and prices will rise dramatically—unless demand declines proportionally or other sources such as coal, extra-heavy oil, tar sands, or gas hydrates become readily available.

(a)

(b)

FIGURE 4.24 Gas hydrates. **(a)** A sample retrieved from the ocean floor shows layers of white icelike gas hydrate mixed with mud. **(b)** Gas hydrates decompose when exposed to surface conditions and release natural gas, which can be ignited.

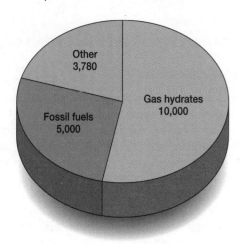

FIGURE 4.25 Organic carbon in Earth reservoirs. Pie diagram of organic carbon in Earth reservoirs, showing that gas hydrates contain twice as much organic carbon as all fossil fuels combined. Values in billions of tons of carbon; "other" includes sources such as soil, peat, and living organisms.

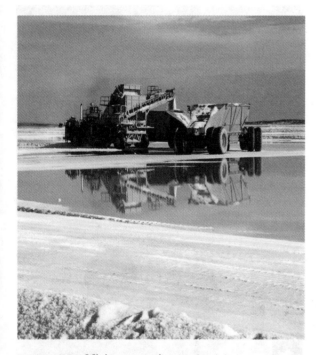

FIGURE 4.26 Mining sea salt. A salt mining operation at Scammon's Lagoon, Baja California, Mexico. Low-lying areas near the lagoon are allowed to flood with seawater, which evaporates in the arid climate and leaves deposits of salt that are then collected.

Halite—common table salt—is widely used for seasoning, curing, and preserving foods. It is also used to de-ice roads, in water conditioners, in agriculture, and in the clothing industry for dying fabric.

In addition, halite is used in the production of chemicals such as sodium hydroxide (to make soap products), sodium hypochlorite (for disinfectants, bleaching agents, and PVC piping), sodium chlorate (for herbicides, matches, and fireworks), and hydrochloric acid (for use in chemical applications and for cleaning scaled pipes). The manufacture and use of salt is one of the oldest chemical industries.[10]

PHOSPHORITE (PHOSPHATE MINERALS) **Phosphorite** is a sedimentary rock consisting of various phosphate minerals containing the element phosphorus, an important plant nutrient. Consequently, phosphate deposits can be used to produce phosphate fertilizer. Although there is currently no commercial phosphorite mining occurring in the oceans, the marine reserve is estimated to exceed 45 billion metric tons (50 billion short tons). Phosphorite occurs in the ocean at depths of less than 300 meters (1000 feet) on the continental shelf and slope in regions of upwelling and high productivity.

Some shallow sand and mud deposits contain up to 18% phosphate. Many phosphorite deposits occur as nodules, with a hard crust formed around a nucleus. The nodules may be as small as a sand grain or as large as 1 meter (3.3 feet) in diameter and may contain more than 25% phosphate. For comparison, most land sources of phosphate have been enriched to more than 31% by groundwater leaching. Florida, for example, has large phosphorite deposits and supplies about one-quarter of the world's phosphates.

MANGANESE NODULES AND CRUSTS *Manganese nodules* are rounded, hard, golf- to tennis-ball-sized lumps of metals that contain significant concentrations of manganese, iron, and smaller concentrations of copper, nickel, and cobalt, all of which have a variety of economic uses. In the 1960s, mining companies began to assess the feasibility of mining manganese nodules from the deep-ocean floor (Figure 4.27). The map in Figure 4.28 shows that vast areas of the sea floor contain manganese nodules, particularly in the Pacific Ocean.

Technologically, mining the deep-ocean floor for manganese nodules is possible. However, the political issue of determining international mining rights at great distances from land has hindered exploitation of this resource. In addition, environmental concerns about mining the deep-ocean floor have not been fully addressed. Evidence suggests that it takes at least several million years for manganese nodules to form and that their formation depends on a particular set of physical and chemical conditions that probably do not last long at any location. In essence, they are a nonrenewable resource that will not be replaced for a very long time once they are mined.

Of the five metals commonly found in manganese nodules, cobalt is the only metal deemed "strategic" (essential to national security) for the United States. It is required to produce dense, strong alloys with other metals for use in high-speed cutting tools, powerful permanent magnets, and jet engine parts. At present, the United States must import all of its cobalt from large deposits in southern Africa. However, the United States has considered deep-ocean nodules and **crusts** (hard coatings on other rocks) as a more reliable source of cobalt.

---

[10]An interesting historical note about salt is that part of a Roman soldier's pay was in salt. That portion was called the *salarium*, from which the word *salary* is derived. If a soldier did not earn it, he was not worth his salt.

FIGURE 4.27 Mining manganese nodules. Manganese nodules can be collected by dredging the ocean floor. This metal dredge is shown unloading nodules onto the deck of a ship.

In the 1980s cobalt-rich manganese crusts were discovered on the upper slopes of islands and seamounts that lie relatively close to shore and within the jurisdiction of the United States and its territories. The cobalt concentrations in these crusts are about one-and-a-half times as rich as the best African ores and at least twice as rich as deep-sea manganese nodules. However, interest in mining these deposits has faded because of lower metal prices from land-based sources.

KEY CONCEPT
Ocean sediments contain many important resources, including petroleum, gas hydrates, sand and gravel, evaporative salts, phosphorite, and manganese nodules and crusts.

FIGURE 4.28 Distribution of manganese nodules on the sea floor. High concentrations of manganese nodules are located on the deep-sea floor, particularly in the Pacific and Atlantic Oceans.

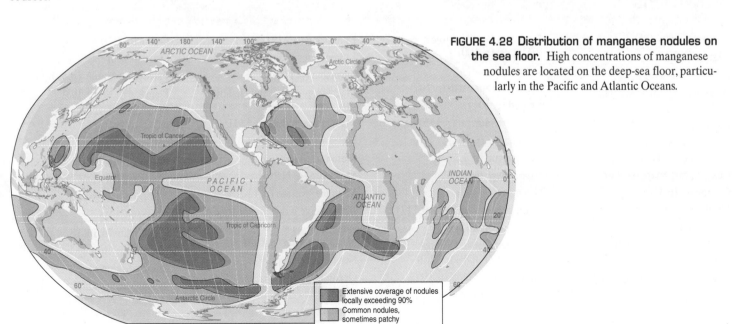

Chapter in Review

• Sediments that accumulate on the ocean floor are *classified by origin* as *lithogenous* (derived from rock), *biogenous* (derived from organisms), *hydrogenous* (derived from water), or *cosmogenous* (derived from outer space).

• The existence of *sea floor spreading was confirmed when the* Glomar Challenger *began the Deep Sea Drilling Project* to sample ocean sediments and the underlying crust, which was continued by the *Ocean Drilling Program's* JOIDES Resolution. Today, the *Integrated Ocean Drilling Program* continues the important work of retrieving sediments from the deep-ocean floor. Analysis and interpretation of marine sediments reveal that *Earth has had an interesting and complex history* including *mass extinctions*, the *drying of entire seas*, *global climate change*, and *movement of plates*.

• *Lithogenous sediments reflect the composition of the rock from which they were derived*. Sediment *texture*—determined in part by the size, sorting, and rounding of particles—is affected greatly by how the particles were transported (by water, wind, ice, or gravity) and the energy conditions under which they were deposited. *Coarse lithogenous material dominates neritic deposits* that accumulate rapidly along the margins of continents, while *fine abyssal clays are found in pelagic deposits*.

• *Biogenous sediment consists of the hard remains* (shells, bones, and teeth) *of organisms*. These are composed of either *silica* (SiO_2) from diatoms and radiolarians or *calcium carbonate* ($CaCO_3$) from foraminifers and coccolithophores. *Accumulations of microscopic shells* (tests) of organisms must comprise at least 30% of the deposit for it to be classified as *biogenic ooze*. *Biogenous oozes are the most common type of pelagic deposits*. The rate of biological productivity relative to the rates of destruction and dilution of biogenous sediment determines whether abyssal clay or oozes will form on the ocean floor. *Siliceous ooze* will form only below areas of high biologic productivity of silica-secreting organisms at the surface. *Calcareous ooze* will form only above the *calcite compensation depth (CCD)*—the depth where seawater dissolves calcium carbonate—although it can be covered and transported into deeper water through sea floor spreading.

• *Hydrogenous sediment* includes manganese nodules, phosphates, carbonates, metal sulfides, and evaporites that *precipitate directly from water* or are formed by the interaction of substances dissolved in water with materials on the ocean floor. Hydrogenous sediments represent a relatively small proportion of marine sediment and are distributed in many diverse environments.

• *Cosmogenous sediment is composed of either macroscopic meteor debris* (such as that produced during the K–T impact event) or *microscopic iron–nickel and silicate spherules* that result from asteroid collisions or extraterrestrial impacts. Minute amounts of cosmogenous sediment are mixed into most other types of ocean sediment.

• Although *most ocean sediment is a mixture of various sediment types*, it is usually dominated by lithogenous, biogenous, hydrogenous, or cosmogenous material.

• *The distribution of neritic and pelagic sediment is influenced by many factors*, including proximity to sources of lithogenous sediment, productivity of microscopic marine organisms, the depth of the ocean floor, and the distribution of various sea floor features. *Fecal pellets* rapidly transport biogenous particles to the deep-ocean floor and cause the composition of sea floor deposits to match the organisms living in surface waters immediately above them.

• *The most valuable nonliving resource from the ocean today is petroleum*, which is recovered from below the continental shelves and used as a source of energy. *Gas hydrates* include vast deposits of icelike material that may someday be used as a source of energy. Other important resources include *sand and gravel* (including deposits of valuable minerals), *evaporative salts*, *phosphorite*, and *manganese nodules and crusts*.

Key Terms

Abyssal clay (p. 105)

Algae (p. 106)

Aragonite (p. 115)

Biogenous sediment (p. 106)

Calcareous ooze (p. 107)

Calcite (p. 106)

Calcite compensation depth (CCD) (p. 111)

Calcium carbonate (p. 106)

Carbonate (p. 110)

Chalk (p. 107)

Coccolith (p. 107)

Coccolithophore (p. 107)

Core (p. 97)

Cosmogenous sediment (p. 115)

Crusts (p. 124)

Deep Sea Drilling Project (DSDP) (p. 100)

Diatom (p. 106)

Diatomaceous earth (p. 107)

Eroded (p. 101)

Evaporite mineral (p. 115)

Foraminifer (p. 107)

Gas hydrate (p. 122)

Glacial deposit (p. 105)

Grain size (p. 103)

Hydrogenous sediment (p. 112)

Ice rafting (p. 105)

Integrated Ocean Drilling Program (IODP) (p. 100)

JOIDES Resolution (p. 100)

K–T event (p. 118)

Limestone (p. 110)

Lithogenous sediment (p. 101)

Lysocline (p. 111)

Macroscopic biogenous sediment (p. 106)

Manganese nodule (p. 114)

Metal sulfide (p. 115)

Meteor (p. 115)

Meteorite (p. 116)

Methane hydrate (p. 122)

Microscopic biogenous sediment (p. 106)

Nannoplankton (p. 107)

Neritic deposit (p. 103)

Ocean Drilling Program (ODP) (p. 100)

Oolite (p. 115)

Ooze (p. 106)

Paleoceanography (p. 99)

Pelagic deposit (p. 103)

Petroleum (p. 122)

Phosphate (p. 114)

Phosphorite (p. 124)

Planktonic (p. 106)

Precipitate (p. 113)

Protozoan (p. 106)

Quartz (p. 101)

Radiolarian (p. 106)

Red clay (p. 105)

Rotary drilling (p. 99)

Salt deposit (p. 123)

Review Questions

1. List and describe the characteristics of the four basic types of marine sediment.

2. Describe the process of how a drill ship like the *JOIDES Resolution* obtains core samples from the deep-ocean floor.

3. How does lithogenous sediment originate?

4. Why is most lithogenous sediment composed of quartz grains? What is the chemical composition of quartz?

5. List the two major chemical compounds of which most biogenous sediment is composed and the organisms that produce them. Sketch these organisms.

6. If siliceous ooze is slowly but constantly dissolving in seawater, how can deposits of siliceous ooze accumulate on the ocean floor?

7. Explain the stages of progression that result in calcareous ooze existing below the CCD.

8. How do oozes differ from abyssal clay? Discuss how productivity, destruction, and dilution combine to determine whether an ooze or abyssal clay will form on the deep-ocean floor.

9. Describe manganese nodules, including what is currently known about how they form.

10. Describe the most common types of cosmogenous sediment and give the probable source of these particles.

11. Describe the K–T event, including evidence for it and its effect on the environment.

12. Why is lithogenous sediment the most common neritic deposit? Why are biogenous oozes the most common pelagic deposits?

13. How do fecal pellets help explain why the particles found in the ocean surface waters are closely reflected in the particle composition of the sediment directly beneath? Why would one not expect this?

14. Discuss the present importance and the future prospects for the production of petroleum; sand and gravel; phosphorite; and manganese nodules and crusts.

15. What are gas hydrates, where are they found, and why are they important?

Critical Thinking Exercises

1. If a deposit has a coarse grain size, what does this indicate about the energy of the transporting medium? Give several examples of various transporting media that would produce such a deposit.

2. What are several reasons diatoms are so remarkable? List products that contain or are produced using diatomaceous earth.

3. Describe the environmental conditions (for example, surface water temperature, productivity, dissolution) that influence the distribution of siliceous and calcareous ooze.

4. What kind of information can be obtained by examining and analyzing core samples?

5. You are on a research cruise in the middle of the Indian Ocean. The water depth is very deep at 5000 meters (16,400 feet). You are 5000 kilometers (3000 miles) from land. The surface water is warm. What is the most likely sediment you would expect to find on the sea floor? Explain.

Oceanography on the Web

Visit the *Essentials of Oceanography* Online Study Guide for Internet resources, including chapter-specific quizzes to test your understanding and Web links to further your exploration of the topics in this chapter.

The *Essentials of Oceanography* Online Study Guide is at http://www.mygeoscienceplace.com/.

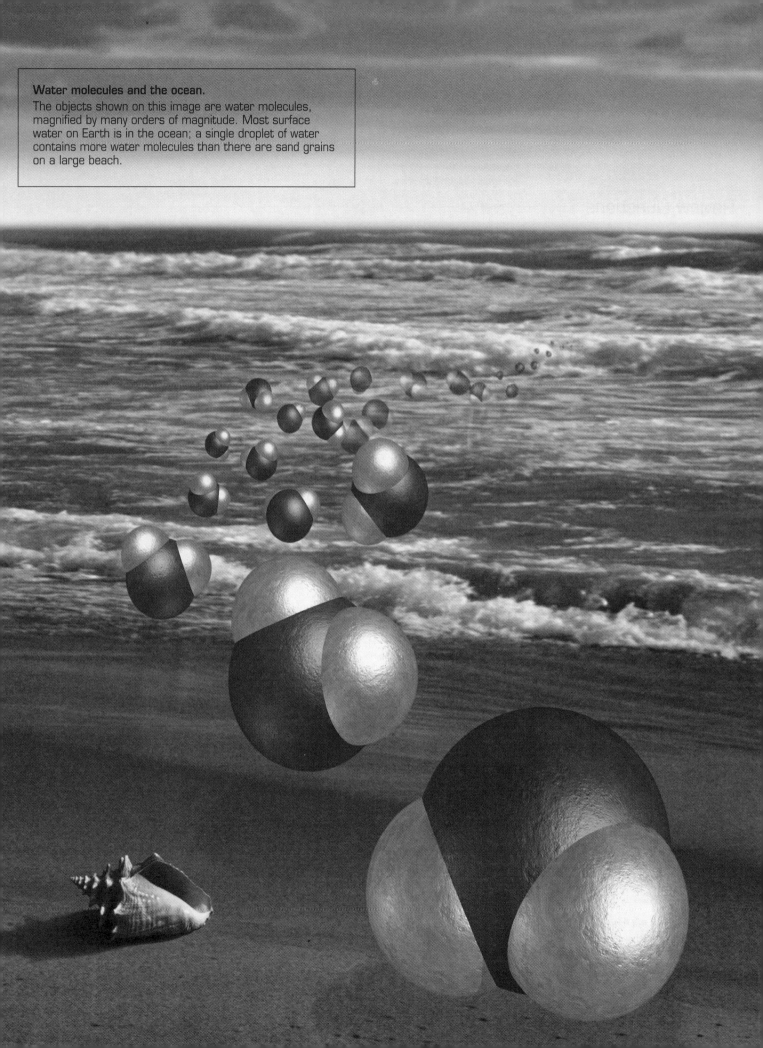

Water molecules and the ocean.
The objects shown on this image are water molecules, magnified by many orders of magnitude. Most surface water on Earth is in the ocean; a single droplet of water contains more water molecules than there are sand grains on a large beach.

"Chemistry . . . is one of the broadest branches of science, if for no other reason that, when we think about it, everything is chemistry."

— *Luciano Caglioti,*
The Two Faces of Chemistry (1985)

5 WATER AND SEAWATER

Why are temperature extremes found at places far from the ocean, while those areas close to the ocean rarely experience severe temperature variations? The mild climates found in coastal regions are made possible by the unique thermal properties of water. These and other properties of water, which stem from the arrangement of its atoms and how its molecules stick together, give water the ability to store vast quantities of heat and to dissolve almost everything.

Water is so common we often take it for granted, yet it is one of the most peculiar substances on Earth. For example, almost every other liquid contracts as it approaches its freezing point, but water actually *expands* as it freezes. Thus water stays at the surface as it starts to freeze, and ice floats—a rare property shared by very few other substances. If its nature were otherwise, all temperate-zone lakes, ponds, rivers, and even oceans would eventually freeze solid from the bottom up, and life as we know it could not exist. Instead, a floating skin of ice cocoons life in the liquid water beneath a layer of insulation, enabling it to persist under the frozen surface.

The chemical properties of water are also essential for sustaining all forms of life. In fact, the primary component of all living organisms is water. The water content of organisms, for instance, ranges from about 65% (humans) to 95% (most plants) to 99% in some jellyfish. Water is the ideal medium to have within our bodies because it facilitates chemical reactions. Our blood, which serves to transport nutrients and remove wastes within our bodies, is 83% water. The very presence of water on our planet makes life possible, and its remarkable properties make our planet livable.

5.1 Why Does Water Have Such Unusual Chemical Properties?

To understand why water has such unusual properties, let's examine its chemical structure.

Atomic Structure

Atoms (*a* = not, *tomos* = cut) are the basic building blocks of all matter. Every physical substance in our world—chairs, tables, books, people, the air we breathe—is composed of atoms. An atom resembles a microscopic sphere (Figure 5.1) and was originally thought to be the smallest form of matter. Additional study has revealed that atoms are composed of even smaller particles, called subatomic particles.[1] As shown in Figure 5.1, the **nucleus** (*nucleos* = a little nut) of an atom is composed

---

[1]It has been discovered that subatomic particles themselves are composed of a variety of even smaller particles such as *quarks*, *leptons*, and *bosons*.

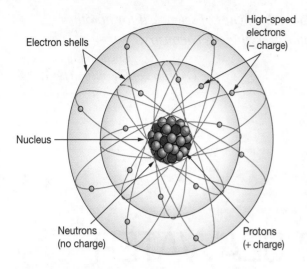

Electron shells

High-speed
electrons
(– charge)

Nucleus

Neutrons
(no charge)

Protons
(+ charge)

FIGURE 5.1 Simplified model of an atom. An atom consists of a central nucleus composed of protons and neutrons that is encircled by electrons.

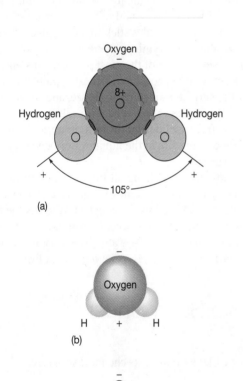

Oxygen
–

8+
O

Hydrogen

Hydrogen

+

+

105°

(a)

–

Oxygen

H   +   H

(b)

–
O

H   +   H

(c)

FIGURE 5.2 The water molecule. (a) Geometry of a water molecule. The oxygen end of the molecule is negatively charged, and the hydrogen regions exhibit a positive charge. Covalent bonds occur between the oxygen and the two hydrogen atoms. **(b)** A three-dimensional representation of the water molecule. **(c)** The water molecule represented by letters (H = hydrogen, O = oxygen).

of **protons** (*protos* = first) and **neutrons** (*neutr* = neutral) which are bound together by strong forces. Protons have a positive electrical charge, whereas neutrons have no electrical charge. Both protons and neutrons have about the same mass, which is extremely small. Surrounding the nucleus are particles called **electrons** (*electro* = electricity) which have about $1/2000$ the mass of either protons or neutrons. Electrical attraction between positively charged protons and negatively charged electrons holds electrons in layers or shells around the nucleus.

The overall electrical charge of most atoms is balanced because each atom contains an equal number of protons and electrons. An oxygen atom, for example, has eight protons and eight electrons. Most oxygen atoms also have eight neutrons, which do not affect the overall electrical charge because neutrons are electrically neutral. The number of protons is what distinguishes atoms of the 118 known chemical elements from one another. For example, an oxygen atom (and only an oxygen atom) has eight protons. Similarly, a hydrogen atom (and only a hydrogen atom) has one proton, a helium atom has two protons, and so on (for more details, see Appendix IV, "A Chemical Background: Why Water has 2 H's and 1 O"). In some cases, an atom will lose or gain one or more electrons and thus have an overall electrical charge. These atoms are called **ions** (*ienai* = to go).

The Water Molecule

A **molecule** (*molecula* = a mass) is a group of two or more atoms held together by mutually shared electrons. It is the smallest form of a substance that can exist yet still retain the original properties of that substance. When atoms combine with other atoms to form molecules, they share or trade electrons and establish chemical bonds. For instance, the chemical formula for water—H_2O—indicates that a water molecule is composed of two hydrogen atoms chemically bonded to one oxygen atom.

GEOMETRY Atoms can be represented as spheres of various sizes, and the more electrons the atom contains, the larger the sphere. It turns out that an oxygen atom (with eight electrons) is about twice the size of a hydrogen atom (with one electron). A water molecule consists of a central oxygen atom covalently bonded to the two hydrogen atoms, which are separated by an angle of about 105 degrees (Figure 5.2a). The **covalent** (*co* = with, *valere* = to be strong) **bonds** in a water molecule are due to the sharing of electrons between oxygen and each hydrogen atom. They are relatively strong chemical bonds, so a lot of energy is needed to break them.

Figure 5.2b shows a water molecule in a more compact representation, and in Figure 5.2c letter symbols are used to represent the atoms in water (O for oxygen, H for hydrogen). Instead of water's atoms being in a straight line, *both hydrogen atoms are on the same side of the oxygen atom.* This curious bend in the geometry of the water molecule is the underlying cause of most of the unique properties of water.

POLARITY The bent geometry of the water molecule gives a slight overall negative charge to the side of the oxygen atom and a slight overall positive charge to the side of the hydrogen atoms (Figure 5.2a). This slight separation of charges gives the entire molecule an electrical **polarity** (*polus* = pole, *ity* = having the quality of) so water molecules are **dipolar** (*di* = two, *polus* =pole) other common dipolar objects are flashlight batteries, car batteries, and bar magnets. Although the electrical charges are weak, water molecules behave as if they contain a tiny bar magnet.

INTERCONNECTIONS OF MOLECULES If you've ever experimented with bar magnets, you know they have polarity and orient themselves relative to one another such that the positive end of one bar magnet is attracted to the negative

Why does a water molecule have the unusual shape that it does?

Based on simple symmetry considerations and charge separations, a water molecule should have its two hydrogen atoms on opposite sides of the oxygen atom, thus producing a linear shape like many other molecules. But water's odd shape where *both* hydrogen atoms are on the same side of the oxygen atom stems from the fact that oxygen has four bonding sites, which are evenly spaced around the oxygen atom. No matter which two bonding sites are occupied by hydrogen atoms, it results in the curious bend of the water molecule.

FIGURE 5.3 Hydrogen bonding in water. Dashed lines indicate locations of hydrogen bonds, which occur between water molecules.

end of another. Water molecules have polarity, too, so they orient themselves relative to one another. In water, the positively charged hydrogen area of one water molecule interacts with the negatively charged oxygen end of an adjacent water molecule, forming a **hydrogen bond** (Figure 5.3). The hydrogen bonds between water molecules are much weaker than the covalent bonds that hold individual water molecules together. In essence, weaker hydrogen bonds form *between* adjacent water molecules and stronger covalent bonds occur *within* water molecules.

Even though hydrogen bonds are weaker than covalent bonds, they are strong enough to cause water molecules to stick to one another and exhibit **cohesion** (*cohaesus* = a clinging together). The cohesive properties of water cause it to "bead up" on a waxed surface, such as a freshly waxed car. They also give water its **surface tension**. Water's surface has a thin "skin" that allows a glass to be filled just above the brim without spilling any of the water. Surface tension results from the formation of hydrogen bonds between the outermost layer of water molecules and the underlying molecules. Water's ability to form hydrogen bonds causes it to have the highest surface tension of any liquid except the element mercury.[2]

WATER: THE UNIVERSAL SOLVENT   Water molecules stick not only to other water molecules, but also to other polar chemical compounds. In doing so, water molecules can reduce the attraction between ions of opposite charges by as much as 80 times. For instance, ordinary table salt—sodium[3] chloride, NaCl—consists of an alternating array of positively charged sodium ions and negatively charged chloride ions (Figure 5.4a). The **electrostatic** (*electro* = electricity, *stasis* = standing) **attraction** between oppositely charged ions produces an **ionic** (*ienai* = to go) **bond**. When solid NaCl is placed in water, the electrostatic attraction (ionic bonding) between the sodium and chloride ions is reduced by 80 times. This, in turn, makes it much easier for the sodium ions and chloride ions to separate. When the ions separate, the positively charged sodium ions become attracted to the negative ends of the water molecules, the negatively charged chloride ions become attracted to the positive ends of the water molecules (Figure 5.4b), and the salt is dissolved in water. The process by which water molecules completely surround ions is called *hydration* (*hydra* = water, *ation* = action or process).

Because water molecules interact with other water molecules and other polar molecules, water is able to dissolve nearly everything.[4] Given enough time, water

A water molecule has a bend in its geometry, with the two hydrogen atoms on the same side of the oxygen atom. This property gives water its polarity and ability to form hydrogen bonds.

(a) Sodium chloride, solid crystal structure

(b) Sodium chloride, in solution

FIGURE 5.4 Water as a solvent. (a) Atomic structure of table salt, which is composed of sodium chloride (Na^+ = sodium ion, Cl^- = chlorine ion). **(b)** As sodium chloride is dissolved, the positively charged ends of water molecules are attracted to the negatively charged Cl^- ion, while the negatively charged ends are attracted to the positively charged Na^+ ion.

---

[2]Mercury is the only metal that is a liquid at normal surface temperatures. Although it is commonly used in thermometers, it is also quite toxic.

[3]Sodium is represented by the letters Na because the Latin term for sodium is *natrium.*

[4]If water is such a good solvent, why doesn't oil dissolve in water? As you might have guessed, the chemical structure of oil is remarkably nonpolar. With no positive or negative ends to attract the polar water molecule, oil will not dissolve in water.

STUDENTS SOMETIMES ASK...

How can it be that water—a liquid at room temperature—can be created by combining hydrogen and oxygen—two gases at room temperature?

It is true that combining two parts hydrogen gas with one part oxygen gas produces liquid water. This can be accomplished as a chemistry experiment, although care should be taken because much energy is released during the reaction (don't try this at home!). Oftentimes, when combining two elements, the product has very different properties than the pure substances. For instance, combining elemental sodium (Na), a highly reactive metal, with pure chlorine (Cl_2) a toxic nerve gas, produces cubes of harmless table salt (NaCl). This is what most people find amazing about chemistry.

can dissolve more substances and in greater quantity than any other known substance. This is why water is called "the universal solvent." It is also why the ocean contains so much dissolved material—an estimated 50 quadrillion tons (50 million billion tons) of salt—which makes seawater taste "salty."

5.2 What Other Important Properties Does Water Possess?

Water's other important properties include its thermal properties (such as water's freezing and boiling points, heat capacity, and latent heats) and its density.

Water's Thermal Properties

Water exists on Earth as a solid, a liquid, and a gas and has the ability to store and release great amounts of heat. Water's thermal properties influence the world's heat budget and are in part responsible for the development of tropical cyclones, worldwide wind belts, and ocean surface currents.

HEAT, TEMPERATURE, AND CHANGES OF STATE Matter around us is usually in one of the three common states: solid, liquid, or gas.[5] What must happen to change the state of a compound? The attractive forces between molecules or ions in the substance must be overcome if the state of the substance is to be changed from solid to liquid or from liquid to gas. These attractive forces include hydrogen bonds and van der Waals forces. The **van der Waals forces**—named for Dutch physicist Johannes Diderik van der Waals (1837–1923)—are relatively weak interactions that become significant only when molecules are very close together, as in the solid and liquid states (but not the gaseous state). Energy must be added to the molecules or ions so they can move fast enough to overcome these attractions.

What form of energy changes the state of matter? Very simply, adding or removing heat is what causes a substance to change its state of matter. For instance, adding heat to ice cubes causes them to melt and removing heat from water causes ice to form. Before proceeding, let's clarify the difference between heat and temperature:

- **Heat** is the *energy transfer from one body to another due to a difference in temperature*. Heat is proportional to the energy level of moving molecules and thus is the total internal energy—both **kinetic** (*kinetos* = moving) **energy** and **potential** (*potentia* = power) **energy**—transferred from one body to another. For example, water can exist as a solid, liquid, or gas depending on the amount of heat added. Heat may be generated by combustion (a chemical reaction commonly called "burning"), through other chemical reactions, by friction, or from radioactivity; it can be transferred by conduction, by convection, or by radiation. A **calorie** (*calor* = heat) is the amount of heat required to raise the temperature of 1 gram of water[6] by 1 degree centigrade. The familiar "calories" used to measure the energy content of foods is actually a *kilocalorie*, 1000 calories. Although the metric unit for thermal energy is the *joule*, calories are directly tied to some of water's thermal properties, as will be discussed in the next section.

---

[5]*Plasma* is widely recognized as a fourth state of matter distinct from solids, liquids, and normal gases. Plasma is a gaseous substance in which atoms have been ionized—that is to say, stripped of electrons. Plasma television monitors take advantage of the fact that plasmas are strongly influenced by electric currents.

[6]One gram (0.035 ounce) of water is equal to about 10 drops.

FIGURE 5.5 Water in the three states of matter: Solid, liquid, and gas. Diagram showing the three states of matter in which water is found on Earth and the processes associated with changes from one state to another. Blue arrows (−) indicate heat released by water (which warms the environment) as it changes state; red arrows (+) indicate heat absorbed by water (which cools the environment).

• **Temperature** is the *direct measure of the average kinetic energy of the molecules that make up a substance.* The greater the temperature, the greater the kinetic energy of the substance. Temperature changes when heat energy is added to or removed from a substance. Temperature is usually measured in degrees centigrade (°C) or degrees Fahrenheit (°F).

Figure 5.5 shows water molecules in the solid, liquid, and gaseous states. In the *solid state* (ice), water has a rigid structure and does not normally flow over short time scales. Intermolecular bonds are constantly being broken and re-formed, but the molecules remain firmly attached. That is, the molecules vibrate with energy but remain in relatively fixed positions. As a result, solids do not conform to the shape of their container.

In the *liquid state* (water), water molecules still interact with each other, but they have enough kinetic energy to flow past each other and take the shape of their container. Intermolecular bonds are being formed and broken at a much greater rate than in the solid state.

In the *gaseous state* (water **vapor**), water molecules no longer interact with one another except during random collisions. Water vapor molecules flow very freely, filling the volume of whatever container they are placed in.

WATER'S FREEZING AND BOILING POINTS   If enough heat energy is added to a solid, it melts to a liquid. The temperature at which melting occurs is the substance's **melting point**. If enough heat energy is removed from a liquid, it freezes to a solid. The temperature at which freezing occurs is the substance's **freezing point**, which is the same temperature as the melting point (Figure 5.5). For pure water, melting and freezing occur at 0°C (32°F).[7]

If enough heat energy is added to a liquid, it converts to a gas. The temperature at which boiling occurs is the substance's **boiling point**. If enough heat energy is removed from a gas, it **condenses** to a liquid. The highest temperature at which condensation occurs is the substance's **condensation point**, which is the same temperature as the boiling point (Figure 5.5). For pure water, boiling and condensation occur at 100°C (212°F).

Both the freezing and boiling points of water are unusually high compared to other similar substances. As shown in Figure 5.6, if water followed the pattern of

Phase Changes of Water

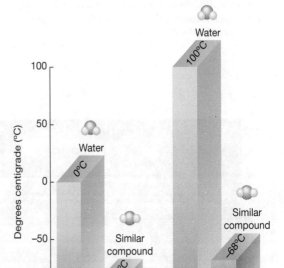

FIGURE 5.6 Comparison of melting and boiling points of water with similar chemical compounds. Bar graph showing the melting and boiling points of water compared to the melting and boiling points of similar chemical compounds. Water would have properties like those of similar chemical compounds if it did not have its unique geometry and resulting polarity.

---

[7]All melting/freezing/boiling points discussed in this chapter assume a standard sea level pressure of 1 atmosphere (14.7 pounds per square inch).

FIGURE 5.7 Specific heat capacity of common substances. Graph showing the specific heat capacity of common substances at 20°C. Note that water has a very high specific heat capacity, which means that it takes a lot of energy to increase water temperature.

other chemical compounds with molecules of similar mass, it should melt at −90°C (−130°F) and boil at −68°C (−90°F). If that were the case, all water on Earth would be in the gaseous state. Instead, water melts and boils at the relatively high temperatures of 0°C (32°F) and 100°C (212°F),[8] respectively, because additional heat energy is required to overcome its hydrogen bonds and van der Waals forces. Thus, if not for the unusual geometry and resulting polarity of the water molecule, all water on Earth would be boiled away and life as we know it would not exist.

WATER'S HEAT CAPACITY AND SPECIFIC HEAT   Heat capacity is *the amount of heat energy required to raise the temperature of a substance by 1 degree centigrade.* Substances that have high heat capacity can absorb (or lose) large quantities of heat with only a small change in temperature. Conversely, substances that change temperature rapidly when heat is applied—such as oil or metals—have lower heat capacity.

The heat capacity per unit mass of a body, called *specific heat capacity* or more simply **specific heat**, is used to more directly compare the heat capacity of substances. For example, as shown in Figure 5.7, pure water has a high specific heat capacity that is exactly 1 calorie per gram,[9] whereas other common substances have much lower specific heats. Note that metals such as iron and copper—which heat up rapidly when heat is applied—have capacity values that are about 10 times lower than water.

Why does water have such high heat capacity? The reason is because it takes more energy to increase the kinetic energy of hydrogen-bonded water molecules than it does for substances in which the dominant intermolecular interaction is the much weaker van der Waals force. As a result, water gains or loses much more heat than other common substances while undergoing an equal temperature change. In addition, water resists any change in temperature, as you may have observed when heating a large pot of water. When heat is applied to the pot, which is made of metal that has a low heat capacity, the pot heats up quickly. The water *inside* the pot, however, takes a long time to heat up (hence, the tale that a watched pot never boils but an unwatched pot boils over!). Making the water boil takes even more heat because all the hydrogen bonds must be broken. The exceptional capacity of water to absorb large quantities of heat helps explain why water is used in home heating, industrial and automobile cooling systems, and home cooking applications.

WATER'S LATENT HEATS   When water undergoes a change of state—that is, when ice melts or water freezes, or when water boils or water vapor condenses—a large amount of heat is absorbed or released. The amount of heat absorbed or released is due to water's high latent (*latent* = hidden) heats and is closely related to water's unusually high heat capacity. As water evaporates from your skin, it cools your body by absorbing heat (this is why sweating cools your body). Conversely, if you ever have been scalded by water vapor—steam—you know that steam releases an enormous amount of latent heat when it condenses to a liquid.

Latent Heat of Melting   The graph in Figure 5.8 shows how latent heat affects the amount of energy needed to increase

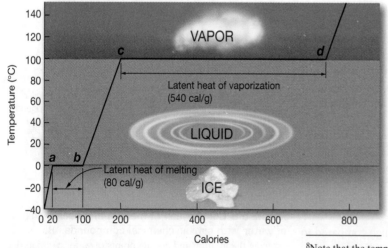

FIGURE 5.8 Latent heats and changes of state of water. The latent heat of melting (80 calories per gram) is much less than the latent heat of vaporization (540 calories per gram). See text for description of points *a*, *b*, *c*, and *d*.

[8]Note that the temperature scale *centigrade* (*centi* = a hundred, *grad* = step) is based on 100 even divisions between the melting and boiling points of pure water. It is also called the Celsius scale after its founder (see Appendix I, "Metric and English Units Compared").

[9]Note that the specific heat capacity of water is used as the unit of heat quantity, the calorie. Thus, water is the standard against which the specific heats of other substances are compared.

water temperature and change the state of water. Beginning with 1 gram of ice (*lower left*), the addition of 20 calories of heat raises the temperature of the ice by 40 degrees, from −40°C to 0°C (point *a* on the graph). The temperature remains at 0°C (32°F) even though more heat is being added, as shown by the plateau on the graph between points *a* and *b*. The temperature of the water does not change until 80 more calories of heat energy have been added. The **latent heat of melting** is the energy needed to break the intermolecular bonds that hold water molecules rigidly in place in ice crystals. The temperature remains unchanged until most of the bonds are broken and the mixture of ice and water has changed completely to 1 gram of water.

After the change from ice to liquid water has occurred at 0°C, additional heat raises the water temperature between points *b* and *c* in Figure 5.8. As it does, it takes 1 calorie of heat to raise the temperature of the gram of water 1°C (or 1.8°F). Therefore, another 100 calories must be added before the gram of water reaches the boiling point of 100°C (212°F). So far, a total of 200 calories has been added to reach point *c*.

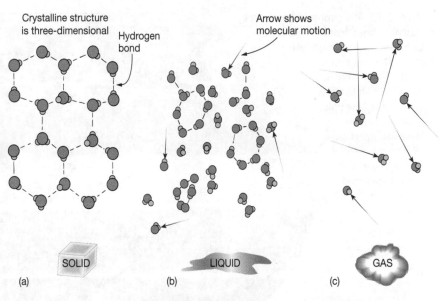

FIGURE 5.9 Hydrogen bonds in H$_2$O and the three states of matter. (a) In the solid state, water exists as ice, in which there are hydrogen bonds between all water molecules. (b) In the liquid state, there are some hydrogen bonds. (c) In the gaseous state, there are no hydrogen bonds and the water molecules are moving rapidly and independently.

Latent Heat of Vaporization   The graph in Figure 5.8 flattens out again at 100°C, between points *c* and *d*. This plateau represents the **latent heat of vaporization**, which is 540 calories per gram for water. This is the amount of heat that must be added to 1 gram of a substance at its boiling point to break the intermolecular bonds and complete the change of state from liquid to vapor (gas).

The drawings in Figure 5.9, which show the structure of water molecules in the solid, liquid, and gaseous states, help explain why the latent heat of vaporization is so much greater than the latent heat of melting. To go from a solid to a liquid, just enough hydrogen bonds must be broken to allow water molecules to slide past one another. To go from a liquid to a gas, however, all of the hydrogen bonds must be completely broken so that individual water molecules can move about freely.

Latent Heat of Evaporation   Sea surface temperatures average 20°C (68°F) or less. How, then, does liquid water convert to vapor at the surface of the ocean? the conversion of a liquid to a gas below the boiling point is called **evaporation**. At ocean surface temperatures, individual molecules converted from the liquid to the gaseous state have less energy than do water molecules at 100°C. To gain the additional energy necessary to break free of the surrounding ocean water molecules, an individual molecule must capture heat energy from its neighbors. In other words, the molecules left behind have lost heat energy to those that evaporate, which explains the cooling effect of evaporation.

It takes more than 540 calories of heat to produce 1 gram of water vapor from the ocean surface at temperatures less than 100°C. At 20°C (68°F), for instance, the **latent heat of evaporation** is 585 calories per gram. More heat is required because more hydrogen bonds must be broken. At higher temperatures, liquid water has fewer hydrogen bonds because the molecules are vibrating and jostling about more.

Latent Heat of Condensation   When water vapor is cooled sufficiently, it condenses to a liquid and releases its **latent heat of condensation** into the surrounding air. On a small scale, the heat released is enough to cook food; this is how a "steamer" works. On a large scale, the heat released is sufficient to power large thunderstorms and even hurricanes (see Chapter 6, "Air–Sea Interaction").

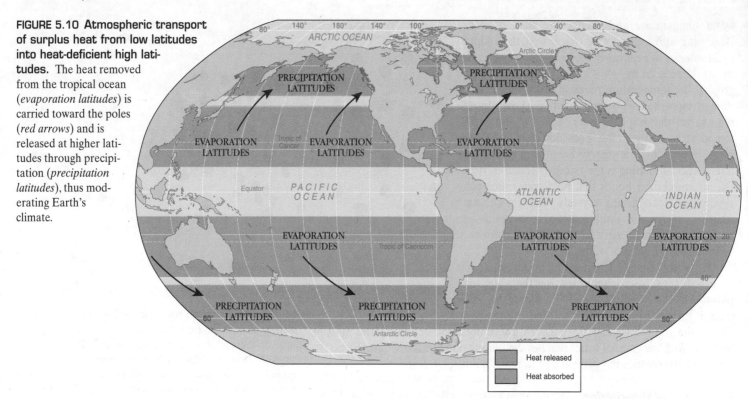

Latent Heat of Freezing Heat is also released when water freezes. The amount of heat released when water freezes is the same amount that was absorbed when the water was melted in the first place. Thus, the **latent heat of freezing** is identical to the latent heat of melting. Similarly, the latent heats of vaporization and condensation are identical.

GLOBAL THERMOSTATIC EFFECTS The **thermostatic** (*thermos* = heat, *stasis* = standing) **effects** of water are those properties that act to moderate changes in temperature, which in turn affect Earth's climate. For example, the huge amount of heat energy exchanged in the evaporation–condensation cycle helps make life possible on Earth. The Sun radiates energy to Earth, where some is stored in the oceans. Evaporation removes this heat energy from the oceans and carries it high into the atmosphere. In the cooler upper atmosphere, water vapor condenses into clouds, which are the basis of **precipitation** (mostly rain and snow) that releases latent heat of condensation. The map in Figure 5.10 shows how this cycle of evaporation and condensation removes huge amounts of heat energy from the low-latitude oceans and adds huge amounts of heat energy to the heat-deficient higher latitudes. In addition, the heat released when sea ice forms further moderates Earth's high-latitude regions.

The exchange of latent heat between ocean and atmosphere is very efficient. For every gram of water that condenses in cooler latitudes, the amount of heat released to warm these regions equals the amount of heat removed from the tropical ocean when that gram of water was evaporated initially. The end result is that the thermal properties of water have prevented wide variations in Earth's temperature, thus moderating Earth's climate. Because rapid change is the enemy of all life, our planet's moderated climate is one of the main reasons life exists on Earth.

Another thermostatic effect of the ocean can be seen in Figure 5.11, which shows the temperature difference between day and night. The map shows that in the ocean, there is only a small difference in temperature between day and night while the land experiences a much greater variation. This difference between ocean and land is due to the higher heat capacity of water, which gives it the ability to absorb the daily gains and minimize the daily losses of heat energy much more

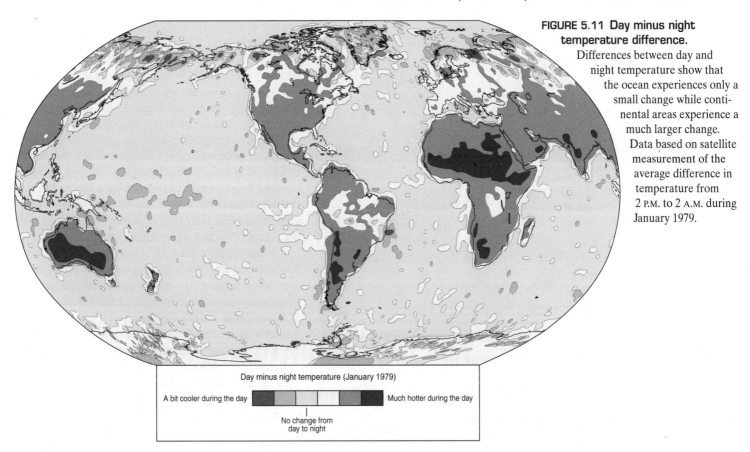

FIGURE 5.11 Day minus night temperature difference.
Differences between day and night temperature show that the ocean experiences only a small change while continental areas experience a much larger change. Data based on satellite measurement of the average difference in temperature from 2 P.M. to 2 A.M. during January 1979.

Day minus night temperature (January 1979)

A bit cooler during the day   Much hotter during the day

No change from
day to night

easily than land materials. The term **marine effect** describes locations that experience the moderating influences of the ocean, usually along coastlines or islands. **Continental effect**—a condition of *continentality*—refers to areas less affected by the sea and therefore having a greater range of temperature differences (both daily and yearly).

Water Density

Recall from Chapter 1 that density is mass per unit volume and can be thought of as *how heavy something is for its size*. Ultimately, density is related to how tightly the molecules or ions of a substance are packed together. Typical units of density are grams per cubic centimeter (g/cm^3). Pure water, for example, has a density of 1.0 g/cm^3. Temperature, salinity, and pressure all affect water density.

The density of most substances increases as temperature decreases. For example, cold air sinks and warm air rises because cold air is denser than warm air. Density increases as temperature decreases because the molecules lose energy and slow down, so the same number of molecules occupy less space. This shrinkage caused by cold temperatures, called **thermal contraction**, also occurs in water, but only to a certain point. As pure water cools to 4°C (39°F), its density increases. From 4°C down to 0°C (32°F), however, its density *decreases*. In other words, water stops contracting and actually expands, which is highly unusual among Earth's many substances. The result is that ice is less dense than liquid water, so ice floats on water. For most other substances, the solid state is denser than the liquid state, so the solid sinks.

Why is ice less dense than water? Figure 5.12 shows how molecular packing changes as water approaches its freezing point. From points *a* to *c* in the figure, the temperature decreases from 20°C (68°F) to 4°C (39°F) and the density increases from 0.9982 g/cm^3 to 1.0000 g/cm^3. Density increases because the

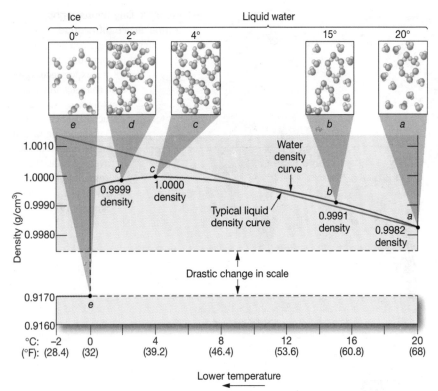

FIGURE 5.12 Water density as a function of temperature and the formation of ice. The density of freshwater (*red curve*) as it freezes (*right to left*); the density of a typical liquid is also shown (*green curve*). Water reaches its maximum density at 4°C, but below that water becomes less dense as ice begins to form. At 0°C, ice forms, its crystal structure expands dramatically, and density decreases. As a result, ice floats.

FIGURE 5.13 Snowflakes. Scanning electron photomicrograph of actual snowflakes magnified about 500 times. Hexagonal snowflakes indicate the internal structure of water molecules held together by hydrogen bonds.

amount of thermal motion decreases, so the water molecules occupy less volume. As a result, the window at point *c* contains more water molecules than the windows at points *a* or *b*. When the temperature is lowered below 4°C (39°F), the overall volume increases again because water molecules begin to line up to form ice crystals. Ice crystals are bulky, open, six-sided structures in which water molecules are widely spaced. Their characteristic hexagonal shape (Figure 5.13) mimics the hexagonal molecular structure resulting from hydrogen bonding between water molecules (see Figure 5.9a). By the time water fully freezes (point *e*), the density of the ice is much less than that of water at 4°C (39°F), the temperature at which water achieves its maximum density.

When water freezes, its volume increases by about 9%. Anyone who has put a beverage in a freezer for "just a few minutes" to cool it down and inadvertently forgotten about it has experienced the volume increase associated with water's expansion as it freezes—usually resulting in a burst beverage container (Figure 5.14). The force exerted when ice expands is powerful enough to break apart rocks, split pavement on roads and sidewalks, and crack water pipes.

Increasing the pressure or adding dissolved substances decreases the temperature of maximum density for freshwater because the formation of bulky ice crystals is inhibited. Increasing pressure increases the number of water molecules in a given volume and inhibits the number of ice crystals that can be created. Increasing amounts of dissolved substances inhibits the formation of hydrogen bonds, which further restricts the number of ice crystals that can form. To produce ice crystals equal in volume to those that could be produced at 4°C (39°F) in freshwater, more energy must be removed, causing a reduction in the temperature of maximum density.

Dissolved solids reduce the freezing point of water, too. It's one of the reasons why most seawater never freezes, except near Earth's frigid poles (and even then, only at the surface). It's also why salt is spread on roads and sidewalks during the winter in cold climates. The salt lowers the freezing point of water, allowing ice-free roads and sidewalks at temperatures that are several degrees below freezing.

Web Table 5.1 summarizes the physical and biological significance of the unusual properties of seawater.

5.3 How Salty Is Seawater?

What is the difference between pure water and seawater? One of the most obvious differences is that seawater contains dissolved substances that give it a distinctly salty taste. These dissolved substances are not simply sodium chloride (table salt)—they include various other salts, metals, and dissolved gases. The oceans, in fact, contain enough salt to cover the entire planet with a layer more than 150 meters (500 feet) thick (about the height of a 50-story skyscraper). Unfortunately, the salt content of seawater makes it unsuitable for drinking or irrigating most crops and causes it to be highly corrosive to many materials.

Salinity

Salinity (*salinus* = salt) is the total amount of solid material dissolved in water including dissolved gases (because even gases become solids at low enough temperatures) but excluding dissolved organic substances. Salinity does *not* include fine particles being held in suspension (turbidity) or solid material in contact with water because these materials are not dissolved. Salinity is the ratio of the mass of dissolved substances to the mass of the water sample.

The salinity of seawater is typically about 3.5%, about 220 times saltier than freshwater. Seawater with a salinity of 3.5% indicates that it also contains 96.5% pure water, as shown in Figure 5.15. Because seawater is mostly pure water, its physical properties are very similar to those of pure water, with only slight variations.

Figure 5.15 and Table 5.1 show that the elements chlorine, sodium, sulfur (as the sulfate ion), magnesium, calcium, and potassium account for over 99% of the dissolved solids in seawater. More than 80 other chemical elements have been identified in seawater—most in extremely small amounts—and probably all of Earth's naturally occurring elements exist in the sea. Remarkably, trace amounts of dissolved components in seawater are vital for human survival (Box 5.1).

Salinity is often expressed in **parts per thousand (‰)**. For example, as 1% is one part in 100, 1‰ is one part in 1000. When converting from percent to parts per thousand, the decimal is simply moved one place to the right. For instance, typical seawater salinity of 3.5% is the same as 35‰. Advantages of expressing salinity in parts per thousand are that decimals are often avoided and values convert directly to grams of salt per kilogram of seawater. For example, 35‰ seawater has 35 grams of salt in every 1000 grams of seawater.[10]

FIGURE 5.14 Glass bottle shattered by frozen water. This glass bottle was filled with water, sealed, and put into a freezer. As water freezes, it expands by 9% as it forms hydrogen bonds and forms an open lattice structure, which increased the pressure and caused the bottle to fracture.

Determining Salinity

Early methods of determining seawater salinity involved evaporating a carefully weighed amount of seawater and weighing the salts that precipitated from it. However, the accuracy of this time-consuming method is limited because some water can remain bonded to salts that precipitate and some substances can evaporate along with the water.

WEB VIDEO

Seawater Evaporating
(Time Lapse)

FIGURE 5.15 Major dissolved components in seawater. Diagrammatic representation of the most abundant components in a kilogram of 35‰ salinity seawater. Constituents are listed in grams per kilogram, which is equivalent to parts per thousand (‰).

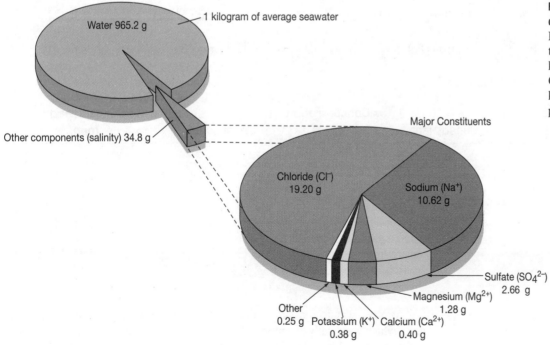

---

[10]Note that the units "parts per thousand" are effectively parts per thousand by weight. Salinity values, however, lack units because the salinity of a water sample is determined as the *ratio* of the electrical conductivity of the sample to the electrical conductivity of a standard. Thus, salinity values are sometimes reported in *p.s.u.*, or *practical salinity units*, which are equivalent to parts per thousand.

TABLE 5.1   SELECTED DISSOLVED MATERIALS IN 35‰ SEAWATER

1. Major Constituents (in parts per thousand, ‰)

Constituent	Concentration (‰)	Ratio of constituent/total salts (%)
Chloride (Cl^-)	19.2	55.04
Sodium (Na^+)	10.6	30.61
Sulfate (SO_4^{2-})	2.7	7.68
Magnesium (Mg^{2+})	1.3	3.69
Calcium (Ca^{2+})	0.40	1.16
Potassium (K^+)	0.38	1.10
Total	**34.58‰**	**99.28%**

2. Minor Constituents (in parts per million, ppm[a])

Gases Constituent	Concentration (ppm)	Nutrients Constituent	Concentration (ppm)	Others Constituent	Concentration (ppm)
Carbon dioxide (CO_2)	90	Silicon (Si)	3.0	Bromide (Br^-)	65.0
Nitrogen (N_2)	14	Nitrogen (N)	0.5	Carbon (C)	28.0
Oxygen (O_2)	6	Phosphorus (P)	0.07	Strontium (Sr)	8.0
		Iron (Fe)	0.002	Boron (B)	4.6

3. Trace Constituents (in parts per billion, ppb[b])

Constituent	Concentration (ppb)	Constituent	Concentration (ppb)	Constituent	Concentration (ppb)
Lithium (Li)	185	Zinc (Zn)	10	Lead (Pb)	0.03
Rubidium (Rb)	120	Aluminum (Al)	2	Mercury (Hg)	0.03
Iodine (I)	60	Manganese (Mn)	2	Gold (Au)	0.005

[a]Note that 1000 ppm = 1‰.
[b]Note that 1000 ppb = 1 ppm.

Another way to measure salinity is to use the *principle of constant proportions*, which was firmly established by chemist William Dittmar when he analyzed the water samples collected during the *Challenger* Expedition (Box 5.2). The **principle of constant proportions** states that the major dissolved constituents responsible for the salinity of seawater occur nearly everywhere in the ocean in the exact same proportions, independent of salinity. The ocean, therefore, is well mixed. When salinity changes, moreover, the salts don't leave (or enter) the

HOW TO AVOID GOITERS

FIGURE 5A A woman with goiters.

The nutritional label on containers of salt usually proclaims "this product contains iodine, a necessary nutrient." Why is iodine necessary in our diets? It turns out that if a person's diet contains an insufficient amount of iodine, a potentially life-threatening disease called **goiters** (*guttur* = throat) may result (Figure 5A).

Iodine is used by the thyroid gland, which is a butterfly-shaped organ located in the neck in front of and on either side of the trachea (windpipe). The thyroid gland manufactures hormones that regulate cellular metabolism essential for mental development and physical growth. If people lack iodine in their diet, their thyroid glands cannot function properly. Often, this results in the enlargement or swelling of the thyroid gland. Severe symptoms include dry skin, loss of hair, puffy face, weakness of muscles, weight increase, diminished vigor, mental sluggishness, and a large nodular growth on the neck called a goiter. If proper steps are not taken to correct this disease, it can lead to cancer. Iodine ingested regularly often begins to reverse the effects. In advanced stages, surgery to remove the goiter or exposure to radioactivity is the only course of action.

How can you avoid goiters? Fortunately, goiters can be prevented with a diet that contains just *trace amounts* of iodine. Where can you get iodine in your diet? All products from the sea contain trace amounts of iodine because iodine is one of the many elements dissolved in seawater. Sea salt, seafood, seaweed, and other sea products contain plenty of iodine to help prevent goiters. Although goiters are rarely a problem in developed nations like the United States, goiters pose a serious health hazard in many underdeveloped nations, especially those far from the sea. In the United States, however, many people get too much iodine in their diet, leading to the overproduction of hormones by the thyroid gland. That's why most stores that sell iodized salt also carry noniodized salt for those people who have a *hyperthyroid* (*hyper* = excessive, *thyroid* = the thyroid gland) condition and must restrict their intake of iodine.

ocean, but water molecules do. Seawater has *constancy of composition*, so the concentration of a single major constituent can be measured to determine the total salinity of a given water sample. The constituent that occurs in the greatest abundance and is the easiest to measure accurately is the chloride ion, Cl^-. The weight of this ion in a water sample is its **chlorinity**.

In any sample of ocean water worldwide, the chloride ion accounts for 55.04% of the total proportion of dissolved solids (Figure 5.15 and Table 5.1). Therefore, by measuring only the chloride ion concentration, the total salinity of a seawater sample can be determined using the following relationship:

$$\text{Salinity (‰)} = 1.80655 \times \text{chlorinity (‰)}^* \qquad (5.1)$$

For example, the average chlorinity of the ocean is 19.2‰, so the average salinity is 1.80655 × 19.2‰ which rounds to 34.7‰. In other words, on average there are 34.7 parts of dissolved material in every 1000 parts of seawater.

Standard seawater consists of ocean water analyzed for chloride ion content to the nearest ten-thousandth of a part per thousand by the Institute of Oceanographic Services in Wormly, England. It is then sealed in small glass vials called *ampules* and sent to laboratories throughout the world for use as a reference standard in calibrating analytical equipment.

Seawater salinity can be measured very accurately with modern oceanographic instruments such as a **salinometer** (*salinus* = salt, *meter* = measure). Most

---

*The number 1.80655 comes from dividing 1 by 0.5504 (the chloride ion's proportion in seawater of 55.04%). However, if you actually divide this, you will get 1.81686, which is different from the original value by 0.57%. Empirically, oceanographers found that seawater's constancy of composition is an approximation and have agreed to use 1.80655 because it more accurately represents the total salinity of seawater.

THE HMS *CHALLENGER* EXPEDITION: BIRTH OF OCEANOGRAPHY

Oceanography as a scientific discipline began in 1872 with the **HMS *Challenger*** expedition, the first large-scale voyage with the express purpose of studying the ocean for scientific purposes. What inspired such a voyage? One of the principal scientific disputes in the mid 1800s was initiated by one of the most influential biologists of his time, Edwin Forbes (see Web Box 15.1), who asserted that life below about 550 meters (1800 feet) was impossible because of high pressure and lack of light. Could life exist in the deep ocean? If so, what were the physical and chemical conditions there? What was the nature of sea floor deposits?

In 1871, the Royal Society of England recommended that funds be raised for an expedition to investigate the distribution of life in the sea as well as the physical and chemical conditions of the water column from the surface to the sea floor. The British government agreed to sponsor such an expedition and in 1872, a reserve warship was refitted to support scientific studies and renamed HMS *Challenger* (Figure 5B, *inset*). It contained a staff of six scientists under the direction of Charles Wyville Thomson, a professor of natural history at Scotland's University of Edinburgh.

From time to time during the course of the voyage, the ship would stop to measure the water depth using a sounding line, the bottom temperature with newly developed thermometers that could withstand the high pressure at depth, and atmospheric and meteorologic conditions. In addition, a sample of the bottom water was collected, and the bottom sediment was dredged. Other measurements included trawling the bottom for life using a net, collecting organisms at the surface, determining temperature at various depths, gathering samples of seawater from certain depths, and recording surface and deep-water currents.

Challenger returned in May 1876, after circumnavigating the globe for nearly three and a half years (Figure 5B). During the 127,500-kilometer (79,200-mile) voyage, the scientists performed 492 deep-sea soundings, dredged the bottom 133 times, trawled the open water 151 times, took 263 water temperature readings, and collected water samples from as deep as 1830 meters (6000 feet). As with most other oceanographic expeditions, the real work of analyzing the data was just beginning. In fact, it took nearly 20 years to compile the expedition results into 50 volumes.

Major accomplishments of the voyage included verifying the existence of life at all ocean depths (thus proving Forbes wrong), classifying 4717 new marine species, measuring a then-record water depth of 8185 meters (26,850 feet) in the Mariana Trench in the western North Pacific Ocean, demonstrating that the ocean floor was not flat but had significant relief, and discovering manganese nodules.

Pioneering work on the chemistry of the oceans was completed, too. Analysis by chemist William Dittmar of 77 ocean water samples collected during the *Challenger* expedition revealed that the oceans had a remarkably consistent chemical composition, even down to minor dissolved substances. Not only were the ratios between various salts constant at the surface from ocean to ocean, but they were also constant at depth. This relationship is the basis of what is now known as the *principle of constant proportions* or *Forchammer's principle*, which has contributed greatly to the understanding of ocean salinity.

FIGURE 5B Route of the HMS *Challenger* and a block print of the ship (*inset*).

salinometers measure seawater's *electrical conductivity* (the ability of a substance to transmit electric current), which increases as more substances are dissolved in water (Figure 5.16). Salinometers can determine salinity to resolutions of better than 0.003‰.

Comparing Pure Water and Seawater

Table 5.2 compares various properties of pure water and seawater. Because seawater is 96.5% water, most of its physical properties are very similar to those of pure water. For instance, the color of pure water and seawater is identical.

The dissolved substances in seawater, however, give it slightly different yet important physical properties as compared to pure water. For example, recall that dissolved substances interfere with pure water changing state. The freezing points and boiling points in Table 5.2 show that dissolved substances decrease the freezing point and increase the boiling point of water. Thus, seawater freezes at a temperature 1.9°C (3.4°F) lower than pure water. Similarly, seawater boils at a temperature 0.6°C (1.1°F) higher than pure water. As a result, the salts in seawater extend the range of temperatures in which water is a liquid. The same principle applies to antifreeze used in automobile radiators. Antifreeze lowers the freezing point of the water in a radiator and increases the boiling point, thus extending the range over which the water remains in the liquid state. Antifreeze, therefore, protects your radiator from freezing in the winter *and* from boiling over in the summer.

Other important properties of seawater (such as pH and density) are discussed in later parts of this chapter.

FIGURE 5.16 Salinity affects water conductivity. Increasing the amount of dissolved substances increases the conductivity of the water. A light bulb with bare electrodes shows that the higher the salinity, the more electricity is transmitted and the brighter the bulb will be lit.

| TABLE 5.2 | COMPARISON OF SELECTED PROPERTIES OF PURE WATER AND SEAWATER |

Property	Pure water	35‰ Seawater
Color (light transmission)		
• Small quantities of water	Clear (high transparency)	Same as for pure water
• Large quantities of water	Blue-green because water molecules scatter blue and green wavelengths best	Same as for pure water
Odor	Odorless	Distinctly marine
Taste	Tasteless	Distinctly salty
pH	7.0 (neutral)	Surface waters range = 8.0–8.3; average = 8.1 (slightly alkaline)
Density at 4°C (39°F)	1.000 g/cm³	1.028 g/cm³
Freezing point	0°C (32°F)	−1.9°C (28.6°F)
Boiling point	100°C (212°F)	100.6°C (213.1°F)

KEY CONCEPT
Seawater salinity can be measured by salinometer and averages 35‰. The dissolved components in seawater give it different yet important physical properties as compared to pure water.

STUDENTS SOMETIMES ASK...

What is the strategy behind adding salt to a pot of water when making pasta? Does it make the water boil faster?

Adding salt to water will not make the water boil faster. It will, however, make the water boil at a slightly higher temperature because *dissolved substances raise* its boiling point (and *lower* its freezing point; see Table 5.2). Thus, the pasta will cook in slightly less time. In addition, the salt adds flavoring, so the pasta may taste better, too. Be sure to add the salt *after* the water has come to a boil, though, or it will take longer to reach a boil. This is a wonderful use of chemical principles—helping you to cook better!

I've seen the labels on electric cords warning against using electrical appliances close to water. Are these warnings because water's polarity allows electricity to be transmitted through it?

Yes and no. Water molecules are polar, so you might assume that water is a good conductor of electricity. Pure water is a very poor conductor, however, because water molecules are neutral overall and will not move toward the negatively or positively charged pole in an electrical system. If an electrical appliance is dropped into a tub of absolutely pure water, the water molecules will transmit no electricity. Instead, the water molecules will simply orient their positively charged hydrogen ends toward the negative pole of the appliance and their negatively charged oxygen ends toward its positive pole, which tends to neutralize the electric field. Interestingly, it is the dissolved substances that transmit electrical current through water (see Figure 5.16). Even slight amounts, such as those in tap water, allow electricity to be transmitted. That's why there are warning labels on the electric cords of household appliances that are commonly used in the bathroom, such as blow dryers, electric razors, and heaters. That's also why it is recommended to stay out of any water—including a bathtub or shower—during a lightning storm!

5.4 Why Does Seawater Salinity Vary?

Using salinometers and other techniques, oceanographers have determined that salinity varies from place to place in the oceans.

Salinity Variations

In the open ocean far from land, salinity varies between about 33 and 38‰. In coastal areas, salinity variations can be extreme. In the Baltic Sea, for example, salinity averages only 10‰ because physical conditions create **brackish** (*brak* = salt, *ish* = somewhat) water. Brackish water is produced in areas where freshwater (from rivers and high rainfall) and seawater mix. In the Red Sea, on the other hand, salinity averages 42‰ because physical conditions produce **hypersaline** (*hyper* = excessive, *salinus* = salt) water. Hypersaline water is typical of seas and inland bodies of water that experience high evaporation rates and limited open-ocean circulation.

Some of the most hypersaline water in the world is found in inland lakes, which are often called seas because they are so salty. The Great Salt Lake in Utah, for example, has a salinity of 280‰, and the Dead Sea on the border of Israel and Jordan has a salinity of 330‰. The water in the Dead Sea, therefore, contains 33% dissolved solids and is almost *10 times saltier than seawater*. As a result, hypersaline waters are so dense and buoyant that one can easily float (Figure 5.17), even with arms and legs sticking up above water level! Hypersaline waters also taste much saltier than seawater.

Salinity of seawater in coastal areas also varies seasonally. For example, the salinity of seawater off Miami Beach, Florida, varies from about 34.8‰ in October to 36.4‰ in May and June when evaporation is high. Offshore of Astoria, Oregon, seawater salinity is always relatively low because of the vast freshwater input from the Columbia River. Here, surface water salinity can be as low as 0.3‰ in April and May (when the Columbia River is at its maximum flow rate) and 2.6‰ in October (the dry season).

Other types of water have much lower salinity. Tap water, for instance, has salinity somewhere below 0.8‰, and good-tasting tap water is usually below 0.6‰. Salinity of premium bottled water is on the order of 0.3‰, with the salinity often displayed prominently on its label, usually as total dissolved solids (TDS) in units of parts per million (ppm), where 1000 ppm equals 1‰.

Processes Affecting Seawater Salinity

Processes affecting seawater salinity change either the amount of water (H_2O molecules) or the amount of dissolved substances within the water. Adding more water, for instance, dilutes the dissolved component and lowers the salinity of the sample. Conversely, removing water increases salinity. Changing the salinity in these ways does not affect the *amount* or the *composition* of the dissolved components, which remain in constant proportions. Let's first examine processes that affect the amount of water in seawater before turning our attention to processes that influence dissolved components.

PROCESSES THAT DECREASE SEAWATER SALINITY   Table 5.3 summarizes the processes affecting seawater salinity. Precipitation, **runoff** (stream discharge), melting icebergs, and melting sea ice *decrease* seawater salinity by adding more freshwater to the ocean. Precipitation is the way atmospheric water returns to Earth as rain, snow, sleet, and hail. Worldwide, about three-quarters of all precipitation falls directly back into the ocean and one-quarter falls onto land. Precipitation falling directly into the oceans adds freshwater, reducing seawater salinity.

FIGURE 5.17 **High-salinity water of the Dead Sea allows swimmers to easily float.** The Dead Sea, which has 330‰ salinity (almost 10 times the salinity of seawater), has high density. As a result, it also has high buoyancy that allows swimmers to float easily.

Most of the precipitation that falls on land returns to the oceans indirectly as stream runoff. Even though this water dissolves minerals on land, the runoff is relatively pure water, as shown in Table 5.4. Runoff, therefore, adds mostly water to the ocean, causing seawater salinity to decrease.

Icebergs are chunks of ice that have broken free (*calved*) from a glacier when it flows into an ocean or marginal sea and begins to melt. Glacial ice originates as snowfall in high mountain areas, so icebergs are composed of freshwater. When icebergs melt in the ocean, they add freshwater, which is another way in which seawater salinity is reduced.

Sea ice forms when ocean water freezes in high-latitude regions and is composed primarily of freshwater. When warmer temperatures return to high-latitude regions in the summer, sea ice melts in the ocean, adding mostly freshwater with a small amount of salt to the ocean. Seawater salinity, therefore, is decreased.

PROCESSES THAT INCREASE SEAWATER SALINITY The formation of sea ice and evaporation *increase* seawater salinity by removing water from the ocean (Table 5.3). Sea ice forms when seawater freezes. Depending on the salinity of seawater and the rate of ice formation, about 30% of the dissolved components in seawater are retained in sea ice. This means that 35‰ seawater creates sea ice with about 10‰ salinity (30% of 35‰ is 10‰). Consequently, the formation of sea ice removes mostly freshwater from seawater, increasing the salinity of the remaining unfrozen water. High-salinity water also has a high density, so it sinks below the surface.

Recall that evaporation is the conversion of water molecules from the liquid state to the vapor state at temperatures below the boiling point. Evaporation removes water from the ocean, leaving its dissolved substances behind. Evaporation, therefore, increases seawater salinity.

THE HYDROLOGIC CYCLE Figure 5.18 shows how the **hydrologic** (*hydro* = water, *logos* = study of) **cycle** relates the processes that affect seawater salinity. These processes recycle water among the ocean, the atmosphere, and the continents, so water is in continual motion between the different components

STUDENTS SOMETIMES ASK...

What would happen to a person if he or she drank seawater?

It depends on the quantity. The salinity of seawater is about four times greater than that of your body fluids. In your body, seawater causes your internal membranes to lose water through *osmosis* (*osmos* = to push) which transports water molecules from higher concentrations (the normal body chemistry of your internal fluids) to areas of lower concentrations (your digestive tract containing seawater). Thus, your natural body fluids would move into your digestive tract and eventually be expelled, causing dehydration.

Don't worry too much if you've inadvertently swallowed some seawater. As a nutritional drink, seawater provides seven important nutrients and contains no fat, cholesterol, or calories. Some people even claim that drinking a small amount of seawater daily gives them good health! However, beware of microbial contaminants in seawater such as viruses and bacteria that can often exist in great quantities.

KEY CONCEPT
Various surface processes either decrease seawater salinity (precipitation, runoff, icebergs melting, or sea ice melting) or increase seawater salinity (sea ice forming and evaporation).

TABLE 5.3	PROCESSES AFFECTING SEAWATER SALINITY

Process	How accomplished	Adds or removes	Effect on salt in seawater	Effect on H$_2$O in seawater	Salinity increase or decrease?	Source of freshwater from the sea?
Precipitation	Rain, sleet, hail, or snow falls directly on the ocean	Adds very fresh water	None	More H$_2$O	Decrease	N/A
Runoff	Streams carry water to the ocean	Adds mostly fresh water	Negligible addition of salt	More H$_2$O	Decrease	N/A
Icebergs melting	Glacial ice calves into the ocean and melts	Adds very fresh water	None	More H$_2$O	Decrease	Yes, icebergs from Antarctic have been towed to South America
Sea ice melting	Sea ice melts in the ocean	Adds mostly fresh water and some salt	Adds a small amount of salt	More H$_2$O	Decrease	Yes, sea ice can be melted and is better than drinking seawater
Sea ice forming	Seawater freezes in cold ocean areas	Removes mostly fresh water	30% of salts in seawater are retained in ice	Less H$_2$O	Increase	Yes, through multiple freezings, called *freeze separation*
Evaporation	Seawater evaporates in hot climates	Removes very pure water	None (essentially all salts are left behind)	Less H$_2$O	Increase	Yes, through evaporation of seawater and condensation of water vapor, called *distillation*

Earth's Water and the Hydrologic Cycle

(*reservoirs*) of the hydrologic cycle. Earth's water supply exists in the following proportions:

- 97.2% in the world ocean
- 2.15% frozen in glaciers and ice caps
- 0.62% in groundwater and soil moisture
- 0.02% in streams and lakes
- 0.001% as water vapor in the atmosphere

In addition, Figure 5.18 shows the average yearly amounts of transfer or *flux* of water between various reservoirs.

Dissolved Components Added to and Removed from Seawater

Seawater salinity is a function of the amount of dissolved components in seawater. Interestingly, dissolved substances do not remain in the ocean forever. Instead, they are cycled into and out of seawater by the processes shown in Figure 5.19. These processes include stream runoff in which streams dissolve ions from continental rocks and carry them to the sea, and volcanic eruptions, both on the land and on the sea floor. Other sources include the atmosphere (which contributes gases) and biologic interactions.

Stream runoff is the primary method by which dissolved substances are added to the oceans. Table 5.4 compares the major components dissolved in stream water with those in seawater. It shows that streams have far lower salinity and a vastly different composition of dissolved substances than seawater. For example, bicarbonate ion (HCO_3^-) is the most abundant dissolved constituent in stream water yet is found in only trace amounts in seawater. Conversely, the most abundant dissolved component in seawater is the chloride ion (Cl^-) which exists in very small concentrations in streams.

If stream water is the main source of dissolved substances in seawater, why do the components of the two not match each other more closely? One of the reasons is that some dissolved substances stay in the ocean and accumulate over time. **Residence time** is the average length of time that a substance resides in the ocean. Long residence times lead to higher concentrations of the dissolved substance. The sodium ion (Na^+) for instance, has a residence time of 260 million years, and, as a result, has a high concentration in the ocean. Other elements such as aluminum have a residence time of only 100 years and occur in seawater in much lower concentrations.

STUDENTS SOMETIMES ASK...

You mentioned that when seawater freezes, it produces ice with about 10‰ salinity. Once that ice melts, can a person drink it with no ill effects?

Early Arctic explorers found out the answer to your question by necessity. Some of these explorers who traveled by ship in high-latitude regions became inadvertently or purposely entrapped by sea ice (see, for example, Web Box 7.1, which describes the voyage of the *Fram*). Lacking other water sources, they used melted sea ice. Although newly formed sea ice contains little salt, it does trap a significant amount of brine (drops of salty water). Depending on the rate of freezing, newly formed ice may have a total salinity from 4 to 15‰. The more rapidly it forms, the more brine it captures and the higher the salinity. Melted sea ice with salinity this high doesn't taste very good, and it still causes dehydration, but not as quickly as drinking 35‰ seawater does. Over time, however, the brine will trickle down through the coarse structure of the sea ice, so its salinity decreases. By the time it is a year old, sea ice normally becomes relatively pure. Drinking melted sea ice enabled these early explorers to survive.

FIGURE 5.18 The hydrologic cycle. All water is in continual motion between the various components (reservoirs) of the hydrologic cycle. Volumes are Earth's average yearly amounts in cubic kilometers; table shows average yearly flux between reservoirs; ice not shown.

380,000 km³ = total water evaporated

Precipitation (land) 96,000 km³

Evaporation and transpiration 60,000 km³

Runoff 36,000 km³

Infiltration

Precipitation (ocean) 284,000 km³

Evaporation 320,000 km³

Annual fluxes between reservoirs	
Pathway	Volume (cubic kilometers per year)
Ocean to atmosphere	320,000
Atmosphere to ocean	284,000
Atmosphere to continent	96,000
Continent to atmosphere	60,000
Continent to ocean	36,000

FIGURE 5.19 The cycling of dissolved components in seawater. Dissolved components are added to seawater primarily by river discharge and volcanic eruptions, while they are removed by adsorption, precipitation, ion entrapment in sea spray, and marine organisms that produce hard parts. Chemical reactions at the mid-ocean ridge add and remove various dissolved components.

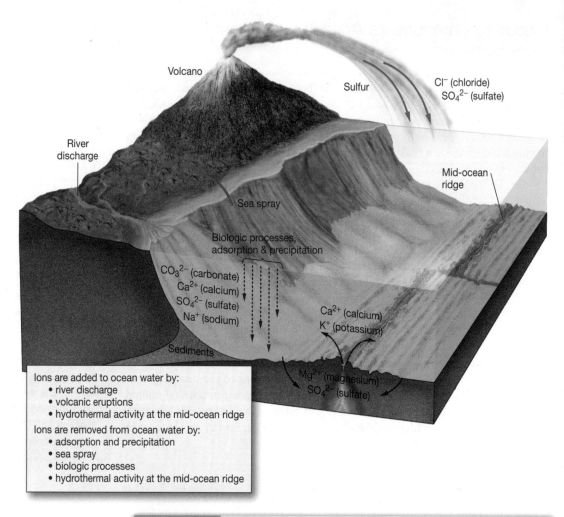

Ions are added to ocean water by:
• river discharge
• volcanic eruptions
• hydrothermal activity at the mid-ocean ridge

Ions are removed from ocean water by:
• adsorption and precipitation
• sea spray
• biologic processes
• hydrothermal activity at the mid-ocean ridge

TABLE 5.4   COMPARISON OF MAJOR DISSOLVED COMPONENTS IN STREAMS WITH THOSE IN SEAWATER

Constituent	Concentration in streams (parts per million)	Concentration in seawater (parts per million)
Bicarbonate ion (HCO_3^-)	58.4	trace
Calcium ion (Ca^{2+})	15.0	400
Silicate (SiO_2)	13.1	3
Sulfate ion (SO_4^{2-})	11.2	2700
Chloride ion (Cl^-)	7.8	19,200
Sodium ion (Na^+)	6.3	10,600
Magnesium ion (Mg^{2+})	4.1	1300
Potassium ion (K^+)	2.3	380
Total (parts per million)	119.2 ppm	34,793 ppm
Total (‰)	0.1192‰	34.8‰

Are the oceans becoming saltier through time? This might seem logical since new dissolved components are constantly being added to the oceans and because most salts have long residence times. However, analysis of ancient marine organisms and sea floor sediments suggests that the oceans have not increased in salinity over time. This must be because the rate at which an element is added to the ocean equals the rate at which it is removed, so the average *amounts* of various elements remain constant (this is called a *steady-state* condition).

Materials added to the oceans are counteracted by several processes that cycle dissolved substances out of seawater. When waves break at sea, for example, sea spray releases tiny salt particles into the atmosphere where they may be blown over land before being washed back to Earth. The amount of material leaving the ocean in this way is enormous: According to a recent study, as much as 3.3 billion metric tons (3.6 billion short tons) of salt as sea spray enter the atmosphere each year. Another example is the infiltration of seawater along mid-ocean ridges near hydrothermal vents (see Figure 5.17), which incorporates magnesium and sulfate ions into sea floor mineral deposits. In fact, chemical studies of seawater indicate that the *entire volume of ocean water* is recycled through this hydrothermal circulation system at the mid-ocean ridge approximately every 3 million years. As a result, the chemical exchange between ocean water and the basaltic crust has a major influence on the composition of ocean water.

Dissolved substances are also removed from seawater in other ways. Calcium, carbonate, sulfate, sodium, and silicon are deposited in ocean sediments within the shells of dead microscopic organisms and animal feces. Vast amounts of dissolved substances can be removed when inland arms of seas dry up, leaving salt deposits called *evaporites* (such as those beneath the Mediterranean Sea; see Web Box 4.1). In addition, ions dissolved in ocean water are removed by adsorption (physical attachment) to the surfaces of sinking clay and biologic particles.

5.5 Is Seawater Acidic or Basic?

An **acid** is a compound that releases hydrogen ions (H^+) when dissolved in water. The resulting solution is said to be *acidic*. A strong acid readily and completely releases hydrogen ions when dissolved in water. An **alkaline** or a **base** is a compound that releases hydroxide ions (OH^-) when dissolved in water. The resulting solution is said to be *alkaline* or *basic*. A strong base readily and completely releases hydroxide ions when dissolved in water.

Both hydrogen ions and hydroxide ions are present in extremely small amounts at all times in water because water molecules dissociate and reform. Chemically, this is represented by the equation:

$$H_2O \overset{\text{dissociate}}{\underset{\text{reform}}{\rightleftharpoons}} H^+ + OH^- \tag{5.2}$$

Note that if the hydrogen ions and hydroxide ions in a solution are due only to the dissociation of water molecules, they are always found in equal concentrations, and the solution is consequently neutral.

When substances dissociate in water, they can make the solution acidic or basic. For example, if hydrochloric acid (HCl) is added to water, the resulting solution will be acidic because there will be a large excess of hydrogen ions from the dissociation of the HCl molecules. Conversely, if a base such as baking soda (sodium bicarbonate, $NaHCO_3$) is added to water, the resulting solution will be basic because there will be an excess of hydroxide ions (OH^-) from the dissociation of $NaHCO_3$ molecules.

The pH Scale

Figure 5.20 shows the **pH** (potential of hydrogen) **scale**, which is a measure of the hydrogen ion concentration of a solution. Values for pH range from 0 (strongly

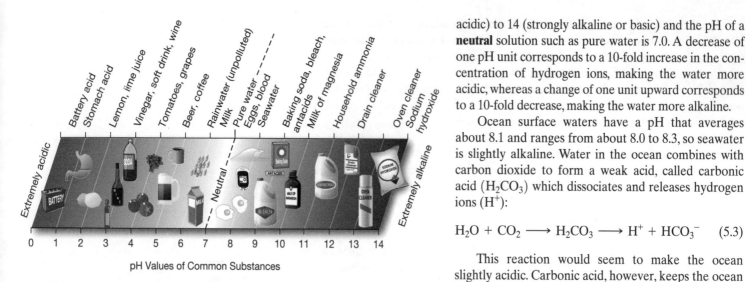

FIGURE 5.20 **The pH scale.** The pH scale ranges from 0 (highly acidic) to 14 (highly alkaline). A pH of 7 is neutral; the pH values of common substances are also shown.

acidic) to 14 (strongly alkaline or basic) and the pH of a **neutral** solution such as pure water is 7.0. A decrease of one pH unit corresponds to a 10-fold increase in the concentration of hydrogen ions, making the water more acidic, whereas a change of one unit upward corresponds to a 10-fold decrease, making the water more alkaline.

Ocean surface waters have a pH that averages about 8.1 and ranges from about 8.0 to 8.3, so seawater is slightly alkaline. Water in the ocean combines with carbon dioxide to form a weak acid, called carbonic acid (H_2CO_3) which dissociates and releases hydrogen ions (H^+):

$$H_2O + CO_2 \longrightarrow H_2CO_3 \longrightarrow H^+ + HCO_3^- \quad (5.3)$$

This reaction would seem to make the ocean slightly acidic. Carbonic acid, however, keeps the ocean slightly alkaline through the process of *buffering*.

The Carbonate Buffering System

The chemical reactions in Figure 5.21 show that carbon dioxide (CO_2) combines with water (H_2O) to form carbonic acid (H_2CO_3). Carbonic acid can then lose a hydrogen ion (H^+) to form the negatively charged bicarbonate ion (HCO_3^-). The bicarbonate ion can lose its hydrogen ion, too, though it does so less readily than carbonic acid. When the bicarbonate ion loses its hydrogen ion, it forms the double-charged negative carbonate ion (CO_3^{2-}) some of which combines with calcium ions to form calcium carbonate ($CaCO_3$). Some of the calcium carbonate is precipitated by various inorganic and organic means and then it sinks and cycles back into the ocean by dissolving at depth.

The equations below Figure 5.21 show how these chemical reactions involving carbonate minimize changes in the pH of the ocean in a process called **buffering**. Buffering protects the ocean from getting too acidic or too basic, similar to how buffered aspirin protects sensitive stomachs. For example, if the pH of the ocean increases (becomes too basic), it causes H_2CO_3 to release H^+ and pH drops. Conversely, if the pH of the ocean decreases (becomes too acidic), HCO_3^- combines with H^+ to remove it, causing pH to rise. In this way, buffering prevents large swings of ocean water pH and allows the ocean to stay within a limited range of pH values. Recently, however, increasing amounts of carbon dioxide from human emissions are beginning to enter the ocean and change the ocean's pH by making it more acidic. For more details on this, see Chapter 16, "The Oceans and Climate Change."

If seawater too basic: $H_2CO_3 \longrightarrow HCO_3^- + H^+$; pH drops
If seawater too acidic: $HCO_3^- + H^+ \longrightarrow H_2CO_3$; pH rises

FIGURE 5.21 **The carbonate buffering system.** Atmospheric carbon dioxide (CO_2) enters the ocean and undergoes chemical reactions. If seawater is too basic, chemical reactions occur that release H^+ into seawater and lower pH. If seawater is too acidic, chemical reactions occur that remove H^+ from seawater and cause pH to rise. Thus, buffering keeps the pH of seawater constant.

Deep-ocean water contains more carbon dioxide than surface water because deep water is cold and has the ability to dissolve more gases. Also, the higher pressures of the deep ocean further aid the dissolution of gases in seawater. Because carbon dioxide combines with water to form carbonic acid, why isn't the cold water of the deep ocean highly acidic? When microscopic marine organisms that make their shells out of calcium carbonate (calcite) die and sink into the deep ocean, they neutralize the acid through buffering. In essence, these organisms act as an "antacid" for the deep ocean analogous to the way commercial antacids use calcium carbonate to neutralize excess stomach acid. As explained in Chapter 4, these shells are readily dissolved below the calcite (calcium carbonate) compensation depth (CCD).

5.6 How Does Seawater Salinity Vary at the Surface and With Depth?

Average seawater salinity is 35‰, but it varies significantly from place to place at the surface and also with depth.

Surface Salinity Variation

Figure 5.22 shows how salinity varies at the surface with latitude. The red curve shows temperature, which decreases at high latitudes and increases near the equator. The green curve shows salinity, which is lowest at high latitudes, highest at the Tropics of Cancer and Capricorn, and dips near the equator.

Why does surface salinity vary in the pattern shown in Figure 5.22? At high latitudes, abundant precipitation and runoff and the melting of freshwater icebergs all decrease salinity. In addition, cool temperatures limit the amount of evaporation that takes place (which would increase salinity). The formation and melting of sea ice balance each other out in the course of a year and are not a factor in changes in salinity.

The pattern of Earth's atmospheric circulation (see Chapter 6, "Air-Sea Interaction") causes warm dry air to descend at lower latitudes near the Tropics of Cancer and Capricorn, so evaporation rates are high and salinity increases. In addition, little precipitation and runoff occur to decrease salinity. As a result, the regions near the Tropics of Cancer and Capricorn are the continental *and* maritime deserts of the world.

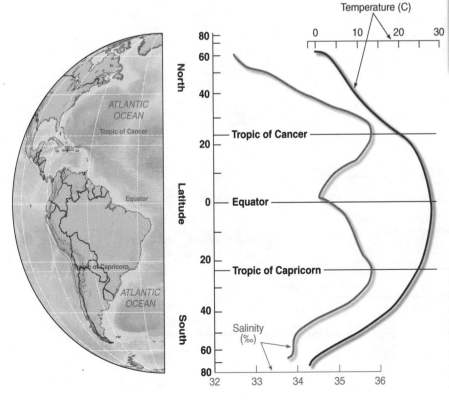

FIGURE 5.22 Surface salinity variation. Sea surface temperature (*red curve*) is lowest at the poles and highest at the equator. Surface seawater salinity (*green curve*) is lowest at the poles, peaks at the Tropics of Cancer and Capricorn, and dips near the equator. The presence of large amounts of runoff from land in far northern latitudes causes salinity to be lower there as compared to equivalent latitudes in the Southern Hemisphere.

Temperatures are warm near the equator, so evaporation rates are high enough to increase salinity. Increased precipitation and runoff partially offsets the high salinity, though. For example, daily rain showers are common along the equator, adding water to the ocean and lowering its salinity.

The map in Figure 5.23 shows how ocean surface salinity varies worldwide. Notice how the overall pattern matches the graph in Figure 5.22. The Atlantic Ocean's higher overall salinity is caused by its proximity to land, which experiences continental effect. This causes high rates of evaporation in the narrow Atlantic, particularly along the Tropics of Cancer and Capricorn.

Salinity Variation with Depth

Figure 5.24 shows how seawater salinity varies with depth. The graph displays data for the open ocean far from land and shows one curve for high-latitude regions and one for low-latitude regions.

For low-latitude regions (such as in the tropics), the curve begins at the surface with relatively high salinity (as was discussed in the preceding section). Even at the equator, surface salinity is still relatively high. With increasing depth, the curve swings toward an intermediate salinity value.

For high-latitude regions (such as near Antarctica or in the Gulf of Alaska), the curve begins at the surface with relatively low salinity (again, see the discussion in the preceding section). With increasing depth, the curve also swings toward an intermediate salinity value that approaches the value of the low-latitude salinity curve at the same depth.

These two curves, which together resemble the outline of a wide Champagne glass, show that salinity varies widely at the surface, but very little in the deep ocean. Why is this so? It occurs because all the processes that affect seawater salinity (precipitation, runoff, melting icebergs, melting sea ice, sea ice forming, and evaporation) occur at the *surface* and thus have no effect on deep water below.

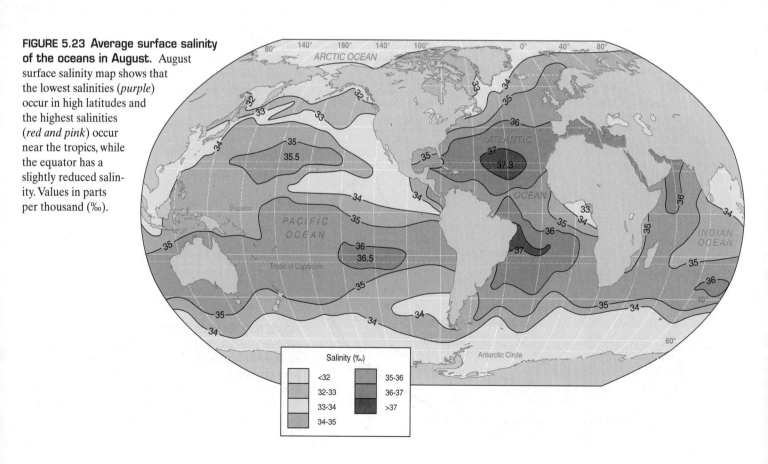

FIGURE 5.23 Average surface salinity of the oceans in August. August surface salinity map shows that the lowest salinities (*purple*) occur in high latitudes and the highest salinities (*red and pink*) occur near the tropics, while the equator has a slightly reduced salinity. Values in parts per thousand (‰).

Salinity (‰)

<32	35-36
32-33	36-37
33-34	>37
34-35	

Halocline

Both curves in Figure 5.24 show a rapid change in salinity between the depths of about 300 meters (980 feet) and 1000 meters (3300 feet). For the low-latitude curve, the change is a *decrease* in salinity. For the high-latitude curve, the change is an *increase* in salinity. In both cases, this layer of rapidly changing salinity with depth is called a **halocline** (*halo* = salt, *cline* = slope). Haloclines separate layers of different salinity in the ocean.

5.7 How Does Seawater Density Vary With Depth?

The density of pure water is 1.000 gram per cubic centimeter (g/cm³) at 4°C (39°F). This value serves as a standard against which the density of all other substances can be measured. Seawater contains various dissolved substances that increase its density. In the open ocean, seawater density averages between 1.022 and 1.030 g/cm³ (depending on its salinity). Thus, the density of seawater is 2 to 3% greater than pure water. Unlike freshwater, seawater continues to increase in density until it freezes at a temperature of −1.9°C (28.6°F) (recall that below 4°C, the density of freshwater actually *decreases*; see Figure 5.12). At its freezing point, however, seawater behaves in a similar fashion to freshwater: Its density decreases dramatically, which is why sea ice floats, too.

Density is an important property of ocean water because density differences determine the vertical position of ocean water and cause water masses to float or sink, thereby creating deep-ocean currents. For example, if seawater with a density of 1.030 g/cm³ were added to freshwater with a density of 1.000 g/cm³, the denser seawater would sink below the freshwater, initiating a deep current.

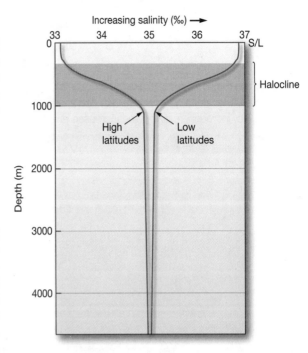

FIGURE 5.24 Salinity variation with depth. Vertical open-ocean profile showing high- and low-latitude salinity variation (horizontal scale in ‰) with depth (vertical scale in meters with sea level at the top). The layer of rapidly changing salinity with depth is the halocline.

Factors Affecting Seawater Density

The ocean, like Earth's interior, is layered according to density. Low-density water exists near the surface and higher density water occurs below. Except for some shallow inland seas with a high rate of evaporation that creates high salinity water, the highest-density water is found at the deepest ocean depths. Let's examine how temperature, salinity, and pressure influence seawater density by expressing the relationships using arrows (up arrow = increase, down arrow = decrease):

- As temperature increases (↑), seawater density decreases (↓)[11] (due to thermal expansion).
- As salinity increases (↑), seawater density increases (↑) (due to the addition of more dissolved material).
- As pressure increases (↑), seawater density increases (↑) (due to the compressive effects of pressure).

Of these three factors, only temperature and salinity influence the density of surface water. Pressure influences seawater density only when very high pressures are encountered, such as in deep-ocean trenches. Still, the density of seawater in the deep ocean is only about 5% greater than at the ocean surface, showing that despite tons of pressure per square centimeter, water is nearly incompressible. Unlike air, which can be compressed and put in a tank for scuba diving, the molecules in liquid water are already close together and cannot be compressed much more. Therefore, pressure has the least effect on influencing the density of surface water and can largely be ignored.

---

[11]A relationship where one variable *decreases* as a result of another variable's *increase* is known as an inverse relationship, in which the two variables are *inversely proportional*.

KEY CONCEPT
Differences in ocean density cause the ocean to be layered. Seawater density increases with decreased temperature, increased salinity, and increased pressure.

Temperature, on the other hand, has the greatest influence on surface seawater density because the range of surface seawater temperature is greater than that of salinity. In fact, only in the extreme polar areas of the ocean, where temperatures are low and remain relatively constant, does salinity significantly affect density. Cold water that also has high salinity is some of the highest-density water in the world. The density of seawater—the result of its salinity and temperature—influences currents in the deep ocean because high-density water sinks below less-dense water.

Temperature and Density Variation with Depth

The four graphs in Figure 5.25 show how seawater temperature and density vary with depth in both low-latitude and high-latitude regions. Let's examine each graph individually.

Figure 5.25a shows how temperature varies with depth in low-latitude regions, where surface waters are warmed by high Sun angles and constant length of days. However, the Sun's energy does not penetrate very far into the ocean. Surface water temperatures remain relatively constant until a depth of about 300 meters (980 feet) because of good surface mixing mechanisms such as surface currents, waves, and tides. Below 300 meters (980 feet), the temperature decreases rapidly until a depth of about 1000 meters (3300 feet). Below 1000 meters, the water's low temperature again remains constant down to the ocean floor.

Figure 5.25b shows how temperature varies with depth in high-latitude regions, where surface waters remain cool year-round and deep-water temperatures are about the same as the surface. The temperature curve for high-latitude regions, therefore, is a straight vertical line, which indicates uniform conditions at the surface and at depth.

The density curve for low-latitude regions in Figure 5.25c shows that density is relatively low at the surface. Density is low because surface water temperatures are high. (Remember that temperature has the greatest influence on density and temperature is inversely proportional to density.) Below the surface, density remains constant also until a depth of about 300 meters (980 feet) because of good surface mixing. Below 300 meters (980 feet), the density increases rapidly until a depth of about 1000 meters (3300 feet). Below 1000 meters, the water's low density again remains constant down to the ocean floor.

The density curve for high-latitude regions (Figure 5.25d) shows very little variation with depth. Density is relatively high at the surface because surface water temperatures are low. Density is high below the surface, too, because water

FIGURE 5.25 Temperature and density variations with depth. (a) Temperature variation with depth in low-latitude regions. The layer of rapidly changing temperature with depth is the thermocline. **(b)** Temperature variation with depth in high-latitude regions. Because the water column is isothermal, there is no thermocline. **(c)** Density variation with depth in low-latitude regions. The layer of rapidly changing density with depth is the pycnocline. **(d)** Density variation with depth in high-latitude regions. Because the water column is isopycnal, there is no pycnocline. Note the inverse relationship between temperature and density by comparing curves *a* and *c* (low latitudes) and curves *b* and *d* (high latitudes).

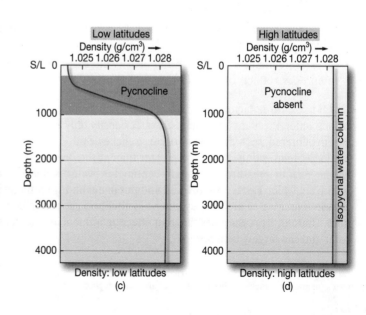

temperature is also low. The density curve for high-latitude regions, therefore, is a straight vertical line, which indicates uniform conditions at the surface and at depth. These conditions allow cold high-density water to form at the surface, sink, and initiate deep-ocean currents.

Temperature is the most important factor influencing seawater density, so the temperature graphs (Figure 5.25a and Figure 5.25b) strongly resemble the corresponding density graphs (Figure 5.25c and Figure 5.25d, respectively). The only difference is that they are *a mirror image of each other*, illustrating that temperature and density are inversely proportional to one another.

Thermocline and Pycnocline

Analogous to the halocline (the layer of rapidly changing salinity shown in Figure 5.24), the low-latitude temperature graph in Figure 5.25a displays a curving line that indicates a layer of rapidly changing temperature called a **thermocline** (*thermo* = heat, *cline* = slope). Similarly, the low-latitude density graph in Figure 5.25c displays a curving line that indicates a **pycnocline** (*pycno* = density, *cline* = slope), which is a layer of rapidly changing density. Note that the high-latitude graphs of temperature (Figure 5.25b) and density (Figure 5.25d) lack both a thermocline and a pycnocline, respectively, because these lines show a constant value with depth (they are straight lines and don't curve). Like a halocline, a thermocline and a pycnocline typically occur between about 300 meters (980 feet) and 1000 meters (3300 feet) below the surface. The temperature difference between water above and below the thermocline can be used to generate electricity (see Web Box 5.1).

When a pycnocline is established in an area, it presents an incredible barrier to mixing between low-density water above and high-density water below. A pycnocline has a high gravitational stability and thus physically isolates adjacent layers of water.[12] The pycnocline results from the combined effect of the thermocline and the halocline, because temperature and salinity influence density. The interrelation of these three layers determines the degree of separation between the upper-water and deep-water masses.

There are essentially three distinct water masses based on density. The **mixed surface layer** occurs above a strong permanent thermocline (and corresponding pycnocline). The water is uniform because it is well mixed by surface currents, waves, and tides. The thermocline and pycnocline occur in a relatively low-density layer called the **upper water**, which is well developed throughout the low and middle latitudes. Denser and colder **deep water** extends from below the thermocline/pycnocline to the deep-ocean floor.

At depths above the main thermocline, divers often experience lesser thermoclines (and corresponding pycnoclines) when descending into the ocean. Thermoclines can develop in swimming pools, ponds, and lakes, too. During the spring and fall, when nights are cool but days can be quite warm, the Sun heats the surface water of the pool yet the water below the surface can be quite cold. If the pool has not been mixed, a thermocline isolates the warm surface layer from the deeper cold water. The cold water below the thermocline can be quite a surprise for anyone who dives into the pool!

In high-latitude regions, the temperature of the surface water remains cold year round, so there is very little difference between the temperature at the surface and in deep water below. Thus, a thermocline and corresponding pycnocline rarely develop in high-latitude regions. Only during the short summer when the days are long does the Sun begin to heat surface waters. Even then, the water

> **KEY CONCEPT**
> A halocline is a layer of rapidly changing salinity, a thermocline is a layer of rapidly changing temperature, and a pycnocline is a layer of rapidly changing density.

---

[12]This is similar to a temperature inversion in the atmosphere, which traps cold (high-density) air underneath warm (low-density) air.

does not heat up very much. Nearly all year, then, the water column in high latitudes is **isothermal** (*iso* = same, *thermo* = heat) and **isopycnal** (*iso* = same, *pycno* = density) allowing good vertical mixing between surface and deeper waters.

5.8 What Methods Are Used to Desalinate SeaWater?

Earth's expanding population uses freshwater in greater volumes each year. In the future, experts warn that more people worldwide will experience water shortage problems, even with increased water use efficiency. Because human need for water is growing yet its supply is dwindling, several countries have begun to use the ocean as a source of freshwater. **Desalination**, or salt removal from seawater, can provide freshwater for business, home, and agricultural use.

Although seawater is mostly just water molecules, its ability to form hydrogen bonds, easily dissolve so many substances, and resist changes in temperature and state makes seawater difficult to desalinate. This is why desalination is so energy-intensive and so expensive. The high cost of desalination, however, is only one issue. Recent studies, for example, indicate that desalination can have unwanted environmental effects through the production of highly concentrated salt brines and potential negative effects on marine life. Still, using the sea as a source of freshwater is attractive to many coastal communities that have few other sources.

Currently, there are more than 13,000 desalination plants worldwide, with the majority very small and located in arid regions of the Middle East, Caribbean, and Mediterranean. The United States produces only about 10% of the world's desalted water, primarily in Florida. To date, only a limited number of desalination plants have been built along the California coast, primarily because the cost of desalination is generally higher than the costs of other water supply alternatives available in California (such as water transfers and groundwater pumping) but also because the extensive permitting process is an impediment to building desalination facilities. However, as drought conditions occur and concern over water availability increases, desalination projects are being proposed at numerous locations in the state.

Because desalinated water requires a lot of energy and thus is expensive to produce, most desalination plants are small-scale operations. In fact, desalination plants provide less than 0.5% of human water needs. More than half of the world's desalination plants use *distillation* to purify water, while most of the remaining plants use *membrane processes*.

Distillation

The process of **distillation** (*distillare* = to trickle) is shown schematically in Figure 5.26. In distillation, saltwater is boiled and the resulting water vapor is passed through a cooling condenser where it condenses and is collected as freshwater. This simple procedure is very efficient at purifying seawater. For instance, distillation of 35‰ seawater produces freshwater with a salinity of only 0.03‰, which is about 10 times fresher than bottled water, so it needs to be mixed with less pure water to make it taste better. Distillation is expensive, however, because it requires large amounts of heat energy to boil the saltwater. Because of water's high latent heat of vaporization, it takes 540 calories to convert only 1 gram (0.035 ounce) of water at the boiling point to the vapor state.[13] Increased efficiency, such as using the waste heat from a power plant, is required to make distillation practical on a large scale.

FIGURE 5.26 Distillation. The process of distillation requires boiling saltwater (*heat distillation*) or using the Sun's energy to evaporate seawater (*solar distillation*). In either case, the water vapor is captured and condensed in a process that produces very pure water.

[13]Even at 100% efficiency, it still requires a whopping *540,000 calories* of heat energy to produce 1 liter (about 1 quart) of distilled water.

Solar distillation, which is also known as **solar humidification**, does not require supplemental heating and has been used successfully in small-scale agricultural experiments in arid regions such as Israel, West Africa, and Peru. Solar humidification is similar to distillation in that saltwater is evaporated in a covered container, but the water is heated by direct sunlight instead (Figure 5.26). Saltwater in the container evaporates, and the water vapor that condenses on the cover runs into collection trays. The major difficulty lies in effectively concentrating the energy of sunlight into a small area to speed evaporation.

Membrane Processes

Electrolysis can be used to desalinate seawater, too. In this method, two volumes of freshwater—one containing a positive electrode and the other a negative electrode—are placed on either side of a volume of seawater. The seawater is separated from each of the freshwater reservoirs by semipermeable membranes. These membranes are permeable to salt ions but not to water molecules. When an electrical current is applied, positive ions such as sodium ions are attracted to the negative electrode, and negative ions such as chloride ions are attracted to the positive electrode. In time, enough ions are removed through the membranes to convert the seawater to freshwater. The major drawback to electrolysis is that it requires large amounts of energy.

Reverse osmosis (*osmos* = to push) may have potential for large-scale desalination. In osmosis, water molecules naturally pass through a thin, semipermeable membrane from a freshwater solution to a saltwater solution. In reverse osmosis, water on the salty side is highly pressurized to drive water molecules—but not salt and other impurities—through the membrane to the freshwater side (Figure 5.27). A significant problem with reverse osmosis is that the membranes are flimsy, become clogged, and must be replaced frequently. Advanced composite materials may help eliminate these problems because they are sturdier, provide better filtration, and last up to 10 years.

Worldwide, at least 30 countries are operating reverse osmosis units. Saudi Arabia—where energy from oil is cheap but water is scarce—has the world's largest reverse osmosis plant, which produces 485 million liters (128 million gallons) of desalted water daily. The largest plant in the United States opened in 2008 in Tampa Bay, Florida, and produces up to 95 million liters (25 million gallons) of freshwater per day, which provides about 10% of the drinking water supply of the Tampa Bay region. Once permits are obtained, a new facility in Carlsbad, California, is designed to produce twice as much freshwater as the Tampa Bay plant. Reverse osmosis is also used in many household water purification units and aquariums.

Other Methods of Desalination

Seawater selectively excludes dissolved substances as it freezes—a process called **freeze separation**. As a result, the salinity of sea ice (once it is melted) is typically 70% lower than seawater. To make this an effective desalination technique, though, the water must be frozen and thawed multiple times, with the salts washed from the ice between each thawing. Like electrolysis, freeze separation requires large amounts of energy, so it may be impractical except on a small scale.

Yet another way to obtain freshwater is to melt naturally formed ice. Imaginative thinkers have proposed towing large icebergs to coastal waters off countries that need freshwater. Once there, the freshwater produced as the icebergs melt could be captured and pumped ashore. Studies have shown that towing large Antarctic icebergs to arid regions would be technologically feasible and, for certain Southern Hemisphere locations, economically feasible, too.

Other novel approaches to desalination include crystallization of dissolved components directly from seawater, solvent demineralization using chemical catalysts, and even making use of salt-eating bacteria!

FIGURE 5.27 Reverse osmosis. The process of reverse osmosis involves applying pressure to salt water and forcing it through a semipermeable membrane, thus removing the salts and producing freshwater.

KEY CONCEPT
Although desalination of seawater is costly, desalination plants use the methods of distillation, solar humidification, electrolysis, freeze separation, and reverse osmosis to purify seawater for domestic use.

Chapter in Review

• *Water's remarkable properties help make life as we know it possible on Earth.* These properties include the arrangement of its atoms, how its molecules stick together, its ability to dissolve almost everything, and its heat storage capacity.

• *The water molecule is composed of one atom of oxygen and two atoms of hydrogen (H_2O).* The two hydrogen atoms, which are covalently bonded to the oxygen atom, are *attached to the same side of the oxygen atom* and produce a bend in the geometry of a water molecule. This geometry makes water molecules *polar*, which allows them to form hydrogen bonds with other water molecules or other substances and gives water its remarkable properties. Water, for example, is *"the universal solvent"* because it can hydrate charged particles (ions), thereby dissolving them.

• *Water is one of the few substances that exists naturally on Earth in all three states of matter* (solid, liquid, gas). Hydrogen bonding gives water *unusual thermal properties*, such as a high freezing point (0°C [32°F]) and boiling point (100°C [212°F]), a high heat capacity and high specific heat (1 calorie per gram), a high latent heat of melting (80 calories per gram), and a high latent heat of vaporization (540 calories per gram). Water's high heat capacity and latent heats have important implications in regulating global thermostatic effects.

• *The density of water increases as temperature decreases,* similar to most substances, and reaches a maximum density at 4°C (39°F). *Below 4°C, however, water density decreases with temperature,* due to the formation of bulky ice crystals. *As water freezes, it expands by about 9% in volume, so ice floats on water.*

• *Salinity is the amount of dissolved solids in ocean water.* It averages about 35 grams of dissolved solids per kilogram of ocean water (*35 parts per thousand [‰]*) but ranges from brackish to hypersaline. Six ions—chloride, sodium, sulfate, magnesium, calcium, and potassium—account for over 99% of the dissolved solids in ocean water. These ions always occur in a *constant proportion* in any seawater sample, so salinity can be determined by measuring the concentration of only one—typically, the chloride ion.

• *The physical properties of pure water and seawater are remarkably similar,* with a few notable exceptions. Compared to pure water, seawater has a higher pH, density, and boiling point (but a lower freezing point).

• *Dissolved components in seawater are added and removed by a variety of processes.* Precipitation, runoff, and the melting of icebergs and sea ice add freshwater to seawater and decrease its salinity. The formation of sea ice and evaporation remove freshwater from seawater and increase its salinity. The hydrologic cycle includes all the reservoirs of water on Earth, including the *oceans*, which contain *97% of Earth's water*. The residence time of various elements indicates how long they stay in the ocean and implies that *ocean salinity has remained constant through time.*

• *A natural buffering system* based on the chemical reaction of carbon dioxide in water *exists in the ocean.* This buffering system *regulates any changes in pH*, creating a stable ocean environment.

• *The salinity of surface water varies considerably due to surface processes,* with the maximum salinity found near the Tropics of Cancer and Capricorn and the minimum salinity found in high-latitude regions. Salinity also varies with depth down to about 1000 meters (3300 feet), but below that the salinity of deep water is very consistent. *A halocline is a layer of rapidly changing salinity.*

• *Seawater density increases as temperature decreases and salinity increases,* though temperature influences surface seawater density more strongly than salinity (the influence of pressure is negligible). Temperature and density vary considerably with depth in low-latitude regions, creating a *thermocline (layer of rapidly changing temperature)* and corresponding *pycnocline (layer of rapidly changing density)*, both of which are generally absent in high latitudes.

• Although *desalination of seawater* is costly, it *provides freshwater for* business, home, and agricultural use. *Distillation, solar humidification, electrolysis, freeze separation,* and *reverse osmosis* are methods currently used to desalinate seawater.

Key Terms

Review Questions

1. Sketch a model of an atom, showing the positions of the subatomic particles protons, neutrons, and electrons.

2. Describe what condition exists in water molecules to make them dipolar.

3. Sketch several water molecules, showing all covalent and hydrogen bonds. Be sure to indicate the polarity of each water molecule.

4. How does hydrogen bonding produce the surface tension phenomenon of water?

5. Discuss how the dipolar nature of the water molecule makes it such an effective solvent of ionic compounds.

6. Why are the freezing and boiling points of water higher than would be expected for a compound of its molecular makeup?

7. How does the specific heat capacity of water compare with that of other substances? Describe the effect this has on climate.

8. The heat energy added as latent heat of melting and latent heat of vaporization does not increase water temperature. Explain why this occurs and where the energy is used.

9. Why is the latent heat of vaporization so much greater than the latent heat of melting?

10. Describe how excess heat energy absorbed by Earth's low-latitude regions is transferred to heat-deficient higher latitudes through a process that uses water's latent heat of evaporation.

11. As water cools, two distinct changes take place in the behavior of molecules: Their slower movement tends to increase density, whereas the formation of bulky ice crystals decreases density. Describe how the relative rates of their occurrence cause pure water to have a temperature of maximum density at 4°C (39.2°F) and make ice less dense than liquid water.

12. What is your state sales tax, in parts per thousand?

13. What are goiters? How can they be avoided?

14. What condition of salinity makes it possible to determine the total salinity of ocean water by measuring the concentration of only one constituent, the chloride ion?

15. List some major achievements of the voyage of HMS *Challenger*.

16. What physical conditions create brackish water in the Baltic Sea and hypersaline water in the Red Sea?

17. Describe the ways in which dissolved components are added and removed from seawater.

18. List the components (reservoirs) of the hydrologic cycle that hold water on Earth and the percentage of Earth's water in each one. Describe the processes by which water moves among these reservoirs.

19. Explain the difference between an acid and an alkali (base) substance. How does the ocean's buffering system work?

20. Why is there such a close association between (a) the curve showing seawater density variation with ocean depth and (b) the curve showing seawater temperature variation with ocean depth?

Critical Thinking Exercises

1. Describe the differences between the three states of matter, using the arrangement of molecules in your explanation.

2. Explain why there is such a wide variation of surface salinity but such a narrow range of salinity at depth.

3. Compare and contrast the following seawater desalination methods: distillation, solar humidification, and reverse osmosis.

Oceanography on the Web

Visit the *Essentials of Oceanography* Online Study Guide for Internet resources, including chapter-specific quizzes to test your understanding and Web links to further your exploration of the topics in this chapter.

The *Essentials of Oceanography* Online Study Guide is at http://www.mygeoscienceplace.com/.

Iceberg above and below water.
Composite image of an iceberg, showing that 90% of an iceberg's mass is below water. Interactions between sea ice, the ocean, and the atmosphere help regulate Earth's climate.

"When the still sea conspires an armor
And her sullen and aborted
Currents breed tiny monsters,
True sailing is dead
Awkward instant
And the first animal is jettisoned . . ."

— *The Doors,*
Horse Latitudes (1972)

6 AIR–SEA INTERACTION

One of the most remarkable things about our planet is that the atmosphere and the ocean act as one interdependent system. Observations of the atmosphere–ocean system show that what happens in one causes changes in the other. Further, the two parts of this system are linked by complex feedback loops, some of which reinforce a change and others that nullify any changes. Surface currents in the oceans, for instance, are a direct result of Earth's atmospheric wind belts. Conversely, certain atmospheric weather phenomena are manifested in the oceans. In order to understand the behavior of the atmosphere and the oceans, their mutual interactions and relationships must be examined.

Solar energy heats the surface of Earth and creates atmospheric winds, which, in turn, drive most of the surface currents and waves in the ocean. Radiant energy from the Sun, therefore, is responsible for motion in the atmosphere and the ocean. Recall from Chapter 5 that the atmosphere and ocean use the high heat capacity of water to constantly exchange this energy, shaping Earth's global weather patterns in the process.

Periodic extremes of atmospheric weather, such as droughts and profuse precipitation, are related to periodic changes in oceanic conditions. For instance, it was recognized as far back as the 1920s that El Niño—an ocean event—was tied to catastrophic weather events worldwide. What is as yet unclear, however, is if changes in the ocean produce changes in the atmosphere that lead to El Niño conditions—or vice versa. El Niño–Southern Oscillation events are discussed in Chapter 7, "Ocean Circulation."

Air–sea interactions have important implications in global warming, too. A multitude of recent studies have confirmed that the atmosphere is experiencing unprecedented warming as a result of human-caused emissions of carbon dioxide and other gases that absorb and trap heat in the atmosphere. This atmospheric heat is being transferred to the oceans and has the potential to cause widespread marine ecosystem changes. This issue is discussed in Chapter 16, "The Oceans and Climate Change."

In this chapter, we'll examine the redistribution of solar heat by the atmosphere and its influence on oceanic conditions. First, large-scale phenomena that influence air–sea interactions are studied, and then smaller scale phenomena are examined.

6.1 What Causes Earth's Seasons?

Earth revolves around the Sun along an elliptical path (Figure 6.1). The plane traced by Earth's orbit is called the **ecliptic**. Earth's axis of rotation is not perpendicular ("upright") on the ecliptic; rather, it tilts at an angle of 23.5 degrees. Figure 6.1 shows that throughout the yearly cycle, Earth's axis *always points in the same direction*, which is toward Polaris, the North Star.

FIGURE 6.1 Earth's seasons. As Earth orbits the Sun during one year, its axis of rotation constantly tilts 23.5 degrees from perpendicular (relative to the plane of the ecliptic) and always points in the same direction, causing different areas to experience vertical rays of the Sun. This tilt causes Earth to have seasons, such as when the Northern Hemisphere is tilted toward the Sun during the summer (*left inset*), and away from the Sun during the winter (*right inset*).

Earth-Sun Relations

The tilt of Earth's rotational axis (and not its elliptical path) causes Earth to have seasons. Spring, summer, fall, and winter occur as follows:

- At the **vernal equinox** (*vernus* = spring; *equi* = equal, *noct* = night), which occurs on or about March 21, the Sun is directly overhead along the equator. During this time, all places in the world experience equal lengths of night and day (hence the name *equinox*). In the Northern Hemisphere, the vernal equinox is also known as the spring equinox.

- At the **summer solstice** (*sol* = the Sun, *stitium* = a stoppage), which occurs on or about June 21, the Sun reaches its most northerly point in the sky, directly overhead along the **Tropic of Cancer**, at 23.5 degrees north latitude (Figure 6.1, *left inset*). To an observer on Earth, the noonday Sun reaches its northernmost or southernmost position in the sky at this time and appears to pause—hence the term *solstice*—before beginning its next six-month cycle.

- At the **autumnal** (*autumnus* = fall) **equinox**, which occurs on or about September 23, the Sun is directly overhead along the equator again. In the Northern Hemisphere, the autumnal equinox is also known as the fall equinox.

- At the **winter solstice**, which occurs on or about December 22, the Sun is directly overhead along the **Tropic of Capricorn**, at 23.5 degrees south latitude (Figure 6.1, *right inset*). In the Southern Hemisphere, the seasons are reversed. Thus, the winter solstice is the time when the Southern Hemisphere is most directly facing the Sun, which is the beginning of the Southern Hemisphere summer.

Because Earth's rotational axis is tilted 23.5 degrees, the Sun's **declination** (angular distance from the equatorial plane) varies between 23.5 degrees north and 23.5 degrees south of the equator on a yearly cycle. As a result, the region between these two latitudes (called the **tropics**) receives much greater annual radiation than polar areas.

Seasonal changes in the angle of the Sun and the length of day profoundly influence Earth's climate. In the Northern Hemisphere, for example, the longest day occurs on the summer solstice and the shortest day on the winter solstice.

Daily heating of Earth also influences climate in most locations. Exceptions to this pattern occur north of the **Arctic Circle** (66.5 degrees north latitude) and south of the **Antarctic Circle** (66.5 degrees south latitude), which at certain times of the year do not experience daily cycles of daylight and darkness. For instance, during the Northern Hemisphere winter, the area north of the Arctic Circle receives no direct solar radiation at all and experiences up to six months of darkness. At the same time, the area south of the Antarctic Circle receives continuous radiation ("midnight Sun"), so it experiences up to six months of light. Half a year later, during the Northern Hemisphere summer (the Southern Hemisphere winter), the situation is reversed.

> **KEY CONCEPT**
> Earth's axis is tilted at an angle of 23.5 degrees, which causes the Northern and Southern Hemispheres to take turns "leaning toward" the Sun every six months and results in the change of seasons.

6.2 How Does Uneven Solar Heating Affect Earth?

The side of Earth facing the Sun (the daytime side) receives a tremendous dose of intense solar energy. This energy drives the global ocean–atmosphere engine, creating pressure and density differences that stir currents and waves in both the atmosphere and the ocean.

Distribution of Solar Energy

If Earth were a flat plate in space, with its flat side directly facing the Sun, sunlight would fall equally on all parts of Earth. Earth is spherical, however, so the amount and intensity of solar radiation received at higher latitudes are much less than at lower latitudes. The following factors influence the amount of radiation received at low and high latitudes:

- Sunlight strikes low latitudes at a high angle, so the radiation is concentrated in a relatively small area (area *A* in Figure 6.2). Sunlight strikes high latitudes at a low angle, so the same amount of radiation is spread over a larger area (area *B* in Figure 6.2).

- Earth's atmosphere absorbs some radiation, so less radiation strikes Earth at high latitudes than at low latitudes, because sunlight passes through more of the atmosphere at high latitudes.

- The **albedo** (*albus* = white) of various Earth materials is the percentage of incident radiation that is reflected back to space. The average albedo of Earth's surface is about 30%. More radiation is reflected back to space at high latitudes because ice has a much higher albedo than soil or vegetation.

- The angle at which sunlight strikes the ocean surface determines how much is absorbed and how much is reflected. If the Sun shines down on a smooth sea from directly overhead, only 2% of the radiation is reflected, but if the Sun is only 5 degrees above the horizon, 40% is reflected back into the atmosphere (Table 6.1). Thus, the ocean reflects more radiation at high latitudes than at low latitudes.

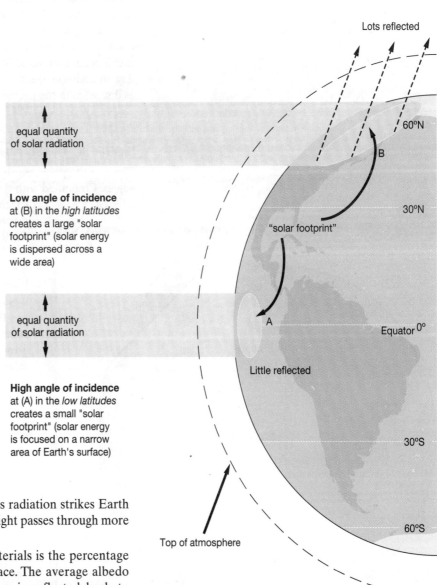

Low angle of incidence at (B) in the *high latitudes* creates a large "solar footprint" (solar energy is dispersed across a wide area)

High angle of incidence at (A) in the *low latitudes* creates a small "solar footprint" (solar energy is focused on a narrow area of Earth's surface)

FIGURE 6.2 Solar radiation received on Earth. Two identical beams of sunlight strike Earth. At *A*, the light beam is focused on a narrow area of Earth's surface and produces a smaller "solar footprint"; at *B*, the light beam is dispersed across a wide area and produces a larger "solar footprint." Additionally, more light is reflected at *B*. Thus, the amount of solar energy received at higher latitudes is much less than that at lower latitudes.

TABLE 6.1	REFLECTION AND ABSORPTION OF SOLAR ENERGY RELATIVE TO THE ANGLE OF INCIDENCE ON A FLAT SEA				
Elevation of the Sun above the horizon	**90°**	**60°**	**30°**	**15°**	**5°**
Reflected radiation (%)	2	3	6	20	40
Absorbed radiation (%)	98	97	94	80	60

Because of all these reasons, the intensity of radiation at high latitudes is greatly decreased compared with that falling in the equatorial region.

Other factors influence the amount of solar energy that reaches Earth. For example, the amount of radiation received at Earth's surface varies *daily* because Earth rotates on its axis so the surface experiences daylight and darkness each day. In addition, the amount of radiation varies *annually* due to Earth's seasons, as discussed in the previous section.

Oceanic Heat Flow

Close to the poles, much incoming solar radiation strikes Earth's surface at low angles. Combined with the high albedo of ice, more energy is reflected back into space than absorbed. In contrast, between about 35 degrees north latitude and 40 degrees south latitude,[1] sunlight strikes Earth at much higher angles and more energy is absorbed than reflected back into space. The graph in Figure 6.3 shows how incoming sunlight and outgoing heat combine on a daily basis for a net heat gain in low-latitude oceans and a net heat loss in high-latitude oceans.

Based on Figure 6.3, you might expect the equatorial zone to grow progressively warmer and the polar regions to grow progressively cooler. The polar regions are always considerably colder than the equatorial zone, but the temperature *difference* remains the same because excess heat is transferred from the equatorial zone to the poles. How is this accomplished? Circulation in both the oceans and the atmosphere transfers the heat.

6.3 What Physical Properties Does the Atmosphere Possess?

The atmosphere transfers heat and water vapor from place to place on Earth. Within the atmosphere, complex relationships exist among air composition, temperature, density, water vapor content, and pressure. Before we apply these relationships, let's examine the atmosphere's composition and some of its physical properties.

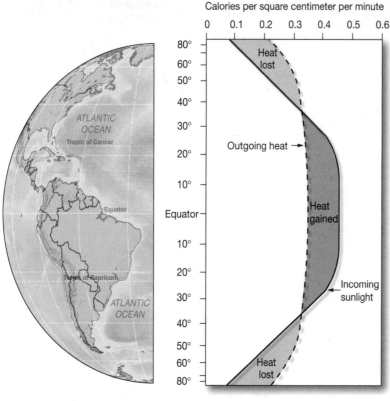

FIGURE 6.3 Heat gained and lost from the ocean varies with latitude. Heat gained by the oceans in equatorial latitudes (*red portion of graph*) equals heat lost in polar latitudes (*blue portion of graph*). On average, the two balance each other, and the excess heat from equatorial latitudes is transferred to heat-deficient polar latitudes by both oceanic and atmospheric circulation.

[1]Note that this latitudinal range extends farther into the Southern Hemisphere because the Southern Hemisphere has more ocean surface area in the middle latitudes than the Northern Hemisphere does.

Composition of the Atmosphere

Figure 6.4 lists the composition of dry air and shows that the atmosphere consists almost entirely of nitrogen and oxygen. Other gases include argon (an inert gas), carbon dioxide, and others in trace amounts. Although these gases are present in very small amounts, they can trap significant amounts of heat within the atmosphere. For more about how these gases trap heat in the atmosphere, see Chapter 16, "The Oceans and Climate Change."

Temperature Variation in the Atmosphere

Intuitively, it seems logical that the higher one goes in the atmosphere, the warmer it should be since it's closer to the Sun. However, as unusual as it seems, the atmosphere is actually heated from *below*. Moreover, the Sun's energy passes through the Earth's atmosphere and heats the Earth's surface (both land and water), which then reradiates this energy as heat into the atmosphere. This process is known as the *greenhouse effect* and will be discussed in more detail in Chapter 16, "The Oceans and Climate Change."

Figure 6.5 shows a temperature profile of the atmosphere. The lowermost portion of the atmosphere, which extends from the surface to about 12 kilometers (7 miles), is called the **troposphere** (*tropo* = turn, *sphere* = a ball) and is where all weather is produced. The troposphere gets its name because of the abundance of mixing that occurs within this layer of the atmosphere, mostly as a result of being heated from below. Within the troposphere, temperature gets cooler with altitude to the point that at high altitudes, the air temperature is well below freezing. If you have ever flown in a jet airplane, for instance, you may have noticed that any water on the wings or inside your window freezes during a high-altitude flight.

Density Variation in the Atmosphere

It may seem surprising that air has density, but since air is composed of molecules, it certainly does. Temperature has a dramatic effect on the density of air. At higher temperatures, for example, air molecules move more quickly, take up more space, and density is decreased. Thus, the general relationship between density and temperature is as follows:

- Warm air is less dense, so it rises; this is commonly expressed as "heat rises."
- Cool air is more dense, so it sinks.

Figure 6.6 shows how a radiator (heater) uses convection to heat a room. The heater warms the nearby air and causes it to expand. This expansion makes the air less dense, causing it to rise. Conversely, a cold window cools the nearby air and causes it to contract, thereby becoming more dense, which causes it to sink. A **convection** (*con* = with, *vect* = carried) **cell** forms, composed of the rising and sinking air moving in a circular fashion, similar to the convection in Earth's mantle discussed in Chapter 2.

Atmospheric Water Vapor Content

The amount of water vapor in air depends in part on the air's temperature. Warm air, for instance, can hold more water vapor than cold air because the air molecules are moving more quickly and come into contact with more water vapor. Thus, warm air is typically moist, and, conversely, cool air is typically dry. As a result, a warm, breezy day speeds evaporation when you hang your laundry outside to dry.

Water vapor influences the density of air. The addition of water vapor decreases the density of air because water vapor has a lower density than air. Thus, humid air is less dense than dry air.

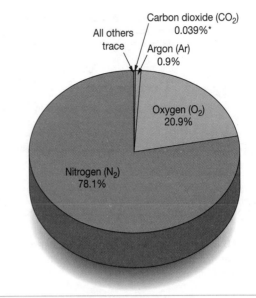

*Note that the concentration of carbon dioxide in the atmosphere is increasing by 0.5% per year due to human activities

FIGURE 6.4 Composition of dry air. Pie chart showing the composition of dry air (without any water vapor). Nitrogen and oxygen gas comprise 99% of the total, with several trace gases making up the rest; the most significant trace gas is carbon dioxide, an important greenhouse gas.

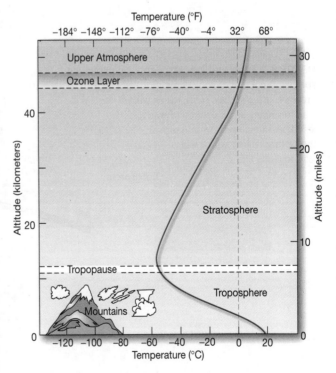

FIGURE 6.5 Temperature profile of the atmosphere. Within the troposphere, the atmosphere gets cooler with increasing altitude. Above the troposphere, the atmosphere generally warms.

FIGURE 6.6 Convection in a room. A circular-moving loop of air (a convection cell) is caused by warm air rising and cool air sinking.

Atmospheric Pressure

Atmospheric pressure is 1.0 atmosphere[2] (14.7 pounds per square inch) at sea level and decreases with increasing altitude. Atmospheric pressure depends on the weight of the column of air above. For instance, a thick column of air produces higher atmospheric pressure than a thin column of air. An analogy to this is water pressure in a swimming pool: The thicker the column of water above, the higher the water pressure. Thus, the highest pressure in a pool is at the bottom of the deep end.

Similarly, the thicker column of air at sea level means air pressure is high at sea level and decreases with increasing elevation. When sealed bags of potato chips or pretzels are taken to a high elevation, the pressure is much lower than where they were sealed, sometimes causing the bags to burst! You may also have experienced this change in pressure when your ears "popped" during the takeoff or landing of an airplane or while driving on steep mountain roads.

Changes in atmospheric pressure cause air movement as a result of changes in the molecular density of the air. The general relationship is shown in Figure 6.7, which indicates that:

- A column of cool, dense air causes high pressure at the surface, which will lead to sinking air (movement *toward* the surface and compression).
- A column of warm, less dense air causes low pressure at the surface, which will lead to rising air (movement *away from* the surface and expansion).

In addition, sinking air tends to warm because of its compression, while rising air tends to cool due to expansion. Note that there are complex relationships among air composition, temperature, density, water vapor content, and pressure.

Movement of the Atmosphere

Air *always* moves from high-pressure regions toward low-pressure regions. This moving air is called **wind**. If a balloon is inflated and let go, what happens to the air inside the balloon? It rapidly escapes, moving from a high-pressure region

FIGURE 6.7 High and low atmospheric pressure zones. A column of cool, dense air causes high pressure at the surface (*left*), which will lead to sinking air. A column of warm, less dense air causes low pressure at the surface (*right*), which will lead to rising air.

[2]The *atmosphere* is a unit of pressure; 1.0 atmosphere is the average pressure exerted by the overlying atmosphere at sea level and is equivalent to 760 millimeters of mercury, 101,300 Pascal, or 1013 millibars.

inside the balloon (caused by the balloon pushing on the air inside) to the lower-pressure region outside the balloon.

An Example: A Nonspinning Earth

Imagine for a moment that Earth is not spinning on its axis but that the Sun rotates around Earth, with the Sun directly above Earth's equator at all times (Figure 6.8). Because more solar radiation is received along the equator than at the poles, the air at the equator in contact with Earth's surface is warmed. This warm, moist air rises, creating low pressure at the surface. This rising air cools (see Figure 6.5) and releases its moisture as rain. Thus, a zone of low pressure and much precipitation occurs along the equator.

As the air along the equator rises, it reaches the top of the troposphere and begins to move toward the poles. Because the temperature is much lower at high altitudes, the air cools, and its density increases. This cool, dense air sinks at the poles, creating high pressure at the surface. The sinking air is quite dry because cool air cannot hold much water vapor. Thus, there are high pressure and clear, dry weather at the poles.

Which way will surface winds blow? Air always moves from high pressure to low pressure, so air travels from the high pressure at the poles toward the low pressure at the equator. Thus, there are strong northerly winds in the Northern Hemisphere and strong southerly winds in the Southern Hemisphere.[3] The air warms as it makes its way back to the equator, completing the loop (called a *convection cell* or *circulation cell*; see Figure 6.6).

Is this fictional case of a nonspinning Earth a good analogy for what is really happening on Earth? Actually, it is not, even though the *principles* that drive the physical movement of air remain the same whether Earth is spinning or not. Let's now examine how Earth's spin influences atmospheric circulation.

6.4 How Does the Coriolis Effect Influence Moving Objects?

The **Coriolis effect** changes the intended path of a moving body. Named after Gaspard Gustave de Coriolis, the French engineer who first calculated its influence in 1835, it is often incorrectly called the Coriolis *force*. It does not accelerate the moving body, so it does not influence the body's speed. As a result, it is an effect and not a true force.

The Coriolis effect causes moving objects on Earth to follow curved paths. In the Northern Hemisphere, an object will follow a path to the *right* of its intended direction; in the Southern Hemisphere, an object will follow a path to the *left* of its intended direction. The directions right and left are the *viewer's perspective looking in the direction in which the object is traveling*. For example, the Coriolis effect very slightly influences the movement of a ball thrown between two people. In the Northern Hemisphere, the ball will veer slightly to its right *from the thrower's perspective*.

The Coriolis effect acts on all moving objects. However, it is much more pronounced on objects traveling long distances, especially north or south. This is why the Coriolis effect has a dramatic effect on atmospheric circulation and the movement of ocean currents.

The Coriolis effect is a result of Earth's rotation toward the east. More specifically, the *difference* in the speed of Earth's rotation at different latitudes causes

---

[3]Notice that winds are named based on the direction *from which they are moving*.

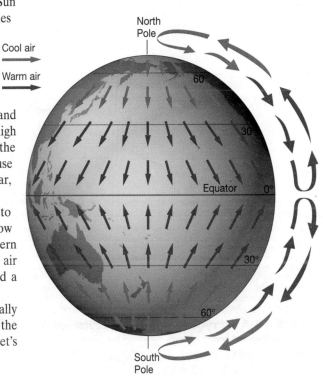

FIGURE 6.8 Atmospheric circulation on a nonspinning Earth. A fictional nonspinning Earth with the Sun rotating around Earth directly above Earth's equator at all times. Arrows show the pattern of winds that would develop due to uneven solar heating on Earth.

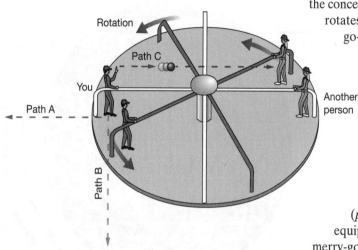

FIGURE 6.9 A merry-go-round spinning counterclock-wise as viewed from above. See text for description of paths *A, B,* and *C.*

the Coriolis effect. In reality, objects travel along straight-line paths,[4] but Earth rotates underneath them, making the objects appear to curve. Let's look at two examples to help clarify this.

Example 1: Perspectives and Frames of Reference on a Merry-Go-Round

A merry-go-round is a useful experimental apparatus with which to test some of the concepts of the Coriolis effect. A merry-go-round is a large circular wheel that rotates around its center. It has bars that people hang onto while the merry-go-round spins, as shown in Figure 6.9.

Imagine that you are on a merry-go-round that is spinning counterclockwise as viewed from above (Figure 6.9). As you are spinning, what will happen to you if you let go of the bar? If you guessed that you would fly off along a straight-line path perpendicular to the merry-go-round (Figure 6.9, *path A*), that's not quite right. Your angular momentum would propel you in a straight line *tangent* to your circular path on the merry-go-round at the point where you let go (Figure 6.9, *path B*). The law of inertia states that a moving object will follow a straight-line path until it is compelled to change that path by other forces. Thus, you would follow a straight-line path (*path B*) until you collide with some object such as other playground equipment or the ground. From the perspective of another person on the merry-go-round, your departure along path B would *appear* to curve to the right due to the merry-go-round's rotation.

Imagine you are again on the merry-go-round, spinning counterclockwise, but you are now joined by another person who is facing you directly but on the opposite side of the merry-go-round. If you were to toss a ball to the other person, what path would it appear to follow? Even though you threw the ball straight at the other person, from *your perspective* the ball's path would appear to curve to the right. That's because the frame of reference (in this example, the merry-go-round) has rotated during the time that it took the ball to reach where the other person had been (Figure 6.9). A person viewing the merry-go-round from directly overhead would observe that the ball did indeed travel along a straight-line path (Figure 6.9, *path C*), just as your path was straight when you let go of the merry-go-round bar. Similarly, the perspective of being on the rotating Earth causes objects to appear to travel along curved paths. This is the Coriolis effect. The merry-go-round spinning in a counterclockwise direction is analogous to the Northern Hemisphere because, as viewed from above the North Pole, Earth is spinning counterclockwise. Thus, moving objects appear to follow curved paths to the *right* of their intended direction in the Northern Hemisphere.

If the other person on the merry-go-round had thrown a ball toward you, it would also appear to have curved. From the perspective of the other person, the ball would appear to curve to its right, just as the ball you threw curved. From your perspective, however, the ball thrown toward you would appear to curve to its *left*. The perspective to keep in mind when considering the Coriolis effect is the one *looking in the same direction that the object is moving.*

To simulate the Southern Hemisphere, the merry-go-round would need to rotate in a *clockwise* direction, which is analogous to Earth when viewed from above the South Pole. Thus, moving objects appear to follow curved paths to the *left* of their intended direction in the Southern Hemisphere.

---

[4]Newton's first law of motion (the law of inertia) states that every body persists in its state of rest or of uniform motion in a straight line unless it is compelled to change that state by forces imposed upon it.

Example 2: A Tale of Two Missiles

The distance that a point on Earth has to travel in a day is shorter with increasing latitude. A location near the pole, for example, travels in a circle not nearly as far in a day as will an area near the equator. Because both areas travel their respective distances in one day, the velocity of the two areas must not be the same. Figure 6.10a shows that as Earth rotates on its axis, the velocity decreases with latitude, ranging from more than 1600 kilometers (1000 miles) per hour at the equator to 0 kilometers per hour at the poles. *This change in velocity with latitude is the true cause of the Coriolis effect.* The following example illustrates how velocity changes with latitude.

   Imagine that we have two missiles that fly in straight lines toward their destinations. For simplicity, assume that the flight of each missile takes one hour regardless of the distance flown. The first missile is launched from the North Pole toward New Orleans, Louisiana, which is at 30 degrees north latitude (Figure 6.10b). Does the missile land in New Orleans? Actually, no. Earth rotates eastward at 1400 kilometers (870 miles) per hour along the 30 degrees latitude line (Figure 6.10a), so the missile lands somewhere near El Paso, Texas, 1400 kilometers west of its target. From your perspective at the North Pole, the path of the missile appears to curve *to its right* in accordance with the Coriolis effect. In reality, New Orleans has moved out of the line of fire due to Earth's rotation.

   The second missile is launched toward New Orleans from the Galápagos Islands, which are directly south of New Orleans along the equator (Figure 6.10b). From their position on the equator, the Galápagos Islands are moving east at 1600 kilometers (1000 miles) per hour, 200 kilometers (124 miles) per hour faster than New Orleans (Figure 6.10a). At takeoff, therefore, the missile is also moving toward the east 200 kilometers per hour faster than New Orleans. Thus, when the missile returns to Earth one hour later at the latitude of New Orleans, it will land offshore of Alabama, 200 kilometers east of New Orleans. Again, from your perspective on the Galápagos Islands, the missile appears to curve *to its right*. Keep in mind that both of these missile examples ignore friction, which would greatly reduce the amount the missiles deflect to the right of their intended courses.

web animation

Coriolis Effect

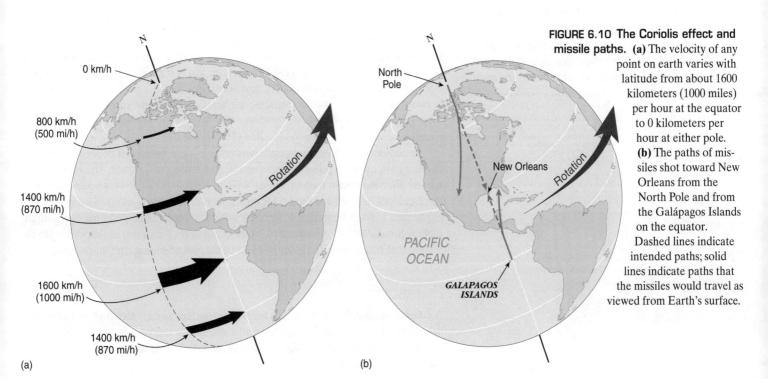

FIGURE 6.10 The Coriolis effect and missile paths. (a) The velocity of any point on earth varies with latitude from about 1600 kilometers (1000 miles) per hour at the equator to 0 kilometers per hour at either pole. **(b)** The paths of missiles shot toward New Orleans from the North Pole and from the Galápagos Islands on the equator. Dashed lines indicate intended paths; solid lines indicate paths that the missiles would travel as viewed from Earth's surface.

(a)   (b)

STUDENTS SOMETIMES ASK...

I've heard that the Coriolis effect is really a force but it is often described as a fictitious force. What is a fictitious force?

The forces you feel in a moving car—those that push you back into your seat when the driver steps on the gas or throw you sideways when the car makes sharp turns—are everyday examples of fictitious forces. In general, these influences arise because the natural frame of reference for a given situation (such as the car) is itself accelerating.

A classic example of these types of apparent influences involves the Coriolis "force" and a pendulum. Consider a back-and-forth swinging pendulum that is suspended directly over the North Pole. To an earthly observer, it would appear to rotate 360 degrees every day and thus would seem to be acted upon by a sideways force (that is, perpendicular to the plane of swing). If you viewed this pendulum from a stationary point in outer space, however, it would appear to swing in a single, fixed plane while Earth turned underneath it. From this outer-space perspective, there is no sideways force deflecting the pendulum's sway. That is why the somewhat pejorative term "fictitious" is attached to this force and also why Coriolis is more properly termed an effect (not a true force). Similarly, in the car, no real force pushes you back into your seat, your senses notwithstanding; what you feel is the moving frame of reference caused by the car's acceleration.

KEY CONCEPT

The Coriolis effect causes moving objects to curve to the right in the Northern Hemisphere and to the left in the Southern Hemisphere. It is at its maximum at the poles and is zero at the equator.

Changes in the Coriolis Effect with Latitude

The first missile (shot from the North Pole) missed the target by 1600 kilometers (1000 miles), while the second missile (shot from the Galápagos Islands) missed its target by only 200 kilometers (124 miles). What was responsible for the difference? Not only does the rotational velocity of points on Earth range from 0 kilometers per hour at the poles to more than 1600 kilometers (1000 miles) per hour at the equator, but the *rate of change* of the rotational velocity (per degree of latitude) increases as the pole is approached from the equator.

For example, the rotational velocity differs by 200 kilometers (124 miles) per hour between the equator (0 degrees) and 30 degrees north latitude. From 30 degrees north latitude to 60 degrees north latitude, however, the rotational velocity differs by 600 kilometers (372 miles) per hour. Finally, from 60 degrees north latitude to the North Pole (where the rotational velocity is zero), the rotational velocity differs by more than 800 kilometers (500 miles) per hour.

Thus, the maximum Coriolis effect is at the poles, and there is no Coriolis effect at the equator. The magnitude of the Coriolis effect depends much more, however, on the length of time the object (such as an air mass or ocean current) is in motion. Even at low latitudes, where the Coriolis effect is small, a large Coriolis deflection is possible if an object is in motion for a long time. In addition, because the Coriolis effect is caused by the *difference* in velocity of different latitudes on Earth, there is no Coriolis effect for those objects moving due east or due west along the equator.

For a summary of the Coriolis effect, see Web Table 6.1.

6.5 What Global Atmospheric Circulation Patterns Exist?

Figure 6.11 shows atmospheric circulation and the corresponding wind belts on a spinning Earth, which presents a more complex pattern than that of the fictional nonspinning Earth (Figure 6.8).

Circulation Cells

The greater heating of the atmosphere over the equator causes the air to expand, to decrease in density, and to rise. As the air rises, it cools by expansion because the pressure is lower, and the water vapor it contains condenses and falls as rain in the equatorial zone. The resulting dry air mass travels north or south of the equator. Around 30 degrees north and south latitude, the air cools off enough to become denser than the surrounding air, so it begins to descend, completing the loop (Figure 6.11). These circulation cells are called **Hadley cells** after noted English meteorologist George Hadley (1685–1768).

In addition to Hadley cells, each hemisphere has a **Ferrel cell** between 30 and 60 degrees latitude and a **polar cell** between 60 and 90 degrees latitude. The Ferrel cell—named after American meteorologist William Ferrel (1817–1891), who invented the three-cell per hemisphere model for atmospheric circulation—is not driven solely by differences in solar heating; if it were, air within it would circulate in the opposite direction. Similar to the movement of interlocking gears, the Ferrel cell moves in the direction that coincides with the movement of the two adjoining circulation cells.

Pressure

A column of cool, dense air moves *toward* the surface and creates high pressure. The descending air at about 30 degrees north and south latitude creates high-pressure zones called the **subtropical highs**. Similarly, descending air at the poles creates high-pressure regions called the **polar highs**.

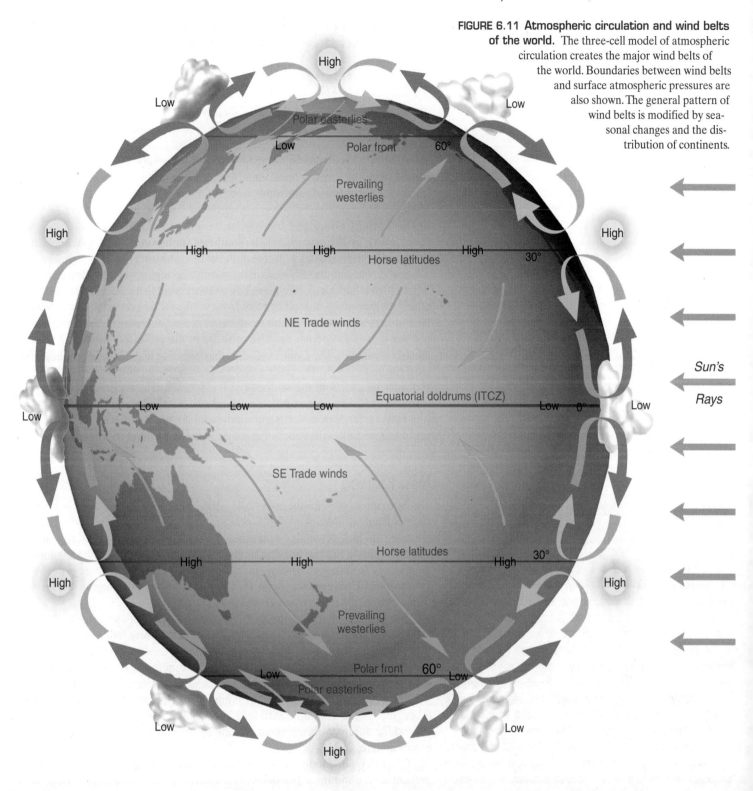

FIGURE 6.11 Atmospheric circulation and wind belts of the world. The three-cell model of atmospheric circulation creates the major wind belts of the world. Boundaries between wind belts and surface atmospheric pressures are also shown. The general pattern of wind belts is modified by seasonal changes and the distribution of continents.

What kind of weather is experienced in these high-pressure areas? Descending air is quite dry and it tends to warm under its own weight, so these areas typically experience dry, clear, fair conditions. The conditions are not necessarily warm (such as at the poles)—just dry and associated with clear skies.

A column of warm, low density air rises *away* from the surface and creates low pressure. Thus, rising air creates a band of low pressure at the equator—the **equatorial low**—and at about 60 degrees north and south latitude—the **subpolar low**.

Global Wind Patterns

The weather in areas of low pressure is dominated by cloudy conditions with lots of precipitation, because rising air cools and cannot hold its water vapor.

Wind Belts

The lowermost portion of the circulation cells—that is, the part that is closest to the surface—generates the major wind belts of the world. The masses of air that move across Earth's surface from the subtropical high-pressure belts toward the equatorial low-pressure belt constitute the **trade winds**. These steady winds are named from the term *to blow trade*, which means to blow in a regular course. If Earth did not rotate, these winds would blow in a north–south direction. In the Northern Hemisphere, however, the **northeast trade winds** curve to the right due to the Coriolis effect and blow *from northeast to southwest*. In the Southern Hemisphere, on the other hand, the **southeast trade winds** curve to the left due to the Coriolis effect and blow *from southeast to northwest*.

Some of the air that descends in the subtropical regions moves along Earth's surface to higher latitudes as the **prevailing westerly wind belts**. Because of the Coriolis effect, the prevailing westerlies blow from southwest to northeast in the Northern Hemisphere and from northwest to southeast in the Southern Hemisphere.

Air moves away from the high pressure at the poles, too, producing the **polar easterly wind belts**. The Coriolis effect is maximized at high latitudes, so these winds are deflected strongly. The polar easterlies blow from the northeast in the Northern Hemisphere, and from the southeast in the Southern Hemisphere. When the polar easterlies come into contact with the prevailing westerlies near the subpolar low pressure belts (at 60 degrees north and south latitude), the warmer, less dense air of the prevailing westerlies rises above the colder, more dense air of the polar easterlies.

Boundaries

The boundary between the two trade wind belts along the equator is known as the **doldrums** (*doldrum* = dull) because, long ago, sailing ships were becalmed there by the lack of winds. Sometimes stranded for days or weeks, the situation was unfortunate but not life-threatening: Daily rain showers supplied sailors with plenty of freshwater. Today, meteorologists refer to this region as the **Intertropical Convergence Zone (ITCZ)**, because it is the region between the tropics where the trade winds converge (Figure 6.11).

The boundary between the trade winds and the prevailing westerlies (centered at 30 degrees north or south latitude) is known as the **horse latitudes**. Sinking air in these regions causes high atmospheric pressure (associated with the *subtropical high pressure*) and results in clear, dry, and fair conditions. Because the air is sinking, the horse latitudes are known for surface winds that are light and variable.

The boundary between the prevailing westerlies and the polar easterlies at 60 degrees north or south latitude is known as the **polar front**. This is a battleground for different air masses, so cloudy conditions and lots of precipitation are common here.

Clear, dry, fair conditions are associated with the high pressure at the poles, so precipitation is minimal. The poles are often classified as cold deserts because the annual precipitation is so low.

Table 6.2 summarizes the characteristics of global wind belts and boundaries.

Circulation Cells: Idealized or Real?

The three-cell model of atmospheric circulation first proposed by Ferrel provides a simplified model of the general circulation pattern on Earth. This circulation model is idealized and does not always match the complexities observed

STUDENTS SOMETIMES ASK...

What is the origin of the name horse latitudes?

The term *horse latitudes* supposedly originates from the days when Spanish sailing vessels transported horses across the Atlantic to the West Indies. Ships would often become becalmed in mid-ocean due to the light winds in these latitudes, thus severely prolonging the voyage; the resulting water shortages would make it necessary for crews to dispose of their horses overboard (see the chapter-opening quote). Alternatively, the term might also have originated by seamen who were paid an advance called the "dead horse" before a long voyage. A few months into the voyage, the "dead horse" was officially worked off; this was also about the same time sailing vessels were stuck in the middle of the ocean without wind, so these regions became known as the horse latitudes.

TABLE 6.2	CHARACTERISTICS OF WIND BELTS AND BOUNDARIES		
Region (north or south latitude)	Name of wind belt or boundary	Atmospheric pressure	Characteristics
Equatorial (0–5 degrees)	Doldrums (boundary)	Low	Light, variable winds. Abundant cloudiness and much precipitation. Breeding ground for hurricanes.
5–30 degrees	Trade winds (wind belt)	—	Strong, steady winds, generally from the east.
30 degrees	Horse latitudes (boundary)	High	Light, variable winds. Dry, clear, fair weather with little precipitation. Major deserts of the world.
30–60 degrees	Prevailing westerlies (wind belt)	—	Winds generally from the west. Brings storms that influence weather across the United States.
60 degrees	Polar front (boundary)	Low	Variable winds. Stormy, cloudy weather year round.
60–90 degrees	Polar easterlies (wind belt)	—	Cold, dry winds generally from the east.
Poles (90 degrees)	Polar high pressure (boundary)	High	Variable winds. Clear, dry, fair conditions, cold temperatures, and minimal precipitation. Cold deserts.

in nature, particularly for the location and direction of motion of the Ferrel and polar cells. Nonetheless, it generally matches the pattern of major wind belts of the world and provides a general framework for understanding why they exist.

Further, the following factors significantly alter the idealized wind, pressure, and atmospheric circulation patterns illustrated in Figure 6.11:

1. The tilt of Earth's rotation axis, which produces seasons

2. The lower heat capacity of continental rock compared to seawater,[5] which makes the air over continents colder in winter and warmer in summer than the air over adjacent oceans

3. The uneven distribution of land and ocean over Earth's surface, which particularly affects patterns in the Northern Hemisphere

During winter, therefore, the continents usually develop atmospheric high-pressure cells from the weight of cold air centered over them and, during the summer, they usually develop low-pressure cells (Figure 6.12). In fact, such seasonal shifts in atmospheric pressure over Asia cause *monsoon winds*, which have a dramatic effect on Indian Ocean currents and will be discussed in Chapter 7, "Ocean Circulation." In general, however, the patterns of atmospheric high- and low-pressure zones shown in Figure 6.12 corresponds closely to those shown in Figure 6.11.

Global wind belts have had a profound effect on ocean explorations (Box 6.1). The world's wind belts also closely match the pattern of ocean surface currents, which are discussed in Chapter 7, "Ocean Circulation."

KEY CONCEPT
The major wind belts in each hemisphere are the trade winds, the prevailing westerlies, and the polar easterlies. The boundaries between these wind belts include the doldrums, the horse latitudes, the polar front, and the polar high.

[5]An object that has low heat capacity heats up quickly when heat energy is applied. Recall from Figure 5.7 that water has one of the highest specific heat capacities of common substances.

FIGURE 6.12 January sea-level atmospheric pressures and winds. Average atmospheric pressure pattern for January. High (*H*) and low (*L*) atmospheric pressure zones correspond closely to those shown in Figure 6.11 but are modified by the change of seasons and the distribution of continents. Arrows show direction of winds, which move from high- to low-pressure regions.

Seasonal Pressure
and Precipitation
Patterns

6.6 What Weather and Climate Patterns Does the Ocean Exhibit?

Because of the ocean's huge extent over Earth's surface and also because of water's unusual thermal properties, the ocean dramatically influences global weather and climate patterns.

Weather Versus Climate

Weather describes the conditions of the atmosphere at a given time and place. **Climate** is the long-term average of weather. If we observe the weather conditions in an area over a long period, we can begin to draw some conclusions about its climate. For instance, if the weather in an area is dry over many years, we can say that the area has an arid climate.

Winds

Recall that air always moves from high pressure toward low pressure and that the movement of air is called *wind*. However, as air moves away from high-pressure regions and toward low-pressure regions, the Coriolis effect modifies its direction. In the Northern Hemisphere, for example, air moving from high to low pressure curves to the right and results in a counterclockwise[6] flow of air around low-pressure cells [called **cyclonic** *(kyklon = moving in a circle)* **flow**]. Similarly, as the air leaves the high-pressure region and curves to the right, it establishes a clockwise flow of air around high-pressure cells (called **anticyclonic flow**). Figure 6.13 shows how a screwdriver can help you remember how air moves around high- and low-pressure regions: High pressures are similar to a high screw that needs to be tightened, so a screwdriver would be turned clockwise; low pressures are similar to a tightened screw that needs to be loosened, so a screwdriver would be turned

---

[6]These directions are reversed in the Southern Hemisphere.

WHY CHRISTOPHER COLUMBUS NEVER SET FOOT ON NORTH AMERICA

The Italian navigator and explorer **Christopher Columbus** is widely credited with discovering North America in the year 1492. However, America was already populated with many natives, and the Vikings predated his voyage to North America by about 500 years. Moreover, the pattern of the major wind belts of the world prevented his sailing ships from reaching continental North America during his four voyages.

Rather than sailing east, Columbus was determined to reach the East Indies (today the country of Indonesia) by sailing west across the Atlantic Ocean. An astronomer in Florence, Italy, named Toscanelli was the first to suggest such a route in a letter to the king of Portugal. Columbus later contacted Toscanelli and was told how far he would have to sail west to reach India. Today, we know that this distance would have carried him just west of North America.

After years of difficulties in initiating the voyage, Columbus received the financial backing of the Spanish monarchs Ferdinand V and Isabella I. He set sail with 88 men and three ships (the *Niña*, the *Pinta*, and the *Santa María*) on August 3, 1492, from the Canary Islands off Africa (Figure 6A). The Canary Islands are located at 28 degrees north latitude and are within the northeast trade winds, which blow steadily from the northeast to the southwest. Instead of sailing directly west, which would have allowed Columbus to reach central Florida, the map in Figure 6A shows that Columbus sailed a more southerly route.

During the morning of October 12, 1492, the first land was sighted; this is generally believed to have been Watling Island in the Bahama Islands southeast of Florida. Based on the inaccurate informa-

tion he had been given, Columbus was convinced that he had arrived in the East Indies and was somewhere near India. Consequently, he called the inhabitants "Indians," and the area is known today as the West Indies. Later during this voyage, he explored the coasts of Cuba and Hispaniola (the island comprising modern-day Haiti and the Dominican Republic).

On his return journey, he sailed to the northeast and picked up the prevailing westerlies, which transported him away from North America and toward Spain. Upon his return to Spain and the announcement of his discovery, additional voyages were planned. Columbus made three more trips across the Atlantic Ocean, following similar paths through

the Atlantic. Thus, his ships were controlled by the trade winds on the outbound voyage and the prevailing westerlies on the return trip. During his next voyage, in 1493, Columbus explored Puerto Rico and the Leeward Islands and established a colony on Hispaniola. In 1498, he explored Venezuela and landed on South America, unaware that it was a new continent to Europeans. On his last voyage in 1502, he reached Central America.

Although he is today considered a master mariner, he died in neglect in 1506, still convinced that he had explored islands near India. Even though he never set foot on the North American mainland, his journeys inspired other Spanish and Portuguese navigators to explore the "New World," including the coasts of North and South America.

FIGURE 6A Route of Christopher Columbus's first voyage (*map*) and a modern-day replica of the *Niña* (*photo*).

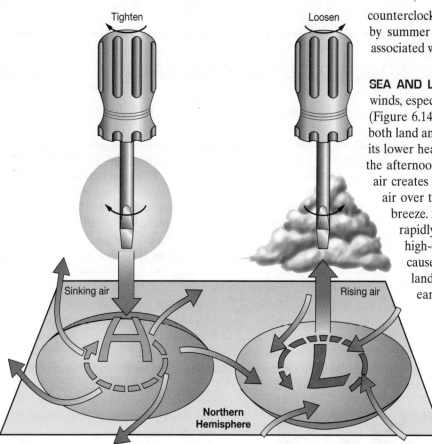

Tighten

Loosen

Sinking air

Rising air

Northern Hemisphere

FIGURE 6.13 High- and low-pressure regions and air flow. As air moves away from a high-pressure region (*H*) toward a low-pressure region (*L*), the Coriolis effect causes the air to curve to the right in the Northern Hemisphere. This results in clockwise winds around high-pressure regions (anticyclonic flow) and counterclockwise winds around low-pressure regions (cyclonic flow). One way to remember this is to think of high pressures as being similar to a high screw that needs tightening (clockwise motion) and low pressures as being similar to a tightened screw that needs loosening (counterclockwise motion).

Cyclones and Anticyclones

Cold Fronts and Warm Fronts

counterclockwise. Because winter high-pressure cells are replaced by summer low-pressure cells over the continents, wind patterns associated with continents often reverse themselves seasonally.

SEA AND LAND BREEZES Other factors that influence regional winds, especially in coastal areas, are **sea breezes** and **land breezes** (Figure 6.14). When an equal amount of solar energy is applied to both land and ocean, the land heats up about five times more due to its lower heat capacity. The land heats the air around it and, during the afternoon, the warm, low-density air over the land rises. Rising air creates a low-pressure region over the land, pulling the cooler air over the ocean toward land, creating what is known as a sea breeze. At night, the land surface cools about five times more rapidly than the ocean and cools the air around it. This cool, high-density air sinks, creating a high-pressure region that causes the wind to blow from the land. This is known as a land breeze, and it is most prominent in the late evening and early morning hours.

Storms and Fronts

At very high and very low latitudes, there is little daily and minor seasonal change in weather.[7] Equatorial regions are usually warm, damp, and typically calm, because the dominant direction of air movement in the doldrums is upward. Midday rains are common, even during the supposedly "dry" season. It is within the *middle latitudes* between 30 and 60 degrees north or south latitude where storms are common.

Storms are atmospheric disturbances characterized by strong winds, precipitation, and often thunder and lightning. Due to the seasonal change of pressure systems over continents, air masses from the high and low latitudes may move into the middle latitudes, meet, and produce severe storms. **Air masses** are large volumes of air that have a definite area of origin and distinctive characteristics. Several air masses influence the United States, including polar air masses and tropical air masses (Figure 6.15). Some air masses originate over land (c = continental) and are therefore dryer, but most originate over the sea (m = maritime) and are moist. Some are colder (P = polar; A = Arctic) and some are warm (T = tropical). Typically, the United States is influenced more by polar air masses during the winter and more by tropical air masses during the summer.

As polar and tropical air masses move into the middle latitudes, they also move gradually in an easterly direction. A **warm front** is the contact between a warm air mass moving into an area occupied by cold air. A **cold front** is the contact between a cold air mass moving into an area occupied by warm air (Figure 6.16).

These confrontations are brought about by the movement of the **jet stream**, which is a narrow, fast-moving, easterly flowing air mass. It exists above the middle latitudes just below the top of the troposphere, centered at an altitude of about 10 kilometers (6 miles). It usually follows a wavy path and may cause unusual weather by steering a polar air mass far to the south or a tropical air mass far to the north.

---

[7]In fact, in equatorial Indonesia, the vocabulary of Indonesians doesn't include the word *seasons*.

Regardless of whether a warm front or cold front is produced, the warmer, less-dense air always rises above the denser cold air. The warm air cools as it rises, so its water vapor condenses as precipitation. A cold front is usually steeper, and the temperature difference across it is greater than a warm front. Therefore, rainfall along a cold front is usually heavier and briefer than rainfall along a warm front.

Tropical Cyclones (Hurricanes)

Tropical cyclones (*kyklon* = moving in a circle) are huge rotating masses of low pressure characterized by strong winds and torrential rain. They are the largest storm systems on Earth, though they are not associated with any fronts. In North and South America, tropical cyclones are called **hurricanes** (*Huracan* = Taino god of wind); in the western North Pacific Ocean, they are called **typhoons** (*tai-fung* = great wind); and in the Indian Ocean, they are called **cyclones**. No matter what they are called, tropical cyclones can be highly destructive. In fact, the energy contained in a *single* hurricane is greater than that generated by all energy sources in the United States over the past 20 years.

ORIGIN   Remarkably, what powers tropical storms is the release of vast amounts of water's *latent heat of condensation*[8] that is carried within water vapor and is released as water condenses to form clouds in a hurricane. A tropical cyclone begins as a low-pressure cell that breaks away from the equatorial low-pressure belt and grows as it picks up heat energy in the

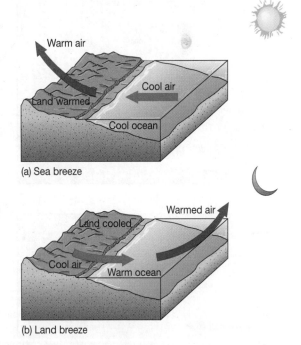

FIGURE 6.14 Sea and land breezes. (a) Sea breezes occur when air warmed by the land rises and is replaced by cool air from the ocean. **(b)** Land breezes occur when the land has cooled, causing dense air to sink and flow toward the warmer ocean.

FIGURE 6.15 Air masses that affect U.S. weather. Polar air masses are shown in blue, and tropical air masses are shown in red. Air masses are classified based on their source region: The designation continental (c) or maritime (m) indicates moisture content, whereas polar (P), Arctic (A), and tropical (T) indicate temperature conditions.

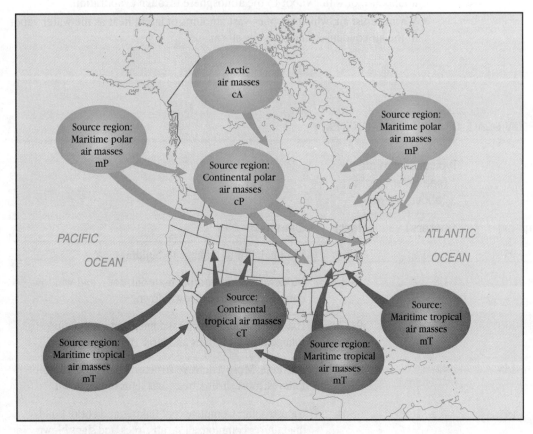

[8]For a discussion of water's latent heats, see Chapter 5.

(a)

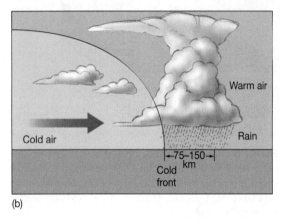

(b)

FIGURE 6.16 Warm and cold fronts. Cross sections through a gradually rising warm front **(a)** and a steeper cold front **(b)**. With both fronts, warm air rises and precipitation is produced.

following manner. Surface winds feed moisture (in the form of water vapor) into the storm. When water evaporates, it stores tremendous amounts of heat in the form of latent heat of evaporation. When water vapor condenses into a liquid (in this case, clouds and rain), it releases this stored heat—latent heat of condensation—into the surrounding atmosphere, which causes the atmosphere to warm and the air to rise. This rising air causes surface pressure to decrease, drawing additional warm moist surface air into the storm. This air, as it rises and cools, condenses into clouds and releases even more latent heat, further powering the storm and continuously repeating itself, each time intensifying the storm.

Tropical storms are classified according to their maximum sustained wind speed:

- If winds are less than 61 kilometers (38 miles) per hour, the storm is classified as a *tropical depression*.
- If winds are between 61 and 120 kilometers (38 and 74 miles) per hour, the storm is called a *tropical storm*.
- If winds exceed 120 kilometers (74 miles) per hour, the storm is a *tropical cyclone*.

The **Saffir-Simpson Scale** of hurricane intensity (Table 6.3) further divides tropical cyclones into categories based on wind speed and damage. In some cases, in fact, the wind in tropical cyclones attains speeds as high as 400 kilometers (250 miles) per hour!

Worldwide, about 100 storms grow to hurricane status each year. The conditions needed to create a hurricane are as follows:

- Ocean water with a temperature greater than 25°C (77°F), which provides an abundance of water vapor to the atmosphere through evaporation.
- Warm, moist air, which supplies vast amounts of latent heat as the water vapor in the air condenses and fuels the storm.

TABLE 6.3   THE SAFFIR-SIMPSON SCALE OF HURRICANE INTENSITY

Category	Wind speed (km/hr)	(mi/hr)	Typical storm surge (sea level height above normal) (meters)	(feet)	Damage
1	120–153	74–95	1.2–1.5	4–5	Minimal: Minor damage to buildings
2	154–177	96–110	1.8–2.4	6–8	Moderate: Some roofing material, door, and window damage; some trees blown down
3	178–209	111–130	2.7–3.7	9–12	Extensive: Some structural damage and wall failures; foliage blown off trees and large trees blown down
4	210–249	131–155	4.0–5.5	13–18	Extreme: More extensive structural damage and wall failures; most shrubs, trees, and signs blown down
5	>250	>155	>5.8	>19	Catastrophic: Complete roof failures and entire building failures common; all shrubs, trees, and signs blown down; flooding of lower floors of coastal structures

- The Coriolis effect, which causes the hurricane to spin counterclockwise in the Northern Hemisphere and clockwise in the Southern Hemisphere. No hurricanes occur directly on the equator because the Coriolis effect is zero there.[9]

These conditions are found during the late summer and early fall, when the tropical and subtropical oceans are at their maximum temperature. Even though hurricanes sometimes form outside of hurricane season (Box 6.2), the official Atlantic basin hurricane season is from June 1 to November 30 each year. These dates conventionally delimit the period when most tropical cyclones form in the Atlantic basin.

MOVEMENT   When hurricanes are initiated in the low latitudes, they are affected by the trade winds and generally move from east to west across ocean basins. Hurricanes typically last from 5 to 10 days and sometimes migrate into the middle latitudes (Figure 6.17). In rare cases, hurricanes have done considerable damage to the northeast United States and have even affected Nova Scotia, Canada. Figure 6.17 also shows how hurricanes are affected by the Coriolis effect: In the Northern Hemisphere, they curve to the right and in the Southern Hemisphere, they curve to the left. Moreover, this serves to carry them out of the tropics and over land or cooler water, where their energy source is cut off, eventually causing the hurricane to dissipate.

The diameter of a typical hurricane is less than 200 kilometers (124 miles), although extremely large hurricanes can exceed diameters of 800 kilometers (500 miles). As air moves across the ocean surface toward the low-pressure center, it is drawn up around the **eye of the hurricane** (Figure 6.18). The air in the vicinity of the eye spirals upward, so horizontal wind speeds may be less than 15 kilometers (25 miles) per hour. The eye of the hurricane, therefore, is usually calm. Hurricanes are composed of spiral rain bands where intense rainfall caused by severe thunderstorms can produce tens of centimeters (several inches) of rainfall per hour.

TYPES OF DESTRUCTION   Destruction from hurricanes is caused by high winds and flooding from intense rainfall. **Storm surge**, however, causes the majority of a hurricane's coastal destruction. In fact, storm surge is responsible for 90% of the deaths associated with hurricanes.

When a hurricane develops over the ocean, its low-pressure center produces a low "hill" of water (Figure 6.19). As the hurricane migrates across the open ocean, the hill moves with it. As the hurricane approaches shallow water near shore, the portion of the hill over which the wind is blowing shoreward produces a mass of elevated, wind-driven water. This mass of water—the storm surge—can be as high as 12 meters (40 feet), resulting in a dramatic increase in sea level at the shore, large storm waves, and tremendous destruction to low-lying coastal areas (particularly if it occurs at high tide). In addition, the area of the coast that is hit with the right front quadrant of the hurricane—where onshore winds further pile up water—experiences the most severe storm surge (Figure 6.19). Table 6.3 shows typical storm surge heights associated with Saffir-Simpson hurricane intensities.

HISTORIC DESTRUCTION   Periodic destruction from hurricanes occurs along the East Coast and the Gulf Coast regions of the United States. In fact, the most deadly natural disaster in U.S. history was caused by a hurricane that struck Galveston Island, Texas, in September 1900. Galveston Island is a thin strip of

Hurricanes

---

[9]An unusual confluence of weather conditions in 2001 created the first-ever documented instance of a tropical cyclone almost directly over the equator. Statistical models indicate that such an event occurs only once every 300–400 years.

6.2   FOCUS ON THE ENVIRONMENT

THE RECORD-BREAKING 2005 ATLANTIC HURRICANE SEASON: HURRICANES KATRINA, RITA, AND WILMA

Although the official Atlantic hurricane season extends each year from June 1 to November 30, the 2005 Atlantic hurricane season persisted into January 2006 and was the most active season on record, shattering numerous records. For example, a record 27 named tropical storms formed, of which a record 15 became hurricanes. Of these, seven strengthened into major hurricanes, a record-tying five became Category 4 hurricanes and a record four reached Category 5 strength, the highest categorization for hurricanes on the Saffir-Simpson Scale of hurricane intensity (see Table 6.3). For the first time ever, NOAA's National Hurricane Center, which oversees the naming of Atlantic Hurricanes, ran out of the usual names for storms and resorted to naming storms using the Greek alphabet.

The most notable storms of the 2005 season were the five Category 4 and Category 5 hurricanes: Dennis, Emily, Katrina, Rita, and Wilma. These storms made a combined twelve landfalls as major hurricanes (Category 3 strength or higher) throughout Cuba, Mexico, and the Gulf Coast of the United States, causing more than $100 billion in damages and over 2000 deaths.

Hurricane Katrina, the sixth-strongest Atlantic hurricane ever recorded, was the costliest and one of the deadliest hurricanes in U.S. history. Katrina formed over the Bahamas on August 23 and crossed southern Florida as a moderate Category 1 hurricane before passing over the warm Loop Current and strengthening rapidly in the Gulf of Mexico, causing it to become one of the strongest hurricanes ever recorded in the Gulf. The storm weakened considerably before making its second landfall as a Category 3 storm on the morning of August 29 in southeast Louisiana (Figure 6B). Still, Katrina was the largest hurricane of its strength to make landfall in the United States in recorded history; its sheer size caused devastation over a

FIGURE 6B Hurricane Katrina, the most destructive hurricane in U.S. history. Satellite view of Hurricane Katrina (*top*) coming ashore along the Gulf Coast on August 29, 2005. Hurricane Katrina, the largest hurricane of its strength to make landfall in the United States in recorded history, had a diameter of about 670 kilometers (415 miles); its counter-clockwise direction of flow and prominent central eye are also visible. Katrina caused levees to breach and flooded New Orleans (*bottom*), which caused damages of more than $75 billion and claimed at least 1600 lives.

radius of 370 kilometers (230 miles). Katrina's 9-meter (30-foot) storm surge—the highest ever recorded in the United States—caused severe damage along the coasts of Mississippi, Louisiana, and Alabama.

Worse yet, Katrina was on a collision course with New Orleans. This scenario was considered a potential catastrophe because nearly all of the New Orleans metropolitan area is below sea level along Lake Pontchartrain. Even without a direct hit, the storm surge from Katrina was forecast to be greater than the height of the levees protecting New Orleans. This risk of devastation was well known; several previous studies warned that a direct hurricane strike on New Orleans could lead to massive flooding, which would lead to thousands of drowning deaths, as well as many more suffering from disease and dehydration after the hurricane passed. Although Katrina passed to the east of New Orleans, levees separating Lake Pontchartrain from New Orleans were breached by Katrina's high winds, storm surge, and heavy rains, ultimately flooding roughly 80% of the city and many neighboring areas (Figure 6B). Damages from Katrina are estimated to have been $75 billion, easily making it the costliest hurricane in U.S. history. The storm also left hundreds of thousands homeless and killed at least 1600 people, making it the deadliest U.S. hurricane since the 1928 Okeechobee Hurricane. The lack of adequate disaster response by the Federal Emergency Management Agency (FEMA) led to a U.S. Senate investigation in 2006 that recommended disbanding the agency and creating a new National Preparedness and Response Agency.

Hurricane Rita set records as the fourth most intense Atlantic hurricane ever recorded and the most intense tropical cyclone observed in the Gulf of Mexico, breaking the record set by Katrina just three weeks earlier. Rita reached its maximum intensity on September 21, with sustained winds of 290 kilometers (180 miles) per hour and an estimated minimum pressure of 89,500 Pascal (895 millibars, or 0.884 atmosphere). Hurricane Rita's unusually rapid intensification in the Gulf can likely be attributed to its passage over the warm Loop Current as well as higher-than-normal sea surface temperatures in the Gulf. Rita made landfall on September 24 near the Texas-Louisiana border as a Category 3 hurricane. Rita's 6-meter (20-foot) storm surge caused extensive damage along the coasts of Louisiana and extreme southeastern Texas, completely destroying some coastal communities and causing $10 billion in damage.

Later during the same season, Hurricane Wilma set numerous records for both strength and seasonal activity. Wilma was only the third Category 5 ever to develop during the month of October, and its pressure of 88,200 Pascal (882 millibars, or 0.871 atmosphere) ranked it as the most intense hurricane ever recorded in the Atlantic basin. Its maximum sustained near-surface wind speed reached 282 kilometers (175 miles) per hour, with gusts up to 320 kilometers (200 miles) per hour. Wilma made several landfalls, with the most destructive effects felt in the Yucatán Peninsula of Mexico, Cuba, and southern Florida. At least 62 deaths were reported, and damage was estimated at $16 to 20 billion ($12.2 billion in the United States), ranking Wilma among the top 10 costliest hurricanes ever recorded in the Atlantic and the sixth costliest storm in U.S. history. Wilma also affected 11 countries with winds or rainfall, more than any other hurricane in recent history.

sand called a barrier island located in the Gulf of Mexico off Texas (Figure 6.20). In 1900, it was a popular beach resort that averaged only 1.5 meters (5 feet) above sea level. At least 6000 people in and around Galveston were killed when the hurricane's 6-meter (20-foot)-high storm surge completely submerged the island, accompanied by heavy rainfall and winds of 160 kilometers (100 miles) per hour.

Category 4 hurricanes like the one in 1900 that made landfall in Galveston have been surpassed by Category 5 hurricanes only three times in the United States: (1) in 1935, an unnamed hurricane[10] flattened the Florida Keys; (2) in 1969, Hurricane Camille struck Mississippi; and (3) in 1992, Hurricane Andrew came ashore in southern Florida, with winds as high as 258 kilometers (160 miles) per hour, ripping down every tree in its path as it crossed the Everglades. Hurricane Andrew did more than $26.5 billion of damage in Florida and along the Gulf Coast. In the aftermath of Hurricane Andrew, more than 250,000 people were left homeless and although most people heeded the warnings to evacuate, 54 were killed.

In October 1998, Hurricane Mitch proved to be one of the most devastating tropical cyclones to affect the Western Hemisphere. At its peak, it was estimated to have winds of 290 kilometers (180 miles) per hour—a strong Category 5 hurricane.

WEB VIDEO

Hurricane Katrina Damage

---

[10]Prior to 1950, Atlantic hurricanes were not named, but this hurricane is often referred to as the "Labor Day Hurricane" because it came ashore then. Today, hurricanes are named by forecasters using an alphabetized list of female and male names.

FIGURE 6.17 Historic tropical cyclone tracks. Color-coded map showing the intensity and paths of tropical cyclones (which, depending on the area, can also be called *hurricanes* or *typhoons*) over the past 150 years. Cyclones originate in low-latitude regions that have warm ocean surface temperatures (*red shading*). Once formed, cyclones are influenced by the trade winds, so generally travel from east to west. Note that cyclones curve to the right north of the equator and to the left south of the equator because of the Coriolis effect, which causes cyclones to track away from the tropics into cooler water or land (and sometimes into the middle latitudes), where they die out.

It hit Central America with winds of 160 kilometers (100 miles) per hour and as much as 130 centimeters (51 inches) of total rainfall, causing widespread flooding and mudslides in Honduras and Nicaragua that destroyed entire towns. The hurricane resulted in more than 11,000 deaths, left more than 2 million homeless, and caused more than $10 billion in damage across the region.

In September 2008, Hurricane Ike reached Category 4 in the Gulf of Mexico and made landfall near Galveston in low-lying Gilchrist, Texas, as a Category 2 hurricane. Ike resulted in 146 deaths and $24 billion in damages (Figure 6.21), making it the third costliest U.S. hurricane of all time, behind only Hurricane Katrina (2005) and Hurricane Andrew (1992).

The majority of the world's tropical cyclones are formed in the waters north of the equator in the western Pacific Ocean. These storms, called typhoons, do enormous damage to coastal areas and islands in Southeast Asia (see Figure 6.17).

Other areas of the world such as Bangladesh experience tropical cyclones on a regular basis. Bangladesh borders the Indian Ocean and is particularly vulnerable because it is a highly populated and low-lying country, much of it only 3 meters (10 feet) above sea level. In 1970, a 12-meter (40-foot)-high storm surge from a tropical cyclone killed an estimated 1 million people. Another tropical cyclone

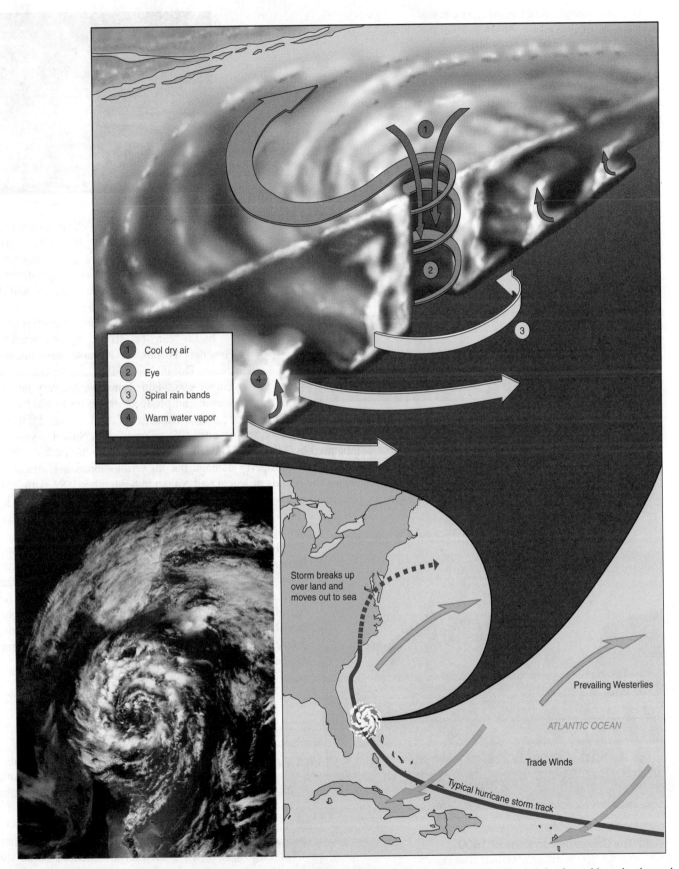

FIGURE 6.18 Typical North Atlantic hurricane storm track and internal structure. Hurricanes in the North Atlantic are blown by the trade winds towards North America. As they curve to the right because of the Coriolis effect, they move northward and often make landfall or pass close to shore. Eventually, they break up and are transported out to sea by the prevailing westerlies. Photo shows subtropical storm Andrea off the East Coast in 2007; internal structure of a hurricane is also shown (*enlargement*).

FIGURE 6.19 Storm surge. As a tropical cyclone in the Northern Hemisphere moves ashore, the low-pressure center around which the storm winds blow combined with strong onshore winds produces a high-water storm surge that floods and batters the coast. The area of the coast that is hit with the right front quadrant of the hurricane—where onshore winds further pile up water—experiences the most severe storm surge. Photograph (*inset*) shows a storm surge in New Jersey caused by Hurricane Felix in August 1995.

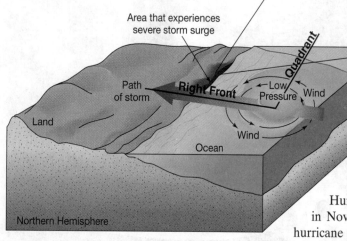

hit the area in 1972 that caused up to 500,000 deaths. In 1991, Hurricane Gorky's winds of 233 kilometers (145 miles per hour) and large storm surge caused extensive damage and killed 200,000 people.

Even islands near the centers of ocean basins can be struck by hurricanes. The Hawaiian Islands, for example, were hit hard by Hurricane Dot in August 1959 and by Hurricane Iwa in November 1982. Hurricane Iwa hit very late in the hurricane season and produced winds up to 130 kilometers (81 miles) per hour. Damage of more than $100 million occurred on the islands of Kauai and Oahu. Niihau, a small island that is inhabited by 230 native Hawaiians, was directly in the path of the storm and suffered severe property damage but no serious injuries. Hurricane Iniki roared across the islands of Kauai and Niihau in September 1992, with 210-kilometer (130-mile)-per-hour winds. It was the most powerful hurricane to hit the Hawaiian Islands in the last 100 years, with property damage that approached $1 billion.

Hurricanes will continue to be a threat to life and property. Because of more accurate forecasts and prompt evacuation, however, the loss of life has been decreasing. Property damage, on the other hand, has been increasing because increasing coastal populations have resulted in more and more construction along the coast. Inhabitants of areas subject to a hurricane's destructive force must be made aware of the danger so that they can be prepared for its eventuality.

The Ocean's Climate Patterns

Just as land areas have climate patterns, so do regions of the oceans. The open ocean is divided into climatic regions that run generally east–west (parallel to lines of latitude) and have relatively stable boundaries that are somewhat modified by ocean surface currents (Figure 6.22).

The **equatorial** region spans the equator, which gets an abundance of solar radiation. As a result, the major

FIGURE 6.20 The Galveston hurricane of 1900. Destruction from the 1900 hurricane at Galveston and location map of Galveston, Texas. At least 6000 people died as a result of the Galveston hurricane, which completely submerged Galveston Island and still stands as the single deadliest U.S. natural disaster.

air movement is upward because heated air rises. Surface winds, therefore, are weak and variable, which is why this region is called the *doldrums*. Surface waters are warm and the air is saturated with water vapor. Daily rain showers are common, which keeps surface salinity relatively low. The equatorial regions just north or south of the equator are also the breeding grounds for tropical cyclones.

Tropical regions extend north or south of the equatorial region up to the Tropic of Cancer and the Tropic of Capricorn, respectively. They are characterized by strong trade winds, which blow from the northeast in the Northern Hemisphere and from the southeast in the Southern Hemisphere. These winds push the equatorial currents and create moderately rough seas. Relatively little precipitation falls at higher latitudes within tropical regions, but precipitation increases toward the equator. Once tropical cyclones form, they gain energy here as large quantities of heat are transferred from the ocean to the atmosphere.

Beyond the tropics are the **subtropical** regions. Belts of high pressure are centered there, so the dry, descending air produces little precipitation and a high rate of evaporation, resulting in the highest surface salinities in the open ocean (see Figure 5.23). Winds are weak and currents are sluggish, typical of the horse latitudes. However, strong boundary currents (along the boundaries of continents) flow north and south, particularly along the western margins of the subtropical oceans.

The **temperate** regions (also called the *middle latitudes* or *midlatitudes*) are characterized by strong westerly winds (the prevailing westerlies) blowing from the southwest in the Northern Hemisphere and from the northwest in the Southern Hemisphere (see Figure 6.11). Severe storms are common, especially during winter, and precipitation is heavy. In fact, the North Atlantic is noted for fierce storms, which have claimed many ships and numerous lives over the centuries.

The **subpolar** region experiences extensive precipitation due to the subpolar low. Sea ice covers the subpolar ocean in winter, but it melts away, for the most part, in summer. Icebergs are common, and the surface temperature seldom exceeds 5°C (41°F) in the summer months.

Surface temperatures remain at or near freezing in the **polar** regions, which are covered with ice throughout most of the year. The polar high pressure dominates the area, which includes the Arctic Ocean and the ocean adjacent to Antarctica. There is no sunlight during the winter and constant daylight during the summer.

FIGURE 6.21 Damage from Hurricane Ike in 2008. Hurricane Ike, which made landfall in Gilchrist, Texas, was the third most destructive hurricane to ever make landfall in the United States.

> **KEY CONCEPT**
> Hurricanes are intense and sometimes destructive tropical storms that form where water temperatures are high, where there is an abundance of warm moist air, and where they can spin.

6.7 How Do Sea Ice and Icebergs Form?

Low temperatures in high-latitude regions cause a permanent or nearly permanent ice cover on the sea surface. The term **sea ice** is used to distinguish such masses of frozen seawater from **icebergs**, which are also found at sea but originate by breaking off (*calving*) from glaciers that originate on land. Sea ice is found throughout the year around the margin of Antarctica, within the Arctic Ocean, and in the extreme high-latitude region of the North Atlantic Ocean.

Formation of Sea Ice

Sea ice is ice that forms directly from seawater (Figure 6.23). It begins as small, needle-like, hexagonal (six-sided) crystals, which eventually become so numerous that a *slush* develops. As the slush begins to form into a thin sheet, it is broken by wind stress and wave action into disk-shaped pieces called **pancake ice** (Figure 6.23a). As further freezing occurs, the pancakes coalesce to form **ice floes** (*flo* = layer).

The rate at which sea ice forms is closely tied to temperature conditions. Large quantities of ice form in relatively short periods when the temperature falls

FIGURE 6.22 The ocean's climatic regions. The ocean's climatic regions are defined primarily by latitude but are modified by ocean currents and wind belts. Red arrows indicate warm surface currents; blue arrows indicate cool surface currents.

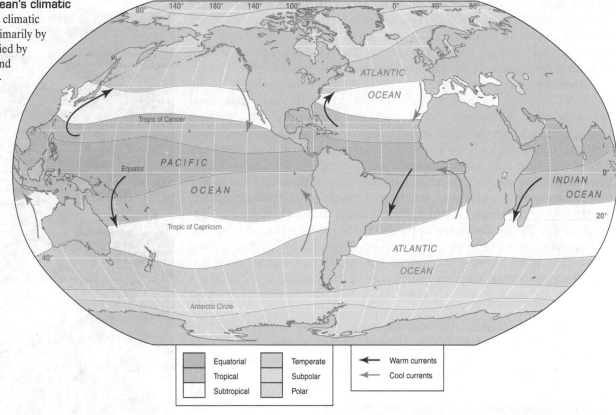

Legend:
- Equatorial
- Tropical
- Subtropical
- Temperate
- Subpolar
- Polar
- Warm currents
- Cool currents

FIGURE 6.23 Sea ice. (a) Pancake ice, which is frozen slush that is broken by wind stress and wave action into disk-shaped pieces. **(b)** Aerial view of the Larsen ice shelf on the Antarctic Peninsula, where ribbons of sea ice (*top*) remain seaward of the shelf ice during September (the beginning of the spring season in the Southern Hemisphere). **(c)** Ice structures associated with rafted ice, which is created as ice floes expand and raft onto one another.

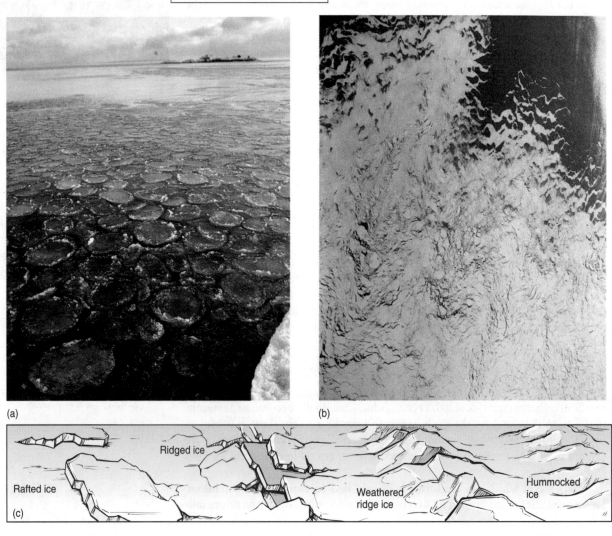

(a)

(b)

Ridged ice

Rafted ice

Weathered ridge ice

Hummocked ice

(c)

to extremely low levels [such as temperatures below −30°C (−22°F)]. Even at these low temperatures, the rate of ice formation slows as sea ice thickens because the ice (which has poor heat conduction) effectively insulates the underlying water from freezing. In addition, calm water enables pancake ice to join together more easily, which aids the formation of sea ice.

The process of sea ice formation tends to be a self-perpetuating process. As sea ice forms at the surface, only a small percentage of the dissolved components can be accommodated into the crystalline structure of ice. As a result, most of the dissolved substances remain in the surrounding seawater, which causes its salinity to increase. Recall from Chapter 5 that increasing the amount of dissolved materials

(a)

(b)

FIGURE 6.24 Icebergs.
(a) Icebergs, such as this small North Atlantic berg, are formed when pieces of ice calve from glaciers that reach the sea. **(b)** Map showing North Atlantic currents (*blue arrows*), typical iceberg distribution (*red triangles*), and site of the 1912 *Titanic* disaster (*green X*). **(c)** Part of a large tabular Antarctic iceberg. **(d)** Satellite view of iceberg C-19, which broke off from Antarctica's Ross Ice Shelf in May 2002. Also shown is iceberg B-15A, which is part of the larger B-15 iceberg that was the size of Connecticut when it calved in March 2000.

(c)

(d)

decreases the freezing point of water, which doesn't appear to enhance ice formation. However, also recall that increasing the salinity of water increases its density and its tendency to sink. As it sinks below the surface, it is replaced by lower-salinity (and lower-density) water from below, which will freeze more readily than the high salinity water it replaced, thereby establishing a circulation pattern that enhances the formation of sea ice.

Recent satellite analyses of the extent of Arctic Ocean sea ice shows that it has decreased dramatically in the past few decades. This accelerated melting appears to be linked to shifts in Northern Hemisphere atmospheric circulation patterns that have caused the region to experience anomalous warming. For more on this topic, see Chapter 16, "The Oceans and Climate Change."

Formation of Icebergs

Icebergs are bodies of floating ice broken away from a glacier (Figure 6.24a) and so are quite distinct from sea ice. Icebergs are formed by vast ice sheets on land, which grow from the accumulation of snow and slowly flow outward to the sea. Once at the sea, the ice either breaks up and produces icebergs there, or, because it is less dense than water, it floats on top of the water, often extending a great distance away from shore before breaking up under the stress of current, wind, and wave action. Most calving occurs during the summer months when temperatures are highest.

In the Arctic, icebergs originate primarily by calving from glaciers that extend to the ocean along the western coast of Greenland (Figure 6.24b). Icebergs are also produced by glaciers along the eastern coasts of Greenland, Ellesmere Island, and other Arctic islands. In all, about 10,000 or so icebergs are calved off these glaciers each year. Many of these icebergs are carried by the East Greenland Current and the West Greenland Current (Figure 6.24b, *arrows*) into North Atlantic shipping lanes, where they become navigational hazards. In recognition of this fact, the area is called Iceberg Alley; it is here that the luxury liner RMS *Titanic* hit an iceberg and sank (see Web Box 6.1). Because of their large size, some of these icebergs take several years to melt, and, in that time, they may be carried as far south as 40 degrees north latitude, which is the same latitude as Philadelphia.

SHELF ICE In Antarctica, where glaciers cover nearly the entire continent, the edges of glaciers form thick floating sheets of ice called **shelf ice** that break off and produce vast plate-like icebergs (Figures 6.24c and 6.24d). In March 2000, for example, a Connecticut-sized iceberg (11,000 square kilometers or 4250 square miles) known as B-15 and nicknamed "Godzilla" broke loose from the Ross Ice Shelf into the Ross Sea. By comparison, the largest iceberg ever recorded in Antarctic waters was nearly three times the size of B-15 and measured an incredible 335 by 97 kilometers (208 by 60 miles)—about the same size as Connecticut and Massachusetts combined.

The icebergs have flat tops that may stand as much as 200 meters (650 feet) above the ocean surface, although most rise less than 100 meters (330 feet) above sea level, and as much as 90% of their mass is below waterline. Once icebergs are created, ocean currents driven by strong winds carry the icebergs north, where they eventually melt. Because this region is not a major shipping route, the icebergs pose little serious navigation hazard except for supply ships traveling to Antarctica. Officers aboard ships sighting these gigantic bergs have, in some cases, mistaken them for land!

The rate at which Antarctica is producing icebergs—especially large icebergs—has recently increased, most likely as a result of Antarctic warming. For more information about Antarctic warming and its relationship to climate change, see Chapter 16, "The Oceans and Climate Change."

KEY CONCEPT
Sea ice is created when seawater freezes; icebergs form when chunks of ice break off from coastal glaciers that reach the sea.

6.8 Can Power from Wind Be Harnessed as a Source of Energy?

The uneven heating of Earth by the Sun drives various small- and large-scale winds. These winds, in turn, can be harnessed to turn windmills or turbines that generate electricity. At various places on land where the wind blows constantly, wind farms have been constructed that consist of hundreds of large turbines mounted on tall towers, thereby taking advantage of this renewable, clean energy source. Similar facilities could be built offshore, where the wind generally blows harder and more steadily than on land. Figure 6.25 shows the offshore areas where the potential for wind farms exist.

Some offshore wind farms have already been built and many more are in the planning stage. In the North Sea north of windswept northern Europe, for example, about 100 sea-based turbines are already operating (Figure 6.26), with hundreds more planned. In fact, Denmark generates 18% of its power by wind—more than any other country—and hopes to increase its proportion of wind power to 50% by 2030. In the United States, America's first offshore wind farm, Cape Wind, is scheduled to be built on Horseshoe Shoal in Nantucket Sound, Massachusetts, 8 kilometers (5 miles) south of Cape Cod. The wind farm expects to be fully functional in 2011 with 130 wind turbines capable of producing 420 megawatts of power, which is capable of supplying the energy needs of nearly 350,000 average U.S. homes.

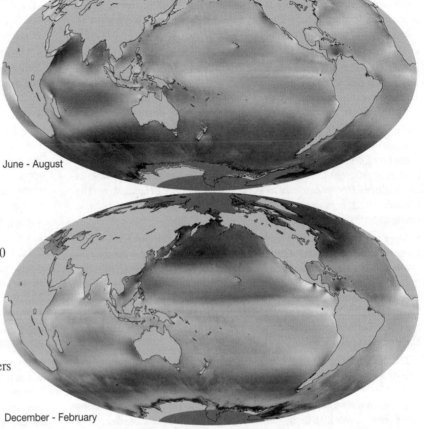

June - August

December - February

Wind Power Density (W/m^2)

0   250 500   1000   2000

FIGURE 6.25 Global ocean wind energy potential. Average ocean wind intensity maps during 2000–2007 for June–August (*top*) and December–February (*bottom*). Areas of high wind power density, where winds are strongest and the potential for wind farms is greatest, are shown in purple, while low power density regions where winds are light are shown in light blue and white.

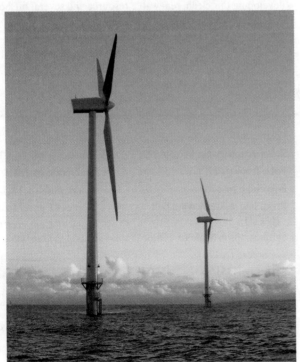

FIGURE 6.26 Offshore wind farm. Offshore wind turbines form a part of a wind farm in the North Sea off the coast of Blyth in the U.K.

Chapter in Review

• *The atmosphere and the ocean act as one interdependent system*, linked by complex feedback loops. There is a close association between most atmospheric and oceanic phenomena.

• *The Sun heats Earth's surface unevenly due to the change of seasons* (*caused by the tilt of Earth's rotational axis*, which is 23.5 degrees from vertical) and the daily cycle of sunlight and darkness (Earth's rotation on its axis). The *uneven distribution of solar energy on Earth* influences most of the physical properties of the atmosphere (such as *temperature, density, water vapor content*, and *pressure differences*) that produce *atmospheric movement*.

• *The Coriolis effect influences the paths of moving objects on Earth and is caused by Earth's rotation.* Because Earth's surface rotates at different velocities at different latitudes, *objects in motion tend to veer to the right in the Northern Hemisphere and to the left in the Southern Hemisphere.* The Coriolis effect is *nonexistent at the equator but increases with latitude*, reaching a maximum at the poles.

• *More solar energy is received than is radiated back into space at low latitudes than at high latitudes.* On the spinning Earth, this creates *three circulation cells in each hemisphere*: a *Hadley cell* between 0 and 30 degrees latitude, a *Ferrel cell* between 30 and 60 degrees latitude, and a *polar cell* between 60 and 90 degrees latitude. High-pressure regions, where dense air descends, are located at about 30 degrees north or south latitude and at the poles. Belts of low pressure, where air rises, are generally found at the equator and at about 60 degrees latitude.

• *The movement of air within the circulation cells produces the major wind belts of the world.* The air at Earth's surface that is moving away from the subtropical highs produces *trade winds* moving toward the equator and *prevailing westerlies* moving toward higher latitudes. The air moving along Earth's surface from the polar high to the subpolar low creates the *polar easterlies*.

• *Calm winds characterize the boundaries between the major wind belts of the world.* The boundary between the two trade wind belts is called the *doldrums*, which coincides with the Intertropical Convergence Zone (ITCZ). The boundary between the trade winds and the prevailing westerlies is called the *horse latitudes*. The boundary between the prevailing westerlies and the polar easterlies is called the *polar front*.

• *The tilt of Earth's axis of rotation*, the *lower heat capacity of rock material* compared to seawater, and the *distribution of continents modify the wind and pressure belts of the idealized three-cell model.* However, the three-cell model closely matches the pattern of the major wind belts of the world.

• *Weather describes the conditions of the atmosphere at a given place and time, while climate is the long-term average of weather.* Atmospheric motion (*wind*) is always from high-pressure regions toward low-pressure regions. In the Northern Hemisphere, therefore, there is a *counterclockwise cyclonic movement* of air around low-pressure cells and a *clockwise anticyclonic movement* around high-pressure cells. Coastal regions commonly experience *sea and land breezes*, due to the daily cycle of heating and cooling.

• *Many storms are due to the movement of air masses.* In the middle latitudes, cold air masses from higher latitudes meet warm air masses from lower latitudes and create *cold and warm fronts* that move from west to east across Earth's surface. *Tropical cyclones (hurricanes) are large, powerful storms that mostly affect tropical regions of the world.* Destruction caused by hurricanes is caused by storm surge, high winds, and intense rainfall.

• *The ocean's climate patterns are closely related to the distribution of solar energy and the wind belts of the world.* Ocean surface currents somewhat modify oceanic climate patterns.

• *In high latitudes, low temperatures freeze seawater and produce sea ice*, which forms as a slush and breaks into pancakes that ultimately grow into ice floes. *Icebergs form when chunks of ice break off glaciers* that form on Antarctica, Greenland, and some Arctic islands. Floating sheets of ice called *shelf ice* near Antarctica produce the largest icebergs.

• *Winds can be harnessed as a source of power.* There is vast potential for developing this clean, renewable resource and several offshore wind farm systems currently exist.

Key Terms

Air mass (p. 176)
Albedo (p. 163)
Antarctic Circle (p. 163)
Anticyclonic flow (p. 174)
Arctic Circle (p. 163)
Autumnal equinox (p. 162)
Climate (p. 174)
Cold front (p. 176)
Columbus, Christopher (p. 175)
Convection cell (p. 165)
Coriolis effect (p. 167)
Cyclone (p. 177)
Cyclonic flow (p. 174)
Declination (p. 162)
Doldrums (p. 172)
Ecliptic (p. 161)

Equatorial (p. 184)
Equatorial low (p. 171)
Eye of the hurricane (p. 179)
Ferrel cell (p. 170)
Hadley cell (p. 170)
Horse latitudes (p. 172)
Hurricane (p. 177)
Ice floe (p. 185)
Icebergs (p. 185)
Intertropical Convergence Zone (ITCZ) (p. 172)
Jet stream (p. 176)
Land breeze (p. 176)
Northeast trade winds (p. 172)
Pancake ice (p. 185)
Polar (p. 185)

Polar cell (p. 170)
Polar easterly wind belt (p. 172)
Polar front (p. 172)
Polar high (p. 170)
Prevailing westerly wind belt (p. 172)
Saffir-Simpson Scale (p. 178)
Sea breeze (p. 176)
Sea ice (p. 185)
Shelf ice (p. 188)
Southeast trade winds (p. 172)
Storm (p. 176)
Storm surge (p. 179)
Subpolar (p. 185)
Subpolar low (p. 171)
Subtropical (p. 185)

Subtropical high (p. 170)
Summer solstice (p. 162)
Temperate (p. 185)
Trade winds (p. 172)
Tropic of Cancer (p. 162)
Tropic of Capricorn (p. 162)
Tropical (p. 185)
Tropical cyclone (p. 177)
Tropics (p. 162)
Troposphere (p. 165)
Typhoon (p. 177)
Vernal equinox (p. 162)
Warm front (p. 176)
Weather (p. 174)
Wind (p. 166)
Winter solstice (p. 162)

Review Questions

1. Sketch a labeled diagram to explain the cause of Earth's seasons.

2. Along the Arctic Circle, how would the Sun appear during the summer solstice? During the winter solstice?

3. If there is a net annual heat loss at high latitudes and a net annual heat gain at low latitudes, why does the temperature difference between these regions not increase?

4. Describe the physical properties of the atmosphere, including its composition, temperature, density, water vapor content, pressure, and movement.

5. Is Earth's atmosphere heated from above or below? Explain.

6. Describe the Coriolis effect in the Northern and Southern Hemispheres and include a discussion of why the strength of the Coriolis effect increases at higher latitudes.

7. Sketch the pattern of surface wind belts on Earth, showing atmospheric circulation cells, zones of high and low pressure, the names of the wind belts, and the names of the boundaries between the wind belts.

8. Why are there high-pressure caps at each pole and a low-pressure belt in the equatorial region?

9. Describe the difference between cyclonic and anticyclonic flow, and show how the Coriolis effect is important in producing both a clockwise and a counterclockwise flow pattern.

10. How do sea breezes and land breezes form? During a hot summer day, which one would be most common and why?

11. Name the polar and tropical air masses that affect U.S. weather. Describe the pattern of movement across the continent and patterns of precipitation associated with warm and cold fronts.

12. What are the conditions needed for the formation of a tropical cyclone? Why do most middle latitude areas only rarely experience a hurricane? Why are there no hurricanes at the equator?

13. Describe the types of destruction caused by hurricanes. Of those, which one causes the majority of fatalities and destruction?

14. How are the ocean's climatic regions (Figure 6.22) related to the broad patterns of air circulation described in Figure 6.11? What are some areas where the two are not closely related?

15. Describe differences between sea ice and icebergs, including how they both form.

Critical Thinking Exercises

1. Describe the effect on Earth as a result of Earth's axis of rotation being angled 23.5 degrees from perpendicular relative to the ecliptic. What would happen if Earth were not tilted on its axis?

2. Discuss why the idealized belts of high and low atmospheric pressure shown in Figure 6.11 are modified (see Figure 6.12).

3. What is the difference between weather and climate? If it rains in a particular area during a day, does that mean that the area has a wet climate? Explain.

Oceanography on the Web

Visit the *Essentials of Oceanography* Online Study Guide for Internet resources, including chapter-specific quizzes to test your understanding and Web links to further your exploration of the topics in this chapter.

The *Essentials of Oceanography* Online Study Guide is at http://www.mygeoscienceplace.com/.

Detection of ocean circulation processes from space.
This composite SeaWiFS/SeaStar satellite view during the austral summer highlights ocean circulation patterns where the deep blue color represents low chlorophyll (phytoplankton) concentrations and the orange and red colors represent high chlorophyll (phytoplankton) concentrations. Note the wavy pattern of eddies between Africa and Antarctica where the Agulhas Current meets the Antarctic Circumpolar Current and is turned to the east, creating the Agulhas Retroflection. Off the west coast of Africa, coastal upwelling is shown in bright red colors.

"The coldest winter I ever spent was a summer in San Francisco."
— *Anonymous, but often attributed to Mark Twain;*
said in reference to San Francisco's cool summer weather
caused by coastal upwelling

7 OCEAN CIRCULATION

Ocean currents are masses of ocean water that flow from one place to another. The amount of water can be large or small, currents can be at the surface or deep below, and the phenomena that create them can be simple or quite complex. Simply put, currents are *water masses in motion*.

Huge current systems dominate the surfaces of the major oceans. These currents transfer heat from warmer to cooler areas on Earth, just as the major wind belts of the world do. Wind belts transfer about two-thirds of the total amount of heat from the tropics to the poles; ocean surface currents transfer the other third. Ultimately, energy from the Sun drives surface currents and they closely follow the pattern of the world's major wind belts. As a result, the movement of currents has aided the travel of prehistoric people across ocean basins. Ocean currents also influence the abundance of life in surface waters by affecting the growth of microscopic algae, which are the basis of most oceanic food webs.

More locally, surface currents affect the climates of coastal continental regions. Cold currents flowing toward the equator on the western sides of continents produce arid conditions. Conversely, warm currents flowing poleward on the eastern sides of continents produce warm, humid conditions. Ocean currents, for example, contribute to the mild climate of northern Europe and Iceland, whereas conditions at similar latitudes along the Atlantic coast of North America (such as Labrador) are much colder. Additionally, water sinks in high-latitude regions, initiating deep currents that help regulate the planet's climate.

7.1 How Are Ocean Currents Measured?

Ocean currents are either *wind driven* or *density driven*. Moving air masses—particularly the major wind belts of the world—set wind-driven currents in motion. Wind-driven currents move water horizontally and occur primarily in the ocean's surface waters, so these currents are called **surface currents**. Density-driven circulation, on the other hand, moves water vertically and accounts for the thorough mixing of the deep masses of ocean water. Some surface waters become high in density—through low temperature and/or high salinity—and so sink beneath the surface. This dense water sinks and spreads slowly beneath the surface, so these currents are called **deep currents**.

Surface Current Measurement

Surface currents rarely flow in the same direction and at the same rate for very long, so measuring average flow rates can be difficult. Some consistency, however, exists in the *overall* surface current pattern worldwide. Surface currents can be measured directly or indirectly.

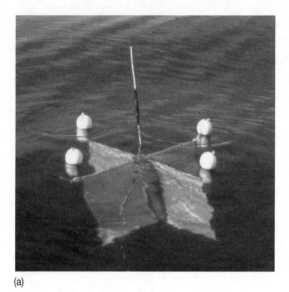

(a)

FIGURE 7.1 Current-measuring devices.
(a) Drift current meter. Depth of metal vanes is
1 meter (3.3 feet). **(b)** Propeller-type flow meter.
Length of instrument is 0.6 meter (2 feet).

(b)

DIRECT METHODS Two main methods are used to
measure currents *directly*. In one, a floating device is
released into the current and tracked through time.
Typically, radio-transmitting float bottles or other devices
are used (Figure 7.1a), but other accidentally released items
also make good drift meters (Box 7.1). The other method is
done from a fixed position (such as a pier) where a current-
measuring device, such as the propeller flow meter shown in
Figure 7.1b, is lowered into the water. Propeller devices can
also be towed behind ships, and the ship's speed is then
subtracted to determine a current's true flow rate.

INDIRECT METHODS Three different methods can be
used to measure surface currents *indirectly*. Water flows
parallel to a pressure gradient, so one method is to
determine the internal distribution of density and the
corresponding pressure gradient across an area of the
ocean. A second method uses radar altimeters—such
as those launched aboard Earth-observing satellites
today—to determine the lumps and bulges at the ocean
surface, which are a result of the shape of the underlying
sea floor (see Box 7.1) as well as current flow. From
these data, *dynamic topography* maps can be produced
that show the speed and direction of surface currents
(Figure 7.2). A third method uses a *Doppler flow meter* to
transmit low-frequency sound signals through the water.
The flow meter measures the shift in frequency between
the sound waves emitted and those backscattered by
particles in the water to determine current movement.

Deep Current Measurement

The great depth at which deep currents exist makes them even more difficult to
measure than surface currents. Most often, they are mapped using underwater
floats that are carried within deep currents. One such unique oceanographic

**FIGURE 7.2 Satellite view of ocean dynamic
topography.** Map showing TOPEX/Poseidon radar
altimeter data in centimeters from September 1992 to
September 1993. Red colors are areas that have higher
than normal sea level; blue colors are areas that are
lower than normal. White arrows indicate the flow direction of currents, with longer arrows indicating
faster flow rates.

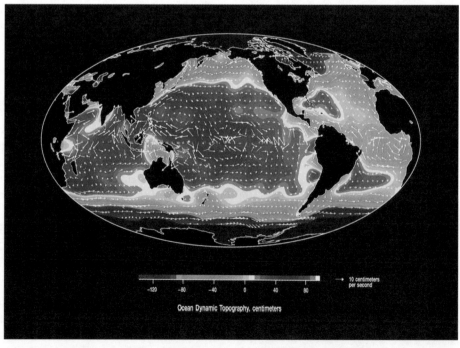

RUNNING SHOES AS DRIFT METERS: JUST DO IT

Any floating object can serve as a makeshift drift meter, as long as it is known where the object entered the ocean and where it was retrieved. The path of the object can then be inferred, providing information about the movement of surface currents. If the time of release and retrieval are known, the speed of currents can also be determined. Oceanographers have long used *drift bottles* (a floating "message in a bottle" or a radio-transmitting device set adrift in the ocean) to track the movement of currents.

Many objects have inadvertently become drift meters when ships lose cargo at sea. Worldwide, in fact, as many as 10,000 shipping containers are lost overboard each year. In this way, Nike athletic shoes and colorful floating bathtub toys (Figure 7A, *right inset*) have advanced the understanding of current movement in the North Pacific Ocean.

In May 1990, the container vessel *Hansa Carrier* was en route from Korea to Seattle, Washington, when it encountered a severe North Pacific storm. The ship was transporting 12.2-meter (40-foot)-long rectangular metal shipping containers, many of which were lashed to the ship's deck for the voyage. During the storm, the ship lost 21 deck containers overboard, including five that held Nike athletic shoes. The shoes floated, so those that were released from their containers were carried east by the North Pacific Current. Within six months, thousands of the shoes began to wash up along the beaches of Alaska, Canada, Washington, and Oregon (Figure 7A, *map*), more than 2400 kilometers (1500 miles) from the site of the spill. A few shoes were found on beaches in northern California, and over two years later, shoes from the spill were even recovered from the north end of the Big Island of Hawaii!

Continued on next page . . .

FIGURE 7A Oceanographer Curtis Ebbesmeyer (*left inset*), path of drifting shoes and recovery locations from the 1990 spill (*map*), and recovered shoes and plastic bathtub toys (*right inset*).

Continued from page 195 . . .

Even though the shoes had spent considerable time drifting in the ocean, they were in good shape and wearable (after barnacles and oil were removed). Because the shoes were not tied together, many beachcombers found individual shoes or pairs that did not match. Many of the shoes retailed for around $100, so people interested in finding matching pairs placed ads in newspapers or attended local swap meets.

With help from the beachcombing public (as well as lighthouse operators), information on the location and number of shoes collected was compiled during the months following the spill. Serial numbers inside the shoes were traced to individual containers, and they indicated that only four of the five containers had released their shoes; evidently, one entire container sank without opening. Thus, a maximum of 30,910 pairs of shoes (61,820

individual shoes) were released. The almost instantaneous release of such a large number of drift items helped oceanographers refine computer models of North Pacific circulation. Before the shoe spill, the largest number of drift bottles purposefully released at one time by oceanographers was about 30,000. Although only 2.6% of the shoes were recovered, this compares favorably with the 2.4% recovery rate of drift bottles released by oceanographers conducting research.

In January 1992, another cargo ship lost 12 containers during a storm to the north of where the shoes had previously spilled. One of these containers held 29,000 packages of small, floatable, colorful plastic bathtub toys in the shapes of blue turtles, yellow ducks, red beavers, and green frogs (Figure 7A, *insets*). Even though the toys were housed in plastic packaging glued to a cardboard backing,

studies showed that after 24 hours in seawater, the glue deteriorated and more than 100,000 of the toys were released.

The floating bathtub toys began to come ashore in southeast Alaska 10 months later, verifying the computer models. The models indicate that many of the bathtub toys will continue to be carried by the Alaska Current, eventually dispersing throughout the North Pacific Ocean. Some may find their way into the Arctic Ocean, where they could spend time within the Arctic Ocean ice pack. From there, the toys may drift into the North Atlantic, eventually washing up on beaches in northern Europe, thousands of kilometers from where they were accidentally released into the ocean.

Oceanographers such as Curtis Ebbesmeyer (Figure 7A, *left inset*) continue to study ocean currents by tracking these and other floating items spilled by cargo ships (see Web Table 7.1).

program that began in 2000 is called **Argo**, which is a global array of free-drifting profiling floats (Figure 7.3b) that move vertically and measure the temperature, salinity, and other water characteristics of the upper 2000 meters (6600 feet) of the ocean. Once deployed, each float sinks to a particular depth, drifts for up to 10 days collecting data, then resurfaces and transmits data on its location and ocean variables, which are made publically available within hours. Each float then sinks back down to a programmed depth and drifts for up to another 10 days collecting more data before resurfacing and repeating the cycle. In 2007, the goal of the program was achieved with the launch of the 3000th Argo float; currently, there are nearly 3300 floats operating worldwide (Figure 7.3a). The program will allow

(a)

(b)

FIGURE 7.3 The Argo system of free-drifting submersible floats. (a) Map showing the locations of Argo floats, which can dive to 2000 meters (6600 feet) and collect data on ocean properties before resurfacing and transmitting their data. (b) Floats are deployed from research or cargo vessels.

oceanographers to develop a forecasting system for the oceans analogous to weather forecasting on land.

Other techniques used for measuring deep currents include identifying the distinctive temperature and salinity characteristics of a deep-water mass or by tracking telltale chemical tracers. Some tracers are naturally absorbed into seawater, while others are intentionally added. Some useful tracers that have inadvertently been added to seawater include tritium (a radioactive isotope of hydrogen produced by nuclear bomb tests in the 1950s and early 1960s) and chlorofluorocarbons (freons and other gases now thought to be depleting the ozone layer).

7.2 How Are Ocean Surface Currents Organized?

Surface currents occur within and above the *pycnocline* (layer of rapidly changing density) to a depth of about 1 kilometer (0.6 mile) and affect only about 10% of the world's ocean water.

Origin of Surface Currents

In a simplistic case, surface currents develop from friction between the ocean and the wind that blows across its surface. Only about 2% of the wind's energy is transferred to the ocean surface, so a 50-knot[1] wind will create a 1-knot current. You can simulate this on a tiny scale simply by blowing gently and steadily across a cup of coffee.

If there were no continents on Earth, the surface currents would generally follow the major wind belts of the world. In each hemisphere, therefore, a current would flow between 0 and 30 degrees latitude as a result of the trade winds, a second would flow between 30 and 60 degrees latitude as a result of the prevailing westerlies, and a third would flow between 60 and 90 degrees latitude as a result of the polar easterlies.

In reality, however, ocean surface currents are driven by more than just the wind belts of the world. The distribution of continents on Earth is one factor that influences the nature and the direction of flow of surface currents in each ocean basin. As an example, Figure 7.4 shows how the trade winds and prevailing westerlies create large circular-moving loops of water in the Atlantic Ocean basin, which is bounded by the irregular shape of continents. These same wind belts affect the other ocean basins, so a similar pattern of surface current flow also exists in the Pacific and Indian Oceans. Other factors that influence surface current patterns include gravity, friction, and the Coriolis effect.

Main Components of Ocean Surface Circulation

Although ocean water continuously flows from one current into another, ocean currents can be organized into discrete patterns within each ocean basin.

SUBTROPICAL GYRES   The large, circular-moving loops of water shown in Figure 7.4 that are driven by the major wind belts of the world are called

FIGURE 7.4 Atlantic Ocean surface circulation pattern. The trade winds (*blue arrows*) in conjunction with the prevailing westerlies (*green arrows*) create circular-moving loops of water (*underlying purple arrows*) at the surface in both parts of the Atlantic Ocean basin. If there were no continents, the ocean's surface circulation pattern would closely match the major wind belts of the world.

---

[1]A *knot* is a speed of 1 nautical mile per hour. A nautical mile is defined as the distance of 1 minute of latitude and is equivalent to 1.15 statute (land) miles or 1.85 kilometers.

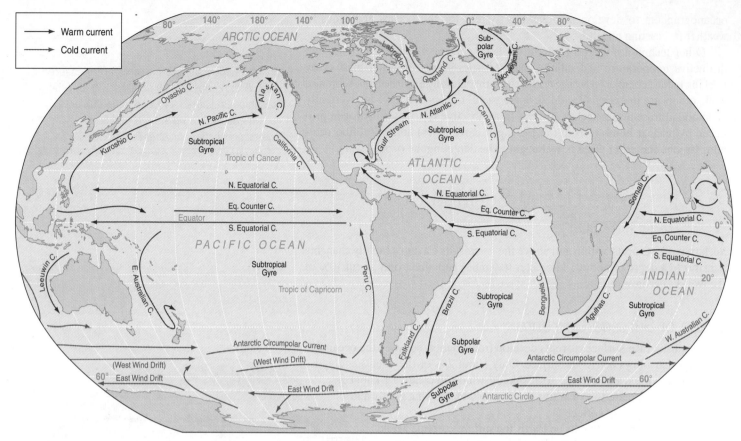

FIGURE 7.5 Wind-driven surface currents. Major wind-driven surface currents of the world's oceans during February–March. The five major subtropical gyres are: (1) the North Pacific (Turtle) Gyre, (2) the South Pacific (Heyerdahl) Gyre, (3) the North Atlantic (Columbus) Gyre, (4) the South Atlantic (Navigator) Gyre, and (5) the Indian Ocean (Majid) Gyre. Smaller subpolar gyres rotate in the reverse direction of their adjacent subtropical gyres.

Ocean Circulation

gyres (*gyros* = a circle). Figure 7.5 shows the world's five **subtropical gyres**: (1) the *North Atlantic Subtropical Gyre*, (2) the *South Atlantic Subtropical Gyre*, (3) the *North Pacific Subtropical Gyre*, (4) the *South Pacific Subtropical Gyre*, and (5) the *Indian Ocean Subtropical Gyre* (which is mostly within the Southern Hemisphere). The reason they are called subtropical gyres is because the center of each gyre coincides with the subtropics at 30 degrees north or south latitude. As shown in Figures 7.4 and 7.5, subtropical gyres rotate clockwise in the Northern Hemisphere and counterclockwise in the Southern Hemisphere. Studies of floating objects (see Box 7.1) indicate that the average drift time in a smaller subtropical gyre such as the North Atlantic Gyre is about three years, whereas in larger subtropical gyres such as the North Pacific Gyre it is about six years.

Oceanographers have given names to the gyres to honor explorers and seafarers—both human and nonhuman, but especially drifters—who have circled and traversed their great expanses:

- The North Atlantic Subtropical Gyre is named the *Columbus Gyre* after the first mariner to exploit its currents in both outbound and homeward journeys (see Box 6.1).
- The South Atlantic Subtropical Gyre is named the *Navigator Gyre* after Portugal's Prince Henry the Navigator, who founded Europe's first navigational school and launched oceanography's Age of Discovery (see Chapter 1).
- The North Pacific Subtropical Gyre is named the *Turtle Gyre* in honor of sea turtles that cross the widest ocean leaving and returning to their ancient breeding beaches in Japan (see Box 2.1).
- The South Pacific Subtropical Gyre is named the *Heyerdahl Gyre* after Thor Heyerdahl, a fearless explorer–scientist that proved an ancient voyage from South America to Polynesia was possible by reenacting it (see Chapter 1).
- The Indian Ocean's gyre is named the *Majid Gyre* after the great 15th-century Arab mariner and author Ahmad Bin Majid, whose maps guided the Portuguese in their globe-spanning voyages.

TABLE 7.1	SUBTROPICAL GYRES AND SURFACE CURRENTS	

	North Pacific (Turtle) Gyre	**North Atlantic (Columbus) Gyre**	**Indian Ocean (Majid) Gyre**
	North Pacific Current	North Atlantic Current	South Equatorial Current
	California Current[a]	Canary Current[a]	Agulhas Current[b]
	North Equatorial Current	North Equatorial Current	West Wind Drift
	Kuroshio (Japan) Current[b]	Gulf Stream[b]	West Australian Current[a]
	South Pacific (Heyerdahl) Gyre	**South Atlantic (Navigator) Gyre**	**Other Major Currents**
Pacific Ocean	South Equatorial Current	South Equatorial Current	Equatorial Countercurrent
	East Australian Current[b]	Brazil Current[b]	North Equatorial Current
	West Wind Drift	West Wind Drift	Leeuwin Current
	Peru (Humboldt) Current[a]	Benguela Current[a]	Somali Current
	Other Major Currents	**Other Major Currents**	
	Equatorial Countercurrent	Equatorial Countercurrent	
	Alaskan Current	Florida Current	
	Oyashio Current	East Greenland Current	
		Labrador Current	
		Falkland Current	

[a]Denotes an eastern boundary current of a gyre, which is relatively *slow*, *wide*, and *shallow* (and is also a *cold-water* current).

[b]Denotes a western boundary current of a gyre, which is relatively *fast*, *narrow*, and *deep* (and is also a *warm-water* current).

Generally, *each subtropical gyre is composed of four main currents* that flow progressively into one another (Table 7.1). The North Atlantic (Columbus) Gyre, for instance, is composed of the North Equatorial Current, the Gulf Stream, the North Atlantic Current, and the Canary Current (Figure 7.5). Let's examine each of the four main currents that comprise subtropical gyres.

Equatorial Currents The trade winds, which blow from the southeast in the Southern Hemisphere and from the northeast in the Northern Hemisphere, set in motion the water masses between the tropics. The resulting currents are called **equatorial currents**, which travel westward along the equator and form the equatorial boundary current of subtropical gyres (Figure 7.5). They are called north or south equatorial currents, depending on their position relative to the equator.

Western Boundary Currents When equatorial currents reach the western portion of an ocean basin, they must turn because they cannot cross land. The Coriolis effect deflects these currents away from the equator as **western boundary currents**, which comprise the western boundaries of subtropical gyres. Western boundary currents are so named because they travel along the western boundary of their respective ocean basins.[2] For example, the Gulf Stream and the Brazil Current,

---

[2]Notice that western boundary currents are off the *eastern* coasts of adjoining continents. It's easy to be confused about this because we have a land-based perspective. From an *oceanic perspective*, however, the western side of the ocean basin is where western boundary currents reside.

which are shown in Figure 7.5, are western boundary currents. They come from equatorial regions, where water temperatures are warm, so they carry warm water to higher latitudes. Note that Figure 7.5 shows warm currents as red arrows.

Northern or Southern Boundary Currents Between 30 and 60 degrees latitude, the prevailing westerlies blow from the northwest in the Southern Hemisphere and from the southwest in the Northern Hemisphere. These winds direct ocean surface water in an easterly direction across an ocean basin [see the North Atlantic Current and the Antarctic Circumpolar Current (West Wind Drift) in Figure 7.5]. In the Northern Hemisphere, these currents comprise the northern parts of subtropical gyres and are called **northern boundary currents**; in the Southern Hemisphere, they comprise the southern parts of subtropical gyres and are called **southern boundary currents**.

Eastern Boundary Currents When currents flow back across the ocean basin, the Coriolis effect and continental barriers turn them toward the equator, creating **eastern boundary currents** of subtropical gyres along the eastern boundary of the ocean basins. Examples of eastern boundary currents include the Canary Current and the Benguela Current,[3] which are shown in Figure 7.5. They come from high-latitude regions where water temperatures are cool, so they carry cool water to lower latitudes. Note that Figure 7.5 shows cold currents as blue arrows.

EQUATORIAL COUNTERCURRENTS   A large volume of water is driven westward due to the north and south equatorial currents. The Coriolis effect is minimal near the equator, so the majority of the water is not turned toward higher latitudes. Instead, the water piles up along the western margin of an ocean basin, which causes average sea level on the western side of the basin to be as much as 2 meters (6.6 feet) higher than on the eastern side. The water on the western margins then flows downhill under the influence of gravity, creating narrow **equatorial countercurrents** that flow to the east counter to and between the adjoining equatorial currents.

Figure 7.5 shows that an equatorial countercurrent is particularly apparent in the Pacific Ocean. This is because of the large equatorial region that exists in the Pacific Ocean and because of a dome of equatorial water that becomes trapped in the island-filled embayment between Australia and Asia. Continual influx of water from equatorial currents builds the dome and creates an eastward countercurrent that stretches across the Pacific toward South America. The equatorial countercurrent in the Atlantic Ocean, on the other hand, is not nearly as well defined because of the shapes of the adjoining continents, which limit the equatorial area that exists in the Atlantic Ocean. The presence of an equatorial countercurrent in the Indian Ocean is strongly influenced by the monsoons, which will be discussed later in this chapter.

SUBPOLAR GYRES   Northern or southern boundary currents that flow eastward as a result of the prevailing westerlies eventually move into subpolar latitudes (about 60 degrees north or south latitude). Here, they are driven in a westerly direction by the polar easterlies, producing **subpolar gyres** that rotate opposite the adjacent subtropical gyres. Subpolar gyres are smaller and fewer than subtropical gyres. Two examples include the subpolar gyre in the Atlantic Ocean between Greenland and Europe (named the *Viking Gyre* in honor of the Viking voyages during the Middle Ages) and in the Weddell Sea off Antarctica (Figure 7.5).

> **KEY CONCEPT**
> The principal ocean surface current pattern consists of subtropical and subpolar gyres that are large, circular-moving loops of water powered by the major wind belts of the world.

---

[3]Currents are often named for a prominent geographic location near where they pass. For instance, the Canary Current passes the Canary Islands, and the Benguela Current is named for the Benguela Province in Angola, Africa.

Other Factors Affecting Ocean Surface Circulation

Several other factors influence circulation patterns in subtropical gyres, including Ekman spiral and Ekman transport, geostrophic currents, and western intensification of subtropical gyres.

EKMAN SPIRAL AND EKMAN TRANSPORT During the voyage of the *Fram* (Web Box 7.1), Norwegian explorer Fridtjof Nansen observed that Arctic Ocean ice moved 20 to 40 degrees to the right of the wind blowing across its surface (Figure 7.6). Not only ice but surface waters in the Northern Hemisphere were also observed to move to the right of the wind direction; in the Southern Hemisphere, surface waters move to the *left* of the wind direction. Why does surface water move in a direction different than the wind? **V. Walfrid Ekman** (1874–1954), a Swedish physicist, developed a circulation model in 1905 called the **Ekman spiral** (Figure 7.7) that explains Nansen's observations as a balance between frictional effects in the ocean and the Coriolis effect.

The Ekman spiral describes the speed and direction of flow of surface waters at various depths. Ekman's model assumes that a uniform column of water is set in motion by wind blowing across its surface. Because of the Coriolis effect, the immediate surface water moves in a direction 45 degrees to the right of the wind (in the Northern Hemisphere). The surface water moves as a thin "layer" on top of deeper layers of water. As the surface layer moves, other layers beneath it are set in motion, thus passing the energy of the wind down through the water column just like how a deck of cards can be fanned out by pressing on and rotating only the top card.

Current speed decreases with increasing depth, however, and the Coriolis effect increases curvature to the right (like a spiral). Thus, each successive layer of water is set in motion at a progressively slower velocity, and in a direction progressively to the right of the one above it. At some depth, a layer of water may move in a direction *exactly opposite from the wind direction that initiated it!* If the water is deep enough, friction will consume the energy imparted by the wind and no motion will occur below that depth. Although it depends on wind speed and latitude, this stillness normally occurs at a depth of about 100 meters (330 feet).

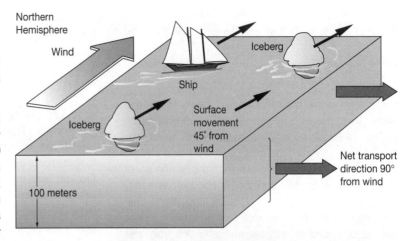

FIGURE 7.6 Transport of floating objects. Fridtjof Nansen first noticed that floating objects, such as icebergs and ships, were carried to the right of the wind direction in the Northern Hemisphere.

Ekman Spiral and Coastal Upwelling/ Downwelling

(a)

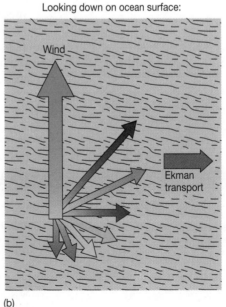

Looking down on ocean surface:

(b)

FIGURE 7.7 Ekman spiral. Perspective view **(a)** and top view **(b)** of Ekman spiral and Ekman transport. Wind drives surface water in a direction 45 degrees to the right of the wind in the Northern Hemisphere. Deeper water continues to deflect to the right and moves at a slower speed with increased depth, causing the Ekman spiral. Ekman transport, which is the average water movement for the entire column, is at a right angle (90 degrees) to the wind direction.

Figure 7.7 shows the spiral nature of this movement with increasing depth from the ocean's surface. The length of each arrow in Figure 7.7 is proportional to the velocity of the individual layer, and the direction of each arrow indicates the direction it moves.[4] Under ideal conditions, therefore, the surface layer should move at an angle of 45 degrees from the direction of the wind. All the layers combine, however, to create a net water movement that is 90 degrees from the direction of the wind. This average movement, called **Ekman transport**, is 90 degrees to the *right* in the Northern Hemisphere and 90 degrees to the *left* in the Southern Hemisphere.

"Ideal" conditions rarely exist in the ocean, so the actual movement of surface currents deviates slightly from the angles shown in Figure 7.7. Generally, surface currents move at an angle somewhat less than 45 degrees from the direction of the wind and Ekman transport in the open ocean is typically about 70 degrees from the wind direction. In shallow coastal waters, Ekman transport may be very nearly the same direction as the wind.

GEOSTROPHIC CURRENTS Ekman transport deflects surface water to the right in the Northern Hemisphere, so a clockwise rotation develops within an ocean basin and produces a **Subtropical Convergence** of water in the middle of the gyre, causing water literally to pile up in the center of the subtropical gyre. Thus, there is a hill of water within all subtropical gyres that is as much as 2 meters (6.6 feet) high.

Surface water in a Subtropical Convergence tends to flow downhill in response to gravity. The Coriolis effect opposes gravity, however, deflecting the water to the right in a curved path (Figure 7.8a) into the hill again. When these two factors balance, the net effect is a **geostrophic** *(geo* = earth, *strophio* = turn*)* **current** that moves in a circular path around the hill and is shown in Figure 7.8a as the *path of ideal geostrophic flow*.[5] Friction between water molecules, however, causes the water to move gradually down the slope of the hill as it flows around it. This is the path of *actual geostrophic flow* labeled in Figure 7.8a.

If you reexamine the satellite image of sea surface elevation in Figure 7.2, you'll see that the hills of water within the subtropical gyres of the Atlantic Ocean are clearly visible. The hill in the North Pacific is visible as well, but the elevation of the equatorial Pacific is not as low as expected because the map shows conditions during a moderate El Niño event,[6] so there is a well-developed warm and anomalously high equatorial countercurrent. Figure 7.2 also shows very little distinction between the North and South Pacific gyres. Moreover, the South Pacific (Heyerdahl) Gyre hill is less pronounced than in other gyres, mostly because it covers such a large area; it lacks confinement by continental barriers along its western margin; and because of interference by numerous islands (really the tops of tall sea floor mountains). The South Indian Ocean hill is rather well developed in the figure, although its northeastern boundary stands high because of the influx of warm Pacific Ocean water through the East Indies islands.

WESTERN INTENSIFICATION OF SUBTROPICAL GYRES Figure 7.8a shows that the apex (top) of the hill formed within a rotating gyre is closer to the western boundary than the center of the gyre. As a result, the western boundary currents of the subtropical gyres are faster, narrower, and deeper than their eastern boundary current counterparts. For example, the Kuroshio Current (a western boundary current) of the North Pacific (Turtle) Gyre is up to 15 times faster, 20 times narrower, and five times as deep as the California Current (an eastern boundary current). This phenomenon is called **western intensification**, and

---

[4]The name Ekman *spiral* refers to the spiral observed by connecting the tips of the arrows shown in Figure 7.7.

[5]The term *geostrophic* for these currents is appropriate, since the currents behave as they do because of Earth's rotation.

[6]El Niño events are discussed later in this chapter, under "Pacific Ocean Circulation."

Northern Hemisphere Subtropical Gyre

FIGURE 7.8 Geostrophic current and western inten-sification. (a) A cross-sectional view of a subtropical gyre showing how water liter-ally piles up in the center, forming a hill up to 2 meters (6.6 feet) high. Gravity and the Coriolis effect balance to create an ideal geostrophic current that flows in equilib-rium around the hill. However, friction makes the current gradually run downs-lope (*actual geostrophic flow*). (b) A map view of the same subtropical gyre, showing that the flow pattern is restricted (lines are closer together) on the western side of the gyre, resulting in western intensification.

currents affected by this phenomenon are said to be *western intensified*. Note that the western boundary currents of *all* subtropical gyres are western intensified, *even in the Southern Hemisphere.*

A number of factors cause western intensification, including the Coriolis effect. The Coriolis effect increases toward the poles, so eastward-flowing high-latitude water turns toward the equator more strongly than westward-flowing equatorial water turns toward higher latitudes. This causes a wide, slow, and shallow flow of water toward the equator across most of each subtropical gyre, leaving only a narrow band through which the poleward flow can occur along the western margin of the ocean basin. If a constant volume of water rotates around the apex of the hill in Figure 7.8b, then the velocity of the water along the western margin will be much greater than the velocity around the eastern side.[7] In Figure 7.8b, the lines are close

---

[7]A good analogy for this phenomenon is a funnel: In the narrow end of a funnel, the flow rates are speeded up (such as in western intensified currents) in the wide end, the flow rates are sluggish (such as in eastern boundary currents).

TABLE 7.2		CHARACTERISTICS OF WESTERN AND EASTERN BOUNDARY CURRENTS OF SUBTROPICAL GYRES				
Current type	Examples	Width	Depth	Speed	Transport volume (millions of cubic meters per second[a])	Comments
Western boundary current	Gulf Stream, Brazil Current, Kuroshio Current	*Narrow:* usually less than 100 kilometers (60 miles)	*Deep:* to depths of 2 kilometers (1.2 miles)	*Fast:* hundreds of kilometers per day	*Large:* as much as 100 Sv[a]	Waters derived from low latitudes and are warm; little or no upwelling
Eastern boundary current	Canary Current, Benguela Current, California Current	*Wide:* up to 1000 kilometers (600 miles)	*Shallow:* to depths of 0.5 kilometer (0.3 mile)	*Slow:* tens of kilometers per day	*Small:* typically 10 to 15 Sv[a]	Waters derived from middle latitudes and are cool; coastal upwelling common

[a] One million cubic meters per second is a flow rate equal to one Sverdrup (Sv).

> **KEY CONCEPT**
> Western intensification is a result of Earth's rotation and causes the western boundary current of all subtropical gyres to be fast, narrow, and deep.

together along the western margin, indicating the faster flow. The end result is a high-speed western boundary current that flows along the hill's steeper westward slope and a slow drift of water toward the equator along the more gradual eastern slope. Table 7.2 summarizes the differences between western and eastern boundary currents of subtropical gyres.

Ocean Currents and Climate

Ocean surface currents directly influence the climate of adjoining landmasses. For instance, warm ocean currents warm the nearby air. This warm air can hold a large amount of water vapor, which puts more moisture (high humidity) in the atmosphere. When this warm, moist air travels over a continent, it releases its water vapor in the form of precipitation. Continental margins that have warm ocean currents offshore (Figure 7.9, *red arrows*) typically have a humid climate. The presence of a warm current off the East Coast of the United States helps explain why the area experiences such high humidity, especially in the summer.

Conversely, cold ocean currents cool the nearby air, which is more likely to have low water vapor content. When the cool, dry air travels over a continent, it results in very little precipitation. Continental margins that have cool ocean currents offshore (Figure 7.9, *blue arrows*) typically have a dry climate. The presence of a cold current off California is part of the reason why the climate is so arid there.

7.3 What Causes Upwelling and Downwelling?

Upwelling is the vertical movement of cold, deep, nutrient-rich water to the surface; **downwelling** is the vertical movement of surface water to deeper parts of the ocean. Upwelling hoists chilled water to the surface. This cold water, rich in

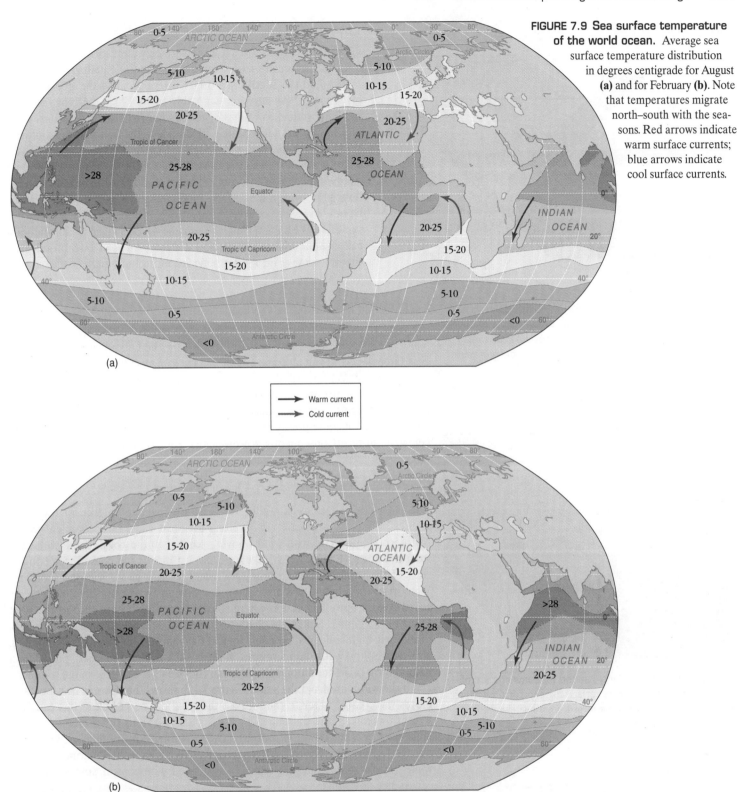

FIGURE 7.9 Sea surface temperature of the world ocean. Average sea surface temperature distribution in degrees centigrade for August **(a)** and for February **(b)**. Note that temperatures migrate north–south with the seasons. Red arrows indicate warm surface currents; blue arrows indicate cool surface currents.

nutrients, creates high **productivity** (an abundance of microscopic algae), which establishes the base of the food web and, in turn, supports incredible numbers of larger marine life like fish and whales. Downwelling, on the other hand, is associated with much lower amounts of surface productivity but carries necessary dissolved oxygen to those organisms living on the deep-sea floor.

Upwelling and downwelling provide important mixing mechanisms between surface and deep waters and are accomplished by a variety of methods.

FIGURE 7.10 Equatorial upwelling. As the southeast trade winds pass over the geographical equator to the meteorological equator, they cause water within the South Equatorial Current north of the equator to veer to the right (northward) and water south of the equator to veer to the left (southward). Thus, surface water diverges, which causes equatorial upwelling.

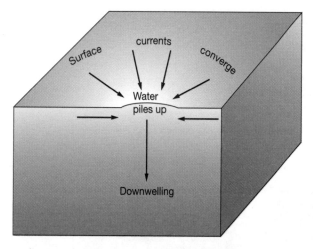

FIGURE 7.11 Downwelling caused by convergence of surface currents. Where surface currents converge, water piles up and slowly sinks downward, creating downwelling.

Diverging Surface Water

Current divergence occurs when surface waters move *away from* an area on the ocean's surface, such as along the equator. As shown in Figure 7.10, the South Equatorial Current occupies the area along the *geographical equator* (most notably in the Pacific Ocean; see Figure 7.5), while the *meteorological equator* (where the doldrums exist) typically occurs a few degrees of latitude to the north. As the southeast trade winds blow across this region, Ekman transport causes surface water north of the equator to veer to the right (northward) and water south of the equator to veer to the left (southward). The net result is a divergence of surface currents along the geographical equator, which causes upwelling of cold, nutrient-rich water. Because this type of upwelling is common along the equator—especially in the Pacific—it is called **equatorial upwelling**, and it creates areas of high productivity that are some of the most prolific fishing grounds in the world.

Converging Surface Water

Current convergence occurs when surface waters move *toward* each other. In the North Atlantic Ocean, for instance, the Gulf Stream, the Labrador Current, and the East Greenland Current all come together in the same vicinity. When currents converge, water stacks up and has no place to go but downward. The surface water slowly sinks in a process called downwelling (Figure 7.11). Unlike upwelling, areas of downwelling are not associated with prolific marine life because the necessary nutrients are not continuously replenished from the cold, deep, nutrient-rich water below the surface. Consequently, downwelling areas have low productivity.

Coastal Upwelling and Downwelling

Coastal winds can cause upwelling or downwelling due to Ekman transport. Figure 7.12 shows a coastal region along the west coast of a continent in the Northern Hemisphere with winds moving parallel to the coast. If the winds are from the north (Figure 7.12a), Ekman transport moves the coastal water to the right of the wind direction, causing the water to flow *away from* the shoreline. Water rises from below to replace the water moving away from shore in a process called **coastal upwelling**. Areas where coastal upwelling occurs, such as the West Coast of the United States, are characterized by high concentrations of nutrients, resulting in high biological productivity and rich marine life. This coastal upwelling also creates low water temperatures in areas such as San Francisco, providing a natural form of air conditioning (and much cool weather and fog) in the summer.

If the winds are from the south, Figure 7.12b shows that Ekman transport still moves the coastal water to the right of the wind direction but, in this case, the water flows *toward* the shoreline. The water stacks up along the shoreline and has nowhere to go but down, in a process called **coastal downwelling**. Areas where coastal downwelling occurs have low productivity and a lack of marine life. If the winds reverse, areas that are typically associated with coastal downwelling can experience upwelling.

A similar situation exists for coastal winds and upwelling/downwelling in the Southern Hemisphere, except that Ekman transport is to the *left* of the wind direction.

Other Causes of Upwelling

Figure 7.13 shows how upwelling can be created by offshore winds, sea floor obstructions, or a sharp bend in a coastline. Upwelling also occurs in high-latitude regions, where there is no pycnocline (a layer of rapidly changing density). The

(a)

(b)

FIGURE 7.12 Coastal upwelling and downwelling. (a) Where northerly coastal winds blow parallel to a west coast in the Northern Hemisphere, Ekman transport carries surface water to the *right* of the wind direction and away from a continent. Upwelling of deeper water replaces the surface water that has moved away from the coast. **(b)** A reversal of the wind direction still causes Ekman transport to the right but results in water piling up against the shore, producing downwelling. A similar situation exists for coastal winds and upwelling/downwelling in the Southern Hemisphere, except that Ekman transport is to the *left* of the wind direction.

> **KEY CONCEPT**
> Upwelling and downwelling cause vertical mixing between surface and deep water. Upwelling brings cold, deep, nutrient-rich water to the surface, which results in high productivity.

absence of a pycnocline allows significant vertical mixing between high-density cold surface water and high-density cold deep water below. Thus, both upwelling and downwelling are common in high latitudes.

7.4 What Are the Main Surface Circulation Patterns in Each Ocean?

The pattern of surface currents varies from ocean to ocean depending upon the geometry of the ocean basin, the pattern of major wind belts, seasonal factors, and other periodic changes.

Antarctic Circulation

Antarctic circulation is dominated by the movement of water masses in the southern Atlantic, Indian, and Pacific Oceans south of about 50 degrees south latitude.

ANTARCTIC CIRCUMPOLAR CURRENT The main current in Antarctic waters is the **Antarctic Circumpolar Current**, which is also called the **West Wind Drift** or the *Penguin Gyre*. This current encircles

(a)

(b)

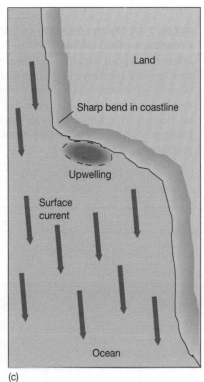

(c)

FIGURE 7.13 Other types of upwelling. Upwelling can be caused by **(a)** offshore winds; **(b)** a sea floor obstruction, in this case, a tablemount; **(c)** a sharp bend in coastal geometry.

FIGURE 7.14 South polar view of Earth showing Antarctic surface circulation. The East Wind Drift is driven by the polar easterlies and flows around Antarctica from the east. The Antarctic Circumpolar Current (West Wind Drift) flows around Antarctica from the west but is further from the continent and is a result of the strong prevailing westerlies. The Antarctic Convergence and Antarctic Divergence are caused by interactions at the boundaries of these two currents.

Antarctica and flows from west to east at approximately 50 degrees south latitude but varies between 40 and 65 degrees south latitude. At about 40 degrees south latitude is the *Subtropical Convergence* (Figure 7.14), which forms the northernmost boundary of the Antarctic Circumpolar Current. The Antarctic Circumpolar Current is driven by the powerful prevailing westerly wind belt, which creates winds so strong that these Southern Hemisphere latitudes have been called the "Roaring Forties," "Furious Fifties," and "Screaming Sixties."

The Antarctic Circumpolar Current is the only current that completely circumscribes Earth and is allowed to do so because of the lack of land at high southern latitudes. It meets its greatest restriction as it passes through the *Drake Passage* [named for the famed English sea captain and ocean explorer Sir Francis Drake (1540–1596)] between the Antarctic Peninsula and the southern islands of South America, which is about 1000 kilometers (600 miles) wide. Although the current is not speedy [its maximum surface velocity is about 2.75 kilometers (1.65 miles) per hour], it transports more water (an average of about 130 million cubic meters per second[8]) than any other surface current.

ANTARCTIC CONVERGENCE AND DIVERGENCE The **Antarctic Convergence** (Figure 7.14) or *Antarctic Polar Front* is where colder, denser, Antarctic waters converge with (and sink sharply below) warmer, less dense sub-Antarctic waters at about 50 degrees south latitude. The Antarctic Convergence marks the northernmost boundary of the Southern or Antarctic Ocean.

The **East Wind Drift**, a surface current propelled by the polar easterlies, moves from an easterly direction around the margin of the Antarctic continent. The East Wind Drift is most extensively developed to the east of the Antarctic Peninsula in the Weddell Sea region and in the area of the Ross Sea (Figure 7.14). As the East Wind Drift and the Antarctic Circumpolar Current flow around Antarctica in opposite directions, they create a surface divergence. Recall that the Coriolis effect deflects moving masses to the left in the Southern Hemisphere, so the East Wind Drift is deflected toward the continent and the Antarctic Circumpolar Current is deflected away from it. This creates a divergence of currents along a boundary called the **Antarctic Divergence**. The Antarctic Divergence has abundant marine life in the Southern Hemisphere summer because of the mixing of these two currents, which supplies nutrient-rich water to the surface through upwelling.

Atlantic Ocean Circulation

Figure 7.15 shows Atlantic Ocean surface circulation, which consists of two large subtropical gyres: the North Atlantic (Columbus) Gyre and the South Atlantic (Navigator) Gyre.

THE NORTH AND SOUTH ATLANTIC SUBTROPICAL GYRES The **North Atlantic Subtropical Gyre** (Columbus Gyre) rotates clockwise and the **South Atlantic Subtropical Gyre** (Navigator Gyre) rotates counterclockwise, due to the combined

---

[8]One million cubic meters per second is a useful flow rate for describing ocean currents, so it has become a standard unit, named the **Sverdrup (Sv)**, after Norwegian meteorologist and physical oceanographer Harald Sverdrup (1888–1957).

effects of the trade winds, the prevailing westerlies, and the Coriolis effect. Figure 7.15 shows that each gyre consists of a poleward-moving warm current (*red*) and an equatorward-moving cold "return" current (*blue*). The two gyres are partially offset by the shapes of the surrounding continents, and the **Atlantic Equatorial Countercurrent** moves in between them.

In the South Atlantic (Navigator) Gyre, the **South Equatorial Current** reaches its greatest strength just below the equator, where it encounters the coast of Brazil and splits in two. Part of the South Equatorial Current moves off along the northeastern coast of South America toward the Caribbean Sea and the North Atlantic. The rest is turned southward as the **Brazil Current**, which ultimately merges with the Antarctic Circumpolar Current (West Wind Drift) and moves eastward across the South Atlantic. The Brazil Current is much smaller than its Northern Hemisphere counterpart, the Gulf Stream, due to the splitting of the South Equatorial Current. The **Benguela Current**, slow moving and cold, flows toward the equator along Africa's western coast, completing the gyre.

Outside the gyre, the *Falkland Current* (Figure 7.15), which is also called the *Malvinas Current*, moves a significant amount of cold water along the coast of Argentina as far north as 25 to 30 degrees south latitude, wedging its way between the continent and the southbound Brazil Current.

THE GULF STREAM   The **Gulf Stream** is the best studied of all ocean currents. It moves northward along the East Coast of the United States, warming coastal states and moderating winters in these and northern European regions.

Figure 7.16 shows the network of currents in the North Atlantic Ocean that contribute to the flow of the Gulf Stream. The **North Equatorial Current** moves parallel to the equator in the Northern Hemisphere, where it is joined by the portion of the South Equatorial Current that turns northward along the South American coast. This flow then splits into the **Antilles Current**, which passes along the Atlantic side of the West Indies, and the **Caribbean Current**, which passes through the Yucatán Channel into the Gulf of Mexico. These masses reconverge as the **Florida Current**.

The Florida Current flows close to shore over the continental shelf at a rate that at times exceeds 35 Sverdrups. As it moves off North Carolina's Cape Hatteras and flows across the deep ocean in a northeasterly direction, it is called the Gulf Stream. The Gulf Stream is a western boundary current, so it is subject to western intensification. Thus, it is only 50 to 75 kilometers (31 to 47 miles) wide, but it reaches depths of 1.5 kilometers (1 mile) and speeds from 3 to 10 kilometers (2 to 6 miles) per hour, making it the fastest current in the world ocean.

The western boundary of the Gulf Stream is usually abrupt, but it periodically migrates closer to and farther away from the shore. Its eastern boundary is very difficult to identify because it is usually masked by meandering water masses that change their position continuously.

The Sargasso Sea   The Gulf Stream gradually merges eastward with the water of the **Sargasso Sea**. The Sargasso Sea is the water that circulates around the rotation center of the North Atlantic gyre. The Sargasso Sea can be thought of as the stagnant eddy of the North Atlantic (Columbus) Gyre. Its name is derived

Currents

A=Antilles	**G**=Guinea
Bg=Benguela	**GS**=Gulf Stream
Br=Brazil	**I**=Irminger
C=Canary	**L**=Labrador
CC=Caribbean	**N**=Norwegian
EC=Equatorial Counter	**NE**=North Equatorial
EG=East Greenland	**SE**=South Equatorial
EW=East Wind Drift	**WW**=West Wind Drift
F=Florida	(Antarctic Circumpolar
Fa=Falkland	Current)

FIGURE 7.15 Atlantic Ocean surface currents. Atlantic Ocean surface circulation is composed primarily of two subtropical gyres.

7.2   HISTORICAL FEATURE

BENJAMIN FRANKLIN: THE WORLD'S MOST FAMOUS PHYSICAL OCEANOGRAPHER

Benjamin Franklin (Figure 7B, *inset*) is well known as a scientist, inventor, economist, statesman, diplomat, writer, poet, international celebrity, and one of the founding fathers of the United States. He even held the position of deputy postmaster general of the colonies from 1753 to 1774. Remarkably, he also became known as one of the first physical oceanographers because he contributed greatly to the understanding of the Gulf Stream, a North Atlantic Ocean surface current. Why would a postmaster general be interested in an ocean current?

Franklin became interested in North Atlantic Ocean circulation patterns because he needed to explain why mail ships coming from Europe to New England took about two weeks less time when they took a longer, more southerly route than when they took a more direct, northerly route. In about 1769 or 1770, Franklin mentioned this dilemma to his cousin, a Nantucket sea captain named Timothy Folger. Folger told Franklin that a strong current with which the mail ships were unfamiliar was impeding their journey because it flowed against them. The whaling ships were familiar with the current because they often hunted whales along its boundaries. The whalers often met the mail ships within the current and told their crews they would make swifter progress if they avoided the current. The British captains of the mail ships, however, would not accept advice from simple American fishers, so they continued to make slow progress within the current. If the winds were light, their ships were actually carried *backward*!

Folger sketched the current on a map for Franklin, including directions for avoiding it by taking a more southerly route when sailing from Europe to North America. Franklin then asked other ship captains for information concerning the movement of surface waters in the North Atlantic Ocean. Franklin inferred that there was a significant current moving northward along the eastern coast of the United States, which then headed east across the North Atlantic. He concluded that this current was responsible for aiding the progress of ships traveling through the North Atlantic to Europe and slowing ships traveling in the reverse direction. He subsequently measured the temperature of the current himself and first published a

map of the current in 1777 based on these observations and distributed it to the captains of the mail ships (who initially ignored it). This strong current is named the *Gulf Stream* because it carries warm water from the Gulf of Mexico and because it is narrow and well defined—similar to a stream, but in the ocean.

In 1969, six scientists studied the Gulf Stream aboard a submersible vessel that was allowed to float for a month underwater wherever the current took her. During the vessel's 2640-kilometer (1650-mile) journey, the scientists observed and measured the properties of and cataloged life forms within the Gulf Stream. Appropriately enough, the vessel was named the *Ben Franklin*.

FIGURE 7B A chart of the Gulf Stream (1786) based on sketches by Ben Franklin (*inset*).

from a type of floating marine alga called *Sargassum* (*sargassum* = grapes) that abounds on its surface.

The transport rate of the Gulf Stream off Chesapeake Bay is about 100 Sverdrups,[9] which suggests that a large volume of water from the Sargasso Sea has combined with the Florida Current to produce the Gulf Stream. By the time

---

[9]The Gulf Stream's flow of 100 Sverdrups equates to a volume of about 100 major league sport stadiums passing by the southeast U.S. coast *each second* and is more than 100 times greater than the combined flow of *all* the world's rivers!

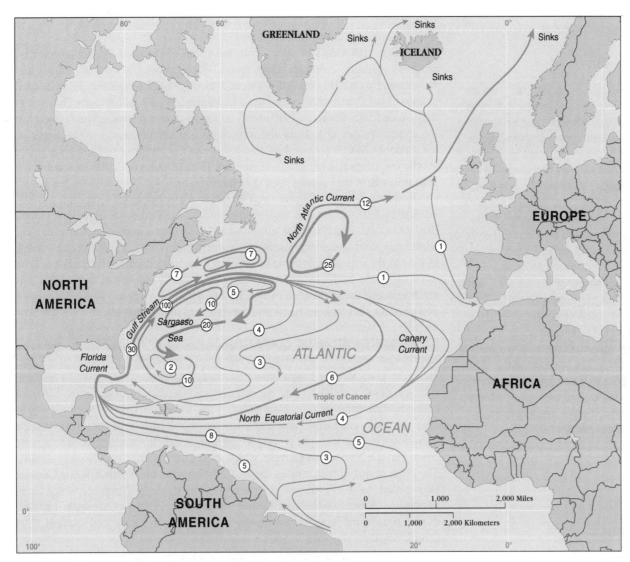

FIGURE 7.16 North Atlantic Ocean circulation. The North Atlantic (Columbus) Gyre, showing average flow rates in *Sverdrups* (1 Sverdrup = 1 million cubic meters per second). The four major currents include the western intensified Gulf Stream, the North Atlantic Current, the Canary Current, and the North Equatorial Current. Some water splits off in the North Atlantic, where it becomes cold and dense, so it sinks. The Sargasso Sea occupies the stagnant eddy in the middle of the subtropical gyre.

the Gulf Stream near Newfoundland, however, the transport rate is only 40 Sverdrups, which suggests that a large volume of water has returned to the diffuse flow of the Sargasso Sea.

Warm- and Cold-Core Rings   The mechanisms that produce the dramatic loss of water as the Gulf Stream moves northward are yet to be determined. Meanders, however, may cause much of it. *Meanders* (*Menderes* = a river in Turkey that has a very sinuous course) are snakelike bends in the current that often disconnect from the Gulf Stream and form large rotating masses of water called *vortexes* (*vortexes* = to turn), which are more commonly known as *eddies* or *rings*. Figure 7.17 shows several of these rings, which are noticeable near the center of each image. The figure also shows that meanders along the north boundary of the Gulf Stream pinch off and trap warm Sargasso Sea water in eddies that rotate clockwise, creating **warm-core rings** (*yellow*) surrounded by cooler (*blue and green*) water. These warm rings contain shallow, bowl-shaped masses of warm water about 1 kilometer (0.6 mile) deep, with diameters of about

Is the Gulf Stream rich in life?

The Gulf Stream *itself* isn't rich in life, but its *boundaries* often are. The oceanic areas that have abundant marine life are typically associated with cool water—either in high-latitude regions, or in any region where upwelling occurs. These areas are constantly resupplied with oxygen- and nutrient-rich water, which results in high productivity. Warm-water areas develop a prominent thermocline that isolates the surface water from colder, nutrient-rich water below. Nutrients used up in warm waters tend not to be resupplied. The Gulf Stream, which is a western intensified, warm-water current, is therefore associated with low productivity and an absence of marine life. New England fishers knew about the Gulf Stream (Box 7.2) because they sought their catch along the *sides* of the current, where mixing and upwelling occur.

Actually, all western intensified currents are warm and are associated with low productivities. The Kuroshio Current in the North Pacific Ocean, for example, is named for its conspicuous absence of marine life. In Japanese, *Kuroshio* means "black current," in reference to its clear, lifeless waters.

100 kilometers (60 miles). Warm-core rings remove large volumes of water as they disconnect from the Gulf Stream.

Cold nearshore water spins off to the south of the Gulf Stream as counterclockwise-rotating **cold-core rings** (*green*) surrounded by warmer (*yellow and red-orange*) water (Figure 7.17). The cold rings consist of spinning cone-shaped masses of cold water that extend over 3.5 kilometers (2.2 miles) deep. These rings may exceed 500 kilometers (310 miles) in diameter at the surface. The diameter of the cone increases with depth and sometimes reaches all the way to the sea floor, where cones have a tremendous impact on sea floor sediment. Cold rings move southwest at speeds of 3 to 7 kilometers (2 to 4 miles) per day toward Cape Hatteras, where they often rejoin the Gulf Stream.

Both warm- and cold-core rings maintain not only unique temperature characteristics, but also unique biological populations. Studies of rings have found they are isolated habitats for either warm-water organisms in a cold ocean or, conversely, cold-water organisms in a warmer ocean. The organisms can survive as long as the ring does; in some cases, rings have been documented to last as long as two years. In addition, cold-core rings are typically associated with high nutrient levels and an abundance of marine life while warm-core rings are zones of downwelling that lack nutrients and are deficient in marine life.

OTHER NORTH ATLANTIC CURRENTS Southeast of Newfoundland, the Gulf Stream continues in an easterly direction across the North Atlantic (Figure 7.16). Here the Gulf Stream breaks into numerous branches, many of which become cold and dense enough to sink beneath the surface. As shown in Figure 7.15, one major branch combines the cold water of the **Labrador Current** with the warm Gulf Stream, producing abundant fog in the North Atlantic. This branch eventually breaks into the **Irminger Current**, which flows along Iceland's west coast, and the **Norwegian Current**, which moves northward along Norway's coast. The other major branch crosses the North Atlantic as the **North Atlantic Current** (also called the *North Atlantic Drift*, emphasizing its sluggish nature), which turns southward to become the cool **Canary Current**. The Canary Current is a broad, diffuse southward flow that eventually joins the North Equatorial Current, thus completing the gyre.

CLIMATIC EFFECTS OF NORTH ATLANTIC CURRENTS The warming effects of the Gulf Stream are far ranging. The Gulf Stream not only moderates temperatures along the East Coast of the United States but also in northern Europe (in conjunction with heat transferred by the atmosphere). Thus, the temperatures across the Atlantic at different latitudes are much higher in Europe than in North America because of the effects of heat transfer from the Gulf Stream to Europe. For example, Spain and Portugal have warm climates, even though they are at the same latitude as the New England states, which are known for severe winters. The warming that northern Europe experiences because of the Gulf Stream is as much as 9°C (20°F), which is enough to keep high-latitude Baltic ports ice free throughout the year.

The warming effects of western boundary currents in the North Atlantic Ocean can be seen on the average sea surface temperature map for February shown in Figure 7.9b. Off the east coast of North America from latitudes 20 degrees north (the latitude of Cuba) to 40 degrees north (the latitude of Philadelphia), for example, there is a 20°C (36°F) difference in sea surface temperatures. On the eastern side of the North Atlantic, on the other hand, there is only a 5°C (9°F) difference in temperature between the same latitudes, indicating the moderating effect of the Gulf Stream.

The average sea surface temperature map for August (see Figure 7.9a) also shows how the North Atlantic and Norwegian Currents (branches of the Gulf Stream) warm northwestern Europe compared with the same latitudes along the

North American coast. On the western side of the North Atlantic, the southward-flowing Labrador Current—which is cold and often contains icebergs from western Greenland—keeps Canadian coastal waters much cooler. During the Northern Hemisphere winter (Figure 7.9b), North Africa's coastal waters are cooled by the southward-flowing Canary Current and are much cooler than waters near Florida and the Gulf of Mexico.

Indian Ocean Circulation

Because of the shape and position of India, the Indian Ocean exists mostly in the Southern Hemisphere. From November to March, equatorial circulation in the Indian Ocean is similar to that in the Atlantic Ocean, with two westward-flowing equatorial currents (North and South Equatorial Currents) separated by an eastward-flowing Equatorial Countercurrent. As compared to circulation in the Atlantic, however, the Equatorial Countercurrent in the Indian Ocean lies in a more southerly position because most of the Indian Ocean lies in the Southern Hemisphere. The shape of the Indian Ocean basin and its proximity to the high mountains of Asia cause it to experience strong seasonal changes.

MONSOONS The winds of the northern Indian Ocean have a seasonal pattern called **monsoon** (*mausim* = season) winds. During winter, air over the Asian mainland rapidly cools, creating high atmospheric pressure, which causes the wind to blow from southwest Asia off the continent and out over the ocean (Figure 7.18a, *green arrows*). These northeast trade winds are called the *northeast monsoon*. During this season, there is little precipitation because the air associated with the high pressure over land is so dry.

During summer, the winds reverse. Because of the lower heat capacity of rocks and soil compared with water, the Asian mainland warms faster than the adjacent ocean, creating low atmospheric pressure over the continent. As a result, the winds blow strongly from the Indian Ocean onto the Asian landmass (Figure 7.18b, *green arrows*), giving rise to the *southwest monsoon*, which may be thought of as a continuation of the southeast trade winds across the equator. During this season, there is heavy precipitation on land because the air brought in from the Indian Ocean is warm and full of moisture.

Not only does this seasonal cycle affect weather patterns on land, it also affects surface current circulation in the Indian Ocean. In fact, the northern Indian Ocean is the only place in the world where reversing seasonal winds

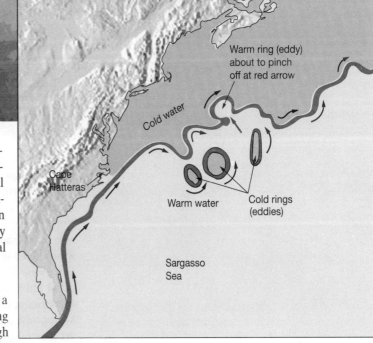

FIGURE 7.17 The Gulf Stream and sea surface temperatures. A NOAA satellite false-color image of sea surface temperature (*upper*) and a schematic diagram of the same area (*lower*). The warm waters of the Gulf stream are shown in red and orange; colder waters are shown in green, blue, and purple. As the Gulf stream meanders northward, some of its meanders pinch off and form either warm-core or cold-core rings.

FIGURE 7.18 Indian Ocean surface currents and the monsoons. Surface currents in the Indian Ocean are influenced by the seasonal monsoons. **(a)** Northeast monsoon, which occurs during winter. **(b)** Southwest monsoon, which occurs during summer.

Currents

A=Agulhas   **SE**=South Equatorial
EC=Equatorial Counter   **SM**=Southwest Monsoon
L=Leeuwin   **WA**=West Australian
NE=North Equatorial   **WW**=West Wind Drift
S=Somali   (Antarctic Circumpolar Current)

actually cause major ocean surface currents to switch direction. During the wintertime northwest monsoon (Figure 7.18a), offshore winds cause the North Equatorial Current to flow from east to west and its extension, the **Somali Current**, flows south along the coast of Africa. An *Equatorial Countercurrent* is also established. During the summertime southwest monsoon (Figure 7.18b), the winds reverse, causing the North Equatorial Current to be replaced by the *Southwest Monsoon Current*, which flows in the opposite direction. The winds cause the Somali Current to reverse as well, which flows rapidly northward with velocities approaching 4 kilometers (2.5 miles) per hour and feeds the Southwest Monsoon Current. By October, the northeast trade winds are reestablished and the North Equatorial Current reappears (Figure 7.18a).

The movement of winds during the summertime southwest monsoon also affects sea surface temperatures, which cool near the Arabian Peninsula because of upwelling as water is drawn away from shore. This cool water also supports large populations of phytoplankton during the summer southwest monsoon (Figure 7.19). Studies of productivity in the Indian Ocean show that upwelling has increased in recent years due to stronger winds caused by warming of the Eurasian landmass, resulting in higher than normal summer productivity in the Arabian Sea.

INDIAN OCEAN SUBTROPICAL GYRE Surface circulation in the southern Indian Ocean (the **Indian Ocean Subtropical Gyre**, or *Majid Gyre*) is similar to subtropical gyres observed in other southern oceans. When the northeast trade winds blow, the South Equatorial Current provides water for the Equatorial Countercurrent and the **Agulhas Current**,[10] which flows southward along Africa's east coast and joins the Antarctic Circumpolar Current (West Wind Drift). The *Agulhas Retroflection* is

---

[10]The Agulhas Current is named for Cape Agulhas, which is the southernmost tip of Africa.

created when the Agulhas Current makes an abrupt turn as it meets the strong Antarctic Circumpolar Current (see the chapter-opening satellite image). Turning northward out of the Antarctic Circumpolar Current is the **West Australian Current**, an eastern boundary current that merges with the South Equatorial Current, completing the gyre.

LEEUWIN CURRENT Eastern boundary currents in other subtropical gyres are cold drifts toward the equator that produce arid coastal climates [that is, they receive less than 25 centimeters (10 inches) of rain per year]. In the southern Indian Ocean, however, the **Leeuwin Current** displaces the West Australian Current offshore. The Leeuwin Current is driven southward along the Australian coast from the warm-water dome piled up in the East Indies by the Pacific equatorial currents.

The Leeuwin Current produces a mild climate in southwestern Australia, which receives about 125 centimeters (50 inches) of rain per year. During El Niño events, however, the Leeuwin Current weakens, so the cold Western Australian Current brings drought instead.

Pacific Ocean Circulation

Two large subtropical gyres dominate the circulation pattern in the Pacific Ocean, resulting in surface water movement and climatic effects similar to those found in the Atlantic. However, the Equatorial Countercurrent is much better developed in the Pacific Ocean than in the Atlantic (Figure 7.20), largely because the Pacific Ocean basin is larger and more unobstructed than the Atlantic Ocean.

NORMAL CONDITIONS "Normal" conditions in the Pacific Ocean are a bit of a misnomer because they are experienced so infrequently. As we'll see, various atmospheric and oceanic disturbances dominate conditions in the Pacific. Still, "normal" conditions provide a baseline from which to measure these disturbances.

North Pacific Subtropical Gyre Figure 7.20 shows that the **North Pacific Subtropical Gyre** (*Turtle Gyre*) includes the North Equatorial Current, which flows westward into the western intensified **Kuroshio Current**[11] near Asia. The warm waters of the Kuroshio Current make Japan's climate warmer than would be expected for its latitude. This current flows into the **North Pacific Current**, which connects to the cool-water **California Current**. The California Current flows south along the coast of California to complete the loop. Some North Pacific Current water also flows to the north and merges into the **Alaskan Current** in the Gulf of Alaska.

South Pacific Subtropical Gyre Figure 7.20 also shows how the **South Pacific Subtropical Gyre** (*Heyerdahl Gyre*) includes the South Equatorial Current, which flows westward into the western intensified **East Australian Current**.[12] From there, it joins the Antarctic Circumpolar Current (West Wind Drift) and

FIGURE 7.19 Seasonal variations in phytoplankton concentration in the Indian Ocean. Paired satellite images showing oceanic phytoplankton pigment, where orange and red colors indicate higher amounts phytoplankton and thus higher biological productivity. **(a)** During the northeast (winter) monsoon, lack of upwelling conditions result in low concentrations of phytoplankton along the coast of Saudi Arabia. **(b)** During the southwest (summer) monsoon, strong winds generate upwelling of nutrient-rich waters, leading to an increase in the concentration of phytoplankton along the coast of Saudi Arabia.

[11]Kuroshio is pronounced "kuhr-ROH-shee-oh." Because of its proximity to Japan, the Kuroshio Current is also called the *Japan Current*.

[12]Note that the western intensified East Australian Current was named because it lies off the *east coast* of Australia, even though it occupies a position along the *western* margin of the Pacific Ocean basin.

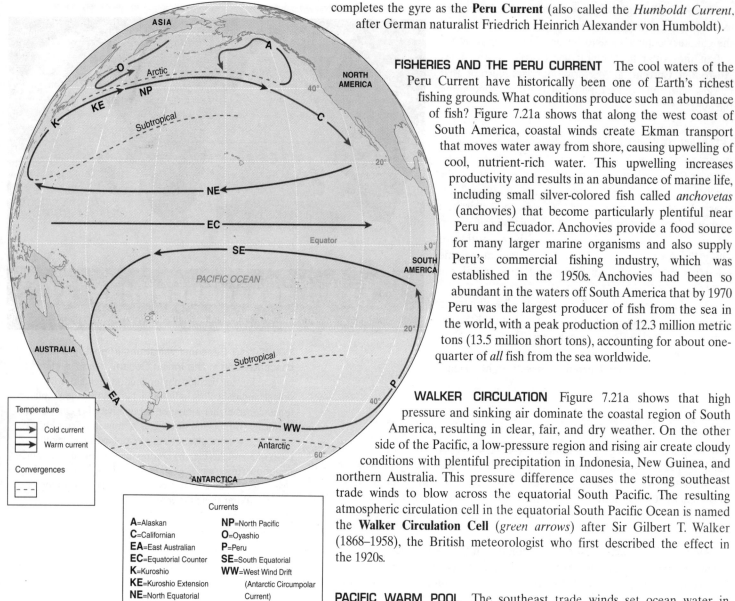

FIGURE 7.20 Pacific Ocean surface currents.
Circulation in the Pacific Ocean consists of two large subtropical gyres similar to those in the Atlantic Ocean. However, the equatorial countercurrent is more strongly developed in the Pacific than in smaller ocean basins.

Temperature

→ Cold current
➔ Warm current

Convergences

- - -

Currents

A=Alaskan	**NP**=North Pacific
C=Californian	**O**=Oyashio
EA=East Australian	**P**=Peru
EC=Equatorial Counter	**SE**=South Equatorial
K=Kuroshio	**WW**=West Wind Drift
KE=Kuroshio Extension	(Antarctic Circumpolar
NE=North Equatorial	Current)

completes the gyre as the **Peru Current** (also called the *Humboldt Current*, after German naturalist Friedrich Heinrich Alexander von Humboldt).

FISHERIES AND THE PERU CURRENT The cool waters of the Peru Current have historically been one of Earth's richest fishing grounds. What conditions produce such an abundance of fish? Figure 7.21a shows that along the west coast of South America, coastal winds create Ekman transport that moves water away from shore, causing upwelling of cool, nutrient-rich water. This upwelling increases productivity and results in an abundance of marine life, including small silver-colored fish called *anchovetas* (anchovies) that become particularly plentiful near Peru and Ecuador. Anchovies provide a food source for many larger marine organisms and also supply Peru's commercial fishing industry, which was established in the 1950s. Anchovies had been so abundant in the waters off South America that by 1970 Peru was the largest producer of fish from the sea in the world, with a peak production of 12.3 million metric tons (13.5 million short tons), accounting for about one-quarter of *all* fish from the sea worldwide.

WALKER CIRCULATION Figure 7.21a shows that high pressure and sinking air dominate the coastal region of South America, resulting in clear, fair, and dry weather. On the other side of the Pacific, a low-pressure region and rising air create cloudy conditions with plentiful precipitation in Indonesia, New Guinea, and northern Australia. This pressure difference causes the strong southeast trade winds to blow across the equatorial South Pacific. The resulting atmospheric circulation cell in the equatorial South Pacific Ocean is named the **Walker Circulation Cell** (*green arrows*) after Sir Gilbert T. Walker (1868–1958), the British meteorologist who first described the effect in the 1920s.

PACIFIC WARM POOL The southeast trade winds set ocean water in motion, which also moves across the Pacific toward the west. The water warms as it flows in the equatorial region and creates a wedge of warm water on the western side of the Pacific Ocean, called the **Pacific warm pool** (see Figure 7.9). Due to the movement of equatorial currents to the west, the Pacific warm pool is thicker along the western side of the Pacific than along the eastern side. The *thermocline* beneath the warm pool in the western equatorial Pacific occurs below 100 meters (330 feet) depth. In the eastern Pacific, however, the thermocline is within 30 meters (100 feet) of the surface. The difference in depth of the thermocline can be seen by the sloping boundary between the warm surface water and the cold deep water in Figure 7.21a.

EL NIÑO–SOUTHERN OSCILLATION (ENSO) CONDITIONS Historically, Peru's residents knew that every few years, a current of warm water reduced the population of anchovies in coastal waters. The decrease in anchovies caused a dramatic decline not only in the fishing industry, but also in marine life such as sea birds and seals that depended on anchovies for food. The warm current also brought about changes in the weather—usually intense rainfall—and even brought such interesting items as floating coconuts from tropical islands near the

(a) Normal conditions

(b) El Niño conditions (strong)

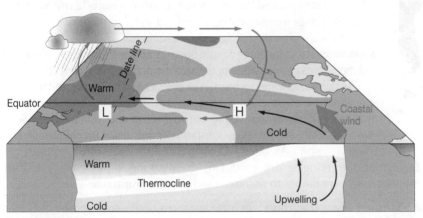

(c) La Niña conditions

FIGURE 7.21 Normal, El Niño, and La Niña conditions. Perspective views of oceanic and atmospheric conditions in the equatorial Pacific Ocean. **(a)** Normal conditions. **(b)** El Niño (ENSO warm phase) conditions. **(c)** La Niña (ENSO cool phase) conditions.

El Niño and La Niña

WEB VIDEO

El Niño

STUDENTS SOMETIMES ASK...

The amount of anchovies produced by Peru is impressive! Besides a topping for pizza, what are some other uses of anchovies?

Anchovies are an ingredient in certain dishes, hors d'oeuvres, sauces, and salad dressing, and they are also used as bait by fishers. Historically, however, most of the *anchoveta* caught in Peruvian waters were exported and used as fishmeal (consisting of ground anchovies). The fishmeal, in turn, was used largely in pet food and as a high-protein chicken feed. As unbelievable as it may seem, El Niños affected the price of eggs! Prior to the collapse of the Peruvian *anchoveta* fishing industry in 1972–1973, El Niño events significantly reduced the availability of *anchovetas*. This drastically cut the export of anchovies from Peru, causing U.S. farmers to pursue more expensive options for chicken feed. Thus, egg prices typically increased.

The collapse of the *anchoveta* fishing industry in Peru was triggered by the 1972–1973 El Niño event but was caused by chronic overfishing in prior years (see Web Box 13.2). Interestingly, the shortage of fishmeal after 1972–1973 led to an increased demand for soyameal, an alternative source of high-quality protein. Increased demand for soyameal increased the price of soy commodities, thereby encouraging U.S. farmers to plant soybeans instead of wheat. Reduced production of wheat, in turn, caused a major global food crisis—all triggered by an El Niño event.

equator. At first, these events were called *años de abundancia* (years of abundance) because the additional rainfall dramatically increased plant growth on the normally arid land. What was once thought of as a joyous event, however, soon became associated with the ecological and economic disaster that is now a well-known consequence of the phenomenon.

This warm-water current usually occurred around Christmas and thus was given the name **El Niño**, Spanish for "the child," in reference to baby Jesus. In the 1920s, Walker was the first to recognize that an east–west atmospheric pressure seesaw accompanied the warm current and he called the phenomenon the **Southern Oscillation**. Today, the combined oceanic and atmospheric effects are

(a) Jan 1998

-4°C -3°C -2°C -1°C 0°C 1°C 2°C 3°C 4°C
Sea Surface Temperature Anomaly

(b) Jan 2000

FIGURE 7.22 Sea surface temperature anomaly maps. Maps showing sea surface temperature anomalies, which represent departures from normal conditions. Red colors indicate water warmer than normal and blue colors represent water cooler than normal. **(a)** Map of the Pacific Ocean in January 1998, showing the anomalous warming during the 1997–1998 El Niño. **(b)** Map of the same area in January 2000, showing cooling in the equatorial Pacific related to La Niña.

called **El Niño–Southern Oscillation (ENSO)**, which periodically alternate between warm and cold phases and cause dramatic environmental changes.

ENSO Warm Phase (El Niño) Figure 7.21b shows the atmospheric and oceanic conditions during an ENSO warm phase, which is known as El Niño. The high pressure along the coast of South America weakens, reducing the difference between the high- and low-pressure regions of the Walker Circulation Cell. This, in turn, causes the southeast trade winds to diminish. In very strong El Niño events, the trade winds actually blow in the *reverse* direction.

Without the trade winds, the Pacific Warm Pool that has built up on the western side of the Pacific begins to flow back across the ocean toward South America. Aided by an increase in the flow of the Equatorial Countercurrent, the Pacific Warm Pool creates a band of warm water that stretches across the equatorial Pacific Ocean (Figure 7.22a). The warm water usually begins to move in September of an El Niño year and reaches South America by December or January. During strong to very strong El Niños, the water temperature off Peru can be up to 10°C (18°F) higher than normal. In addition, the average sea level can increase as much as 20 centimeters (8 inches), simply due to thermal expansion of the warm water along the coast.

As the warm water increases sea surface temperatures across the equatorial Pacific, temperature-sensitive corals are decimated in Tahiti, the Galápagos, and other tropical Pacific islands. In addition, many other organisms are affected by the warm water (see Web Box 13.2). Once the warm water reaches South America, it moves north and south along the west coast of the Americas, increasing average sea level and the number of tropical hurricanes formed in the eastern Pacific.

The flow of warm water across the Pacific also causes the sloped thermocline boundary between warm surface waters and the cooler waters below to flatten out and become more horizontal (Figure 7.21b). Near Peru, upwelling brings warmer, nutrient-depleted water to the surface instead of cold, nutrient-rich water. In fact, *downwelling* can sometimes occur as the warm water stacks up along coastal South America. Productivity diminishes and most types of marine life in the area are dramatically reduced.

As the warm water moves to the east across the Pacific, the low-pressure zone also migrates. In a strong to very strong El Niño event, the low pressure can move across the entire Pacific and remain over South America. The low pressure substantially increases precipitation along coastal South America. Conversely, high pressure replaces the Indonesian low, bringing dry conditions or, in strong to very strong El Niño events, drought conditions to Indonesia and northern Australia.

ENSO Cool Phase (La Niña) In some instances, conditions opposite of El Niño prevail in the equatorial South Pacific; these events are known as ENSO cool phase or **La Niña** (Spanish for "the female child"). Figure 7.21c shows La Niña conditions, which are similar to normal conditions but more intensified because there is a larger pressure difference across the Pacific Ocean. This larger pressure difference creates stronger Walker Circulation and stronger trade winds, which in turn cause more upwelling, a shallower thermocline in the eastern Pacific, and a band of cooler than normal water that stretches across the equatorial South Pacific (Figure 7.22b).

La Niña conditions commonly occur following an El Niño. For instance, the 1997–1998 El Niño was followed by several years of persistent La Niña conditions. The alternating pattern of El Niño–La Niña conditions since 1950 is shown by the multivariate **ENSO index** (Figure 7.23), which is calculated using a weighted average of atmospheric and oceanic factors including atmospheric pressure, winds,

FIGURE 7.23 Multivariate ENSO Index 1950–Present. The multivariate ENSO index is calculated using a variety of atmospheric and oceanic factors. ENSO index values greater than zero (*red areas*) indicate El Niño conditions while ENSO index values less than zero (*blue areas*) indicate La Niña conditions. The greater the value is from zero, the stronger the corresponding El Niño or La Niña. Updates are available at http://www.cdc.noaa.gov/people/klaus.wolter/MEI/.

and sea surface temperatures. Positive ENSO index numbers indicate El Niño conditions, whereas negative numbers reflect La Niña conditions. Normal conditions are indicated by a value near zero, and the greater the index value differs from zero (either negative or positive), the stronger the respective condition.

Table 7.3 compares atmospheric and oceanic conditions during normal, El Niño, and La Niña conditions.

TABLE 7.3	COMPARISON OF ATMOSPHERIC AND OCEANIC CONDITIONS DURING NORMAL, EL NIÑO, AND LA NIÑA CONDITIONS		
	Normal	**El Niño**	**La Niña**
Atmospheric pressure	High over South America; low over Indonesia	High over Indonesia; low over South America	More powerful high over South America; more powerful low over Indonesia
Winds	Strong, steady southeast trade winds	Southeast trade winds weaken and can even reverse	Stronger southeast trade winds
Atmospheric circulation	Normal Walker Circulation	Severely weakened or reversed Walker Circulation	Intensified Walker Circulation
Atmospheric conditions/ weather	Dry, clear weather in South America; humid and rainy weather in Indonesia	Flooding in South America; drought in Indonesia	Can cause drought in South America; flooding in Indonesia
Ocean surface currents	Strong South Equatorial Current	Weakened South Equatorial Current; stronger Equatorial Countercurrent	South Equatorial Current becomes stronger
Coastal upwelling and abundance of marine life	Strong coastal upwelling off South America due to coastal winds; abundant marine life	Coastal winds stop so coastal upwelling off South America ceases; downwelling can occur; lack of marine life	Stronger than normal coastal winds, so intensified coastal upwelling off South America; more abundant marine life
Sea surface temperature	Warm off Indonesia (Pacific Warm Pool); cold off South America (due to upwelling)	Pacific Warm Pool moves to the east and brings warm water to South America; remains warm off Indonesia	Increased upwelling off South America makes for more cold water that spreads farther to the west
Sea surface elevation	Higher off Indonesia, lower off South America	Evens out across the Pacific Ocean as Pacific Warm Pool moves east	Even higher off Indonesia, and even lower off South America
Thermocline	Very close to the surface off South America; deep off Australia	Lowers (deepens) off South America, causing thermocline to even out across the Pacific Ocean	Raised closer to the surface off South America; deepens off Australia

How Often Do El Niño Events Occur?   Records of sea surface temperatures over the past 100 years reveal that throughout the 20th century, El Niño conditions occur on average about every 2 to 10 years, but in a highly irregular pattern. In some decades, for instance, there has been an El Niño event every few years, while in others there may have been only one. Figure 7.23 shows the pattern since 1950, revealing that the equatorial Pacific fluctuates between El Niño and La Niña conditions, with only a few years that could be considered "normal" conditions (represented by an ENSO index value close to zero). Typically, El Niño events last for 12 to 18 months and are followed by La Niña conditions that usually exist for a similar length of time. However, some El Niño or La Niña conditions can last for several years.

Recently recovered sediments from a South American lake provide a continuous 10,000-year record of the frequency of El Niño events. The sediments indicate that between 10,000 and 7000 years ago, no more than five strong El Niños occurred each century. The frequency of El Niños then increased, peaking at about 1200 years ago (and coinciding with the early Middle Ages in Europe), when they occurred every three years or so. If the pattern observed in the lake sediments continues, researchers predict that there should be an increase in El Niños in the early part of the 22nd century.

El Niño events—especially severe ones—may occur more frequently as a result of increased global warming. For instance, the two most severe El Niño events in the 20th century occurred in 1982–1983 and 1997–1998. Presumably, increased ocean temperatures could trigger more frequent and more severe El Niños. However, this pattern could also be a part of a long-term natural climate cycle. Recently, oceanographers have recognized a phenomenon called the **Pacific Decadal Oscillation (PDO)**, which lasts 20 to 30 years and appears to influence Pacific sea surface temperatures. Analysis of satellite data suggests that the Pacific Ocean has been in the warm phase of the PDO from 1977 to 1999 and that it is now in its cool phase, which may suppress the initiation of El Niño events during the next few decades.

Effects of El Niños and La Niñas   Mild El Niño events influence only the equatorial South Pacific Ocean while strong to very strong El Niño events can influence worldwide weather. Typically, stronger El Niños alter the atmospheric jet stream and produce unusual weather in most parts of the globe. Sometimes the weather is drier than normal; at other times, it is wetter. The weather may also be warmer or cooler than normal. It is still difficult to predict exactly how a particular El Niño will affect any region's weather.

Figure 7.24 shows how very strong El Niño events can result in flooding, erosion, droughts, fires, tropical storms, and effects on marine life worldwide. These weather perturbations also affect the production of corn, cotton, and coffee. More locally, the satellite images in Figure 7.25 show that sea surface temperatures off western North America are significantly higher during an El Niño year.

Even though severe El Niños are typically associated with vast amounts of destruction, they can be beneficial in some areas. Tropical hurricane formation, for instance, is generally suppressed in the Atlantic Ocean, some desert regions receive much-needed rain, and organisms adapted to warm-water conditions thrive in the Pacific.

La Niña events are associated with sea surface temperatures and weather phenomena opposite to those of El Niño. Indian Ocean monsoons, for instance, are typically drier than usual in El Niño years but wetter than usual in La Niña years.

Examples from Recent El Niños   Recent El Niños provide an indication of the variability of the effects of El Niño events. For instance, in the winter of 1976, a moderate El Niño event coincided with northern California's worst drought of the 20th century, showing that El Niño events don't always bring torrential rains to the western United States. During that same winter, the eastern United States experienced record cold temperatures.

STUDENTS SOMETIMES ASK ...

Do El Niño events occur in other ocean basins?

Yes, the Atlantic and Indian Oceans both experience events similar to the Pacific's El Niño. These events are not nearly as strong, however, nor do they influence worldwide weather phenomena to the same extent as those that occur in the equatorial Pacific Ocean. The great width of the Pacific Ocean in equatorial latitudes is the main reason that El Niño events occur more strongly in the Pacific.

In the Atlantic Ocean, this phenomenon is related to the North Atlantic Oscillation (NAO), which is a periodic change in atmospheric pressure between Iceland and the Azores Islands. This pressure difference determines the strength of the prevailing westerlies in the North Atlantic, which in turn affects ocean surface currents there. The Atlantic Ocean periodically experiences NAO events, which sometimes cause intense cold in the northeast United States, unusual weather in Europe, and heavy rainfall along the normally arid coast of southwest Africa.

FIGURE 7.24 Effects of severe El Niños. Flooding, erosion, droughts, fires, tropical storms, and effects on marine life are all associated with severe El Niño events.

Marine life impacted	Coastal Erosion	Coral reef damage	Forest Fires
Floods	Drought	Bird life impacted	Tropical Storms

THE 1982–1983 EL NIÑO   The 1982–1983 El Niño is the strongest ever recorded, causing far-ranging effects around the globe. Not only was there anomalous warming in the tropical Pacific, but the warm water also spread along the west coast of North America, influencing sea surface temperatures as far north as Alaska. Sea level was higher than normal (due to thermal expansion of the water), which, when high surf was experienced, caused damage to coastal structures and increased coastal erosion. In addition, the jet stream swung much farther south than normal across the United States, bringing a series of powerful storms that resulted in three times normal rainfall across the southwestern United States. The increased rainfall caused severe flooding and landslides as well as higher than normal snowfall in the Rocky Mountains. Alaska and western Canada had a relatively warm winter, and the eastern United States had its mildest winter in 25 years.

(a) Jan 1998   (b) Jan 1999

Sea Surface Temperature Anomaly

FIGURE 7.25 Sea surface temperatures off western North America during El Niño and La Niña. Satellite-derived sea surface temperature anomaly maps (in °C) along the west coast of North America. Red color represents water that is warmer than normal; blue color represents water that is colder than normal. **(a)** Sea surface temperature anomaly map for January 1998, an El Niño year. **(b)** Sea surface temperature anomaly map of the same region a year later (January 1999), during a La Niña event.

The full strength of El Niño was experienced in western South America. Normally arid Peru was drenched with more than 3 meters (10 feet) of rain, causing extreme flooding and landslides. Sea surface temperatures were so high for so long that temperature-sensitive coral reefs across the equatorial Pacific were decimated. Marine mammals and sea birds, which depend on the food normally available in the highly productive waters along the west coast of South America, went elsewhere or died. In the Galápagos Islands, for example, over half of the island's fur seals and sea lions died of starvation during the 1982–1983 El Niño.

French Polynesia had not experienced a hurricane in 75 years; in 1983, it endured six. The Hawaiian Island of Kauai also experienced a rare hurricane. Meanwhile, in Europe, severe cold weather prevailed. Worldwide, droughts occurred in Australia, Indonesia, China, India, Africa, and Central America. In all, more than 2000 deaths and at least $10 billion in property damage ($2.5 billion in the United States) were attributed to the 1982–1983 El Niño event.

THE 1997–1998 EL NIÑO The 1997–1998 El Niño event began several months earlier than normal and peaked in January 1998. The amount of Southern Oscillation and sea surface warming in the equatorial Pacific was initially as strong as the 1982–1983 El Niño, which caused a great deal of concern. However, the 1997–1998 El Niño weakened in the last few months of 1997 before reintensifying in early 1998. The impact of the 1997–1998 El Niño was felt mostly in the tropical Pacific, where surface water temperatures in the eastern Pacific averaged more than 4°C (7°F) warmer than normal, and, in some locations, reached up to 9°C (16°F) above normal (see Figure 7.22a). High pressure in the western Pacific brought drought conditions that caused wildfires to burn out of control in Indonesia. Also, the warmer than normal water along the west coast of Central and North America increased the number of hurricanes off Mexico.

In the United States, the 1997–1998 El Niño caused killer tornadoes in the Southeast, massive blizzards in the upper Midwest, and flooding in the Ohio River Valley. Most of California received twice the normal rainfall, which caused flooding and landslides in many parts of the state. The lower Midwest, the Pacific Northwest, and the eastern seaboard, on the other hand, had relatively mild weather. In all, the 1997–1998 El Niño caused 2100 deaths and $33 billion in property damage worldwide.

Predicting El Niño Events The 1982–1983 El Niño event was not predicted, nor was it recognized until it was near its peak. Because it affected weather worldwide and caused such extensive damage, the **Tropical Ocean–Global Atmosphere (TOGA)** program was initiated in 1985 to study how El Niño events develop. The goal of the TOGA program was to monitor the equatorial South Pacific Ocean during El Niño events to enable scientists to model and predict future El Niño events. The 10-year program studied the ocean from research vessels, analyzed surface and subsurface data from radio-transmitting sensor buoys, monitored oceanic phenomena by satellite, and developed computer models.

These models have made it possible to predict El Niño events since 1987 as much as one year in advance. After the completion of TOGA, the **Tropical Atmosphere and Ocean (TAO)** project (sponsored by the United States, Canada, Australia, and Japan) has continued to monitor the equatorial Pacific Ocean with a series of 70 moored buoys, providing real-time information about the conditions of the tropical Pacific that is available on the Internet. Although monitoring has improved, the causes of El Niño events are still not fully understood.

KEY CONCEPT
El Niño is a combined oceanic–atmospheric phenomenon that occurs periodically in the tropical Pacific Ocean, bringing warm water to the east. La Niña describes conditions opposite of El Niño.

7.5 What Deep-Ocean Currents Exist?

Deep currents occur in the deep zone below the pycnocline, so they influence about 90% of all ocean water. Density differences create deep currents. Although these density differences are usually small, they are large enough to cause denser waters to sink. Deep-water currents move larger volumes of water and are much slower than surface currents. Typical speeds of deep currents range from 10 to 20 kilometers (6 to 12 miles) per year. Thus, it takes a deep current an *entire year* to travel the same distance that a western intensified surface current can move in *one hour*.

Because the density variations that cause deep ocean circulation are caused by differences in temperature and salinity, deep-ocean circulation is also referred to as **thermohaline** (*thermo* = heat, *haline* = salt) **circulation**.

Origin of Thermohaline Circulation

Recall from Chapter 5 that an increase in seawater density can be caused by a *decrease* in temperature or an *increase* in salinity. Temperature, though, has the greater influence on density. Density changes due to salinity are important only in very high latitudes, where water temperature remains low and relatively constant.

Most water involved in deep-ocean currents (thermohaline circulation) originates in high latitudes *at the surface*. In these regions, surface water becomes cold and its salinity increases as sea ice forms. When this surface water becomes dense enough, it sinks, initiating deep-ocean currents. Once this water sinks, it is removed from the physical processes that increased its density in the first place, so its temperature and salinity remain largely unchanged for the duration it spends in the deep ocean. Thus, a **temperature–salinity (T–S) diagram** can be used to identify deep-water masses based on their characteristic temperature, salinity, and resulting density. Figure 7.26 shows a T–S diagram for the North Atlantic Ocean.

FIGURE 7.26 Temperature–salinity (T–S) diagram. A density T–S diagram for the North Atlantic Ocean. Lines of constant density are in grams/cm^3. After various deep-water masses sink below the surface, they can be identified based on their characteristic temperature, salinity, and resulting density.

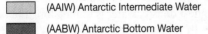

North Atlantic Water Masses:

(AAIW) Antarctic Intermediate Water

(AABW) Antarctic Bottom Water

(NADW) North Atlantic Deep Water

(NACSW) North Atlantic Central Surface Water

(MIW) Mediterranean Intermediate Water

FIGURE 7.27 Atlantic Ocean subsurface water masses. Schematic diagram of the various water masses in the Atlantic Ocean. Similar but less distinct layering based on density occurs in the Pacific and Indian Oceans as well. Upwelling and downwelling occur in the North Atlantic and near Antarctica (*inset*), creating deep-water masses.

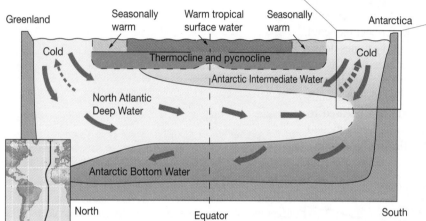

As these surface-water masses become dense and are sinking (downwelling) in high-latitude areas, deep-water masses are also rising to the surface (upwelling). Because the water temperature in high-latitude regions is the same at the surface as it is down below, the water column is isothermal, there is no thermocline or associated pycnocline (see Chapter 5), and upwelling and downwelling can easily be accomplished.

Sources of Deep Water

In southern subpolar latitudes, huge masses of deep water form beneath sea ice along the margins of the Antarctic continent. Here, rapid winter freezing produces very cold, high-density water that sinks down the continental slope of Antarctica and becomes **Antarctic Bottom Water**, the densest water in the open ocean (Figure 7.27). Antarctic Bottom Water slowly sinks beneath the surface and spreads into all the world's ocean basins, eventually returning to the surface perhaps 1000 years later.

In the northern subpolar latitudes, large masses of deep water form in the Norwegian Sea. From there, the deep water flows as a subsurface current into the North Atlantic, where it becomes part of the **North Atlantic Deep Water**. North Atlantic Deep Water also comes from the margins of the Irminger Sea off southeastern Greenland, the Labrador Sea, and the dense, salty Mediterranean Sea. Like Antarctic Bottom Water, North Atlantic Deep Water spreads throughout the ocean basins. It is less dense, however, so it layers on top of the Antarctic Bottom Water (Figure 7.27).

Surface-water masses converge within the subtropical gyres and in the Arctic and Antarctic. Subtropical Convergences do not produce deep water, however, because the density of warm surface waters is too low for them to sink. Major sinking does occur, however, along the **Arctic Convergence** and Antarctic Convergence (Figure 7.27, *inset*). The deep-water mass formed from sinking at the Antarctic Convergence is called the **Antarctic Intermediate Water** mass (Figure 7.27), which remains one of world's most poorly studied water masses.

Figure 7.27 also shows that the highest density water is found along the ocean bottom, with less-dense water above. In low-latitude regions, the boundary between the warm surface water and the deeper cold water is marked by a prominent thermocline and corresponding pycnocline that prevent vertical mixing. There is no pycnocline in high-latitude regions, so substantial vertical mixing (upwelling and downwelling) occurs.

This same general pattern of layering based on density occurs in the Pacific and Indian Oceans as well. They have no source of Northern Hemisphere deep water, however, so they lack a deep-water mass. In the northern Pacific Ocean, the low salinity of surface waters prevents them from sinking into the deep ocean. In the northern Indian Ocean, surface waters are too warm to sink. **Oceanic Common Water**, which is created when Antarctic Bottom Water and North Atlantic Deep Water mix, lines the bottoms of these basins.

Worldwide Deep-Water Circulation

For every liter of water that sinks from the surface into the deep ocean, a liter of deep water must return to the surface somewhere else. However, it is difficult to identify specifically *where* this vertical flow to the surface is occurring. It is generally believed that it occurs as a gradual, uniform upwelling throughout the ocean basins and that it may be somewhat greater in low-latitude regions, where surface temperatures are higher. Alternatively, recent research on turbulent mixing rates between deep-ocean and surface waters in the Southern Ocean suggests that deep water traveling across rugged bottom topography is a major factor in producing the upwelling that returns deep water toward the surface.

CONVEYER-BELT CIRCULATION   An integrated model combining deep thermohaline circulation and surface currents is shown in Figure 7.28. Because the overall circulation pattern resembles a large conveyer belt, the model is called **conveyer-belt circulation**. Beginning in the North Atlantic, surface water carries heat to high latitudes via the Gulf Stream. During the cold winter months, this heat is transferred to the overlying atmosphere, warming northern Europe.

Cooling in the North Atlantic increases the density of this surface water to the point where it sinks to the bottom and flows southward, initiating the lower limb of the "conveyor." Here, seawater flows downward at a rate equal to 100 Amazon Rivers and begins its long journey into the deep basins of all the world's oceans. This limb extends all the way to the southern tip of Africa, where it joins the deep water that encircles Antarctica. The deep water that

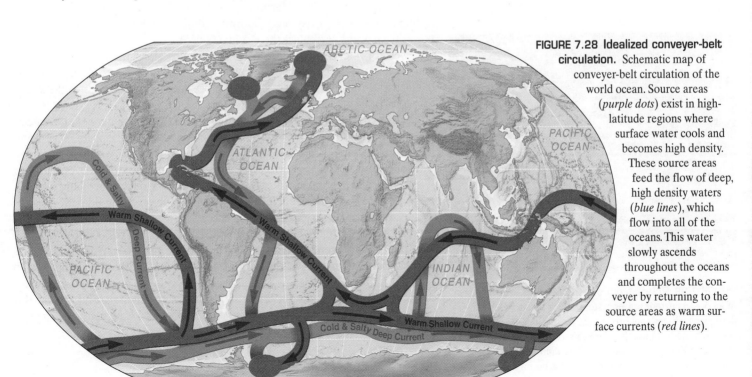

FIGURE 7.28 Idealized conveyer-belt circulation. Schematic map of conveyer-belt circulation of the world ocean. Source areas (*purple dots*) exist in high-latitude regions where surface water cools and becomes high density. These source areas feed the flow of deep, high density waters (*blue lines*), which flow into all of the oceans. This water slowly ascends throughout the oceans and completes the conveyer by returning to the source areas as warm surface currents (*red lines*).

encircles Antarctica includes deep water that descends along the margins of the Antarctic continent. This mixture of deep waters flows northward into the deep Pacific and Indian Ocean basins, where it eventually surfaces and completes the conveyer belt by flowing west and then north again into the North Atlantic Ocean.

DISSOLVED OXYGEN IN DEEP WATER   Cold water can dissolve more oxygen than warm water. Thus, deep-water circulation brings dense, cold, oxygen-enriched water from the surface to the deep ocean. During its time in the deep ocean, deep water becomes enriched in nutrients as well, due to decomposition of dead organisms and the lack of organisms using nutrients there.

At various times in the geologic past, warmer water probably constituted a larger proportion of deep oceanic waters. As a result, the oceans had a lower oxygen concentration than today because warm water cannot hold as much oxygen. Moreover, the oxygen content of the oceans has probably fluctuated widely throughout time.

If high-latitude surface waters did not sink and eventually return from the deep sea to the surface, the distribution of life in the sea would be considerably different. There would be very little life in the deep ocean, for instance, because there would be no oxygen for organisms to breathe. In addition, life in surface waters might be significantly reduced without the circulation of deep water that brings nutrients to the surface.

> **KEY CONCEPT**
> Thermohaline circulation describes the movement of deep currents, which are created at the surface in high latitudes where they become cold and dense, so they sink.

7.6 Can Power From Currents Be Harnessed as a Source of Energy?

The movement of ocean currents has often been considered to be capable of providing a source of renewable, clean energy similar to wind farms (see Chapter 6) but underwater. In fact, currents carry much more energy than winds because water has about 800 times the density of air, so currents have the potential to generate even more power than wind farms do.

One location that has received much consideration as a site for harnessing power from ocean currents is the Florida–Gulf Stream Current System, which is a fast, western intensified surface current that runs along the East Coast of the United States. In fact, researchers have determined that at least 2000 megawatts[13] of electricity could be recovered from this ocean current system along the southeast coast of Florida alone.

Various devices that have been proposed to extract the energy in ocean currents all involve some sort of mechanism for converting the movement of water into electrical energy. For example, a series of underwater turbines similar to windmills could be placed within a current and anchored to the ocean floor (Figure 7.29). The turbines can swivel on their anchors to face oncoming currents, so this system is also useful in locations where strong reversing tidal flows occur. Such a system of six turbines has been successfully tested in the East River near New York City. Once this system is expanded to its capacity of 300 turbines, it will have the ability to generate about 10 megawatts of electricity. However, systems such as these are expensive, difficult to maintain, and can be dangerous to ship traffic. In addition, placing any moving machinery into the marine environment is problematic because seawater tends to corrode most materials. Still, similar turbine systems powered by currents are in use in Strangford Lough, Ireland, and are planned for offshore South Korea.

FIGURE 7.29 Power from ocean currents. A prototype of an ocean current power system, which uses a field of underwater turbines anchored to the ocean floor. As currents flow past the turbines, they turn the rotors and generate electricity. The turbines can swivel on their anchors to face oncoming currents, so this system is also useful in locations where strong tidal flows occur.

[13]Each megawatt of electricity is enough to serve the energy needs of about 800 average U.S. homes.

Chapter in Review

• *Ocean currents are masses of water that flow* from one place to another and can be divided into *surface currents that are wind driven and deep currents that are density driven*. Currents can be measured directly or indirectly.

• *Surface currents occur within and above the pycnocline*. They consist of circular-moving loops of water called gyres, set in motion by the major wind belts of the world. They are modified by the positions of the continents, the Coriolis effect, and other factors. There are *five major subtropical gyres in the world*, which rotate *clockwise in the Northern Hemisphere* and *counterclockwise in the Southern Hemisphere*. Water is pushed toward the center of the gyres, forming low "hills" of water.

• The *Ekman spiral* influences shallow surface water and is *caused by winds and the Coriolis effect*. The average net flow of water affected by the Ekman spiral causes the water to move at *90-degree angles to the wind direction*. At the center of a gyre, the Coriolis effect deflects the water so that it tends to move into the hill, whereas gravity moves the water down the hill. When gravity and the Coriolis effect balance, a *geostrophic current* flowing parallel to the contours of the hill is established.

• *The apex (top) of the hill is located to the west of the geographical center of the gyre* due to Earth's rotation. A phenomenon called *western intensification* occurs in which *western boundary currents of subtropical gyres are faster, narrower, and deeper* than their eastern boundary counterparts.

• *Upwelling and downwelling help vertically mix deep and surface waters*. Upwelling—the movement of *cold, deep, nutrient-rich water to the surface*—stimulates biologic productivity and creates a large amount of marine life. Upwelling and downwelling can occur in a variety of ways.

• *Antarctic circulation is dominated by a single large current, the Antarctic Circumpolar Current* (West Wind Drift), which flows in a clockwise direction around Antarctica and is driven by the Southern Hemisphere's prevailing westerly winds. Between the Antarctic Circumpolar Current and the Antarctic continent is a current called the *East Wind Drift*, which is powered by the polar easterly winds. The two currents flow in opposite directions, so the Coriolis effect deflects them away from each other, creating the *Antarctic Divergence*, an area of abundant marine life due to upwelling and current mixing.

• *The North Atlantic (Columbus) Gyre and the South Atlantic (Navigator) Gyre dominate circulation in the Atlantic Ocean*. A poorly developed equatorial countercurrent separates these two subtropical gyres. The highest velocity and best studied ocean current is the *Gulf Stream*, which carries warm water along the southeastern U.S. Atlantic coast. Meanders of the Gulf Stream produce *warm- and cold-core rings*. The warming effects of the Gulf Stream extend along its route and reach as far away as northern Europe.

• *The Indian Ocean consists of one gyre, the Indian Ocean (Majid) Gyre*, which exists mostly in the Southern Hemisphere. The *monsoon wind system*, which changes direction with the seasons, dominates circulation in the Indian Ocean. The monsoons blow from the northeast in the winter and from the southwest in the summer.

• *Circulation in the Pacific Ocean consists of two subtropical gyres: the North Pacific (Turtle) Gyre and the South Pacific (Heyerdahl) Gyre*, which are separated by a well-developed equatorial countercurrent.

• *A periodic disruption of normal sea surface and atmospheric circulation patterns in the Pacific Ocean is called El Niño–Southern Oscillation (ENSO)*. The *warm phase of ENSO (El Niño)* is associated with the eastward movement of the Pacific warm pool, halting or reversal of the trade winds, a rise in sea level along the equator, a decrease in productivity along the west coast of South America, and, in very strong El Niños, worldwide changes in weather. El Niños fluctuate with the *cool phase of ENSO (La Niña conditions)*, which are associated with cooler than normal water in the eastern tropical Pacific.

• *Deep currents occur below the pycnocline*. They affect much larger amounts of ocean water and move much more slowly than surface currents. Changes in temperature and/or salinity at the surface create slight increases in density, which set deep currents in motion. Deep currents, therefore, are called *thermohaline circulation*.

• *The deep ocean is layered based on density*. Antarctic Bottom Water, the densest deep-water mass in the oceans, forms near Antarctica and sinks along the continental shelf into the South Atlantic Ocean. Farther north, at the Antarctic Convergence, the low-salinity *Antarctic Intermediate Water* sinks to an intermediate depth dictated by its density. Sandwiched between these two masses is the *North Atlantic Deep Water*, which has high nutrient levels after hundreds of years in the deep ocean. Layering in the Pacific and Indian oceans is similar, except there is no source of Northern Hemisphere deep water.

• *Worldwide circulation models that include both surface and deep currents resemble a conveyer belt*. Deep currents carry oxygen into the deep ocean, which is extremely important for life on the planet.

• *Ocean currents can be harnessed as a source of power*. Although there is vast potential for developing this clean, renewable resource, significant problems must be overcome to make this a practical source of energy.

Key Terms

Agulhas Current (p. 214)

Alaskan Current (p. 215)

Antarctic Bottom Water (p. 224)

Antarctic Circumpolar Current (p. 207)

Antarctic Convergence (p. 208)

Antarctic Divergence (p. 208)

Antarctic Intermediate Water (p. 224)

Antilles Current (p. 209)

Arctic Convergence (p. 224)

Argo (p. 196)

Atlantic Equatorial Countercurrent (p. 209)

Benguela Current (p. 209)

Brazil Current (p. 209)

California Current (p. 215)

Canary Current (p. 212)

Caribbean Current (p. 209)

Coastal downwelling (p. 206)

Coastal upwelling (p. 206)

Cold-core ring (p. 212)

Conveyer-belt circulation (p. 225)

Deep current (p. 193)

Downwelling (p. 204)

East Australian Current (p. 215)

East Wind Drift (p. 208)

Eastern boundary current (p. 200)

Ekman spiral (p. 201)

Ekman transport (p. 202)

Ekman, V. Walfrid (p. 201)

El Niño (p. 217)

Review Questions

1. Compare the forces that are directly responsible for creating horizontal and deep vertical circulation in the oceans. What is the ultimate source of energy that drives both circulation systems?

2. Describe the different ways in which currents are measured.

3. What atmospheric pressure is associated with the centers of subtropical gyres? With subpolar gyres? Explain why the subtropical gyres in the Northern Hemisphere move in a clockwise fashion while the subpolar gyres rotate in a counterclockwise pattern.

4. Describe the voyage of the *Fram* and how it helped prove that there was no continent beneath the Arctic ice pack.

5. What causes the apex of the geostrophic "hills" to be offset to the west of the center of the ocean gyre systems?

6. Draw or describe several different oceanographic conditions that produce upwelling.

7. Observing the flow of Atlantic Ocean currents in Figure 7.15, offer an explanation as to why the Brazil Current has a much lower velocity and volume transport than the Gulf Stream.

8. Why did Benjamin Franklin want to know about the surface current pattern in the North Atlantic Ocean?

9. Explain why Gulf Stream eddies that develop northeast of the Gulf Stream rotate clockwise and have warm-water cores, whereas those that develop to the southwest rotate counterclockwise and have cold-water cores.

10. Describe changes in atmospheric pressure, precipitation, winds, and ocean surface currents during the two monsoon seasons of the Indian Ocean.

11. Describe changes in atmospheric and oceanographic phenomena that occur during El Niño/La Niña events, including changes in atmospheric pressure, winds, Walker Circulation, weather, equatorial surface currents, coastal upwelling/downwelling and the abundance of marine life, sea surface temperature and the Pacific warm pool, sea surface elevation, and position of the thermocline.

12. How often do El Niño events occur? Using Figure 7.23, determine how many years since 1950 have been El Niño years. Has the pattern of El Niño events occurred at regular intervals?

13. How is La Niña different from El Niño? Describe the pattern of La Niña events in relation to El Niños since 1950 (see Figure 7.23).

14. Describe the global effects of severe El Niños.

15. Discuss the origin of thermohaline vertical circulation. Why do deep currents form only in high-latitude regions?

16. Name the two major deep-water masses and give the locations of their formation at the ocean's surface.

17. The Antarctic Intermediate Water can be identified throughout much of the South Atlantic based on its temperature, salinity, and dissolved oxygen content. Why is it colder and less salty—and contain more oxygen—than the surface-water mass above it and the North Atlantic Deep Water below it?

Critical Thinking Exercises

1. What would the pattern of ocean surface currents look like if there were no continents on Earth?

2. On a base map of the world, plot and label the major currents involved in the surface circulation gyres of the oceans. Use colors to represent warm versus cool currents and indicate which currents are western intensified. On an overlay, superimpose the major wind belts of the world on the gyres and describe the relationship between wind belts and currents.

3. Diagram and discuss how Ekman transport produces the "hill" of water within subtropical gyres that causes geostrophic current flow. As a starting place on the diagram, use the wind belts (the trade winds and the prevailing westerlies).

4. During flood stage, the largest river in the world—the mighty Amazon River—dumps 200,000 cubic meters of water into the Atlantic Ocean each second. Compare its flow rate with the volume of water transported by the West Wind Drift and the Gulf Stream. How many times larger than the Amazon is each of these two ocean currents?

Oceanography on the Web

Visit the *Essentials of Oceanography* Online Study Guide for Internet resources, including chapter-specific quizzes to test your understanding and Web links to further your exploration of the topics in this chapter.

The *Essentials of Oceanography* Online Study Guide is at http://www.mygeoscienceplace.com/.

Surfer riding a giant wave at Maverick's.
Maverick's in Half Moon Bay off central California is rated
as the world's top big wave surf spot. A unique combination
of oceanographic factors produces waves so large here
that only the most accomplished surfers even attempt to
wade into the surf zone.

"There's no time to put on survival suits or grab a life vest; the boat's moving through the most extreme motion of her life and there isn't even time to shout. The refrigerator comes out of the wall and crashes across the galley. Dirty dishes cascade out of the sink. The TV, the washing machine, the VCR tapes, the men, all go flying. And, seconds later, the water moves in."

—Sebastian Junger,
The Perfect Storm (1997)

8 WAVES AND WATER DYNAMICS

What combination of oceanographic factors causes waves to reach extreme heights at places such as Maverick's? This site, which is rated as the world's premier big wave surf spot, is located 0.5 kilometer (0.3 mile) offshore of Pillar Point in Half Moon Bay along the central California coast. One factor is that Maverick's is located offshore of a prominent point of land, which, as will be explained in this chapter, tends to concentrate wave energy due to *wave refraction*. Another factor is that the point juts directly into the North Pacific Ocean, which is known for its wintertime storms and giant waves. Still another factor is that the shoreline abruptly rises from deep depths to a shallowly submerged rock reef, which causes waves to build up to extreme heights in a very short distance. These factors combined with cold ocean temperatures, unforgiving boulders just below the surface, and the presence of large sharks make the site challenging to even the most skilled surfers. Still, surfing competitions are held every year at Maverick's for those brave enough to catch some of the world's most extreme waves.

Most waves are driven by the wind and are relatively small, so release their energy gently, although ocean storms can build up waves to extreme heights. When these waves come ashore, they often produce devastating effects—or, in the case at Maverick's, a wild ride. Waves are *moving energy* traveling along the interface between ocean and atmosphere, often transferring energy from a storm far out at sea over distances of several thousand kilometers. That's why, even on calm days, the ocean is in continual motion as waves travel across its surface.

8.1 What Causes Waves?

All waves begin as *disturbances*; the energy that causes ocean waves to form is called a **disturbing force**. A rock thrown into a still pond, for example, creates waves that radiate out in all directions. Releases of energy, similar to the rock hitting the water, are the cause of all waves.

Wind blowing across the surface of the ocean generates most ocean waves. The waves radiate out in all directions, just as when the rock is thrown into the pond, but on a much larger scale.

The movement of fluids with different densities can also create waves. These waves travel along the interface (boundary) between two different fluids. Both the air and the ocean are fluids, so waves can be created along interfaces *between* and *within* these fluids as follows:

- Along an *air–water interface*, the movement of air across the ocean surface creates **ocean waves** (simply called *waves*).
- Along an *air–air interface*, the movement of different air masses creates **atmospheric waves**, which are often represented by ripplelike clouds in the sky. Atmospheric waves are especially common when cold fronts (high-density air) move into an area.

(a)

(b) Internal waves, Sulu Sea

FIGURE 8.1 Internal waves. **(a)** An internal wave moving along the density interface (pycnocline) below the ocean surface. **(b)** Internal waves in the Sulu Sea between the Philippines and Malaysia. Image taken April 8, 2003, by the Moderate Resolution Imaging Spectroradiometer (MODIS) instrument aboard the Aqua satellite.

STUDENTS SOMETIMES ASK ...

Can internal waves break?

Internal waves do not break in the way that surface waves break in the surf zone because the density difference across an interface at depth is much smaller than that between the atmosphere and the surface. When internal waves approach the edges of continents, however, they do undergo similar physical changes as waves in the surf zone. This causes the waves to build up and expend their energy with much turbulent motion, in essence "breaking" against the continent.

- Along a *water–water interface*, the movement of water of different densities creates **internal waves**, as shown in Figure 8.1a. Because these waves travel along the boundary between waters of different density, they are associated with a *pycnocline*.[1] Internal waves can be much larger than surface waves, with heights exceeding 100 meters (330 feet). Tidal movement, turbidity currents, wind stress, or even passing ships at the surface create internal waves, which can sometimes be observed from space (Figure 8.1b). Internal waves can even be a hazard for submarines: If submarines are caught in an internal wave while testing their depth limits, the submarines can inadvertently be carried to depths exceeding their designed pressure strength. At the surface, parallel slicks caused by a film of surface debris may indicate the presence of internal waves below. On a smaller scale, internal waves are prominently featured sloshing back and forth in "desktop oceans," which contain two fluids that do not mix.

Mass movement into the ocean, such as coastal landslides or large icebergs that fall from coastal glaciers, also creates waves. These waves are commonly called *splash waves* (see Web Box 8.1 for a description of a large splash wave).

Another way in which large waves are created involves the uplift or down-dropping of large areas of the sea floor, which can release large amounts of energy to the entire water column (compared to wind-driven waves, which affect only surface water). Examples include underwater avalanches (turbidity currents), volcanic eruptions, and fault slippage. The resulting waves are called *seismic sea waves* or *tsunami*, which are discussed later in this chapter. Fortunately, tsunami occur infrequently. When they do, however, they can flood coastal areas and cause large amounts of destruction.

The tides are also a type of wave, in this case caused mainly by the gravitational pull of the Moon and to a lesser extent, the Sun. The tides are actually very extensive, low, and highly predictable waves that are discussed in Chapter 9, "Tides."

Human activities also cause ocean waves. When ships travel across the ocean, they leave behind a *wake*, which is a wave. In fact, smaller boats are often carried along in the wake of larger ships, and marine mammals sometimes play there.

In all cases, though, some type of energy release creates waves. Figure 8.2 shows the distribution of energy in waves, indicating that most ocean waves are wind generated.

8.2 How Do Waves Move?

Waves are energy in motion. Waves transmit energy by means of cyclic movement through matter. The medium itself (solid, liquid, or gas) does not actually travel in the direction of the energy that is passing through it. The particles in the medium simply oscillate, or cycle, back and forth, up and down, or around and around, transmitting energy from one particle to another. If you thump your fist on a table, for example, the energy travels through the table as waves that someone sitting at the other end can feel, but the table itself does not move.

Waves move in different ways. Simple *progressive waves* (Figure 8.3) are waves that oscillate uniformly and progress or travel without breaking. Progressive waves may be *longitudinal*, *transverse*, or a combination of the two motions, called *orbital*.

In **longitudinal waves** (also known as push–pull waves), the particles that vibrate "push and pull" in the same direction that the energy is traveling, like a spring whose coils are alternately compressed and expanded. The shape of the wave (called a *waveform*) moves through the medium by compressing and decompressing

---

[1]As discussed in Chapter 5, a pycnocline is a layer of rapidly changing density.

as it goes. Sound, for instance, travels as longitudinal waves. Clapping your hands initiates a percussion that compresses and decompresses the air as the sound moves through a room. Energy can be transmitted through all states of matter—gaseous, liquid, or solid—by this longitudinal movement of particles.

In **transverse waves** (also known as side-to-side waves), energy travels at right angles to the direction of the vibrating particles. If one end of a rope is tied to a doorknob while the other end is moved up and down (or side to side) by hand, for example, a waveform progresses along the rope and energy is transmitted from the motion of the hand to the doorknob. The waveform moves up and down (or side to side) with the hand, but the motion is at right angles to the direction in which energy is transmitted (from the hand to the doorknob). Generally, transverse waves transmit energy only through solids, because the particles in solids are bound to one another strongly enough to transmit this kind of motion.

Longitudinal and transverse waves are called *body waves* because they transfer energy through a body of matter. Ocean waves are body waves, too, because they transmit energy through the upper part of the ocean near the interface between the atmosphere and the ocean. The movement of particles in ocean waves involves components of *both* longitudinal and transverse waves, so particles move in circular orbits. Thus, waves at the ocean surface are **orbital waves** (also called *interface waves*).

8.3 What Characteristics Do Waves Possess?

Figure 8.4a shows the characteristics of an idealized ocean wave. The simple, uniform, moving waveform transmits energy from a single source and travels along the ocean–atmosphere interface. These waves are also called *sine waves* because their uniform shape resembles the oscillating pattern expressed by a sine curve. Even though idealized waveforms do not exist in nature, they help us understand wave characteristics.

Wave Terminology

As an idealized wave passes a permanent marker (such as a pier piling), a succession of high parts of the waves, called **crests**, alternate with low parts, called **troughs**. Halfway between the crests and the troughs is the **still water level**, or *zero energy level*. This is the level of the water if there were no waves. The **wave height**, designated by the symbol H, is the vertical distance between a crest and a trough.

The horizontal distance between any two corresponding points on successive waveforms, such as from crest to crest or from trough to trough, is the **wavelength**, L. **Wave steepness** is the ratio of wave height to wavelength:

$$\text{Wave steepness} = \frac{\text{wave height }(H)}{\text{wavelength }(L)} \qquad (8.1)$$

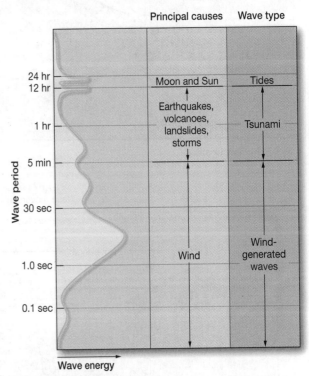

FIGURE 8.2 Distribution of energy in ocean waves. Most of the energy possessed by ocean waves exists as wind-generated waves while other peaks of wave energy represent tsunami and ocean tides.

① **LONGITUDINAL WAVE** Particles (color) move back and forth in direction of energy transmission. These waves transmit energy through all states of matter.

② **TRANSVERSE WAVE** Particles (color) move back and forth at right angles to direction of energy transmission. These waves transmit energy only through solids.

③ **ORBITAL WAVE** Particles (color) move in orbital path. These waves transmit energy along interface between two fluids of different density (liquids and/or gases).

FIGURE 8.3 Types of progressive waves. Diagrammatic view of the three types of progressive waves. Examples of each type include: (1) longitudinal waves = hands clapping or thumping a table; (2) transverse waves = a rope attached to a wall; and (3) orbital waves = the movement of water waves.

(a) Wave characteristics

(b) Calculation of wave base

FIGURE 8.4 Characteristics of progressive waves.
(a) A diagrammatic view of an idealized ocean wave showing its characteristics. **(b)** Enlargement of the orbital motion of water particles in waves, showing that wave base (the depth at which orbital motion ceases) is at a depth of one-half the wavelength, measured from still water level.

If the wave steepness exceeds ⅐, the wave *breaks* (spills forward) because the wave is too steep to support itself. A wave can break anytime the 1:7 ratio is exceeded, either along the shoreline or out at sea. This ratio also dictates the maximum height of a wave. For example, a wave 7 meters long can only be 1 meter high; if the wave is any higher than that, it will break.

The time it takes one full wave—one wavelength—to pass a fixed position (like a pier piling) is the **wave period**, *T*. Typical wave periods range between 6 and 16 seconds. The **frequency** (*f*) is defined as the number of wave crests passing a fixed location per unit of time and is the inverse of the period:

$$\text{Frequency } (f) = \frac{1}{\text{period } (T)} \quad (8.2)$$

For example, consider waves with a period of 12 seconds. These waves have a frequency of ¹⁄₁₂ or 0.083 waves per second, which converts to 5 waves per minute.

Circular Orbital Motion

Waves can travel great distances across ocean basins. In one study, waves generated near Antarctica were tracked as they traveled through the Pacific Ocean basin. After more than 10,000 kilometers (over 6000 miles), the waves finally expended their energy a week later along the shoreline of the Aleutian Islands of Alaska. The water itself doesn't travel the entire distance, but the waveform does. As the wave travels, the water passes the energy along by moving in a circle. This movement is called **circular orbital motion**.

Observation of an object floating in the waves reveals that it moves not only up and down, but also slightly forward and backward with each successive wave. Figure 8.5 shows that a floating object moves up and backward as the crest approaches, up and forward as the crest passes, down and forward after the crest, down and backward as the trough approaches, and rises and moves backward again as the next crest advances. When the movement of the rubber ducky shown in Figure 8.5 is traced as a wave passes, it can be seen that the ducky moves in a circle and returns close to its original position.[2] This motion allows a waveform (the wave's shape) to move forward through the water while the individual water particles that transmit the wave move around in a circle and return to essentially the same place. Wind moving across a field of wheat causes a similar phenomenon: The wheat itself doesn't travel across the field, but the waves do.

The circular orbits of an object floating at the surface have a diameter equal to the wave height (Figure 8.4a). Figure 8.4b shows that circular orbital motion

[2]Actually, the circular orbit does not quite return the floating object to its original position because the half of the orbit accomplished in the trough is slower than the crest half of the orbit. This results in a slight forward movement (net mass transport), which is called *wave drift*.

dies out quickly below the surface. At some depth below the surface, the circular orbits become so small that movement is negligible. This depth is called the **wave base**, and it is equal to one-half the wavelength (*L*/2) *measured from still water level*. Only wavelength controls the depth of the wave base, so the longer the wave, the deeper the wave base.

The decrease of orbital motion with depth has many practical applications. For instance, submarines can avoid large ocean waves simply by submerging below the wave base. Even the largest storm waves will go unnoticed if a submarine submerges to only 150 meters (500 feet). Floating bridges and floating oil rigs are constructed so that most of their mass is below wave base, so they will be unaffected by wave motion. In fact, offshore floating airport runways have been designed using similar principles (Figure 8.6). In addition, seasick scuba divers find relief when they submerge into the calm, motionless water below wave base. Finally, as you walk from the beach into the ocean, you reach a point where it is easier to dive under an incoming wave than to jump over it. It is easier to swim through the smaller orbital motion below the surface than to fight the large waves at the surface.

Deep-Water Waves

If the water depth (*d*) is greater than the wave base (*L*/2), the waves are called **deep-water waves** (Figure 8.7a). Deep-water waves have no interference with the ocean bottom, so they include all wind-generated waves in the open ocean, where water depths far exceed wave base.

Wave speed (*S*) is the rate at which a wave travels. Numerically, it is the distance traveled divided by the travel time; for a wave, it can be calculated as:

$$\text{Wave speed } (S) = \frac{\text{wavelength } (L)}{\text{period } (T)} \tag{8.3}$$

Wave speed is more correctly known as *celerity* (*C*), which is different from the traditional concept of speed. Celerity is used only in relation to waves where no mass is in motion, just the waveform.

According to the equations that govern the movement of progressive waves, the speed of deep-water waves is dependent upon (1) wavelength and (2) several other variables (such as gravitational attraction) that remain constant on Earth.

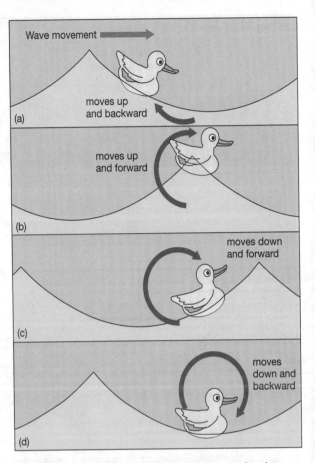

FIGURE 8.5 A floating rubber ducky shows circular orbital motion. As a wave passes to the right, the motion of a floating rubber ducky resembles that of a circle, which is known as circular orbital motion.

KEY CONCEPT

The ocean transmits wave energy by circular orbital motion, where the water particles move in circular orbits and return to approximately the same location.

FIGURE 8.6 Floating runway, Japan. This floating runway called "Mega-Float" was built offshore Yokosuka in Tokyo Bay, Japan, and is the world's largest, with a length of 1000 meters (3300 feet). Stable structures such as runways and bridges can use submerged pontoons to float at the ocean's surface as long as the majority of the structure's mass is below wave base.

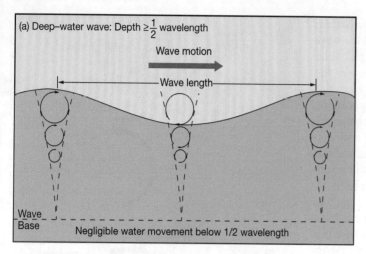

(a) Deep–water wave: Depth $\geq \frac{1}{2}$ wavelength

Wave motion

Wave length

Wave Base

Negligible water movement below 1/2 wavelength

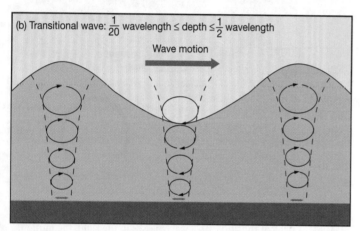

(b) Transitional wave: $\frac{1}{20}$ wavelength $\leq$ depth $\leq \frac{1}{2}$ wavelength

Wave motion

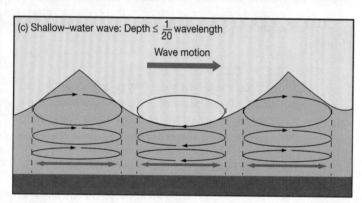

(c) Shallow–water wave: Depth $\leq \frac{1}{20}$ wavelength

Wave motion

FIGURE 8.7 Characteristics of deep-water, shallow-water, and transitional waves. (a) Deep-water waves, showing the diminishing size of the circular orbits with increasing depth. **(b)** Transitional waves, which are intermediate between deep-water and shallow-water waves. **(c)** Shallow-water waves, where the ocean floor interferes with circular orbital motion, causing the orbits to become more flattened. Diagrams are not to scale.

So, by filling in the constants with numbers, the equation for wave speed of deep-water waves varies only with wavelength and becomes (in meters per second):

$$S \text{ (in meters per second)} = 1.25\sqrt{L \text{ (in meters)}} \qquad (8.4)$$

or, in feet per second:

$$S \text{ (in feet per second)} = 2.26\sqrt{L \text{ (in feet)}} \qquad (8.5)$$

We can also determine wave speed knowing only the period (T) because wave speed (S) is defined in Equation 8.3 as L/T. Doing this and filling in the known variables with numbers gives (in meters per second):

$$S \text{ (in meters per second)} = 1.56 \times T \qquad (8.6)$$

or, in feet per second:

$$S \text{ (in feet per second)} = 5.12 \times T \qquad (8.7)$$

The graph in Figure 8.8 uses the above equations to relate the wavelength, period, and speed of deep-water waves. Of the three variables, the wave period is usually easiest to measure. Since all three variables are related, the other two can be determined using Figure 8.8. For example, the vertical red line in Figure 8.8 shows that a wave with a period of 8 seconds has a wavelength of 100 meters. Thus, the speed of the wave is shown by the horizontal red line in Figure 8.8, which is:

$$\text{Speed } (S) = \frac{L}{T} = \frac{100 \text{ meters}}{8 \text{ seconds}} = 12.5 \text{ meters per second} \qquad (8.8)$$

In summary, the general relationship shown by Equations 8.3 through 8.8 (and shown in Figure 8.8) for deep-water waves is *the longer the wavelength, the faster the wave travels*. A fast wave does not necessarily have a large wave height, however, because wave speed depends *only* on wavelength.

Shallow-Water Waves

Waves in which depth (d) is less than ¹⁄₂₀ of the wavelength ($L/20$) are called **shallow-water waves**, or *long waves* (Figure 8.7c). Shallow-water waves are said to *touch bottom* or *feel bottom* because they touch the ocean floor, which interferes with the wave's orbital motion.

The speed of shallow-water waves is influenced only by gravitational acceleration (g) and water depth (d). Since gravitational acceleration remains constant on Earth, the equation for wave speed becomes (in meters per second):

$$S \text{ (in meters per second)} = 3.13\sqrt{d \text{ (in meters)}} \qquad (8.9)$$

or, in feet per second:

$$S \text{ (in feet per second)} = 5.67\sqrt{d \text{ (in feet)}} \qquad (8.10)$$

Equations 8.9 and 8.10 show that wave speed in shallow-water waves is determined only by water depth, where *the deeper the water, the faster the wave travels*.

Examples of shallow-water waves include wind-generated waves that have moved into shallow nearshore areas; *tsunami* (seismic sea waves), generated by earthquakes in the ocean floor; and the *tides*, which are a type of wave generated by the gravitational attraction of the Moon and the Sun. Tsunami and the tides are very long wavelength waves, which far exceed even the deepest ocean water depths.

Particle motion in shallow-water waves is in a very flat elliptical orbit that approaches horizontal (back-and-forth) oscillation. The vertical component of particle motion decreases with increasing depth below sea level, causing the orbits to become even more flattened.

Transitional Waves

Waves that have some characteristics of shallow-water waves and some of deep-water waves are called **transitional waves**. The wavelengths of transitional waves are between two times and twenty times the water depth (Figure 8.7b). The wave speed of shallow-water waves is a function of water depth; for deep-water waves, wave speed is a function of wavelength. Thus, the speed of transitional waves depends partially on water depth and partially on wavelength.

8.4 How Do Wind-Generated Waves Develop?

Most ocean waves are generated by the wind and so are termed *wind-generated waves*.

Wave Development

The life history of a wind-generated wave includes its origin in a windy region of the ocean, its movement across great expanses of open water without subsequent aid of wind, and its termination when it breaks and releases its energy, either in the open ocean or against the shore.

CAPILLARY WAVES, GRAVITY WAVES, AND THE "SEA" As the wind blows over the ocean surface, it creates pressure and stress. These factors deform the ocean surface into small, rounded waves with V-shaped troughs and wavelengths less than 1.74 centimeters (0.7 inch). Commonly called *ripples*, these waves are called **capillary waves** by oceanographers (Figure 8.9, *left*). The name comes from *capillarity*, a property that results from the surface tension of water.[3]

As capillary wave development increases, the sea surface takes on a rougher appearance. The water "catches" more of the wind, allowing the wind and ocean surface to interact more efficiently. As more energy is transferred to the ocean, **gravity waves** develop. These are symmetric waves that have wavelengths exceeding 1.74 centimeters (0.7 inch) (Figure 8.9, *middle*).

The length of gravity waves is generally 15 to 35 times their height. As additional energy is gained, wave height increases more rapidly than wavelength.

---
[3]See Chapter 5 for a description of water's surface tension.

FIGURE 8.8 Speed of deep-water waves. Ideal relations among wavelength, period (*blue line*), and wave speed for deep-water waves. Red lines show an example wave with a wavelength of 100 meters, a period of 8 seconds, and a speed of 12.5 meters per second.

FIGURE 8.9 Wind creates capillary and gravity waves. As wind increases (*left to right*), the height and wavelength of waves increase; they begin as capillary waves and progress to gravity waves. When the wave steepness (*H/L*) exceeds a 1:7 ratio, the waves become unstable and break. (Not to scale.)

The crests become pointed and the troughs are rounded, resulting in a *trochoidal* (*Trokhos* = wheel) waveform (Figure 8.9, *right*).

Energy imparted by the wind increases the height, length, and speed of the wave. When wave speed equals wind speed, neither wave height nor wavelength can change because there is no net energy exchange and the wave has reached its maximum size.

The area where wind-driven waves are generated is called the **sea**, or *sea area*. It is characterized by choppiness and waves moving in many directions. The waves have a variety of periods and wavelengths (most of them short) due to frequently changing wind speed and direction.

FIGURE 8.10 The "sea" and swell. As wind blows across the "sea" (*red dashed line*), wave size increases with increasing wind speed, duration, and fetch. As waves advance beyond their area of origination, they advance across the ocean surface and become sorted into uniform, symmetric swell.

FACTORS AFFECTING WAVE ENERGY Figure 8.10 shows the factors that determine the amount of energy in waves. These factors are (1) the *wind speed*, (2) the *duration*—the length of time during which the wind blows in one direction, and (3) the *fetch*—the distance over which the wind blows in one direction.

Wave height is directly related to the energy in a wave. Wave heights in a sea area are usually less than 2 meters (6.6 feet), but waves with heights of 10 meters (33 feet) and periods of 12 seconds are not uncommon. As "sea" waves gain energy, their steepness increases. When steepness reaches a critical value of ⅐, open ocean breakers—called *whitecaps*—form. The **Beaufort Wind Scale** and the state of the sea (Table 8.1), which was initially devised by Admiral Sir Francis Beaufort (1774–1857) of the British Navy, describes the appearance of the sea surface from dead calm conditions to hurricane-force winds.

Figure 8.11 is a map based on satellite data of average wave heights during October 3–12, 1992. The waves in the Southern Hemisphere are particularly large because the prevailing westerlies between 40 and 60 degrees south latitude reach the highest average wind speeds on Earth, creating the latitudes called the "Roaring Forties," "Furious Fifties," and "Screaming Sixties."

HOW HIGH CAN WAVES BE? According to a U.S. Navy Hydrographic Office bulletin published in the early 1900s, the theoretical maximum height of wind-generated waves should be no higher than 18.3 meters (60 feet); this became known as the "60-foot rule." Although there were some isolated eyewitness accounts of larger waves, the U.S. Navy considered any sightings of waves over 60 feet to be exaggerations. Certainly, embellishment of reported wave height under conditions of extremely rough seas would be understandable. For many years, the "60-foot rule" was accepted as fact.

Careful observations made aboard the 152-meter (500-foot)-long U.S. Navy tanker USS *Ramapo* in 1933 proved the "60-foot rule" incorrect. The ship was caught in a typhoon in the western Pacific Ocean and encountered 108-kilometer- (67-mile-) per-hour winds en route from the Philippines to San Diego. The resulting waves were symmetrical, uniform, and had a period of 14.8 seconds. Because the *Ramapo* was traveling with the waves, the vessel's officers were able to measure the waves accurately. The officers used the dimensions of the ship, including the *eye*

TABLE 8.1	BEAUFORT WIND SCALE AND THE STATE OF THE SEA

Beaufort number	Descriptive term	Wind speed (km/hr)	Wind speed (mi/hr)	Appearance of the sea
0	Calm	<1	<1	Like a mirror
1	Light air	1–5	1–3	Ripples with the appearance of scales, no foam crests
2	Light breeze	6–11	4–7	Small wavelets; crests of glassy appearance, no breaking
3	Gentle breeze	12–19	8–12	Large wavelets; crests begin to break, scattered whitecaps
4	Moderate breeze	20–28	13–18	Small waves, becoming longer; numerous whitecaps
5	Fresh breeze	29–38	19–24	Moderate waves, taking longer form; many whitecaps, some spray
6	Strong breeze	39–49	25–31	Large waves begin to form, whitecaps everywhere, more spray
7	Near gale	50–61	32–38	Sea heaps up and white foam from breaking waves begins to be blown in streaks
8	Gale	62–74	39–46	Moderately high waves of greater length, edges of crests begin to break into spindrift, foam is blown in well-marked streaks
9	Strong gale	75–88	47–54	High waves, dense streaks of foam and sea begins to roll, spray may affect visibility
10	Storm	89–102	55–63	Very high waves with overhanging crests; foam is blown in dense white streaks, causing the sea to appear white; the rolling of the sea becomes heavy; visibility reduced
11	Violent storm	103–117	64–72	Exceptionally high waves (small and medium-sized ships might for a time be lost from view behind the waves), the sea is covered with white patches of foam, everywhere the edges of the wave crests are blown into froth, visibility further reduced
12	Hurricane	118+	73+	The air is filled with foam and spray, sea completely white with driving spray, visibility greatly reduced

Wave Height, meters

FIGURE 8.11 TOPEX/Poseidon wave height, October 3–12, 1992. The TOPEX/Poseidon satellite receives a return of stronger signals from calm seas and weaker signals from seas with large waves. Based on these data, a map of wave height can be produced. The largest average wave heights (*red areas*; scale is in meters) are in the prevailing westerly wind belt in the Southern Hemisphere.

FIGURE 8.12 **USS *Ramapo* in heavy seas.** Bridge officers aboard the USS *Ramapo* measured the largest authentically recorded wave by sighting from the bridge across the crow's nest to the horizon while the ship's stern was directly in the trough of a large wave. A wave height of 34 meters (112 feet) was calculated based on geometric relationships of the vessel and the waves.

WEB VIDEO
Ship in Big Waves

FIGURE 8.13 **Wave damage on the aircraft carrier *Bennington*.** The *Bennington* returns from heavy seas encountered in a typhoon off Okinawa in 1945 with part of its reinforced steel flight deck bent down over its bow. Damage to the flight deck, which is 16.5 meters (54 feet) above still water level, was caused by large waves.

height of an observer on the ship's bridge (Figure 8.12). Geometric relationships revealed that the waves were 34 meters (112 feet) high, which is taller than an 11-story building! These waves proved to be a record that still stands today for the largest authentically recorded wind-generated waves, shattering the "60-foot rule." Although the *Ramapo* was largely undamaged, other ships traveling in rough seas aren't always so lucky (Figure 8.13). In fact, several large ships disappear at sea every year simply due to enormous waves.

FULLY DEVELOPED SEA   For a given wind speed, Table 8.2 lists the minimum fetch and duration of wind beyond which the waves cannot grow. Waves cannot grow because an equilibrium condition, called a **fully developed sea**, has been achieved. Waves can grow no further in a fully developed sea because they lose as much energy breaking as whitecaps under the force of gravity as they receive from the wind. Table 8.2 also lists the average characteristics of waves resulting from a fully developed sea, including the height of the highest 10% of the waves.

SWELL   As waves generated in a sea area move toward its margins, wind speeds diminish and the waves eventually move faster than the wind. When this occurs, wave steepness decreases .and waves become long-crested waves called **swells** (*swellan* = swollen), which are uniform, symmetrical waves that have traveled out of their area of origination. Swells move with little loss of energy over large stretches of the ocean surface, transporting energy away from one sea area and depositing it in another. The movement of swells to distant areas is the reason why there can be waves at a shoreline even though there is no wind.

Waves with longer wavelengths travel faster and thus leave the sea area first. They are followed by slower, shorter **wave trains**, or groups of waves. The progression from long, fast waves to short, slow waves illustrates the principle of **wave dispersion** (*dis* = apart, *spargere* = to scatter)—the sorting of waves by their wavelength. Waves of many wavelengths are present in the generating area. Wave speed depends on wavelength in deep water (see Figure 8.8), however, so the longer waves "outrun" the shorter ones. The distance over which waves change from a choppy "sea" to uniform swell is called the **decay distance**, which can be up to several hundred kilometers.

As a group of waves leaves a sea area and becomes a *swell wave train*, the leading wave keeps disappearing. However, the same number of waves always remains in the group because as the leading wave disappears, a new wave replaces it at the back of the group (Figure 8.14). For example, if four waves are generated, the lead wave keeps dying out as the wave train travels, but one is created in the back, so the wave train stays four waves. Because of the progressive dying out and creation of new waves, the group moves across the ocean surface at only *half* the velocity of an individual wave in the group.

Interference Patterns

When swells from different storms run together, the waves clash, or *interfere* with one another, giving rise to **interference patterns**. An interference pattern produced when two or more wave systems collide is the sum of the disturbance that

TABLE 8.2	CONDITIONS NECESSARY TO PRODUCE A FULLY DEVELOPED SEA AT VARIOUS WIND SPEEDS AND THE CHARACTERISTICS OF THE RESULTING WAVES					
These conditions . . .			. . . produce these waves			
Wind speed in km/hr (mi/hr)	Fetch in km (mi)	Duration in hours	Average height in m (ft)	Average wavelength in m (ft)	Average period in seconds	Highest 10% of waves in m (ft)
20 (12)	24 (15)	2.8	0.3 (1.0)	10.6 (34.8)	3.2	0.8 (2.5)
30 (19)	77 (48)	7.0	0.9 (2.9)	22.2 (72.8)	4.6	2.1 (6.9)
40 (25)	176 (109)	11.5	1.8 (5.9)	39.7 (130.2)	6.2	3.9 (12.8)
50 (31)	380 (236)	18.5	3.2 (10.5)	61.8 (202.7)	7.7	6.8 (22.3)
60 (37)	660 (409)	27.5	5.1 (16.7)	89.2 (292.6)	9.1	10.5 (34.4)
70 (43)	1093 (678)	37.5	7.4 (24.3)	121.4 (398.2)	10.8	15.3 (50.2)
80 (50)	1682 (1043)	50.0	10.3 (33.8)	158.6 (520.2)	12.4	21.4 (70.2)
90 (56)	2446 (1517)	65.2	13.9 (45.6)	201.6 (661.2)	13.9	28.4 (93.2)

each wave would have produced individually. Figure 8.15 shows that the result may be a larger or smaller trough or crest, depending on conditions.

CONSTRUCTIVE INTERFERENCE   **Constructive interference** occurs when wave trains having the same wavelength come together *in phase*, meaning crest to crest and trough to trough. If the displacements from each wave are added together,

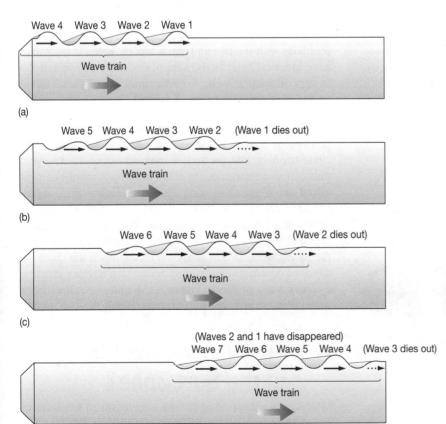

(a)

(b)

(c)

(d)

STUDENTS SOMETIMES ASK...

I know that swell is what surfers hope for. Is swell always big?

Not necessarily. Swell is defined as waves that have moved out of their area of origination, so these waves do not have to be a certain wave height to be classified as swell. It is true, however, that the uniform and symmetrical shape of most swell delights surfers.

STUDENTS SOMETIMES ASK...

What is the difference between "groundswell" and "wind swell"?

The term *groundswell* was originally a sailor's word (and is now a surfer's term) for deep-ocean swell, such as might be generated by a distant storm or earthquake. In its original sense, groundswell referred to waves so huge that their troughs bared the "ground" of the sea bottom. Groundswell is essentially the same thing as *wind swell*, although groundswell often refers to very large waves from a distant origin whereas wind swell refers to smaller, locally produced waves.

FIGURE 8.14 Movement of a wave train. As energy in the leading waves (**a**, *waves 1 and 2*) is transferred into circular orbital motion, the waves in front die out and are replaced by new waves from behind (**b**). Even though new waves take up the lead (**c** and **d**), the length of the wave train and the total number of waves remain the same. This causes the group speed to be one-half that of the individual wave.

FIGURE 8.15 Constructive, destructive, and mixed interference patterns. Constructive interference (*left*) occurs when waves of the same wavelength come together in phase (crest to crest and trough to trough), producing waves of greater height. Destructive interference (*center*) occurs when overlapping waves have identical characteristics but come together out of phase, resulting in a canceling effect. More commonly, waves of different lengths and heights encounter one another and produce a complex, mixed interference pattern (*right*).

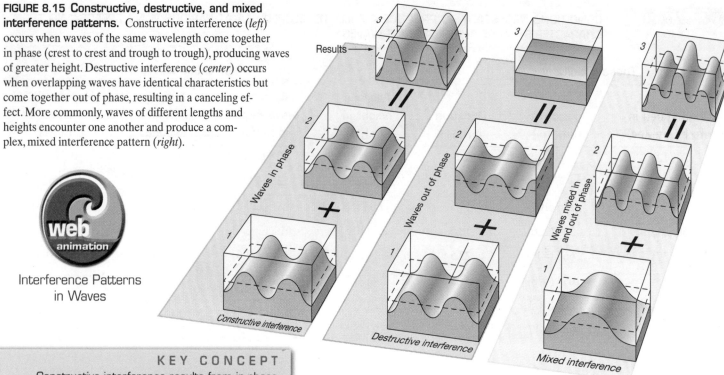

web animation

Interference Patterns in Waves

the interference pattern results in a wave with the same wavelength as the two overlapping wave systems, but with a wave height equal to the sum of the individual wave heights (Figure 8.15, *left*).

DESTRUCTIVE INTERFERENCE **Destructive interference** occurs when wave trains having the same wavelength come together *out of phase*, meaning the crest from one wave coincides with the trough from a second wave. If the waves have identical heights, the sum of the crest of one and the trough of another is zero, so the energies of these waves cancel each other (Figure 8.15, *center*).

MIXED INTERFERENCE In most ocean areas, it is likely that two or more swells of different heights and lengths will come together and produce a mixture of constructive and destructive interference. In this scenario, a more complex **mixed interference** pattern develops (Figure 8.15, *right*). Mixed interference patterns explain the varied sequence of higher and lower waves called **surf beat** that most people notice at the beach as well as other irregular wave patterns that occur when two or more swells approach the shore. In the open ocean, several swell systems often interact, creating complex wave patterns (Figure 8.16), and sometimes, large waves that can be hazardous to ships (Box 8.1).

8.5 How Do Waves Change in the Surf Zone?

Most waves generated in the sea area by storm winds move across the ocean as swell. These waves then release their energy along the margins of continents in the **surf zone**,

FIGURE 8.16 Mixed interference pattern. The observed wave pattern in the ocean (*above*) is often the result of mixed interference of many different overlapping wave sets (*below*).

ROGUE WAVES: SHIPS BEWARE!

Rogue waves are massive, solitary, spontaneous ocean waves that can reach enormous height and often occur at times when normal ocean waves are not unusually large. In a sea of 2-meter (6.5-foot) waves, for example, a 20-meter (65-foot) rogue wave may suddenly appear. *Rogue* means "unusual" and, in this case, the waves are unusually large. Rogue waves—sometimes called *superwaves, monster waves, sleeper waves,* or *freak waves*—are defined as individual waves of exceptional height or abnormal shape that are more than twice the average of the highest one-third of all the wave heights in a given wave record. Mariners often describe rogue wave crests as "mountains of water" and their troughs as "holes in the sea," creating a roller-coaster ride that can be disastrous.

Because of their size and destructive power, rogue waves have been popularized in literature and movies such as *The Perfect Storm* and the recent film remake *Poseidon.* The impressive size of some rogue waves makes them quite hazardous to oil-drilling platforms and vessels at sea. In 1966, for example, the Italian luxury liner *Michelangelo* received extensive damage from a rogue wave it encountered during a storm in the North Atlantic (Figure 8A). In a nearby area in 1995, the giant luxury liner *Queen Elizabeth II,* which carries 1500 passengers, plowed through a 29-meter (95-foot) wave generated by Hurricane Luis.

In the open ocean, 1 wave in 23 will be over twice the height of the wave average, 1 in 1175 will be three times as high, and 1 in 300,000 will be four times as high. The chances of a truly monstrous wave, therefore, are only 1 in several billion. Nevertheless, rogue waves do occur, and satellite observations over a three-week period in 2001 confirmed that rogue waves occur more frequently than were previously thought: The study documented more than 10 individual giant waves around the globe of over 25 meters (82 feet) in height. Even with satellite monitoring of ocean waves (see Web Table 3.1), it remains difficult to forecast specifically

FIGURE 8A Damage to the *Michelangelo* from a rogue wave. In April 1966, while making a crossing of the North Atlantic Ocean, the Italian luxury liner *Michelangelo* encountered a rogue wave amid a storm. As the wave crashed aboard the ship, it ripped off part of the ship's bow, tore a hole in its superstructure, smashed bridge windows 24 meters (80 feet) above the waterline, killed three people, and injured dozens more.

when or where rogue waves will arise. For instance, the 17-meter (56-foot) NOAA research vessel R/V *Ballena* was flipped and sunk in 2000 by a 4.6-meter (15-foot) rogue wave off the California coast while conducting a survey in shallow, calm water. Fortunately, the three people on board survived the incident.

Worldwide each year, about 10 large ships such as supertankers or container-ships are reported missing without a trace; as many as 1000 vessels of all sizes are lost each year, with rogue waves the suspected cause of many of the sinkings. Still, scientists lack detailed shipboard measurements of rogue waves because they tend to appear without warning, and bobbing ships make poor observations platforms.

The main cause of rogue waves is theorized to be an extraordinary case of constructive wave interference where multiple

waves overlap in-phase to produce an extremely large wave. Rogue waves also tend to occur more frequently near weather fronts and downwind from islands or shoals. Recent modeling of the wave conditions in the Pacific that caused a Japanese fishing vessel to capsize in 2008 suggests that rogue waves can be created when the low- and high-frequency components of ordinary ocean waves interact and channel their energy into a narrow frequency band.

Another way in which rogue waves can be created is when strong ocean currents focus and amplify opposing swells. Such conditions exist along the "Wild Coast" off the southeast coast of Africa, where the Agulhas Current flows directly against large Antarctic storm waves, creating rogue waves that can crash onto a ship's bow, overcome its structural capacity, and sink even large, well-constructed ships (Figure 8B).

FIGURE 8B Rogue waves along Africa's "Wild Coast."

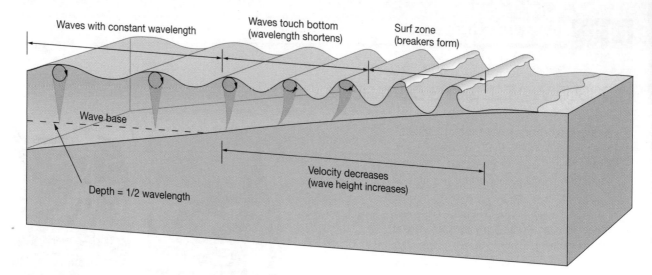

Waves with constant wavelength

Waves touch bottom (wavelength shortens)

Surf zone (breakers form)

Wave base

Depth = 1/2 wavelength

Velocity decreases (wave height increases)

FIGURE 8.17 Physical changes of a wave in the surf zone. As waves approach the shore and encounter water depths of less than one-half wavelength, the waves "feel bottom." The *wave speed decreases* and waves stack up against the shore, causing the *wavelength to decrease*. This results in an *increase in wave height* to the point where the wave *steepness is increased* beyond the 1:7 ratio, causing the wave to pitch forward and break in the surf zone.

Wave Motion and
Wave Refraction

which is the zone of breaking waves. Breaking waves exemplify power and persistence, sometimes moving objects weighing several tons. In doing so, energy from a distant storm can travel thousands of kilometers until it is finally expended along a distant shoreline in a few wild moments.

Physical Changes as Waves Approach Shore

As deep-water waves of swell move toward continental margins over gradually **shoaling** (*shold* = shallow) water, they eventually encounter water depths that are less than one-half of their wavelength (Figure 8.17) and become transitional waves. Actually, any shallowly submerged obstacle (such as a coral reef, sunken wreck, or sand bar) will cause waves to release some energy. Navigators have long known that breaking waves indicate dangerously shallow water.

Many physical changes occur to a wave as it encounters shallow water, becomes a shallow-water wave, and breaks. The shoaling depths interfere with water particle movement at the base of the wave, so the *wave speed decreases*. As one wave slows, the following waveform, which is still moving at its original speed, moves closer to the wave that is being slowed, causing a *decrease in wavelength*. Although some wave energy is lost due to friction, the wave energy that remains must go somewhere, so *wave height increases*. This increase in wave height combined with the decrease in wavelength causes an *increase in wave steepness* (H/L). When the wave steepness reaches the 1:7 ratio, the waves break as surf (Figure 8.17).

If the surf is swell that has traveled from distant storms, breakers will develop relatively near shore in shallow water. The horizontal motion characteristic of shallow-water waves moves water alternately toward and away from the shore as an oscillation. The surf will be characterized by parallel lines of relatively uniform breakers.

If the surf consists of waves generated by local winds, the waves may not have been sorted into swell. The surf may be mostly unstable, deep-water, high-energy waves with steepness already near the 1:7 ratio. In this case, the waves will break shortly after feeling bottom some distance from shore, and the surf will be rough, choppy, and irregular.

When the water depth is about one and one-third times the wave height, the crest of the wave breaks, producing surf.[4] When the water depth becomes less than ¹⁄₂₀ the wavelength, waves in the surf zone begin to behave like shallow-water waves (see Figure 8.7). Particle motion is greatly impeded by the bottom, and a significant transport of water toward the shoreline occurs (Figure 8.17).

---

[4]Using this relationship provides a handy way of estimating water depth in the surf zone: The depth of the water where waves are breaking is one and one-third times the breaker height.

Waves break in the surf zone because particle motion near the bottom of the wave is severely restricted, slowing the waveform. At the surface, however, individual orbiting water particles have not yet been slowed because they have no contact with the bottom. In addition, the wave height increases in shallow water. The difference in speed between the top and bottom parts of the wave causes the top part of the wave to overrun the lower part, which results in the wave toppling over and breaking. Breaking waves are analogous to a person who leans too far forward. If you don't catch yourself, you may also "break" something when you fall.

> **KEY CONCEPT**
> As waves come into shallow water and feel bottom, their speed and wavelength decrease while their wave height and wave steepness increase; this action causes waves to break.

Breakers and Surfing

There are three main types of breakers. Figure 8.18a shows a **spilling breaker**, which is a turbulent mass of air and water that runs down the front slope of the wave as it breaks. Spilling breakers result from a gently sloped ocean bottom, which gradually extracts energy from the wave over an extended distance and produces breakers with low overall energy. As a result, spilling breakers have a longer life span and give surfers a long—but somewhat less exciting—ride than other breakers.

Figure 8.18b shows a **plunging breaker**, which has a curling crest that moves over an air pocket. The curling crest occurs because the particles in the crest literally outrun the wave, and there is nothing beneath them to support their motion. Plunging breakers form on moderately steep beach slopes and are the best waves for surfing (see the chapter-opening photo).

When the ocean bottom has an abrupt slope, the wave energy is compressed into a shorter distance and the wave will surge forward, creating a **surging breaker** (Figure 8.18c). These waves build up and break right at the shoreline, so board surfers tend to avoid them. For body surfers, however, these waves present the greatest challenge.

Surfing is analogous to riding a gravity-operated water sled by balancing the forces of gravity and buoyancy. The particle motion of ocean waves (see Figure 8.4) shows that water particles move up into the front of the crest. This force, along with the buoyancy of the surfboard, helps maintain a surfer's position in front of a breaking wave. The trick is to perfectly balance the force of gravity (directed downward) with the buoyant force (directed perpendicular to the

(a)

(b)

(c)

FIGURE 8.18 Types of breakers. (a) Spilling breaker, resulting from a gradual beach slope. **(b)** Plunging breaker, resulting from a steep beach slope; these are the best waves for surfing. **(c)** Surging breaker, resulting from an abrupt beach slope.

Why is surfing so much better along the West Coast of the United States than along the East Coast?

There are three main reasons why the U.S. West Coast has better surfing conditions:

- The waves are generally bigger in the Pacific. The Pacific is larger than the Atlantic, so the fetch is larger, allowing bigger waves to develop in the Pacific.
- The beach slopes are generally steeper along the West Coast. Along the East Coast, the gentle slopes often create spilling breakers, which are not as favorable for surfing. The steeper beach slopes along the West Coast cause plunging breakers, which are better for surfing.
- The wind is more favorable. Most of the United States is influenced by the prevailing westerlies, which blow toward shore and enhance waves along the West Coast. Along the East Coast, the wind blows away from shore.

Wave Motion and
Wave Refraction

KEY CONCEPT

Wave refraction is the bending of waves caused when slow in shallow water; wave reflection is the bouncing back of wave energy caused when waves strike a hard barrier.

wave face) to enable a surfer to be propelled forward by the wave's energy. A skillful surfer, by positioning the board properly on the wave front, can regulate the degree to which the propelling gravitational forces exceed the buoyancy forces, and speeds up to 40 kilometers (25 miles) per hour can be obtained while moving along the face of a breaking wave. When the wave passes over water that is too shallow to allow the upward movement of water particles to continue, the wave has expended its energy and the ride is over.

Wave Refraction

Waves seldom approach a shore at a perfect right angle (90 degrees). Instead, some segment of the wave will "feel bottom" first and will slow before the rest of the wave. This results in the **refraction** (*refringere* = to break up) or *bending*, of each *wave crest* (also called a *wave front*) as waves approach the shore.

Figure 8.19a shows how waves coming toward a straight shoreline are refracted and tend to align themselves *nearly* parallel to the shore. This explains why all waves come almost straight in toward a beach, no matter what their original orientation was. Figure 8.19b shows how waves coming toward an irregular shoreline refract so that they, too, nearly align with the shore. Figure 8.19c shows a classic example of wave refraction around Rincon Point in California.

The refraction of waves along an irregular shoreline distributes wave energy unevenly along the shore. To help illustrate how this works, notice the long black arrows in Figure 8.19b, which are called **orthogonal** (*ortho* = straight, *gonia* = angle) **lines** or *wave rays*. Orthogonal lines are drawn perpendicular to the wave crests (so they indicate the direction that waves travel) and are spaced so that the energy between lines is equal at all times. Far from shore, notice how the orthogonals in Figure 8.19b are evenly spaced. As they approach the shore, however, notice how the orthogonals *converge* on headlands that jut into the ocean and *diverge* in bays. This means that wave energy is focused against the headlands but dispersed in bays. As a result, large waves occur at headlands, which are areas of good surfing[5] and sites of erosion. Conversely, smaller waves occur in bays, which often provide areas for boat anchorages and are also associated with sediment deposition. In addition, waves approaching shore are also influenced by sea floor features such as shallow banks or submarine canyons.

Wave Reflection

Not all wave energy is expended as waves rush onto the shore. A vertical barrier, such as a seawall or a rock ledge, can reflect waves back into the ocean with little loss of energy—a process called **wave reflection** (*reflecten* = to bend back), which is similar to how a mirror reflects (bounces) back light. If the incoming wave strikes the barrier at a right (90-degree) angle, for example, the wave energy is reflected back parallel to the incoming wave, often interfering with the next incoming wave and creating unusual waveforms. More commonly, waves approach the shore at an angle, causing wave energy to be reflected at an angle equal to the angle at which the wave approached the barrier.

THE WEDGE: A CASE STUDY OF WAVE REFLECTION AND CONSTRUCTIVE INTERFERENCE   An outstanding example of wave reflection and constructive interference occurs in an area called *The Wedge*, which develops west of the jetty that protects the harbor entrance at Newport Harbor, California (Figure 8.20). The jetty is a solid human-made object that extends into the ocean 400 meters (1300 feet) and has a near-vertical side facing the waves. As incoming waves strike the vertical side of the jetty at an angle, they are reflected at an equivalent angle.

---

[5]Sailors have long known that "the points draw the waves." Surfers also know how wave refraction causes good "point breaks."

(a)

(b)

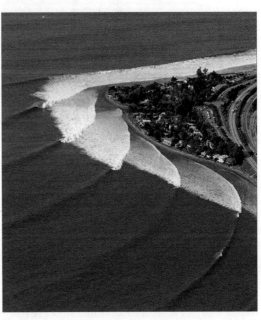

(c)

FIGURE 8.19 Wave refraction. **(a)** Wave refraction along a straight shoreline. Waves approaching the shore at an angle first "feel bottom" close to shore. This causes the segment of the wave in shallow water to slow, causing the crest of the wave to refract or bend so that the waves arrive at the shore nearly parallel to the shoreline. Red arrows represent direction and speed of the wave. **(b)** Wave refraction along an irregular shoreline. As waves first "feel bottom" in the shallows off the headlands, they are slowed, causing the waves to refract and align nearly parallel to the shoreline. Evenly spaced orthogonal lines (*long black arrows*) show that wave energy is concentrated on headlands (causing erosion) and dispersed in bays (resulting in deposition). **(c)** Wave refraction at Rincon Point, California, looking west.

WEB VIDEO

Wave Refraction and
Longshore Current

Because the original waves and the reflected waves have the same wavelength, a constructive interference pattern develops, creating plunging breakers that may exceed 8 meters (26 feet) in height (Figure 8.20, *inset*). Too dangerous for board surfers, these waves present a fierce challenge to the most experienced body surfers. The Wedge has crippled and even killed many who have come to challenge it.

STANDING WAVES, NODES, AND ANTINODES   Standing waves (also called *stationary waves*) can be produced when waves are reflected at right angles to a barrier. Standing waves are the sum of two waves with the same wavelength moving in opposite directions, resulting in no net movement. Although the water particles continue to move vertically and horizontally, there is none of the circular motion that is characteristic of a progressive wave.

Figure 8.21 shows the movement of water during the wave cycle of a standing wave. Lines along which there is no vertical movement are called *nodes* (*nodus* = knot), or *nodal lines*. *Antinodes*, which are crests that alternately become troughs, are the points of greatest vertical movement within a standing wave.

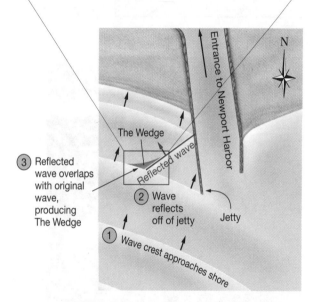

FIGURE 8.20 Wave reflection and constructive interference at The Wedge, Newport Harbor, California. As waves approach the shore (*1*), some of the wave energy is reflected off the long jetty at the entrance to the harbor (*2*). The reflected wave overlaps and constructively interferes with the original wave (*3*), resulting in a wedge-shaped wave (*dark blue triangle*) that may reach heights exceeding 8 meters (26 feet). Photo (*inset*) shows a boogie boarder making an airborne escape from The Wedge; note the end of the jetty in the background.

Tsunami

When water sloshes back and forth in a basin, the maximum vertical displacements are at the antinodes. When water moves from crest to trough at an antinode, the displaced volume of water has to move horizontally to raise the water level of the adjacent antinode from trough to crest. As a result, there is no vertical motion at the node; instead, there is only horizontal motion. At the antinodes, however, the movement of water particles is entirely vertical.

We'll consider standing waves further when tidal phenomena are discussed in Chapter 9, "Tides." Under certain conditions, the development of standing waves significantly affects the tidal character in coastal regions.

8.6 How Are Tsunami Created?

The Japanese term for the large, sometimes destructive waves that occasionally roll into their harbors is **tsunami** (*tsu* = harbor, *nami* = wave[s]) Tsunami originate from sudden changes in the topography of the sea floor caused by such events as slippage along underwater faults, underwater avalanches such as turbidity currents or the collapse of large oceanic volcanoes, and underwater volcanic eruptions. Many people mistakenly call them "tidal waves," but tsunami are unrelated to the tides. The mechanisms that trigger tsunami are typically seismic events, so tsunami are *seismic sea waves*.

The majority of tsunami are caused by *fault movement*. Underwater fault movement displaces Earth's crust, generates earthquakes, and, if it ruptures the sea floor, produces a sudden change in water level at the ocean surface (Figure 8.22a). Faults that produce *vertical* displacements (the uplift or downdropping of ocean floor) change the volume of the ocean basin, which affects the entire water column and generates tsunami. Conversely, faults that produce *horizontal* displacements (such as the lateral movement associated with transform faulting) do not generally generate tsunami because the side-to-side movement of these faults does not change the volume of the ocean basin. Much less common events, such as underwater avalanches triggered by shaking or underwater volcanic eruptions—which create the largest waves—also produce tsunami. In addition, large objects that splash into the ocean, such as above-water coastal landslides (see Web Box 8.1) or meteorite impacts, produce **splash waves**, which are a type of tsunami.

During the 20th century, 498 measurable tsunami occurred worldwide, with 66 resulting in fatalities. The source events were earthquakes (86%), volcanic activity (5%), landslides (4%), or a combination of those processes (5%). Tsunami generated by meteorite or asteroid impacts occur much less frequently.

The wavelength of a typical tsunami exceeds 200 kilometers (125 miles), so it is a shallow-water wave everywhere in the ocean.[6] Because tsunami are shallow-water

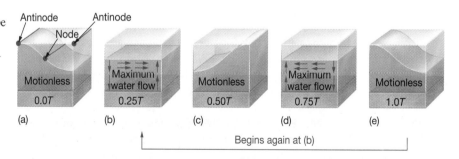

FIGURE 8.21 Sequence of motion in a standing wave. In a standing wave, water is motionless when antinodes reach maximum displacement (*a, c,* and *e; a* and *e* are identical). Water movement is at a maximum (*blue arrows*) when the water is horizontal (*b* and *d*). Movement is vertical beneath the antinodes, and maximum horizontal movement occurs beneath the node. After *e*, cycle begins again at *b*.

[6]Recall that the depth of the wave base is equal to one-half a wave's wavelength. Thus, tsunami can typically be felt to depths of 100 kilometers (62 miles), which is deeper than even the deepest ocean trenches.

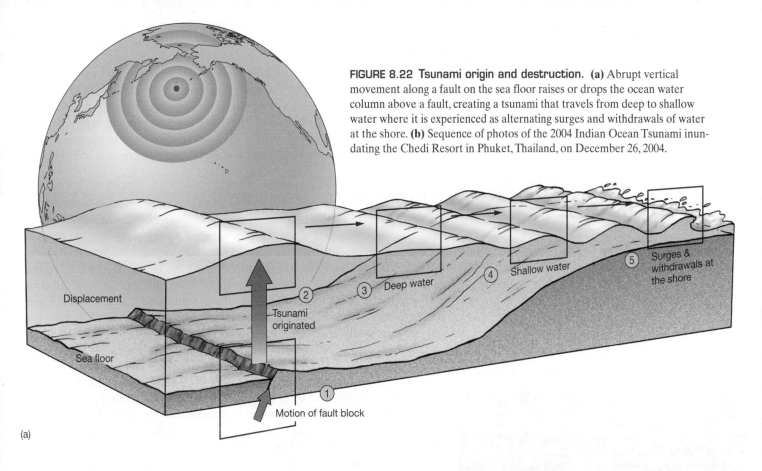

FIGURE 8.22 Tsunami origin and destruction. (a) Abrupt vertical movement along a fault on the sea floor raises or drops the ocean water column above a fault, creating a tsunami that travels from deep to shallow water where it is experienced as alternating surges and withdrawals of water at the shore. (b) Sequence of photos of the 2004 Indian Ocean Tsunami inundating the Chedi Resort in Phuket, Thailand, on December 26, 2004.

(a)

(b)

waves, their speed is determined only by water depth. In the open ocean, tsunami move at well over 700 kilometers (435 miles) per hour—they can easily keep pace with a jet airplane—and have heights of only about 0.5 meter (1.6 feet). Even though they are fast, tsunami are small in the open ocean and pass unnoticed in deep water until they reach shore, where they slow in the shallow water and undergo physical changes (just as wind-generated waves do) that cause the tsunami to increase in wave height.

Coastal Effects

Contrary to popular belief, a tsunami does not form a huge breaking wave at the shoreline. Instead, it is a strong flood or surge of water that causes the ocean to advance (or, in certain cases, retreat) dramatically. In fact, a tsunami resembles a sudden, *extremely* high tide, which is why they are misnamed "tidal waves." It may take many minutes for the tsunami to express itself fully, during which time sea level can rise up to 40 meters (131 feet) above normal, with normal waves superimposed on top of the higher sea level. The strong surge of water can rush into low-lying areas with destructive results (Figure 8.22b).

As the trough of the tsunami arrives at the shore, the water will rapidly drain off the land. In coastal areas, it will look like a sudden and *extremely* low tide, where sea level is many meters lower than even the lowest low tide. Because tsunami are typically a series of waves, there is often an alternating series of dramatic surges and withdrawals of water that are widely separated in time. The first surge is only rarely the largest; instead, the third, fourth—or even seventh—surge may be the largest and can occur several hours later.

Depending on the geometry of sea floor motion that creates a tsunami, the trough can sometimes arrive at a coast first. For example, on the side of a fault where the sea floor drops down, the first part of the wave to propagate outward will be the trough, followed by the crest. Conversely, on the side of the fault that moves upward, the crest leads the trough. At a coast where the trough arrives first, the water drains out and exposes parts of the lowermost shoreline that are rarely seen. For people at the shoreline, the temptation is to explore these newly exposed areas and catch stranded organisms. Within a few minutes, however, a strong surge of water (the crest of the tsunami) is due to arrive.

The alternating surges and retreats of water by tsunami can severely damage coastal structures and can injure or kill people as well. The speed of the advance—up to 4 meters (13 feet) per second—is faster than any human can run. Those who are caught in a tsunami are often drowned or crushed by floating debris (Figure 8.23).

FIGURE 8.23 Tsunami damage in Hilo, Hawaii.
Flattened parking meters in Hilo, Hawaii, caused by the 1946 tsunami that resulted in more than $25 million in damage and 159 deaths.

Some Examples of Historic and Recent Tsunami

Although many small tsunami are created each year, most go unnoticed. On average, 57 noticeable tsunami occur every decade, with a large tsunami occurring somewhere in the world every two to three years and an extremely large and damaging one occurring every 15 to 20 years.

Where do most tsunami occur? About 86% of all great waves are generated in the Pacific Ocean because large-magnitude earthquakes occur along the series of trenches that ring its ocean basin where oceanic plates are subducted along convergent plate boundaries. Volcanic activity is also common along the *Pacific Ring of Fire*, and the large earthquakes that occur along its margin are capable of producing extremely large tsunami. Figure 8.24 shows that since 1990 a number of destructive tsunami have occurred along the Pacific Ring of Fire.

THE ERUPTION OF KRAKATAU (1883) One of the most destructive tsunami ever generated came from the eruption of the volcanic island of Krakatau[7] on

---

[7]The island Krakatau (which is *west* of Java) is also called Krakatoa.

FIGURE 8.24 Large tsunami since 1990 and their destruction. Worldwide tsunami have claimed more than 300,000 lives since 1990. These killer waves are most often generated by earthquakes along colliding tectonic plates of the Pacific Rim, although the most deadly tsunami in history was the 2004 Indian Ocean Tsunami (*red X*). Locations of ocean trenches are shown in purple; Pacific Ring of Fire is shown by pink shading.

August 27, 1883. Approximately the size of a small Hawaiian Island in what is now Indonesia, Krakatau exploded with the greatest release of energy from Earth's interior ever recorded in historic times. The island, which stood 450 meters (1500 feet) above sea level, was nearly obliterated. The sound of the explosion was heard throughout the Indian Ocean up to 4800 kilometers (3000 miles) away and remains the loudest noise on human record. Dust from the explosion ascended into the atmosphere and circled Earth on high-altitude winds, producing brilliant red sunsets worldwide for nearly a year.

Not many people were killed by the outright explosion of the volcano because the island was uninhabited. However, the displacement of water from the energy released during the explosion was enormous, creating a tsunami that exceeded 35 meters (116 feet)—as high as a 12-story building. It devastated the coastal region of the Sunda Strait between the nearby islands of Sumatra and Java, drowning more than 1000 villages and taking more than 36,000 lives. The energy carried by this wave reached every ocean basin and was even detected by tide-recording stations as far away as London and San Francisco.

Like most of the other approximately 130 active volcanoes in Indonesia, Krakatau was formed along the Sunda Arc, a 3000-kilometer (1900-mile) curving chain of volcanoes associated with the subduction of the Australian Plate beneath the Eurasian Plate. Where these two sections of Earth's crust meet, earthquakes and volcanic eruptions are common.

THE SCOTCH CAP, ALASKA/HILO, HAWAII TSUNAMI (1946) A strong and damaging tsunami hit the Hawaiian Islands on April 1, 1946, with north-facing shores including the port city of Hilo receiving the majority of damage. The tsunami was from a magnitude $M_w = 7.3$ earthquake in the Aleutian Trench off the island of Unimak, Alaska, more than 3000 kilometers (1850 miles) away. From that direction, the offshore bathymetry in Hilo Bay focused the tsunami's energy directly toward town, so the city of Hilo experienced tsunami surges of tremendous heights. In this case, the tsunami expressed itself as a strong recession followed by a surge of water nearly 17 meters (55 feet) above normal high tide, causing more than $25 million in damage and killing 159 people. Remarkably, it stands as Hawaii's worst natural disaster (Figure 8.23).

STUDENTS SOMETIMES ASK...

What is the record height of a tsunami?

Japan, which is in close proximity to several subduction zones and endures more tsunami than any other place on Earth (followed by Chile and Hawaii), holds the record. The largest documented tsunami occurred in the Ryukyu Islands of southern Japan in 1971, when one raised normal sea level by 85 meters (278 feet). In low-lying coastal areas, such an enormous vertical rise can send water many kilometers inland, causing flooding and widespread damage.

Closer to the source of the earthquake, the tsunami was considerably larger. The tsunami struck Scotch Cap, Alaska, on Unimak Island, where a two-story reinforced concrete lighthouse stood 14 meters (46 feet) above sea level at its base. The lighthouse was destroyed by a wave that is estimated to have reached 36 meters (118 feet), killing all five people inside the lighthouse at the time. Vehicles on a nearby mesa 31 meters (103 feet) above water level were also moved by the onrush of water.

PAPUA NEW GUINEA (1998) In July 1998, off the north coast of Papua New Guinea in the western part of the Pacific Ring of Fire, a magnitude $M_w = 7.1$ earthquake was followed shortly thereafter by a 15-meter (49-foot) tsunami, which was up to five times larger than expected for a quake that size. The tsunami completely overtopped a heavily populated low-lying sand bar, destroying three entire villages and resulting in at least 2200 deaths. Researchers who mapped the sea floor after the tsunami discovered the remains of a huge underwater landslide, which was apparently triggered by the shaking and caused the unusually large tsunami.

INDIAN OCEAN (2004) Although most tsunami are associated with offshore trenches where plates experience subduction along the rim of the Pacific Ocean, tsunami sometimes occur in other ocean basins. On December 26, 2004, for example, a magnitude $M_w = 9.3$ earthquake occurred about 100 kilometers (60 miles) off the coast of Sumatra, Indonesia, and uplifted the sea floor, which generated a devastating tsunami that was felt throughout the Indian Ocean and caused widespread damage (Box 8.2).

Tsunami Warning System

In response to the tsunami that struck Hawaii in 1946, a tsunami warning system was established throughout the Pacific Ocean. It led to what is now the **Pacific Tsunami Warning Center (PTWC)**, which coordinates information from 25 Pacific Rim countries and is headquartered in Ewa Beach (near Honolulu), Hawaii. The tsunami warning system uses seismic waves—some of which travel through Earth at speeds 15 times faster than tsunami—to forecast destructive tsunami. In addition, oceanographers have recently established a network of sensitive pressure sensors on the deep-ocean floor of the Pacific. The program, called **Deep-ocean Assessment and Reporting of Tsunamis (DART)**, utilizes sea floor sensors that are capable of picking up the small yet distinctive pressure pulse from a tsunami passing above. The pressure sensors relay information to a buoy at the surface that transmits the data via satellite, allowing oceanographers to detect the passage of a tsunami in the open ocean (Figure 8.25). DART buoys, which are essential components of tsunami warning systems, have now been deployed in all oceans.

TSUNAMI WATCHES AND TSUNAMI WARNINGS When a seismic disturbance occurs beneath the ocean surface that is large enough to be tsunamigenic (capable of producing a tsunami), a *tsunami watch* is issued. At this point, a tsunami may or may not have been generated, but the potential for one exists.

The PTWC is linked to a series of sea floor pressure sensors, ocean buoys, and tide-measuring stations throughout the Pacific, so the recording stations nearest the earthquake are closely monitored for any indication of unusual wave activity. If unusual wave activity is verified, the tsunami watch is upgraded to a *tsunami warning*. Generally, earthquakes smaller than magnitude $M_w = 6.5$ are not tsunamigenic because they lack the duration of ground shaking necessary to initiate a tsunami. Additionally, transform faults do not usually produce tsunami because lateral movement does not offset the ocean floor and impart energy to the water column in the same way that vertical fault movements do.

WEB VIDEO
The 2004 Indian Ocean Tsunami

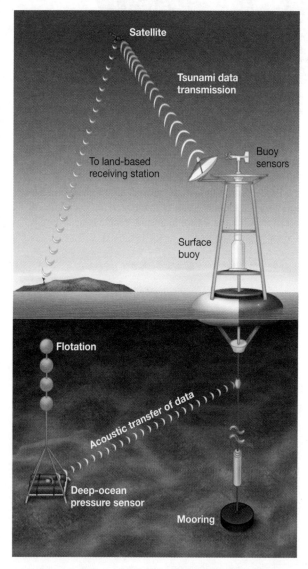

FIGURE 8.25 Deep-ocean Assessment and Reporting of Tsunamis (DART). The DART system consists of a deep-ocean pressure sensor that can detect a tsunami passing above. The pressure sensor relays information to a buoy at the surface that transmits the data via satellite, allowing oceanographers to detect the passage of a tsunami in the open ocean.

8.2 OCEANS AND PEOPLE

WAVES OF DESTRUCTION: THE 2004 INDIAN OCEAN TSUNAMI

On December 26, 2004, an enormous earthquake struck off the west coast of Sumatra in Indonesia. Known as the Sumatra–Andaman Earthquake, it was the second biggest earthquake recorded during the past century and the largest to be recorded by modern seismograph equipment. The earthquake was so large that it changed Earth's gravity field, triggered small earthquakes as far away as Alaska, and even altered Earth's rotation. Initially, it was deemed a magnitude $M_w = 9.0$, but it was subsequently upgraded to magnitude $M_w = 9.3$. The earthquake occurred about 30 kilometers (19 miles) beneath the sea floor near the Sunda Trench where the Indian Plate is being subducted beneath the Eurasian Plate. Moreover, about 1200 kilometers (750 miles) of sea floor was ruptured along the interface of these two tectonic plates, thrusting sea floor upward and generating about 10 meters (33 feet) of vertical displacement. This abrupt vertical movement of the sea floor is what generated the deadliest tsunami in history.

Once generated, the tsunami spread out at jetliner speeds across the Indian Ocean. Only 15 minutes after the earthquake, the tsunami hit the shores of Sumatra with a series of alternating rapid withdrawals and strong surges up to 35 meters (115 feet) high. Many coastal villages were completely washed away (Figure 8C), causing several hundred thousand deaths. Sites farther from the quake zone experienced smaller but nevertheless deadly waves. Particularly affected were Thailand (see Figure 8.22b), which was struck by the tsunami about 75 minutes after the quake occurred, and Sri Lanka and India, which were pounded by devastating waves about three hours after the earthquake. After seven hours and at a distance of more than 5000 kilometers (3000 miles), the tsunami hit the east coast of Africa, where it still had enough power to kill more than a dozen people.

Although much smaller, the tsunami was also detected in the Atlantic, Pacific, and Arctic Oceans.

In a remarkable coincidence, the Jason-1 satellite happened to be passing over the Indian Ocean two hours after the tsunami originated (Figure 8D). The satellite's radar altimeter, which is designed to accurately measure the elevation of the ocean surface (see Box 3.1), was able to detect the crests and troughs of the tsunami as it radiated out across the Indian Ocean with a wavelength of about 500 kilometers (300 miles). Although this sighting occurred about an hour before the first waves struck Sri Lanka and India, the satellite data couldn't have been used to warn tsunami victims because scientists needed several hours to analyze the information. However, these satellite data are particularly valuable because they will allow scientists to check the accuracy of open-ocean tsunami travel models, which are based on seismic

(a) Before: January 10, 2003

(b) After: December 29, 2004

FIGURE 8C Satellite views of tsunami destruction in Indonesia. High-resolution satellite images of Lhoknga, in the province of Aceh, west coast of Sumatra, Indonesia. **(a)** Before the tsunami, on January 10, 2003. **(b)** The same area on December 29, 2004, three days after the tsunami that inundated the city with a 15-meter (50-foot) surge of water. In both images, note the mosque (*white circular feature*), which was one of the few buildings that remained standing.

Continued on next page . . .

Continued from page 253...
data, bathymetric information, and coastal tide gauges.

In all, nearly 300,000 people in 11 countries were killed by the tsunami, ranking this tragedy as the most deadly tsunami in recorded history. The tsunami also caused billions of dollars of damage throughout the region and left millions homeless. Why was there such a large loss of life during the tsunami? One factor was the lack of a warning system in the Indian Ocean like the network of buoys and deep-sea instruments that monitors earthquake and wave activity in the Pacific Ocean, where most tsunami have historically occurred. Another is the lack of an emergency response system to warn beachgoers and coastal communities. Still another was the lack of good public awareness in recognizing the signs of an impending tsunami, such as when a rapid withdrawal of water is observed at the shore, which is caused by the trough of the tsunami arriving first and indicates that an equally strong surge of water will soon follow.

Studies of the effect of the tsunami on different coastlines suggest that those areas lacking protective coral reefs or mangroves received stronger surges. In many cases, the shape of the coastline as well as the geometry of the offshore sea floor affected the height of the tsunami and the amount of coastal destruction. Sediment cores reveal that several other large tsunami have occurred in the region during the past 1000 years.

On July 17, 2006, another strong earthquake—this time an $M_w = 7.7$ earthquake associated with faulting in the Java Trench off the southern coast of Java, Indonesia—triggered a 2-meter (6.6-foot) tsunami that killed more than 637 people, injured at least 600, and destroyed many coastal structures. This destruction near the area that experienced even greater damage from the 2004 tsunami emphasized the fact that the region still lacked a comprehensive tsunami warning system. In 2010, however, the Indian Ocean Tsunami Warning and Mitigation System became fully operational, with its network of deep-ocean pressure sensors, buoys, land seismographs, tidal gauges, data centers, and communications upgrades. With this new warning system in place and enhanced public education about what to do in the event of a tsunami, all countries bordering the Indian Ocean will be much better prepared for the destructive power of future tsunami.

FIGURE 8D Jason-1 satellite detects the Indian Ocean Tsunami. The Indian Ocean Tsunami was initiated by a large earthquake offshore Sumatra on December 26, 2004 (*red star*). By a fortuitous circumstance, the Jason-1 satellite passed over the Indian Ocean (*black line*) two hours after the tsunami was generated. Its radar altimeter detected the crests and troughs of the tsunami (*colors*), which showed a wave height of about 1 meter (3.3 feet) in the open ocean. The graph of the satellite's overpass (*below*) shows the difference between the measured sea level from satellite data (*black line*) and the modeled wave height (*blue curve*).

When a tsunami is detected, warnings are sent to all the coastal regions that might encounter the destructive wave, along with its estimated time of arrival. This warning, usually just a few hours in advance of the tsunami, makes it possible to evacuate people from low-lying areas and remove ships from harbors before the waves arrive. If the disturbance is nearby, however, there is not enough time to issue a warning because a tsunami travels so rapidly. Unlike hurricanes, whose high winds and waves threaten ships at sea and send them to the protection of a coastal harbor, a tsunami washes ships from their coastal moorings into the open ocean or onto shore. The best strategy during a tsunami warning is to move ships out of coastal harbors and into deep water, where tsunami are not easily felt.

EFFECTIVENESS OF TSUNAMI WARNINGS Since the PTWC was established in 1948, it has effectively prevented loss of life due to tsunami when people have heeded the evacuation warnings. Property damage, however, has increased as more buildings have been constructed close to shore. To combat the damage caused by tsunami, countries that are especially prone to tsunami, such as Japan, have invested in shoreline barriers, seawalls, and other coastal fortifications.

Perhaps one of the best strategies to limit tsunami damage and loss of life is to restrict construction projects in low-lying coastal regions where tsunami have frequently struck in the past. However, the long time interval between large tsunami can lead people to forget past disasters.

> **STUDENTS SOMETIMES ASK...**
>
> *If there is a tsunami warning issued, what is the best thing to do?*
>
> The *smartest* thing to do is to stay out of coastal areas, but people often want to see the tsunami firsthand. For instance, when an earthquake of magnitude $M_w = 7.7$ occurred offshore of Alaska in May 1986, a tsunami warning was issued for the West Coast of the United States. In Southern California, people flocked to the beach to observe the phenomenon. Fortunately, the tsunami was only a few centimeters high by the time it reached Southern California, so it went unnoticed. Since 1982, in fact, 16 tsunami warnings have been issued for U.S. shores.
>
> If you *must* go to the beach to observe a tsunami, expect crowds, road closings, and general mayhem. It would be a good idea to stay at least 30 meters (100 feet) above sea level. If you happen to be at a remote beach where the water suddenly withdraws, evacuate immediately to higher ground (Figure 8.26). And, if you happen to be at a beach where an earthquake occurs and shakes the ground so hard that you can't stand up, then *RUN*—don't walk—for high ground as soon as you *can* stand up!
>
> After the first surge of the tsunami, stay out of low-lying coastal areas for several hours because several more surges (and withdrawals) can be expected. There are many documented cases of curious people being killed when they were caught in the third or fourth (. . . or ninth) surge of a tsunami.

FIGURE 8.26 Tsunami warning sign. This tsunami warning sign in coastal Oregon advises residents to evacuate low-lying areas during a tsunami.

8.7 Can Power From Waves Be Harnessed as a Source of Energy?

Moving water has a huge amount of energy, which is why there are so many hydroelectric power plants on rivers. Even greater energy exists in ocean waves, but significant problems must be overcome for the power to be harnessed efficiently. For example, a serious obstacle to the use of any device to harness wave energy is the monumental engineering problem of preventing the devices from being destroyed by the wave force they are built to harness.

Another key disadvantage of wave energy is that the system produces significant power only when large storm waves break against it, so the system could serve only as a power supplement. In addition, a series of one hundred or more of these structures along the shore would be required. Structures of this type could have a significant impact on the environment, with negative effects on marine organisms that rely on wave energy for dispersal, transporting food supplies, or removing wastes. Also, harnessing wave energy might alter the transport of sand along the coast, causing erosion in areas deprived of sediment.

Still, the immense power contained in waves could be used for generating electricity. Offshore wave-generating plants would be able to tap into the higher wave energy found offshore, but they are more likely to be damaged in large waves and more difficult to maintain. The most promising locations for coastal

(a)

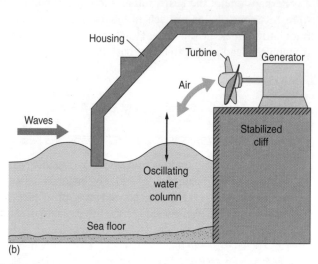

(b)

FIGURE 8.27 How a wave power plant works.
(a) LIMPET 500, the world's first commercial wave power plant. **(b)** Cutaway view of LIMPET 500, showing how the power plant generates electricity. As a wave advances into the power plant, it causes water to surge into the structure, forcing air out through a turbine. As the wave recedes, air is sucked back through the turbine. Electricity is generated as air moves both ways past the turbine as waves advance and recede.

power generation from waves are where waves refract (bend) and converge, such as at headlands, which tend to focus wave energy (see Figure 8.19b). Using this advantage, an array of wave power plants might extract up to 10 megawatts of power[8] per 1 kilometer (0.6 mile) of shoreline.

Internal waves are a potential source of energy, too. Along shores that have favorable sea floor shape for focusing wave energy, internal waves may be effectively concentrated by refraction and thus could power an energy-conversion device that generates electricity.

Wave Power Plants and Wave Farms

In 2000, the world's first commercial wave power plant began generating electricity. The small plant, called **LIMPET 500** (*L*and *I*nstalled *M*arine *P*owered *E*nergy *T*ransformer), is located on Islay, a small island off the west coast of Scotland. The plant was constructed at a cost of about $1.6 million and allows waves to compress air in a partially submerged chamber that, in turn, rotates a turbine for the generation of power (Figure 8.27). As waves recede, air is sucked back into the chamber and rotates the turbine in the other direction, which also generates power. Under peak operating capacity, the facility is capable of producing 500 kilowatts of power, which is capable of supplying the energy needs of about 400 average U.S. homes. Economic conditions in the future may lead to the construction of larger wave plants that are capable of using this renewable source of energy.

In 2008, Ocean Power Delivery completed the world's first wave farm off the coast of northern Portugal. This project uses three 150-meter- (500-foot-) long devices that resemble giant segmented snakes and float half-submerged in the ocean (Figure 8.28). As each segment surges up or down with the crest of an oncoming wave, its hydraulic power plant pumps a biodegradable hydraulic fluid through a turbine, thus generating electricity. These wave-energy devices are already supplying up to 2.25 megawatts of power to Portugal's electrical grid, with 25 more devices planned in the future.

Currently, about 50 wave-energy projects are in development at various sites around the world. These projects use different methods to harness wave power, including floats or submerged pistons that move up and down with each passing wave, tethered paddles that oscillate back and forth, and collection of water from breaking waves that overtops coastal structures and then using it to turn turbines as it returns to the ocean.

---

[8]Each megawatt of electricity is enough to serve the energy needs of about 800 average U.S. homes.

FIGURE 8.28 Harnessing the power of ocean waves. This wave energy device resembles a large segmented floating snake and is designed to flex as waves pass, thus generating electricity. A wave farm of three of these devices is currently generating electricity off northern Portugal, with 25 more planned.

Global Coastal Wave Energy Resources

Leading estimates suggest that the global resource for wave energy lies between 1 and 10 terawatts; the world currently produces about 12 terawatts from all sources. Where are the best places to develop additional wave power plants and wave farms? Figure 8.29 shows the average wave height experienced along coastal regions and indicates the sites most favorable for wave energy generation (*red areas*). The map shows that west-to-east movement of storm systems in the middle latitudes between 30 and 60 degrees north or south latitude causes the western coasts of continents to be struck by larger waves than eastern coasts. Thus, more wave energy is generally available along western than eastern shores. Furthermore, some of the largest waves (and greatest potential for wave power) are associated with the prevailing westerly wind belt in the middle latitude Southern Hemisphere.

KEY CONCEPT
Ocean waves produce large amounts of energy. Although significant problems exist in harnessing wave energy effectively, several types of devices are extracting wave energy today.

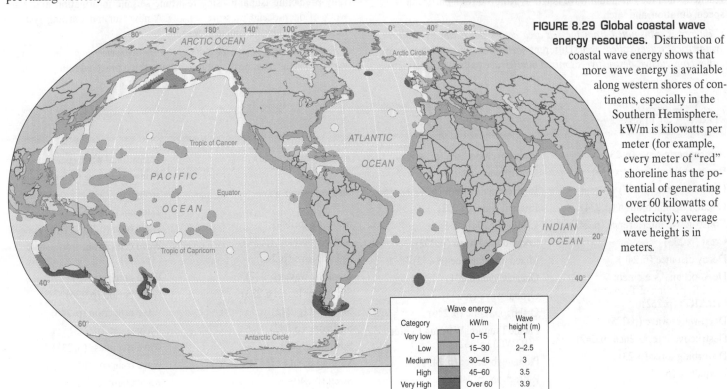

FIGURE 8.29 Global coastal wave energy resources. Distribution of coastal wave energy shows that more wave energy is available along western shores of continents, especially in the Southern Hemisphere. kW/m is kilowatts per meter (for example, every meter of "red" shoreline has the potential of generating over 60 kilowatts of electricity); average wave height is in meters.

	Wave energy	
Category	kW/m	Wave height (m)
Very low	0–15	1
Low	15–30	2–2.5
Medium	30–45	3
High	45–60	3.5
Very High	Over 60	3.9

Chapter in Review

• *All ocean waves begin as disturbances caused by releases of energy.* The releases of energy include wind, the movement of fluids of different densities (which create internal waves), mass movement into the ocean, underwater sea floor movements, the gravitational pull of the Moon and the Sun on Earth, and human activities in the ocean.

• Once initiated, *waves transmit energy through matter by setting up patterns of oscillatory motion* in the particles that make up the matter. Progressive waves are longitudinal, transverse, or orbital, depending on the pattern of particle oscillation. Particles in ocean waves move primarily in orbital paths.

• *Waves are described according to their wavelength* (L), *wave height* (H), *wave steepness* (H/L), *wave period* (T), *frequency* (f), *and wave speed* (S). As a wave travels, the water passes the energy along by moving in a circle, called *circular orbital motion.* This motion advances the waveform, not the water particles themselves. *Circular orbital motion decreases with depth,* ceasing entirely at wave base, which is equal to one-half the wavelength measured from still water level.

• If water depth is greater than one-half the wavelength, a progressive wave travels as a *deep-water wave with a speed that is directly proportional to wavelength.* If water depth is less than $\frac{1}{20}$ wavelength (*L*/20), the wave moves as a *shallow-water wave with a speed that is directly proportional to water depth. Transitional waves* have wavelengths between deep- and shallow-water waves, with speeds that depend on both wavelength and water depth.

• As wind-generated waves form in a sea area, *capillary waves* with rounded crests and wavelengths less than 1.74 centimeters (0.7 inch) *form first. As the energy of the waves increases, gravity waves form,* with increased wave speed, wavelength, and wave height. Factors that influence the size of wind-generated waves include wind *speed, duration* (time), and *fetch* (distance). An equilibrium condition called a *fully developed sea* is reached when the maximum wave height is achieved for a particular wind speed, duration, and fetch.

• *Energy is transmitted from the sea area across the ocean by uniform, symmetrical waves called swell.* Different wave trains of swell can create either *constructive, destructive,* or *mixed interference* patterns. Constructive interference produces unusually large waves called rogue waves or superwaves.

• *As waves approach shoaling water near shore, they undergo many physical changes.* Waves release their energy in the surf zone when their steepness exceeds a 1:7 ratio and break. If waves break on a relatively flat surface, they produce *spilling breakers.* The curling crests of *plunging breakers,* which are the best for surfing, form on steep slopes, and abrupt beach slopes create *surging breakers.*

• When swell approaches the shore, *segments of the waves that first encounter shallow water are slowed* whereas other segments of the wave in deeper water move at their original speed, *causing each wave to refract, or bend.* Refraction concentrates wave energy on headlands, while low-energy breakers are characteristic of bays.

• *Reflection of waves off seawalls or other barriers* can cause an interference pattern called a *standing wave.* The crests of standing waves do not move laterally as in progressive waves but alternate with troughs at antinodes. Between the antinodes are nodes, where there is no vertical movement of the water.

• *Sudden changes in the elevation of the sea floor, such as from fault movement or volcanic eruptions, generate tsunami, or seismic sea waves.* These waves often have lengths exceeding 200 kilometers (125 miles) and travel across the open ocean with undetectable heights of about 0.5 meter (1.6 feet) at speeds in excess of 700 kilometers (435 miles) per hour. Upon approaching shore, a tsunami produces a *series of rapid withdrawals and surges,* some of which may increase the height of sea level by 40 meters (131 feet) or more. *Most tsunami occur in the Pacific Ocean,* where they have caused millions of dollars of coastal damage and taken tens of thousands of lives. However, the *2004 Indian Ocean Tsunami killed nearly 300,000,* making it the most deadly tsunami in history. The *Pacific Tsunami Warning Center (PTWC)* has dramatically reduced fatalities by successfully predicting tsunami using real-time seismic information and a network of deep-ocean pressure sensors. A new tsunami warning system is being installed in the Indian Ocean.

• *Ocean waves can be harnessed to produce hydroelectric power,* but significant problems must be overcome to make this a practical source of energy.

Key Terms

Atmospheric wave (p. 231)

Beaufort Wind Scale (p. 238)

Capillary wave (p. 237)

Circular orbital motion (p. 234)

Constructive interference (p. 241)

Crest (p. 233)

Decay distance (p. 240)

Deep-ocean Assessment and Reporting of Tsunamis (DART) (p. 252)

Deep-water wave (p. 235)

Destructive interference (p. 242)

Disturbing force (p. 231)

Frequency (p. 234)

Fully developed sea (p. 240)

Gravity wave (p. 237)

Interference pattern (p. 240)

Internal wave (p. 232)

LIMPET 500 (p. 256)

Longitudinal wave (p. 232)

Mixed interference (p. 242)

Ocean wave (p. 231)

Orbital wave (p. 233)

Orthogonal line (p. 246)

Pacific Tsunami Warning Center (PTWC) (p. 252)

Plunging breaker (p. 245)

Refraction (p. 246)

Rogue wave (p. 243)

Sea (p. 238)

Shallow-water wave (p. 236)

Shoaling (p. 244)

Spilling breaker (p. 245)

Splash wave (p. 248)

Standing wave (p. 247)

Still water level (p. 233)

Surf beat (p. 242)

Surf zone (p. 242)

Surfing (p. 245)

Surging breaker (p. 245)

Swell (p. 240)

Transitional wave (p. 237)

Transverse wave (p. 233)

Trough (p. 233)

Tsunami (p. 248)

Wave base (p. 235)

Wave dispersion (p. 240)

Wave height (p. 233)

Wave period (p. 234)

Wave reflection (p. 246)

Wave speed (p. 235)

Wave steepness (p. 233)

Wave train (p. 240)

Wavelength (p. 233)

Review Questions

1. Discuss several different ways in which waves form. How are most ocean waves generated?

2. Why is the development of internal waves likely within the pycnocline?

3. Discuss longitudinal, transverse, and orbital wave phenomena, including the states of matter in which each can transmit energy.

4. Can a wave with a wavelength of 14 meters ever be more than 2 meters high? Why or why not?

5. What physical feature of a wave is related to the depth of the wave base? What is the difference between the *wave base* and *still water level*?

6. Calculate the speed (S) in meters per second for deep-water waves with the following characteristics:

    a. $L = 351$ meters, $T = 15$ seconds

    b. $T = 12$ seconds

    c. $f = 0.125$ wave per second

7. Define *swell*. Does swell necessarily imply a particular wave size? Why or why not?

8. Describe the physical changes that occur to a wave's wave speed (S), wavelength (L), height (H), and wave steepness (H/L) as a wave moves across shoaling water to break on the shore.

9. Describe the three different types of breakers and indicate the slope of the beach that produces the three types. How is the energy of the wave distributed differently within the surf zone by the three types of breakers?

10. Using examples, explain how wave refraction is different from wave reflection.

11. Using orthogonal lines, illustrate how wave energy is distributed along a shoreline with headlands and bays. Identify areas of high- and low-energy release.

12. Why is it more likely that a tsunami will be generated by faults beneath the ocean along which vertical rather than horizontal movement has occurred?

13. How large was the largest wave ever authentically recorded? Where did it occur, and how did it form?

14. While shopping in a surf shop, you overhear some surfing enthusiasts mention that they would really like to ride the curling wave of a tidal wave at least once in their life, because it is a single breaking wave of enormous height. What would you say to these surfers?

15. Explain what it would look like at the shoreline when the trough of a tsunami arrives there first. What is the impending danger?

16. Explain how the tsunami warning system in the Pacific Ocean works. Why must the tsunami be verified at the closest tide recording station?

17. Discuss some environmental problems that might result from developing facilities for conversion of wave energy to electrical energy.

Critical Thinking Exercises

1. Draw a diagram of a simple progressive wave. From memory, label the crest, trough, wavelength, wave height, wave base, and still water level.

2. Using the information about the giant waves experienced by the USS *Ramapo* in 1933, determine the waves' wavelength and speed.

3. Explain why the following statements for deep-water waves are either true or false:

    a. The longer the wave, the deeper the wave base.

    b. The greater the wave height, the deeper the wave base.

    c. The longer the wave, the faster the wave travels.

    d. The greater the wave height, the faster the wave travels.

    e. The faster the wave, the greater the wave height.

4. Waves from separate sea areas move away as swell and produce an interference pattern when they come together. If Sea A has wave heights of 1.5 meters (5 feet) and Sea B has wave heights of 3.5 meters (11.5 feet), what would be the height of waves resulting from constructive interference and destructive interference? Illustrate your answer (see Figure 8.15).

5. What ocean depth would be required for a tsunami with a wavelength of 220 kilometers (136 miles) to travel as a deep-water wave? Is it possible that such a wave could become a deep-water wave any place in the world ocean? Explain.

Oceanography on the Web

Visit the *Essentials of Oceanography* Online Study Guide for Internet resources, including chapter-specific quizzes to test your understanding and Web links to further your exploration of the topics in this chapter.

The *Essentials of Oceanography* Online Study Guide is at http://www.mygeoscienceplace.com/.

Extreme tidal variation.
High and low tides in a small harbor near Blomidon Provincial Park, Nova Scotia, Canada, demonstrate the dramatic change of sea level experienced daily in the Bay of Fundy, which has the world's largest tidal range.

"I derive from the celestial phenomena the forces of gravity with which bodies tend to the sun and several planets. Then from these forces, by other propositions which are also mathematical, I deduce the motions of the planets, the comets, the moon, and the sea."

—Sir Isaac Newton,
Philosophiae Naturalis Principia Mathematica
(Philosophy of Natural Mathematical Principles) (1686)

9 TIDES

Tides are the periodic raising and lowering of sea level that occurs daily throughout the ocean. As sea level rises and falls, the edge of the sea slowly shifts landward and seaward each day; as it rises, it often destroys sand castles that were built during low tide. Knowledge of tides is important in many coastal activities, including tide pooling, shell collecting, surfing, fishing, navigation, and preparing for storms. Tides are so important that accurate records have been kept at nearly every port for several centuries and there are many examples of the term *tide* in everyday vocabulary (for instance, "to tide someone over," "to go against the tide," or to wish someone "good tidings").

There is no doubt that early coastal peoples noticed the tides yet the earliest written record of tides is in about 450 B.C. Even the earliest sailors knew the Moon had some connection with the tides because both followed a similar pattern. For example, high tides were associated with either a full or new moon. However, it wasn't until **Isaac Newton** (1642–1727) developed the universal law of gravitation that the tides could adequately be explained.

Although the study of the tides can be complex, tides are fundamentally very long and regular shallow-water waves. As we shall see, their wavelengths are measured in thousands of kilometers and their heights range to more than 15 meters (50 feet).

9.1 What Causes the Tides?

Simplistically, the gravitational attraction of the Sun and Moon on Earth creates ocean tides. In a more complete analysis, tides are generated by forces imposed on Earth that are caused by a combination of *gravity* and *motion* among Earth, the Moon, and the Sun.

Tide-Generating Forces

Newton's work on quantifying the forces involved in the Earth–Moon–Sun system led to the first understanding of the underlying forces that keep bodies in orbit around each other. It is well known that gravity is the force that interconnects the Sun, its planets, and their moons and keeps them in relatively fixed orbits. For example, most of us are taught that "the Moon orbits Earth," but it is not quite that simple. The two bodies actually rotate around a common center of mass called the **barycenter** (*barus* = heavy, *center* = center), which is the *balance point* of the system, located 1600 kilometers (1000 miles) beneath Earth's surface (Figure 9.1a). Why isn't the barycenter halfway in between the two bodies? It's because Earth's mass is so much greater than that of the Moon. This can be visualized by imagining Earth and its Moon as ends of an object that is much heavier on one end than the other. A good example of this is a sledgehammer, which has a lighter handle and a much heavier head, with its balance point within the head of the hammer. Now imagine that the

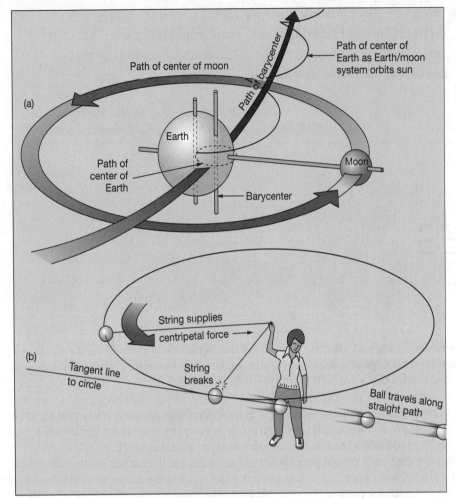

FIGURE 9.1 Earth–Moon system rotation. (a) The center of mass (*barycenter*) of the Earth–Moon system moves in a nearly circular orbit around the Sun. **(b)** If a ball with a string attached is swung overhead, it stays in a circular orbit because the string exerts a centripetal (center-seeking) force on the ball. If the string breaks, the ball will fly off along a straight path along a tangent to the circle.

WEB VIDEO

Tidal Change along a
Coast (Time Lapse)

sledgehammer is flung into space, tumbling slowly end over end about its balance point. This is exactly the situation that describes the movement of the Earth–Moon system. The purple arrow in Figure 9.1a shows the smooth, nearly circular path of the Earth–Moon barycenter around the Sun.

If the Moon and Earth are attracted to one another, why don't the two collide? Moreover, the Earth–Moon system is involved in a mutual orbit held together by gravity and motion, which prevents the Moon and Earth from colliding. This is how orbits are established that keep objects at more or less fixed distances.

Newton's work also allowed an understanding of why the tides behave as they do. Just as gravity and motion serve to keep bodies in mutual orbits, they also exert an influence on every particle of water on Earth, thus creating the tides.

GRAVITATIONAL AND CENTRIPETAL FORCES IN THE EARTH–MOON SYSTEM To understand how *tide-generating* forces influence the oceans, let's examine how *gravitational forces* and *centripetal forces* affect objects on Earth within the Earth–Moon system. (We'll ignore the influence of the Sun for the moment.)

The **gravitational force** is derived from **Newton's law of universal gravitation**, which states that *every object that has mass in the universe is attracted to every other object.* An object can be as small as an individual atomic particle or as large as a sun. The basic equation for this relationship is:

$$F_g = \frac{Gm_1m_2}{r^2} \qquad (9.1)$$

What this equation states is that the gravitational force (F_g) is directly proportional to the product of the masses of the two bodies (m_1, m_2) and is inversely proportional to the square of the distance between the two masses (r^2). Note that G is the gravitational constant, so it does not change.

Let's simplify Newton's law of universal gravitation and examine the effect of both mass and distance on the gravitational force, which can be expressed with arrows (up arrow = increase, down arrow = decrease):

If mass increases ($\uparrow$), then gravitational force increases ($\uparrow$).

A practical example of this can be seen in an object with a large mass (such as the Sun), which produces a large gravitational attraction (Figure 9.2a).

Looking at how distance influences gravitational force, the relationship is:

If distance increases ($\uparrow$), then gravitational force greatly decreases ($\downarrow\downarrow$).

Equation 9.1 shows that the gravitational attraction varies with the *square* of distance, so even a small *increase* in the distance between two objects significantly *decreases* the gravitational force between them, hence the double arrows in the distance relationship illustrated above. What this means is that when an object is twice as far away, the gravitational attraction is only one-quarter as strong. As a practical example, this is why astronauts experience weightlessness in space when they get far enough from Earth's gravitational pull (Figure 9.2b). In summary, then, the *greater* the mass of the objects and (especially) the *closer* they are together, the greater their gravitational attraction.

Figure 9.3 shows how gravitational forces for points on Earth (caused by the Moon) vary depending on their distances from the Moon. The greatest gravitational attraction (the longest arrow) is at Z, the **zenith** (*zenith* = a path over the head), which is the point closest to the Moon. The gravitational attraction is weakest at N, the **nadir** (*nadir* = opposite the zenith), which is the point farthest from the Moon. The direction of the gravitational attraction between most particles and the center of the Moon is at an angle relative to a line connecting the center of Earth and the Moon (Figure 9.3). This angle causes the force of gravitational attraction between each particle and the Moon to be slightly different.

The **centripetal** (*centri* = the center, *pet* = seeking) **force**[1] required to keep planets in their orbits is provided by the gravitational attraction between each of them and the Sun. Centripetal force connects an orbiting body to its parent, pulling the object *inward* toward the parent, "seeking the center" of its orbit. For example, if you tie a string to a ball and swing the ball around your head (Figure 9.1b), the string pulls the ball toward your hand. The string exerts a *centripetal force* on the ball, forcing the ball to *seek the center* of its orbit. If the string should break, the force is gone and the ball can no longer maintain its circular orbit. The ball flies off in a *straight* line,[2] *tangent* (*tangent* = touching) to the circle (Figure 9.1b).

The Earth and Moon are interconnected, too, not by strings but by gravity. Gravity provides the centripetal force that holds the Moon in its orbit around Earth. If all gravity in the solar system could be shut off, centripetal force would vanish, and the momentum of the celestial bodies would send them flying off into space along straight-line paths, tangent to their orbits.

RESULTANT FORCES Particles of identical mass rotate in identical-sized paths due to the Earth–Moon rotation system (Figure 9.4). Each particle requires an identical centripetal force to maintain it in its circular path. Gravitational

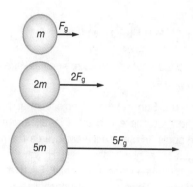

(a) The effect of mass on gravitational attraction

(b) The effect of distance on gravitational attraction

FIGURE 9.2 The relationship of gravitational force to mass and distance. (a) Gravitational force (F_g) is proportional to a body's mass; as mass increases, so does the gravitational force. **(b)** Gravitational forces between two bodies decrease rapidly as distance (r) increases.

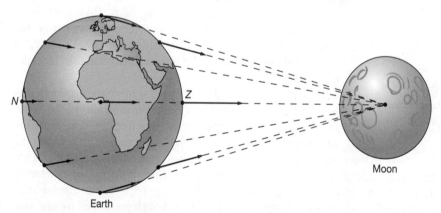

Moon

Earth

FIGURE 9.3 Gravitational forces on Earth due to the Moon. The gravitational forces on objects located at different places on Earth due to the Moon are shown by arrows. The length and orientation of the arrows indicate the strength and direction of the gravitational force. Notice the length and angular differences of the arrows for different points on Earth. The letter Z represents the zenith; N represents the nadir. Distance between Earth and Moon not shown to scale.

To Moon

FIGURE 9.4 Required centripetal (center-seeking) forces. Centripetal forces required to keep identical-sized particles in identical-sized orbits as a result of the rotation of the Earth–Moon system around its barycenter. Notice that the arrows are all the same length and are oriented in the same direction for all points on Earth. Z = zenith; N = nadir.

---

[1]This is not to be confused with the so-called *centrifugal* (*centri* = the center, *fug* = flee) *force*, an apparent or fictitious force that is oriented outward.

[2]At the moment that the string breaks, the ball will continue along a straight-line path, obeying Newton's first law of motion (the *law of inertia*), which states that moving objects follow straight-line paths until they are compelled to change that path by other forces.

Centripetal force
Gravitational attraction
Moon
Earth

→ Centripetal force
→ Gravitational attraction of moon
→ Resultant force

FIGURE 9.5 Resultant forces. Red arrows indicate centripetal forces (*C*), which are not equal to the black arrows that indicate gravitational attraction (*G*). The small blue arrows show resultant forces, which are established by constructing an arrow from the tip of the centripetal (*red*) arrow to the tip of the gravity (*black*) arrow and located where the red and black arrows begin. *Z* = zenith; *N* = nadir. Distance between Earth and Moon not shown to scale.

KEY CONCEPT
The tides are caused by an imbalance between the required centripetal and the provided gravitational forces acting on Earth. This difference produces residual forces, the horizontal component of which pushes ocean water into two equal tidal bulges on opposite sides of Earth.

attraction between the particle and the Moon supplies the centripetal force, but the *supplied* force is different than the *required* force (because gravitational attraction varies with distance from the Moon) except at the center of Earth. This difference creates tiny **resultant forces**, which are the mathematical difference between the two sets of arrows shown in Figures 9.3 and 9.4.

Figure 9.5 combines Figures 9.3 and Figure 9.4 to show that resultant forces are produced by the difference between the required centripetal (*C*) and supplied gravitational (*G*) forces. However, do not think that both of these forces are being applied to the points, because (*C*) is a force that would be required to keep the particles in a perfectly circular path, while (*G*) is the force actually provided for this purpose by gravitational attraction between the particles and the Moon. The resultant forces (*blue arrows*) are established by constructing an arrow from the tip of the centripetal (*red*) arrow to the tip of the gravity (*black*) arrow and located where the red and black arrows begin.

TIDE-GENERATING FORCES Resultant forces are small, averaging about one-millionth the magnitude of Earth's gravity. If the resultant force is vertical to Earth's surface, as it is at the zenith and nadir (oriented upward) and along an "equator" connecting all points halfway between the zenith and nadir (oriented downward), it has no tide-generating effect (Figure 9.6). However, if the resultant force has a significant *horizontal component*—that is, tangential to Earth's surface—it produces tidal bulges on Earth, creating what are known as the **tide-generating forces**. These tide-generating forces are quite small but reach their maximum value at points on Earth's surface at a "latitude" of 45 degrees relative to the "equator" between the zenith and nadir (Figure 9.6).

As previously discussed, gravitational attraction is inversely proportional to the *square* of the distance between two masses. The tide-generating force, however, is inversely proportional to the *cube* of the distance between each point on Earth and the *center* of the tide-generating body (Moon or Sun). Although the tide-generating force is derived from the gravitational force, it is not linearly proportional to it. As a result, distance is a more highly weighted variable for tide-generating forces.

The tide-generating forces push water into two simultaneous bulges: one on the side of Earth directed *toward* the Moon (the zenith) and the other on the side directed *away from* the Moon (the nadir) (Figure 9.7). On the side directly facing the Moon, the bulge is created because the provided gravitational force is greater than the required centripetal force. Conversely, on the side facing away from the Moon, the bulge is created because the required centripetal force is greater than the provided gravitational force. Although the forces are oriented in opposite directions on the two sides of Earth, the resultant forces are equal in magnitude, so the bulges are equal, too.

Tidal Bulges: The Moon's Effect

It is easier to understand how tides on Earth are created if we consider an ideal Earth and an ideal ocean. The ideal Earth has two tidal bulges, one toward the Moon and one away from the Moon (called the **lunar bulges**), as shown in Figure 9.7. The ideal ocean has a uniform depth, with no friction between the seawater and the sea floor. Newton made these same simplifications when he first explained Earth's tides.

If the Moon is stationary and aligned with the ideal Earth's equator, the maximum bulge will occur on the equator on opposite sides of Earth. If you were standing on the equator, you would experience two high tides each day. The time between high tides, which is the **tidal period**, would be 12 hours. If you moved to any latitude north or south of the equator, you would experience the same tidal period, but the high tides would be less high, because you would be at a lower point on the bulge.

In most places on Earth, however, high tides occur every 12 hours 25 minutes because tides depend on the lunar day, not the solar day. The **lunar day** (also called a *tidal day*) is measured from the time the Moon is on the meridian of an observer—that is, directly overhead—to the next time the Moon is on that meridian and is 24 hours 50 minutes.[3] The **solar day** is measured from the time the Sun is on the meridian of an observer to the next time the Sun is on that meridian and is 24 hours. Why is the lunar day 50 minutes longer than the solar day? During the 24 hours it takes Earth to make a full rotation, the Moon has continued moving another 12.2 degrees to the east in its orbit around Earth (Figure 9.8). Thus, Earth must rotate an additional 50 minutes to "catch up" to the Moon so that the Moon is again on the meridian (directly overhead) of our observer.

The difference between a solar day and a lunar day can be seen in some of the natural phenomena related to the tides. For example, alternating high tides are normally 50 minutes *later* each successive day and the Moon rises 50 minutes *later* each successive night.

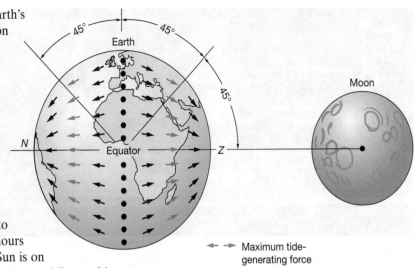

FIGURE 9.6 Tide-generating forces. Where the resultant force acts vertically relative to Earth's surface, the tide-generating force is zero. This occurs at the zenith (*Z*) and nadir (*N*), and along an "equator" connecting all points halfway between the zenith and nadir (*black dots*). However, where the resultant force has a significant *horizontal component*, it produces a tide-generating force on Earth. These tide-generating forces reach their maximum value at points on Earth's surface at a "latitude" of 45 degrees (*blue arrows*) relative to the "equator" mentioned here. Distance between Earth and Moon not shown to scale.

Tidal Bulges: The Sun's Effect

The Sun affects the tides, too. Like the Moon, the Sun produces tidal bulges on opposite sides of Earth, one oriented *toward* the Sun and one oriented *away from* the Sun. These **solar bulges**, however, are much smaller than the lunar bulges. Although the Sun is 27 million times more massive than the Moon, its tide-generating force is not 27 million times greater than the Moon's. This is because the Sun is 390 times farther from Earth than the Moon (Figure 9.9). Moreover, tide-generating forces vary inversely as the *cube* of the distance between objects. Thus, the tide-generating force is reduced by the cube of 390, or about 59 million times compared with that of the Moon. These conditions result in the Sun's tide-generating force being $^{27}/_{59}$ that of the Moon, or 46% (about one-half). Consequently, the solar bulges are only 46% the size of the lunar bulges and, as a result, the Moon exerts over two times the gravitational pull of the Sun on the tides.

Even though the Moon exerts over two times the gravitational pull of the Sun on Earth's tides, note that the Sun does not exert a smaller gravitational force on Earth as compared to the Moon. In fact, the Sun's total "pull" on all points on Earth is much greater than that of the Moon's, but the *difference* across Earth is small because the diameter of Earth is very small in relation to the distance from the Sun. In contrast, the diameter of Earth is quite large in relation to the distance to the center of the Moon. In summary, the reason why the Moon controls tides far more than the Sun is because the Moon is much closer to Earth, although it is much smaller in size and mass as compared to the Sun.

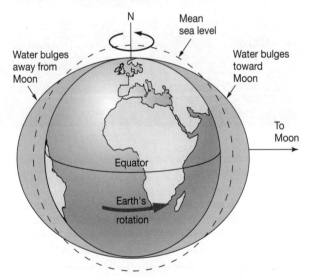

FIGURE 9.7 Idealized tidal bulges. In an idealized case, the Moon creates two bulges in the ocean surface: one that extends *toward* the Moon and the other *away from* the Moon. As Earth rotates, it carries various locations into and out of the two tidal bulges so that all points on its surface (except the poles) experience two high tides daily.

> **KEY CONCEPT**
> A solar day (24 hours) is shorter than a lunar day (24 hours and 50 minutes). The extra 50 minutes is caused by the Moon's movement in its orbit around Earth.

---

[3]A lunar day is exactly 24 hours, 50 minutes, 28 seconds long.

FIGURE 9.8 **The lunar day.** A lunar day is the time that
elapses between when the Moon is directly overhead and
the next time the Moon is directly overhead. During one
complete rotation of Earth (the 24-hour solar day), the
Moon moves eastward 12.2 degrees, and Earth must rotate
an additional 50 minutes for the Moon to be in the exact
same position overhead. Thus, a lunar day is 24 hours
50 minutes long.

Earth's Rotation and the Tides

The tides appear to move water in toward shore (the **flood tide**) and to move
water away from shore (the **ebb tide**). However, according to the nature of the
idealized tides presented so far, *Earth's rotation carries various locations into and
out of the tidal bulges,* which are in fixed positions relative to the Moon and the
Sun. In essence, alternating high and low tides are created as
Earth constantly rotates inside fluid bulges that are supported by the Moon and the Sun.

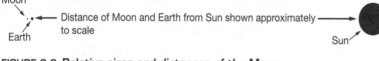

FIGURE 9.9 **Relative sizes and distances of the Moon,
Earth, and Sun.** *Top:* The relative sizes of the Moon, Earth,
and Sun, showing the diameter of the Moon is roughly one-
fourth that of Earth, while the diameter of the Sun is 109 times
the diameter of Earth. *Bottom:* The relative distances of the
Moon, Earth, and Sun are shown to scale.

9.2 How Do Tides Vary During a Monthly Tidal Cycle?

The monthly tidal cycle is 29½ days because that's how long it
takes the Moon to complete an orbit around Earth.[4] During
its orbit around Earth, the Moon's changing position influences tidal conditions on Earth.

The Monthly Tidal Cycle

During the monthly tidal cycle, the phase of the Moon
changes dramatically. When the Moon is between Earth and
the Sun, it cannot be seen at night; this phase is called **new
moon**. When the Moon is on the side of Earth opposite the Sun, its entire disk is
brightly visible; this phase is called **full moon**. A **quarter moon**—a moon that is
half lit and half dark as viewed from Earth—occurs when the Moon is at right angles to the Sun relative to Earth.

Figure 9.10 shows the positions of the Earth, Moon, and Sun at various points
during the 29½-day lunar cycle. When the Sun and Moon are aligned, either with
the Moon between Earth and the Sun (new moon; Moon in *conjunction*) or with
the Moon on the side opposite the Sun (full moon; Moon in *opposition*), the tide-
generating forces of the Sun and Moon combine (Figure 9.10, *top*). At this time,
the **tidal range** (the vertical difference between high and low tides) is large (very
high high tides and quite *low* low tides) because there is *constructive interference*[5]
between the lunar and solar tidal bulges. The maximum tidal range is called

---

[4]The 29½-day monthly tidal cycle is also called a *lunar cycle,* a *lunar month,* or a *synodic (synod =
meeting) month.*

[5]As mentioned in Chapter 8, *constructive interference* occurs when two waves (or, in this case, two
tidal bulges) overlap crest to crest and trough to trough.

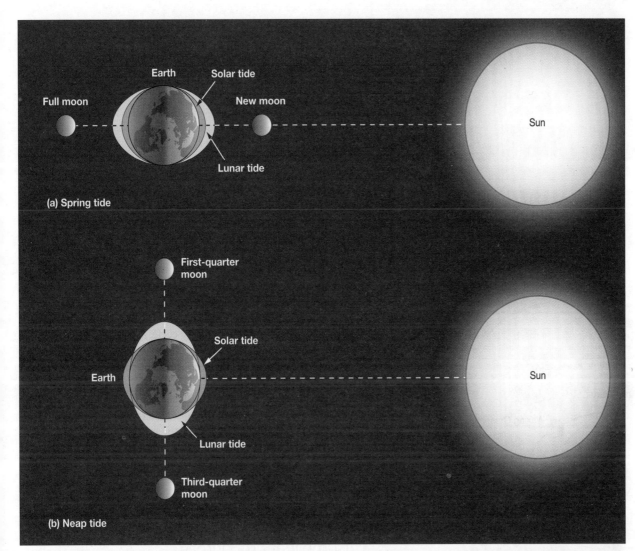

(a) Spring tide

(b) Neap tide

FIGURE 9.10 Earth–Moon–Sun positions and the tides.
Top: When the Moon is in the new or full position, the tidal bulges created by the Sun and Moon are aligned, there is a large tidal range on Earth, and spring tides are experienced. *Bottom:* When the Moon is in the first- or third-quarter position, the tidal bulges produced by the Moon are at right angles to the bulges created by the Sun. Tidal ranges are smaller and neap tides are experienced. Note that there is only one moon in orbit around Earth.

Monthly Tidal Cycle

a **spring** (*springen* = to rise up) **tide**,[6] because the tide is extremely large or "springs forth." When the Earth–Moon–Sun system is aligned, the Moon is said to be in **syzygy** (*syzygia* = union).

When the Moon is in either the first- or third-quarter[7] phase (Figure 9.10, *bottom*), the tide-generating force of the Sun is working at right angles to the tide-generating force of the Moon. The tidal range is small (*lower* high tides and *higher* low tides) because there is *destructive interference*[8] between the lunar and solar tidal bulges. This is called a **neap** (*nep* = scarcely or barely touching) **tide**,[9] and the Moon is said to be in **quadrature** (*quadra* = four).

The time between successive spring tides (full moon and new moon) or neap tides (first quarter and third quarter) is one-half the monthly lunar cycle, which is about two weeks. The time between a spring tide and a successive neap tide is one-quarter the monthly lunar cycle, which is about one week.

[6]Spring tides have no connection with the spring season; they occur twice a month during the time when the Earth–Moon–Sun system is aligned.

[7]The third-quarter moon is often called the last-quarter moon, which is not to be confused with certain sports that have a fourth quarter.

[8]*Destructive interference* occurs when two waves (or, in this case, two tidal bulges) match up crest to trough and trough to crest.

[9]To help you remember a *neap tide*, think of it as one that has been *"nipped in the bud,"* indicating a small tidal range.

KEY CONCEPT
Spring tides occur during the full and new moon, when the lunar and solar tidal bulges constructively interfere, producing a large tidal range. Neap tides occur during the quarter moon phases, when the lunar and solar tidal bulges destructively interfere, producing a small tidal range.

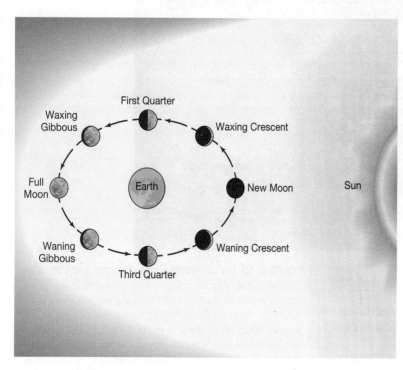

FIGURE 9.11 Phases of the Moon. As the Moon moves around Earth during its 29½-day lunar cycle, its phase changes depending on its position relative to the Sun and Earth. During a new moon, the dark side of the Moon faces Earth while during a full moon, the lit side of the Moon faces Earth. Moon phases are shown diagrammatically as seen from Earth.

Figure 9.11 shows the pattern that the Moon experiences as it moves through its monthly cycle. As the Moon progresses from new moon to first-quarter phase, the Moon is a **waxing crescent** (*waxen* = to increase; *crescere* = to grow). In between the first-quarter and full moon phase, the Moon is a **waxing gibbous** (*gibbus* = hump). Between the Moon's full and third-quarter phase, it is a **waning gibbous** (*wanen* = to decrease). And, in between the third-quarter and new moon phase, the Moon is a **waning crescent**. The Moon has identical periods of rotation on its axis and revolution around Earth (a property called *synchronous rotation*). As a result, the same side of the Moon always faces Earth.

Complicating Factors

Besides Earth's rotation and the relative positions of the Moon and the Sun, there are many other factors that influence tides on Earth. Two of the most prominent of these factors are the declination of the Moon and Sun and the elliptical shapes of Earth's and the Moon's orbits. Let's examine both of these factors.

DECLINATION OF THE MOON AND SUN Up to this point, we have assumed that the Moon and Sun have remained directly overhead at the equator, but this is not usually the case. Most of the year, in fact, they are either north or south of the equator. The angular distance of the Sun or Moon above or below Earth's equatorial plane is called **declination** (*declinare* – to turn away).

Earth revolves around the Sun along an invisible ellipse in space. The imaginary plane that contains this ellipse is called the **ecliptic** (*ekleipein* = to fail to appear). Recall from Chapter 6 that Earth's axis of rotation is tilted 23.5 degrees with respect to the ecliptic and that this tilt causes Earth's seasons. It also means the maximum declination of the Sun relative to Earth's equator is 23.5 degrees.

To complicate matters further, the plane of the Moon's orbit is tilted 5 degrees with respect to the ecliptic. Thus, the maximum declination of the Moon's orbit relative to Earth's equator is 28.5 degrees (5 degrees plus the 23.5 degrees of Earth's tilt). The declination changes from 28.5 degrees south to 28.5 degrees north and back to 28.5 degrees south of the equator during the multiple lunar cycles within one year. As a result, tidal bulges are rarely aligned with the equator. Instead, they occur mostly north and south of the equator. The Moon affects

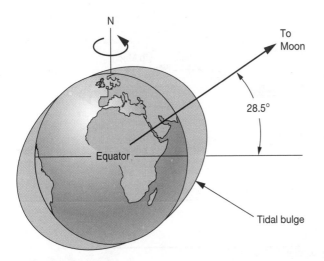

FIGURE 9.12 Maximum declination of tidal bulges from the equator. The center of the tidal bulges may lie at any latitude from the equator to a maximum of 28.5 degrees on either side of the equator, depending on the season of the year (solar angle) and the Moon's position.

Earth's tides more than the Sun, so tidal bulges follow the Moon, ranging from a maximum of 28.5 degrees north to a maximum of 28.5 degrees south of the equator (Figure 9.12).

EFFECTS OF ELLIPTICAL ORBITS   Earth revolves around the Sun in an elliptical orbit (Figure 9.13) such that Earth is 148.5 million kilometers (92.2 million miles) from the Sun during the Northern Hemisphere winter and 152.2 million kilometers (94.5 million miles) from the Sun during summer. Thus, the distance between Earth and the Sun varies by 2.5% over the course of a year. Tidal ranges are largest when Earth is near its closest point, called **perihelion** (*peri* = near, *helios* = Sun) and smallest near its most distant point, called **aphelion** (*apo* = away from, *helios* = Sun). Thus, the greatest tidal ranges typically occur in January each year.

The Moon revolves around Earth in an elliptical orbit, too. The Earth–Moon distance varies by 8% (between 375,000 kilometers [233,000 miles] and 405,800 kilometers [252,000 miles]). Tidal ranges are largest when the Moon is closest to Earth, called **perigee** (*peri* = near, *geo* = Earth), and smallest when most distant, called **apogee** (*apo* = away from, *geo* = Earth) (Figure 9.13, *top*). The Moon cycles between perigee, apogee, and back to perigee every 27½ days. Spring tides happen to coincide with perigee about every one and a half years, producing **proxigean** (*proximus* = nearest, *geo* = Earth) or "closest of the close moon" tides. During this time, the tidal range is especially large and often results in the flooding of low-lying coastal areas; if a storm occurs simultaneously, damage can be extreme. In 1962, for example, a winter storm that occurred at the same time as a proxigean tide caused widespread damage along the entire U.S. East Coast.

The elliptical orbits of Earth around the Sun and the Moon around Earth change the distances between Earth, the Moon, and

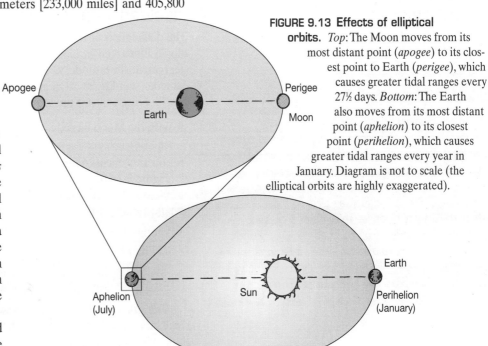

FIGURE 9.13 Effects of elliptical orbits. *Top:* The Moon moves from its most distant point (*apogee*) to its closest point to Earth (*perigee*), which causes greater tidal ranges every 27½ days. *Bottom:* The Earth also moves from its most distant point (*aphelion*) to its closest point (*perihelion*), which causes greater tidal ranges every year in January. Diagram is not to scale (the elliptical orbits are highly exaggerated).

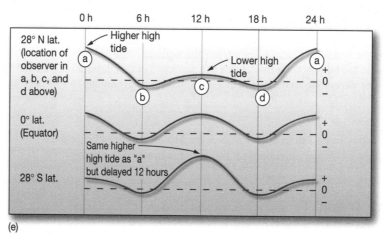

FIGURE 9.14 Predicted idealized tides. (a)—(d) Sequence showing the tide experienced every 6 lunar hours at 28 degrees north latitude when the declination of the Moon is 28 degrees north. (e) Tide curves for 28 degrees north, 0 degrees, and 28 degrees south latitudes during the lunar day shown in the sequence above. The tide curves for 28 degrees north and 28 degrees south latitude show that the higher high tides occur 12 hours later.

the Sun, thus affecting Earth's tides. The net result is that spring tides have greater ranges during the Northern Hemisphere winter than in the summer, and spring tides have greater ranges when they coincide with perigee.

Idealized Tide Prediction

The declination of the Moon determines the position of the tidal bulges. The example illustrated in Figure 9.14 shows that the Moon is directly overhead at 28 degrees north latitude when its declination is 28 degrees north of the equator. Imagine standing at 28 degrees north latitude and experiencing tidal conditions during a day, which is the sequence shown in Figure 9.14a-d:

- With the Moon directly overhead, the tidal conditions experienced will be high tide (Figure 9.14a).
- Low tide occurs 6 lunar hours later (6 hours 12½ minutes solar time) (Figure 9.14b).
- Another high tide, but one much lower than the first, occurs 6 lunar hours later (Figure 9.14c).
- Another low tide occurs 6 lunar hours later (Figure 9.14d).
- Six lunar hours later, at the end of a 24-lunar-hour period (24 hours 50 minutes solar time), you will have passed through a complete lunar-day cycle of two high tides and two low tides (returns to Figure 9.14a).

The graphs in Figure 9.14e show the heights of the tides observed during the same lunar day at 28 degrees north latitude, the equator, and 28 degrees south latitude when the declination of the Moon is 28 degrees north of the equator. Tide curves for 28 degrees north and 28 degrees south latitude have identically timed highs and lows, but the *higher* high tides and *lower* low tides occur 12 hours later. The reason that they occur out of phase by 12 hours is because the bulges in the two hemispheres are on opposite sides of Earth in relation to the Moon. Web Table 9.1 summarizes the characteristics of the tides on the idealized Earth.

9.3 What Do Tides Really Look Like in the Ocean?

If tidal bulges are wave crests separated by a distance of one-half Earth's circumference—about 20,000 kilometers (12,420 miles)—one would expect the bulges to move across Earth at about 1600 kilometers (1000 miles) per hour. Tides, however, are an extreme example of shallow-water waves, so their speed is proportional to the water depth. For a tide wave to travel at 1600 kilometers (1000 miles) per hour, the ocean would have to be 22 kilometers (13.7 miles) deep! Instead, the average depth of the ocean is only 3.7 kilometers (2.3 miles), so tidal bulges move as *shallow-water waves*, with their speed determined by ocean depth.

Based on the average ocean depth, the average speed at which tide waves can travel across the open ocean is only about 700 kilometers (435 miles) per hour. Thus, the idealized bulges that are oriented toward and away from a tide-generating body cannot exist because they cannot keep up with the rotational speed of Earth. Instead, ocean tides break up into distinct large circulation units called *cells*.

Amphidromic Points and Cotidal Lines

In the open ocean, the crests and troughs of the tide wave rotate around an **amphidromic** (*amphi* = around, *dromus* = running) **point** near the center of each cell. There is essentially no tidal range at amphidromic points, but radiating from each point are **cotidal** (*co* = with, *tidal* = tide) **lines**, which connect all nearby locations where high tide occurs simultaneously. The labels on the cotidal lines in Figure 9.15 indicate the time of high tide in hours as they rotate around the cell.

The times in Figure 9.15 indicate that the tide wave rotates counterclockwise in the Northern Hemisphere and clockwise in the Southern Hemisphere. The wave must complete one rotation during the tidal period (usually 12 lunar hours), so this limits the size of the cells.

Low tide occurs 6 hours after high tide in an amphidromic cell. If high tide is occurring along the cotidal line labeled "10," for example, then low tide is occurring along the cotidal line labeled "4."

Effect of the Continents

The continents affect tides, too, because they interrupt the free movement of the tidal bulges across the ocean surface. Tides are expressed in each ocean basin as free-standing waves that are affected by the position and shape of the continents that ring the ocean basin. In fact, two of the most important factors that influence tidal conditions along a coast are coastline shape and offshore depth.

Just like surface waves that undergo physical changes as they move into shallow water (such as slowing down and increasing in height; see Chapter 8), tides experience similar physical changes as they enter the shallow water of continental shelves. These changes tend to amplify the tidal range as compared to the deep ocean, where the maximum tidal range is only about 45 centimeters (18 inches).

In addition, increased turbulent mixing rates in deep water over areas of rough bottom topography (as discussed in Chapter 7) are associated with internal waves created by tides breaking on this rough topography and against continental slopes. These tide-generated internal waves have recently been observed along

FIGURE 9.15 Cotidal map of the world. Cotidal lines indicate times of the main lunar daily high tide in lunar hours after the Moon has crossed the Greenwich Meridian (0 degrees longitude). Tidal ranges generally increase with increasing distance along cotidal lines away from the amphidromic points (center of the cell). Where cotidal lines terminate at both ends in amphidromic points, maximum tidal range will be near the midpoints of the lines.

Tidal Patterns

the chain of Hawaiian Islands, have heights of up to 300 meters (1000 feet), and contribute to increased turbulence and mixing, which strongly affect the tides.

Other Considerations

A detailed analysis of all the variables that affect the tides at any particular coast reveals that nearly 400 factors are involved, which are far more than can adequately be addressed here. The combination of all these factors creates some conditions that are unexpected based on a simple tidal model. For example, high tide rarely occurs when the Moon is at its highest point in the sky. Instead, the time between the Moon crossing the meridian and a corresponding high tide varies from place to place.

Because of the complexity of the tides, a completely mathematical model of the tides is beyond the limits of marine science. Instead, a combination of mathematical analysis and observation is required to adequately model the tides. Moreover, successful models must take into account at least 37 independent factors related to tides (the two most important are the Moon and the Sun) and are usually quite successful in predicting future tides.

9.4 What Types of Tidal Patterns Exist?

In theory, most areas on Earth should experience two high tides and two low tides of unequal heights during a lunar day. In practice, however, the various depths, sizes, and shapes of ocean basins modify tides so they exhibit three different patterns in different parts of the world. The three tidal patterns, which are illustrated in

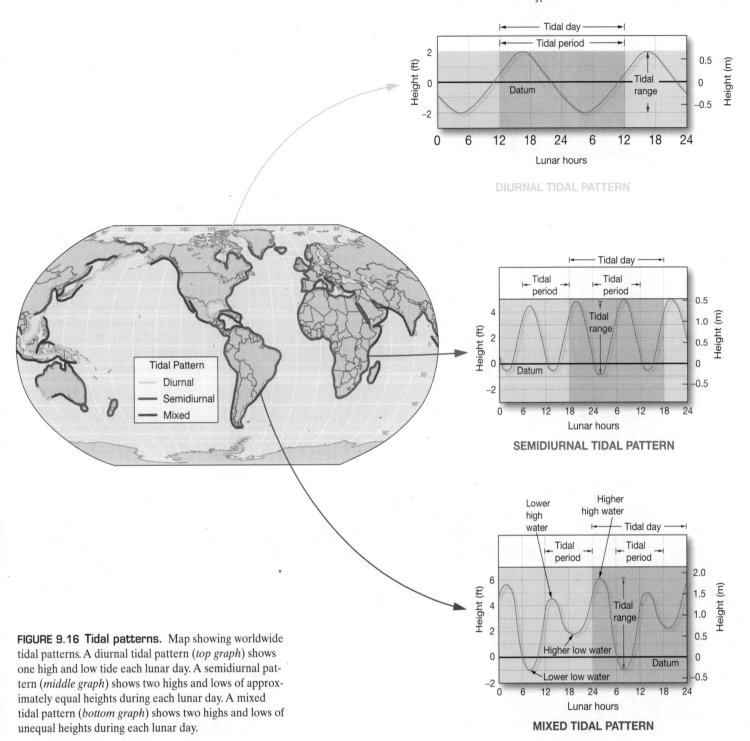

FIGURE 9.16 Tidal patterns. Map showing worldwide tidal patterns. A diurnal tidal pattern (*top graph*) shows one high and low tide each lunar day. A semidiurnal pattern (*middle graph*) shows two highs and lows of approximately equal heights during each lunar day. A mixed tidal pattern (*bottom graph*) shows two highs and lows of unequal heights during each lunar day.

Figure 9.16, are *diurnal* (*diurnal* = daily) *semidiurnal* (*semi* = twice, *diurnal* = daily) and *mixed*.[10]

Diurnal Tidal Pattern

A **diurnal tidal pattern** has one high tide and one low tide each lunar day. These tides are common in shallow inland seas such as the Gulf of Mexico and along the coast of Southeast Asia. Diurnal tides have a tidal period of 24 hours 50 minutes.

[10]Sometimes a *mixed* tidal pattern is referred to as *mixed semidiurnal*.

KEY CONCEPT

A diurnal tidal pattern exhibits one high and one low tide each lunar day; a semidiurnal tidal pattern exhibits two high and two low tides daily of about the same height; a mixed tidal pattern usually has two high and two low tides of different heights daily but may also exhibit diurnal characteristics.

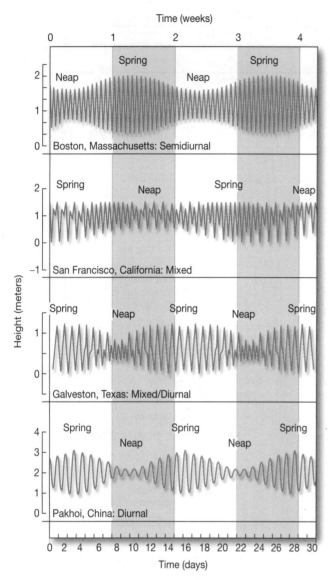

FIGURE 9.17 Monthly tidal curves. *Top*: Boston, Massachusetts, showing a semidiurnal tidal pattern. *Upper middle*: San Francisco, California, showing a mixed tidal pattern. *Lower middle*: Galveston, Texas, showing a mixed tidal pattern with strong diurnal tendencies. *Bottom*: Pakhoi, China, showing a diurnal tidal pattern.

Semidiurnal Tidal Pattern

A **semidiurnal tidal pattern** has two high tides and two low tides each lunar day. The heights of successive high tides and successive low tides are approximately the same.[11] Semidiurnal tides are common along the Atlantic Coast of the United States. The tidal period is 12 hours 25 minutes.

Mixed Tidal Pattern

A **mixed tidal pattern** may have characteristics of both diurnal and semidiurnal tides. Successive high tides and/or low tides will have significantly different heights, a condition called *diurnal inequality*. Mixed tides commonly have a tidal period of 12 hours 25 minutes, but they may also exhibit diurnal periods. Mixed tides are the most common type in the world, including along the Pacific Coast of North America.

Figure 9.17 shows examples of monthly tidal curves for various coastal locations. Even though a tide at any particular location follows a single tidal pattern, it still may pass through stages of one or both of the other tidal patterns. Typically, however, the tidal pattern for a location remains the same throughout the year. Also, the tidal curves in Figure 9.17 clearly show the weekly switching of the spring tide-neap tide cycle.

9.5 What Tidal Phenomena Occur in Coastal Regions?

Remember that the tides are fundamentally a wave. When tide waves enter coastal waters, they are subject to reflection and amplification similar to what wind-generated waves experience. In certain locations, reflected wave energy causes water to slosh around in a bay, producing *standing waves*.[12] As a result, interesting tidal phenomena are sometimes experienced in coastal waters.

Large lakes and coastal rivers experience tidal phenomena, too. In some low-lying rivers, for instance, a *tidal bore* is produced by an incoming high tide (Box 9.1). Further, the tides profoundly affect the behavior of certain marine organisms (Box 9.2).

An Example of Tidal Extremes: The Bay of Fundy

The largest tidal range in the world is found in Nova Scotia's **Bay of Fundy**. With a length of 258 kilometers (160 miles), the Bay of Fundy has a wide opening into the Atlantic Ocean. At its northern end, however, it splits into two narrow basins, Chignecto Bay and Minas Basin (Figure 9.18). The period of free oscillation in the bay—the oscillation that occurs when a body is displaced and then released—is very nearly that of the tidal period. The resulting constructive interference—along with the narrowing and shoaling of the bay to the north—causes a buildup of tidal energy in the northern end of the bay. In addition, the bay curves to the right, so the Coriolis effect in the Northern Hemisphere adds to the extreme tidal range.

---

[11]Because tides are always growing higher or lower at any location due to the spring tide-neap tide sequence, successive high tides and successive low tides can never be *exactly* the same at any location.

[12]See Chapter 8 for a discussion of standing waves, including the terms *node* and *antinode*.

TIDAL BORES: BORING WAVES THESE ARE NOT!

A **tidal bore** (*bore* = crest or wave) is a wall of water that moves up certain low-lying rivers due to an incoming tide. Because it is a wave created by the tides, it is a *true* tidal wave. When an incoming tide rushes up a river, it develops a steep forward slope because the flow of the river resists the advance of the tide (Figure 9A). This creates a tidal bore, which may reach heights of 5 meters (16.4 feet) or more and move at speeds up to 24 kilometers (15 miles) per hour.

Conditions necessary for the development of tidal bores include (1) a large spring tidal range of at least 6 meters (20 feet); (2) a tidal cycle that has a very abrupt rise of the flood tide phase and an elongated ebb tide phase; (3) a low-lying river with a persistent seaward current during the time when an incoming high tide begins; (4) a progressive shallowing of the sea floor as the basin progresses inland; and (5) a progressive narrowing of the basin toward its upper reaches. Because of these unique circumstances, only about 60 places on Earth experience tidal bores.

Although tidal bores do not commonly attain the size of waves in the surf zone, tidal bores have successfully been rafted, kayaked, and even surfed (Figure 9B). They can give a surfer a very long ride because the bore travels many kilometers upriver. If you miss the bore, though, you have to wait about half a day before the next one comes along because the incoming high tide occurs only twice a day.

The Amazon River is probably the longest estuary affected by oceanic tides: Tides can be measured as far as 800 kilometers (500 miles) from the river's mouth, although the effects are quite small at this distance. Tidal bores near the mouth of the Amazon River can reach heights up to 5 meters (16.4 feet) and are locally called *pororocas*—the name means "mighty noise." Other rivers that have notable tidal bores include the Qiantang River in China (which has the largest tidal bores in the world, often reaching 8 meters [26 feet] high); the Petitcodiac River in New Brunswick, Canada; the River Seine in France; the Trent and Severn Rivers in England; and Cook Inlet near Anchorage, Alaska (where the largest tidal bore in the United States can be found). Although the Bay of Fundy has the world's largest tidal range, its tidal bore rarely exceeds 1 meter (3.3 feet), mostly because the bay is so wide.

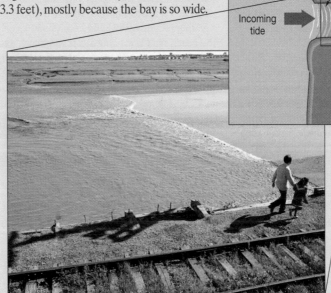

FIGURE 9A How a tidal bore forms (*figure*) and a tidal bore moving quickly upriver near Chignecto Bay, New Brunswick, Canada (*photo*).

FIGURE 9B Brazilian surf star Alex "Picuruta" Salazar tidal bore surfing on the Amazon River.

GRUNION: DOING WHAT COMES NATURALLY ON THE BEACH

From March through September, shortly after the maximum spring tide has occurred, **grunion** (*Leuresthes tenuis*) come ashore along sandy beaches of Southern California and Baja, California, to bury their eggs. Grunion—slender, silvery fish up to 15 centimeters (6 inches) long—are the only marine fish in the world that come completely out of water to spawn. The name *grunion* comes from the Spanish *gruñón*, which means "grunter" and refers to the faint noise they make during spawning.

A mixed tidal pattern occurs along Southern California and Baja, California, beaches. On most lunar days (24 hours and 50 minutes), there are two high and two low tides. There is usually a significant difference in the heights of the two high tides that occur each day. During the summer months, the higher high tide occurs at night. The night high tide becomes higher each night as the maximum spring tide range is approached, causing sand to be eroded from the beach (Figure 9C, *graph*). After the maximum spring tide has occurred, the night high tide diminishes each night. As neap tide is approached, sand is deposited on the beach.

Grunion spawn only after each night's higher high tide has peaked on the three or four nights following the night of the highest spring high tide. This assures that their eggs will be covered deeply in sand deposited by the receding higher high tides each succeeding night. The fertilized eggs buried in the sand are ready to hatch nine days after spawning. By this time, another spring tide is approaching, so the night high tide is getting progressively higher each night again. The beach sand is eroding again, too, which exposes the eggs to the waves that break ever higher on the beach. The eggs hatch about three minutes after being freed in the water. Tests done in laboratories have shown that the grunion eggs will not hatch until agitated in a manner that simulates that of the eroding waves.

The spawning begins as the grunion come ashore immediately following an appropriate high tide, and it may last from one to three hours. Spawning usually peaks about an hour after it starts and may last an additional 30 minutes to an hour. Thousands of fish may be on the beach at this time. During a run, the females, which are larger than the males, move

high on the beach. If no males are near, a female may return to the water without depositing her eggs. In the presence of males, she drills her tail into the semifluid sand until only her head is visible. The female continues to twist, depositing her eggs 5 to 7 centimeters (2 to 3 inches) below the surface.

The male curls around the female's body and deposits his milt against it (Figure 9C, *photo*). The milt runs down the body of the female to fertilize the eggs. When the spawning is completed, both fish return to the water with the next wave.

Larger females are capable of producing up to 3000 eggs for each series of spawning runs, which are separated by the two-week period between spring tides. As soon as the eggs are deposited, another group of eggs begins to form within the female. These eggs will be deposited during the next spring tide run. Early in the season, only older fish spawn. By May, however, even the one-year-old females are in spawning condition.

Young grunion grow rapidly and are about 12 centimeters (5 inches) long when they are a year old and ready for their first spawning. They usually live two or three years, but four-year-olds have been recovered. The age of a grunion can be determined by its scales. After growing rapidly during the first year, they grow very slowly thereafter. There is no growth at all during the six-month spawning season, which causes marks to form on each scale that can be used to identify the grunion's age.

It is not known exactly how grunion are able to time their spawning behavior so precisely with the tides. Research suggests that grunion are somehow able to sense very small changes in hydrostatic pressure caused by rising and falling sea level due to changing tides. Certainly, a very dependable detection mechanism keeps the grunion accurately informed of the tidal conditions, because their survival depends on a spawning behavior precisely tuned to the tides.

New Moon
Spring tide

First Quarter
Neap tide

Full Moon
Spring tide

Tidal height

Days

Grunion deposit eggs in beach sand during early stages of the ebb of higher high tides on the three or four days following maximum spring tidal range.

Flood tides erode sand and free grunion eggs during higher high tide as maximum spring tidal range is approached.

Maximum spring tidal range

FIGURE 9C The tidal cycle and spawning grunion. During summer months and for 3 or 4 days after the highest spring tides (*graph*), grunion deposit their eggs on sandy beaches (*photo*). The successively lower high tides during the approaching neap tide conditions won't wash the eggs from the sand until they are ready to hatch about 10 days later. As the next spring tide is approached, successively higher high tides wash the eggs free and allow them to hatch. The spawning cycle begins a few days later after the peak of spring tide conditions with the next cycle of successively lower high tides.

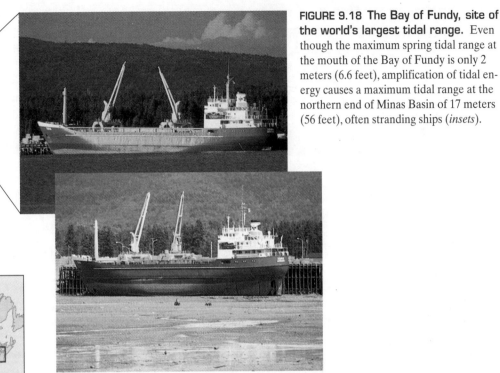

FIGURE 9.18 The Bay of Fundy, site of the world's largest tidal range. Even though the maximum spring tidal range at the mouth of the Bay of Fundy is only 2 meters (6.6 feet), amplification of tidal energy causes a maximum tidal range at the northern end of Minas Basin of 17 meters (56 feet), often stranding ships (*insets*).

During maximum spring tide conditions, the tidal range at the mouth of the bay (where it opens to the ocean) is only about 2 meters (6.6 feet). However, the tidal range increases progressively from the mouth of the bay northward. In the northern end of Minas Basin, the maximum spring tidal range is 17 meters (56 feet), which leaves boats high and dry during low tide (Figure 9.18, *insets*).

Coastal Tidal Currents

The current that accompanies the slowly turning tide crest in a Northern Hemisphere basin rotates counterclockwise, producing a **rotary current** in the open portion of the basin. Friction increases in nearshore shoaling waters, so the rotary current changes to an alternating or **reversing current** that moves into and out of restricted passages along a coast.

The velocity of rotary currents in the open ocean is usually well below 1 kilometer (0.6 mile) per hour. Reversing currents, however, can reach velocities up to 44 kilometers (28 miles) per hour in restricted channels such as between islands of coastal waters.

Reversing currents also exist in the mouths of bays (and some rivers) due to the daily flow of tides. Figure 9.19 shows that a **flood current** is produced when water rushes into a bay (or river) with an incoming high tide. Conversely, an **ebb current** is produced when water drains out of a bay (or river) because a low tide is approaching. No currents occur for several minutes during either **high slack water** (which occurs at the peak of each high tide) or **low slack water** (at the peak of each low tide).

WEB VIDEO
Tidal Bore and Tidal Bore Surfing

WEB VIDEO
Grunion Run

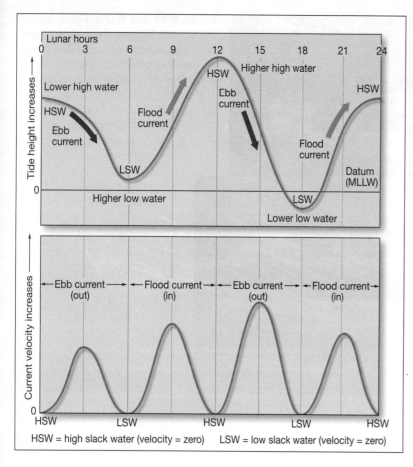

FIGURE 9.19 Reversing tidal currents in a bay. *Top*: Tidal curve for a bay, showing ebb currents are created by an outgoing low tide and flood currents are created by an incoming high tide. No currents occur during either high slack water (*HSW*) or low slack water (*LSW*). The datum MLLW stands for *mean lower low water,* which is the average of the lower of the two low tides that occur daily in a mixed tidal pattern. *Bottom*: Corresponding chart showing velocity of ebb and flood currents.

KEY CONCEPT

Coastal tidal phenomena include large tidal ranges (the largest of which occurs in the Bay of Fundy, where reflection and amplification produce a maximum spring tide range of 17 meters 56 feet), tidal currents, and rapidly spinning vortices called whirlpools.

Reversing currents in bays can sometimes reach speeds of 40 kilometers (25 miles) per hour, creating a navigation hazard for ships. On the other hand, the daily flow of these currents often keeps sediment from closing off the bay and replenishes the bay with seawater and ocean nutrients.

Tidal currents can be significant even in deep ocean waters. For example, tidal currents were encountered shortly after the discovery of the remains of the *Titanic* at a depth of 3795 meters (12,448 feet) on the continental slope south of Newfoundland's Grand Banks in 1985. These tidal currents were so strong that they forced researchers to abandon the use of the camera-equipped, tethered, remotely-operated vehicle *Jason Jr.*

Whirlpools: Fact or Fiction?

A **whirlpool**—a rapidly spinning body of water, which is also termed a *vortex* (*vertere* = to turn)—can be created in some restricted coastal passages due to reversing tidal currents. Whirlpools most commonly occur in shallow passages connecting two large bodies of water that have different tidal cycles. The different tidal heights of the two bodies cause water to move vigorously through the passage. As water rushes through the passage, it is affected by the shape of the shallow sea floor, causing turbulence, which, along with spin due to opposing tidal currents, creates whirlpools. The larger the tidal difference between the two bodies of water and the smaller the passage, the greater the vortex caused by the tidal currents. Because whirlpools can have high flow rates of up to 16 kilometers (10 miles) per hour, they can cause ships to spin out of control for a short time.

One of the world's most famous whirlpools is the *Maelstrom* (*malen* = to grind in a circle, *strom* = stream), which occurs in a passage off the west coast of Arctic Norway (Figure 9.20). This and another famous whirlpool in the Strait of Messina, which separates mainland Italy from Sicily, are probably the source of ancient legends of huge churning funnels of water that destroy ships and carry mariners to their deaths, although they are not nearly as deadly as legends suggest. Other notable whirlpools occur off the west coast of Scotland, in the Bay of Fundy at the border between Maine and the Canadian province of New Brunswick, and off Japan's Shikoku Island.

9.6 Can Tidal Power Be Harnessed as a Source of Energy?

Throughout history, ocean tides have been used as a source of power. During high tide, water can be trapped in a basin and then harnessed to do work as it flows back to the sea. In the 12th century, for example, water wheels driven by the tides were used to power gristmills and sawmills. During the 17th and 18th centuries, much of Boston's flour was produced at a tidal mill.

Today, tidal power is considered a clean, renewable resource with vast potential. The initial cost of building a tidal power-generating plant may be higher than a conventional thermal power plant, but the operating costs would be less because it does not use fossil fuels or radioactive substances to generate electricity.

One disadvantage of tidal power, however, is the periodicity of the tides, allowing power to be generated only during a portion of a 24-hour day. People

FIGURE 9.20 The Maelstrom. The Maelstrom, located off the west coast of Norway, is one of the strongest whirlpools in the world and can cause ships to spin out of control. It is created by tidal currents that pass through a narrow, shallow passage between Vest Fjord and the Norwegian Sea.

operate on a solar period, but tides operate on a lunar period, so the energy available from the tides would coincide with need only part of the time. Power would have to be distributed to the point of need at the moment it was generated, which could be a great distance away, resulting in an expensive transmission problem. The power could be stored, but even this alternative presents a large and expensive technical problem.

To generate electricity effectively, electrical turbines (generators) need to run at a constant speed, which is difficult to maintain when generated by the variable flow of tidal currents in two directions (flood tide and ebb tide). Specially designed turbines that allow both advancing and receding water to spin their blades are necessary to solve the problem of generating electricity from the tides.

Another disadvantage of tidal power is harm to wildlife and other unwanted environmental effects resulting from the modification of tidal current flow. In addition, a tidal power plant would likely interfere with many traditional uses of coastal waters, such as transportation and fishing.

Tidal Power Plants

Tidal power can be harnessed in one of two ways: (1) Tidal water trapped behind coastal barriers in bays and estuaries can be used to turn turbines and generate electrical energy, and (2) tidal currents that pass through narrow channels can be used to turn underwater pivoting turbines, which produce energy (see Chapter 7). Although the first type is much more commonly employed, Norway, the United Kingdom, and the United States have recently installed offshore turbines that harness swift coastal tidal currents and plan to expand these devices into tidal energy farms.

Worldwide, there are only a few small tidal power plants that use water trapped behind coastal barriers. One successful tidal power plant has been operating in the

FIGURE 9.21 La Rance tidal power plant at St. Malo, France. Electricity is generated at the La Rance tidal power plant at St. Malo, France, when water from a rising tide (*1*) flows into the estuary and turns turbines; electricity is also generated when water from a falling tide (*2*) exits the estuary and turns turbines in the other direction.

One tidal cycle = 12 hours 25 minutes

① Rising tide

Side toward sea

Turbine generator unit

② Falling tide

Side toward estuary

Turbine generator unit

ENGLAND

English Channel

50°

St. Malo

La Rance River

FRANCE

5°

Area enlarged at left

estuary of La Rance River in northern France (Figure 9.21) since 1967. The estuary has a surface area of approximately 23 square kilometers (9 square miles), and the tidal range is 13.4 meters (44 feet). Usable tidal energy increases as the area of the basin increases and as the tidal range increases.

The power-generating barrier was built across the estuary a little over 3 kilometers (2 miles) upstream to protect it from storm waves. The barrier is 760 meters (2500 feet) wide and supports a two-lane road (Figure 9.21). Water passing through the barrier powers 24 electricity-generating units that operate beneath the power plant. At peak operating capacity, each unit can generate 10 megawatts of electricity for a total of 240 megawatts.[13]

To generate electricity, the La Rance plant needs a sufficient water height between the estuary and the ocean—which only occurs about half of the time. Annual power production of about 540 million kilowatt-hours can be increased to 670 million kilowatt-hours by using the turbine generators as pumps to move water into the estuary at proper times.

Within the Bay of Fundy, which has the largest tidal range in the world, the Canadian province of Nova Scotia constructed a small tidal power plant in 1984 that can generate 20 megawatts of electricity. The plant is built on the Annapolis River estuary, an arm of the Bay of Fundy (see Figure 9.18), where maximum tidal range is 8.7 meters (26 feet).

---

[13]Each megawatt of electricity is enough to serve the energy needs of about 800 average U.S. homes.

In 2006, the first Asian tidal power plant came online in Daishan County of eastern China's Zhejiang province. This small power station has the capability to produce 40 kilowatts of electricity, and China has proposed building another larger plant.

Larger power plants that avoid some of the shortcomings of smaller plants have often been considered. For example, a tidal power plant could be made to generate electricity continually if it were located on the Passamaquoddy Bay near the U.S.–Canadian border near the entrance to the Bay of Fundy. Although a tidal power plant across the Bay of Fundy has often been proposed, it has never been built. Potentially, the usable tidal energy seems large compared to the La Rance plant, because the flow volume is over 100 times greater.

Recognizing the benefits of tidal power, the United Kingdom has proposed building a tidal power barrage across the Severn Estuary that separates England and Wales. The Severn River has the second-largest tidal range in the world and is a prime target for producing tidal power. If completed, it would be the world's largest tidal power plant with a 12-kilometer- (7.5-mile-) long dam that could produce 8.6 gigawatts of energy, or about 5% of the electricity currently used in the United Kingdom.

> **KEY CONCEPT**
> The daily change in water level as a result of ocean tides can be harnessed as a source of energy. In spite of significant drawbacks, several tidal power plants in coastal estuaries successfully extract tidal energy today.

Chapter in Review

• *Gravitational attraction of the Moon and Sun create Earth's tides*, which are fundamentally long wavelength waves. According to a *simplified model of tides*, which assumes an ocean of uniform depth and ignores the effects of friction, small horizontal forces (the tide-generating forces) tend to push water into *two bulges on opposite sides of Earth*. One bulge is directly facing the tide-generating body (the Moon and the Sun), and the other is directly opposite.

• Despite its vastly smaller size, *the Moon has about twice the tide-generating effect of the Sun* because the Moon is so much closer to Earth. The tidal bulges due to the Moon's gravity (the lunar bulges) dominate, so lunar motions dominate the periods of Earth's tides. However, the changing position of the solar bulges relative to the lunar bulges modifies tides. According to the simplified idealized tide theory, *Earth's rotation carries locations on Earth into and out of the various tidal bulges*.

• Tides would be easy to predict if Earth were a uniform sphere covered with an ocean of uniform depth. For most places on Earth, *the time between successive high tides would be 12 hours 25 minutes (half a lunar day)*. The 29½ monthly tidal cycle would consist of tides with maximum tidal range (spring tides) and minimum tidal range (neap tides). *Spring tides would occur each new moon and full moon, and neap tides would occur each first- and third-quarter phases of the Moon*.

• The *declination of the Moon* varies between 28.5 degrees north or south of the equator during the lunar month, and the *declination of the Sun* varies between 23.5 degrees north or south of the equator during the year, so *the location of tidal bulges usually creates two high tides and two low tides of unequal height per lunar day*. Tidal ranges are greatest when Earth is nearest the Sun and Moon.

• *When friction and the true shape of ocean basins are considered, the dynamics of tides becomes more complicated*. Moreover, the two bulges on opposite sides of Earth cannot exist because they cannot keep up with the rotational speed of Earth. Instead, the bulges are broken up into *several tidal cells that rotate around an amphidromic point*—a point of zero tidal range. Rotation is counterclockwise in the Northern Hemisphere and clockwise in the Southern Hemisphere. *Many other factors influence tides on Earth*, too, such as the positions of the continents, the varying depth of the ocean, and coastline shape.

• The *three types of tidal patterns* observed on Earth are *diurnal* (a single high and low tide each lunar day), *semidiurnal* (two high and two low tides each lunar day), and *mixed* (characteristics of both). Mixed tidal patterns usually consist of semidiurnal periods with significant diurnal inequality. Mixed tidal patterns are the most common type in the world.

• There are many types of *observable tidal phenomena in coastal areas*. *Tidal bores are true tidal waves* (a wave produced by the tides) that occur in certain rivers and bays due to an incoming high tide. The effects of constructive interference together with the shoaling and narrowing of coastal bays creates the *largest tidal range in the world—17 meters (56 feet)—at the northern end of Nova Scotia's Bay of Fundy*. Tidal currents follow a rotary pattern in open-ocean basins but are converted to *reversing currents* along continental margins. The maximum velocity of reversing currents occurs during flood and ebb currents when the water is halfway between high and low slack waters. *Whirlpools* can be created in some restricted coastal passages due to reversing tidal currents. *The tides are also important to many marine organisms*. For instance, *grunion*—small silvery fish that inhabit waters along the West Coast of North America—time their spawning cycle to match the pattern of the tides.

• *Tides can be used to generate power* without need for fossil or nuclear fuel. There are some *significant drawbacks*, however, to creating successful tidal power plants. Still, many sites worldwide have the *potential for tidal power generation*.

Key Terms

Amphidromic point (p. 271)
Aphelion (p. 269)
Apogee (p. 269)
Barycenter (p. 261)
Bay of Fundy (p. 274)
Centripetal force (p. 263)
Cotidal line (p. 271)
Declination (p. 268)
Diurnal tidal pattern (p. 273)
Ebb current (p. 277)
Ebb tide (p. 266)
Ecliptic (p. 268)
Flood current (p. 277)
Flood tide (p. 266)

Full moon (p. 266)
Gravitational force (p. 262)
Grunion (*Leuresthes tenuis*) (p. 276)
High slack water (p. 277)
Low slack water (p. 277)
Lunar bulge (p. 264)
Lunar day (p. 265)
Mixed tidal pattern (p. 274)
Nadir (p. 263)
Neap tide (p. 267)
New moon (p. 266)

Newton, Isaac (p. 261)
Newton's law of universal gravitation (p. 262)
Perigee (p. 269)
Perihelion (p. 269)
Proxigean (p. 269)
Quadrature (p. 267)
Quarter moon (p. 266)
Resultant force (p. 264)
Reversing current (p. 277)
Rotary current (p. 277)
Semidiurnal tidal pattern (p. 274)
Solar bulge (p. 265)

Solar day (p. 265)
Spring tide (p. 267)
Syzygy (p. 267)
Tidal bore (p. 275)
Tidal period (p. 265)
Tidal range (p. 266)
Tide (p. 261)
Tide-generating force (p. 264)
Waning crescent (p. 268)
Waning gibbous (p. 268)
Waxing crescent (p. 268)
Waxing gibbous (p. 268)
Whirlpool (p. 278)
Zenith (p. 263)

Review Questions

1. Explain why the Sun's influence on Earth's tides is only 46% that of the Moon, even though the Sun is so much more massive than the Moon.

2. Why is a lunar day 24 hours 50 minutes long, while a solar day is 24 hours long?

3. Which is more technically correct: The tide comes in and goes out; or Earth rotates into and out of the tidal bulges? Why?

4. Explain why the maximum tidal range (spring tide) occurs during new and full moon phases and the minimum tidal range (neap tide) at first-quarter and third-quarter moons.

5. If Earth did not have the Moon orbiting it, would there still be tides? Why or why not?

6. What is declination? Discuss the degree of declination of the Moon and Sun relative to Earth's equator. What are the effects of declination of the Moon and Sun on the tides?

7. Are tides considered deep-water waves anywhere in the ocean? Why or why not?

8. Describe the number of high and low tides in a lunar day, the period, and any inequality of the following tidal patterns: diurnal, semidiurnal, and mixed.

9. Discuss factors that help produce the world's largest tidal range in the Bay of Fundy.

10. Discuss the difference between rotary and reversing tidal currents.

11. Of flood current, ebb current, high slack water, and low slack water, when is the best time to enter a bay by boat? When is the best time to navigate in a shallow, rocky harbor? Explain.

12. Describe the spawning cycle of grunion, indicating the relationship among tidal phenomena, where grunion lay their eggs, and the movement of sand on the beach.

13. Discuss at least two positive and two negative factors related to tidal power generation.

14. Explain how a tidal power plant works, using as an example an estuary that has a mixed tidal pattern. Why does potential for usable tidal energy increase with an increase in the tidal range?

Critical Thinking Exercises

1. From memory, draw the positions of the Earth–Moon–Sun system during a complete monthly tidal cycle. Indicate the tide conditions experienced on Earth, the phases of the Moon, the time between those phases, and syzygy and quadrature.

2. Assume that there are two moons in orbit around Earth that are on the same orbital plane but always on opposite sides of Earth and that each moon is the same size and mass of our Moon. How would this affect the tidal range during spring and neap tide conditions?

3. Diagram the Earth–Moon system's orbit about the Sun. Label the positions on the orbit at which the Moon and Sun are closest to and farthest from Earth, stating the terms used to identify them. Discuss the effects of the Moon's and Earth's positions on Earth's tides.

4. Observe the Moon from a reference location every night at about the same time for two weeks. Keep track of your observations about the shape (phase) of the Moon and its position in the sky. Then compare these to the reported tides in your area and report your findings.

Oceanography on the Web

Visit the *Essentials of Oceanography* Online Study Guide for Internet resources, including chapter-specific quizzes to test your understanding and Web links to further your exploration of the topics in this chapter.

The *Essentials of Oceanography* Online Study Guide is at http://www.mygeoscienceplace.com/.

A building falling into the sea at Réunion Island, Indian Ocean.

When coastal structures are built too close to the sea, they could collapse into it, as did this building at Saint-Paul de la Réunion in 2007. Understanding coastal dynamics and shoreline processes can help prevent damage such as this.

"The waves which dash upon the shore are, one by one, broken, but the ocean conquers nevertheless. It overwhelms the Armada, it wears out the rock."

— *Lord Byron (1821)*

10 THE COAST: BEACHES AND SHORELINE PROCESSES

CHAPTER AT A GLANCE

- Sand is moved toward and away from shore by seasonal changes in wave energy; sand is also transported upcoast/downcoast by waves that approach the beach at an angle.

- Erosional shores are characterized by features such as cliffs, sea arches, sea stacks, and marine terraces; depositional shores are characterized by features such as spits, tombolos, barrier islands, deltas, and beach compartments.

- Hard stabilization involves placing human-made structures at the beach, all of which alter the coastal environment and result in changes in the shape of the beach.

Humans have always been attracted to the coastal regions of the world for their moderate climate, seafood, transportation, recreational opportunities, and commercial benefits. In the United States, for example, 80% of the population now lives within easy access of the Atlantic, Pacific, and Gulf Coasts, increasing the stress on these important national resources.

The coastal region is constantly changing because waves crash along most shorelines more than 10,000 times a day, releasing their energy from distant storms. Waves cause erosion in some areas and deposition in others, resulting in changes that occur hourly, daily, weekly, monthly, seasonally, and yearly.

In this chapter, we'll examine the major features of the seacoast and shore and the processes that modify them. We'll also discuss ways people interfere with these processes, creating hazards to themselves and to the environment.

10.1 How Are Coastal Regions Defined?

The **shore** is a zone that lies between the lowest tide level (low tide) and the highest elevation on land that is affected by storm waves. The **coast** extends inland from the shore as far as ocean-related features can be found (Figure 10.1). The width of the shore varies between a few meters and hundreds of meters. The width of the coast may vary from less than 1 kilometer (0.6 mile) to many tens of kilometers. The **coastline** marks the boundary between the shore and the coast. It is the landward limit of the effect of the highest storm waves on the shore.

Beach Terminology

The beach profile in Figure 10.1 shows features characteristic of a cliffed shoreline. The shore is divided into the **backshore** and the **foreshore**.[1] The backshore is above the high tide shoreline and is covered with water only during storms. The foreshore is the portion exposed at low tide and submerged at high tide. The **shoreline** migrates back and forth with the tide and is the water's edge. The **nearshore** extends seaward from the low tide shoreline to the low tide breaker line. It is never exposed to the atmosphere, but it is affected by waves that touch bottom. Beyond the low-tide breakers is the **offshore** zone, which is deep enough that waves rarely affect the bottom.

A **beach** is a deposit of the shore area. It consists of wave-worked sediment that moves along the **wave-cut bench** (a flat, wave-eroded surface). A beach may continue from the coastline across the nearshore region to the line of breakers. Thus, the beach is the entire active area of a coast that

---

[1]The foreshore is often referred to as the *intertidal zone*, or *littoral (litoralis = the shore) zone*.

FIGURE 10.1 Landforms and terminology of coastal regions. The beach is the entire active area affected by waves that extends from the low tide breaker line to the base of the coastal cliffs.

KEY CONCEPT
The beach is the coastal area affected by breaking waves and includes the berm, beach face, longshore trough, and longshore bar.

experiences changes due to breaking waves. The area of the beach above the shoreline is often called the *recreational beach*.

The **berm** is the dry, gently sloping region at the foot of the coastal cliffs or dunes. The berm is often composed of sand, making it a favorite place of beachgoers. The **beach face** is the wet, sloping surface that extends from the berm to the shoreline. It is more fully exposed during low tide and is also known as the *low tide terrace*. The beach face is a favorite place for runners because the sand is wet and hard packed. Offshore beyond the beach face is one or more **longshore bars**—sand bars that parallel the coast. A longshore bar may not always be present throughout the year, but when one is, it may be exposed during extremely low tides. Longshore bars can "trip" waves as they approach shore and cause them to begin breaking. Separating the longshore bar from the beach face is a **longshore trough**.

Beach Composition

Beaches are composed of whatever material is locally available. When this material—sediment—comes from the erosion of beach cliffs or nearby coastal mountains, beaches are composed of mineral particles from these rocks and may be relatively coarse in texture. When the sediment comes primarily from rivers that drain lowland areas, beaches are finer in texture. Often, mud flats develop along the shore because only tiny clay-sized and silt-sized particles are emptied into the ocean. Such is the case for muddy coastlines such as along the coast of Suriname in South America and the Kerala coast of southwest India.

Other beaches have a significant biologic component. For example, in low-relief, low-latitude areas such as southern Florida, where there are no mountains or other sources of rock-forming minerals nearby, most beaches are composed of shell fragments and the remains of organisms that live in coastal waters. Many beaches on volcanic islands in the open ocean are composed of black or green fragments of the basaltic lava that comprise the islands, or of coarse debris from coral reefs that develop around islands in low latitudes.

Regardless of the composition, though, the material that comprises the beach does not stay in one place. Instead, the waves that crash along the shoreline are constantly moving it. Thus, beaches can be thought of as *material in transit along the shoreline*.

10.2 How Does Sand Move on the Beach?

The movement of sand on the beach occurs both perpendicular to the shoreline (*toward* and *away from* shore) and parallel to the shoreline (often referred to as *upcoast* and *downcoast*).

Movement Perpendicular to Shoreline

Sand on the beach moves perpendicular to the shoreline as a result of breaking waves.

Summertime/ Wintertime Beach Conditions

MECHANISM   As each wave breaks, water rushes up the beach face toward the berm. Some of this **swash** soaks into the beach and eventually returns to the ocean. However, most of the water drains away from shore as **backwash**, though usually not before the next wave breaks and sends its swash over the top of the previous wave's backwash.

While standing in ankle-deep water at the shoreline, you can see that swash and backwash transport sediment up and down the beach face perpendicular to the shoreline. Whether swash or backwash dominates determines whether sand is deposited or eroded from the berm.

LIGHT VERSUS HEAVY WAVE ACTIVITY   During *light wave activity* (characterized by less energetic waves), much of the swash soaks into the beach, so backwash is reduced. The swash dominates the transport system, therefore causing a net movement of the sand up the beach face toward the berm, which creates a wide, well-developed berm.

During *heavy wave activity* (characterized by high-energy waves), the beach is saturated with water from previous waves, so very little of the swash soaks into the beach. Backwash dominates the transport system, therefore causing a net movement of sand down the beach face, which erodes the berm. When a wave breaks, moreover, the incoming swash comes *on top of* the previous wave's backwash, effectively protecting the beach from the swash and adding to the eroding effect of the backwash.

During heavy wave activity, where does the sand from the berm go? The orbital motion in waves is too shallow to move the sand very far offshore. Thus, the sand accumulates just beyond where the waves break and forms one or more offshore sand bars (the longshore bars).

SUMMERTIME AND WINTERTIME BEACHES   Light and heavy wave activity alternate seasonally at most beaches, so the characteristics of the beaches they produce change, too (Table 10.1). For example, light wave activity produces a wide sandy berm and an overall steep beach face—a **summertime beach**—at the expense of the longshore bar (Figure 10.2a). Conversely, heavy wave activity produces a narrow rocky berm and an overall flattened beach face—a **wintertime beach**—and builds prominent longshore bars (Figure 10.2b). A wide berm that takes several months to build can be destroyed in just a few hours by high-energy wintertime storm waves.

Movement Parallel to Shoreline

At the same time that movement occurs perpendicular to shore, movement parallel to shoreline also occurs.

MECHANISM   Recall from Chapter 8 that within the surf zone, waves *refract* (bend) and line up *nearly* parallel to shore. With each breaking wave, the swash moves up onto the exposed beach at a slight angle; then gravity pulls the backwash down the beach face at a slight downcoast angle. As a result, water moves in a zigzag fashion along the shore.

LONGSHORE CURRENT AND LONGSHORE DRIFT (LONGSHORE TRANSPORT)   This zigzag movement of water along the shore is called a **longshore current**

(a) Summertime beach (fair weather)

(b) Wintertime beach (storm)

FIGURE 10.2 Summertime and wintertime beach conditions. Dramatic differences occur between **(a)** summertime and **(b)** wintertime beach conditions at Boomer Beach in La Jolla, California.

KEY CONCEPT
Smaller, low-energy waves move sand up the beach face toward the berm and create a summertime beach while larger, high-energy waves scour sand from the berm and create a wintertime beach.

TABLE 10.1	CHARACTERISTICS OF BEACHES AFFECTED BY LIGHT AND HEAVY WAVE ACTIVITY	
	Light wave activity	Heavy wave activity
Berm/longshore bars	Berm is built at the expense of the longshore bars	Longshore bars are built at the expense of the berm
Wave energy	Low wave energy (nonstorm conditions)	High wave energy (storm conditions)
Time span	Long time span (weeks or months)	Short time span (hours or days)
Characteristics	Creates summertime beach: sandy, wide berm, steep beach face	Creates wintertime beach: rocky, narrow berm, flattened beach face

web animation

Longshore Current and Longshore (Beach) Drift

(a)

(Figure 10.3). Longshore currents have speeds up to 4 kilometers (2.5 miles) per hour. Speeds increase as beach slope increases, as the angle at which breakers arrive at the beach increases, as wave height increases, and as wave frequency increases.

Swimmers can inadvertently be carried by longshore currents and find themselves carried far from where they initially entered the water. This demonstrates that longshore currents are strong enough to move people as well as a vast amount of sand in a zigzag fashion along the shore.

Longshore drift (also called **longshore transport**, *beach drift*, or *littoral drift*) is the movement of *sediment* in a zigzag fashion caused by the longshore current (Figure 10.3b). Both longshore currents and longshore transport occur only within the surf zone and not farther offshore because the water is too deep there. Recall from Chapter 8 that the depth of *wave base* is one-half a wave's wavelength, measured from still water level. Below this depth, waves don't touch bottom, they don't refract, and, as a result, longshore currents can't form.

THE BEACH: A RIVER OF SAND By various processes, both rivers and coastal zones move water and sediment from one area (*upcoast* or *upstream*) to another (*downcoast* or *downstream*). As a result, the beach has often been referred to as a "river of sand." There are, however, differences between how beaches and rivers transport sediment. For example, a longshore current moves in a zigzag fashion while rivers flow mostly in a turbulent, swirling fashion. In addition, the direction of flow of longshore currents along a shoreline can change, whereas rivers always flow in the same basic direction (downhill). The longshore current can change direction because the waves that approach the beach typically come from different directions in different seasons. Nevertheless, the longshore current generally flows *southward along both the Atlantic and Pacific shores of the United States.*

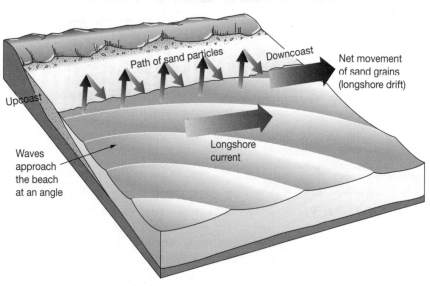

FIGURE 10.3 Longshore current and longshore drift. (a) Waves approaching the beach at a slight angle near Oceanside, California, producing a longshore current moving toward the right of the photo. **(b)** A longshore current, caused by refracting waves, moves water in a zigzag fashion along the shoreline. This causes a net movement of sand grains (longshore drift) from upcoast to downcoast ends.

(b)

10.3 What Features Exist Along Erosional and Depositional Shores?

Sediment eroded from the beach is transported along the shore and deposited in areas where wave energy is low. Even though all shores experience some degree of both erosion and deposition, shores can often be identified primarily as one type or the other. **Erosional shores** typically have well-developed cliffs and are in areas where tectonic uplift of the coast occurs, such as along the U.S. Pacific Coast.

The U.S. southeastern Atlantic Coast and the Gulf Coast, on the other hand, are primarily **depositional shores**. Sand deposits and offshore barrier islands are common there because the shore is gradually subsiding. Erosion can still be a major problem on depositional shores, especially when human development interferes with natural coastal processes.

Features of Erosional Shores

Because of wave refraction, wave energy is concentrated on any **headlands** that jut out from the continent, while the amount of energy reaching the shore in bays is reduced. Headlands, therefore, are eroded and the shoreline retreats. Some of these erosional features are shown in Figure 10.4.

Waves pound relentlessly away at the base of headlands, undermining the upper portions, which eventually collapse to form **wave-cut cliffs**. The waves may form **sea caves** at the base of the cliffs.

As waves continue to pound the headlands, the caves may eventually erode through to the other side, forming openings called **sea arches** (Figure 10.5). Some sea arches are large enough to allow a boat to maneuver safely through them. With continued erosion, the tops of sea arches eventually crumble to produce **sea stacks** (Figure 10.5). Waves also erode the bedrock of the bench. Uplift of the wave-cut bench creates a gently sloping **marine terrace** above sea level (Figure 10.6).

Rates of coastal erosion are influenced by the degree of exposure to waves, the amount of tidal range, and the composition of the coastal bedrock. Regardless

Coves

Blowhole

Sea cliffs

Headland

Sea cave

Sea stack

Uplifted marine terrace

Headland

Sea arch

Wave-cut bench

Sediments

FIGURE 10.4 Features of erosional coasts. Diagrammatic view of features characteristic of erosional coasts.

KEY CONCEPT

Longshore currents are produced by waves approaching the beach at an angle and create longshore drift, which transports and along the coast in a zigzag fashion.

10.1   OCEANS AND PEOPLE

WARNING: RIP CURRENTS . . . DO YOU KNOW WHAT TO DO?

The backwash from breaking waves usually returns to the open ocean as a flow of water across the ocean bottom, so it is commonly referred to as "sheet flow." Some of this water, however, flows back in surface **rip currents**. Rip currents typically flow perpendicular to the beach and move away from the shore.

Rip currents are between 15 and 45 meters (15 and 150 feet) wide and can attain velocities of 7 to 8 kilometers (4 to 5 miles) per hour—faster than most people can swim for any length of time. In fact, it is useless to swim for long against a current stronger than about 2 kilometers (1.2 miles) per hour. Rip currents can travel hundreds of meters from shore before they break up. If a light-to-moderate swell is breaking, numerous rip currents may develop that are moderate in size and velocity. A heavy swell usually produces fewer, more concentrated, and stronger rips. They can often be recognized by the way they interfere with incoming waves, by their characteristic brown color caused by suspended sediment, or by their foamy and choppy surface (Figure 10A).

The rip currents that occur during heavy swell are a significant hazard to coastal swimmers. In fact, 80% of rescues at beaches by lifeguards involve people who are trapped in rip currents. Swimmers caught in a rip current can escape by swimming parallel to the shore for a short distance (simply swimming out of the narrow rip current) and then riding the waves in toward the beach. However, even excellent swimmers who panic or try to fight the current by swimming directly into it are eventually overcome by exhaustion and may drown. Even though most beaches have warnings posted and are frequently patrolled by lifeguards, many people lose their lives each year because of rip currents.

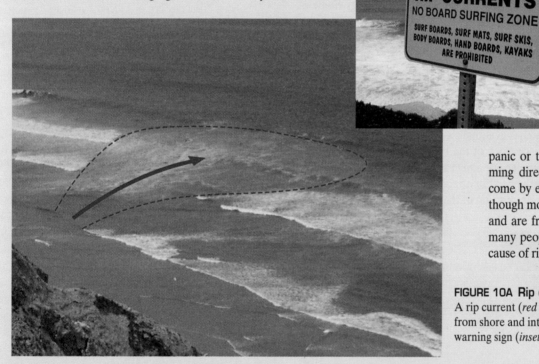

FIGURE 10A Rip current and warning sign. A rip current (*red arrow*), which extends outward from shore and interferes with incoming waves, and warning sign (*inset*).

STUDENTS SOMETIMES ASK...

What is the difference between a rip current and a rip tide? Are they the same thing as an undertow?

Like tidal waves (tsunami), rip tides are a misnomer and have nothing to do with the tides. Rip tides are more correctly called *rip currents*. Perhaps rip currents have incorrectly been called rip tides because they occur suddenly (like an incoming tide). The origin of rip currents and their associated dangers are discussed in Box 10.1.

An undertow, similar to a rip current, is a flow of water away from shore. An undertow is much wider, however, and is usually more concentrated along the ocean floor. An undertow is really a continuation of backwash that flows down the beach face and is strongest during heavy wave activity. Undertows can be strong enough to knock people off their feet, but they are confined to the immediate floor of the ocean and only within the surf zone.

WEB VIDEO

Rip Currents

WEB VIDEO

Wave Refraction and
Longshore Current

FIGURE 10.5 Sea arches and sea stack at Praia da Marinha Beach, near Armacao de Pera, Algarve, Portugal. When the roof of a sea arch (*behind*) collapses, a sea stack (*middle*) is formed.

of the erosion rate, all coastal regions follow the same developmental path. As long as there is no change in the elevation of the landmass relative to the ocean surface, the cliffs will continue to erode and retreat until the beaches widen sufficiently to prevent waves from reaching them. The eroded material is carried from high-energy areas and deposited in low-energy areas.

Features of Depositional Shores

Coastal erosion of sea cliffs produces large amounts of sediment. Additional sediment, which is carried to the shore by rivers, comes from the erosion of inland rocks. Waves then distribute all of this sediment along the continental margin.

FIGURE 10.6 Wave-cut bench and marine terrace. A wave-cut bench is exposed at low tide along the California coast at Bolinas Point near San Francisco. An elevated wave-cut bench, called a marine terrace, is shown at right.

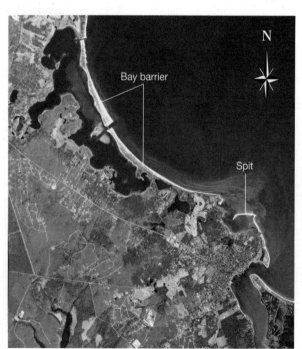

FIGURE 10.7 Features of depositional coasts.
Diagrammatic view of features characteristic of depositional coasts.

Figure 10.7 shows some of the features of depositional coasts. These features are primarily deposits of sand moved by longshore drift but are also modified by other coastal processes. Some are partially or wholly separated from the shore.

A **spit** (*spit* = spine) is a linear ridge of sediment that extends in the direction of longshore drift from land into the deeper water near the mouth of a bay. The end of the spit normally curves into the bay due to the movement of currents.

Tidal currents or currents from river runoff are usually strong enough to keep the mouth of the bay open. If not, the spit may eventually extend across the bay and connect to the mainland, forming a **bay barrier**, or **bay-mouth bar** (Figure 10.8a), which cuts off the bay from the open ocean. Although a bay barrier is a buildup of sand usually less than 1 meter (3.3 feet) above sea level, permanent buildings are often constructed on them.

A **tombolo** (*tombolo* = mound) is a sand ridge that connects an island or sea stack to the mainland (Figure 10.8b). Tombolos can also connect two adjacent islands. Formed in the wave-energy shadow of an island, tombolos are usually oriented perpendicular to the average direction of wave crests.

BARRIER ISLANDS Extremely long offshore deposits of sand that are parallel to the coast are called **barrier islands** (Figure 10.9). They form a first line of defense against rising sea level and high-energy storm waves, which would otherwise exert their full force directly against the shore. The origin of barrier islands is complex, but many appear to have developed during the worldwide rise in sea level that is associated with the melting of glaciers at the end of the most recent ice age about 18,000 years ago.

At least 280 barrier islands ring the Atlantic and Gulf Coasts of the United States. They are nearly continuous from Massachusetts to Florida and continue through the Gulf of Mexico, where they exist well south of the Mexican border.

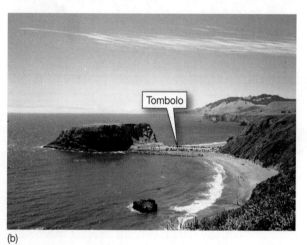

FIGURE 10.8 Coastal depositional features. **(a)** Barrier coast, spit, and bay barrier along the coast of Martha's Vineyard, Massachusetts. **(b)** Tombolo at Goat Rock Beach, California.

**FIGURE 10.9
Barrier islands.**
(a) Barrier islands along North Carolina's Outer Banks.
(b) Barrier islands along the south Texas coast. **(c)** A portion of a heavily developed barrier island near Tom's River, New Jersey.

(a)

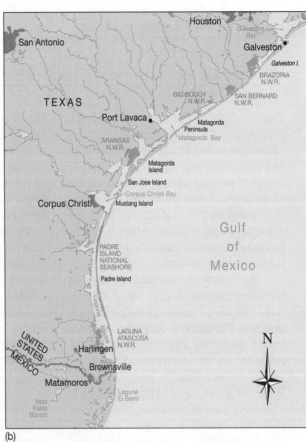

(b)

Barrier islands may exceed 100 kilometers (60 miles) in length, have widths of several kilometers, and are separated from the mainland by a lagoon. Notable barrier islands include Fire Island off the New York coast, North Carolina's Outer Banks, and Padre Island off the coast of Texas.

One human-related environmental issue of barrier islands is their proximity to the ocean, which is often considered a prime building site. Although it seems unwise to build a coastal structure on a narrow, low-lying, shifting strip of sand, many large buildings have been constructed on barrier islands (see Figure 10.9c). Some of these structures have either fallen into the ocean or have needed to be moved (Box 10.2).

Features of Barrier Islands A typical barrier island has the physiographic features shown in Figure 10.10a. From the ocean landward, they are (1) ocean beach, (2) dunes, (3) barrier flat, (4) high salt marsh, (5) low salt marsh, and (6) lagoon between the barrier island and the mainland.

During the summer, gentle waves carry sand to the *ocean beach,* so it widens and becomes steeper. During the winter, higher energy waves carry sand offshore and produce a narrow, gently sloping beach.

Winds blow sand inland during dry periods to produce coastal *dunes,* which are stabilized by dune grasses. These plants can withstand salt spray and burial by sand. Dunes protect the lagoon against excessive flooding during storm-driven high tides. Numerous passes exist through the dunes, particularly along the southeastern Atlantic Coast, where dunes are less well developed than to the north.

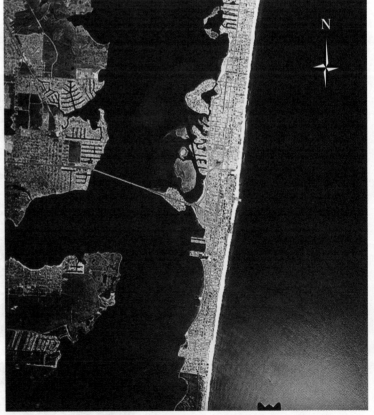

(c)

THE MOVE OF THE CENTURY: RELOCATING THE CAPE HATTERAS LIGHTHOUSE

Despite efforts to protect structures that are too close to the shore, such structures can still be in danger of being destroyed by receding shorelines and the destructive power of waves. Such was the case for one of the nation's most prominent landmarks, the candy-striped lighthouse at Cape Hatteras, North Carolina, which is 21 stories tall—the nation's tallest lighthouse and the tallest brick lighthouse in the world.

The lighthouse was built in 1870 on the Cape Hatteras barrier island 457 meters (1500 feet) from the shoreline to guide mariners through the dangerous offshore shoals known as the "Graveyard of the Atlantic." As the barrier island began migrating toward land, its beach narrowed. When the waves began to lap just 37 meters (120 feet) from its brick and granite base, there was concern that even a moderate-strength hurricane could trigger beach erosion sufficient to topple the lighthouse.

In 1970, the U.S. Navy built three groins in front of the lighthouse in an effort to protect the lighthouse from further erosion. The groins initially slowed erosion but disrupted sand flow in the surf zone, which caused the flattening of nearby dunes and the formation of a bay south of the lighthouse. Attempts to increase the width of the beach in front of the lighthouse included beach nourishment and artificial offshore beds of seaweed, both of which failed to widen the beach substantially. In the 1980s, the U.S. Army Corps of Engineers proposed building a massive stone seawall around the lighthouse but decided the eroding coast would eventually move out from under the structure, leaving it stranded at sea on its own island. In 1988, the U.S. National Academy of Sciences determined that the shoreline in front of the lighthouse would retreat so far as to destroy the lighthouse and recommended relocation of the tower as had been done with smaller lighthouses. In 1999, the U.S. National Park Service, which owns the lighthouse, finally authorized moving the structure to a safer location.

Moving the lighthouse, which weighs 4400 metric tons (4800 short tons), was accomplished by severing it from its foundation and carefully hoisting it onto a platform of steel beams fitted with roller dollies. Once on the platform, it was slowly rolled along a specially designed steel track using a series of hydraulic jacks. A strip of vegetation was cleared to make a runway along which the lighthouse crept 1.5 meters (5 feet) at a time, with the track picked up from behind and reconstructed in front of the tower as it moved. During June and July 1999, the lighthouse was gingerly transported 884 meters (2900 feet) from its original location, making it one of the largest structures ever moved successfully.

After its $12 million move, the lighthouse now resides in a scrub oak and pine woodland 488 meters (1600 feet) from the shore (Figure 10B). Although it now stands further inland, the light's slightly higher elevation makes it visible just as far out to sea, where it continues to warn mariners of hazardous shoals. At the current rate of shoreline retreat, the lighthouse should be safe from the threat of waves for at least another century.

FIGURE 10B Relocation of the Cape Hatteras lighthouse, North Carolina. In 1999, the Cape Hatteras lighthouse was moved inland along a cleared path (*photo*) because it was in danger of falling into the sea.

(a)

(b)

FIGURE 10.10 Features and migration of barrier islands. (a) Diagrammatic view showing the major physiographic zones of a barrier island. The peat bed represents ancient marsh environments. (b) Sequence (*1–4*) showing how a barrier island migrates toward the mainland in response to rising sea level and exposes peat deposits that have been covered by the island.

The *barrier flat* forms behind the dunes from sand driven through the passes during storms. Grasses quickly colonize these flats and seawater washes over them during storms. If storms wash over the barrier flat infrequently enough, the plants undergo natural biological succession, with the grasses successively replaced by thickets, woodlands, and eventually forests.

Salt marshes typically lie inland of the barrier flat. They are divided into the *low marsh*, which extends from about mean sea level to the high neap-tide line, and the *high marsh*, which extends to the highest spring-tide line. The low marsh is by far the most biologically productive part of the salt marsh.

New marshland is formed as overwash carries sediment into the lagoon, filling portions so they become intermittently exposed by the tides. Marshes may be poorly developed on parts of the island that are far from floodtide inlets. Their development is greatly restricted on barrier islands, where people perform artificial dune enhancement and fill inlets, which help prevent overwashing and flooding.

Movement of a Barrier Island in Response to Rising Sea Level

The gradual sea level rise experienced along the eastern North American coast is causing barrier islands to migrate landward. The movement of the barrier island is similar to a slowly moving tractor tread, with the entire island rolling over itself, impacting structures built on these islands. *Peat deposits*, which are formed by the accumulation of organic matter in marsh environments, provide further evidence of barrier island migration (Figure 10.10b). As the island slowly rolls over itself and migrates toward land, it buries ancient peat deposits. These peat deposits can be found beneath the island and may even be exposed on the ocean beach when the barrier island has moved far enough.

DELTAS   Some rivers carry more sediment to the ocean than longshore currents can distribute. These rivers develop a **delta** (*delta* = triangular) deposit at their mouths. The Mississippi River, which empties into the Gulf of Mexico (Figure 10.11a), forms one of the largest deltas on Earth. Deltas are fertile, flat, low-lying areas that are subject to periodic flooding.

Delta formation begins when a river has filled its mouth with sediment. The delta then grows through the formation of *distributaries*, which are branching channels that deposit sediment as they radiate out over the delta in finger-like extensions (Figure 10.11a). When the fingers get too long, they become choked with sediment. At this point, a flood may easily shift the distributary's course and provide sediment to low-lying areas between the fingers. When depositional processes exceed coastal erosion and transportation processes, a branching "bird's foot" Mississippi-type delta results.

When erosion and transportation processes exceed deposition, on the other hand, a delta shoreline is smoothed to a gentle curve, like that of the Nile River Delta in Egypt (Figure 10.11b). The Nile Delta is presently eroding because sediment is trapped behind the Aswan High Dam. Before the completion of the dam in 1964, the Nile carried huge volumes of sediment into the Mediterranean Sea.

BEACH COMPARTMENTS   **Beach compartments** consist of three main components: (1) a series of rivers that supply sand to a beach; (2) the beach itself where sand is moving due to longshore transport; and (3) offshore submarine

(a)

(b)

FIGURE 10.11
Deltas.
(a) Satellite image of the branching "bird's foot" structure of the Mississippi River Delta, which flows into the Gulf of Mexico and shows suspended sediment in the water. **(b)** Photograph from the space shuttle of Egypt's Nile River Delta, which has a smooth, curved shoreline as it extends into the Mediterranean Sea.

FIGURE 10.12 Beach compartments. Southern California has several beach compartments, which include rivers that bring sediment to the beach, the beach that experiences longshore transport, and the submarine canyons that remove sand from the beaches. Average longshore transport is toward the south.

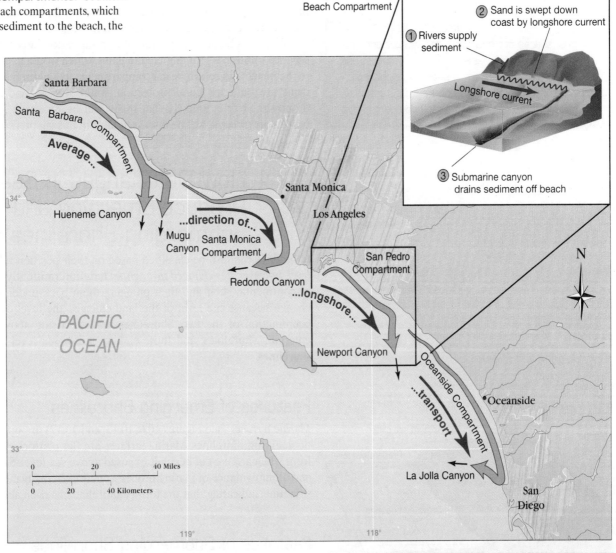

canyons where sand is drained away from the beach. The map in Figure 10.12 shows that the coast of Southern California contains four separate beach compartments.

Within an individual beach compartment, sand is supplied primarily by rivers (Figure 10.12, *inset*) but in areas that have coastal bluffs, a substantial proportion of sand may also be supplied by sea cliff erosion. The sand moves south with the longshore current, so beaches are wider near the southern (*downcoast*) end of each beach compartment. Although some sand is washed offshore along the way or blows onshore to produce coastal sand dunes, most sand eventually moves near the head of a submarine canyon, many of which come surprisingly close to shore. The sand is drained off away from the beach and onto the ocean floor, lost from the beach forever. To the south of this beach compartment, the beaches are typically thin and rocky, without much sand. The process begins all over again at the upcoast end of the next beach compartment, where rivers add their sediment. Farther downcoast, the beach widens and has an abundance of sand until that sand is also diverted down a submarine canyon.

Beach Starvation Human activities have altered the natural system of beach compartments. When a dam is built along one of the rivers that feed into a beach compartment, it deprives the beach of sand. Lining rivers with concrete for flood control further reduces the sediment load delivered to coastal regions. Longshore

Movement of Sand in a Beach Compartment

transport continues to sweep the shoreline's sand into the submarine canyons, so the beaches become narrower and experience **beach starvation**. If all the rivers are blocked, the beaches may nearly disappear.

What can be done to prevent beach starvation in beach compartments? One obvious solution is to eliminate the dams, which would allow rivers to supply sand to the beach and return beach compartments to a natural balance. However, most dams are built for flood protection, water storage, and the generation of hydropower, so it is unlikely that many will be removed. Another option, called *beach nourishment*, will be discussed later in this chapter.

10.4 How Do Changes in Sea Level Produce Emerging and Submerging Shorelines?

Shorelines can also be classified based on their position relative to sea level. *Sea level, however, has changed throughout time*, intermittently exposing large regions of continental shelf and then plunging them back under the sea. Sea level can change because the level of the land changes, the level of the sea changes, or a combination of the two. Shorelines that are rising above sea level are called **emerging shorelines**, and those sinking below sea level are called **submerging shorelines**.

Features of Emerging Shorelines

Marine terraces (see Figures 10.6, 10.13, and 10.17) are one feature characteristic of emerging shorelines. Marine terraces are flat platforms backed by cliffs, which form when a wave-cut bench is exposed above sea level. **Stranded beach deposits** and other evidence of marine processes may exist many meters above the present shoreline, indicating that the former shoreline has risen above sea level.

Features of Submerging Shorelines

Features characteristic of submerging shorelines include **drowned beaches** (Figure 10.13), **submerged dune topography**, and **drowned river valleys** along the present shoreline.

FIGURE 10.13 Evidence of ancient shorelines. Marine terraces result from exposure of ancient sea cliffs and wave-cut benches above present sea level. Below sea level, drowned beaches indicate the sea level has risen relative to the land.

Changes in Sea Level

What causes the changes in sea level that produce submerging and emerging shorelines? One mechanism is to raise or lower the land surface relative to sea level through the movement of Earth's crust. Another mechanism is to affect the level of the sea itself through worldwide changes in sea level.

MOVEMENT OF EARTH'S CRUST The elevation of Earth's crust relative to sea level can be affected by tectonic movements and by isostatic adjustment.[2] These are termed changes in relative sea level, because it's the land that has changed, not the sea.

Tectonic Movements The most dramatic changes in sea level during the past 3000 years have been caused by *tectonic movements*, which affect the elevation of

---

[2]Isostatic adjustment of Earth's crust is discussed in Chapter 1.

the land. These changes include uplift or subsidence of major portions of continents or ocean basins, as well as localized folding, faulting, or tilting of the continental crust.

Most of the U.S. Pacific Coast, for example, is an emerging shoreline because continental margins where plate collisions occur are tectonically active, producing earthquakes, volcanoes, and mountain chains paralleling the coast. Most of the U.S. Atlantic Coast, on the other hand, is a submerging shoreline. When a continent moves away from a spreading center (such as the Mid-Atlantic Ridge), its trailing edge subsides because of cooling and the additional weight of accumulating sediment. Passive margins experience only a low level of tectonic deformation, earthquakes, and volcanism, making the Atlantic Coast far more quiet and stable than the Pacific Coast.

Isostatic Adjustment Earth's crust also undergoes *isostatic adjustment*: It sinks under the accumulation of heavy loads of ice, vast piles of sediment, or outpourings of lava, and it rises when heavy loads are removed.

For example, at least four major accumulations of glacial ice—and dozens of smaller ones—have occurred in high-latitude regions over the past 3 million years. Although Antarctica is still covered by a very large, thick ice cap, much of the ice that once covered northern Asia, Europe, and North America has melted.

The weight of ice sheets as much as 3 kilometers (2 miles) thick caused the crust beneath to sink. Today, these areas are still slowly rebounding, 18,000 years after the ice began to melt. The floor of Hudson Bay, for example, which is now about 150 meters (500 feet) deep, will be close to or above sea level by the time it stops isostatically rebounding. Another example is the Gulf of Bothnia (between Sweden and Finland), which has isostatically rebounded 275 meters (900 feet) during the last 18,000 years.

Generally, tectonic and isostatic changes in sea level are confined to a segment of a continent's shoreline. For a *worldwide* change in sea level, there must be a change in seawater volume or ocean basin capacity.

WORLDWIDE (EUSTATIC) CHANGES IN SEA LEVEL Changes in sea level that are experienced worldwide due to changes in seawater volume or ocean basin capacity are called **eustatic** (*eu* = good, *stasis* = standing)[3] **sea level changes**. The formation or destruction of large inland lakes, for example, causes small eustatic changes in sea level. When lakes form, they trap water that would otherwise run off the land into the ocean, so sea level is lowered worldwide. When lakes are drained and release their water back to the ocean, sea level rises.

Another example of a eustatic change in sea level is through changes in sea floor spreading rates, which can change the capacity of the ocean basin and affect sea level worldwide. Fast spreading, for instance, produces larger rises, such as the East Pacific Rise, which displace more water than slow-spreading ridges such as the Mid-Atlantic Ridge. Thus, fast spreading raises sea level, whereas slower spreading lowers sea level worldwide. Significant changes in sea level due to changes in spreading rate typically take hundreds of thousands to millions of years and may have changed sea level by 1000 meters (3300 feet) or more in the geologic past.

Changes to Sea Level during Ice Ages Ice ages cause eustatic sea level changes, too. As glaciers form, they tie up vast volumes of water on land, eustatically lowering sea level. An analogy to this effect is a sink of water representing an ocean basin. To simulate an ice age, some of the water from the sink is removed and frozen, causing the water level of the sink to be lower. In a similar fashion,

---

[3]The term *eustatic* refers to a highly idealized situation in which all of the continents remain static (in *good standing*), while only the sea rises or falls.

STUDENTS SOMETIMES ASK...

Because of plate motions, I know that the continents have not always remained in the same geographic position. Has the movement of the continents ever affected sea level?

Remarkably, yes. When plate motion moves large continental masses into polar regions, thick continental glaciation can occur (such as in Antarctica today). Glacial ice forms from water vapor in the atmosphere (in the form of snow), which is ultimately derived from the evaporation of seawater. Thus, water is removed from the oceans when continents assume positions close to the poles that provide a platform for large land-based ice accumulation, thereby lowering sea level worldwide.

FIGURE 10.14 Sea level change during the most recent advance and retreat of Pleistocene glaciers. Sea level dropped worldwide by about 120 meters (400 feet) as the last glacial advance removed water from the oceans and transferred it to continental glaciers. About 18,000 years ago, sea level began to rise as the glaciers melted and water was returned to the oceans.

> ### KEY CONCEPT
> Sea level is affected by the movement of land and changes in seawater volume or ocean basin capacity. Sea level has changed dramatically in the past because of changes in Earth's climate.

worldwide sea level is lower during an ice age. During interglacial stages (such as the one we are in at present), the glaciers melt and release great volumes of water that drain to the sea, eustatically raising sea level. This would be analogous to putting the frozen chunk of ice on the counter near the sink and letting the ice melt, causing the water to drain into the sink and raise "sink level."

During the *Pleistocene Epoch*,[4] glaciers advanced and retreated many times on land in middle- to high-latitude regions, causing sea level to fluctuate considerably. The thermal contraction and expansion of the ocean as its temperature decreased and increased, respectively, affected sea level, too. The thermal contraction and expansion of seawater work much like a mercury thermometer: As the mercury inside the thermometer warms, it expands and rises up the thermometer; as it cools, it contracts. Similarly, cooler seawater contracts and occupies less volume, thereby eustatically *lowering* sea level. Warmer seawater expands, eustatically *raising* sea level.

For every 1°C (1.8°F) change in the average temperature of ocean surface waters, sea level changes about 2 meters (6.6 feet). Microfossils in Pleistocene ocean sediments suggest that ocean surface waters may have been as much as 5°C (9°F) lower than at present. Therefore, thermal contraction of the ocean water may have lowered sea level by about 10 meters (33 feet).

Although it is difficult to state definitely the range of shoreline fluctuation during the Pleistocene, evidence suggests that it was at least 120 meters (400 feet) below the present shoreline (Figure 10.14). It is also estimated that if *all* the remaining glacial ice on Earth were to melt, sea level would rise another 70 meters (230 feet). Thus, the maximum sea level change during the Pleistocene would have been on the order of 190 meters (630 feet), most of which was due to the capture and release of Earth's water by land-based glaciers and polar ice sheets.

The combination of tectonic and eustatic changes in sea level is very complex, so it is difficult to classify coastal regions as purely emergent or submergent. In fact, most coastal areas show evidence of *both* submergence and emergence in the recent past. Evidence suggests, however, that until recently sea level has experienced only minor changes as a result of melting glacial ice during the last 3000 years.

More recently, there has been a documented sea level rise as a result of human-induced climate change. This topic is discussed in Chapter 16, "The Oceans and Climate Change."

10.5 What Characteristics Do U.S. Coasts Exhibit?

Whether the dominant process along a coast is erosion or deposition depends on the combined effect of many variables, such as composition of coastal bedrock, the degree of exposure to ocean waves, tidal range, tectonic subsidence or emergence, isostatic subsidence or emergence, and eustatic sea level change.

Although many factors contribute to shoreline retreat, sea level rise is the main factor driving worldwide coastal land loss. In fact, more than 70% of the world's sandy beaches are currently eroding, and the percentage increases to nearly 90% for well-studied U.S. sandy coasts. Studies supported by the U.S. Geological Survey produced the rates of shoreline change presented in Figure 10.15, where erosion rates are shown as *negative* values and deposition rates are shown as *positive* values.

---

[4]The Pleistocene Epoch of geologic time, which is also called the "Ice Age," occurred 2.6 million to 10,000 years ago (see the Geologic Time Scale, Figure 1.24).

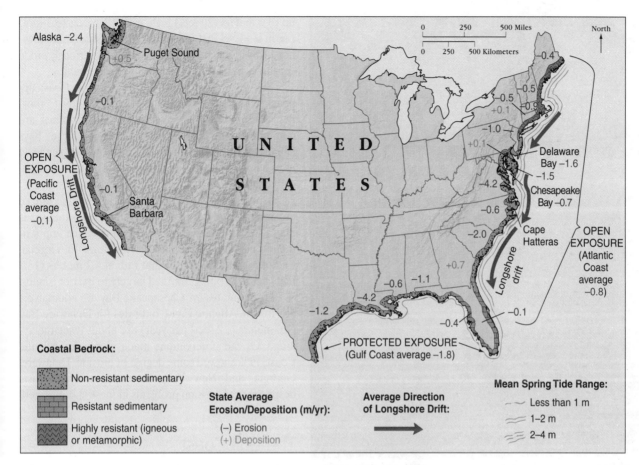

FIGURE 10.15 Factors affecting U.S. coasts and rates of erosion and deposition.
Map showing U.S. coastal bedrock type (*yellow, blue,* and *brown colors*), the mean spring-tide range (*light blue lines*), degree of exposure, and average direction of longshore drift (*purple arrows*). Also, for each coastal state, the map shows the average rate of erosion (indicated by *red negative numbers*) or deposition (indicated by *green positive numbers*) between 1979 and 1983 in meters per year.

The Atlantic Coast

Figure 10.15 shows that the U.S. Atlantic Coast has a variety of complex coastal conditions:

- Most of the Atlantic Coast is exposed to storm waves from the open ocean. Barrier islands from Massachusetts southward, however, protect the mainland from large storm waves.

- Tidal ranges generally increase from less than 1 meter (3.3 feet) along the Florida coast to more than 2 meters (6.5 feet) in Maine.

- Bedrock for most of Florida is a resistant type of sedimentary rock called *limestone*. Most of the bedrock northward through New Jersey, however, consists of nonresistant sedimentary rocks formed in the recent geologic past. As these rocks rapidly erode, they supply sand to barrier islands and other depositional features common along the coast. The bedrock north of New York consists of very resistant rock types.

- From New York northward, continental glaciers affected the coastal region directly. Many coastal features, including Long Island and Cape Cod, are glacial deposits (called *moraines*) left behind when the glaciers melted.

North of Cape Hatteras in North Carolina, the coast is subject to very high-energy waves during fall and winter when powerful storms called *nor'easters* (north-easters) blow in from the North Atlantic. The energy of these storms generates waves

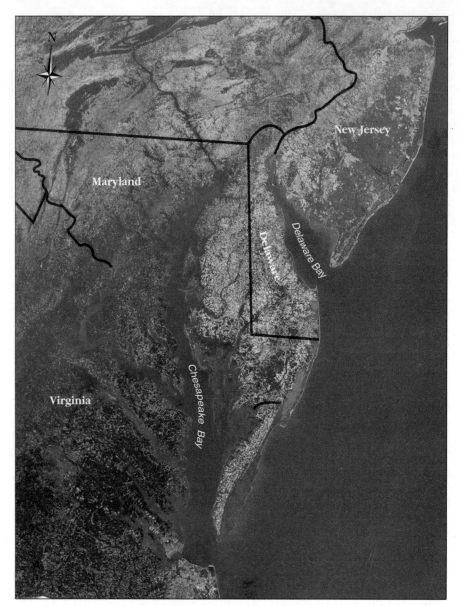

FIGURE 10.16 Drowned river valleys. Satellite false-color image of drowned river valleys along the East Coast of the United States, including the Chesapeake and Delaware Bays, which were formed by a relative rise in sea level that followed the end of the Pleistocene Ice Age.

up to 6 meters (20 feet) high, with a 1-meter (3.3-foot) rise in sea level that follows the low pressure as it moves northward. Such high-energy conditions seriously erode coastlines that are predominantly depositional.

Sea level along most of the Atlantic Coast appears to be rising at a rate of about 0.3 meter (1 foot) per century. Drowned river valleys, for instance, are common along the coast and form large bays (Figure 10.16). In northern Maine, however, sea level may be dropping as the continent rebounds isostatically from the melting of the Pleistocene ice sheet.

The Atlantic Coast has an average annual rate of erosion of 0.8 meter (2.6 feet), which means that sea is migrating landward each year by a distance approximately equal to the length of your legs! In Virginia, the loss is over five times that rate at 4.2 meters (13.7 feet) per year but is confined largely to barrier islands.

Erosion rates for Chesapeake Bay are about average for the Atlantic Coast, but rates for Delaware Bay (1.6 meters [5.2 feet] per year) are about twice the average. Of the observations made along the Atlantic Coast, 79% showed some degree of erosion. Delaware, Georgia, and New York have depositional coasts despite serious erosion problems in these states as well.

The Gulf Coast

The Mississippi River Delta, which is deposited in an area with a tidal range of less than 1 meter (3.3 feet), dominates the Louisiana–Texas portion of the Gulf Coast. Except during the hurricane season (June to November), wave energy is generally low. Tectonic subsidence is common throughout the Gulf Coast, and the average rate of sea level rise is similar to that of the southeast Atlantic Coast, about 0.3 meter (1 foot) per century. Some areas of coastal Louisiana have experienced a 1-meter (3.3-foot) rise during the last century due to the compaction of Mississippi River sediments by overlying weight.

The average rate of erosion is 1.8 meters (6 feet) per year in the Gulf Coast. The Mississippi River Delta experiences the greatest rate, averaging 4.2 meters (13.7 feet) per year. Erosion is made worse by barge channels dredged through marshlands, and Louisiana has lost more than 1 million acres of delta since 1900. Louisiana is now losing marshland at a rate exceeding 130 square kilometers (50 square miles) per year.

Although all Gulf states show a net loss of land, and the Gulf Coast has a greater erosion rate than the Atlantic Coast, only 63% of the shore is receding because of erosion. The high average rate of erosion reflects the heavy losses in the Mississippi River Delta.

The Pacific Coast

The Pacific Coast is generally experiencing less erosion than the Atlantic and Gulf Coasts. Along the Pacific Coast, relatively young and easily eroded sedimentary rocks dominate the bedrock, with local outcrops of more resistant rock types. Tectonically, the coast is rising, as shown by marine (wave-cut) terraces (Figure 10.17). Sea level still shows at least small rates of rise, except for segments along the coast of Oregon and Alaska. The tidal range is mostly between 2.0 and 3.6 meters (6.6 and 12 feet).

The Pacific Coast is fully exposed to large storm waves and as a result is said to have *open exposure*. High-energy waves may strike the coast in winter, with typical wave heights of 1 meter (3.3 feet). Frequently, the wave height increases to 2 meters (6.6 feet), and a few times per year 6-meter (20-foot) waves hammer the shore! These high-energy waves erode sand from many beaches. The exposed beaches, which are composed primarily of pebbles and boulders during the winter months, regain their sand during the summer when smaller waves occur.

Many Pacific Coast rivers have been dammed for flood control and hydroelectric power generation. The amount of sediment supplied by rivers to the shoreline for longshore transport is reduced, resulting in beach starvation in some areas.

With an average erosion rate of only 0.005 meter (0.016 foot)[5] per year and only 30% of the coast showing erosion loss, the Pacific Coast is eroded much less than the Atlantic and Gulf Coasts. Nevertheless, high wave energy and relatively soft rocks result in high erosion rates of 0.3 meters (1 foot) per year or more in some parts of the Pacific Coast. In some parts of Alaska, for example, the average rate of erosion is 2.4 meters (7.9 feet) per year.

Of the Pacific states, only Washington shows a net sediment deposition. The long, protected Washington shoreline within Puget Sound helps skew the Pacific Coast values (see Figure 10.15). Although the average erosion rate for California is only 0.1 meter (4 inches) per year, over 80% of the California coast is experiencing erosion, with rates as high as 0.6 meter (2 feet) per year.

FIGURE 10.17 Marine (wave-cut) terraces. Each marine terrace on San Clemente Island offshore of Southern California was created by wave activity at sea level. Subsequently, each terrace has been exposed by tectonic uplift. The highest (oldest) terraces near the top of the photo are now about 400 meters (1320 feet) above sea level.

KEY CONCEPT
U.S. coastal regions are affected by many variables, including composition of the coastal bedrock, degree of exposure to waves, and tidal range. Most U.S. coastal regions are experiencing erosion.

STUDENTS SOMETIMES ASK...

I have the opportunity to live in a house at the edge of a coastal cliff where there is an incredible view along the entire coast. Is it safe from coastal erosion?

Based on what you've described, most certainly not! Geologists have long known that cliffs are naturally unstable. Even if cliffs appear to be stable (or have been stable for a number of years), one significant storm can severely damage them.

The most common cause of coastal erosion is direct wave attack, which undermines the support and causes the cliff to fail. You might want to check the base of the cliff and examine the local bedrock to determine for yourself if you think it will withstand the pounding of powerful storm waves that can move rocks weighing several tons. Other dangers include drainage runoff, weaknesses in the bedrock, slumps and landslides, seepage of water through the cliff, and even burrowing animals. Although all states enforce a setback from the edge of the cliff for all new buildings, sometimes that isn't enough because large sections of "stable" cliffs can fail all at once. For instance, several city blocks of real estate have been eroded from the edge of cliffs during the last 100 years in some areas of Southern California. Even though the view sounds outstanding, you may find out the hard way that the house is built a little *too* close to the edge of a cliff!

[5]0.005 meter is equal to 5 millimeters (0.2 inch).

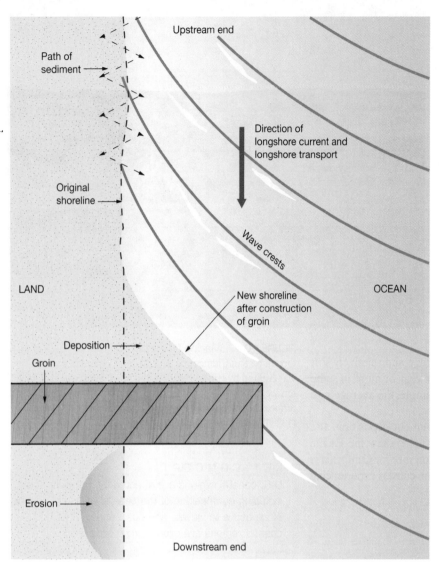

FIGURE 10.18 Interference of sand movement. Hard stabilization like the groin shown here interferes with the movement of sand along the beach, causing deposition of sand upcoast of the groin and erosion immediately downcoast, modifying the shape of the beach.

10.6 What Is Hard Stabilization?

Coastal residents continually modify coastal sediment erosion/deposition in attempts to improve or preserve their property. Structures built to protect a coast from erosion or to prevent the movement of sand along a beach are known as **hard stabilization**, or *armoring of the shore*. Hard stabilization can take many forms and often results in predictable yet unwanted outcomes.

Groins and Groin Fields

One type of hard stabilization is a **groin** (*groin* = ground). Groins are built perpendicular to a coastline and are specifically designed to trap sand moving along the coast in longshore transport (Figure 10.18). They are constructed of many types of material, but large blocks of rocky material called **rip-rap** is most common. Sometimes groins are even constructed of sturdy wood pilings (similar to a fence built out into the ocean).

Although a groin traps sand on its *upcoast side*, erosion occurs immediately downcoast of the groin because the sand that is normally found just downcoast of the groin is trapped on the groin's upcoast side. To lessen the erosion, another groin can be constructed downcoast, which in turn also creates erosion downcoast from it. More groins are needed to alleviate the beach erosion, and soon a **groin field** is created (Figure 10.19).

Does a groin (or a groin field) actually retain more sand on the beach? Sand eventually migrates around the end of the groin, so there is no additional sand on the beach; it is only *distributed differently*. With proper engineering and by taking into account the regional

FIGURE 10.19 Groin field. A series of groins has been built along the shoreline north of Ship Bottom, New Jersey, in an attempt to trap sand, altering the distribution of sand on the beach. The view is toward the north, and the primary direction of longshore current is toward the bottom of the photo (toward the south).

sand transport budget and seasonal wave activity, an equilibrium may be reached that allows sufficient sand to move along the coast before excessive erosion occurs downcoast from the last groin. However, some serious erosional problems have developed in many areas resulting from attempts to stabilize sand on the beach by the excessive use of groins.

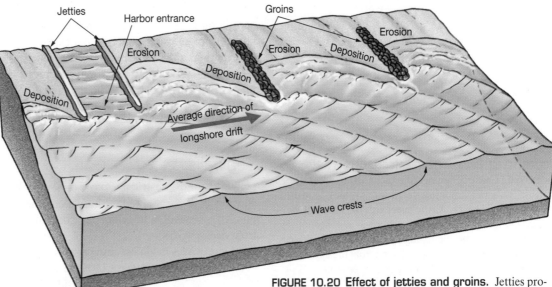

FIGURE 10.20 Effect of jetties and groins. Jetties protect a harbor entrance and usually occur in pairs. Groins are built specifically to trap sand moving in the longshore transport system and occur individually or as a groin field. Both structures cause deposits of sand on their upcoast sides and an equal amount of erosion downcoast.

Jetties

Another type of hard stabilization is a **jetty** (*jettee* = to project outward). A jetty is similar to a groin because it is built perpendicular to the shore and is usually constructed of rip-rap. The purpose of a jetty, however, is to protect harbor entrances from waves and only secondarily does it trap sand (Figure 10.20). Because jetties are usually built in closely spaced pairs and can be quite long, they can cause more pronounced upcoast deposition and downcoast erosion than groins (Figure 10.21).

Breakwaters

Figure 10.22 shows a **breakwater**—hard stabilization built parallel to a shoreline—that was constructed to create the harbor at Santa Barbara, California. California's longshore drift is predominantly southward, so the breakwater on the western side of the harbor accumulated sand that had migrated eastward along the coast. The beach to the west of the harbor continued to grow until finally the sand moved around the breakwater and began to fill in the harbor (Figure 10.22).

While abnormal deposition occurred to the west, erosion proceeded at an alarming rate east of the harbor. The waves east of the harbor were no greater than before, but the sand that had formerly moved down the coast was now trapped behind the breakwater.

A similar situation occurred in Santa Monica, California, where a breakwater was built to provide a boat anchorage. A bulge in the beach soon formed behind (inshore of) the breakwater and severe erosion occurred downcoast (Figure 10.23). The breakwater interfered with the natural transport of sand by blocking the waves that used to keep the sand moving. If something was not done to put energy back into the system, the breakwater would soon be attached by a tombolo of sand, and further erosion downcoast might destroy coastal structures.

In Santa Barbara and Santa Monica, dredging was used to compensate for erosion downcoast from the breakwater and to keep the harbor or anchorage from filling with sand. Sand dredged from behind the breakwater is pumped down the coast so it can reenter the longshore drift and replenish the eroded beach.

Coastal Stabilization Structures

FIGURE 10.21 Jetties at Santa Cruz Harbor, California. These jetties protect the inlet to Santa Cruz Harbor and interrupt the flow of sand, which is toward the right (southward). Notice the buildup of sand to the left (upcoast) of the jetties and the corresponding erosion to the right (downcoast).

The dredging operation has stabilized the situation in Santa Barbara, but at a considerable (and ongoing) expense. In Santa Monica, dredging was conducted until the breakwater was largely destroyed during winter storms in 1982–1983. Shortly thereafter, wave energy was able to move sand along the coast again, and the system was restored to normal conditions. When people interfere with natural processes in the coastal region, they must provide the energy needed to replace what they have misdirected through modification of the shore environment.

Seawalls

One of the most destructive types of hard stabilization is a **seawall** (Figure 10.24), which is built parallel to the shore along the landward side of the berm. The purpose of a seawall is to armor the coastline and protect landward developments from ocean waves.

Once waves begin breaking against a seawall, however, turbulence generated by the abrupt release of wave energy quickly erodes the sediment on its seaward side, which can eventually cause it to collapse into the surf (Figure 10.24). In many cases where seawalls have been used to protect property on barrier islands, the seaward slope of the island beach has steepened and the rate of erosion has increased, causing the destruction of the recreational beach.

A well-designed seawall may last for many decades, but the constant pounding of waves eventually takes its toll (Figure 10.25). In the long run, the cost of repairing or replacing seawalls will be more than the property is worth, and the sea will claim more of the coast through the natural processes of erosion. It's just a matter of time for homeowners who live too close to the coast, many of whom are gambling that their houses won't be destroyed in their lifetimes.

FIGURE 10.22 Breakwater at Santa Barbara Harbor, California. Construction of a shore-connected breakwater at Santa Barbara Harbor interfered with the longshore drift, creating a broad beach. As the beach extended around the breakwater into the harbor, the harbor was in danger of being closed off by accumulating sand. As a result, dredging operations were initiated to move sand from the harbor downcoast, where it helped reduce coastal erosion.

FIGURE 10.23 Breakwater at Santa Monica, California. (a) The shoreline and pier at Santa Monica as it appeared in 1931. **(b)** The same area in 1949, showing that the construction of a breakwater to create a boat anchorage disrupted the longshore transport of sand and caused a bulge of sand in the beach. North is to the right in both images.

(a) September 18, 1931

(b) October 21, 1949

FIGURE 10.24 Seawalls and beaches. When a seawall is built along a beach (such as on this barrier island) to protect beachfront property **(a)**, a large storm can remove the beach from the seaward side of the wall and steepen its seaward slope **(b)**. Eventually, the wall is undermined and falls into the sea **(c)**. The property is lost **(d)** as the oversteepened beach slope advances landward in its effort to reestablish a natural slope angle.

10.7 What Alternatives to Hard Stabilization Exist?

Is it better to preserve the houses of a few people who have built too close to the shore at the expense of armoring the coast with hard stabilization and destroying the recreational beach? If you own coastal property, your response would probably be different from the general beachgoing public. Because hard stabilization has been shown to have negative environmental consequences, alternatives have been sought.

Construction Restrictions

One of the simplest alternatives to the use of hard stabilization is to restrict construction in areas prone to coastal erosion. Unfortunately, this is becoming less and less an option as coastal regions experience population increases and governments increase the risk of damage and injuries because of programs like the *National Flood Insurance Program* (*NFIP*). Since its inception in 1968, NFIP has paid out billions of dollars in federal subsidy to repair or replace high-risk

FIGURE 10.25 Seawall damage. A seawall in Solana Beach, California, that has been damaged by waves and needs repair. Although seawalls appear to be sturdy, they can be destroyed by the continual pounding of high-energy storm waves.

coastal structures. As a result, NFIP has actually *encouraged* construction in exactly the unsafe locations it was designed to prevent![6] Further, many homeowners spend large amounts of money rebuilding structures and fortifying their property.

Beach Replenishment

Another alternative to hard stabilization is **beach replenishment** (also called **beach nourishment**), in which sand is added to the beach to replace lost sediment (Figure 10.26). Although rivers naturally supply sand to most beaches, dams on rivers restrict the sand supply that would normally arrive at beaches. When dams are built, their effect on beaches far downcoast is rarely considered. It's not until beaches begin disappearing that the rivers are seen as parts of much larger systems that operate along the coast.

Beach replenishment is expensive, however, because huge volumes of sand must be continually supplied to the beach. The cost of beach replenishment depends on the type and quantity of material placed on the beach, how far the material must be transported, and how it is to be distributed on the beach. Most sand used for replenishment comes from offshore areas, but sand that is dredged from nearby rivers, drained dams, harbors, and lagoons is also used.

The average cost of sand used to replenish beaches is between $5 and $10 per 0.76 cubic meter (1 cubic yard). In comparison, a typical top-loading trash dumpster holds about 2.3 cubic meters (3 cubic yards) of material, and a typical dump truck has a volume of about 45 cubic meters (60 cubic yards). The drawbacks of beach replenishment projects are that a huge volume of sand must be moved and that new

FIGURE 10.26 Beach replenishment. Beach replenishment projects, such as this one in Carlsbad, California, are used to widen beaches. Beach replenishment involves dredging sand from offshore or coastal locations, pumping it through a pipe (*lower right*), and spreading it across the beach.

[6]Recent changes in regulations of the Federal Emergency Management Agency (FEMA), which oversees NFIP, are intended to curb this practice.

sand must be supplied on a regular basis. These problems often cause replenishment projects to exceed the monetary limits of what can be reasonably accomplished. For example, a small beach replenishment project of several hundred cubic meters can cost around $10,000 per year. Larger projects—several thousand cubic meters of sand—cost several million dollars per year.

Relocation

U.S. coastal policy has recently shifted from defending coastal property in high-hazard areas to removing structures and letting nature reclaim the beach. This approach is called **relocation**, which involves moving structures to safer locations as they become threatened by erosion. One example of the successful use of this technique is the relocation of the Cape Hatteras Lighthouse in North Carolina (see Box 10.2). Relocation, if used wisely, can allow humans to live in balance with the natural processes that continually modify beaches.

> **KEY CONCEPT**
> Hard stabilization includes groins, jetties, breakwaters, and seawalls, all of which alter the coastal environment and result in changes in the shape of the beach. Alternatives to hard stabilization include construction restrictions, beach replenishment, and relocation.

Chapter in Review

- *The coastal region changes continuously.* The *shore* is the region of contact between the oceans and the continents, lying between the lowest low tides and the highest elevation on the continents affected by storm waves. The *coast* extends inland from the shore as far as marine-related features can be found. The *coastline* marks the boundary between the shore and the coast. The shore is divided into the *foreshore*, extending from low tide to high tide, and the *backshore*, extending beyond the high tide line to the coastline. Seaward of the low tide shoreline are the *nearshore* zone, extending to the breaker line, and the *offshore* zone beyond.

- *A beach is a deposit of the shore area,* consisting of wave-worked sediment that moves along a wave-cut bench. It includes the *recreational beach, berm, beach face, low tide terrace,* one or more *longshore bars,* and *longshore trough.* Beaches are composed of whatever material is locally available.

- *Waves that break at the shore move sand perpendicular to shore* (toward and away from shore). In *light wave activity,* swash dominates the transport system and sand is moved up the beach face toward the berm. In *heavy wave activity,* backwash dominates the transport system and sand is moved down the beach face away from the berm toward longshore bars. In a natural system, there is a *balance between light and heavy wave activity,* alternating between sand piled on the berm (*summertime beach*) and sand stripped from the berm (*wintertime beach*), respectively.

- *Sand is moved parallel to the shore, too.* Waves breaking at an angle to the shore create a *longshore current that results in a zigzag movement of sediment called longshore drift* (longshore transport). Each year, *millions of tons of sediment are moved from upcoast to downcoast ends of beaches.* Most of the year, *longshore drift moves southward along both the Pacific and Atlantic shores* of the United States.

- *Erosional shores are characterized by headlands, wave-cut cliffs, sea caves, sea arches, sea stacks, and marine terraces* (caused by uplift of a wave-cut bench). Wave erosion increases as more of the shore is exposed to the open ocean, tidal range decreases, and bedrock weakens.

- *Depositional shores are characterized by beaches, spits, bay barriers, tombolos, barrier islands, deltas, and beach compartments.* Viewed from ocean side to lagoon side, barrier islands commonly have an ocean beach, dunes, barrier flat, and salt marsh. Deltas form at the mouths of rivers that

carry more sediment to the ocean than the longshore current can carry away. *Beach starvation* occurs in beach compartments and other areas where the sand supply is interrupted.

- *Shorelines can also be classified as emerging or submerging based on their position relative to sea level.* Ancient wave-cut cliffs and stranded beaches well above the present shoreline may indicate a drop in sea level relative to land. Old drowned beaches, submerged dunes, wave-cut cliffs, or drowned river valleys may indicate a rise in sea level relative to land. *Changes in sea level may result from tectonic processes causing local movement of the landmass or from eustatic processes changing the amount of water in the oceans or the capacity of ocean basins.* Melting of continental ice caps and glaciers during the past 18,000 years has caused a *eustatic rise in sea level of about 120 meters (400 feet).*

- *Sea level is rising along the Atlantic Coast* about 0.3 meter (1 foot) per century, and the average erosion rate is 0.8 meter (2.6 feet) per year. *Along the Gulf Coast,* sea level is rising 0.3 meter (1 foot) per century, and the average rate of erosion is 1.8 meters (6 feet) per year. The Mississippi River Delta is eroding at 4.2 meters (13.7 feet) per year, resulting in a large loss of wetlands every year. *Along the Pacific Coast,* the average erosion rate is only 0.005 meter (0.016 foot) per year. Different shorelines erode at different rates depending on wave exposure, amount of uplift, and type of bedrock.

- *Hard stabilization, such as groins, jetties, breakwaters, and seawalls, is often constructed in an attempt to stabilize a shoreline.* Groins (built to trap sand) and *jetties* (built to protect harbor entrances) widen the beach by trapping sediment on their upcoast side, but erosion usually becomes a problem downcoast. Similarly, *breakwaters* (built parallel to a shore) trap sand behind the structure but cause unwanted erosion downcoast. *Seawalls* (built to armor a coast) often cause loss of the recreational beach. Eventually, the constant pounding of waves destroys all types of hard stabilization.

- *Alternatives to hard stabilization* include *construction restrictions* in areas prone to coastal erosion, *beach replenishment* (*beach nourishment*), which is an expensive and temporary way to reduce beach starvation, and *relocation,* which is a technique that has been successfully used to protect coastal structures

Key Terms

Backshore (p. 285)
Backwash (p. 287)
Barrier island (p. 292)
Bay barrier (bay-mouth bar) (p. 292)
Beach (p. 285)
Beach compartment (p. 296)
Beach face (p. 286)
Beach replenishment (beach nourishment) (p. 308)
Beach starvation (p. 298)
Berm (p. 286)
Breakwater (p. 305)
Coast (p. 285)
Coastline (p. 285)

Delta (p. 296)
Depositional shore (p. 289)
Drowned beach (p. 298)
Drowned river valley (p. 298)
Emerging shoreline (p. 298)
Erosional shore (p. 289)
Eustatic sea level change (p. 299)
Foreshore (p. 285)
Groin (p. 304)
Groin field (p. 304)
Hard stabilization (p. 304)
Headland (p. 289)
Jetty (p. 305)
Longshore bar (p. 286)

Longshore current (p. 287)
Longshore drift (longshore transport) (p. 288)
Longshore trough (p. 286)
Marine terrace (p. 289)
Nearshore (p. 285)
Offshore (p. 285)
Relocation (p. 309)
Rip current (p. 290)
Rip-rap (p. 304)
Sea arch (p. 289)
Sea cave (p. 289)
Sea stack (p. 289)
Seawall (p. 306)

Shore (p. 285)
Shoreline (p. 285)
Spit (p. 292)
Stranded beach deposit (p. 298)
Submerged dune topography (p. 298)
Submerging shoreline (p. 298)
Summertime beach (p. 287)
Swash (p. 287)
Tombolo (p. 292)
Wave-cut bench (p. 285)
Wave-cut cliff (p. 289)
Wintertime beach (p. 287)

Review Questions

1. Describe differences between summertime and wintertime beaches. Explain why these differences occur.

2. What variables affect the speed of longshore currents?

3. What is longshore drift, and how is it related to a longshore current?

4. How is the flow of water in a stream similar to a longshore current? How are the two different?

5. Why does the direction of longshore current sometimes reverse in direction? Along both U.S. coasts, what is the primary direction of annual longshore current?

6. Describe the formation of rip currents. What is the best strategy to ensure that you won't drown if you are caught in a rip current?

7. Discuss the formation of such erosional features as wave-cut cliffs, sea caves, sea arches, sea stacks, and marine terraces.

8. Describe the origin of these depositional features: spit, bay barrier, tombolo, and barrier island.

9. Describe the response of a barrier island to a rise in sea level. Why do some barrier islands develop peat deposits running through them from the ocean beach to the salt marsh?

10. Discuss why some rivers have deltas and others do not. What are the factors that determine whether a "bird's-foot" delta (like the Mississippi Delta) or a smoothly curved delta (like the Nile Delta) will form?

11. Describe all parts of a beach compartment. What will happen when dams are built across all of the rivers that supply sand to the beach?

12. Compare the causes and effects of tectonic versus eustatic changes in sea level.

13. List the two basic processes by which coasts advance seaward, and list their counterparts that lead to coastal retreat.

14. List and discuss four factors that influence the classification of a coast as either erosional or depositional.

15. Describe the tectonic and depositional processes causing subsidence along the Atlantic Coast.

16. List the types of hard stabilization and describe what each is intended to do.

17. Describe alternatives to hard stabilization, including potential drawbacks of each.

Critical Thinking Exercises

1. To help reinforce your knowledge of beach terminology, construct and label your own diagram similar to Figure 10.1 from memory.

2. Compare the Atlantic Coast, Gulf Coast, and Pacific Coast by describing the conditions and features of emergence—submergence and erosion—deposition that are characteristic of each.

3. Draw an aerial view of a shoreline to show the effect on erosion and deposition caused by constructing a groin, a jetty, a breakwater, and a seawall within the coastal environment.

Oceanography on the Web

Visit the *Essentials of Oceanography* Online Study Guide for Internet resources, including chapter-specific quizzes to test your understanding and Web links to further your exploration of the topics in this chapter.

The *Essentials of Oceanography* Online Study Guide is at http://www.mygeoscienceplace.com/.

Gash in the hull of the cargo freighter *Cosco Busan* after it hit the Bay Bridge.

In November 2007, the *Cosco Busan* hit a support structure of California's San Francisco–Oakland Bay Bridge (*background*) while underway in heavy fog. As a result of the collision, the vessel leaked an estimated 200,000 million liters (53,500 million gallons) of toxic bunker fuel oil, which washed up throughout the bay and floated out of the bay with the tides, spreading onto northern California beaches. The spill necessitated a cleanup that is estimated to have cost $70 million.

"Most people think of oceans as so immense and bountiful that it's difficult to imagine any significant impact from human activity. Now we've begun to recognize how much of an impact we do have."

—*Jane Lubchenco,*
marine ecologist (2002)

11

THE COASTAL OCEAN

The coastal ocean is a very busy place, filled with life, commerce, recreation, fisheries, and waste. Of the world fishery,[1] about 95% is obtained within 320 kilometers (200 miles) of shore. Coastal waters also support about 95% of the total mass of life in the oceans. Further, coastal estuary and wetland environments are among the most biologically productive ecosystems on Earth and serve as nursery grounds for many species of marine organisms that inhabit the open ocean. In addition, these waters are the focal point of most shipping routes, oil and gas production, and recreational activities.

Coastal waters are also the conduits through which land-derived compounds must pass to reach the open ocean. Numerous chemical, physical, and biological processes occur in these environments that tend to protect the quality of the water in the open ocean. The ocean has a tremendous ability to assimilate waste materials, yet negative results are beginning to be felt worldwide. Recently, the effects of cumulative stresses on the oceans have become large enough for humans to finally acknowledge the finiteness and fragility of the world environment. In the United States, for example, comprehensive reports such as the U.S. Commission on Ocean Policy and the Pew Oceans Commission have identified an emerging national crisis regarding damage being done to ocean and coastal resources, calling for a plan of action to restore coastal environments.

Earth's rapidly expanding human population has put an ever-increasing stress on the marine environment. Human activities are increasingly altering coastal environments in two main ways: (1) the destruction of coastal ecosystems through development and exploitation and (2) the addition of land-based waste products into coastal waters. Pollution in coastal waters comes from many sources, such as accidental spills of petroleum, the accumulation of sewage, and certain chemicals (such as DDT, PCBs, and mercury). These pollutants—either alone or in combination with each other—often have severe deleterious effects on marine organisms.

In this chapter, we'll first examine the legal framework of who owns the ocean. Then we'll explore the properties of coastal waters before discussing how they're being affected and what can be done to reduce or eliminate pollution from coastal waters.

11.1 What Laws Govern Ocean Ownership?

Who owns the ocean? Who owns the sea floor? If a company wanted to drill for oil offshore between two different countries, would it have to obtain permission from either country? The current extraction of minerals and petroleum on the coastal sea floor necessitates laws that unambiguously answer these questions. Further offshore, exploration and development of marine resources is also occurring

---

[1]The term *fishery* refers to fish caught by commercial fishers. Marine fisheries are discussed in Chapter 13, "Biological Productivity and Energy Transfer."

far from the jurisdiction of any country. Furthermore, overfishing and pollution are worsening. Are these kinds of problems covered by long-established laws? The answer is yes . . . and no.

Mare Liberum and the Territorial Sea

In 1609, Hugo Grotius, a Dutch jurist and scholar whose writings eventually helped formulate international law, urged freedom of the seas to all nations in his treatise *Mare liberum* (*mare* = sea, *liberum* = free), which was premised on the assumption that the sea's major known resource—fish—exists in inexhaustible supply. Nevertheless, controversy continued over whether nations could control a *portion* of an ocean, such as the ocean adjacent to a nation's coastline.

Dutch jurist Cornelius van Bynkershoek attempted to solve this problem in *De dominio maris* (*de* = of, *dominio* = domain, *maris* = sea) published in 1702. It provided for national domain over the sea out to the distance that could be protected by cannons from the shore, an area called the **territorial sea**. Just how far from shore did the territorial sea extend? The British had determined in 1672 that cannon range extended 1 league (3 nautical miles) from shore. Thus, every country with a coastline maintained ownership over a *three-mile territorial limit* from shore.

Law of the Sea

In response to new technology that facilitated mining the ocean floor, the first **United Nations Conference on the Law of the Sea**, held in 1958 in Geneva, Switzerland, established that prospecting and mining of minerals on the continental shelf was under the control of the country that owned the nearest land. Because the continental shelf is that portion of the sea floor extending from the coastline to where the slope markedly increases, the seaward limit of the shelf is subject to interpretation. Unfortunately, the continental shelf was not well defined in the treaty, which led to disputes. In 1960, the second United Nations Conference on the Law of the Sea was also held in Geneva, but it made little progress toward an unambiguous and fair treaty concerning ownership of the coastal ocean.

Meetings of the third Law of the Sea Conference were held during 1973–1982. A new Law of the Sea treaty was adopted by a vote of 130 to 4, with 17 abstentions. Most developing nations that could benefit significantly from the treaty voted to adopt it. The United States, Turkey, Israel, and Venezuela opposed the new treaty because it made sea floor mining unprofitable. The abstaining countries included the Soviet Union, Great Britain, Belgium, the Netherlands, Italy, and West Germany, all of which were interested in sea floor mining, too. Nevertheless, the treaty was ratified by the required 60th nation in 1993, establishing it as international law. Negotiations removed the objections of nations interested in sea floor mining, and the United States signed the revised treaty in 1994. Despite the fact that 153 coastal nations have ratified the treaty and have made it the definitive word on coastal law, the United States has still not officially ratified it, which means that the United States doesn't have the legal right to extend its maritime claims or hold a seat on the commission that reviews the plans of other countries. Recently, U.S. policymakers have advocated ratifying the treaty.

The Law of the Sea treaty specifies how coastal nations watch over their natural resources, settle maritime boundary disputes, and—especially in the Arctic—extend their rights to any riches on or beneath the adjacent sea floor. The primary components of the treaty are as follows:

1. **Coastal nations jurisdiction.** The treaty established a uniform 12-mile (19-kilometer) territorial sea and a 200-nautical-mile (370-kilometer) **exclusive economic zone (EEZ)** from all land (including islands) within a nation. Each of the 151 coastal nations has jurisdiction over mineral resources, fishing, and pollution regulation within its EEZ. If the continental shelf

(defined geologically) exceeds the 200-mile EEZ, the EEZ is extended to 350 nautical miles (648 kilometers) from shore.

2. **Ship passage.** The right of free passage for all vessels on the high seas is preserved. The right of free passage is also provided within territorial seas and through straits used for international navigation.

3. **Deep-ocean mineral resources.** Private exploitation of sea floor resources may proceed under the regulation of the International Seabed Authority (ISA), within which a mining company will be strictly controlled by the United Nations. This provision, which caused some industrialized nations to oppose ratification, required mining companies to fund two mining operations—their own and one operated by the regulatory United Nations. Recently, this portion of the law was modified to eliminate some of the regulatory components, thus favoring free market principles and development by private companies. Still, this portion of the Law of the Sea has been one of the most contentious issues in international law.

4. **Arbitration of disputes.** A United Nations Law of the Sea tribunal will arbitrate any disputes in the treaty or disputes concerning ownership rights.

The Law of the Sea puts 42% of the world's oceans under the control of coastal nations. The EEZ of the United States consists of about 11.5 million square kilometers (4.2 million square miles) (Figure 11.1), which is about 30% more than the entire land area of the United States and its territories. This huge offshore area is widely believed to have tremendous economic potential.

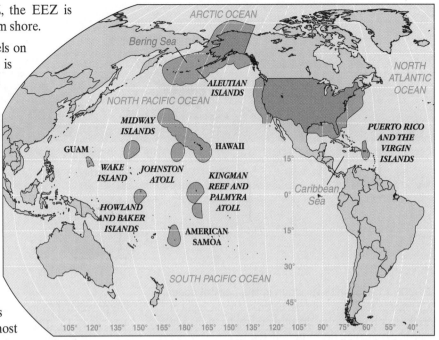

FIGURE 11.1 The U.S. exclusive economic zone (EEZ). A country's EEZ extends from shore to a distance of 200 nautical miles (370 kilometers) from the continent or islands. If the continental shelf (defined geologically) exceeds the 200-mile EEZ, the EEZ is extended to 350 nautical miles (648 kilometers) from shore.

> **KEY CONCEPT**
> Ownership of the ocean and sea floor is regulated by the internationally ratified Law of the Sea, which gives nations control of waters immediately adjacent to their coasts.

11.2 What Characteristics Do Coastal Waters Exhibit?

Coastal waters are those relatively shallow-water areas that adjoin continents or islands. If the continental shelf is broad and shallow, coastal waters can extend several hundred kilometers from land. If it has significant relief or drops rapidly onto the deep-ocean basin, on the other hand, coastal waters will occupy a relatively thin band near the margin of the land. Beyond coastal waters lies the *open ocean*.

Because of their proximity to land, coastal waters are directly influenced by processes that occur on or near land. River runoff and tidal currents, for example, have a far more significant effect on coastal waters than on the open ocean.

Salinity

Freshwater is less dense than seawater, so river runoff does not mix well with seawater along the coast. Instead, the freshwater forms a wedge at the surface, which creates a well-developed **halocline**[2] (Figure 11.2a). When water is shallow enough, however, tidal mixing causes freshwater to mix with seawater, thus reducing the salinity of the water column (Figure 11.2c). There is no halocline here; instead, the water column is **isohaline** (*iso* = same, *halo* = salt).

Freshwater runoff from the continents generally lowers the salinity of coastal regions compared to the open ocean. Where precipitation on land is mostly rain,

---

[2]Recall that a halocline (*halo* = salt, *cline* = slope) is a layer of rapidly changing salinity, as discussed in Chapter 5.

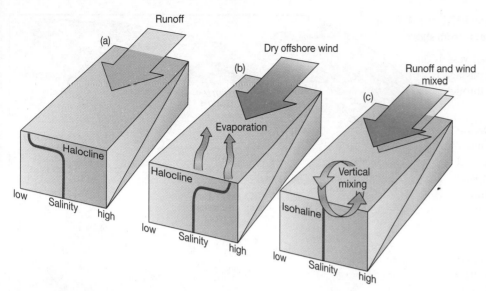

FIGURE 11.2 Salinity variation in the coastal ocean.
Changes in coastal salinity can be caused by the input of freshwater runoff **(a)**, by dry offshore winds causing a high rate of evaporation **(b)**, or by both **(c)**.

river runoff peaks in the rainy season. Where runoff is due mainly to melting snow and ice, on the other hand, runoff always peaks in summer.

Prevailing offshore winds can increase the salinity in some coastal regions. As winds travel over a continent, they usually lose most of their moisture. When these dry winds reach the ocean, they typically evaporate considerable amounts of water as they move across the surface of the coastal waters. The increased evaporation rate increases surface salinity, creating a halocline (Figure 11.2b). The gradient of the halocline, however, is reversed compared to the one developed from the input of freshwater (Figure 11.2a).

Temperature

In low-latitude coastal regions, where circulation with the open ocean is restricted, surface waters are prevented from mixing thoroughly, so sea surface temperatures may approach 45°C (113°F) (Figure 11.3a). Alternatively, sea ice forms in many high-latitude coastal areas where water temperatures are uniformly cold—generally lower than −2°C (28.4°F) (Figure 11.3b). In both low- and high-latitude coastal waters, **isothermal** (*iso* = same, *thermo* = heat) conditions prevail.

Surface temperatures in middle latitude coastal regions are coolest in winter and warmest in late summer. A strong **thermocline**[3] may develop from surface water being warmed during the summer (Figure 11.3c) and cooled during the

FIGURE 11.3 Temperature variation in the coastal ocean. Changes in coastal temperature depend on latitude. In low latitudes **(a)**, coastal waters may become uniformly warm. In high latitudes **(b)**, the temperature of coastal waters remains uniformly cold (near freezing). In the middle latitudes, coastal surface water is significantly warmed during summer **(c)** and cooled during the winter **(d)**.

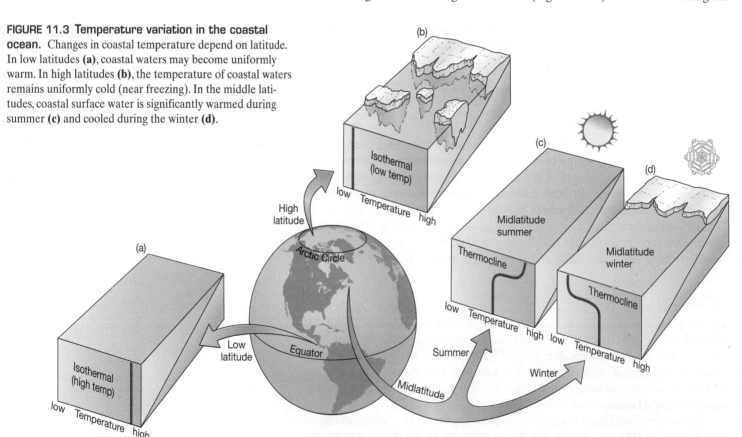

[3]Recall that a *thermocline* (*thermo* = heat, *cline* = slope) is a layer of rapidly changing temperature, as discussed in Chapter 5.

winter (Figure 11.3d). In summer, very high-temperature surface water may form a relatively thin layer. Vertical mixing reduces the surface temperature by distributing the heat through a greater volume of water, thus pushing the thermocline deeper and making it less pronounced. In winter, cooling increases the density of surface water, which causes it to sink.

Prevailing offshore winds can significantly affect surface water temperatures. These winds are relatively warm during the summer, so they increase the ocean surface temperature and seawater evaporation. During winter, they are much cooler than the ocean surface, so they absorb heat and cool surface water near shore. Mixing from strong winds may drive the thermoclines in Figures 11.3c and 11.3d deeper and even mix the entire water column, producing isothermal conditions. Tidal currents can also cause considerable vertical mixing in shallow coastal waters.

Coastal Geostrophic Currents

Recall from Chapter 7 that *geostrophic* (*geo* = earth, *strophio* = turn) *currents* move in a circular path around the middle of a current gyre. Wind and runoff create geostrophic currents in coastal waters, too, where they are called **coastal geostrophic currents**.

Where winds blow in a certain direction parallel to a coastline, they transport water toward the coast where it piles up along the shore. Gravity eventually pulls this water back toward the open ocean. As it runs downslope away from the shore, the Coriolis effect causes it to curve to the right in the Northern Hemisphere and to the left in the Southern Hemisphere. Thus, in the Northern Hemisphere, the coastal geostrophic current curves *northward* on the western coast and *southward* on the eastern coast of continents. These currents are reversed in the Southern Hemisphere.

A high-volume runoff of freshwater produces a surface wedge of freshwater that slopes away from the shore (Figure 11.4). This causes a surface flow of low-salinity water toward the open ocean, which the Coriolis effect curves to the right in the Northern Hemisphere and to the left in the Southern Hemisphere.

Coastal geostrophic currents are variable because they depend on the wind and the amount of runoff for their strength. If the wind is strong and the volume of runoff is high, then the currents are relatively strong. They are bounded on the ocean side by the steadier eastern or western boundary currents of subtropical gyres.

An example of a coastal geostrophic current is the **Davidson Current** that develops along the coast of Washington and Oregon during winter (Figure 11.4). Heavy precipitation (which produces high volumes of runoff) combines with strong southwesterly winds to produce a relatively strong northward-flowing current. It flows between the shore and the southward-flowing California Current.

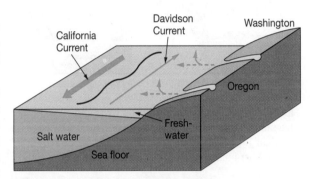

FIGURE 11.4 Davidson coastal geostrophic current. The Davidson Current is a coastal geostrophic current that flows north along the coast of Washington and Oregon. During the winter, runoff produces a freshwater wedge (*light blue*) that thins away from shore. This causes a surface flow of low-salinity water toward the open ocean, which is acted upon by the Coriolis effect and curves to the right.

KEY CONCEPT
The shallow coastal ocean adjoins land and experiences changes in salinity and temperature that are more dramatic than the open ocean. Coastal geostrophic currents can also develop.

11.3 What Types of Coastal Waters Exist?

The most important types of coastal waters include estuaries, lagoons, and marginal seas.

Estuaries

An **estuary** (*aestus* = tide) is a partially enclosed coastal body of water in which freshwater runoff dilutes salty ocean water. The most common estuary is a river mouth, where the river empties into the sea. Many bays, inlets, gulfs, and sounds may be considered estuaries, too. All estuaries exhibit large variations in temperature and/or salinity.

The mouths of large rivers form the most economically significant estuaries because many are seaports, centers of ocean commerce, and important commercial

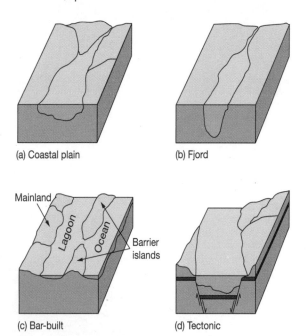

(a) Coastal plain

(b) Fjord

Mainland

Lagoon

Ocean

Barrier islands

(c) Bar-built

(d) Tectonic

FIGURE 11.5 Classifying estuaries by origin. Diagrammatic views of the four types of estuaries based on origin: **(a)** Coastal plain estuary; **(b)** glacially-carved fjord; **(c)** bar-built estuary; **(d)** tectonic estuary.

fisheries. Examples include Baltimore, New York, San Francisco, Buenos Aires, London, Tokyo, and many others.

ORIGIN OF ESTUARIES The estuaries of today exist because sea level has risen approximately 120 meters (400 feet) since major continental glaciers began melting 18,000 years ago. As described in Chapter 10, these glaciers covered portions of North America, Europe, and Asia during the Pleistocene Epoch, which is also referred to as the *Ice Age*. Four major classes of estuaries can be identified based on their origin (Figure 11.5):

1. A **coastal plain estuary** forms as sea level rises and floods existing river valleys. These estuaries, such as the Chesapeake Bay in Maryland and Virginia, are called *drowned river valleys* (see Figure 10.16).

2. A **fjord**[4] forms as sea level rises and floods a glaciated valley. Water-carved valleys have V-shaped profiles, but fjords are U-shaped valleys with steep walls. Commonly, a shallowly submerged glacial deposit of debris (called a *moraine*) is located near the ocean entrance, marking the farthest extent of the glacier. Fjords are common along the coasts of Alaska, Canada, New Zealand, Chile, and Norway (Figure 11.6a).

3. A **bar-built estuary** is shallow and is separated from the open ocean by sand bars that are deposited parallel to the coast by wave action. Lagoons that separate *barrier islands* from the mainland are bar-built estuaries. They are common along the U.S. Gulf and East Coasts, including Laguna Madre in Texas and Pamlico Sound in North Carolina (see Figure 10.9).

FIGURE 11.6 Estuaries. **(a)** Aerial view of an Alaskan fjord with an active glacier that extends into the upper part of the estuary. Fjords are steep-sided, deep, glacially formed estuaries that are flooded by the sea. **(b)** Aerial view of San Francisco Bay in California, which is a tectonic estuary that was created by the down-dropping of land between the two faults (*red lines*).

(a)

San Francisco Bay

S. F. City

0   5   10 MILES

0   5   10 KILOMETERS

(b)

---

[4]The Norwegian term *fjord* is pronounced "FEE-yord" and means a long, narrow sea inlet bordered by steep cliffs.

4. A **tectonic estuary** forms when faulting or folding of rocks creates a restricted downdropped area into which rivers flow. San Francisco Bay is in part a tectonic estuary (Figure 11.6b), formed by movement along faults, including the San Andreas Fault.

WATER MIXING IN ESTUARIES Generally, freshwater runoff moves across the upper layer of the estuary toward the open ocean, whereas denser seawater moves in a layer just below toward the head of the estuary. Mixing takes place at the contact between these water masses.

Estuaries are marine environments whose pH, salinity, and water levels vary, depending on the mixing between the river that feeds the estuary and the ocean from which it derives its salinity. Based on the physical characteristics of the estuary and the resulting mixing of freshwater and seawater, estuaries are classified into one of four main types, as shown in Figure 11.7:

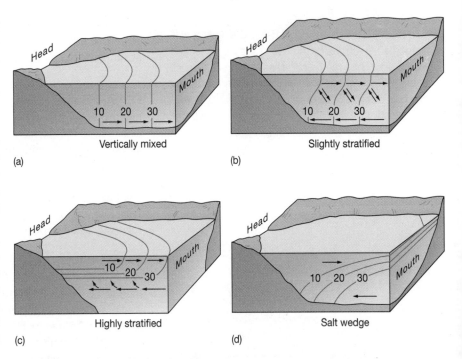

FIGURE 11.7 **Classifying estuaries by mixing.** The basic flow pattern in an estuary is a surface flow of less dense freshwater toward the ocean and an opposite flow in the subsurface of salty seawater into the estuary. Numbers represent salinity in ‰; arrows indicate flow directions. **(a)** Vertically mixed estuary. **(b)** Slightly stratified estuary. **(c)** Highly stratified estuary. **(d)** Salt wedge estuary.

1. A **vertically mixed estuary** is a shallow, low-volume estuary where the net flow always proceeds from the head of the estuary toward its mouth. Salinity at any point in the estuary is uniform from surface to bottom because river water mixes evenly with ocean water at all depths. Salinity simply increases from the head to the mouth of the estuary, as shown in Figure 11.7a. Salinity lines curve at the edge of the estuary because the Coriolis effect influences the inflow of seawater.

2. A **slightly stratified estuary** is a somewhat deeper estuary in which salinity increases from the head to the mouth at any depth, as in a vertically mixed estuary. However, two water layers can be identified. One is the less-saline, less-dense upper water from the river, and the other is the more saline, more dense deeper water from the ocean. These two layers are separated by a zone of mixing. The circulation that develops in slightly stratified estuaries is a net surface flow of low-salinity water toward the ocean and a net subsurface flow of seawater toward the head of the estuary (Figure 11.7b), which is called an **estuarine circulation pattern**.

3. A **highly stratified estuary** is a deep estuary in which upper-layer salinity increases from the head to the mouth, reaching a value close to that of open-ocean water. The deep-water layer has a rather uniform open-ocean salinity at any depth throughout the length of the estuary. An estuarine circulation pattern is well developed in this type of estuary (Figure 11.7c). Mixing at the interface of the upper water and the lower water creates a net movement from the deep-water mass into the upper water. Less-saline surface water simply moves from the head toward the mouth of the estuary, growing more saline as water from the deep mass mixes with it. Relatively strong haloclines develop at the contact between the upper and lower water masses.

4. A **salt wedge estuary** is an estuary in which a wedge of salty water intrudes from the ocean beneath the river water. This kind of estuary is typical of the mouths of deep, high-volume rivers. No horizontal salinity gradient exists at the surface because surface water is essentially fresh throughout the length of—and even beyond—the estuary (Figure 11.7d). There is, however, a *horizontal* salinity gradient at depth and a very pronounced vertical salinity gradient (a halocline) at any location throughout the length of the estuary. This halocline is shallower and more highly developed near the mouth of the estuary.

Within all estuaries, the predominant mixing pattern may vary with location, season, or tidal conditions. In addition, mixing patterns in real estuaries are rarely as simple as the models presented here.

ESTUARIES AND HUMAN ACTIVITIES Estuaries are important breeding grounds and protective nurseries for many marine animals, so the ecological well-being of estuaries is vital to fisheries and coastal environments worldwide. Nevertheless, estuaries support shipping, logging, manufacturing, waste disposal, and other activities that can potentially damage the environment.

Estuaries are most threatened where human population is large and expanding, but they can be severely damaged where populations are still modest, too. Development in the Columbia River estuary, for example, demonstrates how a relatively small population can damage an estuary.

Columbia River Estuary The Columbia River, which forms most of the border between Washington and Oregon, has a long salt-wedge estuary at its entrance to the Pacific Ocean (Figure 11.8). The strong flow of the river and tides drive a salt wedge as far as 42 kilometers (26 miles) upstream and raise the river's water level more than 3.5 meters (12 feet). When the tide falls, the huge flow of freshwater (up to 28,000 cubic meters [1,000,000 cubic feet] per second) creates a freshwater wedge that can extend hundreds of kilometers into the Pacific Ocean.

Most rivers create floodplains along their lower courses, which have rich soil that can be used for growing crops. In the late 19th century, farmers moved onto the floodplains to establish agriculture along the Columbia River. Eventually, protective dikes were built to prevent agricultural damage done by annual flooding. Flooding brings new nutrients, however, so the dikes deprived the floodplain of the nutrients necessary to sustain agriculture.

The river has been the principal conduit for the logging industry, which dominated the region's economy through most of its modern history. Fortunately, the river's ecosystem has largely survived the additional sediment caused by clear cutting by the logging industry. The construction of more than 250 dams along the river and its tributaries, on the other hand, has permanently altered the river's ecosystem. Many of these dams, for example, do not have salmon ladders, which help fish "climb" in short vertical steps around the dams to reach their spawning grounds at the headwaters of their home streams.

Even though the dams have caused a multitude of problems, they do provide flood control, electrical power, and a dependable source of water, all of which have become necessary to the region's economy. To aid shipping operations, the river receives periodic dredging of sediment, which brings an increased risk for pollution. If these kinds of problems have developed in such sparsely populated areas as the Columbia River estuary, then larger environmental effects must exist in more highly populated estuaries, such as the Chesapeake Bay.

Chesapeake Bay Estuary Chesapeake Bay is about 320 kilometers (200 miles) long and 56 kilometers (35 miles) wide at its widest point, making it the largest (and best studied) estuary in the United States (Figure 11.9). It drains a watershed of about 166,000 square kilometers (64,000 square miles) spread over six states that includes a population of over 15 million people. The length of the bay's shoreline is an astonishing 17,700 kilometers (11,000 miles) because of all the inlets created by the 19 major rivers and 400 creeks and tributaries that flow into it. The bay formed when the lower parts of the Susquehanna River were drowned by rising sea level after the most recent ice age.

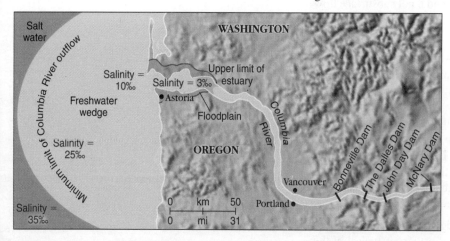

FIGURE 11.8 Columbia River estuary. The long estuary at the mouth of the Columbia River has been severely affected by interference with floodplains that have been diked, by logging activities, and—most significantly—by the construction of hydroelectric dams. The tremendous outflow of the Columbia River creates a large wedge of low-density freshwater that remains traceable far out at sea.

Chesapeake Bay is a slightly stratified estuary that experiences large seasonal changes in salinity, temperature, and dissolved oxygen. Figure 11.9a shows the estuary's average surface salinity, which increases oceanward. The salinity lines are oriented virtually north–south in the middle of the bay because of the Coriolis effect. Recall that the Coriolis effect causes flowing water to curve to the right in the Northern Hemisphere, so seawater entering the bay tends to hug the bay's *eastern* side, and freshwater flowing through the bay toward the ocean tends to hug its *western* side.

With maximum river flow in the spring, a strong halocline (and *pycnocline*[5]) develops, preventing the fresh surface water and saltier deep water from mixing. Beneath the pycnocline, which can be as shallow as 5 meters (16 feet), waters may become **anoxic** (*a* = without, *oxic* = oxygen) from May through August, as dead organic matter decays in the deep water (Figure 11.9b). Major kills of commercially important blue crab, oysters, and other bottom-dwelling organisms occur during this time.

The degree of stratification and extent of mortality of bottom-dwelling animals have increased since the early 1950s. Increased nutrients from sewage and agricultural fertilizers have been added to the bay during this time, too, which has increased the productivity of microscopic algae (algal blooms). When these organisms die, their remains accumulate as organic matter at the bottom of the bay and promote the development of anoxic conditions. In drier years with less river runoff, however, anoxic conditions aren't as widespread or severe in bottom waters (Figure 11.9c) because fewer nutrients are supplied.

Lagoons

Landward of barrier islands lie protected, shallow bodies of water called **lagoons** (see Figure 11.5c). Lagoons form in a bar-built type of estuary. Because of restricted circulation between lagoons and the ocean, three distinct zones can usually be identified within lagoons (Figure 11.10): (1) a *freshwater zone* that lies near the head of the lagoon where rivers enter; (2) a *transitional zone* of brackish[6] water that occurs near the middle of the lagoon, and (3) a *saltwater zone* that lies close to the lagoon's mouth.

Salinity within a lagoon is highest near the entrance and lowest near the head (Figure 11.10b). In latitudes that have seasonal variations in temperature and precipitation, ocean water flows through the entrance during a warm, dry summer to compensate for the volume of water lost through evaporation, thus increasing the salinity in the lagoon. Lagoons actually may become hypersaline[7] in arid regions, where evaporation rates are extremely high. Even though water flows into the lagoon from the open ocean to replace water lost by evaporation, the dissolved components do not evaporate and sometimes accumulate to extremely high levels. During the rainy season, the lagoon becomes much less saline as freshwater runoff increases.

Tidal effects are greatest near the entrance to the lagoon (Figure 11.10c) and diminish inland from the saltwater zone until they are nearly undetectable in the freshwater zone.

LAGUNA MADRE Laguna Madre is located along the Texas coast between Corpus Christi and the mouth of the Rio Grande (Figure 11.11). This long, narrow body of water is protected from the open ocean by Padre Island, a barrier island

---

[5]Recall that a *pycnocline* (*pycno* = density, *cline* = slope) is a layer of rapidly changing density, as discussed in Chapter 5. A pycnocline is caused by a change in temperature and/or salinity with depth.

[6]Brackish water is water with salinity between that of freshwater and seawater.

[7]Hypersaline conditions are created when water becomes excessively salty.

(a)

(b)

(c)

FIGURE 11.9 Chesapeake Bay. (a) Map of Chesapeake Bay, showing average surface salinity (*blue lines*) in ‰. The purple area in the middle of the bay represents anoxic (oxygen-poor) waters. **(b)** Profile along length of Chesapeake Bay showing dissolved oxygen concentration (in ppm) during July–August 1980, indicating deep anoxic waters (*purple*). **(c)** Comparison profile showing normal dissolved oxygen concentrations (in ppm) during July 1950.

(a) Geometry

(b) Salinity

(c) Tidal effects

FIGURE 11.10 Lagoons. A lagoon's typical **(a)** geometry, **(b)** salinity, and **(c)** tidal effects.

KEY CONCEPT

High evaporation rates in the Mediterranean Sea cause it to have a shallow inflow of surface seawater and a subsurface high-salinity outflow—a circulation pattern opposite that of most estuaries.

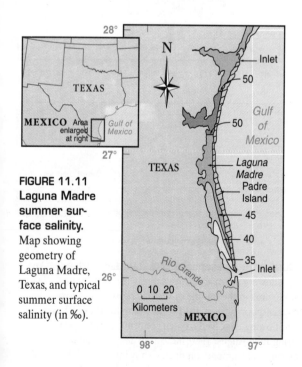

FIGURE 11.11 Laguna Madre summer surface salinity. Map showing geometry of Laguna Madre, Texas, and typical summer surface salinity (in ‰).

160 kilometers (100 miles) long. The lagoon probably formed about 6000 years ago as sea level approached its present height.

The tidal range of the Gulf of Mexico in this area is about 0.5 meter (1.6 feet). The inlets at each end of Padre Island are quite narrow (Figure 11.11), so there is very little tidal interchange between the lagoon and the open sea.

Laguna Madre is a hypersaline lagoon and much of it is less than 1 meter (3.3 feet) deep. As a result, there are large seasonal changes in temperature and salinity. Water temperatures reach 32°C (90°F) in the summer and can dip below 5°C (41°F) in winter. Salinities range from 2‰ when infrequent local storms provide large volumes of freshwater to over 100‰ during dry periods. High evaporation generally keeps salinity well above 50‰.[8]

Because even salt-tolerant marsh grasses cannot withstand such high salinities, the marsh has been replaced by an open sand beach on Padre Island. At the inlets, ocean water flows in as a surface wedge *over* the denser water of the lagoon and water from the lagoon flows out as a *subsurface* flow, which is the exact opposite of a typical estuarine circulation pattern.

Marginal Seas

At the margins of the ocean are relatively large semi-isolated bodies of water called **marginal seas.** Most of these seas result from tectonic events that have isolated low-lying pieces of ocean crust between continents, such as the Mediterranean Sea, or are created behind volcanic island arcs, such as the Caribbean Sea. These waters are shallower than and have varying degrees of exchange with the open ocean, depending on climate and geography; as a result, salinities and temperatures are substantially different from those of typical open ocean seawater.

A CASE STUDY: THE MEDITERRANEAN SEA The **Mediterranean** (*medi* = middle, *terra* = land) **Sea** is actually a number of small seas connected by narrow necks of water into one larger sea. It is the remnant of the ancient Tethys Sea that existed when all the continents were combined about 200 million years ago. It is more than 4300 meters (14,100 feet) deep and is one of the few inland seas in the world underlain by oceanic crust. Thick salt deposits and other evidence on the floor of the Mediterranean suggest that it nearly dried up about 6 million years ago, only to refill with a large salt water waterfall (see Web Box 4.1).

The Mediterranean is bounded by Europe and Asia Minor on the north and east and Africa to the south (Figure 11.12a). It is surrounded by land except for very shallow and narrow connections to the Atlantic Ocean through the Strait of Gibraltar (about 14 kilometers [9 miles] wide), and to the Black Sea through the Bosporus (roughly 1.6 kilometers [1 mile] wide). In addition, the Mediterranean Sea has a human-made passage to the Red Sea via the Suez Canal, a waterway 160 kilometers (100 miles) long that was completed in 1869. The Mediterranean Sea has a very irregular coastline, which divides it into subseas such as the Aegean Sea and Adriatic Sea, each of which has a separate circulation pattern.

An underwater ridge called a **sill**, which extends from Sicily to the coast of Tunisia at a depth of 400 meters (1300 feet), separates the Mediterranean into two major basins. This sill restricts the flow between the two basins, resulting in strong currents that run between Sicily and the Italian mainland through the Strait of Messina (Figure 11.12a).

Mediterranean Circulation The Mediterranean Sea has a very unusual and unique circulation pattern. This circulation is caused by the dry, intense heat of

---

[8]Recall that normal salinity in the open ocean averages 35‰.

the Middle East, where a huge volume of water evaporates from the eastern Mediterranean and causes a tremendous surface inflow of Atlantic Ocean water through the Strait of Gibraltar to replace the evaporated water. In fact, the water level in the eastern Mediterranean is generally 15 centimeters (6 inches) lower than at the Strait of Gibraltar. The surface flow follows the northern coast of Africa throughout the length of the Mediterranean and spreads northward across the sea (Figure 11.12a).

FIGURE 11.12 **Mediterranean Sea bathymetry and circulation.** (a) Map of the Mediterranean Sea region showing its subseas, depths, sills (underwater ridges), surface flow, and intermediate flow. (b) Diagrammatic view of Mediterranean circulation in the Gibraltar Sill area.

The remaining Atlantic Ocean water continues eastward to Cyprus. During winter, it sinks to form what is called the *Mediterranean Intermediate Water*, which has a temperature of 15°C (59°F) and a salinity of 39.1‰. This water flows westward at a depth of 200 to 600 meters (660 to 2000 feet) and returns to the North Atlantic as a *subsurface* flow through the Strait of Gibraltar (Figure 11.12b).

By the time the Mediterranean Intemediate Water passes through Gibraltar, its temperature has dropped to 13°C (55°F) and its salinity to 37.3‰ It is still denser than even Antarctic Bottom Water and much denser than water at this depth in the Atlantic Ocean, so it moves down the continental slope. While descending, it mixes with Atlantic Ocean water and becomes less dense. At a depth of about 1000 meters (3300 feet) its density equals that of the surrounding Atlantic Ocean, so it spreads in all directions (Figure 11.12b), sometimes forming deep-ocean eddies that last for more than two years and can be detected by satellite as far north as Iceland.

Circulation between the Mediterranean Sea and the Atlantic Ocean is typical of closed, restricted basins where evaporation exceeds precipitation. Low-latitude restricted basins such as this always lose water rapidly to evaporation, so surface flow from the open ocean must replace it. Evaporation of inflowing water from the open ocean increases the sea's salinity to very high values. This denser water eventually sinks and returns to the open ocean as a subsurface flow.

This circulation pattern, which is called **Mediterranean circulation**, is opposite that of most estuaries, which experience estuarine circulation where freshwater flows at the surface into the open ocean and salty water flows below the surface into the estuary. In estuaries, however, freshwater input exceeds water loss to evaporation, whereas evaporation exceeds input in the Mediterranean.

STUDENTS SOMETIMES ASK...

How can Mediterranean Intermediate Water sink if it's so warm?

While it is true that warm water has low density, remember that *both* salinity and temperature affect seawater density. In the case of the Mediterranean Intermediate Water, it has high enough salinity to increase its density despite being warm. Once its density increases enough, it sinks beneath the surface and retains its temperature and salinity characteristics as it flows out through the Strait of Gibraltar into the North Atlantic.

11.4 What Issues Face Coastal Wetlands?

Wetlands are ecosystems in which the water table is close to the surface, so they are typically saturated most of the time. Wetlands can border either freshwater or coastal environments. Coastal wetlands occur along the margins of coastal waters such as estuaries, lagoons, and marginal seas and include swamps, tidal flats, coastal marshes, and bayous.

Types of Coastal Wetlands

The two most important types of coastal wetlands are **salt marshes** and **mangrove swamps**. Both are intermittently submerged by ocean water, and both have oxygen-poor mud and accumulations of organic matter called *peat deposits*. Salt marshes support a variety of salt-tolerant grasses and other low-lying plants that are termed *halophytic* (*halo* = salt, *phyto* = plant), while mangrove swamps support various species of mangrove trees. Salt marshes generally occur between about 30 and 65 degrees latitude (Figures 11.13a and 11.13b), whereas mangroves are restricted to tropical regions (below 30 degrees latitude; Figures 11.13a and 11.13c).

Characteristics of Coastal Wetlands

Wetlands are some of the most highly productive ecosystems on Earth and provide enormous economic benefits when left alone. Salt marshes, for example, serve as nurseries for more than half the species of commercially important fishes in the southeastern United States. Other fish, such as flounder and bluefish, use marshes for feeding and protection during the winter. Fisheries of oysters, scallops, clams, eels, and smelt are located directly in marshes, too. Mangrove ecosystems are important nursery areas and habitats for commercially valuable shrimp, prawn, shellfish, and fish species. Both marshes and mangroves also serve as important stopover points for many species of waterfowl and migrating birds.

Wetlands are amazingly efficient at cleansing polluted water. Just 0.4 hectare (1 acre) of wetlands, for example, can filter up to 2,760,000 liters (730,000 gallons) of water each year, cleaning agricultural runoff, toxins, and other pollutants long before they reach the ocean. Wetlands remove inorganic nitrogen compounds (from sewage and fertilizers) and metals (from groundwater polluted by land sources), which become attached to clay-sized particles in wetland mud. Some nitrogen compounds trapped in sediment are decomposed by bacteria that release the nitrogen to the atmosphere as gas, and many of the remaining nitrogen compounds fertilize plants, further increasing the productivity of wetlands. As marsh plants die, their remains either accumulate as peat deposits or are broken up to become food for bacteria, fungi, and fish.

In addition, wetlands can also buffer coastal regions from flooding by absorbing excess water and protect shorelines from erosion, particularly during severe storms or tsunami. The 2004 Indian Ocean tsunami, for example, devastated some coastal regions, yet others with protective offshore coral reefs or coastal mangroves experienced much less damage. And, the loss of protective coastal wetlands in the Mississippi River Delta contributed to the extensive flooding associated with the storm surge caused by Hurricane Katrina in 2005 (see Box 6.2).

Serious Loss of Valuable Wetlands

Despite all the benefits they provide, more than half of the nation's wetlands have vanished. Of the original 87 million hectares (215 million acres) of wetlands that once existed in the conterminous United States, only about 43 million hectares (106 million acres) remain (Figure 11.14). Wetlands have been filled in and devel-

> **KEY CONCEPT**
> Coastal wetlands such as salt marshes and mangrove swamps are highly productive areas that serve as important nurseries for many marine organisms and act as filters for polluted runoff.

(a)

(b)

(c)

FIGURE 11.13 Salt marshes and mangrove swamps.
(a) Map showing the distribution of salt marshes (higher latitudes) and mangrove swamps (lower latitudes). (b) A typical salt marsh along the coast of Germany that borders the North Sea. (c) Red mangrove trees on Isla Espiritu Santo in the Sea of Cortez, Mexico.

oped for housing, industry, and agriculture, because people want to live near the oceans and because they often view wetlands as unproductive, useless land that harbors diseases. In many places, wetlands loss is compounded by the lack of fresh sediment from regular river floods. Instead, flooding rivers and their sediment are channeled away from wetland areas.

Louisiana's coastal wetlands, for example, are among those that are steadily disappearing. The soil in wetlands naturally compresses over time, a process called *subsidence*. Normally, the growth of plants and the infusion of fresh sediment from river floodwaters offset subsidence. With these factors reduced or eliminated, many wetlands are sinking into the ocean faster than they are building up.

Other countries have experienced similar losses of wetlands, too. In fact, scientists estimate that 50% of wetlands worldwide have been destroyed in the past century. Mangroves, for example, are already critically endangered or approaching extinction in 26 out of the 120 countries that have mangroves; the Philippines

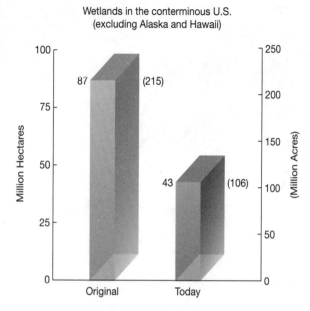

Wetlands in the conterminous U.S.
(excluding Alaska and Hawaii)

FIGURE 11.14 Wetland loss in the conterminous United States. Bar graph illustrating the amount of wetland loss in the conterminous United States (excluding Alaska and Hawaii), showing a reduction by more than half. Wetlands have been drained and converted to other uses (primarily development, industry, and agriculture).

alone has reported losing 70% of its original mangrove cover. At the current rate of mangrove loss, there is increasing concern that all mangrove ecosystems worldwide will be destroyed within the next 100 years.

To help prevent the loss of remaining wetlands, the U.S. Environmental Protection Agency (EPA) established an Office of Wetlands Protection (OWP) in 1986. At that time, wetlands were being lost to development at a rate of 121,000 hectares (300,000 acres) per year! As recently as 1997, the rate of coastal wetland loss had slowed to about 8100 hectares (20,000 acres) per year. The goal of the OWP is to reduce the loss of wetlands in the U.S. to zero by actively enforcing regulations against wetlands pollution and identifying the most valuable wetlands to be protected or restored.

Recent trends suggest an overall increase in U.S. wetlands. In fact, a study from 1998 to 2004 revealed that the conterminous U.S. gained an estimated 13,000 hectares (32,000 acres) of wetlands each year. This small gain was primarily due to the large increase in freshwater wetlands; coastal wetlands were found to still be decreasing, but at a slower rate than previously. The fact that coastal regions were losing wetlands despite the national trend of a net gain in wetlands points to the need for more research on the natural and human forces behind these trends and to an expanded effort on conservation of wetlands, particularly in coastal areas.

A rise in sea level is predicted to exacerbate the loss of wetlands. Even using a conservative estimate of sea level rise over the next 100 years of 50 centimeters (20 inches), it is estimated that 38% to 61% of existing U.S. coastal wetlands would be lost. Some of this wetland loss, however, would be partially offset by new wetland formation on former upland areas, although even under ideal circumstances not all lost wetlands would be replaced.

11.5 What Is Pollution?

As the use of coastal areas has increased for residences, recreation, and commerce, pollution of coastal waters has increased as well.

Marine Pollution: A Definition

Pollution can broadly be defined as *any harmful substance*, but how do scientists determine which substances are harmful? For example, a substance may be esthetically unappealing to people yet is not harmful to the environment. Conversely, certain types of pollution cannot easily be detected by humans, yet they can do harm to the environment. A substance may not immediately be harmful, but it may cause harm years, decades, or even centuries later. Also, to whom must this harm be done? For instance, some marine species thrive when exposed to a particular compound that is quite toxic to other species. Interestingly, natural conditions in coastal waters, such as dead seaweed on the beach, may be considered "pollution" by some people. It should be remembered, however, that although nature may produce conditions we dislike, it does not pollute. The amount of a pollutant is also important: If a substance that causes pollution is present in extremely tiny amounts, can it still be characterized as a pollutant? All of these questions are difficult to answer.

The World Health Organization defines pollution of the marine environment as follows:

The introduction by man, directly or indirectly, of substances or energy into the marine environment, including estuaries, which results or is likely to result in such deleterious effects as harm to living resources and marine life, hazards to human health, hindrance to marine activities, including fishing and other legitimate uses of the sea, impairment of quality for use of sea water and reduction of amenities.

It is often difficult to determine the degree to which pollution affects the marine environment. Most areas were not studied sufficiently before they were polluted, so scientists do not have an adequate baseline from which to determine how pollutants have altered the marine environment. The marine environment is affected by decade- to century-long cycles, too, so it is difficult to determine whether a change is due to a natural biologic cycle or any number of introduced pollutants, many of which combine to produce new compounds.

Environmental Bioassay

One of the most widely used techniques for determining the concentration of pollutants that negatively affect the living resources of the ocean is to conduct a carefully controlled experiment to assess how a particular pollutant impacts marine organisms. Such an experiment is called an *environmental biological assay*, or **environmental bioassay** (*bio* = biologic, *essaier* = to weigh out). For example, regulatory agencies such as the U.S. EPA use an environmental bioassay to determine the concentration of a pollutant that causes 50% mortality among a specific group of test organisms within a prescribed period of time. If a pollutant exceeds a 50% mortality rate, then concentration limits are established for the discharge of the pollutant into coastal waters.

There are several drawbacks to using a specific environmental bioassay to draw general conclusions about a pollutant. One shortcoming is that it does not predict the long-term effect of pollution on marine organisms. Another is that it does not take into account how pollutants may combine with other substances, creating new types of pollutants. In addition, environmental bioassays are often time-consuming, laborious, and organism-specific and so may result in data that isn't applicable to other species.

The Issue of Waste Disposal in the Ocean

Waste disposal facilities on land (such as landfills) have limited capacities that are already being exceeded in many cases. Should additional waste be discarded in the open ocean? Unlike coastal areas, the open ocean has mixing mechanisms (waves, tides, and currents) that distribute pollutants over a wide area—including an entire ocean basin. Diluting pollutants often renders them less harmful. On the other hand, do we really want to distribute a pollutant across an entire ocean without knowing what its long-term effects might be?

Some experts believe that we should not dump *anything* in the ocean, while others believe that the ocean can be a repository for many of society's wastes, as long as proper monitoring is conducted. Unfortunately, there are no easy answers and the issues are complex. What is clear is that more research is needed to assess the impact of pollutants in the ocean.

11.6 What Are the Main Types of Marine Pollution?

Marine pollution comes from substances such as petroleum, sewage, and various chemical compounds, all of which can have severe deleterious effects on marine organisms, particularly in coastal environments. Generally, coastal waters are more polluted than the open ocean because of two main reasons: (1) Most pollution from land is dumped into nearby coastal waters, and (2) coastal waters are shallower and not as well circulated as the open ocean.

Petroleum

Major oil (**petroleum**) spills into the ocean are a fact of our modern oil-powered economy. Some oil spills are the result of loading/unloading accidents, collisions, or tankers running aground, such as the 1989 spill from the *Exxon Valdez* in Prince William Sound, Alaska (Box 11.1). Although large spills such as from the *Exxon*

KEY CONCEPT

Marine pollution is difficult to define but includes any human-induced substance that is harmful to the marine environment.

STUDENTS SOMETIMES ASK...

Is dilution the solution to ocean pollution?

That's certainly a catchy phrase, but the implications are controversial. It suggests that the oceans can be used as a repository for society's wastes, as long as the wastes are diluted to the point that they no longer threaten marine organisms (which is often difficult to determine). Because the oceans are vast and consist of a good solvent (water), they appear ideally suited to this disposal strategy. In addition, the oceans have good mixing mechanisms (currents, waves, and tides), which dilute many forms of pollution.

Air pollution was once viewed in a similar manner. Disposal of pollutants into the atmosphere was thought to be acceptable, as long as they were dispersed widely and high enough—so tall smokestacks were constructed. Over time, however, pollutants such as nitric acid and acid sulfates increased in the atmosphere to the point that acid rain is now a problem. The ocean, like the atmosphere, has a finite *holding capacity* for pollutants and even experts disagree on exactly how much that is.

As disposal sites on land begin to fill, the ocean is increasingly evaluated as an area for disposal of society's wastes. One thing that we can *all* do is to limit the amount of waste we generate, alleviating some of the problem of where to put waste. It is likely, however, that the ocean will continue to be used as a dumping ground in the foreseeable future. Despite many new disposal techniques, a long-term "solution" to ocean pollution hasn't yet appeared.

THE *EXXON VALDEZ* OIL SPILL: NOT THE WORST SPILL EVER

A large percentage of oil enters the oceans from spills by tankers and transportation operations. One of the most publicized oil spills was from the supertanker *Exxon Valdez*, which occurred in Prince William Sound, Alaska, and is the largest oil spill in U.S. territorial waters.

Crude oil produced from the North Slope of Alaska is carried by pipeline to the southern port of Valdez, Alaska, where it is loaded onto supertankers like the *Exxon Valdez*, which are capable of holding almost 200 million liters (53 million gallons) when full. On March 29, 1989, the tanker left Valdez with a full load of crude oil and was headed toward refineries in California. She was only 40 kilometers (25 miles) out of Valdez when the ship's officers noted icebergs from nearby Columbia Glacier within the shipping channel. While maneuvering around the icebergs, the ship

ran aground on a shallowly submerged rocky outcrop known as Bligh Reef (Figure 11A), rupturing 8 of the ship's 11 cargo tanks. About 22% of her cargo— almost 44 million liters (about 11.6 million gallons) of oil—spilled into the pristine waters of Prince William Sound, where it subsequently spread into the Gulf of Alaska and fouled over 1775 kilometers (1100 miles) of shoreline.

Estimates suggest that at least 1000 sea otters and between 100,000 and 7,000,000 seabirds were killed outright by the spill based on an extrapolation of the number of oiled carcasses that were collected on beaches and from the water. The area's remote location and the size of the affected area limit an accurate accounting of marine animal fatalities.

Immediately after the spill, Exxon spent more than $2 billion in cleanup

efforts and another $900 million in subsequent years for restoration. Absorbent materials and skimming devices were used to remove oil from the water, whereas super hot water (60°C [140°F]) sprayed through high-pressure hoses was used to clean oil from the rocky beaches. The hot water removed the oil but also killed most shoreline organisms. Analysis of the cleanup effort, when compared to areas that were left to biodegrade naturally, reveals that the beaches that were left alone recovered more quickly and more completely than the cleaned beaches.

Oil from the *Exxon Valdez* spill that settled on active shorelines, where wave action or microbes could break it down, disappeared fairly fast. But surface puddles of crude oil from the spill are still found more than 20 years later, and

FIGURE 11A The 1989 *Exxon Valdez* oil spill, Prince William Sound, Alaska. Map showing location of the oil spill (*left*), the *Exxon Valdez* on Bligh Reef (*upper right*), and spilled oil coating a beach (*lower right*).

TABLE 11A		THE WORLD'S LARGEST OIL SPILLS			

Rank	Date	Location	Source of spill	Size of spill	
				million liters	million gallons
1	1/1991	Kuwait, Saudi Arabia	Oil terminals, tankers	908	240
2	6/1979	Gulf of Mexico	Ixtoc #1 oil well	530	140
3	3/1992	Uzbekistan	Oil well	333	88
4	2/1983	Iran	Oil well	303	80
5	8/1983	Near the coast of South Africa	*Castillo de Bellver* tanker	299	79
6	3/1978	Near the coast of France	*Amoco Cadiz* tanker	261	69
…	…	…	…	…	…
53	3/1989	Prince William Sound, Alaska	*Exxon Valdez* tanker	44.0	11.6

pockets of undegraded oil rest just below the surface of some beaches and in coastal wetlands. Experts state that marine animals are no longer at risk of exposure to toxic oil and that natural processes will continue to biodegrade the remaining oil.

As large and damaging as the *Exxon Valdez* spill was, it ranks as only the *53rd* largest oil spill worldwide (Table 11A). The world's largest oil spill occurred because of intentional dumping by the Iraqi army during their invasion of Kuwait during the 1991 Persian Gulf War. By the time the Iraqi were driven out of Kuwait and the leaking oil wells and sabotaged production facilities were brought under control, more than 908 million liters (240 million gallons) of oil had spilled into the Persian Gulf (Figure 11B)—more than *20 times* the amount spilled by the *Exxon Valdez*.

FIGURE 11B Oil pollution from the 1991 Persian Gulf War. Map showing the location of the spilled oil, which was confined to the northwest coast of the Persian Gulf by currents and southeasterly winds, and a Saudi Arabian government official examining some of the damage (*inset*).

Valdez occur infrequently, smaller-scale spills are more common. In fact, nearly 100 documented spills of at least 3800 liters (1000 gallons) of oil and more than 10,000 smaller spills have been reported annually in U.S. waters. Other oil spills are intentionally created, such as the oil that was spilled during the Persian Gulf War in 1991. Still others are caused by the blowout of undersea oil wells during drilling or pumping. The largest such spill occurred in June 1979 in the Gulf of Mexico, when the

FIGURE 11.15 Blowout from the Ixtoc #1 oil well, Gulf of Mexico. Location of the 1979 Bay of Campeche blowout and oil slick that affected the Texas coast. The well blew out, caught fire, and flowed for 10 months, spilling 530 million liters (140 million gallons) of oil into the Gulf of Mexico. The accident produced the world's largest oil spill from an oil well.

FIGURE 11.16 Recovery of organisms affected by the *Exxon Valdez* oil spill. The populations of several key organisms in the Prince William Sound area of Alaska have rebounded after the 1989 *Exxon Valdez* oil spill. The bald eagle is so numerous that it was removed from the endangered species list in 1996. The collapse of the Pacific herring's population is thought to be unrelated to effects of the oil spill.

Petroleus Mexicanos (PEMEX) oil-drilling station Ixtoc #1 in the Bay of Campeche off the Yucatán peninsula, Mexico, blew out and caught fire. Before it was capped nearly 10 months later, it spewed 530 million liters (140 million gallons) of oil into the Gulf of Mexico, some of which washed up along the coast of Texas (Figure 11.15).

Oil is a mixture of various **hydrocarbons**, which means it is composed of the elements *hydrogen* and *carbon*. Hydrocarbons are organic substances, so they can be broken down or *biodegraded* by microorganisms. Because hydrocarbons are largely biodegradable, many marine pollution experts consider oil to be among the *least* damaging pollutants introduced into the ocean! Certainly oil spills appear ghastly as the oil coats the water, the shore, and helpless marine organisms including seabirds, and it can cause grievous short-term damage. But oil dissipates and breaks down, becoming food for various microbes. As an example, vast quantities of oil were spilled in the Pacific and, especially, the Atlantic during World War II. In fact, some U.S. East Coast beaches were coated by oil several centimeters deep, yet not a trace of those spills remains today. In a broader view, some natural undersea oil seeps have occurred for millions of years, and the ocean ecosystem seems unaffected—or even *enhanced*—by them (because oil is a source of energy). As we'll see, other types of pollutants last far longer and can do much more damage than an oil spill.

Data from the *Exxon Valdez* oil spill are a case in point. The oil spill released almost 44 million liters (11.6 million gallons) of oil into a pristine wilderness area in Alaska. The affected waters were expected to have a long, slow recovery, but the fisheries that closed in 1989 bounced back with record takes in 1990. A study conducted 10 years after the spill revealed that several key species had rebounded to the point where their numbers were greater than before the spill (Figure 11.16).

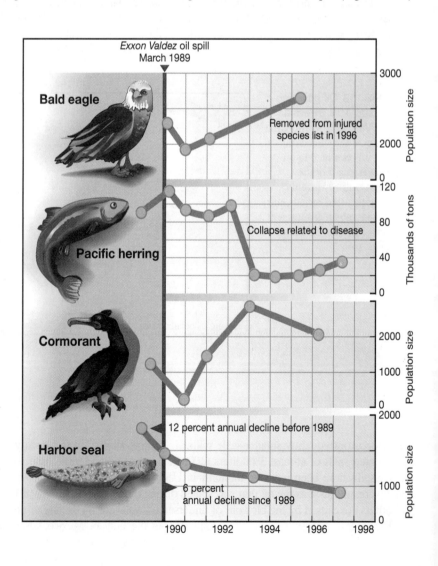

Recent research on the long-term effects of the spill, however, reveals that a significant amount of poorly weathered oil remains in intertidal subsurface sediments and is still affecting marine ecosystems. Because of Alaska's relatively cold subarctic climate, the spilled oil is biodegrading very slowly, so it will continue to be an ecological problem for decades.

Another concern is that oil is a complex mixture of various hydrocarbons and other substances, including the elements oxygen, nitrogen, sulfur, and various trace metals. When this complex chemical mixture combines with seawater—another complex chemical mixture, which also contains organisms—the results are usually devastating for marine organisms. Many are killed outright when they are coated by oil, rendering their insulating feathers or fur useless (Figure 11.17).

There is also concern about the long-term effects of oil spills, such as chronic, delayed, or indirect impacts, many of which are often difficult to document and link to the spill because of the considerable time lag. For example, the 2002 spill in the Bay of Biscay north of Spain caused by the ruptured oil tanker *Prestige*, which leaked an estimated 26.5 million liters (7 million gallons) of fuel oil, will cause negative impacts to the region's shorelines and fisheries for years to come. Another example is the oil tanker that ran aground in the Galápagos Islands in 2001, spilling roughly 3 million liters (800,000 gallons) of diesel and bunker oil. The oil spread westward and was dispersed by strong currents, so only a few marine animals were immediately killed. Marine iguanas on a nearby island, however, suffered a massive 62% mortality in the year after the accident, due to a small amount of residual oil contamination in the sea.

In addition, spills from oil tankers may release a wide variety of petroleum products (not just crude oil), each of which contains different concentrations of **toxic** (*toxicum* = poison) **compounds**[9] and behaves differently in the environment. For example, refined oil such as fuel oil is rich in compounds that are much more toxic to the environment than crude oil.

Although spills from oil tankers receive much media attention, they are not the primary source of oil to the oceans. Figure 11.18 shows that 47% of worldwide oil to the oceans is caused by underwater *natural oil seeps* (many of which occur in U.S. waters); the remaining 53% comes from *human sources*. The figure also shows that of human-caused oil to the oceans, 72% comes from *petroleum consumption*, which includes nontank vessels, runoff from increasingly paved urban areas, and individual car, boat, and watercraft owners; 22% comes from *petroleum transportation*, including refining and distribution activities; and only 6% comes from *petroleum extraction*, which are activities associated with oil and gas exploration or production. Remarkably, the overwhelming majority of the petroleum that enters the oceans due to human activity is a result of small but frequent and widespread releases of oil related to activities that consume petroleum.

CLEANING OIL SPILLS   When oil enters the ocean, it initially floats because oil is less dense than water and forms a slick at the surface, where it starts to break down through natural processes (Figure 11.19). The volatile, lighter components of crude oil evaporate over the first few days, leaving behind a more viscous substance that aggregates into tar balls and eventually sinks. The tarry oil also coats suspended particles, which settle to the sea floor, too.

If the floating oil hasn't dispersed, it can be collected with specially designed skimmers or absorbent materials. The collected oil (or oiled materials), however, must still be disposed of elsewhere. Waves, winds, and currents serve to further disperse an oil slick and mix the remaining oil with water to make a frothy emulsion called *mousse*. In addition, bacteria and photooxidation act to break down the oil into compounds that dissolve in water.

Microorganisms such as bacteria and fungi naturally biodegrade oil, so they can be used to help clean oil spills—a method called **bioremediation** (*bio* = biologic,

[9]A *toxic compound* is a poisonous substance that has the capability of causing injury or death, especially by chemical means.

FIGURE 11.17 A bird covered by oil from the *Exxon Valdez* oil spill. When marine organisms are covered by oil from an oil spill, their feathers or fur lose their insulation properties, resulting in high fatality rates. Some marine organisms such as this cormorant were rescued and cleaned of oil.

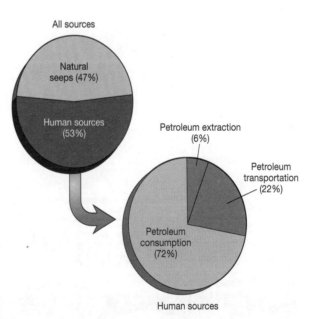

FIGURE 11.18 Sources of oil to the oceans. Of worldwide oil to the oceans, 47% comes from natural seeps, while 53% comes from human sources. Of all human sources, 72% comes from petroleum consumption activities such as individual car and boat owners, nontank vessels, and runoff from increasingly paved urban areas. Surprisingly, combined petroleum transportation and extraction account for only 28% of all human-caused oil to the oceans.

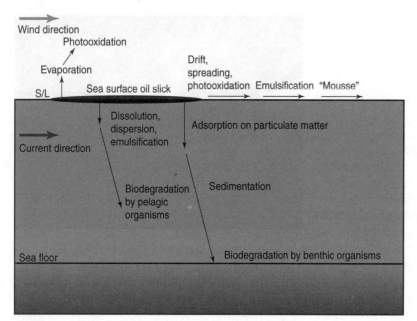

FIGURE 11.19 Processes acting on oil spills. After an oil spill enters the ocean, it is acted upon by various natural processes that break up the spill. The lighter components evaporate, while the heavier components form tar balls or coat suspended particles and sink. The remaining dispersed oil photo oxidizes or can mix with water, creating a frothy substance called "mousse."

WEB VIDEO

Oil Spill Issues

FIGURE 11.20 Who is at fault?

remedium = to heal again). Virtually all marine ecosystems harbor naturally occurring bacteria that degrade hydrocarbons. Although certain types of bacteria and fungi can break down particular kinds of hydrocarbons, none is effective against all forms. In 1980, however, microbiologists discovered a microorganism capable of breaking down nearly two-thirds of the hydrocarbons in most crude oil spills.

Releasing bacteria directly into the marine environment is one form of bioremediation. For example, a strain of oil-degrading bacteria was released into the Gulf of Mexico to test its effectiveness in cleaning up about 15 million liters (4 million gallons) of crude oil spilled after an explosion disabled the tanker *Mega Borg* in 1990. Preliminary results indicate that the bacteria reduced the amount of oil with no negative effects on the ecology due to the bacteria.

Providing conditions that stimulate the growth of naturally occurring oil-degrading bacteria is another form of bioremediation. Exxon, for example, spent $10 million dollars to spread fertilizers rich in phosphorus and nitrogen on Alaskan shorelines to boost the growth of indigenous oil-eating bacteria after the *Exxon Valdez* spill (Box 11.1). The resulting cleanup rate was more than twice that under natural conditions.

PREVENTING OIL SPILLS One of the best ways to protect areas from oil spills is to prevent spills from occurring in the first place. Because our society relies on petroleum products, however, oil spills are a likely occurrence in the future (Figure 11.20), especially as petroleum reserves beneath the continental shelves of the world are increasingly exploited.

After the *Exxon Valdez* oil spill in 1989, Congress enacted the Oil Pollution Act of 1990, which defined responsibility for fiscal damage and cleanup. The act also phased out single-hulled oil tankers traveling in U.S. waters and mandated double-hulled construction. Currently, single-hulled tankers are now barred from U.S. ports, while European countries such as France and Spain do not allow them within 320 kilometers (200 miles) of their coast. The double hull houses two layers: An inner hull can prevent oil spillage if damage should occur to the outer hull. Studies of hull designs during groundings and collisions indicate that double-hull designs are more effective overall at reducing oil spills. However, analysis of the *Exxon Valdez* spill suggests that even a double-hulled tanker would not have prevented the disaster. Tanker designs are also being modified to limit the amount of oil spilled should there be a hull rupture.

In February 1999, the Japanese-owned freighter M/V *New Carissa* ran aground just offshore of Coos Bay, Oregon, with nearly 1,500,000 liters (400,000 gallons) of tarlike fuel oil aboard and began leaking oil through cracks in its hull. When the ship washed into the surf zone and an approaching storm threatened to tear it apart, federal and state authorities decided to ignite the vessel and its fuel rather than risk a larger oil spill (Figure 11.21). This was the first time that oil on a ship in U.S. waters was intentionally burned to prevent an oil spill. Eventually, the ship split in two and about half of its oil burned, limiting the amount of oil spilled into the ocean. Most of the remaining oil was sunk with the wrecked ship a month later when it was towed offshore and sunk in water 3 kilometers (1.9 miles) deep by Naval gunfire and a torpedo.

Sewage Sludge

Another main type of marine pollution is **sewage sludge**. Sewage treated at a facility typically undergoes **primary treatment**, where solids are allowed to settle and dewater, and **secondary treatment**, where it is exposed to bacteria-killing chlorine. Sewage sludge is the semisolid material that remains after such treatment. It contains a toxic brew of human waste, oil, zinc, copper, lead, silver, mercury, pesticides, and other chemicals. Since the 1960s, at least 500,000 metric tons (550,000 short tons) of sewage sludge have been dumped into the coastal waters of Southern California, and more than 8 million metric tons (8.8 million short tons) have been dumped in the New York Bight between Long Island and the New Jersey shore.

Although the Clean Water Act of 1972 prohibited the dumping of sewage into the ocean after 1981, the high cost of treating and disposing of sewage sludge on land resulted in extension waivers being granted to many municipalities. In the summer of 1988, however, nonbiodegradable debris including medical waste—probably carried by heavy rains into the ocean through storm drains—washed up on Atlantic coast beaches and adversely affected the tourist business. Although this event was completely unrelated to sewage disposal at sea, it focused public awareness on ocean pollution and helped pass new legislation to terminate sewage disposal at sea.

NEW YORK'S SEWAGE SLUDGE DISPOSAL AT SEA   Sewage sludge from New York and Philadelphia has traditionally been transported offshore by barge and dumped in the ocean at sites totaling 150 square kilometers (58 square miles) within the New York Bight Sludge Site and the Philadelphia Sludge Site (Figure 11.22).

The water depth is about 29 meters (95 feet) at the New York Bight Sludge Site and about 40 meters (130 feet) at the Philadelphia Sludge Site. The water column in such shallow water is relatively uniform, so even the smallest sludge particles reach the bottom without undergoing much horizontal transport, and the ecology of the dump site can be severely affected. At the very least, such a concentration of organic and inorganic matter seriously disrupts the chemical cycling of nutrients. Greatly reduced species diversity results, and in some locations the environment becomes devoid of oxygen (*anoxic*).

In 1986, the shallow-water sites were abandoned, and sewage was subsequently transported to a deep-water site 171 kilometers (106 miles) out to sea (Figure 11.22). The deep-water site is beyond the continental shelf break, so there is usually a well-developed density gradient that separates low-density, warmer surface water from high-density, colder deep water. Internal waves moving along this density gradient can horizontally transport particles at rates 100 times greater than they sink.

Local fishermen reported adverse effects on their fisheries soon after deep-water dumping began. Also, concern was expressed that the sewage could be transported great distances in eddies of the Gulf Stream (see Chapter 7), even as far as the coast of the United Kingdom. This program was terminated in 1993, and municipalities must now dispose of their sewage on land.

BOSTON HARBOR SEWAGE PROJECT   Some 48 different communities that comprise the greater Boston area have, until recently, used an antiquated sewage system to dump sludge and partially treated sewage at the entrance to Boston Harbor. Tidal currents often swept the sewage back into the bay, and at other times, the system became overloaded and dumped raw sewage directly into the bay, making Boston Harbor one of the most polluted bays in the country.

A court-ordered cleanup of Boston Harbor in the 1980s resulted in the construction of a new waste treatment facility at Deer Island that came online in 1998. It treats all sewage with bacteria-killing chlorine and carries it through a tunnel 15.3 kilometers (9.5 miles) long into deeper waters offshore (Figure 11.23a), which prevents it from returning to the bay. Since the cleanup of Boston Harbor, beaches have reopened, clammers are digging again, and marine life—including harbor seals, porpoises, and even whales—has returned. To pay for the $3.8 million sewage system, however, the average annual sewage bill for a Boston-area household is now about $1200, more than five times what it used to be.

FIGURE 11.21 The *New Carissa* on fire off the Oregon coast. When the freighter M/V *New Carissa* ran aground in 1999 in shallow water offshore Coos Bay, Oregon, and began leaking oil, it was intentionally set on fire to prevent further oil from spilling into the ocean.

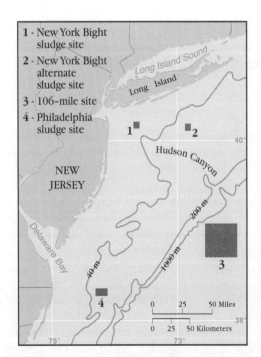

FIGURE 11.22 Atlantic sewage sludge disposal sites. More than 8 million metric tons of sewage sludge was dumped by barge annually at the New York Bight Sludge Site (*1*) and the Philadelphia Sludge Site (*4*). After 1986, the new dump site is the larger and deeper-water 170-kilometer (106-mile) site (*3*).

(a)

(b)

FIGURE 11.23 Boston Harbor sewage project.
(a) Diagrammatic view of the Boston Harbor Project tunnels that transport sewage to an outfall 15 kilometers (9.5 miles) offshore at a depth of 76 meters (250 feet) beneath the ocean floor. **(b)** Bathymetric map of the coastal ocean in the Boston–Cape Cod area, showing the proximity of the new sewage outfall (*red x*) to Stellwagen Bank, which is a National Marine Sanctuary.

Some fear that the project will degrade the environment in Cape Cod Bay and Stellwagen Bank (Figure 11.23b), which is an important whale habitat. The area's recent designation as a National Marine Sanctuary may affect the feasibility of dumping there.

DDT and PCBs

The pesticide **DDT** (dichloro-diphenyl-trichloroethane) and the industrial chemicals called **PCBs** (polychlorinated biphenyls) are now found throughout the marine environment. They are persistent, biologically active chemicals that have been introduced into the oceans entirely as a result of human activities. Because of their toxicity, long life, and propensity for being accumulated in food chains, these and other chemicals have been classified as *persistent organic pollutants (POPs)* capable of causing cancer, birth defects, and other grave harm.

DDT was widely used in agriculture during the 1950s and improved crop production throughout developing countries for several decades. However, its extreme effectiveness as an insecticide and persistence as a toxin in the environment eventually resulted in a host of environmental problems including devastating effects on marine food chains.

PCBs are industrial chemicals that were once widely used as a liquid coolant and insulation in industrial equipment such as power transformers, where they were released into the environment. PCBs were also widely used in wiring, paints, caulking, hydraulic oils, carbonless copy paper, and a host of other products. PCBs have been shown to cause liver cancer and harmful genetic mutations in animals. PCBs can also affect animal reproduction: They have been indicated as causes of spontaneous abortions in sea lions and the death of shrimp in Escambia Bay, Florida.

DDT AND EGGSHELLS Since 1972, the EPA has banned the use of DDT in the United States. Worldwide, the pesticide is banned from agricultural use, but it continues to be used in limited quantities for public health purposes. Ironically, U.S. companies continue to produce DDT and supply it to other countries.

The danger of excessive use of DDT and similar pesticides first became apparent in the marine environment when it affected marine bird populations. During the 1960s, there was a serious decline in the brown pelican population of Anacapa Island off Southern California (Figure 11.24). High concentrations of DDT in the fish eaten by the birds had caused them to produce eggs with excessively thin shells.

The osprey is a common bird of prey in coastal waters that is similar to a large hawk. The osprey population of Long Island Sound declined in the late 1950s and 1960s because DDT contamination caused them to produce eggs with thin shells, too. Since the ban on DDT, the osprey, brown pelican, and many other species affected by the chemical are making remarkable comebacks.

DDT AND PCBs LINGER IN THE ENVIRONMENT   DDT and PCBs (which were banned in 1977) generally enter the ocean through the atmosphere and river runoff. They are initially concentrated in the thin slick of organic chemicals at the ocean surface, and then they gradually sink to the bottom, attached to sinking particles. A study off the coast of Scotland indicated that open-ocean concentrations of DDT and PCBs are 10 and 12 times less, respectively, than in coastal waters. Long-term studies have shown that DDT residue in mollusks along the U.S. coasts peaked in 1968.

Although most countries have banned their use, DDT and PCBs are so pervasive in the marine environment that even Antarctic marine organisms contain measurable quantities of them. There has been no agriculture or industry in Antarctica to introduce them directly, so they must have been transported from distant sources by winds and ocean currents.

Mercury and Minamata Disease

The metal **mercury**, which is a silvery liquid at room temperature, has many industrial uses. When it enters the ecosystem, however, mercury forms an organic compound (*methyl mercury*) that is generally toxic to most living things.

A chemical plant built in 1938 on Minamata Bay, Japan, produced acetaldehyde, which requires mercury in its manufacture. Mercury was discharged into Minamata Bay, where bacteria degraded it into methyl mercury that was later ingested and concentrated in the tissues of larger marine organisms. The first ecological changes in Minamata Bay were reported in 1950 and human effects were noted as early as 1953. The mercury poisoning that is now known as **Minamata disease** became epidemic in 1956, when the plant was only 18 years old.

Minamata disease is a degenerative neurological disorder that affects the human nervous system and causes sensory disturbances including blindness and tremor, brain damage, birth defects, paralysis, and even death. This mercury poisoning was the first major human disaster resulting from ocean pollution. However, the Japanese government did not declare mercury as the cause of the disease until 1968. The plant was immediately shut down, but more than 100 people were known to suffer from the disease by 1969 (Figure 11.25), almost half of whom died. A second acetaldehyde plant was closed in 1965 in Niigata, Japan, because it, too, was discharging mercury that poisoned people. Between 1965 and 1970, 47 fishing families contracted Minamata disease. Today the concentration of mercury in Minamata Bay is no longer unusually high, indicating that there has been enough time for the mercury to be widely dispersed within the marine environment.

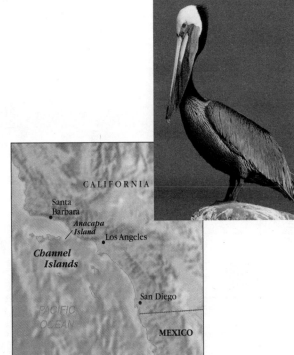

FIGURE 11.24 Survival of brown pelicans threatened by DDT. Brown pelicans (*Pelecanus occidentalis*) that breed on Anacapa Island offshore Southern California were found to have high levels of DDT, which decreased the thickness of their eggshells. Since DDT has been banned, healthy pelicans have returned to these waters, such as this one in breeding plumage (*photo*).

FIGURE 11.25 A victim of Minamata disease. Ingestion or contact with the toxic metal mercury can cause Minamata a disease, which affects the human nervous system and can result in brain damage, birth defects, paralysis, and even death.

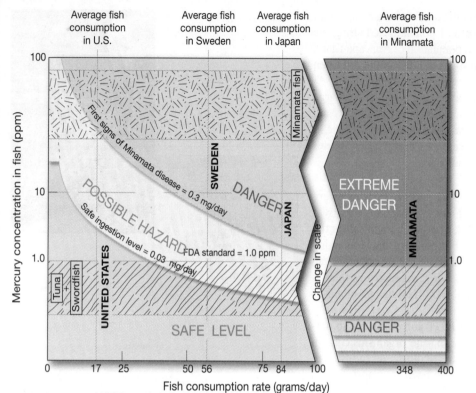

FIGURE 11.26 Mercury concentrations in fish versus consumption rates for various populations. Graph showing the relative risk of contracting Minamata disease based on the amount of fish consumed and the concentration of mercury in fish for people in the United States, Sweden, and Japan—including Minamata. It shows that the safe ingestion level of 0.03 milligrams of mercury per day is within the Food and Drug Administration's standard safety level of 1.0 ppm for fish and that tuna and most swordfish are safe to consume.

BIOACCUMULATION AND BIOMAGNIFICATION

During the 1960s and 1970s methyl mercury contamination in seafood received considerable attention. Certain marine organisms concentrate within their tissues many substances found in minute concentrations in seawater in a process called **bioaccumulation**. When animals eat other animals, some of these substances (including toxic chemicals) move up food chains and become concentrated in the tissues of larger animals in a process called **biomagnification**. Because the amount of mercury in the ocean has been increasing (mostly from the mercury in disposable batteries), some seafood such as tuna and swordfish were thought to contain unusually high amounts of mercury.

Studies done on the amount of seafood consumed by various human populations helped establish safe levels of mercury in marketed fish. To establish these levels, three variables were considered:

1. The rate at which each group of people consumed fish
2. The mercury concentration in the fish consumed by that population
3. The minimum ingestion rate of mercury that induces disease symptoms

These three variables help establish a maximum allowable mercury concentration that will safeguard people from mercury poisoning, as long as they don't exceed the recommended intake of fish.

Figure 11.26 shows the relative risk of contracting Minamata disease for people in the United States, Sweden, and Japan, including those from the Minamata fishing community. The graph shows that the risk increases with increased consumption of fish and that the higher the mercury concentration of the fish, the greater the risk.

Scientists have determined that the minimum level of mercury consumption that causes poisoning symptoms is 0.3 milligrams per day over a 200-day period. Figure 11.26 shows that for people in the United States who have an average daily consumption of 17 grams of fish per day, mercury poisoning symptoms occur when mercury concentrations in fish exceed 20 parts per million (ppm). Using a safety factor of 10 times, the maximum concentration of mercury in fish that can safely be consumed by people in the United States is 2.0 ppm.

The U.S. Food and Drug Administration (FDA) doubled the safety factor and established a limit of mercury concentration for fish at 1 ppm. Based on consumption rates, this limit has adequately protected the health of U.S. citizens because essentially all tuna and most swordfish fall below this concentration. Still, the FDA issued an advisory in 2001 stating that pregnant women, women of childbearing age, nursing mothers, and young children should avoid eating certain kinds of fish that may contain high levels of methyl mercury, such as swordfish, sharks, king mackerel, and tilefish. A recent study, however, found that mercury in fish might not be as harmful as thought because the form of the metal in seafood (methyl mercury cysteine) differs from that used in toxicology models (aqueous methyl mercury chloride).

Figure 11.26 shows that for people in Sweden and Japan, the mercury concentration of fish deemed to be at a safe level is lower because these populations eat more fish. The graph also shows the extreme danger to which residents of Minamata were inadvertently subjected when they ate so much of the highly contaminated fish from Minamata Bay.

Non-Point-Source Pollution and Trash

Non-point-source pollution—also called *poison runoff*—is any type of pollution entering the ocean from multiple sources rather than from a single discrete source, point, or location. In most urban areas, non-point-source pollution arrives at the ocean via runoff from storm drains, many of which now have labels indicating that they lead to the ocean (Figure 11.27). The U.S. National Academy of Sciences estimates that 5.8 million metric tons (6.4 million short tons) of litter enters the world's oceans each year.

Because non-point-source pollution comes from many different locations, it is difficult to pinpoint where it originates, although the *cause* of the pollution may readily be apparent. Trash that is washed down a storm drain to the ocean is one such example. Others include pesticides and fertilizers from agriculture and oil from automobiles that are washed to the ocean whenever it rains. In fact, the amount of road oil and improperly disposed oil regularly discharged each year into U.S. waters as non-point-source pollution is as much as 26 times the amount of the *Exxon Valdez* oil spill!

Trash enters the ocean as a result of ocean dumping, too. According to existing laws (Figure 11.28), certain types of trash such as glass, metal, rags, and food can legally be dumped in the ocean—as long as they are dumped far enough away from shore or ground up small enough. Mostly, this material sinks or biodegrades and does not accumulate at the surface. The exception is plastic material.

PLASTICS   Globally, **plastic** constitutes the vast majority of marine debris. About 80% of marine debris comes from land-based sources, and the majority of that is plastic. When plastic enters the ocean, it floats and is not readily biodegradable. As such, plastic can remain in the marine environment almost indefinitely, affecting marine organisms through entanglement and ingestion. In fact, there are many documented cases of plastic waste such as six-pack rings or packing straps strangling fish, marine mammals, and birds that have been entangled in plastic trash (Figures 11.29a and Figure 11.29b). Marine birds have also ingested so much floating plastic trash that it fills their stomach and they die from starvation (Figure 11.29c). In probably the most well-known case of lethal ingestion of plastic trash, marine turtles have been killed when they eat floating plastic bags, evidently mistaking them for

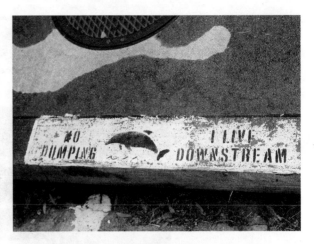

FIGURE 11.27 A labeled storm drain that leads to the ocean. Although many people believe that storm drain runoff is processed by sewage treatment plants, any material that enters storm drains goes directly into streams or the ocean.

STUDENTS SOMETIMES ASK...

Don't storm drains receive treatment before emptying into the ocean?

Contrary to popular belief, water (and any other material) that goes down a storm drain does *not* receive any treatment before being emptied into a river or directly into the ocean. Sewage treatment plants receive enough waste to process without the additional runoff from storms, so it is important to monitor carefully what is disposed into storm drains. For instance, some people discharge used motor oil into storm drains, thinking that it will be processed by a sewage plant. A good rule of thumb is this: *Don't put anything down a storm drain that you wouldn't put directly into the ocean itself.*

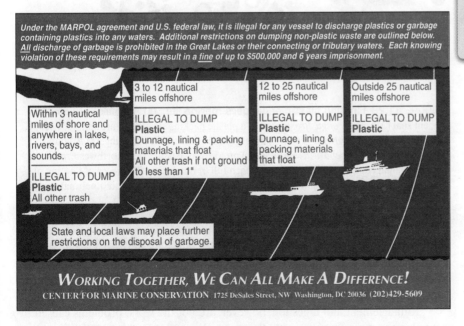

Under the MARPOL agreement and U.S. federal law, it is illegal for any vessel to discharge plastics or garbage containing plastics into any waters. Additional restrictions on dumping non-plastic waste are outlined below. *All* discharge of garbage is prohibited in the Great Lakes or their connecting or tributary waters. Each knowing violation of these requirements may result in a *fine* of up to $500,000 and 6 years imprisonment.

Within 3 nautical miles of shore and anywhere in lakes, rivers, bays, and sounds.
ILLEGAL TO DUMP
Plastic
All other trash

3 to 12 nautical miles offshore
ILLEGAL TO DUMP
Plastic
Dunnage, lining & packing materials that float
All other trash if not ground to less than 1"

12 to 25 nautical miles offshore
ILLEGAL TO DUMP
Plastic
Dunnage, lining & packing materials that float

Outside 25 nautical miles offshore
ILLEGAL TO DUMP
Plastic

State and local laws may place further restrictions on the disposal of garbage.

WORKING TOGETHER, WE CAN ALL MAKE A DIFFERENCE!
CENTER FOR MARINE CONSERVATION 1725 DeSales Street, NW Washington, DC 20036 (202)429-5609

FIGURE 11.28 Current law regulating ocean dumping. Many types of trash can legally be dumped in the ocean, as long as it is ground fine enough and not composed of plastic. In fact, plastic is the only substance that cannot be dumped anywhere in the ocean.

FIGURE 11.29 Floating plastic endangers marine life. (a) A female northern elephant seal (*Mirounga angustirostris*) with a plastic packing strap tight around her neck. (b) A herring gull (*Larus argentatus*) entangled in a plastic six-pack ring. (c) A young laysan albatross (*Phoebastria immutabilis*) on Midway Island at the northwestern end of the Hawaiian chain that died from a stomach full of more than 500 pieces of floating plastic trash (*right*) including lighters, bottle caps, electrical connectors, and other materials unintentionally fed to it by its parents.

STUDENTS SOMETIMES ASK ...

All this pollution is distressing. Is there anything I can do about it?

Yes, there are many things you can do to help protect the ocean, some of which are listed in this book's Afterword. They all involve making intelligent choices and minimizing your impact on the environment. Non-point-source pollution, for example, is something that the general public is directly responsible for, so one of the best methods of prevention may be educating people. Once people understand the impact our choices have on the environment, then the solution is up to *all* of us.

jellyfish or other transparent plankton on which they typically feed. Despite the fact that plastics are one of the few substances that are illegal to dump anywhere in the ocean (see Figure 11.28), their properties and abundant usage in society contribute to their increasing profusion in the marine environment (Box 11.2).

Entanglement and ingestion, however, are not the worst problems caused by the ubiquitous plastic pollution in the ocean. Researchers have recently discovered that floating plastic pieces have a high affinity for non-water-soluble toxic compounds, most notably DDT, PCBs, and other oily pollutants. As a result, some plastic

FROM A TO Z IN PLASTICS: THE MIRACLE SUBSTANCE?

I often struggle to find words that will communicate the vastness of the Pacific Ocean to people who have never been to sea. Day after day, Alguita was the only vehicle on a highway without landmarks, stretching from horizon to horizon. Yet as I gazed from the deck at the surface of what ought to have been a pristine ocean, I was confronted, as far as the eye could see, with the sight of plastic.

— *Capt. Charles Moore (2003)*

Even though plastic products have been used for over a century, their commercial development occurred during World War II, when shortages of rubber and other materials created great demand for alternative products. Plastic products are *lightweight, strong, durable,* and *inexpensive,* so they have many advantages over other materials. Today, everything from airplane parts to zippers is made of plastic (Figure 11C). Humans wear plastics, cook in plastics, drive in plastics, and even have internal artificial parts made of plastics. The convenience of plastic items intended for one-time use has also contributed to their popularity.

What was once thought of as a miracle substance, however, has been found to have several disadvantages. Disposing of plastics has already strained the capacity of land-based solid-waste disposal systems. Plastic waste is now an increasingly abundant component of oceanic flotsam (floating refuse). In fact, plastics constitute the vast majority of floating trash in all oceans worldwide. Unfortunately, the very same properties that make plastics so advantageous make them unusually persistent and damaging when released into the marine environment:

- They are *lightweight*, so they float and concentrate at the surface.
- They are *strong*, so they entangle marine organisms.
- They are *durable*, so they don't biodegrade easily, causing them to last almost indefinitely.
- They are *inexpensive*, so they are mass-produced and used in almost everything.

Small pellets called *nurdles* ranging in size from a BB to a pea are used to produce nearly all plastic

FIGURE 11C Plastic products.

FIGURE 11D Plastic pellets (*nurdles*) found at a beach.

products (Figure 11D). They are transported in bulk aboard commercial vessels and are found throughout the oceans, probably due to spillage at loading terminals. In coastal waters, plastic products used in fishing are commonly thrown overboard by recreational and commercial vessels. Plastic trash also finds its way into the open-ocean waters from non-point-source pollution by careless people on land.

Because of ocean currents that wash plastics ashore, plastic pellets and trash can be found on all beaches—even in remote areas. In one of the best-documented studies of trash on beaches, for example, researchers painstakingly counted all debris larger than a pinhead along selected transits in Orange County, California. Based on what was collected during the six-week sampling period, researchers project that each year Orange County beaches receive 106.9 million pieces of debris, an astonishing 98% (105.2 million) of which are nurdles. Other studies have shown that some Bermuda beaches contain up to 10,000 nurdles per square meter (10.7 square feet) and some beaches on Martha's Vineyard in Massachusetts contain 16,000 nurdles per square meter (10.7 square feet). Plastic trash is not limited to beaches. In fact, floating plastic trash is beginning to accumulate in unprecedented amounts in the open ocean. For example, in the centers

Continued on next page . . .

Continued from page 339...

of the major subtropical gyres, which have a sluggish circular motion and tend to accumulate floating debris, recent surveys indicate that the mass of floating plastic trash now outnumbers the mass of marine organisms six to one. Indeed, equipment deployed from research vessels often returns entangled in plastic trash such as six-pack rings, Styrofoam, and fishing lines, nets, and floats.

What can be done to limit the amount of plastic in the marine environment? For starters, people can limit their use of single-use plastic, recycle plastic material, and dispose of their plastic trash properly, including not dumping any plastic at sea. Recently, some California municipalities have banned single-use plastic bags and polystyrene takeout containers, with mounting pressure to enforce statewide

prohibition on these items. (China, Australia, South Africa, Bangladesh, Tanzania, and several other countries have already banned plastic grocery bags.) And, beach cleanups are responsible for removing an amazing amount of trash from beaches. By taking these simple actions, the amount of plastics in the world's oceans would be greatly reduced.

WEB VIDEO

Plastic Pollution

pieces accumulate poisons to levels as high as a million times their concentrations in seawater. When marine organisms ingest the toxic plastic pieces, they accumulate vast quantities of the toxic materials.

What makes matters worse is that over time, floating plastics *photodegrade*, a process in which sunlight breaks them into progressively smaller pieces, which only serves to facilitate the ingestion of plastics by all types of marine organisms, particularly microscopic organisms that constitute lower levels of marine food webs. So, plastics rarely if ever leave the ocean—they just break down into smaller pieces and enter marine food webs at progressively lower levels.

Studies have revealed that marine plastic particles increased tenfold every 10 years in the 1970s and 1980s—and then tenfold again in just 3 years in the 1990s. Where does all this floating plastic trash go? Some of it washes up on various beaches, and some is eaten by marine animals, but most of it remains at sea, constantly breaking down into smaller pieces. Oceanographers have recently discovered large floating regions of trash in all oceans of the world where plastics outnumber marine organisms several times over. These regions are located where major current systems converge within the world's subtropical gyres (see Chapter 7). One of the best studied of these regions is the **Eastern Pacific Garbage Patch** (Figure 11.30), which is about twice the size of Texas and is estimated to contain a staggering 91 million metric tons (100 million short tons) of debris.

What are the laws regulating ocean dumping? In the 1980s, increasing concern about floating trash—in particular syringes and other medical waste that closed long stretches of beaches in the New York area—prompted nations of the world to come together to try to correct the problem. In 1988, the International Convention for the Prevention of Pollution from Ships, which is commonly known as **MARPOL** (short for "Marine Pollution"), proposed a treaty banning the disposal of all plastics and regulating the dumping of most other garbage at sea (see Figure 11.28). By 2005, 122 nations had ratified MARPOL. Some studies suggest that MARPOL has reduced both marine debris and entanglements by discarded fishing nets in some places, most notably in waters off Alaska and California. Other studies, however, show no improvement in areas such as the Southern Ocean, South Atlantic, and Hawaiian Islands. As with many environmental protections and international treaties, enforcement lags far behind stated intentions. And although an annex to MARPOL requires that nations that have signed the treaty provide shore-based facilities where ships can easily dispose of their garbage, many developing countries have not been able to provide these facilities. As

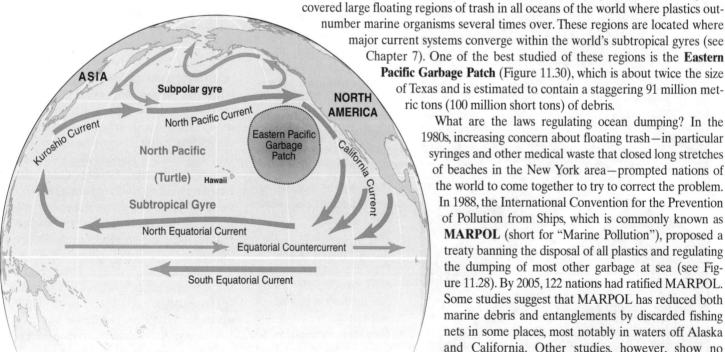

FIGURE 11.30 The Eastern Pacific Garbage Patch.
Map showing the location of the Eastern Pacific Garbage Patch in the North Pacific (Turtle) Gyre. Other subtropical gyres contain similar garbage patches, although this one is roughly twice the size of Texas.

a result, even well-meaning captains and shippers who want to comply with existing international marine pollution laws may not be able to do so.

Biological Pollution: Non-Native Species

Non-native species (also called *exotic*, *alien*, or *invasive species*) are species that originate in a particular area but are introduced into new environments either by the deliberate or accidental actions of humans and so are classified as biological pollutants. Because nonnative species inhabit new areas where they lack predators or other natural controls, they can wreak ecological havoc by outcompeting and dominating native populations. Nonnative species can also introduce new parasites and/or diseases. In some cases, non-native species completely transform ecosystems. In the United States alone, more than 7000 introduced species (not counting microorganisms) have been documented, of which about 15% cause ecological and economic damage. In fact, invasive species cause an estimated $137 billion in loss and damages in the United States each year.

The seaweed *Caulerpa taxifolia*, which is native in tropical waters, is one example of an invasive, non-native marine species. It is ideal as a decorative alga in saltwater aquariums because it is hardy, fast growing, and not edible by most fish. However, when it is introduced into suitable new habitats (probably as a result of the dumping of household saltwater aquariums), it becomes a dominant and persistent species that displaces native seaweeds and other marine life. In 1984, a cold-tolerant clone of *Caulerpa taxifolia* produced for the aquarium industry was first introduced into the Mediterranean Sea, where it has overwhelmed aquatic ecosystems and continues to spread. This clone has also been found in the lagoons of Southern California (Figure 11.31), where it was first reported in 2000, but eradication efforts appear to have been successful. Because *Caulerpa taxifolia* can regenerate from very small fragments, however, repeated surveys are being conducted in these lagoons to eliminate all remaining occurrences of the seaweed. Recently, a new infestation of *Caulerpa taxifolia* has been reported near Sydney, Australia.

Another example of a non-native aquatic species is the **zebra mussel** (*Dreissena polymorpha*), which has invaded the Great Lakes region. After entering North America more than a decade ago (probably in the ballast water[10] of a freighter from Europe), these mussels have proliferated rapidly in waters of eastern Canada and the United States. In doing so, they've driven out native mussels, altered the ecology of freshwater lakes and streams, and blocked the water-carrying pipes of power plants and many other industrial facilities. Although zebra mussels are exceedingly hardy organisms, researchers are working to identify predators, parasites, and infectious microbes that can kill zebra mussels but leave native populations unharmed.

FIGURE 11.31 Invasion of *Caulerpa taxifolia*. The seaweed *Caulerpa taxifolia* is thought to have been illegally dumped from an aquarium into Southern California coastal lagoons. The alga was eradiated largely because of good public awareness and quick action by local authorities.

---

[10]Ballast water is taken into the hold of a ship to enhance stability and then released in a port when it is no longer needed.

KEY CONCEPT
Examples of marine pollution include petroleum from
oil spills; sewage sludge; chemicals such as
DDT, PCBs, and mercury; non-point-source pollution
such as road oil and trash (including plastics); and
biological pollution such as non-native species.

Other notable examples of harmful non-native aquatic species include the Atlantic comb jelly *Mnemiopsis leidyi*, which was transported in ballast water to the Black Sea and has done extensive damage; the Atlantic cordgrass *Spartina alterniflora*, which has invaded soft-bottom coasts of California and Washington; the water hyacinth *Eichhornia crassipes*, which infests tropical estuaries and other water bodies; and the European green crab *Carcinus maenas*, which has invaded the Pacific Coast and is altering coastal food webs.

Chapter in Review

• *Coastal waters support about 95% of the total mass of life in the oceans*, and they are important areas for commerce, recreation, fisheries, and the disposal of waste. *Coastal law is specified in the United Nations Convention on the Law of the Sea*, which has been ratified by 153 coastal nations and in force since 1994. The treaty delineates *national obligations, rights, and jurisdiction in coastal waters*. In spite of its near-universal acceptance, *the United States has still not ratified the treaty*.

• *The temperature and salinity of the coastal ocean vary over a greater range than the open ocean* because the coastal ocean is shallow and experiences river runoff, tidal currents, and seasonal changes in solar radiation. *Coastal geostrophic currents are produced from freshwater runoff and coastal winds*.

• *Estuaries are semienclosed bodies of water where freshwater runoff from the land mixes with ocean water.* Estuaries are *classified by their origin* as coastal plain, fjord, bar built, or tectonic. Estuaries are also *classified by their mixing patterns* of fresh and salt water as vertically mixed, slightly stratified, highly stratified, and salt wedge. *Typical circulation in an estuary consists of a surface flow of low-salinity water toward its mouth and a sub-surface flow of marine water toward its head.*

• *Estuaries provide important breeding and nursery areas for many marine organisms* but often suffer from human population pressures. The *Columbia River Estuary*, for example, has degraded from agriculture, logging, and the construction of dams upstream. In the *Chesapeake Bay*, an anoxic zone occurs during the summer that kills many commercially important species.

• *Long offshore deposits called barrier islands protect marshes and lagoons.* Some lagoons have restricted circulation with the ocean, so water temperatures and salinity may vary widely with the seasons.

• *Circulation in the Mediterranean Sea is characteristic of restricted bodies of water in areas where evaporation greatly exceeds precipitation.* Called *Mediterranean circulation*, it is the reverse of estuarine circulation.

• *Wetlands are some of the most biologically productive regions on Earth. Salt marshes and mangrove swamps are important examples of coastal wetlands. Wetlands are ecologically important* because they *remove land-derived pollutants* from water before it reaches the ocean. Nevertheless, *human activities continue to destroy wetlands*.

• *Although marine pollution seems easily defined, an all-encompassing definition is quite detailed.* It is often difficult to establish the degree to which pollution affects ocean areas. The most widely used technique for determining the effects of pollution is the *environmental bioassay*, which determines the concentration of a pollutant that causes a *50% mortality*

rate among test organisms. The debate continues about whether society's wastes should be dumped in the ocean.

• *Oil is a complex mixture of hydrocarbons and other substances*, most of which are naturally *biodegradable*. Thus, *many marine pollution experts consider oil to be among the least damaging of all substances* introduced into the marine environment. In areas that have experienced oil spills, *recovery can be as rapid as a few years*. Still, *oil spills can cover large areas and kill many animals*. After the much publicized *Exxon Valdez* oil spill in Alaska, *many novel approaches were used to clean the spilled oil*, including oil-eating bacteria (*bioremediation*).

• *Millions of tons of sewage sludge have been dumped offshore in coastal waters.* Although 1972 legislation required an *end to dumping of sewage* in the coastal ocean by 1981, *exceptions continue to be made*. Increased public concern resulted in new legislation to prohibit sewage dumping in the ocean.

• *DDT and PCBs are persistent, biologically hazardous chemicals that have been introduced into the ocean by human activities.* DDT pollution produced a decline in the Long Island *osprey population* in the 1950s and the *brown pelican population* of the California coast in the 1960s. *Virtual cessation of DDT use* in the Northern Hemisphere in 1972 allowed the *recovery of both populations*. The DDT thinned the eggshells and reduced the number of successful hatchings. PCBs have been implicated in causing health problems in sea lions and shrimp.

• *Mercury poisoning was the first major human disaster resulting from ocean pollution.* It is now called *Minamata disease* after the bay in Japan where it first occurred in 1953. *Mercury bioaccumulates in the tissues of many large fish*, most notably tuna and swordfish, and *works its way up the food web* in a process called *biomagnification*. To prevent mercury poisonings in the United States, *stringent mercury contamination levels in fish have been established by the FDA*.

• *Non-point-source pollution includes road oil and trash.* Plastics are light-weight, strong, durable, and inexpensive. Unfortunately, these same properties make them a relentless *source of floating trash* in the ocean, especially because they *break down into progressively smaller pieces* over time. *The amount of plastic accumulating in the oceans has increased dramatically.* Certain forms of plastic are known to be *lethal to marine mammals, birds, and turtles*. International legislation such as *MARPOL regulates the disposal of trash in the ocean* but lacks enforcement.

• The introduction of *biological pollution* such as *non-native species* (including *Caulerpa taxifolia* and zebra mussels) into new environments can cause *severe ecological and economic damage*.

Key Terms

Anoxic (p. 321)

Bar-built estuary (p. 318)

Bioaccumulation (p. 336)

Biomagnification (p. 336)

Bioremediation (p. 331)

Caulerpa taxifolia (p. 341)

Coastal geostrophic current (p. 317)

Coastal plain estuary (p. 318)

Coastal water (p. 315)

Davidson Current (p. 317)

DDT (p. 334)

Review Questions

1. For coastal oceans where deep mixing does not occur, discuss the effect that offshore winds and freshwater runoff will have on salinity distribution. How will the winter and summer seasons affect the temperature distribution in the water column?

2. How does coastal runoff of low-salinity water produce a coastal geostrophic current?

3. Describe the difference between vertically mixed and salt wedge estuaries in terms of salinity distribution, depth, and volume of river flow. Which displays the more classical estuarine circulation pattern?

4. Discuss factors that cause the surface salinity of the Chesapeake Bay to be greater along its east side, and why periods of summer anoxia in deep water are becoming increasingly severe with time.

5. Name the two types of coastal wetland environments and the latitude ranges where each will likely develop. How do wetlands contribute to the biology of the oceans and the cleansing of polluted river water?

6. What factors lead to a wide seasonal range of salinity in Laguna Madre?

7. Describe the circulation between the Atlantic Ocean and the Mediterranean Sea, and explain how and why it differs from estuarine circulation.

8. Why would many marine pollution experts consider oil among the *least* damaging pollutants in the ocean?

9. Discuss techniques used to clean oil spills. Why is it important to begin the cleanup immediately?

10. When and where was the world's largest oil spill? How many times larger was it than the *Exxon Valdez* oil spill?

11. How would dumping sewage in deeper water off the East Coast help reduce the negative effects to the ocean bottom?

12. Discuss the animal populations that clearly suffered from the effects of DDT and the way in which this negative effect was manifested.

13. What causes Minamata disease? What are the symptoms of the disease in humans?

14. What is non-point-source pollution and how does it get to the ocean? What other ways does trash get into the ocean?

15. What properties contributed to plastics being considered a miracle substance? How do those same properties cause them to be unusually persistent and damaging in the marine environment?

16. What are non-native species? Why can they be so damaging to ecosystems?

Critical Thinking Exercises

1. Discuss reasons why less-developed nations believe that the open ocean is the common heritage of all, whereas the more developed nations believe that the open ocean's resources belong to those who recover them.

2. Based on their origin, draw and describe the four major classes of estuaries.

3. List and describe the three main problems that floating plastic trash presents to marine organisms. Of the three, which one is potentially the most serious threat? Explain.

4. Without consulting the textbook, define pollution. Then consider these items and determine if each one is a pollutant based on your definition (and refine your definition as necessary):

    a. Dead seaweed on the beach

    b. Natural oil seeps

    c. A small amount of sewage

    d. Warm water from a power plant dumped into the ocean

    e. Sound from boats in the ocean

Oceanography on the Web

Visit the *Essentials of Oceanography* Online Study Guide for Internet resources, including chapter-specific quizzes to test your understanding and Web links to further your exploration of the topics in this chapter.

The *Essentials of Oceanography* Online Study Guide is at http://www.mygeoscienceplace.com/.

Unique adaptations of marine life.
The goosefish (*Lophius americanus*; also called monkfish, or angler) has unique adaptations, including feathery appendages as camouflage and a modified dorsal fin that serves as a lure to attract prey. It has been described as mostly mouth with a tail attached and it can eat prey almost as big as itself. The bottom-dwelling goosefish lives in water as deep as 800 meters (2600 feet) and ranges from the Grand Banks and northern Gulf of St. Lawrence south to Cape Hatteras, North Carolina.

"A species is a masterpiece of evolution, a million-year-old entity encoded by five billion genetic letters, exquisitely adapted to the niche it inhabits."

—E. O. Wilson,
biologist and global conservation advocate (2001)

12 MARINE LIFE AND THE MARINE ENVIRONMENT

A wide variety of organisms inhabits the marine environment. These organisms range in size from microscopic bacteria and algae to the blue whale, which is as long as three buses lined up end to end. Marine biologists have identified over 250,000 marine species; this number is constantly increasing as new organisms are discovered.

Most marine organisms live within the sunlit surface waters of the ocean. Strong sunlight supports photosynthesis by marine algae, which either directly or indirectly provides food for the vast majority of marine organisms. All marine algae live near the surface because they need the sunlight; most marine animals live near the surface because this is where food can be obtained. In shallow-water areas close to land, sunlight reaches all the way to the ocean floor, resulting in an abundance of marine life.

There are advantages and disadvantages to living in the marine environment. One advantage is that there is an abundance of water available, which is necessary for supporting all types of life. One disadvantage is that maneuvering in water can be difficult because the high density of water impedes movement. The individual success of species depends on their ability to find food, avoid predators, and cope with the many physical barriers to their movement.

12.1 What Are Living Things, and How Are They Classified?

Living things are classified based on their physical characteristics, with organisms that are closely related to one another sharing a host of common traits. Recently, genome sequencing of the DNA of many organisms (including human, mouse, dog, cat, cow, elephant, honeybee, platypus, diatom, red algae, sea urchin, dolphin, and hundreds of bacteria and viruses, amongst others) has allowed genetic comparison, sometimes confirming many of the classification groupings based on structure and other times indicating some unexpected relationships. First, however, let's examine what characteristics qualify an entity as being alive.

A Working Definition of Life

It might seem easy to differentiate those that are living from the nonliving, but the unusual nature of some life forms makes defining life a challenging task. Also, both living and nonliving things are composed of the same basic building blocks: atoms, which move continuously in and out of living and nonliving systems. This free exchange of identical components between life and nonlife is one of the factors that complicates attempts at formally defining life.

A simple definition of life is that it consumes energy from its environment. Using this definition, a car engine could probably be classified as alive. An engine, however, cannot self-replicate or otherwise reproduce itself, which is another key component of life.

Several other qualities are crucial in defining life. Water probably needs to be a part of a living organism because living things need a solvent for biochemical reactions—though ammonia or sulfuric acid might also work. A living thing probably has to have some sort of a membrane to distinguish itself from its environment. In addition, most living things tend to respond to stimuli or adapt to their environment. Lastly, life as we know it is carbon-based, since carbon is so useful in making chemical compounds. Because NASA's definition of life must encompass the potential of extraterrestrial life, they have been using a fairly simple working definition of life: "Life is a self-sustained chemical system capable of undergoing Darwinian evolution."[1] Even this definition is problematic in that it would likely require observation of several successive generations over a considerable length of time to verify evolution in a life form.

A good working definition of life, then, should incorporate most of these ideas: that living things can capture, store, and transmit energy; they are capable of reproduction; they can adapt to their environment; and they change through time.

The Three Domains of Life

All living things belong to one of three domains or "superkingdoms" of life: Bacteria (or Eubacteria), Archaea, and Eukarya (Figure 12.1a). Domain **Bacteria** (*bakterion* = rod) includes simple life forms with cells that usually lack a nucleus, including purple bacteria, green nonsulfur bacteria, and cyanobacteria (blue-green algae). Domain **Archaea** (*achaeo* = ancient) is a group of simple, microscopic,

FIGURE 12.1 The three domains of life and the five kingdoms of organisms. Starting with a common ancestral community of primitive cells, life on Earth can be visualized as branching out into **(a)** the three domains of life and **(b)** the five kingdoms of organisms, which shows representative organisms in each kingdom.

(a) The three domains of life

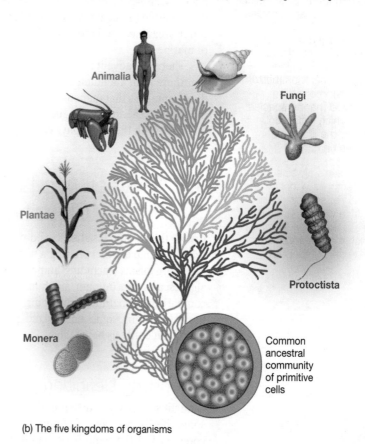

(b) The five kingdoms of organisms

---

[1]See Box 1.3 for a description of Darwinian evolution.

bacteria-like creatures that includes methane producers and sulfur oxidizers that inhabit deep-sea vents and seeps,[2] as well as other forms—many of which prefer environments with extreme temperatures and/or pressures. Domain **Eukarya** (*eu* = good, *karuon* = nut) includes complex organisms: multicellular plants; multicellular animals; fungi; and protoctists, which are a diverse array of mostly microscopic organisms that don't fit into any other group. The main component of eukaryotes, DNA, is housed in a discrete nucleus, and their cells contain structures that supply energy to build the cell and maintain its functions.

What were the ancestors of these three domains of life? The ancestors of the three domains are thought to have consisted of a community of early primitive cells, some of which apparently acquired new genetic material by engulfing microbial neighbors including their genetic codes. These groups of organisms helped each other coexist for their mutual benefit, and as a result evolved into new organisms that contained merged genes. Today, in fact, it is well established that such adoption of foreign genetic material is common among single-celled bacteria and other microbes but also occurs in some fungi, plants, insects, worms, and other animals. For example, a recent study of venomous jellyfish has revealed that one of the genes necessary for jellyfish to sting is identical to a gene in bacteria, suggesting that the ancestors of jellyfish picked up the gene from microbes. This process, called *lateral gene transfer*, was likely quite important in the evolution of some of the first complex cells.

The Five Kingdoms of Organisms

Within the three domains of life, a system of five kingdoms was first proposed by ecologist and biologist Robert H. Whittaker in 1969. Although the five kingdoms have been modified somewhat since they were first proposed, the five kingdoms are Monera, Plantae, Animalia, Fungi, and Protoctista (or Protista) (Figure 12.1b). More recently, some biologists now recognize additional kingdoms within the Archaea domain.

Kingdom **Monera** (*monos* = single) includes some of the simplest organisms. These organisms are single celled but lack discrete nuclei and the internal organelles present in all other organisms. Included in this kingdom are cyanobacteria (blue-green algae), heterotrophic bacteria, and archaea. Recent discoveries have shown bacteria to be a much more important part of marine ecology than previously believed. These organisms are found throughout the breadth and depth of the oceans.

Kingdom **Plantae** (*planta* = plant) comprises the multicelled plants, all of which photosynthesize. Only a few species of true plants—such as surf grass (*Phyllospadix*) and eelgrass (*Zostera*)—inhabit shallow coastal environments. In the ocean, photosynthetic marine algae occupy the ecological niche of land plants. However, certain plants are vital parts of coastal ecosystems, including mangrove swamps and salt marshes.

Kingdom **Animalia** (*anima* = breath) comprises the multicelled animals. Organisms from kingdom Animalia range in complexity from the simple sponges to complex vertebrates (animals with backbones), which also includes humans.

Kingdom **Fungi** (*fungus* = [probably from Greek *sp(h)ongos* = sponge]) includes 100,000 species of mold and lichen, though less than one-half of 1% of them are sea dwellers. Fungi exist throughout the marine environment, but they are much more common in the intertidal zone, where they live with cyanobacteria or green algae to form lichen. Other fungi remineralize organic matter and function primarily as decomposers in the marine ecosystem.

Kingdom **Protoctista** (*proto* = first, *ktistos* = to establish) includes a diverse collection of single- and multicelled organisms that have a nucleus. Examples of

---

[2]A *seep* is an area where various fluids trickle out of the sea floor.

Genus • *Delphinus*
Species • *delphis*
(Common dolphin)

FAMILY • DELPHINIDAE
ORDER • CETACEA
CLASS • MAMMALIA
PHYLUM • CHORDATA
KINGDOM • ANIMALIA

FIGURE 12.2 A visualization of Linnaeus's classification scheme. The Linnaean system of classification can be visualized as a series of nested boxes, with genus and species the most specific groupings (smallest boxes). The box-in-box representation shows genealogical connections amongst organisms.

organisms in kingdom Protoctista include various types of marine *algae* (aquatic photosynthetic organisms that can be either single-celled and microscopic or multicelled and macroscopic) and single-celled animals called **protozoa** (*proto* = first, *zoa* = animal).

Linnaeus and Taxonomic Classification

In an effort to determine the relationships of all living things on Earth, Swedish botanist Carl von Linné—who Latinized his name to **Carolus Linnaeus** (1707–1778)—created a system in 1758 that is the basis of the modern scientific system of classification used today. Linnaeus developed his system similar to the social hierarchy of his day, with its kingdoms, countries, provinces, parishes, and villages. Linnaeus was a gifted observationist and tireless collector who spent much of his time naming species and organizing them into groups. In fact, Linnaeus's original names for the roughly 12,000 organisms he examined over the course of his life became the starting point for all biological classification. Linnaeus's organizational scheme can be visualized as a series of nested boxes (Figure 12.2).

Today, the systematic classification of organisms—called **taxonomy** (*taxix* = arrangement, *nomia* = a law)—involves using physical characteristics as well as genetic information to recognize organism similarities and then grouping them into the following increasingly specific categories:

- Kingdom   (Less specific grouping)
- Phylum[3]
- Class
- Order
- Family
- Genus
- Species   (More specific grouping)

All organisms that share a common category (for instance, a *family*—such as the cat or dolphin family) have certain characteristics and evolutionary similarities. In some cases, subdivisions of these categories are also used, such as subphylum (Table 12.1). The categories assigned to an individual species must be agreed upon by an international panel of experts.

The fundamental unit of taxonomic classification is the **species** (*species* = a kind). Species consist of populations of genetically similar, interbreeding (or potentially interbreeding) individuals that share a collection of inherited characteristics whose combination is unique.

As an offshoot of his classification scheme, Linnaeus also invented *binomial nomenclature*, where every living thing is known by just two Latin names (previously, organisms were known by a combination of as many as a dozen Latin names). In this way, every type of organism has a unique two-word scientific name

KEY CONCEPT
Living organisms use energy, reproduce, adapt, and change through time. Living things can be classified into one of three domains and five kingdoms, each of which is split into increasingly specific groupings of phylum, class, order, family, genus, and species.

---

[3]Note that for plants, the term division is used instead of phylum; the current International Code of Botanical Nomenclature, however, allows the use of either term.

TABLE 12.1	TAXONOMIC CLASSIFICATION OF SELECTED ORGANISMS				
Category	**Human**	**Common dolphin**	**Killer whale**	**Bat star**	**Giant kelp**
Kingdom	Animalia	Animalia	Animalia	Animalia	Protoctista
Phylum	Chordata	Chordata	Chordata	Echinodermata	Phaeophyta
Subphylum	Vertebrata	Vertebrata	Vertebrata		
Class	Mammalia	Mammalia	Mammalia	Asteroidea	Phaeophycae
Order	Primates	Cetacea	Cetacea	Valvatida	Laminariales
Family	Hominidae	Delphinidae	Delphinidae	Oreasteridae	Lessoniaceae
Genus	*Homo*	*Delphinus*	*Orcinus*	*Asterina*	*Macrocystis*
Species	*sapiens*	*delphis*	*orca*	*miniata*	*pyrifera*

using its genus and species, which is italicized with the first letter of the generic (genus) name capitalized—for example, *Delphinus delphis*. Most organisms also have one or more common names. *Delphinus delphis*, for instance, is the common dolphin, and *Orcinus orca* is the killer whale or orca. If the scientific name is referred to repeatedly within a document, it is often shortened by abbreviating the genus name to its first letter. Thus, *Delphinus delphis* becomes *D. delphis*.

The Linnaean system, even in its modern form, is far from perfect. New evidence routinely requires taxonomists to move species from one genus to another, or even to an entirely different order. Linnaeus, however, is credited with forging a single, flexible, universally applicable scientific language that is still in use over 250 years after he invented it.

12.2 How Are Marine Organisms Classified?

Marine organisms can be classified according to where they live (their habitat) and how they move (their mobility). Organisms that inhabit the water column can be classified as either *plankton* (drifters) or *nekton* (swimmers). All other organisms are *benthos* (bottom dwellers).

Plankton (Drifters)

Plankton (*planktos* = wandering) include all organisms—algae, animals, and bacteria—that drift with ocean currents. An individual organism is called a **plankter**. Just because plankters drift does not mean they are unable to swim. In fact, many plankters can swim but either move only weakly or move only vertically. As such, they cannot determine their horizontal position within the ocean.

Plankton are unbelievably abundant and important within the marine environment. In fact, *most of Earth's* **biomass**—*the mass of living organisms*—*consists of plankton adrift in the oceans*. Even though 98% of marine *species* are bottom dwelling, the vast majority of the ocean's *biomass* is planktonic.

TYPES OF PLANKTON   Plankton can be classified based on their feeding styles. If an organism can photosynthesize and therefore produce its own food, it is termed **autotrophic** (*auto* = self, *tropho* = nourishment). Autotrophic plankton are called **phytoplankton** (*phyto* = plant, *planktos* = wandering) and can range in size from microscopic algae to larger species of drifting kelp. If an organism cannot produce its own food and relies instead on food produced by other organisms, it is termed **heterotrophic** (*hetero* = different, *tropho* = nourishment). Heterotrophic plankton are called **zooplankton** (*zoo* = animal, *planktos* = wandering), which includes drifting marine animals. Representative members of each group are shown in Figure 12.3.

Plankton also include bacteria. It has recently been discovered that free-living **bacterioplankton** are much more abundant and far more widely distributed than previously thought. Having an average diameter of only one-half of a micrometer[4] (0.00002 inch), they were missed in earlier studies because they are so incredibly small. Recently, microbiologists have begun to study oceanic bacterioplankton and have even discovered an extremely small yet abundant bacterium that has been estimated to constitute at least half of the ocean's total photosynthetic biomass and is likely the most abundant photosynthetic organism on Earth.

Plankton also include viruses, which are called **virioplankton**. Virioplankton are an order of magnitude smaller than bacterioplankton and are similarly little known. The role of viruses in planktonic communities is not well understood, but they may limit the abundance of other types of plankton through infection.

Although plankton can be classified as either phytoplankton, zooplankton, bacterioplankton, or virioplankton, they can also be classified according to the portion of their life cycle spent as plankton. Organisms that spend their entire lives as plankton are **holoplankton** (*holo* = whole, *planktos* = wandering). Many organisms that spend their adult lives as nekton or benthos spend their juvenile and/or larval stages as plankton

FIGURE 12.3 Phytoplankton and zooplankton (floaters). Schematic drawings of various phytoplankton (*above*) and zooplankton (*below*). Not drawn to scale; typical maximum dimension is in parentheses. **Phytoplankton: (a)** and **(b)** Coccolithophoridae (15 microns, or 0.0006 in). **(c)–(l)** Diatoms (80 microns, or 0.0032 in): **(c)** *Corethron*; **(d)** *Asteromphalus*; **(e)** *Rhizosolenia*; **(f)** *Coscinodiscus*; **(g)** *Biddulphia favus*; **(h)** *Chaetoceras*; **(i)** *Licmophora*; **(j)** *Thalassiosira*; **(k)** *Biddulphia mobiliensis*; **(l)** *Eucampia*. **(m)–(s)** Dinoflagellates (100 microns, or 0.004 in): **(m)** *Ceratium reticulatum*; **(n)** *Goniaulax scrippsae*; **(o)** *Gymnodinium*; **(p)** *Goniaulax triacantha*; **(q)** *Dynophysis*; **(r)** *Ceratium bucephalum*; **(s)** *Peridinium*. **Zooplankton: (a)** Fish egg (1 mm, or 0.04 in). **(b)** Fish larva (5 cm, or 2 in). **(c)** Radiolaria (0.5 mm, or 0.02 in). **(d)** Foraminifer (1 mm, or 0.04 in). **(e)** Jellyfish (30 cm, or 12 in). **(f)** Arrowworms (3 cm, or 1.2 in). **(g)** and **(h)** Copepods (5 mm, or 0.2 in). **(i)** Salp (10 cm, or 4 in). **(j)** Tunicate (*Doliolum*) (10 cm, or 4 in). **(k)** Siphonophore (30 cm, or 12 in). **(l)** Worm larva (1 mm, or 0.04 in). **(m)** Fish larva (5 cm, or 2 in). **(n)** Tintinnid (1 mm, or 0.04 in). **(o)** Foraminifer (1 mm, or 0.04 in). **(p)** Dinoflagellate (*Noctiluca*) (1 mm, or 0.04 in).

---

[4]One micrometer (also known as a *micron*) is one-millionth of a meter and is designated by the symbol μm.

(Figure 12.4). These organisms are called **meroplankton** (*mero* = a part, *planktos* = wandering).

Lastly, plankton can also be classified based on size. For example, large floating animals and algae, such as jellyfish and Sargassum,[5] are called **macroplankton** (*macro* = large, *planktos* = wandering) and measure 2 to 20 centimeters (0.8 to 8 inches). Plankton also include *bacterioplankton,* which are so small that they can be removed from the water only with special microfilters. These very tiny drifters are called **picoplankton** (*pico* = small, *planktos* = wandering) and measure 0.2 to 2 microns (0.000008 to 0.00008 inch).

Nekton (Swimmers)

Nekton (*nektos* = swimming) include all animals capable of moving independently of the ocean currents by swimming or other means of propulsion. They are capable not only of determining their own positions within the ocean but also, in many cases, of long migrations. Nekton include most adult fish and squid, marine mammals, and marine reptiles (Figure 12.5). When you go ocean swimming, you become nekton, too.

Although nekton move freely, they are unable to move throughout the breadth of the ocean. Gradual changes in temperature, salinity, viscosity, and availability of nutrients effectively limit their lateral range. The deaths of large numbers of fish, for example, can be caused by temporary horizontal shifts of water masses in the ocean. Water pressure normally limits the vertical range of nekton.

Fish may appear to exist everywhere in the oceans, but they are more abundant near continents and islands and in colder waters. Some fish, such as salmon, ascend freshwater rivers to spawn. Many eels do just the reverse, growing to maturity in freshwater and then descending the streams to breed in the great depths of the ocean.

Benthos (Bottom Dwellers)

The term **benthos** (*benthos* = bottom) describes organisms living on or in the ocean bottom. **Epifauna** (*epi* = upon, *fauna* = animal) live on the surface of the sea floor, either attached to rocks or moving along the bottom. **Infauna** (*in* = inside, *fauna* = animal) live buried in the sand, shells, or mud. Some benthos, called **nektobenthos**, live on the bottom yet also have the ability to swim or crawl through the water above the ocean floor (such as flat-fish, octopuses, crabs, and sea urchins). Examples of benthos are shown in Figure 12.6.

The shallow coastal ocean floor contains a wide variety of physical and nutritive conditions, which have allowed a great number of animal species to develop. Moving across the bottom from the shore into deeper water, the *number* of benthos species per square meter may remain relatively constant, but the *biomass* of benthos organisms decreases. In addition, the shallow coastal areas are the only locations where large marine algae (often called "seaweeds") attached to the bottom are found because *these* are the only areas of the sea floor that receive sufficient sunlight.

Throughout most of deeper parts of the sea floor, animals live in perpetual darkness, where photosynthetic production cannot occur. They must feed on each other or on whatever outside nutrients fall from the productive zone near the surface.

The deep-sea bottom is an environment of coldness, stillness, and darkness. Under these conditions, life progresses slowly, and organisms that live in the deep

[5]*Sargassum* is a floating type of brown macro marine algae commonly referred to as a "seaweed" that is particularly abundant in the Sargasso Sea.

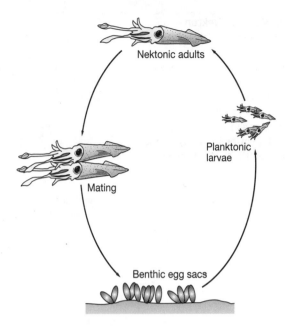

FIGURE 12.4 Typical life cycle of a squid. Squid are meroplankton because they are planktonic only during their larval stage. Adult squid are nekton and their egg sacs are benthos.

FIGURE 12.5 Nekton (swimmers). Schematic drawing of various nektonic organisms. Not drawn to scale; typical maximum dimension is in parentheses. **(a)** Bluefin tuna (2 m, or 6.6 ft). **(b)** Bottlenose dolphin (4 m, or 13 ft). **(c)** Nurse shark (3 m, or 10 ft). **(d)** Barracuda (1 m, or 3.3 ft). **(e)** Striped bass (0.5 m, or 1.6 ft). **(f)** Sardine (15 cm, or 6 in). **(g)** Deep-ocean fish (8 cm, or 3 in). **(h)** Squid (1 m, or 3.3 ft). **(i)** Anglerfish (5 cm, or 2 in). **(j)** Lantern fish (8 cm, or 3 in). **(k)** Gulper (15 cm, or 6 in).

sea usually are widely distributed because physical conditions vary little on the deep-ocean floor, even over great distances.

HYDROTHERMAL VENT BIOCOMMUNITIES Prior to the discovery of deep-sea hydrothermal vent biocommunities in 1977, marine scientists believed that only sparse and small life existed on the deep-ocean floor. Then the first biocommunity at a hydrothermal vent was discovered in waters 2500 meters (8200 feet) deep in the Galápagos Rift off South America, demonstrating for the first time that high concentrations of abundant and large deep-ocean benthos are possible. Because the primary factor that limits life on the deep-ocean floor is sparse food supply, the scientists wondered how the hydrothermal vent organisms were able to obtain enough food to exist.

It turns out that bacteria-like archaea, which produce food not by photosynthesis (for no sunlight is available) but instead thrive on sea floor chemicals, are the base of this marine food web. As a result, the size of individuals and the total biomass in hydrothermal communities far exceed those previously known for deep-ocean benthos. These biocommunities are discussed in Chapter 15, "Animals of the Benthic Environment."

KEY CONCEPT
Marine organisms can be classified according to their habitat and mobility as plankton (drifters), nekton (swimmers), or benthos (bottom dwellers).

FIGURE 12.6 Benthos (bottom dwellers): Representative intertidal and shallow subtidal forms. Schematic drawing of various benthos organisms. Not drawn to scale; typical maximum dimension is in parentheses. **(a)** Sand dollar (8 cm, or 3 in). **(b)** Clam (30 cm, or 12 in). **(c)** Crab (30 cm, or 12 in). **(d)** Abalone (30 cm, or 12 in). **(e)** Sea urchins (15 cm, or 6 in). **(f)** Sea anemone (30 cm, or 12 in). **(g)** Brittle star (20 cm, or 8 in). **(h)** Sponge (30 cm, or 12 in). **(i)** Acorn barnacles (2.5 cm, or 1 in). **(j)** Snail (2 cm, or 0.8 in). **(k)** Mussels (25 cm, or 10 in). **(l)** Gooseneck barnacles (8 cm, or 3 in). **(m)** Sea star (30 cm, or 12 in). **(n)** Brain coral (50 cm, or 20 in). **(o)** Sea cucumber (30 cm, or 12 in). **(p)** Lamp shell (10 cm, or 4 in). **(q)** Sea lily (10 cm, or 4 in). **(r)** Sea squirt (10 cm, or 4 in).

12.3 How Many Marine Species Exist?

The total number of catalogued species on Earth in both marine and terrestrial environments is currently 1.8 million; the figure is constantly increasing as new species are discovered. Quite certainly, there are many marine species (maybe millions) that have not yet been identified due in large part to the difficulty and expense of exploring the deep sea. Overall, as many as 2000 new species are cataloged each year. Therefore, the total number of species on Earth, known and still undiscovered, has been estimated to be between 3 million and 100 million; the most likely total number of species on Earth is estimated to be between 6 million and 12 million.[6] And, not all newly discovered species are microbes or small invertebrates. In fact, species of frogs, lizards, birds, fish, and even mammals previously unknown to science have been recently discovered in remote areas of the world.

---

[6]Note that this figure does not include the millions of species throughout geologic time that were once living but are now extinct.

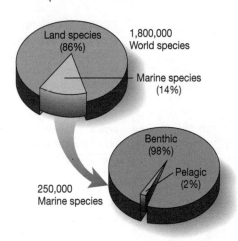

FIGURE 12.7 Distribution of species on Earth. Of the 1.8 million known species on Earth, 86% inhabit land environments and 14% inhabit the ocean. Of the 250,000 known marine species, 98% inhabit the benthic environment and live in or on the ocean floor, while only 2% inhabit the pelagic environment and live within the water column as either plankton or nekton.

STUDENTS SOMETIMES ASK...

Which group of organisms has the most species on Earth?

Although you might expect that bacteria or other microbes comprise the largest number of species on Earth, it's actually... (wait for it)... insects, which comprise 56% of total species on Earth (more than 1 million species identified). Of insect species, nearly half—or one out of every four species on Earth—are beetles, such as ladybugs, fireflies, rhinoceros beetles, soldier beetles, leaf beetles, rove beetles, click beetles, dung beetles, bark beetles, scarabs, and weevils. Even though insect species are incredibly abundant on land, only 1400 species—less than a quarter of 1%—inhabit the ocean. Of those, just five species (sea skaters of the genus *Halobates*) live in the open ocean; the rest are coastal. Apparently, the lack of solid surfaces in the open ocean is what has kept insects at bay.

KEY CONCEPT
Marine species represent 14% of the total number of known species on Earth. The benthic environment, which has large environmental variability, is home to 98% of the 250,000 known marine species.

Some of the difficulties of describing the extent to which the marine environment is inhabited include the immense size of the marine habitat and its inaccessibility. In addition, so little is known about marine organisms and some populations fluctuate greatly each season. An ambitious program called the *Census of Marine Life (CoML)* began in 2000 as a 10-year project by a team of 2000 researchers in more than 70 countries to assess and explain the diversity, distribution, and abundance of marine organisms in the world's oceans. While CoML has discovered a large number of marine species and will undoubtedly add more, there are currently 250,000 catalogued marine species, which represent only about 14% of all known species on Earth (Figure 12.7).

Why Are There So Few Marine Species?

If the ocean is such a prime habitat for life and if life originated there, why do so few of the world's species live in the ocean? The disparity is likely a result of the fact that the marine environment is more stable than the terrestrial environment. A major factor that leads to the creation of different species is the variability of the environment: The more variable the environment, the more species are generally present. The higher environmental variability on land presents many opportunities for natural selection to produce new species to inhabit varied new niches, which is one reason why tropical rainforests have such a high diversity of species. Conversely, the relatively uniform conditions of the open ocean do not pressure organisms to adapt, so there are fewer species there. In addition, ocean temperatures are not only stable but also relatively low below the sunlit surface waters. The rate of chemical reaction is slowed, which may further reduce the tendency for speciation to occur.

Species in Pelagic and Benthic Environments

Figure 12.7 also shows that only 2% or about 5000 of the 250,000 known marine species inhabit the **pelagic** (*pelagios* = of the sea) **environment** and live within the water column. The other 98% inhabit the **benthic** (*benthos* = bottom) **environment** and live either in or on the sea floor. These numbers are minimums, however, because recent discoveries indicate that many more species may inhabit the benthic environment than previously thought.

Why do most marine species inhabit the benthic environment? The ocean floor contains numerous benthic environments (such as rocky, sandy, muddy, flat, sloped, irregular, and mixed bottoms) that create different habitats to which organisms have adapted. On the other hand, most of the pelagic environment—especially that below the sunlit surface waters—is a watery world that is quite uniform from one region to the next and does not experience extreme environmental variability to which organisms need to be adapted in order to survive.

12.4 How Are Marine Organisms Adapted for the Physical Conditions of the Ocean?

For organisms to survive, they must be able to adapt to conditions of their environment. The ocean's physical conditions provide benefits but also present challenges to anything living within it.

For example, the marine environment—particularly its temperature—is far more stable than the terrestrial environment. As a result, ocean-dwelling organisms have not developed highly specialized regulatory systems to adjust to sudden changes that might occur within their environment. Marine organisms can, therefore, be affected adversely by very small changes in temperature, salinity, turbidity, pressure, or other environmental conditions.

Water constitutes more than 80% of the mass of **protoplasm** (*proto* = first, *plasm* = something molded), which is the substance of living matter. In fact, more than 65% of your body's weight—and 95% of a jellyfish's weight—is water (Figure 12.8). Water carries dissolved within it the gases and minerals organisms need to survive. Water is also a raw material in the photosynthesis of food by marine phytoplankton.

Land plants and animals have developed complex "plumbing systems" to retain water and to distribute it throughout their bodies. The inhabitants of the open ocean do not risk atmospheric *desiccation* (drying out), however, because they live in an environment of abundant water.

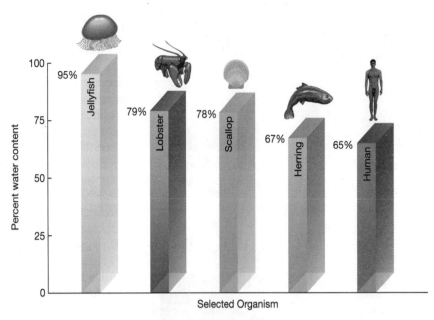

FIGURE 12.8 Percent water content of selected organisms. Bar graph showing the water content of selected organisms. Jellyfish are 95% water, whereas humans are 65% water.

Need for Physical Support

One basic need of all plants and animals is for simple physical support. Land plants, for example, have vast root systems that anchor the plants securely to the ground. Land animals have skeletons and combinations of appendages—legs, arms, fingers, and toes—to support their entire weight.

In the ocean, water physically supports marine plants and animals. Organisms such as photosynthetic phytoplankton, which must live in the upper surface waters of the ocean, depend primarily upon buoyancy and frictional resistance to sinking to maintain their desired position. Still, maintaining position can be difficult, so some organisms have developed special adaptations to increase their efficiency. These adaptations are discussed in this and succeeding chapters.

Water's Viscosity

Viscosity (*viscos* = sticky) is a substance's *internal resistance to flow*. Recall from Chapter 1 that a substance with high resistance to flow (high viscosity)—such as toothpaste—does not flow easily. Conversely, a substance that has low viscosity—such as water—flows more readily. Viscosity is strongly affected by temperature. Tar, for example, must be heated to decrease its viscosity before it can be spread onto roofs or roads.

The viscosity of ocean water increases as salinity increases and temperature decreases. Thus, single-celled organisms that float in colder, higher viscosity waters have less need for extensions to help them maintain their positions near the surface. Figure 12.9 shows, for example, that a warm-water floating crustacean has ornate, featherlike appendages, whereas a cold-water variety does not.

THE IMPORTANCE OF ORGANISM SIZE The basic requirements of phytoplankton are that they (1) stay in the upper portion of ocean water where solar radiation is available, (2) have available necessary nutrients, (3) efficiently take in these nutrients from surrounding waters, and (4) expel waste materials. Their ingenious size and shape help single-celled phytoplankton satisfy these requirements without needing specialized multiple cells.

Phytoplankton cannot propel themselves, so they use frictional resistance to maintain their general position near the surface of the water. Frictional resistance to sinking increases as an

FIGURE 12.9 Water temperature and appendages. **(a)** Copepod (*Oithona*) displays the ornate plumage characteristic of warm-water varieties. **(b)** Copepod (*Calanus*) displays the less ornate appendages found on temperate and cold-water forms.

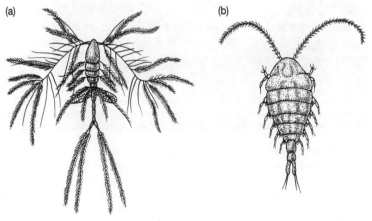

Cube a
Side = 1
Surface = 6
Volume = 1

$$\frac{S}{V} = \frac{6}{1} = 6$$

(a)

Cube b
Side = 2
Surface = $2^2 \times 6 = 24$
Volume = $2^3 = 8$

$$\frac{S}{V} = \frac{24}{8} = 3$$

(b)

Cube c
Side = 4
Surface = $4^2 \times 6 = 96$
Volume = $4^3 = 64$

$$\frac{S}{V} = \frac{96}{64} = 1.5$$

(c)

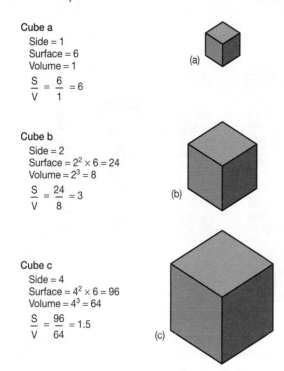

FIGURE 12.10 Surface area to volume ratio of cubes of different sizes. As the linear dimension of a cube increases, the ratio of surface area to volume decreases. Thus, smaller bodies have a higher surface area to volume ratio, which allows them to stay afloat more easily and efficiently exchange nutrients and wastes.

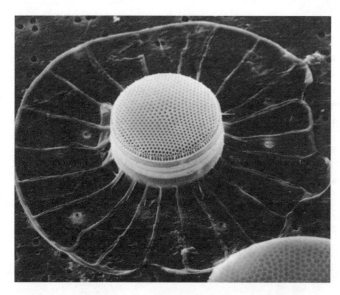

FIGURE 12.11 Warm-water diatom. Scanning electron micrograph of the warm-water diatom *Planktoniella sol,* which has a prominent marginal ring to increase its surface area and prevent it from sinking (diameter = 60 microns, or 0.0024 inch).

organism's ratio of surface area to volume (mass) increases. For example, Figure 12.10 shows the surface area to volume ratio of three different cubes and illustrates that the ratio increases as an organism's size decreases. In the figure, cube a has twice the surface area per unit of volume of cube b and four times the surface area per unit of volume as cube c. If the cubes were plankton, cube a would have four times the resistance to sinking per unit of mass as cube c, so cube a would need to exert far less energy to stay afloat. Single-celled organisms, which make up the bulk of photosynthetic marine life, clearly benefit from being as small as possible. They are so small, in fact, that one needs a microscope to see them!

Photosynthetic cells take in nutrients from surrounding water and expel waste through their cell membranes. The efficiency of both functions increases with a higher surface area to volume ratio. Thus, if cubes a and c in Figure 12.10 were planktonic algae, cube a could take in nutrients and dispose of waste four times more efficiently than cube c. This is why cells in all plants and animals are microscopic, regardless of the overall size of the organism.

Diatoms—one of the most important groups of phytoplankton—often have unusual appendages, needlelike extensions, or even rings (Figure 12.11) to increase their surface area, thus preventing them from sinking below sunlit surface waters. Other planktonic marine organisms—particularly warm-water species—use similar strategies to stay afloat.

Some small organisms produce a tiny droplet of oil, which lowers their overall density and increases buoyancy. Accumulations of vast amounts of these organisms in sediment can produce offshore oil deposits if their droplets of oil are combined, sufficiently matured, and trapped in a reservoir.

Despite adaptations to remain in the upper layers of the ocean, organisms still have a higher density than seawater, so they tend to sink, if ever so slowly. This is not a serious handicap, however, because wind causes considerable mixing and turbulence near the surface. Turbulence, in turn, keeps these organisms positioned to bask in the solar radiation needed to photosynthesize, producing the energy used by essentially all other members of the marine community.

VISCOSITY AND STREAMLINING As organisms increase in size, viscosity ceases to enhance survival and instead becomes an obstacle. This is particularly true of large organisms that swim freely in the open ocean. They must pursue prey or flee predators, yet the faster they swim, the more the viscosity of water impedes their progress. Not only must water be displaced ahead of the swimmer, but water also must move in behind it to occupy the space that the animal has vacated.

Figure 12.12 shows the advantage of **streamlining**, which is having a shape that offers the least resistance to fluid flow. Streamlining allows marine organisms to overcome water's viscosity and move more easily through water. A streamlined shape usually consists of a flattened body, which presents a small cross section at the front end and a gradual tapering at the back end to reduce the wake created by eddies. It is exemplified in the shape of free-swimming fish (and in marine mammals such as whales and dolphins).

Temperature

Figure 12.13 compares extremes in land and ocean surface temperatures and shows that ocean temperatures have a far narrower range than temperatures on land. The minimum surface temperature of the open ocean is seldom much below −2°C (28.4°F) and the maximum surface temperature seldom exceeds 32°C (89.6°F), except in some shallow-water coastal regions, where the temperature may reach 40°C (104°F). On land, however, extremes in temperatures have ranged from −88°C (−127°F) to 58°C (136°F), which represents a temperature range more than four times greater than that experienced by the ocean. This *continental effect* was discussed in Chapter 5.

Further, the ocean has a smaller daily, seasonal, and annual temperature range than that experienced on land, which provides a stable environment for marine organisms. The reasons for this are fourfold:

1. Recall from Chapter 5 that the heat capacity of water is much higher than that of land, which causes land to heat up by a greater amount and much more rapidly than the ocean.

2. The warming of the ocean is reduced substantially because of evaporation, a cooling process that stores excess heat as latent heat.

3. Radiation received at the surface of the ocean can penetrate several tens of meters deep and distribute its energy throughout a very large mass. In contrast, solar radiation absorbed by land heats only a very thin surface layer.

4. Unlike solid land surfaces, water has good mixing mechanisms such as currents, waves, and tides that allow heat from one area to be transported to other areas.

In addition, the small daily and seasonal temperature variations are confined to ocean surface waters and decrease with depth, becoming insignificant throughout the deeper parts of the ocean. At ocean depths that exceed 1.5 kilometers (0.9 mile), for example, temperatures hover around 3°C (37.4°F) year-round, regardless of latitude.

COMPARING COLD- AND WARM-WATER SPECIES   Cold water is denser and has a higher viscosity than warm water. These factors, among others, profoundly influence marine life, resulting in the following differences between warm-water and cold-water species in the marine environment:

- Floating organisms are physically smaller in warm waters than in colder waters. Small organisms expose more surface area per unit of body mass, which helps them maintain their position in the lower viscosity and density of warm seawater more easily.

- Warm-water species often have ornate plumage to increase surface area, which is strikingly absent in the larger cold-water species (see Figures 12.9 and 12.11).

FIGURE 12.12 Streamlining. A streamlined shape (*bottom*) enables efficient movement in water by allowing a marine organism's body to produce as little stress as possible as it moves through and displaces water. In addition, it allows water to flow in behind the body with minimal eddy action.

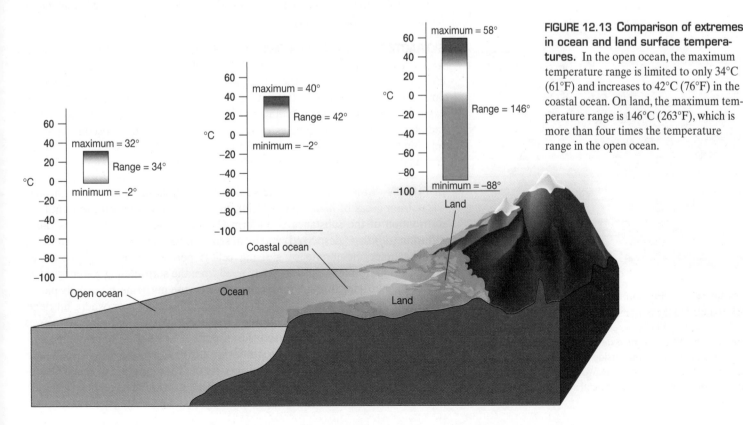

FIGURE 12.13 Comparison of extremes in ocean and land surface temperatures. In the open ocean, the maximum temperature range is limited to only 34°C (61°F) and increases to 42°C (76°F) in the coastal ocean. On land, the maximum temperature range is 146°C (263°F), which is more than four times the temperature range in the open ocean.

- Warmer temperatures increase the rate of biological activity, which more than doubles with an increase of 10°C (18°F). Tropical organisms apparently grow faster, have a shorter life expectancy, and reproduce earlier and more frequently than those in colder water.

- There are more *species* in warm waters, but the total *biomass* of plankton in colder, high-latitude waters greatly exceeds that of the warmer tropics. Note that the high biomass of plankton in high-latitude regions is not directly caused by temperature or viscosity but rather indirectly by allowing the upwelling of nutrients for phytoplankton.

Some animal species can live only in cooler waters, whereas others can live only in warmer waters. Many of these organisms can withstand only very small temperature changes and are called **stenothermal** (*steno* = narrow, *thermo* = temperature). Stenothermal organisms are found predominantly in the open ocean at depths where large temperature ranges do not occur.

Other species are little affected by different temperatures and can withstand large and even rapid changes in temperature. These organisms are called **eurythermal** (*eury* = wide, *thermo* = temperature) and are predominantly found in shallow coastal waters—where the largest temperature ranges are found—and in surface waters of the open ocean.

Salinity

The sensitivity of marine animals to changes in their environment varies from organism to organism. Those that inhabit estuaries, for example, such as oysters, must be able to withstand considerable fluctuations in salinity. The daily rise and fall of the tides forces salty ocean water into river mouths and draws it out again, changing the salinity considerably. During floods, the salinity in estuaries can reach extremely low levels. The coastal organisms that can tolerate large changes in salinity are known as **euryhaline** (*eury* = wide, *halo* = salt).

Marine organisms that inhabit the open ocean, on the other hand, are seldom exposed to a large variation in salinity. They have adapted to a constant salinity and can tolerate only very small changes. These organisms are called **stenohaline** (*steno* = narrow, *halo* = salt).

EXTRACTION OF SALINITY COMPONENTS Some organisms extract minerals from ocean water—particularly *silica* (SiO_2) and *calcium carbonate* ($CaCO_3$)—to construct the hard parts of their bodies, which serve as protective coverings. In doing so, they reduce the amount of dissolved material in ocean water. For example, phytoplankton (including diatoms) and microscopic protozoans such as radiolarians and silicoflagellates extract silica from seawater. Coccolithophores, foraminifers, most mollusks, corals, and some algae that secrete a calcium carbonate skeletal structure extract calcium carbonate from seawater.

DIFFUSION Molecules of soluble substances, such as nutrients, move through water from areas of *high* concentration to areas of *low* concentration until the distribution of the substance is uniform (Figure 12.14a). This process is called **diffusion** (*diffuse* = dispersed) and is caused by random motion of molecules.

The outer membrane of a living cell is permeable to many molecules. Organisms may take in nutrients they need from the surrounding water by diffusion of the nutrients through their cell walls. Because nutrients are usually plentiful in seawater, they pass through the cell wall into the interior, where nutrients are less concentrated (Figure 12.14b). In addition to passive diffusion, organisms also import nutrients to cells by active transport.

After a cell uses the energy stored in nutrients, it must dispose of waste. Waste passes out of a cell by diffusion, too. As the concentration of waste materials becomes greater within the cell than in the water surrounding it, these materials pass from within the cell into the surrounding fluid. The waste products are then

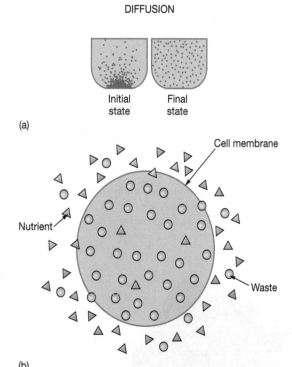

FIGURE 12.14 Diffusion. (a) A water-soluble substance that is added to the bottom of a container of water (*initial state*) will eventually become evenly distributed throughout the water by diffusion (*final state*). **(b)** Nutrients (*triangles*) are in high concentration outside the cell and diffuse into the cell through the cell membrane. Waste particles (*circles*) are in high concentration inside the cell and diffuse out of the cell through the membrane.

carried away by circulating fluid that services cells in higher animals, or by the water that surrounds simple one-celled organisms.

OSMOSIS   When water solutions of unequal salinity are separated by a semipermeable membrane (such as skin or the membrane around a living cell), water molecules (but not dissolved ions) diffuse through the membrane. Water molecules always move from the *less* concentrated solution into the *more* concentrated solution in a process called **osmosis** (*osmos* = to push) (Figure 12.15a). **Osmotic pressure** is the pressure that must be applied to the more concentrated solution to prevent water molecules from passing into it.

Osmosis causes water to move through an organism's skin (its semipermeable membrane) and affects both marine and freshwater organisms. If the salinity of an organism's body fluid equals that of the ocean, it is **isotonic** (*iso* = same, *tonos* = tension), has equal osmotic pressure, and no net transfer of water will occur through the membrane in either direction (Figure 12.15b).

If seawater has a lower salinity than the fluid within an organism's cells, seawater will pass through the cell walls into the cells (always toward the more concentrated solution). This organism is **hypertonic** (*hyper* = over, *tonos* = tension), which means it is saltier than the surrounding seawater.

If the salinity within an organism's cells is less than that of the surrounding seawater, water from the cells will pass through the cell membranes out into the seawater (toward the more concentrated solution). This organism is **hypotonic** (*hypo* = under, *tonos* = tension) relative to the water outside its body.

In essence, osmosis is diffusion that produces a net transfer of water molecules through a semipermeable membrane from the side with the *greatest concentration* of water molecules to the side with the *lesser concentration* of water molecules.

During osmosis, three things can occur simultaneously across the cell membrane:

1. Water molecules move through the semipermeable membrane toward the side with the lower concentration of water.

2. Nutrient molecules or ions move from where they are more concentrated into the cell, where they are used to maintain the cell.

3. Waste molecules move from within the cell to the surrounding seawater.

Molecules or ions of all the substances in the system are passing through the membrane in both directions. A net transport of molecules of a given substance always occurs from the side on which they are most highly concentrated to the side where the concentration is less, until equilibrium is attained.

The body fluids of marine invertebrates (those without backbones) such as worms, mussels, and octopuses, and the seawater in which they live, are nearly isotonic. As a result, these organisms have not had to evolve special mechanisms to maintain their body fluids at a proper concentration. This gives them an advantage over their freshwater relatives, whose body fluids are hypertonic.

AN EXAMPLE OF OSMOSIS: MARINE VERSUS FRESHWATER FISH   Marine fish have body fluids that are only slightly more than one-third as saline as ocean water, possibly because they evolved in low-salinity coastal waters. They are, therefore, hypotonic (less salty) compared to the surrounding seawater.

This salinity difference means that saltwater fish, without some means of regulation, would lose water from their body fluids into the surrounding ocean and eventually dehydrate. This loss is counteracted, however, because marine fish drink ocean water and excrete the salts through special chloride-releasing cells located in their gills. These fish also help maintain their body water by discharging a very small amount of very highly concentrated urine (Figure 12.16a).

Freshwater fish are hypertonic (internally more saline) compared to the very dilute water in which they live. The osmotic pressure of the body fluids of such fish may be 20 to 30 times greater than that of the freshwater that surrounds them, so freshwater fish risk rupturing cell walls from excessive quantities of water taken on through osmosis.

OSMOSIS

(a)

(b)

FIGURE 12.15 Osmosis. (a) A semipermeable membrane that separates two water solutions of different salinities allows water molecules (but not dissolved substances) to pass through it by the process of osmosis. Water molecules will diffuse through the membrane from the less concentrated (hypotonic) solution (*left*) into the more concentrated (hypertonic) solution (*right*). **(b)** If the salinity of the two solutions is the same (isotonic), there is no net movement of water molecules.

STUDENTS SOMETIMES ASK...

Why do my fingers get wrinkly when I stay in the water for a long time?

It's caused by water molecules passing through your skin (a semipermeable membrane) due to osmosis. The water molecules outside your body—contained in either pure water or seawater—flow into your skin cells in an attempt to dilute the dissolved particles inside those cells. After a short time in water, your skin cells contain many more water molecules than before, which hydrates your skin and causes it to look wrinkly. The effect is most obvious on appendages such as fingers and toes because they have a high surface area per unit of volume. It's only a temporary condition, though, because your body absorbs and excretes the excess water molecules after you leave the water.

FIGURE 12.16
Salinity adaptations of marine and freshwater fish.
Osmotic processes cause these two types of fish to have different adaptations to the environment.

(a) MARINE FISH
(Hypotonic)

- Drink large quantities of water
- Secrete salt through special cells
- Small volume of highly concentrated urine

(b) FRESHWATER FISH
(Hypertonic)

- Do not drink
- Cells absorb salt
- Large volume of dilute urine

KEY CONCEPT

Osmosis produces a net transfer of water molecules through a semipermeable membrane from the side with the greatest concentration of water molecules to the side with the lesser concentration.

To prevent this, freshwater fish do not drink water and their cells have the capacity to absorb salt. They also excrete large volumes of very dilute urine to reduce the amount of water in their cells (Figure 12.16b).

Dissolved Gases

The amount of gases that dissolve in seawater increases as the temperature of seawater decreases, so cold water dissolves more gas than warm water. This helps vast phytoplankton communities develop in high latitudes during summer, when solar energy becomes available for photosynthesis. These cold waters contain an abundance of dissolved gases, specifically carbon dioxide (which phytoplankton need for photosynthesis) and oxygen (which all organisms need to metabolize their food). In addition, the cold, oxygen-rich water of high-latitude regions sinks and flows along the ocean bottom, supplying deep-sea organisms with an abundant supply of dissolved oxygen.

Most animals that live in the ocean—except air-breathing marine mammals and certain fishes—must extract dissolved oxygen from seawater. How do they do this? Most marine animals have specially designed fibrous respiratory organs called **gills** that exchange oxygen and carbon dioxide directly with seawater. Most fish, for instance, take water in through their mouths (which gives them the appearance of "breathing" underwater), pass it through their gills to extract oxygen, and then expel it through the gill slits on the sides of their bodies (Figure 12.17). Most fish need at least 4.0 parts per million (ppm) of dissolved oxygen in seawater to survive for long periods, and even more for activity and rapid growth. That's why aquariums need a pump to continually resupply oxygen to the water in the tank.

During low-oxygen conditions, most marine animals with gills cannot simply breathe air at the surface. Their adaptations allow them to use only the oxygen dissolved in water. If dissolved oxygen levels become low enough (such as after an algae bloom when decomposition consumes dissolved oxygen), many marine organisms will suffocate and die.

Gill structure and location vary among animals of different groups. In fishes, gills are located at the rear of the mouth and contain capillaries. In higher aquatic invertebrates, they protrude from the body surface and contain extensions of the vascular system. In mollusks, they are inside the mantle cavity. In higher vertebrates (including humans), they occur as rudimentary, nonfunctional gill slits, which disappear during embryonic development.

Water in

Water out

Gills
(Internal)

(extract oxygen)

FIGURE 12.17 Gills on fish. Water is taken in through the mouth and passes through the gills, which extract dissolved oxygen. Afterward, water is exited through the gill slits. Photo (*inset*) shows a blue-streaked cleaner wrasse (*Labroides dimidiatus*) cleaning the gills of a map puffer (*Arothron mappa*) in the Solomon Islands.

Water's High Transparency

Water—including seawater—has relatively high transparency compared to many other substances, allowing sunlight to penetrate to a depth of about 1000 meters (3300 feet) in the open ocean. The actual depth depends on the amount of turbidity (suspended sediment) in the water, the amount of plankton in the water, latitude, time of day, and the season.

Because of water's high transparency, many marine organisms have developed keen eyesight, which helps them locate and capture prey. To combat keen-eyed predators, many marine organisms such as jellyfish are themselves nearly transparent, which helps them blend into their environment (Figure 12.18). In fact, almost all open-ocean animals not otherwise protected by teeth, toxins, speed, or small size have some degree of invisibility. Only at depths where sunlight never penetrates is transparency uncommon. Not only can transparency help organisms elude their predators, it can also help organisms stalk their prey.

Other organisms hide by using their coloration pattern as camouflage (Figure 12.19a). Still others use **countershading**, which means they are dark colored on top and light colored on bottom (Figure 12.19b), to blend into their environment. Many fish—especially flat fish—have countershading so they cannot easily be seen against the dark background of deep water or the ocean floor and they blend into the sunlight when viewed from below. Other organisms undertake a daily vertical migration to deeper, darker parts of the ocean to avoid becoming prey (Box 12.1).

In contrast to species trying to blend into their environment, many species of tropical fish display bright colors (Figure 12.20). Why would they be brightly colored if it makes them easily seen by predators? The bright markings of tropical fish may be an example of **disruptive coloration**, where large, bold patterns of contrasting colors tend to make an object blend in when viewed against an equally variable, contrasting background such as a tropical reef. Zebras use this principle to evade predators, tigers use it to conceal themselves from their prey, and military uniforms are camouflaged in a similar way.

Even considering disruptive coloration, many tropical fish still don't seem to blend into their environment. Perhaps the bright colors and distinctive markings that make tropical fish more apparent make it easier to advertise their identity, to attract mates, or to display weaponry such as spines or poison. Scientists have yet to agree on why tropical fish have such vivid colors, but it must serve some biological advantage or the fish wouldn't be so brightly colored.

FIGURE 12.18 Jellyfish. Jellyfish such as these moon jellies (*Aurelia aurita*) are nearly transparent, which makes them difficult for predators to see, especially in dim light.

WEB VIDEO
Camouflage

(a)

(b)

FIGURE 12.19 Camouflage and countershading. (a) The head and eye of a well-camouflaged rock fish. **(b)** Halibut on a dock in Alaska show countershading.

12.1   RESEARCH METHODS IN OCEANOGRAPHY

A FALSE BOTTOM: THE DEEP SCATTERING LAYER (DSL)

Within most parts of the ocean, there exists a curious feature called the **deep scattering layer (DSL)**. It was discovered when the U.S. Navy was testing sonar equipment to detect enemy submarines early in World War II. On many of the sonar recordings, a mysterious sound-reflecting surface appeared that was much too shallow to be the ocean floor. It was often referred to as a "false bottom" (see Figure 3.1). What was even more surprising was that the depth of the deep scattering layer changed with time. It was at a depth of about 100 to 200 meters (330 to 660 feet) during the night but was as deep at 900 meters (3000 feet) during the day.

With the help of marine biologists, sonar specialists were able to determine that sonar signals were reflecting off densely packed concentrations of marine organisms (Figure 12A). Investigation with plankton nets, submersibles, and detailed sonar revealed that the DSL contains many different organisms, including copepods (which constitute a large proportion of planktonic animals), krill, and lantern fish (family Myctophidae).

The daily movement of the deep scattering layer is caused by the vertical migration of marine organisms that feed in the highly productive surface waters but must protect themselves from being seen by predators. Organisms within the DSL ascend to the surface only at night to feed under cover of darkness and then migrate to deeper (darker) water to hide during the day. Studies reveal that the daily migration of the DSL causes increased vertical mixing of ocean waters.

Today, fish-finding sonar is still used on commercial and sport fishing trips to track the movement of fish below the surface, often quite successfully.

FIGURE 12A Daily movement and organisms of the deep scattering layer.

Daily Movement of the Deep Scattering Layer (DSL)

Pressure

Water pressure increases about 1 kilogram per square centimeter (1 atmosphere or 14.7 pounds per square inch) with every 10 meters (33 feet) of water depth. Humans are not well adapted to the high pressures that exist below the surface (Box 12.2). Even when diving to the bottom of the deep end of a swimming pool, one can feel the dramatic increase in pressure in one's ears.

In the deep ocean, water pressure is on the order of several hundred kilograms per square centimeter (several hundred atmospheres, or several tons per square inch). How do deep-water marine organisms withstand pressures that can easily kill humans? Most marine organisms lack large compressible air pockets inside their bodies. They do not have lungs, ear canals, or other passageways as we do, so these organisms don't feel the high pressure pushing in on their bodies. Water is nearly incompressible, moreover, so their water-filled bodies have the same amount of pressure pushing outward and they are unaffected by the high pressures found in deep-ocean environments.

A few species appear to be extremely tolerant of pressure changes. In fact, some marine species that are found in nearshore areas can also be found at depths of several kilometers.

12.5 What Are the Main Divisions of the Marine Environment?

The oceans can be divided into two main environments. The *ocean water itself is the pelagic environment*, where drifters and swimmers play out their lives in a complex food web. The *ocean bottom is the benthic environment*, where marine algae and animals that do not float or swim (or at least not very well) spend their lives.

Pelagic (Open Sea) Environment

The pelagic environment can be divided into distinctive life zones called **biozones** that possess unique physical characteristics, as shown in Figure 12.21.

FIGURE 12.20 Use of color by tropical fish. Many tropical fish such as this mandarinfish (*Synchiropus splendidus*) have bright colors and bold patterns, which allow them to blend into the environment by using disruptive coloration. Alternatively, they may also stand out so that they can advertise their identity, sex, or weaponry.

> **KEY CONCEPT**
> The ocean's physical support, viscosity, temperature, salinity, sunlit surface waters, dissolved gases, high transparency, and pressure create conditions to which marine organisms are superbly adapted.

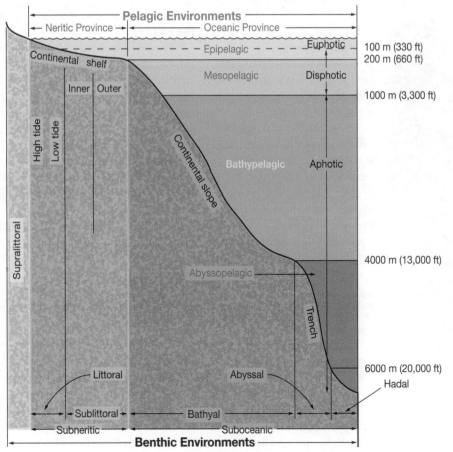

FIGURE 12.21 Oceanic biozones of the pelagic and benthic environments. Pelagic environments are shown in blue, and benthic environments are shown in brown. Pelagic and benthic environments are both based on depth, not necessarily on distance from shore. Sea floor features and sunlight zones are shown in black lettering.

DIVING INTO THE MARINE ENVIRONMENT

Throughout history, humans have submerged themselves in the marine environment to observe it directly for scientific exploration, profit, or adventure (Figure 12B). As early as 4500 B.C., brave and skillful divers reached depths of 30 meters (100 feet) on one breath of air to retrieve red coral and mother-of-pearl shells. Later, diving bells (bell-shaped structures full of trapped air) were lowered into the sea to provide passengers or underwater divers with an air supply. In 360 B.C., Aristotle, in his *Problematum*, recorded the use by Greek sponge divers of kettles full of air lowered into the sea. However, technology to move around freely while breathing underwater was not developed until 1943, when Jacques-Yves Cousteau and Émile Gagnan invented the fully automatic, compressed-air Aqualung. The equipment was later dubbed **scuba**, an acronym for *self*-contained *underwater breathing apparatus*, and it is used by millions of recreational divers today. By using scuba, divers can experience the ocean firsthand, leading to a fuller appreciation of the wonder and beauty of the marine environment.

Those who venture underwater must contend with many obstacles inherent in ocean diving, such as low temperatures, darkness, and the effects of greatly increased pressure. To combat low temperatures, specially designed clothing is worn. Waterproof, high-intensity diving lights are used to combat darkness. To combat the deleterious effects of pressure, depth and duration of dives must be limited. As a result, most scuba divers rarely venture below a depth of 30 meters (100 feet)—where the pressure is three times that at the surface—and they stay there less than 30 minutes.

It is relatively dangerous for humans to enter the marine environment because our bodies are adapted to living in the relatively low pressure of the atmosphere. In water, pressure increases rapidly with depth, to which anyone who has been to the bottom of the deep end of a swimming pool can attest. The increased pressure at depth in the ocean can cause problems for divers.

For instance, higher pressure causes more nitrogen to be dissolved in a diver's body and may cause a disorienting condition known as *nitrogen narcosis* or *rapture of the deep*. Further, if a diver surfaces too rapidly, expanding gases within the body can catastrophically rupture cell membranes (a condition called *barotrauma*).

In addition, when divers return to the surface, they may experience *decompression sickness*, which is also called *caisson disease*, or the *bends*. The bends affects divers who ascend to the lower pressure at the surface too rapidly, causing nitrogen bubbles to form in the bloodstream and other tissues (analogous to the bubbles that form in a carbonated beverage when the container is opened). Various symptoms can result, from nosebleed and joint pain (which causes divers to stoop over, hence the term the bends) to permanent neurological injury and even fatal paralysis. To avoid it, divers must ascend slowly, allowing time for excess dissolved nitrogen to be eliminated from the blood via the lungs.

Despite these risks, divers venture to greater and greater depths in the ocean. In 1962, Hannes Keller and Peter Small made an open-ocean dive from a diving bell to a then record-breaking depth of 304 meters (1000 feet). Although they used a special gas mixture, Small died once they returned to the surface. Presently, the record ocean dive is 534 meters (1750 feet), but researchers who study the physiology of deep divers have simulated a dive to 701 meters (2300 feet) in a pressure chamber using a special mix of oxygen, hydrogen, and helium gases. Researchers believe that humans will eventually be able to stay underwater for extended periods of time at depths below 600 meters (1970 feet).

FIGURE 12B Oceanographer and explorer Willard Bascom in early diving gear.

The pelagic environment is divided into neritic and oceanic provinces (Figure 12.21). The **neritic** (*neritos* = of the coast) **province** extends from the shore seaward and includes all water less than 200 meters (660 feet) deep. Seaward of the neritic province is the **oceanic province**, where depth increases beyond 200 meters (660 feet). The oceanic province is further subdivided into four biozones as follows:

1. The **epipelagic** (*epi* = top, *pelagios* = of the sea) **zone** from the surface to a depth of 200 meters (660 feet).

2. The **mesopelagic** (*meso* = middle, *pelagios* = of the sea) **zone** from 200 to 1000 meters (660 to 3280 feet).

3. The **bathypelagic** (*bathos* = depth, *pelagios* = of the sea) **zone** from 1000 to 4000 meters (3300 to 13,000 feet).

4. The **abyssopelagic** (*a* = without, *byssus* = bottom, *pelagios* = of the sea) **zone**, which includes all the deepest parts of the ocean below 4000 meters (13,000 feet).

The single most important factor that determines the distribution of life in the oceanic province is the availability of sunlight. Thus, in addition to the four biozones, the distribution of life in the ocean is also divided into zones based on the availability of sunlight as follows:

- The **euphotic** (*eu* = good, *photos* = light) **zone** extends from the surface to a depth where enough light still exists to support photosynthesis, which is rarely deeper than 100 meters (330 feet). The euphotic zone—often called the thin sunlit surface layer—accounts for only about 2.5% of the marine environment, but as discussed in subsequent chapters, it is quite important for marine life.

- The **disphotic** (*dis* = apart from, *photos* = light) **zone** has small but measurable quantities of light. It extends from the euphotic zone to a depth where light no longer exists—usually about 1000 meters (3300 feet).

- The **aphotic** (*a* = without, *photos* = light) **zone** has no light, so it exists below about 1000 meters (3300 feet).

EPIPELAGIC ZONE   The upper half of the epipelagic zone is the only place in the ocean where there is sufficient light to support photosynthesis. The boundary between the epipelagic and mesopelagic zones, at 200 meters (660 feet), is also where the level of dissolved oxygen begins to decrease significantly (Figure 12.22, *red curve*).

Oxygen decreases at this depth because no photosynthetic algae live below about 150 meters (500 feet), and dead organic tissue descending from the biologically productive upper waters is decomposing by bacterial oxidation. Nutrient content also increases abruptly below 200 meters (600 feet) (Figure 12.22, *green curve*) and it is the approximate bottom of the mixed layer, seasonal thermocline, and surface water mass.

MESOPELAGIC ZONE   A dissolved **oxygen minimum layer (OML)** occurs at a depth of about 700 to 1000 meters (2300 to 3280 feet) (Figure 12.22). The intermediate-water masses that move horizontally in this depth range often possess the highest levels of nutrients in the ocean.

Organisms capable of **bioluminescence** (*bio* = life, *lumen* = light, *esc* = becoming), which have the ability to produce light biologically and "glow in the dark," are common in the mesopelagic and deeper zones. In these areas below the sunlit surface waters, having the ability to produce light has many advantages and so the vast majority of organisms are capable of producing light. Examples of bioluminescent organisms include certain species of shrimp, squid, and especially deep-sea fish (Figure 12.23). The mechanism involved in allowing organisms to bioluminesce is discussed more fully in Chapter 14, "Animals of the Pelagic Environment."

BATHYPELAGIC AND ABYSSOPELAGIC ZONES   The aphotic (lightless) bathypelagic and abyssopelagic zones represent over 75% of the living space in the oceanic province. Many completely blind fish exist in this region of total darkness and all are small, bizarre-looking, and predaceous.

STUDENTS SOMETIMES ASK ...

If animals that have large air pockets inside are affected by the extreme pressures at depth, how are sperm whales able to dive so deeply?

All marine mammals have lungs and breathe air and certain ones have special adaptations that allow them to make extremely deep dives. Sperm whales, for example, can dive to more than 2800 meters (9200 feet) and stay submerged for more than two hours during their search for food! They are able to use small amounts of oxygen very efficiently and have a collapsible rib cage, which forces air out and collapses the lungs, thereby closing the air cavities inside their bodies. Marine mammals and their adaptations are discussed in Chapter 14, "Animals of the Pelagic Environment."

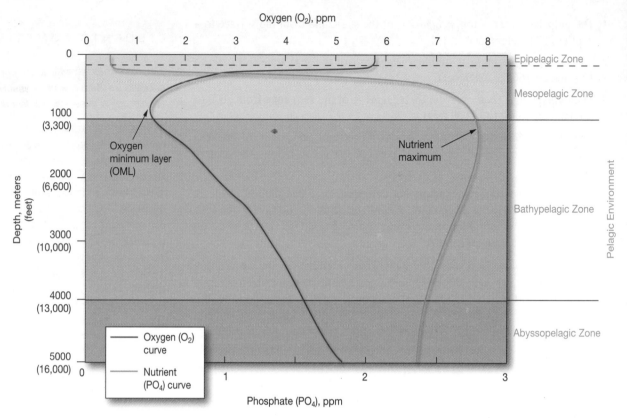

FIGURE 12.22 Abundance of dissolved oxygen and nutrients with depth. In surface water, oxygen is abundant due to mixing with the atmosphere and plant photosynthesis, and nutrient content (phosphate) is low due to uptake by algae. At deeper depths, oxygen decreases and produces an oxygen minimum layer (OML), which coincides with a nutrient maximum. Below that, nutrient levels remain high and oxygen increases as it is replenished with high-oxygen cold water from polar regions (*ppm* = parts per million).

FIGURE 12.23 Deep-sea bioluminescent anglerfish.
A deep-sea anglerfish (*Lophiiformes*), which has large, sharp teeth, small eyes, and bioluminescent spots along its body. The structure projecting from its head is a bioluminescent lure, which has many uses, including attracting prey. Length of the fish is about 10 centimeters (4 inches).

Many species of shrimp that normally feed on **detritus**[7] become predators at these depths, where the food supply is greatly reduced compared to surface waters. Animals that live in these deep zones feed mostly upon one another. They have evolved impressive warning devices and unusual apparatuses to make them extremely efficient predators (Figure 12.23). Many also have sharp teeth and extremely large mouths relative to their body size.

Oxygen content increases with depth below the oxygen minimum layer because it is replenished by deep currents originating in polar regions as cold surface water high in oxygen. The abyssopelagic zone is the realm of the bottom-water masses, which commonly move in the direction opposite the deep-water masses in the bathypelagic zone.

Benthic (Sea Bottom) Environment

The transitional region from land to sea floor above the spring high tide line is called the **supralittoral** (*supra* = above, *littoralis* = the shore) **zone** (see Figure 12.21).

---

[7]*Detritus* (*detritus* = to lessen) is a catchall term for dead and decaying organic matter, including waste products.

Commonly called the spray zone, it is covered with water only during periods of extremely high tides and when tsunami or large storm waves break on the shore.

The rest of the benthic, or sea floor, environment is divided into two main units that correspond to the neritic and oceanic provinces of the pelagic environment (see Figure 12.21):

- The **subneritic province** extends from the spring high tide shoreline to a depth of 200 meters (660 feet), approximately encompassing the continental shelf.
- The **suboceanic province** includes the benthic environment below 200 meters (660 feet).

SUBNERITIC PROVINCE   The subneritic province is subdivided into the littoral and sublittoral zones. The *intertidal zone* (the zone between high and low tides) coincides with the **littoral** (*littoralis* = the shore) **zone**. The **sublittoral** (*sub* = below, *littoralis* = the shore) **zone**, or *shallow subtidal zone,* extends from low tide shoreline out to a depth of 200 meters (660 feet).

The sublittoral zone consists of inner and outer regions. The **inner sublittoral zone** extends to the depth at which marine algae no longer grow attached to the ocean bottom (approximately 50 meters [160 feet]), so the seaward boundary varies. All photosynthesis seaward of the inner sublittoral zone is carried out by floating microscopic algae.

The **outer sublittoral zone** extends from the inner sublittoral zone out to a depth of 200 meters (660 feet) or the shelf break, which is the seaward edge of the continental shelf.

SUBOCEANIC PROVINCE   The suboceanic province is subdivided into bathyal, abyssal, and hadal zones. The **bathyal** (*bathus* = deep) **zone** extends from a depth of 200 to 4000 meters (660 to 13,000 feet) and corresponds generally to the continental slope.

The **abyssal** (*a* = without, *byssus* = bottom) **zone** extends from a depth of 4000 to 6000 meters (13,000 to 20,000 feet) and includes more than 80% of the benthic environment. The ocean floor of the abyssal zone is covered by soft oceanic sediment, primarily abyssal clay. Tracks and burrows of animals that live in this sediment can be seen in Figure 12.24.

The **hadal** (*hades* = hell)[8] **zone** extends below 6000 meters (20,000 feet), so it consists only of deep trenches along the margins of continents. Animal communities that are found in these deep environments have been isolated from each other, often resulting in unique adaptations.

FIGURE 12.24 Benthic organisms produce tracks on the ocean floor. As benthic organisms—such as this sea urchin (*below*) and brittle star (*above*)—move across or burrow through the ocean bottom, they often leave tracks in the sediment on the ocean floor.

KEY CONCEPT
The pelagic environment includes the water column and the benthic environment includes the sea bottom. Subdivisions of pelagic and benthic environments are based on depth, which influences the amount of sunlight.

---

[8]The inhospitable high-pressure environment of the hadal zone is, in fact, aptly named.

Chapter in Review

• *A wide variety of organisms lives in the ocean*, ranging in size from microscopic bacteria and algae to blue whales. *All living things belong to one of three major domains (branches) of life: Archaea*, simple microscopic bacteria-like creatures; *Bacteria*, simple life forms consisting of cells that usually lack a nucleus; and *Eukarya*, complex organisms (including plants and animals) consisting of cells that have a nucleus.

• *Organisms are further divided into five kingdoms: Monera*, single-celled organisms without a nucleus; *Protoctista*, single- and multicelled organisms with a nucleus; *Fungi*, mold and lichen; *Plantae*, many-celled plants; and *Animalia*, many-celled animals. *Classification of organisms involves placing individuals within the kingdoms into increasingly specific groupings of phylum, class, order, family, genus, and species*, the last two of which denote an organism's scientific name. Many organisms also have one or more common names.

• *Marine organisms can be classified into one of three groups based on habitat and mobility. Plankton* are free-floating forms with little power of locomotion; *nekton* are swimmers; and *benthos* are bottom dwellers. *Most of the ocean's biomass is planktonic.*

• *Only about 14% of all known species inhabit the ocean, and more than 98% of marine organisms are benthic.* The *marine environment*—especially the pelagic environment—*is much more stable than the terrestrial environment*, so there is less pressure on marine organisms to diversify.

• *Marine organisms are well adapted to life in the ocean.* Those organisms that have established themselves on land have had to develop complex systems for support and for acquiring and retaining water.

• Both *algae*, which must stay in surface waters to receive sunlight, and *small animals* that feed on them *lack an effective means of locomotion.* To keep from sinking below sunlit surface waters, they depend on their *small size* and other adaptations to *increase their ratio of surface area to body mass*, which gives them high frictional resistance to sinking. Their small size also allows them to efficiently absorb nutrients and dispose of wastes.

Many nektonic organisms have developed *streamlined bodies so they can overcome the viscosity of seawater* and move through it more easily.

• *Surface temperature of the world ocean does not vary* on a daily, seasonally, or yearly basis *as much as on land. Organisms living in warm water tend to be individually smaller, have ornate plumage, comprise a greater number of species, and constitute a much smaller total biomass than organisms living in cold water.* Warm-water organisms also tend to live shorter lives and reproduce earlier and more frequently than cold-water organisms.

• *Osmosis is the passing of water molecules through a semipermeable membrane from a region of higher concentration to a region of lower concentration.* If the body fluids of an organism and ocean water are separated by a membrane that allows water molecules to pass through, the organism may become severely dehydrated from osmosis. Many marine invertebrates are essentially *isotonic*—the salinity of their body fluids is similar to that of ocean water. Most marine vertebrates are *hypotonic*—the salinity of their body fluids is lower than that of ocean water, so they tend to lose water through osmosis. Freshwater organisms are essentially all *hypertonic*—the salinity of their body fluids is greater than the water in which they live, so they tend to gain water through osmosis.

• *Most marine animals extract oxygen through their gills.* Many marine organisms have well-developed eyesight because water is so transparent. *To avoid being seen and consumed by predators*, many marine organisms are transparent, camouflaged, countershaded, or disruptively colored. Unlike humans, most *marine organisms are unaffected by the high pressure at depth* because they do not have large internal air pockets that can be compressed.

• *The marine environment is divided into pelagic (open sea) and benthic (sea bottom) environments.* These regions are further divided based on depth and have varying physical conditions to which marine life is superbly adapted. One of the most important layers of the pelagic environment is the *euphotic zone*, which includes the sunlit surface waters and *contains enough sunlight to support photosynthesis.*

Key Terms

Abyssal zone (p. 367)	Countershading (p. 361)	Hadal zone (p. 367)	Nekton (p. 351)
Abyssopelagic zone (p. 365)	Deep scattering layer (DSL) (p. 362)	Heterotrophic (p. 350)	Neritic province (p. 364)
Animalia (p. 347)		Holoplankton (p. 350)	Oceanic province (p. 364)
Aphotic zone (p. 365)	Detritus (p. 366)	Hypertonic (p. 359)	Osmosis (p. 359)
Archaea (p. 346)	Diffusion (p. 358)	Hypotonic (p. 359)	Osmotic pressure (p. 359)
Autotrophic (p. 349)	Disphotic zone (p. 365)	Infauna (p. 351)	Outer sublittoral zone (p. 367)
Bacteria (p. 346)	Disruptive coloration (p. 361)	Inner sublittoral zone (p. 367)	Oxygen minimum layer (OML) (p. 365)
Bacterioplankton (p. 350)	Epifauna (p. 351)	Isotonic (p. 359)	
Bathyal zone (p. 367)	Epipelagic zone (p. 365)	Linnaeus, Carolus (p. 348)	Pelagic environment (p. 354)
Bathypelagic zone (p. 365)	Eukarya (p. 347)	Littoral zone (p. 367)	Phytoplankton (p. 349)
Benthic environment (p. 354)	Euphotic zone (p. 365)	Macroplankton (p. 351)	Picoplankton (p. 351)
Benthos (p. 351)	Euryhaline (p. 358)	Meroplankton (p. 351)	Plankter (p. 349)
Bioluminescence (p. 365)	Eurythermal (p. 358)	Mesopelagic zone (p. 365)	Plankton (p. 349)
Biomass (p. 349)	Fungi (p. 347)	Monera (p. 347)	Plantae (p. 347)
Biozone (p. 363)	Gill (p. 360)	Nektobenthos (p. 351)	Protoctista (p. 347)

Protoplasm (p. 355)
Protozoa (p. 348)
Scuba (p. 364)
Species (p. 348)

Stenohaline (p. 358)
Stenothermal (p. 358)
Streamlining (p. 356)
Sublittoral zone (p. 367)

Subneritic province (p. 367)
Suboceanic province (p. 367)
Supralittoral zone (p. 366)
Taxonomy (p. 348)

Virioplankton (p. 350)
Viscosity (p. 355)
Zooplankton (p. 350)

Review Questions

1. List the three major domains of life and the five kingdoms of organisms. Describe the fundamental criteria used in assigning organisms to these divisions.

2. Describe the lifestyles of plankton, nekton, and benthos. Why is it true that plankton account for a much larger percentage of the ocean's biomass than the benthos and nekton?

3. List the subdivisions of plankton and benthos and the criteria used for assigning individual species to each.

4. List the relative number of species of animals found in the terrestrial, pelagic, and benthic environments, and discuss the factors that may account for this distribution.

5. Discuss some adaptations other than size that are used by organisms to increase their resistance to sinking.

6. Changes in water temperature significantly affect the density, viscosity of water, and ability of water to hold gases in solution. Discuss how decreased water temperature changes these variables and how these changes affect marine life.

7. List differences between cold- and warm-water species in the marine environment.

8. What do the prefixes *eury-* and *steno-* mean? Define the terms *eurythermal/stenothermal* and *euryhaline/stenohaline*. Where in the marine environment will organisms displaying a well-developed degree of each characteristic be found?

9. Describe the process of osmosis. How is it different from diffusion? What three things can occur simultaneously across the cell membrane during osmosis?

10. What is the problem requiring osmotic regulation faced by hypotonic fish in the ocean? How have these animals adapted to meet this problem?

11. How does water temperature affect the water's ability to hold gases? How do marine organisms extract the dissolved oxygen from seawater?

12. How does the depth of the deep scattering layer vary over the course of a day? Why does it do this? Which organisms comprise the DSL?

Critical Thinking Exercises

1. Discuss the major differences between marine algae and land plants and explain the reasons why there is greater complexity in land plants.

2. Determine the surface to volume ratio of an organism whose average linear dimension is (a) 1 centimeter (0.4 inch); (b) 3 centimeters (1.1 inches);

and (c) 5 centimeters (2 inches). Which one is better able to resist sinking and why?

3. Construct a table listing the subdivisions of the pelagic and benthic environments and the physical factors used in assigning their boundaries.

Oceanography on the Web

Visit the *Essentials of Oceanography* Online Study Guide for Internet resources, including chapter-specific quizzes to test your understanding and Web links to further your exploration of the topics in this chapter.

The *Essentials of Oceanography* Online Study Guide is at
http://www.mygeoscienceplace.com/.

Tarpon feeding on silversides at Grand Cayman Island,
British West Indies.

Marine organisms generally feed on organisms smaller than
they are, although some animals prove to be exceptions to
this rule. All marine food webs are based on the passing of
nutrients from one organism to another, mostly accomplished through eating.

"We cannot cheat on DNA. We cannot get round photosynthesis. We cannot say I am not going to give a damn about phytoplankton. All these tiny mechanisms provide the preconditions of our planetary life."

—*Barbara Ward,*
Who Speaks for Earth? *(1973)*

13 BIOLOGICAL PRODUCTIVITY AND ENERGY TRANSFER

CHAPTER AT A GLANCE

- Productivity is essentially another word for photosynthesis; it is accomplished by a wide variety of marine organisms—mostly microscopic—and is affected by sunlight and nutrients.

- In polar oceans, productivity peaks during the summer; in tropical oceans, productivity is low year-round; in temperate oceans, productivity varies as sunlight and nutrients change seasonally.

- Linear feeding relationships are best displayed as a food chain whereas a food web displays a branching network of feeding relationships; the oceanic biomass pyramid shows the energy transfer between tropic (feeding) levels.

- The marine fishing industry suffers from overfishing, wasteful practices that produce a large amount of unwanted bycatch, and a lack of adequate fisheries management.

Producers are organisms that photosynthesize their own food from carbon dioxide, water, and sunlight. Their ability to capture solar energy and bind it into their food sugars is the basis of food for all other organisms in the marine biological community (except those near hydrothermal vents,[1] where *chemosynthesis* is the major source of "food" energy). As such, the ocean's producers are the foundation of the oceanic food web.

Photosynthetic producers in the ocean include plants, algae, and bacteria. Because there are few true marine plants and large species of marine algae play only a minor role, microscopic marine algae and bacteria comprise the majority of organisms responsible for the conversion of solar energy. These microscopic organisms—called *phytoplankton*—are mostly scattered throughout the ocean's sunlit surface waters and represent the largest community of organisms in the marine environment.

In this chapter, we'll examine primary productivity and the factors that cause it to vary, describe various types of photosynthetic marine organisms, discuss productivity in different regions of the ocean, examine feeding relationships such as food chains and food webs, and explore environmental issues related to marine fisheries.

13.1 What Is Primary Productivity?

Primary productivity is the rate at which energy is stored by organisms through the formation of organic matter (carbon-based compounds) using energy derived from solar radiation during **photosynthesis** (*photo* = light, *syn* = with, *thesis* = an arranging) or from chemical reactions during **chemosynthesis** (*chemo* = chemistry, *syn* = with, *thesis* = an arranging).[2] This organic matter can then be used as food for other organisms. Although chemosynthesis supports hydrothermal vent biocommunities along oceanic spreading centers, it is much less significant than photosynthesis in worldwide marine primary production. In fact, 99.9% of the ocean's **biomass**[3] relies either directly or indirectly on organic matter supplied by photosynthetic primary productivity as its source of food. As such, the discussion of primary productivity presented here will focus on photosynthetic productivity.

Chemically, photosynthesis is a reaction in which energy from the Sun is stored in organic molecules. In photosynthesis (Figure 13.1, *top*), plant cells capture light energy and store it as sugars. As a chemical reaction, the photosynthetic equation is reversible; this process is called respiration (Figure 13.1, *middle*). The equations are also shown chemically (Figure 13.1, *bottom*). Note that this

---

[1]Hydrothermal vent biocommunities are discussed in more detail in Chapter 15, "Animals of the Benthic Environment."

[2]More details about chemosynthesis can be found in Chapter 15, "Animals of the Benthic Environment."

[3]Recall that *biomass* is the mass of living organisms.

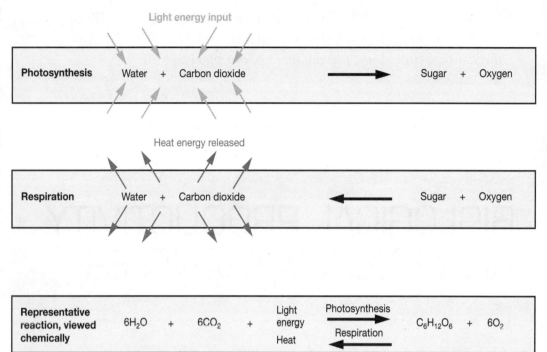

FIGURE 13.1 Photosynthesis (*top*), respiration (*middle*), and representative reactions viewed chemically (*bottom*). The process of photosynthesis, which is accomplished by plants, is represented in the upper panel. The second panel shows respiration, which is done by animals. Both processes are shown chemically in the third panel. (Note that this is the same image as Figure 1.20.)

KEY CONCEPT
Primary productivity is the rate at which carbon (organic matter) is produced by microbes, algae, and plants mostly through photosynthesis but also includes chemosynthesis.

is the same figure from Chapter 1, where photosynthesis and respiration were previously discussed.

Measurement of Primary Productivity

Various properties of the ocean can be measured to give an approximation of the amount of primary productivity. One of the most direct at-sea methods is to capture plankton in cone-shaped nylon **plankton nets** (Figure 13.2). These fine mesh nets—which resemble windsocks at airports—filter plankton from the ocean as they are towed at a specific depth by research vessels. Analysis of the amounts and types of organisms captured reveals much about the productivity of the area.

Other methods include lowering specially designed bottles into the ocean, analyzing the amount of radioactive carbon in seawater, or even monitoring ocean color with orbiting satellites. Photosynthetic organisms such as **phytoplankton** (*phyto* = plant, *planktos* = wandering) use the green pigment **chlorophyll** (*khloros* = green, *phylum* = leaf) to capture energy from the Sun and perform photosynthesis. The color of surface waters is strongly affected by the amount of chlorophyll, so ocean color can be used as an approximation of phytoplankton abundance and, in turn, productivity. One such instrument that conducts ocean color measurements is the **SeaWiFS** (*Sea*-viewing *Wi*de *F*ield-of-View *S*ensor) instrument aboard the SeaStar satellite, which began operating in 1997. It replaced Nimbus-7's Coastal Zone Color Scanner instrument, which operated between 1978 and 1986. Today, SeaWiFS measures the color of Earth's surface with a radiometer and provides global coverage of estimated ocean chlorophyll levels as well as land vegetation every two days.

Factors Affecting Primary Productivity

In the ocean, the two main factors that limit the amount of photosynthetic primary productivity are the availability of nutrients and the availability of solar radiation. Sometimes other variables—such as the amount of carbon dioxide—can also limit primary productivity if they become scarce in seawater.

AVAILABILITY OF NUTRIENTS The distribution of life throughout the ocean's breadth and depth depends mainly on the availability of nutrients such as nitrate, phosphorus, iron, and silica that are needed by phytoplankton. Where the physical conditions supply large quantities of nutrients, marine populations reach their greatest concentration. To understand where these areas are found, the sources of nutrients must be considered.

Water in the form of runoff erodes the continents, carrying material to the oceans and depositing it as sediment on the continental margins. Runoff also dissolves and transports substances such as nitrates and phosphates, which are the basic nutrients for phytoplankton. Nitrates and phosphates are also the basic ingredients in all garden and farm fertilizers.

Through photosynthesis, phytoplankton combine these nutrients with carbon dioxide and water to produce the carbohydrates, proteins, and fats that the rest of the ocean's biological community depends upon for food.

The continents are the major sources of these nutrients, so the greatest concentrations of marine life are found along the continental margins. The concentration of marine life decreases, however, as the distance from the continental margins into the open sea increases. The vast depth of the world's oceans and the great distance between the open ocean and the coastal regions where nutrients are concentrated account for these differences.

Often, the lack of certain nutrients can limit productivity, particularly nitrogen (as nitrates) and phosphorus. As a result, these compounds are among the most studied in chemical oceanography. Comparatively, nitrogen compounds involved in photosynthesis may be 10 times the total nitrogen compound concentration that can be measured as a yearly average. This level implies that the soluble nitrogen compounds must be completely recycled up to 10 times per year. Available phosphates may be turned over up to four times per year.

Carbon is an important element in productivity, too, because carbon is the basic component of all organic compounds (including carbohydrates, proteins, and fats). In the ocean, however, various forms of carbon are quite abundant, so there is no scarcity of carbon for photosynthetic production. Thus, carbon does not limit productivity.

When nutrients are not limiting productivity, the ratio of carbon to nitrogen to phosphorus in the tissues of algae is in the proportion of 106:16:1 (C:N:P), which is called the *Redfield ratio* after American oceanographer Alfred C. Redfield, who first described it in 1963. This ratio is also observed in zooplankton that feed on diatoms, and in most ocean water samples taken worldwide. Moreover, phytoplankton take up nutrients in the ratio in which they are available in the ocean water and pass them on to zooplankton in the same ratio. When these plankton and animals die, carbon, nitrogen, and phosphorus are restored to the water in this same ratio.

Recent studies in the waters near Antarctica and the Galápagos Islands reveal that photosynthetic production is low even though the concentration of all nutrients—except iron—is high.[4] Production is high only in regions of shallow water downcurrent from islands or landmasses where a significant amount of iron from rocks and sediments is dissolved in water.

FIGURE 13.2 Plankton nets. These large, cone-shaped, fine-mesh plankton nets being washed are lowered into the water and towed behind a research vessel to collect plankton.

AVAILABILITY OF SOLAR RADIATION   Photosynthesis cannot proceed unless light energy (solar radiation) is available. Despite the atmosphere's thickness of more than 80 kilometers (50 miles), its high transparency allows sunlight to penetrate it quite readily, so land-based plants almost always have an abundance of solar radiation to conduct photosynthesis.

In the clearest ocean water, solar energy may be detected to depths of only about 1 kilometer (0.6 mile) and, even then, the amount reaching these depths is inadequate for photosynthesis. Photosynthesis in the ocean, therefore, is restricted to the uppermost surface waters and those areas of the sea floor where the water is shallow enough to allow light to penetrate.

The depth at which net photosynthesis becomes zero is called the **compensation depth for photosynthesis**. The **euphotic** (*eu* = good, *photos* = light) **zone** extends from the surface down to the compensation depth for photosynthesis, which is approximately 100 meters (330 feet) in the open ocean. Near the coast, the euphotic zone may extend to less than 20 meters (66 feet) because the water contains more suspended inorganic material (turbidity) or microscopic organisms that limit light penetration.

How do the two factors necessary for photosynthesis—the supply of nutrients and the presence of solar radiation—differ between coastal areas and the open ocean? In the open ocean (far from continental margins), solar energy

---

[4]The idea of fertilizing the ocean with iron to stimulate productivity and increase the amount of carbon dioxide gas absorbed by the ocean is discussed in Chapter 16, "The Oceans and Climate Change."

extends deeper into the water column, but concentration of nutrients is low. In coastal regions, on the other hand, light penetration is much less, but the concentration of nutrients is much higher. Because the coastal zone is much more productive, nutrient availability must be the most important factor affecting the distribution of life in the oceans.

Light Transmission in Ocean Water

The graph in Figure 13.3 shows that most solar energy falls in the range of wavelengths called **visible light**. This radiant energy from the Sun powerfully affects three major components of the oceans:

1. The major wind belts of the world, which produce ocean currents and wind-driven ocean waves, ultimately derive their energy from solar radiation. Wind belts and ocean currents strongly influence world climates.

2. A thin layer of warm water at the ocean surface, created by solar heating, overlies the great mass of cold water that fills most of the ocean basins. This is the "life layer" where most marine life exists.

3. Photosynthesis can occur only where sunlight penetrates the ocean water, so phytoplankton and most animals that eat them must live where the light is, in the relatively thin layer of sunlit surface water.

THE ELECTROMAGNETIC SPECTRUM   The Sun radiates a wide range of wavelengths of electromagnetic radiation. Together they comprise the **electromagnetic spectrum**, which is shown in the upper part of Figure 13.3. Only a very narrow portion of the electromagnetic spectrum is visible to humans as visible light. We call it "visible" light because our electromagnetic sensors—our eyes—are adapted to detect only the wavelengths in the visible region. In essence, our eyes "tune into" the visible light wavelengths, just as a radio "tunes into" specific radio waves.

Visible light can be further divided by wavelength into violet, blue, green, yellow, orange, and red energy levels. Together, these different wavelengths produce white light. The shorter wavelengths of energy to the left of visible light (for example, X rays and gamma rays) damage tissue in high enough doses. The longer wavelengths of energy to the right of visible light (for example, infrared, microwaves, and radio waves) are used for heat transfer and communication.

THE COLOR OF OBJECTS   Light from the Sun includes all the visible colors. Most of the light we see is reflected from objects. All objects absorb and reflect different wavelengths of light, and each wavelength represents a color in the visible spectrum. Vegetation, for example, absorbs most wavelengths except green and yellow, which they reflect, so most plants look green. Similarly, a red jacket absorbs all wavelengths of color except red, which is reflected.

The lower part of Figure 13.3 shows how the ocean selectively absorbs the longer wavelength colors (red, orange, and yellow) of visible light. The true colors of objects can be observed in natural light only in the surface waters because only there can all wavelengths of the visible spectrum be found. Red light is absorbed within the upper 10 meters (33 feet) of the ocean, and yellow is completely absorbed before a depth of 100 meters (330 feet). Thus, the shorter wavelength portion of the visible spectrum is all that can be transmitted to greater depths (mostly blue light with some violet and green wavelengths), and even then, their intensity is low. In the open ocean, sunlight strong enough to support photosynthesis occurs only with the euphotic zone to a depth of 100 meters (330 feet), and no sunlight penetrates below a depth of about 1000 meters (3300 feet).

FIGURE 13.3 The electromagnetic spectrum and transmission of visible light in seawater. The electromagnetic spectrum (*top*) runs from extremely short cosmic rays (*left side*) with progressively increasing wavelength shown toward the right. The narrow portion of the spectrum that we see as visible light is shown passing through seawater (*bottom*), which absorbs the longer wavelengths (red, orange, and yellow) above a depth of 100 meters.

FIGURE 13.4 Using a Secchi disk. A Secchi disk is used to measure the depth of penetration of sunlight, thus indicating the clarity of the water.

A **Secchi** (pronounced "SECK-ee") **disk**, such as the one shown in Figure 13.4, is used to measure water transparency, and based on that, the depth of light penetration can be estimated. The Secchi disk is named after its inventor, Angelo Secchi, an Italian astronomer who first used the device to measure water clarity of lakes in 1865. It consists of a disk about 40 centimeters (16 inches) in diameter attached to a line that is marked off at regular intervals. After the disk is lowered into the ocean, the depth at which it can last be seen indicates the water's clarity. Increased turbidity, which includes microorganisms and suspended sediment, increases the degree of light absorption, thus decreasing the depth to which visible light can penetrate into the ocean.

WATER COLOR AND LIFE IN THE OCEANS The color of the ocean ranges from deep indigo (blue) to yellow-green. Why are some areas of the ocean blue, whereas others appear green? Ocean color is influenced by (1) the amount of turbidity from runoff and (2) the amount of photosynthetic pigment, which increases with increasing biological production.

Coastal waters and upwelling areas are biologically very productive and almost always yellow-green in color because they contain large amounts of yellow-green microscopic marine algae and suspended particles. These materials disperse solar radiation so that the wavelengths for greenish or yellowish light are scattered most.

Water in the open ocean—particularly in the tropics—lacks productivity (and turbidity), so it is usually a clear, indigo-blue color. Water molecules disperse solar radiation so that the wavelength for blue light is scattered most. The atmosphere scatters blue light, too, which is why clear skies are blue.

Although photosynthetic marine algae and bacteria are microscopic, they occur in such large numbers that they can change the color of ocean to such a degree that orbiting satellites are able to measure that change from space. Figure 13.5, for example, shows a SeaStar satellite/SeaWiFS instrument view of ocean chlorophyll, which is an approximation for productivity. The figure shows high chlorophyll concentrations (highly productive areas) in light green color, which are called **eutrophic** (*eu* = good, *tropho* = nourishment). Generally, eutrophic waters are found in shallow-water coastal regions, areas of upwelling, and high-latitude regions. Alternatively, areas of low chlorophyll concentration (low productivity) are shown in dark blue color, are called **oligotrophic** (*oligo* = few, *tropho* = nourishment), and are found in the open oceans of the tropics.

Why Are the Margins of the Oceans So Rich in Life?

If the stability of the ocean environment is ideal for sustaining life, why are the richest concentrations of marine organisms in the very margins of the oceans, where conditions are the most *un*stable? For example, characteristics of the coastal ocean include:

- Water depths that are shallow, allowing much greater seasonal variations in temperature and salinity than the open ocean.
- A water column that varies in thickness in the nearshore region in response to tides that periodically cover and uncover a thin strip of land along the margins of the continents.
- Breaking waves in the surf zone that release large amounts of energy, which has been carried for great distances across the open ocean.

Each of these conditions stresses organisms. In spite of hardships, however, new species have evolved over the vast expanse of geologic time that spans billions

Chlorophyll Concentration (mg/m³)

0.01 0.03 0.1 0.3 1 3 10 30 60

FIGURE 13.5 Satellite image of ocean chlorophyll.
Satellite data (September 1997-August 2007) showing average ocean chlorophyll concentration, which is an approximation for productivity. Data gathered by the SeaWiFS instrument aboard the SeaStar satellite, which detects changes in seawater color caused by changing concentrations of chlorophyll that varies with photosynthetic productivity. Chlorophyll concentrations are reported in milligrams per cubic meter (mg/m³).

of years by the process of natural selection[5] to fit every imaginable biological niche—even in environments that pose difficulties for organisms. In fact, many organisms have adapted to live under adverse conditions—such as coastal environments—as long as nutrients are available.

Along continental margins, some areas have more abundant life than others. What characteristics create such an uneven distribution of life? Again, only those basic requirements for the production of food need be considered. For example, areas that have the greatest biomass have the lowest water temperatures, too, because cold water contains higher amounts of nutrients than warm water. These nutrients stimulate phytoplankton growth and phytoplankton growth, in turn, profoundly affects the distribution of all other life in the oceans.

UPWELLING AND NUTRIENT SUPPLY   As discussed in Chapter 7, **upwelling** is a flow of deep water toward the surface that brings water from depths below the euphotic zone. This deep water is rich in nutrients and dissolved gases because there are no phytoplankton at these depths to consume these compounds. When chilled water from below the surface rises, it hoists nutrients from the depths to the surface, where phytoplankton thrive and make food for larger organisms—copepods, fish, and on up to larger organisms such as whales.

Highly productive areas of *coastal upwelling* are found along the western margins of continents, where surface currents are moving toward the equator (Figure 13.6). Ekman transport (see Chapter 7) causes surface water to move away from these coasts, so nutrient-rich water from depths of 200 to 1000 meters (660 to 3300 feet) constantly rises to replace it.

---

[5]See Box 1.3 for a description of evolution and natural selection.

KEY CONCEPT
Photosynthetic productivity is limited in the marine environment by the amount of sunlight and the supply of nutrients. Upwelling greatly enhances the conditions for life by lifting cold, nutrient-rich water to the sunlit surface.

(a)

(b)

FIGURE 13.6 Coastal upwelling. (a) Coastal winds (*black arrows*) cause Ekman transport, which drives surface water away from the west coasts of continents (*blue arrows*). **(b)** Block diagram showing how coastal upwelling is created by surface water that moves away from shore, bringing cold, nutrient-rich water to the surface. **(c)** SeaWiFS image of chlorophyll concentration along the southwest coast of Africa (February 21, 2000). High chlorophyll concentrations indicate high phytoplankton biomass, which is caused by coastal upwelling. Concentration is reported in milligrams of chlorophyll per cubic meter (mg/m^3).

13.2 What Kinds of Photosynthetic Marine Organisms Exist?

Many types of marine organisms photosynthesize. Mostly, they are represented by microscopic bacteria and algae but also include larger forms of algae and seed-bearing plants.

Seed-Bearing Plants (Anthophyta)

The only members of kingdom Plantae that exist in the marine environment belong to the highest group of plants, the seed-bearing members of phylum Anthophyta (*antho* = a flower, *phytum* = a plant), which occur exclusively in shallow coastal areas. Eelgrass (*Zostera*), for example, is a grasslike plant with true roots that exists primarily in the quiet waters of bays and estuaries from the low-tide zone to a depth of 6 meters (20 feet). Surf grass (*Phyllospadix*) (Figure 13.7), which is also a seed-bearing plant with true roots, is typically found in the high-energy environment of exposed rocky coasts from the intertidal zones down to a depth of 15 meters (50 feet).

Other seed-bearing plants are found in salt marshes and include grasses (mostly of the genus *Spartina*), whereas mangrove swamps contain primarily mangroves (genera *Rhizophora* and *Avicennia*). All of these plants are important sources of food and protection for the marine animals that inhabit nearshore environments.

FIGURE 13.7 Surf grass. Green surf grass (*Phyllospadix*) and various species of brown algae are exposed during an extremely low tide in this California tide pool. When the tide rises, the anchored surf grass floats and provides a protective hiding place for many tide pool organisms.

Macroscopic (Large) Algae

Various types of marine macro algae (the "seaweeds") are typically found in shallow waters along the ocean margins. These algae are usually attached to the bottom, but a few species float. Algae are classified in part on the color of the pigment they contain (Figure 13.8). Although modern classification of algae uses more than just its color, the division of algae into groups based on color is still a useful means of describing the different types of algae.

BROWN ALGAE The brown algae of the phylum Phaeophyta (*phaeo* = dusky, *phytum* = a plant) include the largest members of the attached (not free-floating) species of marine algae. Their color ranges from very light brown to black. Brown algae occur primarily in temperate and cold-water areas.

The sizes of the brown algae range widely. One of the smallest is *Ralfsia*, which occurs as a dark brown encrusting patch in upper and middle intertidal zones. One of the largest is bull kelp (*Pelagophycus*), which may grow in water deeper than 30 meters (100 feet) and extend to the surface. Other types of brown algae include *Sargassum* (Figure 13.8a) and *Macrocystis* (Figure 13.8b).

GREEN ALGAE Although green algae of phylum Chlorophyta (*khloros* = green, *phytum* = a plant) are common in freshwater environments, they are not well represented in the ocean. Most marine species are intertidal or grow in shallow bay waters. They contain the pigment chlorophyll, which gives them their green color. They grow only to moderate size, seldom exceeding 30 centimeters (12 inches) in the largest dimension. Forms range from finely branched filaments to thin sheets.

Various species of sea lettuce (*Ulva*), a thin membranous sheet only two cell layers thick, are widely scattered throughout colder water areas. Sponge weed (*Codium*), a two-branched form more common in warm waters, can exceed 6 meters (20 feet) in length (Figure 13.8c).

RED ALGAE Red algae of phylum Rhodophyta (*rhodos* = red, *phytum* = a plant) are the most abundant and widespread of marine macroscopic algae. Over 4000 species occur from the very highest intertidal levels to the outer edge of the

Ekman Spiral and Coastal Upwelling/Downwelling

(a)

(b)

(c)

(d)

FIGURE 13.8 Macroscopic algae. (a) Brown algae, *Sargassum.* This attached form is similar to the floating form that is the namesake of the Sargasso Sea. **(b)** A small strand of brown algae, *Macrocystis,* which is a major component of kelp beds. **(c)** Green algae, *Codium fragile,* also known as sponge weed or dead man's fingers. **(d)** Red algae of two different types: *Bossiella californica* (*left, center*) and *Corallina sp.* (*right*). Both have tips that show portions of their internal calcareous skeleton (*white*).

WEB VIDEO

Bioluminescent
Organisms

inner sublittoral zone. Many are attached to the bottom, either as branching forms (Figure 13.8d) or as forms that encrust surfaces. They are very rare in freshwater. Red algae range from those just barely visible to the unaided eye to 3 meters (10 feet) long. While found in both warm and cold waters, the warm-water varieties are relatively small.

The color of red algae varies considerably depending on its depth in the intertidal or inner sublittoral zones. In upper, well-lighted areas, it may be green to black or purplish. In deeper water zones, where less light is available, it may be brown to pinkish red.

The vast majority of marine photosynthetic productivity occurs within the surface layer of the ocean to a depth of 100 meters (330 feet), which corresponds to the depth of the euphotic zone. At this depth, the amount of light is reduced to 1% of that available at the surface. Remarkably, some deep-water species can survive on the very faint amount of sunlight that exists below the euphotic zone. For example, a species of red alga has been documented growing at a depth of 268 meters (880 feet) on a seamount near San Salvador in the Bahamas where available light is only 0.0005% of that available at the surface.

Microscopic (Small) Algae

Microscopic algae are either directly or indirectly the source of food for more than 99% of marine animals. Most microscopic algae are phytoplankton—photosynthetic organisms that live in the upper surface waters and drift with currents—although some live on the bottom in the nearshore environment, where sunlight reaches the shallow ocean floor.

GOLDEN ALGAE   The golden algae of phylum Chrysophyta (*chrysus* = golden, *phytum* = a plant) contain the orange-yellow pigment *carotin*. They consist of diatoms and coccolithophores, both of which store food as carbohydrates and oils and were discussed in Chapter 4.

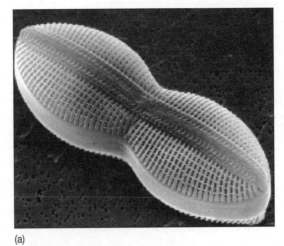

Diatoms **Diatoms** (*diatoma* = cut in half) are a class of algae that are contained in a microscopic shell called a **test** (*testa* = shell). Diatom tests are composed of opaline silica ($SiO_2 \cdot nH_2O$) and are important geologically because they accumulate on the ocean bottom, producing **diatomaceous earth**. Some deposits of diatomaceous earth that have been elevated above sea level by tectonic forces are mined and used in filtering devices and numerous other applications (see Box 4.2). Diatoms are the most productive group of marine algae.

Diatom tests have a variety of shapes, but all have a top and bottom half that fit together (Figure 13.9a). The single cell is contained within this test, and it exchanges nutrients and waste with the surrounding water through holes in its test.

(a)

(b)

(c)

(d)

FIGURE 13.9 Microscopic algae. **(a)** Peanut-shaped diatom *Diploneis* (length = 50 microns, or 0.002 inch). **(b)** Coccolithophore *Emiliania huxleyi*, showing disk-shaped calcium carbonate ($CaCO_3$) plates—called coccoliths—that cover the organism (bar scale = 1 micron, or 0.00004 inch). **(c)** Dinoflagellate *Protoperidinium divergens* (length = 70 microns, or 0.003 inch). **(d)** Leaflike tropical dinoflagellate *Heterodinium whittingae* (length = 100 microns, or 0.004 inch).

Coccolithophores **Coccolithophores** (*coccus* = berry, *lithos* = stone, *phorid* = carrying) are covered with small calcareous plates called **coccoliths**, made of calcium carbonate ($CaCO_3$) (Figure 13.9b). The individual plates are about the size of a bacterium, and the entire organism is too small to be captured in plankton nets. Coccolithophores contribute significantly to calcareous deposits in temperate and warmer oceans.

DINOFLAGELLATES   **Dinoflagellates** (*dino* = whirling, *flagellum* = a whip) belong to the phylum Pyrrophyta (*pyrrhos* = fire, *phytum* = a plant) (Figures 13.9c and d). They possess **flagella** (small, whiplike structures) for locomotion, giving them a slight capacity to move into areas that are more favorable for photosynthetic productivity. Dinoflagellates are rarely important geologically because their tests are made of cellulose, which is biodegradable and not preserved as deposits on the sea floor.

Dinoflagellates sometimes exist in such great abundance that they color surface waters red, producing the phenomenon known as a **red tide** (Box 13.1), which has nothing to do with tidal phenomena. Red tides and associated algal blooms that do not color the water red are more accurately called **harmful algal blooms (HABs)** because they are marked by an overabundance of algae that is detrimental to marine animals, humans, or the environment. In addition, many of the 1100 species of dinoflagellates undergo structural changes in response to changes in their environment (see Web Box 13.1).

Many dinoflagellates are associated with various types of seafood poisoning. One example is **ciguatera**, which is a type of seafood poisoning caused by ingestion

RED TIDES: WAS ALFRED HITCHCOCK'S *THE BIRDS* BASED ON FACT?

Oceanographic conditions sometimes stimulate the productivity of certain dinoflagellates. During these times, up to 2 million dinoflagellates may be found in 1 liter (about 1 quart) of water, giving the water a reddish color and causing what is known as a *red tide* (Figure 13A). Red tides are by no means a new phenomenon. In fact, the Old Testament makes reference to waters turning blood red, which is most likely how the Red Sea got its name.

Although many red tides are harmless to marine animals and humans, they can still be responsible for mass die-offs of marine organisms. When huge numbers of dinoflagellates die, oxygen is removed from seawater during decomposition and many types of marine life literally suffocate to death. In other cases, dinoflagellates that are responsible for many red tides produce toxins that can spread to many different types of organisms—including humans (Figure 13B). *Karenia* and *Gonyaulax*, for example, are two common genera of dinoflagellates in red tides that produce water-soluble toxins. Certain filter-feeding shellfish called bivalves—various clams, mussels, and oysters—then strain the dinoflagellates from the water for food. *Karenia* toxin kills fish and shellfish. *Gonyaulax* toxin is

not poisonous to shellfish, but it concentrates in their tissues and is poisonous to humans who eat the shellfish, even after the shellfish are cooked. This malady is called *paralytic shellfish poisoning (PSP)*.

The symptoms of PSP in humans are similar to those of drunkenness—incoherent speech, uncoordinated movement, dizziness, and nausea—and can occur only

30 minutes after ingesting contaminated shellfish. There is no known antidote for the toxin, which attacks the human nervous system, but the critical period usually passes within 24 hours. At least 300 fatal and 1750 nonfatal cases of PSP have been documented worldwide.

April through September are particularly dangerous months for red tides in

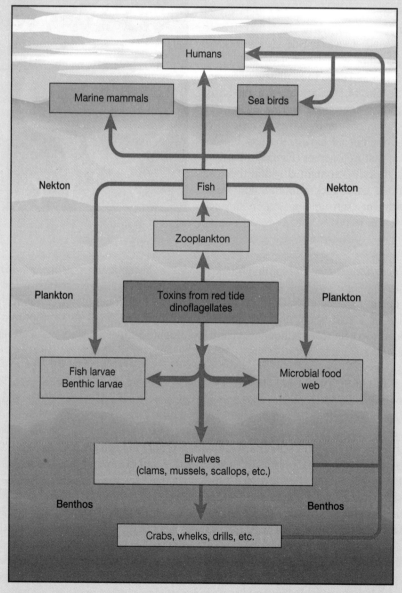

FIGURE 13B Routes through which dinoflagellate toxins spread to marine organisms and humans.

FIGURE 13A Red tide in the ocean.

the Northern Hemisphere. In most areas, quarantines exist to prohibit harvesting those shellfish that feed on toxic microscopic organisms.

Worldwide, increasing numbers of mysterious poisonings are implicating species of toxic marine microorganisms that can spread throughout the marine food web and to humans. For instance, domoic acid—a toxin produced by a diatom (*Pseudonitzschia*)—was first recognized in 1987 as the poison that infected more than 100 people who ate contaminated mussels from Prince Edward Island, Canada. Four of the victims died and 10 suffered permanent memory loss, which led researchers to call poisoning by domoic acid *amnesic shellfish poisoning.*

Domoic acid poisoning may also be responsible for birds attacking humans in California's Monterey Bay in 1961. The incident—reported to have inspired Alfred Hitchcock's classic 1963 thriller *The Birds* (Figure 13C)—apparently happened after seagulls consumed fish loaded with domoic acid produced by a bloom of diatoms. Infected by the poison, erratically flying birds smashed into structures, rammed cars, and pecked eight people. In the same area in September 1991, brown pelicans and Brandt's cormorants exhibited similar behavior—they acted drunk, swam in circles, and made loud squawking sounds. Research revealed that toxic diatoms (*Pseudonitzschia australis*) were ingested by unaffected anchovies that were subsequently eaten by birds, causing more than 100 birds to wash up dead at the shore. In 1998, another toxic diatom bloom in Monterey Bay caused the death of 400 California sea lions that ate fish contaminated with domoic acid.

FIGURE 13C Actress Tippi Hedren fights off a menacing seagull in Hitchcock's 1963 classic suspense film, *The Birds.*

of certain tropical reef fish (most notably barracuda, red snapper, and grouper) that have high levels of naturally occurring dinoflagellate toxins. Symptoms of ciguatera in humans usually involve a combination of gastrointestinal, neurological, and cardiovascular disorders. Worldwide, ciguatera causes more cases of human illness than any other form of seafood poisoning.

Photosynthetic Bacteria

Until recently, the role of marine bacteria in photosynthesis has been largely ignored. Because of the extremely small size of bacteria, earlier samplings of marine life completely overlooked them. Recent improvements in sampling methods for bacteria-sized organisms and genome sequencing studies have revealed bacteria's incredible abundance and importance in the oceans.

For example, one of the first types of marine photosynthetic bacteria to be identified was *Synechococcus*, which are extremely abundant in coastal and open-ocean environments, sometimes reaching densities greater than 100,000 cells per milliliter (0.03 ounce) of seawater. At certain times and places, these cells can be responsible for as much as half of the primary production of food in the ocean. More recently, microbiologists have discovered an extremely small but abundant bacteria named *Prochlorococcus* (Figure 13.10) that reaches concentrations many

> **KEY CONCEPT**
> Marine photosynthetic organisms include seed-bearing plants (such as surf grass), macroscopic algae (seaweeds), microscopic algae (diatoms, coccolithophores, and dinoflagellates), and bacteria.

FIGURE 13.10 Photosynthetic bacteria *Prochlorococcus*. The bacteria *Prochlorococcus* is the most abundant and smallest of the marine phytoplankton, reaching only about 0.6 microns (0.00002 inch) in diameter.

times that of *Synechococcus*. In fact, *Prochlorococcus* has been estimated to constitute at least half of the world ocean's total photosynthetic biomass, which means that it is probably the most abundant photosynthetic organism on Earth.

In addition, recent large-scale gene sequencing of microbes in the Sargasso Sea has revealed a host of new types of bacteria, suggesting substantial yet previously unrecognized oceanic microbial diversity. Clearly, microbes exert a critical influence on marine ecosystems and carry significant implications for sustainability, global climate change, ocean system cycles, and human health.

13.3 How Does Regional Primary Productivity Vary?

Primary photosynthetic production in the oceans varies dramatically from place to place (see Figure 13.5). Typical units of photosynthetic production are in weight of carbon (*grams of carbon*) per unit of area (*square meter*) per unit of time (*year*), which is abbreviated as $gC/m^2/yr$. Values range from as low as $1\ gC/m^2/yr$ in some areas of the open ocean to as much as $4000\ gC/m^2/yr$ in some highly productive coastal estuaries (Table 13.1). This variability is the result of the uneven distribution of nutrients throughout the photosynthetic zone and seasonal changes in the availability of solar energy.[6]

About 90% of the biomass generated in the euphotic (sunlit) zone of the open ocean is decomposed into inorganic nutrients before descending below this zone. The remaining 10% of this organic matter sinks into deeper water, where all but about 1% of it is decomposed. The 1% that reaches the deep-ocean floor accumulates there. The process of removing material from the euphotic zone to the sea floor is called a **biological pump** because it "pumps" carbon dioxide and

TABLE 13.1	VALUES OF NET PRIMARY PRODUCTIVITY FOR VARIOUS ECOSYSTEMS

Ecosystem	Primary Productivity	
	Range ($gC/m^2/yr$)	Average ($gC/m^2/yr$)
Oceanic		
Algae beds and coral reefs	1000–3000	2000
Estuaries	500–4000	1800
Upwelling zone	400–1000	500
Continental shelf	300–600	360
Open ocean	1–400	125
Land		
Freshwater swamp and marsh	800–4000	2500
Tropical rainforest	1000–5000	2000
Middle latitude forest	600–2500	1300
Cultivated land	100–4000	650

[6]For a review of Earth's seasons, see Chapter 6.

nutrients from the upper ocean and concentrates them in deep-sea waters and sea floor sediments.

Throughout much of the subtropical gyres, a permanent **thermocline** (and resulting **pycnocline**[7]) develops. It forms a barrier to vertical mixing, so it prevents the resupply of nutrients to the sunlit surface layer. In the middle latitudes, a thermocline develops only during the summer season and, in polar regions, a thermocline does not usually develop. The degree to which waters develop a thermocline profoundly affects the patterns of biological production observed at different latitudes.

Productivity in Polar Oceans

Polar regions such as the Arctic Ocean's Barents Sea, which is off the northern coast of Europe, experience continuous darkness for about three months of winter and continuous illumination for about three months during summer. Diatom productivity peaks in the Barents Sea during May (Figure 13.11a), when the Sun rises high enough in the sky so that there is deep penetration of sunlight into the water. As soon as diatoms develop, zooplankton—mostly small crustaceans (Figure 13.11d)—begin feeding on them. The zooplankton biomass peaks in June and continues at a relatively high level until winter darkness begins in October.

In the Antarctic region—particularly at the southern end of the Atlantic Ocean—productivity is somewhat greater. This is caused by the upwelling of North Atlantic Deep Water, which forms on the opposite side of the ocean basin, where it sinks and moves southward below the surface. Hundreds of years later, it rises to the surface near Antarctica, carrying with it high concentrations of nutrients (Figure 13.11b). When the Sun provides sufficient solar radiation in summer, there is an explosion of biological productivity. A recent study of Antarctic waters, however, documented as much as a 12% decrease in phytoplankton productivity because of increased ultraviolet radiation as a result of the Antarctic ozone hole.

FIGURE 13.11 Productivity in polar oceans.(a) A springtime increase of diatom mass is closely followed by an increase in zooplankton abundance. **(b)** The continuous upwelling of North Atlantic Deep Water keeps Antarctic waters rich in nutrients. **(c)** Polar water shows nearly uniform temperature with depth (an isothermal water column). **(d)** Copepods of the genus *Calanus*, each about 8 millimeters (0.3 inch) in length.

(a) Barents Sea productivity

(b) Antarctic upwelling

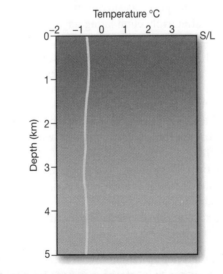
(c) Typical polar temperature profile

(d) Copepods

[7]Recall that a *thermocline* is a layer of rapidly changing temperature and a *pycnocline* is a layer of rapidly changing density. Development of ocean thermoclines and pycnoclines is discussed in Chapter 5.

Blue whales—the largest of all whales (see Figure 14.20)—eat mostly zooplankton and time their migration through temperate and polar oceans to coincide with maximum zooplankton productivity. This enables the whales to develop and support calves that can exceed 7 meters (23 feet) in length at birth. The mother blue whale suckles the calf with rich, high-fat milk for six months. By the time the calf is weaned, it is over 16 meters (50 feet) long. In two years, it will be 23 meters (75 feet) long, and after about three years, it will weigh 55 metric tons (60 short tons)! This phenomenal growth rate gives some indication of the enormous biomass of small copepods and krill upon which these large mammals feed.[8]

Density and temperature change very little with depth in polar regions (Figure 13.11c), so these waters are **isothermal** (*iso* = same, *thermo* = temperature) and there is no barrier to mixing between surface waters and deeper, nutrient-rich waters. In the summer, however, melting ice creates a thin, low-salinity layer that does not readily mix with the deeper waters. This stratification is crucial to summer production because it helps prevent phytoplankton from being carried into deeper, darker waters. Instead, they are concentrated in the sunlit surface waters, where they reproduce continuously.

Nutrient concentrations (mostly nitrates and phosphates) are usually adequate in high-latitude surface waters, so the availability of solar energy limits photosynthetic productivity in these areas more than the availability of nutrients.

Productivity in Tropical Oceans

Perhaps surprisingly, productivity is low in tropical regions of the open ocean. Because the Sun is more directly overhead, light penetrates much more deeply into tropical oceans than temperate and polar waters, and solar energy is available year-round, but productivity is low in tropical regions of the open ocean because a permanent thermocline produces a stratification (layering) of water masses. This prevents mixing between surface waters and nutrient-rich deeper waters, effectively eliminating any supply of nutrients from deeper waters below (Figure 13.12).

At about 20 degrees north and south latitude, phosphate and nitrate concentrations are commonly less than 1/100 of their concentrations in temperate oceans during winter. In fact, nutrient-rich waters in the tropics lie below 150 meters (500 feet), with the highest concentrations between 500 and 1000 meters (1640 and 3300 feet). So, productivity in tropical regions is limited by the lack of nutrients (unlike polar regions, where productivity is limited by the lack of sunlight).

Generally, primary production in tropical oceans occurs at a steady but rather low rate. The total annual production of tropical oceans is only about half of that found in temperate oceans.

Exceptions to the general pattern of low productivity in tropical oceans include the following:

1. **Equatorial upwelling.** Where trade winds drive westerly equatorial currents on either side of the equator, Ekman transport causes surface water to diverge toward higher latitudes (see Figure 7.10). This surface water is replaced by nutrient-rich water from depths of up to 200 meters (660 feet). Equatorial upwelling is best developed in the eastern Pacific Ocean.

2. **Coastal upwelling.** Where the prevailing winds blow toward the equator and along western continental margins, surface waters are driven away from the coast. They are replaced by nutrient-rich waters from depths of 200 to

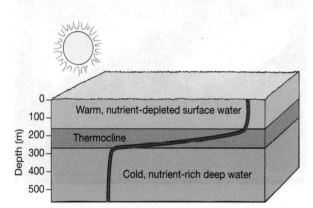

FIGURE 13.12 Productivity in tropical oceans.
Although tropical regions receive adequate sunlight year-round, a permanent thermocline prevents the mixing of surface and deep water. As phytoplankton consume nutrients in the surface layer, productivity is limited because the thermocline prevents replenishment of nutrients from deeper water. Thus, productivity remains at a steady, low level. Red curve indicates temperature of the water column, with high temperature toward the right.

---

[8]As a similar size analogy, consider how many ants you would have to eat as a child to grow to adult size!

900 meters (660 to 2950 feet). This upwelling promotes high primary production along the west coasts of continents (see Figure 13.6), which can support large fisheries.

3. Coral reefs. Organisms that comprise and live among coral reefs are superbly adapted to low-nutrient conditions, similar to the way certain organisms are adapted to desert life on land. Symbiotic algae living within the tissues of coral and other species allow coral reefs to be highly productive ecosystems. Coral reefs also tend to retain and recycle what little nutrients exist. Coral reef ecosystems are discussed further in Chapter 15, "Animals of the Benthic Environment."

Productivity in Temperate Oceans

Productivity is limited by available sunlight in polar regions and by nutrient supply in the low-latitude tropics. In temperate (middle latitude) regions, a combination of these two limiting factors controls productivity as shown in Figure 13.13a (which shows the pattern for the Northern Hemisphere; in the Southern Hemisphere, the seasons are reversed).

STUDENTS SOMETIMES ASK...

The number and variety of tropical species on land is astounding. I don't understand how the tropical oceans can have such low productivity.

Life on land does not necessarily correspond to life in the ocean! Tropical rainforests support an amazing diversity of species and an enormous biomass. In the tropical ocean, however, a strong, permanent thermocline limits the availability of nutrients that are necessary for the growth of phytoplankton. Without abundant phytoplankton, not much else can live in the ocean. In fact, these areas are often considered biological deserts. It is ironic that the clear blue water of the tropics so prominently displayed in tourist brochures indicates seawater that is biologically quite sterile!

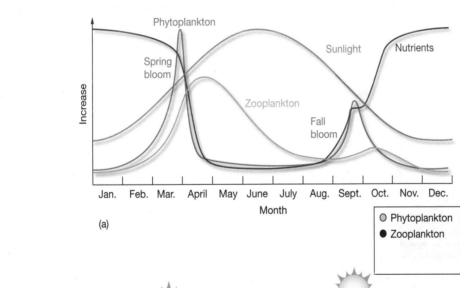

FIGURE 13.13 Productivity in temperate oceans (Northern Hemisphere).
(a) Relationship among phytoplankton, zooplankton, amount of sunlight, and nutrient levels for surface waters in northern temperate latitudes. **(b)** The seasonal cycle of sunlight affects the presence and depth of the thermocline, which affects the availability of nutrients. This, in turn, affects the abundance of phytoplankton and other organisms such as zooplankton that rely on phytoplankton for food.

Oceanic Midlatitude
Productivity

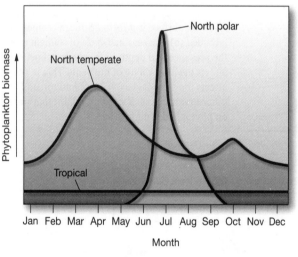

FIGURE 13.14 Comparison of productivity in tropical, temperate, and polar oceans (Northern Hemisphere). Seasonal variations in phytoplankton biomass, where the total area under each curve represents annual photosynthetic productivity.

WINTER Productivity in temperate oceans is very low during winter, even though nutrient concentration is *highest* at this time (Figure 13.13a). The water column is isothermal, too, similar to polar regions, so nutrients are well distributed throughout the water column. Figure 13.13b (*winter*) shows, however, that the Sun is at its lowest position above the horizon during winter, so a high percentage of the available solar energy is reflected, leaving only a small percentage to be absorbed into surface waters. As a result, the compensation depth for photosynthesis is so shallow that phytoplankton do not grow much. The absence of a thermocline, moreover, allows algal cells to be carried down beneath the euphotic zone for extended periods by turbulence associated with winter waves.

SPRING The Sun rises higher in the sky during spring (Figure 13.13b, *spring*), so the compensation depth for photosynthesis deepens. A **spring bloom** of phytoplankton occurs (Figure 13.13a) because solar energy and nutrients are available, and a seasonal thermocline develops (due to increased solar heating) that traps algae in the euphotic zone (Figure 13.13b). This creates a tremendous demand for nutrients in the euphotic zone, so the supply becomes limited, causing productivity to decrease sharply. Even though the days are lengthening and sunlight is increasing, productivity during the spring bloom is limited by the lack of nutrients. In most areas of the Northern Hemisphere, therefore, phytoplankton populations decrease in April due to insufficient nutrients and because their population is being consumed by zooplankton (grazers).

SUMMER The Sun rises even higher in the summer (Figure 13.13b, *summer*), so surface waters in temperate parts of the ocean continue to warm. A strong seasonal thermocline is created at a depth of about 15 meters (50 feet). The thermocline, in turn, prevents vertical mixing, so nutrients depleted from surface waters cannot be replaced by those from deeper waters. Throughout summer, the phytoplankton population remains relatively low (Figure 13.13a). Even though the compensation depth for photosynthesis is at its maximum, phytoplankton can actually become scarce in late summer.

FALL Solar radiation diminishes in the fall as the Sun moves lower in the sky (Figure 13.13b, *fall*), so surface temperatures drop and the summer thermocline breaks down. Nutrients return to the surface layer as increased wind strength mixes surface waters with deeper waters. These conditions create a **fall bloom** of phytoplankton, which is much less dramatic than the spring bloom (Figure 13.13a). The fall bloom is very short-lived because sunlight (not nutrient supply, as in the spring bloom) becomes the limiting factor as winter approaches to repeat the seasonal cycle.

Comparing Regional Productivity

Figure 13.14 compares the seasonal variation in phytoplankton biomass of tropical, north polar, and north temperate regions, where the total area under each curve represents photosynthetic productivity. The figure shows the dramatic peak in productivity in polar oceans during the summer; the steady, low rate of productivity year-round in the tropical ocean; and the seasonal pattern of productivity that occurs in temperate oceans. It also shows that the highest overall productivity occurs in temperate regions.

Regional productivity can also vary due to human influence. Nutrients added to the ocean, for example, can result in dangerous phytoplankton blooms and other unwanted effects (Box 13.2).

OCEAN EUTROPHICATION AND THE DEAD ZONE

Ocean **eutrophication** (*eu* = good, *tropho* = nourishment, *ation* = action) is the artificial enrichment of waters by a previously scarce nutrient that can result in *harmful algal blooms (HABs)*. Human activities have been shown to contribute to ocean eutrophication when excess nutrients in the form of fertilizer, sewage, and animal waste make their way into coastal waters. Ocean eutrophication has been linked to the increasing size and frequency of red tides (see Box 13.1) as well as outbreaks of toxic dinoflagellates (see Box 13.1).

Large areas of ocean eutrophication are associated with extensive *hypoxic* (*hypo* = under, *oxic* = oxygen) **dead zones** of oxygen-poor water that often occur near the mouths of major rivers after large spring runoffs. When rivers deliver excess nutrients to the ocean, they feed profuse, widespread blooms of algae that later die and decompose, robbing the water of oxygen. Oxygen levels within these dead zones drop from above 5.0 parts per million (ppm) to below 2.0 ppm, which is lower than most marine animals can tolerate. Some of the more mobile marine organisms can flee the area, but it suffocates and kills many bottom-dwelling organisms that cannot swim or crawl to other areas. Low oxygen levels have also been shown to limit the growth and reproduction of marine life.

One of the most prominent **dead zones** is the one that forms each summer near the mouth of the Mississippi River in the Gulf of Mexico off Louisiana (Figure 13D). In 2002, in fact, it reached a record size of 22,000 square kilometers (8500 square miles)—about the same size as the state of New Jersey. Smaller dead zones have occurred each summer in the region for decades, but they dramatically increased in size after the record-breaking 1993 Midwest floods.

The Gulf's dead zone appears to be related to runoff of nutrients—especially nitrate—from agricultural activities that are washed down the Mississippi River and eventually reach the Gulf, where they trigger algal blooms. Once these algae die and rain down on the sea floor, bacteria feed on them and on fecal matter, depleting the water of oxygen along the bottom. Similar nutrient pollution has degraded more than half of U.S. estuaries.

Worldwide, scientists have documented more than 400 dead zones, although the Gulf's dead zone is the largest in the Western Hemisphere. Proposals to combat the spread of the Gulf's dead zone include controlling nutrient runoff from agriculture, preserving and utilizing wetlands that filter runoff before it enters the Gulf, planting buffer strips of trees and grasses between farm fields and streams, altering the times when fertilizers are applied, improving crop rotation, and enforcing existing clean water regulations. In this way, scientists, land planners, and policy makers are working to institute an action plan that would shrink the yearly Gulf of Mexico dead zone.

FIGURE 13D The Gulf of Mexico dead zone. Map (*above*) showing Mississippi River drainage basin (*gold*) and enlargement (*below*) showing extent of the 1999 Gulf of Mexico dead zone (*red*). The dead zone is a low-oxygen region related to excess nutrients from agricultural runoff from the Mississippi River that stimulates algal blooms. When the algae die, decomposition consumes vast amounts of oxygen, creating an anoxic dead zone that affects a multitude of marine life.

13.4 How Are Energy and Nutrients Passed Along in Marine Ecosystems?

A **biotic community** is the assemblage of organisms that live together within some definable area. An **ecosystem** includes the biotic community plus the environment with which it exchanges energy and chemical substances. A kelp forest biotic

FIGURE 13.15 Energy flow through a photosynthetic marine ecosystem. Energy enters a marine ecosystem as radiant solar energy and is converted to chemical energy through photosynthesis by producers. Metabolism in the fish (a consumer) then releases the chemical energy for conversion to mechanical energy. Energy is also dissipated within the ecosystem as heat energy. Decomposers work to break down the remaining energy after an organism dies.

community, for instance, includes all organisms living within or near the kelp and receiving some benefit from it. A kelp forest ecosystem, on the other hand, includes all those organisms plus the surrounding seawater, the hard substrate onto which the kelp is attached, and the atmosphere where gases are exchanged.

Two of the most important commodities passed along in marine ecosystems are energy and nutrients.

Flow of Energy in Marine Ecosystems

Energy flow in photosynthetic marine ecosystems is not a cycle but a *unidirectional flow* based on the input of solar energy. Consider an algae-supported biotic community (Figure 13.15), where energy enters the system when algae absorb solar radiation. Photosynthesis converts this solar energy into chemical energy, which is used for the algae's respiration. This chemical energy is also passed on to the animals that consume the algae for their growth and other life functions. The animals expend mechanical and heat energy, which are progressively less recoverable forms of energy, until this residual energy becomes dissipated within the ecosystem. In essence, the ecosystem relies on a constant input of energy in the form of sunlight.

PRODUCERS, CONSUMERS, AND DECOMPOSERS Generally, three basic categories of organisms exist within an ecosystem: **producers**, **consumers**, and **decomposers** (Figure 13.15).

Producers can nourish themselves through either photosynthesis or chemosynthesis. Examples of producers include algae, plants, archaea, and photosynthetic bacteria, all of which are called **autotrophic** (*auto* = self, *tropho* = nourishment) organisms. Consumers and decomposers, on the other hand, are called **heterotrophic** (*hetero* = different, *tropho* = nourishment) organisms because they depend either directly or indirectly on the organic compounds produced by autotrophs for their food supply.

Consumers eat other organisms and are categorized as either **herbivores** (*herba* = grass, *vora* = eat), which feed directly on plants or algae; **carnivores** (*carni* = meat, *vora* = eat), which feed only on other animals; **omnivores** (*omni* = all, *vora* = eat), which feed on both; or **bacteriovores** (*bacterio* = bacteria, *vora* = eat), which feed only on bacteria.

Decomposers such as bacteria break down organic compounds that comprise **detritus** (*detritus* = to lessen)—dead and decaying remains and waste products of organisms—for their own energy requirements. In the decomposition process, compounds are released that are again available for use by autotrophs as nutrients.

Flow of Nutrients in Marine Ecosystems

Unlike the noncyclic, unidirectional flow of energy through a biotic community, the flow of nutrients depends on **biogeochemical cycles**.[9] That is, matter does not dissipate (as energy does) but is *cycled* from one chemical form to another by the various members of the biotic community.

BIOGEOCHEMICAL CYCLING Figure 13.16 shows the biogeochemical cycling of matter within the marine environment. The chemical components of organic

[9]Biogeochemical cycling is so named because it involves *bio*logical, *geo*logical (Earth processes), and *chemical* components.

matter enter the biological system through photosynthesis (or, less commonly, through chemosynthesis at hydrothermal vents). These chemical components are passed on to animal populations (consumers) through feeding. When organisms die, some of the material is used and reused within the euphotic zone, while some sinks as detritus. Some of this detritus feeds organisms living in deep water or on the sea floor, while some undergoes bacterial or other decomposition processes that convert organic remains into useable nutrients (nitrates and phosphates). When upwelling hoists these nutrients to the surface again, they can be used by algae and plants to begin the cycle anew.

13.5 What Oceanic Feeding Relationships Exist?

As producers make food (organic matter) available to the consuming animals of the ocean, the food passes from one feeding population to the next. Only a small percentage of the energy taken in at any level is passed on to the next because energy is consumed and lost at each level. As a result, the producers' biomass in the ocean is many times greater than the mass of the top consumers, such as sharks or whales.

Feeding Strategies

For most marine animals, obtaining food occupies the majority of their time. Some animals are fast and agile and are able to obtain food through active predation. Other animals move more leisurely or not at all and instead obtain food by filtering it from seawater or locating it as deposits on the sea floor.

In **suspension feeding**, which is also called **filter feeding**, organisms use specially designed structures to filter plankton from seawater (Figure 13.17a). Clams, for instance, bury themselves in sediment and extend siphons up to the surface. They pump in overlying water and filter from it suspended plankton and other organic matter.

In **deposit feeding**, organisms feed on food items that occur as deposits. These deposits include detritus—dead and decaying organic matter and waste products—and the sediment itself, which is coated with organic matter. Some deposit feeders, such as the segmented worm *Arenicola* (Figure 13.17b), feed by ingesting sediment and extracting organic matter from it. Others, such as the amphipod *Orchestoidea* (Figure 13.17c), feed on more concentrated deposits of organic matter (detritus) on the sediment surface.

In **carnivorous feeding**, organisms directly capture and eat other animals. This predation can be either passive or active. Passive predation involves waiting for prey items and ensnaring them such as how a sea anemone feeds. Active predation involves seeking prey; examples include sharks and the sand star *Astropecten* (Figure 13.17d), which can burrow rapidly into sandy beaches and feeds voraciously on crustaceans, mollusks, worms, and other echinoderms.

Trophic Levels

Chemical energy stored in the mass of the ocean's algae (the "grass of the sea") is transferred to the animal community mostly through feeding. Zooplankton are *herbivores*, like cows,[10] so they eat diatoms and other microscopic marine algae.

[10]In fact, zooplankton could be considered the miniature drifting "cows of the sea."

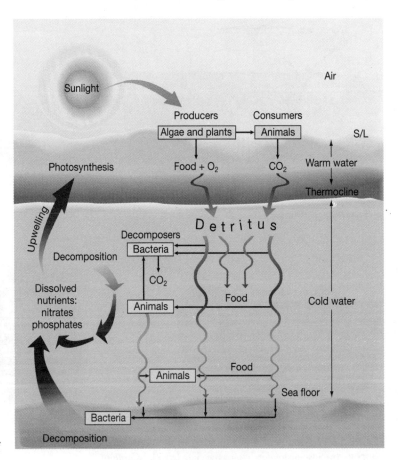

FIGURE 13.16 Biogeochemical cycling of matter. The chemical components of organic matter enter the biological system through photosynthesis and are passed on to consumers through feeding. Detritus sinks and feeds organisms living below the surface or undergoes decomposition, which returns nutrients to the water that can be hoisted to the surface by upwelling.

FIGURE 13.17 Modes of feeding along sediment-covered shores. (a) Suspension feeding by the clam (cockle) *Cardium*, which uses its siphon to filter plankton and other organic matter that is suspended in the water. (b) Deposit feeding by the segmented worm *Arenicola*, which feeds by ingesting sediment and extracting organic matter from it. (c) Deposit feeding by the amphipod *Orchestoidea*, which feeds on more concentrated deposits of organic matter (detritus) on the sediment surface. (d) Carnivorous feeding of a clam by the sand star *Astropecten*.

FIGURE 13.18 Passage of energy through trophic levels. As food mass initially produced by phytoplankton passes from herbivores to carnivores, a large percentage is excreted by feces, used during respiration, or dies uneaten. Thus, only about 10% of the food mass consumed by herbivores is available for consumption by carnivores.

Larger herbivores feed on the larger algae and marine plants that grow attached to the ocean bottom near shore.

The herbivores are then eaten by larger animals, the *carnivores*. They, in turn, are eaten by another population of larger carnivores, and so on. Each of these feeding stages is called a **trophic** (*tropho* = nourishment) **level**.

Generally, individual members of a feeding population are larger—but not too much larger—than the organisms they eat. There are conspicuous exceptions, however, such as the blue whale. At 30 meters (100 feet) long, it is possibly the largest animal that has ever existed on Earth, yet it feeds on krill, which have a maximum length of only 6 centimeters (2.4 inches).

The transfer of energy from one population to another is a continuous *flow* of energy. Small-scale recycling and storage interrupt the flow; this in turn slows the conversion of potential (chemical) energy to kinetic energy, then to heat energy, and finally the energy is so dissipated it becomes useless.

Transfer Efficiency

The transfer of energy between trophic levels is very inefficient. The efficiencies of different algal species vary, but the average is only about 2%, which means that 2% of the light energy absorbed by algae is ultimately synthesized into food and made available to herbivores.

The **gross ecological efficiency** at any trophic level is the ratio of energy passed on to the next higher trophic level divided by the energy received from the trophic level below. The ecological efficiency of herbivorous anchovies, for example, would be the energy consumed by carnivorous tuna that feed on the anchovies divided by the energy contained in the phytoplankton that the anchovies consumed.

Figure 13.18 shows that some of the chemical energy taken in as food by herbivores is excreted as feces and the rest is assimilated. Of the assimilated chemical energy, much is converted through respiration to kinetic energy for maintaining life, and what remains is available for growth and reproduction. Thus, only about 10% of the food mass consumed by herbivores is available to the next trophic level.

Figure 13.19 shows the passage of energy between trophic levels through an entire ecosystem, from the solar energy assimilated by phytoplankton through all trophic levels to the ultimate carnivore—humans. Because energy is lost at each trophic level, it takes thousands of smaller marine organisms to produce a *single* fish that is so easily consumed during a meal!

The efficiency of energy transfer between trophic levels depends on many variables. Young animals, for example, have a higher growth

**FIGURE 13.19
Ecosystem
energy flow and
efficiency.**
For every 500,000
units of radiant
energy input avail-
able to the produc-
ers (phytoplankton),
only one unit of
equivalent mass is
added to the fifth
trophic level
(humans). Average
phytoplankton
transfer efficiency is
2% (98% loss), and
all other trophic lev-
els average 10%
efficiency (90% loss).

efficiency than older animals. In addition, when food is plentiful, animals expend
more energy in digestion and assimilation than when food is scarce.

Most ecological efficiencies in natural ecosystems average about 10% but
range between 6% and 15%. There is some evidence, however, that ecological
efficiencies in populations important to present fisheries may run as high as 20%.
The true value of this efficiency is of practical importance because it determines
the size of the fish harvest that can safely be taken from the oceans without damaging the ecosystem.

Food Chains, Food Webs, and the Biomass Pyramid

The loss of energy between each feeding population limits the number of feeding
populations in an ecosystem. If there were too many levels, there would not be
enough energy to support the organisms in higher and higher trophic levels. In
addition, each feeding population must necessarily have less mass than the population it eats. As a result, individual members of a feeding population are generally
larger in size and *less numerous* than their prey.

FOOD CHAINS   A **food chain** is a sequence of organisms through which energy
is transferred, starting with an organism that is the primary producer, then an
herbivore, then one or more carnivores, finally culminating with the "top carnivore,"

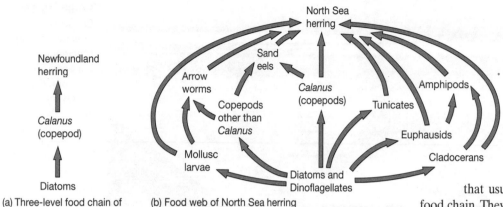

Newfoundland
herring

↑

Calanus
(copepod)

↑

Diatoms

(a) Three-level food chain of
Newfoundland herring

(b) Food web of North Sea herring
containing many food chains

FIGURE 13.20 Comparison between a food chain and a food web. **(a)** A food chain, showing the passage of energy along a single path, such as from diatoms to copepods to Newfoundland herring in three trophic levels. **(b)** A food web, showing multiple paths for food sources of the North Sea herring, which may be at the third or fourth trophic level.

which is not usually preyed upon by any other organism.

Because energy transfer between trophic levels is inefficient, it is advantageous for fishers to choose a population that feeds as close to the primary producing population as possible. This increases the biomass available for food and the number of individuals available to be taken by the fishery. Newfoundland herring, for example, are an important fishery that usually represents the third trophic level in a food chain. They feed primarily on small crustaceans (copepods) that feed, in turn, upon diatoms (Figure 13.20).

FOOD WEBS Feeding relationships are rarely as simple as that of the Newfoundland herring. more often, top carnivores in a food chain feed on a number of different animals, each of which has its own simple or complex feeding relationships. This constitutes a **food web**, as shown in Figure 13.20b for North Sea herring.

Animals that feed through a food web rather than a food chain are more likely to survive because they have alternative foods to eat should one of their food sources diminish in quantity or even disappear. Newfoundland herring, on the other hand, eat only copepods, so the disappearance of copepods would catastrophically affect their population. Conversely, Newfoundland herring are more likely to have a larger biomass to eat, because they are only two steps removed from the producers, whereas North Sea herring are three steps removed in some of the food chains within their web.

BIOMASS PYRAMID The ultimate effect of energy transfer between trophic levels can be seen in the oceanic **biomass pyramid** shown in Figure 13.21. It shows that for the survival of each large marine organism, many levels of progressively larger populations of smaller-sized organisms must exist to support those higher on the pyramid. In essence, the *number of individuals* and *total biomass* decrease at successive trophic levels because the amount of available energy decreases. The figure also shows that organisms *increase in size* at successive trophic levels up the pyramid.

In some marine environments, "inverted" biomass pyramids can occur. An "inverted" biomass pyramid can exist, for example, where a smaller population of phytoplankton with a very high turnover rate supports a larger population of zooplankton. As a result, oceanic biomass pyramids can have a variety of shapes, depending on the turnover rates of different trophic levels.

Killer whale (tertiary carnivore)

Bonito (secondary carnivore)

Anchovies (primary carnivore)

Killer whale
10X mass of killer whale
100X mass of killer whale
1000X mass of killer whale

Zooplankton (herbivore)

10,000X mass of killer whale

Phytoplankton (producer)

FIGURE 13.21 Oceanic biomass pyramid. A huge mass of phytoplankton constitutes the base of the biomass pyramid. At each step up the pyramid, there are larger organisms but fewer individuals and a smaller total biomass because transfer efficiency between steps averages only 10%.

13.6 What Issues Affect Marine Fisheries?

Since well before the beginning of recorded history, humans have used the sea as a source of food. Over the past several decades, **fisheries** (fish caught from the ocean by commercial fishers) have provided billions of people around the world nearly 20% of their protein intake, with less-developed nations relying on fish for 27% of their dietary protein.

Marine Ecosystems and Fisheries

Figure 13.22 shows that the world marine fishery is drawn from five ecosystems. In descending order, they are (1) nontropical shelves, (2) tropical shelves, (3) upwellings, (4) coastal and coral systems, and (5) open ocean. The largest proportion of the marine fishery is found in highly productive shallow shelf and coastal waters, whereas low productivity open ocean areas comprise only 3.8% of the total. Nearly 21% of the world's total catch is from very highly productive upwelling areas, which represent only about 0.1% of the ocean surface area.

Overfishing

Fisheries harvest from the **standing stock** of a population, which is the mass present in an ecosystem at a given time. Successful fisheries leave enough individuals from the standing stock to repopulate the ecosystem after fisheries have made their harvest.

Overfishing occurs when harvesting of fish stocks takes place so rapidly that the majority of the population is sexually immature and is therefore unable to reproduce. Predictably, overfishing results in the decline of marine fish populations and the reduction of a fishery's **maximum sustainable yield (MSY)** (the maximum fishery biomass that can be removed yearly and still be sustained by the fishery ecosystem).

According to a report by the Food and Agriculture Organization (FAO) of the United Nations, 80% of the 523 world marine fish stocks for which assessment information is available are classified as fully exploited, overexploited, or depleted/recovering from depletion (Figure 13.23). In U.S. waters, the story is much the same: 80% of the 191 commercial fish stocks are fully exploited or overfished. In U.K. waters, stocks of palatable fish—such as cod—have been reduced by overfishing to less than 10% of what they were 100 years ago.

Overfishing also affects the size of fish in fisheries. For example, recent studies indicate that fishing practices have removed 90% of large predatory fish species and, as a result, the fishing industry has concentrated on smaller fish that occupy successively lower trophic levels (Box 13.3). Not only are big fish disappearing at an alarming rate, but the ocean's top predators are now only about one-half to one-fifth the size they once were, which affects entire marine ecosystems. As a case in point, the removal of large predatory sharks along the East Coast by

KEY CONCEPT

A food chain is a linear feeding relationship among producers and one or more consumers while a food web is a branching network of feeding relationships among many different organisms. The oceanic biomass pyramid shows energy transfer between trophic levels.

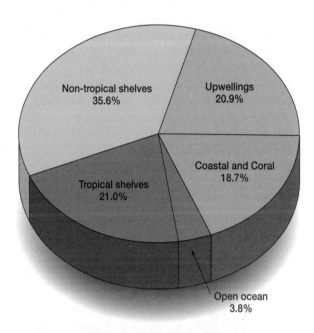

FIGURE 13.22 Marine fishery ecosystems. Pie diagram showing the relative contribution of various ecosystems to the total world marine fishery.

FIGURE 13.23 Exploitation status of world marine fisheries. Bar graph showing the current status of world fishery stocks, including depleted/recovering from depletion, overexploited, fully exploited, moderately exploited, and underexploited. The only fisheries safe to increase are those that are moderately exploited and underexploited.

13.3   FOCUS ON THE ENVIRONMENT

FISHING DOWN THE FOOD WEB: SEEING IS BELIEVING

Marine scientists can measure the health of an ecosystem by determining its original fish abundance, diversity, and size. But how can these variables be assessed effectively for periods before extensive scientific field surveys were conducted? Recently, scientists have been using novel ways to estimate these parameters. A new field of research called *historical marine ecology* uses items such as old photographs, newspaper accounts, ships' logs, cannery records, and even old restaurant menus to estimate the type and quantity of fish that used to live in the sea.

Striking evidence of past fish abundance and size comes from old photographs. Certainly, people have always enjoyed having their picture taken with the fish they catch. Loren McClenachan, a graduate student at Scripps Institute of Oceanography at the University of California, San Diego, found a historical archive of old photographs in Key West, Florida, in the Monroe County Public Library. The archive allowed her to examine fish caught by day-trippers at coral reef sites aboard a series of vessels called *Gulf Stream* and *Greyhound*, which have operated out of Key West for the past 50 years.

By comparing old photographs with newer ones (Figure 13E), it is apparent that there has been a pronounced decrease in both fish abundance and fish size through the years. Research suggests that chronic overfishing by both commercial and recreational fishers is the likely source of this decline. In fact, some species completely disappear over time, reflecting a loss of the largest fish from the coral reef environment. For example,

in the 1950s, fishers caught huge grouper and sharks. In the 1970s, they landed a few grouper but more jack. Today's main catch lacks grouper and instead consists of small snapper, which once weren't even deemed worthy of a photograph; instead, they were just piled up below the hanging racks. Historical records from other regions throughout the world also reveal astonishing declines in most fish stocks. Scientists use the phrase "fishing down the food web" to describe how key large species in healthy functioning ecosystems have been replaced by progressively smaller, less valuable species that occupy lower levels of the food web.

Worldwide, fishers typically catch the biggest animals first, whether turtles, whales, cod, or grouper. Then they catch whatever is left—including animals so young that they haven't reproduced yet—until, in some cases, the animals are gone. To change human habits, it is important to gain a clearer picture of what has been lost. In the Florida Keys, historical photographs provide such a window into a more pristine coral reef ecosystem that existed a half century ago.

FIGURE 13E Decreasing size of fish catch. Historical photos from chartered fishing vessels that concentrated on the fish of the coral reefs surrounding Key West, Florida, show decreasing catch size and abundance from 1958 (*above*), 1980s (*middle*), and 2007 (*below*).

fishing practices during the past 35 years has allowed one of their prey items, the cownose ray (*Rhinoptera bonasus*), to increase 20-fold. As a result, shellfish populations such as the bay scallop—which are a major prey item of the rays—have been decimated. In fact, this overabundance of rays caused the closure of North Carolina's century-old bay scallop fishery in 2004.

Recent research shows that fishing can induce inherited changes that cut the average growth rate, maturing time, and size in fish from generation to generation, which has some severe implications for the health and longevity of fisheries. In fact, a recent study of the effect of pollution and fisheries on marine ecosystem biodiversity projects that fish stocks will be depleted by 2048. Not only will the loss of seafood threaten humans' food supplies but the loss of fish will also seriously damage marine ecosystems.

Although it is widely assumed that recreational fishing has a minimal influence on most species of fish, recreational fishing has been shown to have an impact on fish populations, too. A recent rigorous analysis of multiple U.S. fisheries records shows that for some threatened sportfishing species such as red drum, bocaccio rockfish, and red snapper, recreational fishing actually poses more of a threat than commercial fishing because of the size and number of fish taken by recreational fishers. Thus, new fishing regulations that target recreational fishers are needed to complement existing catch restrictions on the commercial sector.

Figure 13.24 shows the world total fish production in marine waters since 1950. After increasing steadily for 35 years, the world catch of ocean fish finally leveled off in the 1990s. In 1998, in fact, it dipped to 79.6 million metric tons (87.6 million short tons).

How much fish can the oceans produce? The National Research Council estimated in 1999 that the maximum catch that might be expected from the oceans is about 100 million metric tons (110 million short tons). This amount might be exceeded, however, if new species—such as Antarctic krill, squid, and pelagic crabs—become significant new fisheries in the future. Based on current yields of traditional fisheries, the United Nations FAO estimates that the maximum catch that might be expected from the oceans is about 120 million metric tons (132 million short tons).

The reported worldwide catch, however, does not include additional organisms caught but deemed undesirable and discarded, so the actual catch is likely much higher than the reported value. Unfortunately, this suggests that the amount of biomass removed by fishing exceeds that produced in the ocean, which means that the oceans are being overfished.

Incidental Catch

Incidental catch, or **bycatch**, includes any marine organisms that are caught incidentally by fishers seeking commercial species. On average, close to one-fourth of the catch is discarded, although for some fisheries, such as shrimp, the incidental catch may be up to eight times larger than the catch of the target species. Incidental catch includes birds, turtles, sharks, and dolphins, as well as many species of noncommercial fish. In most cases, these animals die before they are thrown back overboard, even though some of them are protected by U.S. and international law. Globally, an estimated 20 million metric tons (32 million short tons) of bycatch is produced each year by the fishing industry, accounting for nearly one-fourth of the world's total marine fish catch.

TUNA AND DOLPHINS   Schools of yellowfin tuna are commonly found swimming beneath spotted and spinner dolphins in the eastern Pacific Ocean (Figure 13.25). Fishers commonly used these dolphins to locate tuna and set a *purse seine net* around the entire school (Figure 13.26). When an underwater line is drawn tight,

FIGURE 13.24 World total marine fish production since 1950. Graph showing the increasing amount of reported world total marine fish production, which begins to level off during the 1990s. The catch actually dipped to 79.6 million metric tons in 1998.

FIGURE 13.25 Spotted dolphin (*Stenella attnuata*), which are commonly associated with yellowfin tuna. Eastern Pacific spotted dolphins are often found swimming with yellowfin tuna, but the dolphins do not eat those fish. Although the prey items of spotted dolphins and yellowfin tuna are similar (squid and small fish), they probably feed at different levels.

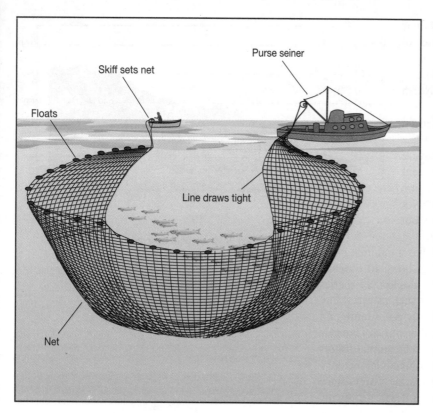

FIGURE 13.26 Purse seiner. Purse seine nets are set around schools of yellowfin tuna, often trapping dolphins at the surface as bycatch.

STUDENTS SOMETIMES ASK...

Is tuna labeled as "dolphin-safe" really safe to dolphins?

It depends on where the tuna is from, but the answer is probably yes. Tuna and tuna products harvested in the eastern tropical Pacific Ocean can only be labeled as "dolphin-safe" in the United States if no nets were intentionally set on dolphins during fishing and no dolphins were killed or seriously injured during the set in which the tuna were caught. In the United States, the National Marine Fisheries Service (NMFS) has developed an extensive monitoring, tracking, and verification program to ensure that only tuna and tuna products that meet the definition of dolphin-safe are indeed labeled as "dolphin-safe." This program, along with consumer awareness, has substantially reduced yearly dolphin mortality, which numbered in the hundreds of thousands in the 1980s. Recently, however, changes to the definition of "dolphin-safe" have been accepted by the NMFS that address international trade concerns and allow more tuna to be imported from international sources, particularly from Mexico. Tuna from international sources caught along with dolphins may be labeled "dolphin-safe" in the United States as long as observers aboard fishing vessels certify that no dolphins were killed or seriously injured during the catch—but this relies on the honesty of the observers.

---

the net traps the tuna underwater as well as the dolphins at the surface.

The problem of dolphin deaths caused by tuna fishing was graphically presented to the world in 1988 through video footage taken by biologist Samuel F. La Budde of dolphins struggling in tuna fishing nets. In 1990, under intense public outcry and a boycott on tuna, the U.S. tuna canning industry declared that it would not buy or sell tuna caught using methods that kill or injure dolphins. In 1992, a special addendum was added to the **Marine Mammals Protection Act**, further protecting dolphins. As a result of these measures, purse seine nets were modified so that dolphins could be released alive. In spite of reducing dolphin mortality as bycatch, dolphin populations have not rebounded accordingly. Research suggests that tuna fishing operations are still having a negative effect on dolphin populations by reducing dolphin survival and birth rates.

DRIFTNETS Another means of netting tuna and other species is by use of **driftnets**, or **gill nets**, which are made of monofilament fishing line that is virtually invisible and cannot be detected by most marine animals. Depending on the size of the holes in the net, it is highly effective at catching anything large enough to become entangled in it. As a result, driftnets often have high amounts of bycatch.

Up until 1993, Japan, Korea, and Taiwan had the largest driftnet fleets, deploying as many as 1500 fishing vessels into the North Pacific and setting over 48,000 kilometers (30,000 miles) of driftnets in one day. Although driftnetting was supposed to be restricted to specific fisheries, some fishers who claimed to be fishing for squid were involved in illegally taking large quantities of salmon and steelhead trout. Driftnetters were also targeting immature tuna in the South Pacific, which could result in the reduced abundance of South Pacific tuna. In addition, tens of thousands of birds, turtles, dolphins, and other species were killed annually in these nets.

A prohibition against the importation of fish caught in driftnets was included in the International Convention of Pacific Long Driftnet Fishing, signed in 1989. Although driftnets are now banned by international law, some fishers continue to use them illegally.

Fisheries Management

Fisheries management is the organized effort directed at regulating fishing activity with the goal of maintaining a long-term fishery. Fisheries management practices include assessing ecosystem health, determining fish stocks, analyzing fishing practices including recommending gear modification, establishing closed areas, and setting and enforcing catch limits. Unfortunately, however, fisheries management has historically been more concerned with maintaining human employment than preserving a self-sustaining marine ecosystem. For example, fisheries such as anchovy, cod, flounder, haddock, herring, and sardine are suffering from overfishing in spite of being managed (see Web Box 13.2).

One of the most pressing problems facing fisheries management results from the fact that some fisheries encompass the waters of many different countries, including a variety of ecosystems. Some species of commercial fish, for instance, are raised in coastal estuaries and migrate long distances across international waters to their preferred environment. Fishing limits are difficult to enforce internationally and if human interference occurs at any location where the fish exist, these species can be severely reduced in number. Other problems include the degradation of many ecosystems that sustain fisheries, limited scientific analysis, a lack of regulations enforcement (particularly on illegal/private fishers), poaching, misreporting of catch and bycatch, political barriers, and inadequate guidance for minimally regulated new fisheries.

REGULATION OF FISHING VESSELS   A major regulatory failure has been the absence of restrictions on the number of fishing vessels. In 2004, according to the FAO, the world's fishing fleet consisted of about 4 million vessels. Of these, about 1.3 million were engine-powered, mechanized decked vessels engaged in commercial fishing, including 40,000 vessels over 100 gross tons in size (generally more than 24 meters [80 feet] in length). Figure 13.27 shows that the number of decked fishing vessels in the world more than doubled between 1970 and 1995, and continues to increase. Many of these larger vessels use nets that can hold up to 27,000 kilograms (60,000 pounds) of fish in one haul. In addition, there are more than 2.1 million smaller nondecked fishing vessels that are owned and operated by artisanal fishers, mostly in Asia, Africa, and the Near East.

The increase in fishing vessels has resulted in an increased fishing effort, which often leads to overfishing. In some locations, the fish are becoming so scarce that the fishing effort costs more than what the catch is worth! In 1995, for instance, the world fishing fleet spent $124 billion to catch $70 billion worth of fish. To make up for the shortfall, many governments have given fishers subsidies in the form of cash payments totaling an estimated $30–34 billion yearly, which compounds the problem by maintaining (or even *increasing*) the number of fishing vessels.

FISHERIES IN THE NORTHWEST ATLANTIC   The effects of inadequate fisheries management are illustrated by the history of fisheries in the northwest Atlantic. Under management by the International Commission for the Northwest Atlantic Fisheries, the fishing capacity of the international fleet increased 500% from 1966 to 1976; the total catch, however, rose by only 15%. This was a significant decrease in the catch per unit of effort, which is a good indication that the fishing stocks of the Newfoundland–Grand Banks area were being overexploited. The biologists who recommended the total allowable fishing quotas for the major species within this region complained that enforcement was lacking and that countries' quotas were being bartered in a game of international politics. As a result, fishers exceeded the total allowable catch set by the commission.

The difficulty of enforcing regulations by the international commission was largely responsible for Canada's unilateral decision to extend its right to control fish stocks for a distance of 200 nautical miles (370 kilometers) from its shores beginning January 1, 1977. The United States followed with a similar action only two months later.

Claiming coastal waters, however, proved to have limited effectiveness. After essentially all coastal nations assumed regulatory control over their coastal waters, things continued to deteriorate and overfishing became even more of a problem. The Canadian government, in fact, had to shut down the Grand Banks fishery off Newfoundland in 1992, which resulted in the loss of about 40,000 jobs and subsequent government outlays of more than $3 billion in welfare. This cost far exceeds the value of the fishery, which generated no more than $125 million during one of its best years.

A similar situation has emerged on Georges Bank, which lies in Canadian and U.S. waters. On Georges Bank, however, tough international restrictions and proper enforcement are beginning to bring back haddock and yellowtail flounder fisheries.

In spite of protection, some fish stocks in the North Atlantic have not rebounded as anticipated. Atlantic cod stocks, for example, continue to decrease despite sharply curtailed annual catches. To help halt the cod's decline, the Canadian government in 2003 declared cod—one of the North Atlantic's most impacted fish species—completely off-limits to fishing. A similar decline in cod stocks is also occurring in European waters, but so far officials have rejected a proposed cod-fishing ban.

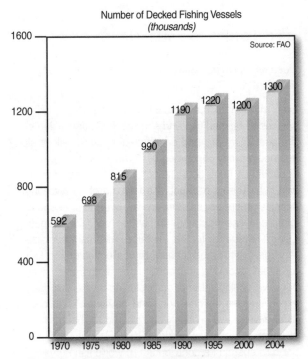

FIGURE 13.27 Number of decked fishing vessels in the world (in thousands).   Bar graph showing the worldwide number of engine-powered, mechanized decked vessels engaged in commercial fishing. The number has more than doubled since 1970 and continues to increase, which results in an increased fishing effort and often leads to overfishing.

Does fish farming relieve some of the demand for wild fish?

Even though global production of the nearly 250 species of farmed fish and shellfish has quadrupled in the past 20 years and now provides nearly half of all seafood directly consumed by humans, some types of aquaculture have actually *increased* the demand for wild fish. This is because the farming of carnivorous species such as salmon, tuna, cod, and seabass requires large inputs of wild fish for feed. Some aquaculture systems further reduce wild fish supplies through habitat modification, the collection of wild fish for initially stocking aquaculture operations, and other negative ecological impacts including waste disposal, exotic species introduction, and pathogen invasions, all of which have probably contributed to the collapse of fishery stocks worldwide. If the aquaculture industry is to sustain its contribution to world fish supplies, it must reduce wild fish inputs in feed and adopt more ecologically sound management practices.

KEY CONCEPT
The marine fishing industry suffers from overfishing, wasteful practices that produce a large amount of unwanted bycatch, and a lack of adequate fisheries management.

DEEP-WATER FISHERIES One of the results of depleting and/or banning certain fish stocks is that the fishing industry then expands its efforts into the deep sea, where there are few regulations. As compared to surface species, most deep-water species have low metabolic and reproduction rates, which cause them to be severely impacted by fishing. For example, the collapse of Atlantic cod stocks resulted in fishers seeking the deep-water Greenland halibut as a substitute. Predictably, that species in now in danger of becoming overfished throughout the Atlantic.

The deep-water orange roughy fishery near Australia is another prime example. It was developed to satisfy the middle-American market for a bland white fish. Even the name was picked through careful supermarket research (its original moniker—the slimehead—sounded far less appealing). And when that fishery began its inevitable decline, the industry moved on to another deep-water species, the Patagonian toothfish. It was renamed the Chilean sea bass, even though it is neither a bass nor exclusively Chilean. The precipitous decline of these deep-water fish has qualified them for endangered status.

Deep-sea ecosystems are beginning to feel the effect of this increased fishing effort, too. For example, tall seamounts rise precipitously from the deep sea floor and provide a unique environment that harbors many species of fish and deep-water coral. To effectively catch fish here, fishers use large bottom-dragging trawl nets. These nets, however, do long-lasting damage to the sea floor and have proven to negatively affect these slow-growing yet important ecosystems.

ECOSYSTEM-BASED FISHERY MANAGEMENT The historic record of fishery management shows many examples of attempts to regulate a fish stock looking only at an individual species. If fisheries are to remain viable in the future, marine ecosystems must be studied to document the natural relationships among organisms in marine food webs, the critical environmental factors for the health of the fishery, and the effects of removing so many organisms as fisheries catch. In addition, critical fish habitats must be protected and fishing limits must be upheld despite political factors. Only after such obstacles are overcome can a fishery be successfully managed.

To ensure sustainable fisheries and a healthy marine environment in U.S. waters, there has been a recent push to institute *ecosystem-based fishery management,* which employs a more comprehensive approach to understanding fish stocks including analysis of such variables as fish habitat, migration routes, and predator-prey interactions. Ecosystem-based fishery management essentially reverses the order of management priorities, starting with an ecosystem rather than a target species. It also focuses on rebuilding fisheries on a global basis.

Research has shown that sustainable fisheries can be achieved if management strategies are adopted that remove subsidies and give individual fishers a right to a proportion of the total catch. By removing competition, fishers of all types would then be encouraged to act to sustain the entire fishery because, as the common fish stock improves, each individual's quota will increase. In this way, fishers will have the incentive to manage the stock sustainably, thus avoiding overfishing and the eventual collapse of the fishery.

Recently, a study was conducted on the effectiveness of fisheries management practices. Scientists analyzed six key parameters, including the scientific quality of management recommendations, the transparency of converting recommendations into policy, the enforcement of policies, the influence of subsidies, fishing effort, and the extent of fishing by foreign entities. Results of the study (Figure 13.28) show that fisheries management, despite broad acceptance and commitments by governments to initiatives for improvements, remains largely ineffective.

Seafood Choices

Consumer demand has driven some fish populations to the brink of disappearing. However, consumers can help by making wise choices in the fish they consume by purchasing only those fish that are from healthy, thriving fisheries. Certainly,

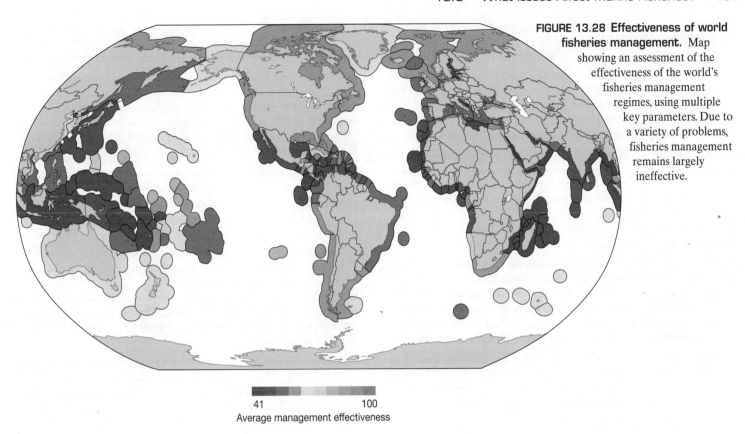

FIGURE 13.28 Effectiveness of world fisheries management. Map showing an assessment of the effectiveness of the world's fisheries management regimes, using multiple key parameters. Due to a variety of problems, fisheries management remains largely ineffective.

41   100
Average management effectiveness

some types of seafood carry less environmental impact than others because of differences in abundance, how they're caught, and how well fishing is managed. Figure 13.29 shows some recommendations for seafood (both fish and shellfish) in three categories: best choices (*green*), good alternatives (*yellow*), and seafood to avoid (*red*).

FIGURE 13.29 Recommended seafood choices. The Monterey Bay Aquarium Seafood Watch shows recommended seafood choices (*green*), seafood with some concerns (*yellow*), and seafood to avoid (*red*). Printable regional pocket guides are available at http://www.seafoodwatch.org.

Best Choices	Good Alternatives	Avoid	Support Ocean-friendly Seafood

Arctic Char (farmed)
Barramundi (US farmed)
Catfish (US farmed)
Clams (farmed)
Cod: Pacific (Alaska longline)*
   (trap or hook & line-caught)
Crab: Dungeness, Snow
Halibut: Pacific*
Lobster: Spiny (US)
Mussels (farmed)
Oysters (farmed)
Pollock (Alaska wild)*
Salmon (Alaska wild)*
Scallops: Bay (farmed)
Striped Bass (farmed or wild*)
Sturgeon, Caviar (farmed)
Tilapia (US farmed)
Trout: Rainbow (farmed)
Tuna: Albacore US*, British
   Columbia troll/pole)
Tuna: Skipjack (troll/pole)
	Clams (wild)
	Cod Pacific (trawled)
	Crab Blue*, King (US), Snow
	Crab: Imitation/Surimi
	Flounders, Soles (Pacific)
	Herring: Atlantic/Sardines
	Lobster: American/Maine
	Mahi mahi/Dolphinfish (US)
	Oysters (wild)*
	Scallops: Sea
	Shrimp (US farmed or wild)
	Squid
	Swai, Basa (farmer)
	Swordfish (US)*
	Tuna: Bigeye, Yellowfin (troll/pole)
	Tuna: canned light, canned
	   white/Albacore*
	Yellowtail (US farmed)
		Chilean Seabass/Toothfish*
		Cod: Atlantic
		Crab: King (imported)
		Flounders, Soles (Atlanitc)
		Groupers*
		Halibut: Atlantic
		Lobster: Spiny (Caribbean imported)
		Mahi mahi/Dolphinfish (imported)
		Marlin: Blue* , Striped*
		Monkfish
		Orange Roughy*
		Rockfish (Pacific trawled)
		Salmon (farmed, including Atlantic)*
		Sharks*
		Shrimp (imported farmed or wild)
		Snapper: Red
		Sturgeon*, Caviar (imported wild)
		Swordfish (imported)*
		Tuna: Albacore, Bigeye, Yellowfin
		   (longline)*
		Tuna: Bluefin*
		Yellowtail (Australia or Japan,
		farmed)
			Best Choices are abundant, well-managed and caught or farmed in environmental friendly ways.
			
			Good Alternatives are an option, but there are concerns with how they're caught or farmed-or with the health of their habitat due to other human impacts.
			
			Avoid for now as these items are caught or farmed in ways that harm other marine life or the environment.
			
			Key
			* Limit consumption due to concerns about mercury or other contaminants, Visit www.edf.org/seafood
			
			* Some or all of this fishery is certified as sustainable to the Marine Stewardship Council standard. Visit www. msc.org
			
			Seafood may appear in more than one column

Chapter in Review

• *Microscopic planktonic bacteria and algae that photosynthesize represent the largest biomass in the ocean.* They are the ocean's *primary producers*—the foundation of the ocean's food web. Organic biomass is also produced near deep-sea hydrothermal springs through *chemosynthesis,* in which bacteria-like organisms trap chemical energy by the oxidation of hydrogen sulfide.

• *The availability of nutrients and the amount of solar radiation limit the photosynthetic productivity in the oceans. Nutrients*—such as *nitrate, phosphorus, iron,* and *silica*—are most abundant in coastal areas, due to runoff and upwelling. The depth at which net photosynthesis is zero is the *compensation depth for photosynthesis.* Generally, algae cannot live below this depth, which may be less than 20 meters (65 feet) in turbid coastal waters or as much as 100 meters (330 feet) in the open ocean.

• *Marine life is most abundant along continental margins,* where nutrients and sunlight are optimal. It decreases with distance from the continents and with increased depth. In addition, *cool water typically supports more abundant life than warm water* because cool water can dissolve more of the gases necessary for life (oxygen and carbon dioxide). *Areas of upwelling bring cold, nutrient-rich water to the surface and have some of the highest productivities.*

• *Ocean water selectively absorbs the colors of the visible spectrum. Red and yellow light are absorbed at relatively shallow depths,* whereas *blue and green light are the last to be removed.* Ocean water of *low biologic productivity* scatters the short wavelengths of visible light, producing a *blue color.* Turbidity and photosynthetic algae in *more productive ocean water* scatter more green light wavelengths, which produces a *green color.*

• *There are many different types of photosynthetic marine organisms.* The seed-bearing Anthophyta are represented by a few genera of *nearshore plants* such as eelgrass (*Zostera*), surf grass (*Phyllospadix*), marsh grass (*Spartina*), and mangrove trees (genera *Rhizophora* and *Avicennia*). *Macroscopic algae* include *brown algae* (Phaetophyta), *green algae* (Chlorophyta), and *red algae* (Rhodophyta). *Microscopic algae* include *diatoms* and *coccolithophores* (Chrysophyta), and *dinoflagellates* (Pyrrophyta, which are responsible for *red tides*).

• *A thermocline is generally absent in high-latitude (polar) areas, so upwelling can readily occur.* The *availability of solar radiation limits* productivity more than the availability of nutrients. In *low-latitude (tropical) regions,* however, a *strong thermocline* may exist year-round, so the *lack of nutrients limits productivity,* except in areas of upwelling or near coral reefs. In *middle latitude (temperate) regions,* productivity peaks in the spring and fall and is limited by lack of solar radiation in the winter and lack of nutrients in the summer.

• *Radiant energy captured by algae is converted to chemical energy* and passed through the different *trophic levels* of a *biotic community.* It is expended as *mechanical and heat energy* and ultimately becomes biologically useless. Upon death, organisms are *decomposed* to an inorganic form that algae can use again for nutrients.

• *Marine ecosystems are composed of populations of organisms called producers* (which photosynthesize or chemosynthesize), *consumers* (which eat producers), and *decomposers* (which break down detritus). Animals can be categorized as *herbivores* (eat plants), *carnivores* (eat animals), *omnivores* (eat both), or *bacteriovores* (eat bacteria). Through *biogeochemical cycles,* the organisms of a biotic community *cycle nutrients and other chemicals from one form to another.*

• *Feeding strategies* include *suspension* or *filter feeding* (filtering planktonic organisms from seawater), *deposit feeding* (ingesting sediment and detritus), and *carnivorous feeding* (preying directly upon other organisms). On average, *only about 10% of the mass taken in at one feeding level is passed on to the next.* As a result, the *size of individuals increases* but the *number of individuals decreases* with each *trophic level* of a *food chain* or *food web.* Overall, the *total biomass of populations decreases the higher they are in the biomass pyramid.*

• *Marine fisheries harvest standing stocks of populations from various ecosystems,* particularly shallow shelf and coastal waters and areas of upwelling. *Overfishing occurs when adult fish are harvested faster than they can reproduce* and results in the decline of fish populations as well as a reduction of a fishery's *maximum sustainable yield (MSY).* Many fishing practices capture unwanted *bycatch.* Despite the *management of fisheries, many fish stocks worldwide are declining. Wise seafood choices can help* reverse the decline in fish populations.

Key Terms

Autotrophic (p. 390)

Bacteriovore (p. 390)

Biogeochemical cycle (p. 390)

Biological pump (p. 384)

Biomass (p. 371)

Biomass pyramid (p. 394)

Biotic community (p. 389)

Bycatch (p. 397)

Carnivore (p. 390)

Carnivorous feeding (p. 391)

Chemosynthesis (p. 371)

Chlorophyll (p. 372)

Ciguatera (p. 381)

Coccolith (p. 381)

Coccolithophore (p. 381)

Compensation depth for
   photosynthesis (p. 373)

Consumer (p. 390)

Dead zone (p. 389)

Decomposer (p. 390)

Deposit feeding (p. 391)

Detritus (p. 390)

Diatom (p. 381)

Diatomaceous earth (p. 381)

Dinoflagellate (p. 381)

Driftnet (p. 398)

Ecosystem (p. 389)

Electromagnetic spectrum (p. 374)

Euphotic zone (p. 373)

Eutrophic (p. 376)

Eutrophication (p. 389)

Fall bloom (p. 388)

Filter feeding (p. 391)

Fisheries (p. 394)

Fisheries management (p. 398)

Flagella (p. 381)

Food chain (p. 393)

Food web (p. 394)

Gill net (p. 398)

Gross ecological efficiency (p. 392)

Harmful algal bloom (HAB)
   (p. 381)

Herbivore (p. 390)

Heterotrophic (p. 390)

Incidental catch (p. 397)

Isothermal (p. 386)

Marine Mammals Protection
   Act (p. 398)

Maximum sustainable yield
   (MSY) (p. 395)

Oligotrophic (p. 376)

Omnivore (p. 390)

Overfishing (p. 395)

Photosynthesis (p. 371)

Phytoplankton (p. 372)

Plankton net (p. 372)

Review Questions

1. Discuss chemosynthesis as a method of primary productivity. How does it differ from photosynthesis?

2. An important variable in determining the distribution of life in the oceans is the availability of nutrients. How are the following variables related: proximity to the continents, availability of nutrients, and the concentration of life in the oceans?

3. Another important determinant of productivity is the availability of solar radiation. Why is biological productivity relatively low in the tropical open ocean, where the penetration of sunlight is greatest?

4. Discuss the characteristics of the coastal ocean where unusually high concentrations of marine life are found.

5. Why does everything in the ocean at depths below the shallowest surface water take on a blue-green appearance?

6. What factors create the color difference between coastal waters and less-productive open-ocean water? What color is each?

7. Compare the macroscopic algae in terms of color, maximum depth in which they grow, common species, and size.

8. The golden algae include two classes of important phytoplankton. Compare their composition and the structure of their tests and explain their importance in the geologic fossil record.

9. How does paralytic shellfish poisoning (PSP) differ from amnesic shellfish poisoning? What types of microorganisms create each?

10. Describe how a biological pump works. What percentage of organic material from the euphotic zone accumulates on the sea floor?

11. Generally, the productivity in tropical oceans is rather low. What are three environments that are exceptions to this, and what factors contribute to their higher productivity?

12. What conditions create ocean eutrophication (dead zones)? What can be done to limit their spread?

13. Describe the flow of energy through the biotic community and include the forms into which solar radiation is converted. How does this flow differ from the manner in which matter is moved through the ecosystem?

14. Describe the advantage that a top carnivore gains by eating from a food web as compared to a single food chain.

15. When a species is overfished, what changes are there in the standing stock and the maximum sustainable yield? What are some problems with marine fisheries management?

16. Of the following types of seafood on a menu, which is the best choice for supporting sustainable fisheries: (a) farmed salmon, (b) monkfish, (c) orange roughy, (d) Atlantic cod, or (e) Pacific halibut?

Critical Thinking Exercises

1. Compare the biological productivity of polar, temperate, and tropical regions of the oceans. Consider seasonal changes, the development of a thermocline, the availability of nutrients, and solar radiation.

2. What is the average efficiency of energy transfer between trophic levels? Use this efficiency to determine how much phytoplankton mass is required to add 1 gram of new mass to a killer whale, which is a third-level carnivore. Include a diagram that shows the different trophic levels and the relative size and abundance of organisms at different levels. How would your answer change if the efficiency were half the average rate, or twice the average rate?

Oceanography on the Web

Visit the *Essentials of Oceanography* Online Study Guide for Internet resources, including chapter-specific quizzes to test your understanding and Web links to further your exploration of the topics in this chapter.

The *Essentials of Oceanography* Online Study Guide is at
http://www.mygeoscienceplace.com/.

A superbly streamlined shark glides through the ocean.
Sharks like this silky shark (*Carcharhinus falciformis*) have
unique adaptations that make them efficient ocean predators.

"What we are dealing with here is a perfect engine, an eating machine. It's really a miracle of evolution. All this machine does is swim and eat and make little sharks, and that's all."

— Matt Hooper,
a character in Peter Benchley's film Jaws (1975)

14 ANIMALS OF THE PELAGIC ENVIRONMENT

CHAPTER AT A GLANCE

- Pelagic organisms employ a variety of adaptations to help them survive in the marine environment, including swim bladders, schooling, symbiosis, and, for most deep-water nekton, bioluminescence.

- Marine (and most land) mammals share the following characteristics: they all have warm blood, breathe air, have hair, bear live young, and suckle their young.

- Marine mammals include orders Carnivora (sea otters, polar bears, and pinnipeds—walrus, seals, sea lions, and fur seals), Sirenia (manatees and dugongs), and Cetacea (whales, dolphins, and porpoises).

Pelagic organisms live suspended in seawater (not on the ocean floor) and comprise the vast majority of the ocean's **biomass**.[1] Phytoplankton and other photosynthesizing microbes live within the sunlit surface waters of the ocean and are the food source for nearly all other marine life. As a result, many marine animals live in surface waters so they can be close to their food supply. One of the most important challenges facing many marine organisms is to stay afloat and not sink below surface waters into the immense depth of the oceans.

Phytoplankton and other photosynthesizing microbes depend primarily on their small size to provide a high degree of frictional resistance to sinking. Most animals, however, are more dense than ocean water and have less surface area per unit of body mass. Therefore, they tend to sink more rapidly than phytoplankton.

To remain in surface waters where the food supply is greatest, pelagic marine animals must increase their buoyancy or swim continually. Animals apply one or both of these strategies in a wonderful variety of adaptations and lifestyles.

14.1 How Are Marine Organisms Able to Stay Above the Ocean Floor?

Some animals increase their buoyancy to remain in near-surface waters. They may have containers of gas, which significantly reduce their average density, or they may have soft bodies void of hard, high-density parts. Larger animals often have the ability to swim but if their bodies are denser than seawater, they must exert more energy to propel themselves through the water.

Use of Gas Containers

Air is approximately 1000 times less dense than water at sea level, so even a small amount of air inside an organism can dramatically increase its buoyancy. Generally, animals use either a rigid gas container or a swim bladder to achieve *neutral buoyancy*, which means the amount of air in their bodies regulates their density, so they can remain at a particular depth.

RIGID GAS CONTAINERS Some animals, such as the cephalopods (*cephalo* = the head, *poda* = a foot), have rigid gas containers in their bodies. For instance, the genus *Nautilus* has an external shell,

---

[1]Remember that *biomass* is the mass of living organisms.

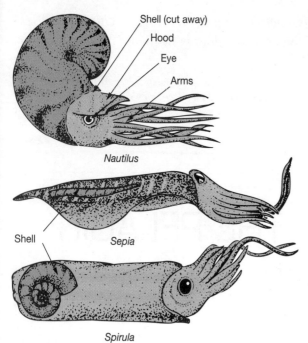

Nautilus

Shell (cut away)
Hood
Eye
Arms

Shell

Sepia

Spirula

FIGURE 14.1 Gas containers in cephalopods. The *Nautilus* has an external chambered shell, while *Sepia* and *Spirula* have rigid internal chambered structures that can be filled with gas to provide buoyancy.

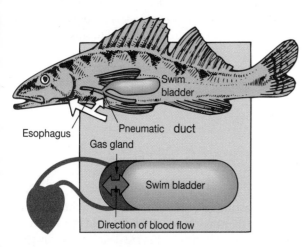

Swim bladder

Esophagus

Pneumatic duct
Gas gland

Swim bladder

Direction of blood flow

FIGURE 14.2 Swim bladder. Some bony fish have a swim bladder, which is connected to the esophagus by the pneumatic duct, allowing air to be added or removed rapidly. In fish with no pneumatic duct, all gas must be added or removed through the blood, which requires more time.

KEY CONCEPT

Marine organisms use a variety of adaptations to stay within the sunlit surface waters, such as rigid gas containers, swim bladders, spines to increase their surface area, soft bodies, or the ability to swim.

---

whereas the cuttlefish *Sepia*[2] and deep-water squid *Spirula* have an internal chambered structure (Figure 14.1).

Because the pressure in their air chambers is always 1 kilogram per square centimeter (1 atmosphere, or 14.7 pounds per square inch), the *Nautilus* must stay above a depth of approximately 500 meters (1640 feet) to prevent collapse of its chambered shell. The *Nautilus*, therefore, rarely ventures below about 250 meters (800 feet).

SWIM BLADDERS   Alternatively, some slow-moving fish use an internal organ called a **swim bladder** (Figure 14.2) to achieve neutral buoyancy. Very active swimmers (such as tuna) or fish that live on the bottom, however, do not usually have a swim bladder because they don't have a problem maintaining their positions in the water column.

A change in depth either expands or contracts the swim bladder, so fish must remove or add gas to maintain a constant volume. In some fish, a pneumatic duct connects the swim bladder to the esophagus, so these fish can quickly add or remove gases through the duct. In other fish without the pneumatic duct, the gases of the swim bladder must be added or removed more slowly by an interchange with the blood, so they cannot withstand rapid changes in depth.

The composition of gases in the swim bladders of shallow-water fish is similar to that of the atmosphere. At the surface, the concentration of oxygen in the swim bladder is about 20% and as depth increases, the oxygen concentration increases to more than 90%. Fish with swim bladders have been captured from as deep as 7000 meters (23,000 feet), where the pressure is 700 kilograms per square centimeter (700 atmospheres, or 10,300 pounds per square inch). Pressure this high compresses the gas to a density of 0.7 gram per cubic centimeter.[3] This is approximately the same density as fat and as a result, many deep-water fish have special organs for buoyancy that are filled with fat instead of compressed gas.

Ability to Float

Floating animals range in size from microscopic shrimplike organisms to relatively large species, such as the familiar jellyfish. These floating organisms—collectively called *zooplankton*—comprise the second largest biomass in the ocean after phytoplankton and other photosynthesizing microbes. Microscopic forms of zooplankton usually have a hard shell called a **test** (*testa* = shell). Many larger forms have soft, gelatinous bodies with little if any hard tissue, which reduces their density and allows them to stay afloat.

Microscopic zooplankton are incredibly abundant in the ocean. They are primary consumers because they eat microscopic phytoplankton, the primary producers. Thus, many zooplankton are herbivores. Others are omnivores because they eat other zooplankton in addition to phytoplankton. Most types of microscopic zooplankton have adaptations to increase the surface area of their bodies (or shells) so they can remain in the sunlit surface waters near their food source.[4]

In addition, some organisms produce low-density fats or oils to stay afloat. Many zooplankton, for example, produce tiny droplets of oil to help maintain neutral or near-neutral buoyancy. Another example is sharks, which have a very large, oil-rich liver to help reduce their density and float more easily.

---

[2]Many species of cephalopods have an inking response. In fact, the ink of *Sepia* was used as writing ink (with the brand name Sepia) before alternatives were developed.

[3]For comparison, note that the density of water is 1.0 gram per cubic centimeter.

[4]For a more complete discussion of how increased surface area affects an organism's ability to float, see Chapter 12.

FIGURE 14.3 Radiolarians. Scanning electron micrographs of various radiolarians: **(a)** *Euphysetta elegans* (magnified 280 times), **(b)** *Anthocyrtidium ophirense* (magnified 230 times), **(c)** *Larcospira quadrangula* (magnified 190 times), and **(d)** *Heliodiscus asteriscus* (magnified 200 times).

(a) *Euphysetta elegans, x280*

(b) *Anthocyrtidium ophirense, x230*

Ability to Swim

Many larger pelagic animals such as fish and marine mammals can maintain their position in the water column by swimming and can also swim easily against currents. These organisms are called *nekton* (*nektos* = swimming). Because of their swimming ability, some of these organisms undertake long migrations.

The Diversity of Planktonic Animals

Diversity in planktonic marine animals stems from a shifting balance between competition for food and avoidance of predators. As a result, a wide variety of planktonic animals inhabit the oceans.

EXAMPLES OF MICROSCOPIC ZOOPLANKTON Three of the most important groups of microscopic zooplankton are the radiolarians, foraminifers (both of which are discussed in more detail in Chapter 4, "Marine Sediments"), and copepods.

Radiolarians (*radio* = a spoke or ray) are single-celled, microscopic protozoans (*proto* = first, *zoa* = animal) that build their hard shells (*tests*) out of silica (Figure 14.3). Their tests have intricate ornamentation including long projections. Although the spikes and spines appear to be a defense mechanism against predators, they increase the test's surface area so the organism won't sink through the water column.

(c) *Larcospira quadrangula, x190*

(d) *Heliodiscus asteriscus, x200*

Foraminifers (*foramen* = an opening) are microscopic to (barely) macroscopic single-celled protozoans. While the most abundant types of foraminifers are planktonic, the most diverse (in terms of number of species) are benthic. Foraminifers produce a hard test made of calcium carbonate (Figure 14.4) that is segmented or chambered with a prominent opening in one end. The tests of both radiolarians and foraminifers are common components of deep-sea sediment.

Copepods (*kope* = oar, *poda* = a foot) are microscopic shrimplike animals of the subphylum Crustacea, which also includes shrimps, crabs, and lobsters. Like other crustaceans, copepods have a hard exoskeleton (*exo* = outside) and a segmented body with jointed legs (Figure 14.5). Most copepods have forked tails and distinct and elaborate antennae.

More than 7500 species of copepods exist, with most possessing special adaptations for filtering tiny floating food particles from water. Some copepods are herbivores that eat algae, others are carnivores that eat other zooplankton, and still others are parasitic.

All copepods lay eggs, which are sometimes carried in egg sacs attached to the abdomen but generally released into seawater, where they hatch in about a day. Their rapid reproduction allows great numbers of copepods to occur wherever favorable conditions—generally an abundance of food, which is mostly algae—exist.

Although copepods are small (only a few species are larger than 1 mm or 0.04 inch), they are extremely numerous in the ocean. They are so abundant, in fact, that they are one of the most numerically dominant types of multicelled organisms on the planet. As such, copepods comprise the majority of the ocean's

FIGURE 14.4 Foraminifers. Photomicrograph of various species of foraminifers, the largest of which is 1 millimeter (0.04 inch) long. These pelagic foraminifers were collected from the Ontong Java Plateau in the western Pacific Ocean.

(a)

(b)

(c)

(d)

FIGURE 14.5 Copepods. Line drawings of various copepods (shown many times their actual size) from Wilhelm Giesbrecht's 1892 book on the flora and fauna of the Gulf of Naples. **(a)** The adult female *Sapphirina auronitens* carries a pair of lobe-like egg sacs. **(b)** Copulating pair of *Oncaea conifera*. **(c)** *Calocalanus pavo* showing elaborate feathery appendages that are characteristic of warm-water species. **(d)** *Copilia vitrea* uses its appendages to cling to large particles in the water column or to larger zooplankton.

zooplankton biomass and are a vital link in many marine food webs between phytoplankton (producers) and larger species such as plankton-eating fish.

EXAMPLES OF MACROSCOPIC ZOOPLANKTON Many types of zooplankton are large enough to be seen without the aid of a microscope. Two of the most important groups of macroscopic zooplankton are krill and various types of cnidarians.

Krill, which means "young fry of fish" in Norwegian, are actually in the subphylum Crustacea (genus *Euphausia*) and resemble minishrimp or large copepods (Figure 14.6). There are more than 1500 species of krill, most of which achieve a length no longer than 5 centimeters (2 inches). They are abundant near Antarctica and form a critical link in the food web there, supplying food for many organisms from sea birds to the largest whales in the world.

Cnidarians [*cnid* = nematocyst (*nemato* = thread, *cystis* = bladder)], which were formerly known as *coelenterates* (*coel* = hollow, *enteron* = the intestines), have soft bodies that are more than 95% water and tentacles armed with stinging cells called *nematocysts*. Macroscopic zooplankton that are cnidarians fall into one of two basic groups: the *hydrozoans* and the *scyphozoans* (jellyfish).

Hydrozoan (*hydro* = water, *zoa* = animal) *cnidarians* are represented in all oceans by the Portuguese man-of-war (genus *Physalia*) and the "by-the-wind sailor" (genus *Velella*). Their gas chambers, called *pneumatophores* (*pneumato* = breath, *phoros* = bearing), serve as floats and sails that allow the wind to push them across the ocean surface (Figure 14.7a, *left*). Sometimes the wind pushes large numbers of these organisms toward a beach, where they can wash ashore and die. In the living organism, a colony of tiny individuals is suspended beneath the float. Portuguese man-of-war tentacles may be many meters long and, because they are armed with nematocysts, they have been known to inflict a painful and occasionally dangerous neurotoxin poisoning in humans.

Jellyfish, or **scyphozoan** (*skyphos* = cup, *zoa* = animal) *cnidarians*, have a bell-shaped body with a fringe of tentacles and a mouth at the end of a clapper-like extension hanging beneath the bell-shaped float (Figure 14.7). Ranging in size from nearly microscopic to 2 meters (6.6 feet) in diameter, most jellyfish are less than 0.5 meter (1.6 feet) in diameter. The largest jellyfish can have tentacles as long as 60 meters (200 feet).

Jellyfish move by muscular contraction. Water enters the cavity under the bell and is forced out when muscles that circle the bell contract, jetting the animals ahead in short spurts. To allow the animal to swim generally in an upward direction, light-sensitive or gravity-sensitive organs exist around the outer edge of the bell. The ability to orient is important because jellyfish feed by swimming to the surface and sinking slowly through the rich surface waters.

Other types of macroscopic zooplankton include tunicates and salps (barrel-shaped, often colonial organisms), ctenophores (comb jellies or sea gooseberries), and chaetognaths (arrowworms).

EXAMPLES OF SWIMMING ORGANISMS Swimming, or *nektonic*, organisms include invertebrate squids, fish, sea turtles, and marine mammals.

Swimming squid include the common squid (genus *Loligo*), flying squid (*Ommastrephes*), and giant squid (*Architeuthis*), all of which are active predators of fish. Most squid possess long, slender bodies with paired fins (Figure 14.8) and must remain active to stay afloat. However, a few species such as *Sepia* and *Spirula* (see Figure 14.1) have a hollow gas-filled chamber in their bodies to help them remain afloat and so they can be less active.

Squid can swim about as fast as any fish their size and do so by drawing water into their body cavity and then expelling the water out through their siphon,

FIGURE 14.6 Krill. Krill that has washed up on a beach in Antarctica and close-up view of *Meganyctiphanes norvegica*, which is about 3.8 centimeters (1.5 inches) long (*inset*).

(a)

(b)

FIGURE 14.7 Planktonic cnidarians. (a) Line drawings of a Portuguese man-of-war (*Physalia*) (*left*) and a typical medusa jellyfish (*right*). (b) Photo of a medusa jellyfish (*Cyanea capillata*), which has a bell that is 50 centimeters (20 inches) wide.

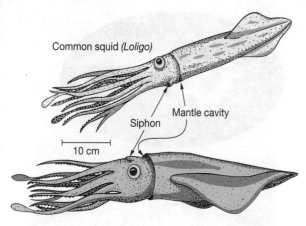

Common squid (Loligo)

Mantle cavity

Siphon

10 cm

Flying squid (Ommastrephes)

FIGURE 14.8 Squid. Squid move by trapping water in their mantle cavity between their soft body and penlike shell. They then jettison the water through their siphon for rapid propulsion.

WEB VIDEO

Giant Squid Encounter

propelling themselves backward. To capture prey, squid use two long arms with pads containing suction cups at the ends (Figure 14.8). Eight shorter arms with suckers convey the prey to the mouth, where it is crushed by a mouthpiece that resembles a parrot's beak.

In fish, locomotion occurs when a wave of lateral body curvature passes from the front of the fish to the back. This is achieved by the alternate contraction and relaxation of muscle segments, called *myomeres* (*myo* = muscle, *merous* = parted), along the sides of the body. The backward pressure of the fish's body and fins produced by the movement of this wave provides the forward thrust (Figure 14.9).

FIN DESIGNS IN FISH Most active swimming fish use two sets of paired fins— *pelvic fins* and *pectoral* (*pectoralis* = breast) *fins*—to turn, brake, and balance (Figure 14.9). When not in use, these fins can be folded against the body. Vertical fins, both *dorsal* (*dorsum* = back) and *anal*, serve primarily as stabilizers.

The fin that is most commonly used to propel high-speed fish is the tail fin, which is called the *caudal* (*cauda* = tail) *fin*. Caudal fins flare vertically to increase the surface area available to develop thrust against the water.[5] The increased surface area also increases frictional drag. The efficiency of the design of a caudal fin depends on its shape, which is one of the five basic forms illustrated in Figure 14.10 and keyed by letter to the following descriptions:

a) *Rounded fins* are flexible and useful in accelerating and maneuvering at slow speeds.

b) and c) *Truncate fins* (b) and *forked fins* (c) are found on faster fish; the fins are somewhat flexible for better propulsion but are also used for maneuvering.

d) *Lunate fins* are found on fast-cruising fish such as tuna, marlin, and swordfish; the fins are very rigid and useless for maneuverability but very efficient for propulsion.

e) *Heterocercal* (*hetero* = uneven, *cercal* = tail) *fins* are asymmetrical, with most of their mass and surface area in the upper lobe. Sharks have a heterocercal

Alternate contraction and relaxation of the myomeres sends a wave of body curvature back along the body to produce a forward thrust.

Caudal fin

Soft dorsal fin

Spiny dorsal fin

Anal fin

Myomeres

Pelvic fin

Lateral line

Operculum (gill covering)

Pectoral fin

FIGURE 14.9 Swimming motion and general features of fish. Fish send a wave of body curvature along their bodies to produce a forward thrust (*left*). General features of fish (*right*), with the major fins labeled.

[5]This is equivalent to humans donning swimming fins on their feet to enable them to swim more efficiently.

FIGURE 14.10 Caudal fin shapes. **(a)** Rounded fin on a blue-face angel (other examples: sculpin, flounder). **(b)** Truncate fin on a gray angelfish (other examples: salmon, bass). **(c)** Forked fin on a yellowfin doctorfish (other examples: herring, goatfish). **(d)** Lunate fin on a striped marlin (other examples: bluefish, tuna). **(e)** Heterocercal fin on a gray reef shark (other examples: many other types of sharks).

fin, which produces significant lift and is necessary because sharks have no swim bladder and tend to sink when they stop moving. In fact, the fundamental body design of sharks has many adaptations to compensate for the shark's negative buoyancy. The pectoral (chest) fins, for example, are large and flat and positioned so they function like airplane wings to lift the front of the shark's body, balancing the rear lift supplied by its heterocercal caudal fin. Although the shark gains tremendous lift from this adaptation of its pectoral fins, it sacrifices maneuverability. This is why sharks tend to swim in broad circles—like a circling airplane—and do not make sharp turns while swimming.

> **KEY CONCEPT**
> Fish use their fins for swimming and staying afloat within the water column. The fin that provides the most thrust is the caudal (tail) fin, which can have a variety of shapes depending on the lifestyle of the fish.

14.2   What Adaptations Do Pelagic Organisms Possess for Seeking Prey?

Pelagic organisms possess several adaptations that are designed to enhance their ability to seek and capture food. These adaptations include mobility (lunging versus cruising), swimming speed, body temperature, and specially designed circulatory systems. In addition, deep-water nekton have some unique adaptations to help them succeed in capturing prey in their world of darkness.

Mobility: Lungers versus Cruisers

Some fish wait patiently for prey and exert themselves only in short bursts as they lunge at the prey. Others cruise relentlessly through the water, seeking prey. A marked difference occurs in the musculature of fish that use these different styles of obtaining food.

For example, **lungers** (such as the grouper shown in Figure 14.11a) sit and wait for prey to come close by. Lungers have truncate caudal fins for speed and maneuverability, and almost all their muscle tissue is white.

14.1 OCEANS AND PEOPLE

SOME MYTHS (AND FACTS) ABOUT SHARKS

Sharks (Figure 14A) are the fish humans most fear. Their strength, large size, sharp teeth, and unpredictable nature are enough to keep some people from *ever* entering the ocean. The publicity generated by the occasional shark attack on humans has led to many myths about sharks, including the following:

- *Myth #1: All sharks are dangerous.* Of the world's 370 shark species, 80% are unable to hurt people or rarely encounter people. The largest shark is the whale shark (*Rhincodon typus*), which reaches lengths of up to 15 meters (50 feet) but eats only plankton and so is not considered dangerous.

- *Myth #2: Sharks are voracious eaters that must eat continuously.* Like other large animals, sharks eat periodically depending upon their metabolism and the availability of food. Humans are not a primary food source of any shark, and many large sharks prefer the higher fat content of seals and sea lions.

- *Myth #3: Most people attacked by a shark are killed.* Of every 100 people attacked by sharks, 85 survive. Many large sharks commonly attack by biting their prey to immobilize it before trying to eat it. Consequently, many potential prey escape and survive. The most common targets of shark attacks are surfers (49%), swimmers/ waders (29%), divers/ snorkelers (15%), and kayakers (6%). Most shark encounters with humans are investigative, not predatory.

- *Myth #4: Many people are killed by sharks each year.* The chances of a person being killed by a shark are quite low (Table 14A). Sharks kill an average of only 5 to 15 people worldwide each year. Humans, on the other hand, kill as many as 100 million sharks a year (mostly as bycatch from fishing activities). Compared to many other fish, sharks have low reproduction rates and

FIGURE 14A Great white shark (*Carcharodon carcharias*).

grow slowly, which may result in many sharks being designated as endangered species in the future.

- *Myth #5: The great white shark is a common, abundant species found off most beaches.* Great white sharks are relatively uncommon predators that prefer cooler waters. At most beaches, great whites are rarely encountered.

- *Myth #6: Sharks are not found in freshwater.* A specialized osmoregulatory system enables some species (such as the bull shark) to cope with dramatic changes in salinity, from the high salinity of seawater to the low salinity of freshwater rivers and lakes.

- *Myth #7: All sharks need to swim constantly.* Some sharks can remain at rest for long periods on the bottom and obtain enough oxygen by opening and closing their mouths to pump oxygen through their gills. Typically, sharks

TABLE 14A	TYPES AND NUMBERS OF OCCURRENCES IN THE UNITED STATES

Occurrence to people in the U.S.	Average number per year
Transportation fatalities	42,000
Death involving slipping, tripping, or stumbling	565
Struck by lightning	352
Killed by lightning	50
Bitten by a squirrel in New York City	88
Killed by a dog bite	26
Killed by a snake bite	12
Bitten by a shark	10
Killed by a shark	0.4

swim very slowly—cruising speeds are less than 9 kilometers (6 miles) per hour—but they can swim at bursts of over 37 kilometers (23 miles) per hour.

- *Myth #8: Sharks have poor vision.* The lens of a shark's eye is up to seven times more powerful than that of a human's. Sharks can even distinguish color.
- *Myth #9: Eating shark meat makes one aggressive.* There is no indication that eating shark meat will alter a person's

temperament. The firm texture, white flesh, low fat content, and mild taste of shark meat have made it a favorite seafood in many countries.

- *Myth #10: No one would ever want to enter water filled with sharks.* Long regarded with fear and suspicion, sharks have more recently been viewed as skilled predators that are vitally important to the health of ocean ecosystems. Diving tours specializing in close

encounters with sharks are becoming increasingly popular.

Today I could not, for instance, portray the shark as a villain, especially not as a mindless omnivore that attacks boats and humans with reckless abandon. No, the shark in an updated Jaws could not be the villain; it would have to be written as the victim, for, world-wide, sharks are much more the oppressed than the oppressors.

—Peter Benchley (2005),
author of Jaws

On the other hand, **cruisers** (such as the tuna shown in Figure 14.11b) actively seek prey. Less than half of a cruiser's muscle tissue is white; most is red.

What is the significance of red versus white muscle tissue? Red muscle tissue contains fibers that are 25 to 50 microns in diameter (0.01 to 0.02 inch), whereas the fibers in white muscle tissue are 135 microns (0.05 inch) and contain much lower concentrations of **myoglobin** (*myo* = muscle, *globus* = sphere), a red pigment with an affinity for oxygen. Moreover, red muscle tissue supplies a much greater amount of oxygen and supports a much higher metabolic rate than white tissue. This is why cruisers have so much red muscle tissue: it allows them to have the endurance needed to support their active lifestyle.

Lungers, on the other hand, need very little red tissue because they do not move continually. Instead, they need white tissue, which fatigues much more rapidly than red tissue, for quick bursts of speed to capture prey. Cruisers use white tissue, too, for short periods of acceleration while on the attack.

STUDENTS SOMETIMES ASK...

Do sharks ever get cancer?

Legend has it that sharks don't get cancer, making the creature's cartilage popular in the alternative health market as a cure for the disease. However, researchers who study tumors in animals have recently reported that sharks and their close relatives—skates and rays—can and do get cancer.

Swimming Speed

Although rapid swimming consumes much energy, it can help organisms capture prey. Fish normally swim slowly when cruising, fast when hunting for prey, and fastest of all when trying to escape from predators.

Generally, when comparing fish of similar shapes, the larger the fish, the faster it can swim. For tuna, well adapted for sustained cruising and short, high-speed

FIGURE 14.11 Feeding styles of lungers and cruisers. (a) Lungers, such as this tiger grouper, sit patiently on the bottom and capture prey with quick, short lunges. **(b)** Cruisers, such as these yellowfin tuna, swim constantly in search of prey and capture it with short periods of high-speed swimming.

(a)

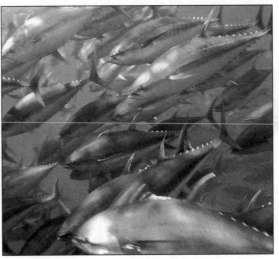

(b)

bursts, cruising speed averages about three body lengths per second. They can, however, maintain a maximum speed of about 10 body lengths per second, but only for about one second. Remarkably, yellowfin tuna (*Thunnus albacares*) have been clocked at 74.6 kilometers (46 miles) per hour! Even though this speed is more than 20 body lengths per second, the tuna could maintain it for only a *fraction* of a second. Theoretically, a 4-meter (13-foot) bluefin tuna (*Thunnus thynnus*) can reach speeds up to about 144 kilometers (90 miles) per hour.[6]

Like fish, many of the toothed whales are fast swimmers, too. For instance, spotted dolphins of the genus *Stenella* have been clocked at 40 kilometers (25 miles) per hour, and killer whales may exceed 55 kilometers (34 miles) per hour during short bursts.

Cold-Blooded versus Warm-Blooded Organisms

Fish are mostly **cold-blooded**, or **poikilothermic** (*poikilos* = spotted, *theromos* = heat), so their body temperatures are nearly the same as their environment. Usually, these fish are not fast swimmers. The mackerel (*Scomber*), yellowtail (*Seriola*), and bonito (*Sarda*), on the other hand, are indeed fast swimmers. They also have body temperatures that are 1.3, 1.4, and 1.8°C (2.3, 2.5, and 3.2°F), respectively, higher than the surrounding seawater.

Mackerel sharks (genera *Lamna* and *Isurus*) and Tuna (genera *Thunnus*) have body temperatures much higher than their environment. Bluefin tuna can maintain a body temperature of 30 to 32°C (86 to 90°F) regardless of the water temperature, which is characteristic of organisms that are **warm-blooded**, or **homeothermic** (*homeo* = alike, *thermos* = heat). Although these tuna are more commonly found in warmer water, where the temperature difference between fish and water is no more than 5°C (9°F), body temperatures of 30°C (86°F) have been measured in bluefin tuna swimming in 7°C (45°F) water.

Why do these fish exert so much energy to maintain their body temperatures at high levels, when other fish do quite well with ambient body temperatures? It may be that for cruisers, any adaptation (high temperature and high metabolic rate) that increases the power output of their muscle tissue helps them seek and capture prey.

Adaptations of Deep-Water Nekton

Living below the surface water but still above the ocean floor are deep-water nektonic species—mostly various species of fish—that are specially adapted to the deep-water environment, where it is very still and completely dark. Their food source is either **detritus** (*detritus* = to lessen)—dead and decaying organic matter including waste products that slowly sink downward from surface waters—or each other. The lack of abundant food limits the *number* of organisms (total biomass) and the *size* of these organisms. As a result, small populations of these organisms exist and most individuals are less than 30 centimeters (1 foot) long. Many have low metabolic rates to conserve energy, too.

These **deep-sea fish** (Figure 14.12) have special adaptations to efficiently find and collect food. They have good sensory devices, for example, such as long antennae or sensitive lateral lines that can detect movement of other organisms within the water column.

Well over half of deep-sea fish and even some deep-water species of shrimp and squid can **bioluminesce** (*bios* = life, *lumen* = light, *esc* = becoming), which means they can produce light biologically and "glow in the dark." Fireflies and glowworms are well-known animals on land that have bioluminescent capability. Approximately 80% of bioluminescent organisms have light-producing cells called **photophores** (*photo* = light, *phoros* = bearing), which are glandular cells

FIGURE 14.12 Deep-sea fish. Line drawings of a **(a)** hatchet fish, **(b)** lantern fish, **(c)** stomiatoid, **(d)** hatchet fish, **(e)** gulper eel, and **(f)** female deep-sea anglerfish, with attached parasitic male **(g)**. Photo of a female deep-sea anglerfish (*Himantolophus danae*) **(h)** that washed ashore in Carlsbad, California, in 2001.

[6]Imagine how difficult it would be to clock a bluefin tuna in the ocean at this speed!

containing luminescent bacteria surrounded by dark pigments. Some photophores even contain lenses to amplify the emission of light.

Bioluminescence is produced when molecules of *luciferin* (*lucifer* = light bringing) are excited and emit photons of light in the presence of oxygen. Only a 1% loss of energy is required to produce this illumination.

In a world of darkness, the ability to bioluminesce is useful for a variety of purposes, including:

- Searching for food items in the dark.
- Attracting prey (for example, the deep-sea anglerfish in Figure 14.12f uses its specially modified dorsal fin as a bioluminescent lure).
- Staking out territory by constantly patrolling an area.
- Communicating or seeking a mate by sending signals.
- Escaping from predators by using a flash of light to temporarily blind or distract them.
- Avoiding predators by use of a "burglar alarm" by attracting unwanted attention with brilliant displays of bioluminescence.
- Camouflaging by using belly lights to match the color and intensity of dim filtered sunlight from above and obliterate a telltale shadow. This is known as **counterillumination**.

To take advantage of bioluminescent light, many deep-sea fish species have large and sensitive eyes—perhaps 100 times more sensitive to light than human eyes—that enable them to see potential prey. To avoid being prey, most species are dark in color so that they blend into the environment. Still other species are blind and rely on senses such as smell to track down prey.

Other adaptations that various deep-sea fish species possess include large sharp teeth, expandable bodies to accommodate large food items, hinged jaws that can unlock to open widely, and mouths that are huge in proportion to their bodies (Figure 14.13). These adaptations allow deep-sea fish to ingest species

STUDENTS SOMETIMES ASK ...

Those deep-sea fish look frightening. Do they ever come to the surface? Are they related to piranhas?

They never come to the surface, and that is fortunate for us because they are vicious predators. They are only distantly related to piranhas (they are within the same group of bony fish), but their similarly-adapted, large, sharp teeth may be a good example of *convergent evolution*: the evolution of similar characteristics on different organisms independent of one another yet adapted to the same problem (in this case, a low food supply).

WEB VIDEO

Bioluminescent
Organisms

KEY CONCEPT
Adaptations of pelagic organisms for seeking prey include mobility (lunging versus cruising), high swimming speed, and high body temperature. Deep-water nekton exhibit a host of unusual adaptations—including bioluminescence—that allow them to survive in deeper waters.

(b)

FIGURE 14.13 Adaptations of deep-sea fish. (a) Large teeth, hinged jaw, and swallowing mechanism of the deep-sea viper fish *Chauliodus sloani*. **(b)** Ingestion capability of *Chiasmodon niger*, with a curled-up fish in its stomach that is longer than it is.

10 cm

(a)

that are larger than they are and to process food efficiently whenever it is captured.

14.3 What Adaptations Do Pelagic Organisms Possess to Avoid Being Prey?

Many animals have unique adaptations to avoid being captured and eaten. Examples of adaptations that organisms use to enhance their survival include schooling and symbiosis.

Schooling

The term **school** refers to large numbers of fish, squid, or shrimp that form well-defined social groupings. Although vast populations of phytoplankton and zooplankton may be highly concentrated in certain areas of the ocean, they are not usually referred to as schools.

The number of individuals in a school can vary from a few larger predaceous fish (such as bluefin tuna) to hundreds of thousands of small filter feeders (such as anchovies). Within the school, individuals move in the same direction and are evenly spaced. Spacing is probably maintained through visual contact and, in the case of fish, by use of the lateral line system (see Figure 14.9) that detects vibrations of swimming neighbors. The school can turn abruptly or reverse direction as individuals at the head or rear of the school assume leadership positions (Figure 14.14).

What are the advantages of schooling? One advantage is that during spawning, schooling ensures that there will be males to release sperm to fertilize the eggs released into the water or deposited on the bottom by females. Another advantage is that schools of smaller fish can invade the territory of larger aggressive species and feed there because the "owner" of the territory can never chase away the whole school. The most important function of schooling in small fish, however, is protection from predators.

It may seem illogical that schooling would be protective. For instance, schooling creates tighter groupings of organisms so that any predator lunging into a school would surely catch something, just as land predators run a herd of grazing animals until one weakens and becomes a meal. So, aren't the smaller fish making it easier for the predators by forming a large target?

Scientists who study fish behavior suggest that schooling does indeed serve to protect a group of organisms based on strategies that give them "safety in numbers" much like flocking in birds. In many parts of the marine environment such as the open ocean where there is no place to hide, schooling has the following advantages:

1. When members of a species form schools, they reduce the percentage of ocean volume in which a cruising predator might find one of their kind.

2. When a predator encounters a large school, it is less likely to consume the entire unit than if it encounters a small school or an individual.

3. The school may appear as a single large and dangerous opponent to the potential predator and prevent some attacks.

FIGURE 14.14 Schooling. A school of soldier fish near a reef in the Maldives, Indian Ocean. Schooling increases chances of survival, and more than half of all fish species are known to join schools during at least a portion of their lives.

4. Predators may find the continually changing position and direction of movement of fish within the school confusing, making attack particularly difficult for predators, which can attack only one fish at a time.

In addition, the fact that more than half of all fish species join schools during at least a portion of their lives suggests that schooling enhances survival of species, especially for those with no other means of defense. Schooling may also help fish swim greater distances than individuals because each schooling fish gets a boost from the vortex created by the fish swimming in front of it.

Recently, a new ocean predator has developed a method to take advantage of the schooling behavior of fish. Human fishers have developed nets large enough to encircle whole schools of fish, which is very efficient at catching fish but has led to the decline of many fish stocks (see Chapter 13).

Symbiosis

Many marine organisms enter into relationships with other organisms to help them survive. One such relationship is **symbiosis** (*sym* = together, *bios* = life), which occurs when two or more organisms associate in a way that benefits at least one of them. There are three main types of symbiotic relationships: commensalism, mutualism, and parasitism.

In **commensalism** (*commensal* = sharing a meal, *ism* = a process), a smaller or less dominant participant benefits without harming its host, which affords subsistence or protection to the other. A remora, for example, attaches itself to a shark or another fish to obtain food and transportation, generally without harming its host (Figure 14.15a).

(a)

(b)

(c)

FIGURE 14.15 Types of symbiosis. (a) Commensalism occurs when an organism benefits without harming its host, such as these remoras attached to a lemon shark. **(b)** Mutualism occurs when both participants benefit, such as this cinnamon clown fish and sea anemone. **(c)** Parasitism occurs when one participant benefits at the expense of the other, such as this isopod that has attached itself to the head of a whitetip soldierfish.

In **mutualism** (*mutuus* = borrowed, *ism* = a process), both participants benefit. For example, the stinging tentacles of the sea anemone protect the clown fish (Figure 14.15b), and the clown fish, which is small but aggressive, chases away any fish that tries to feed on the anemone itself. In addition, the clown fish helps clean the anemone and may even supply scraps of food. Remarkably, clown fish are not stung by the anemone because clown fish have a protective agent in the mucus that coats their bodies.

In **parasitism** (*parasitos* = a person who eats at someone else's table, *ism* = a process), one participant (the parasite) benefits at the expense of the other (the host). Many fish are hosts to isopods, which attach to the fish and derive their nutrition from the body fluids of the fish, thereby robbing the host of some of its energy supply (Figure 14.15c). Usually, the parasite does not rob enough energy to kill the host because if the host dies, so does the parasite.

Recently, symbiosis had been discovered to be an important component that drives evolution. For example, the sequencing of the genome of a species of diatom reveals that it apparently acquired new genes by engulfing microbial neighbors. The research suggests that early on in the evolution of diatoms, the most significant acquisition was an algal cell that provided the diatom with photosynthetic machinery.

Other Adaptations

Marine animals exhibit a variety of behaviors that serve as defensive mechanisms to help them ward off predators—or to be more successful predators themselves. These include using speed, secreting poisons, and mimicry of other poisonous or distasteful species. Others use transparency, camouflage, or countershading, as discussed in Chapter 12.

14.4 What Characteristics Do Marine Mammals Possess?

Marine mammals include some of the largest, best known, and most charismatic animals in the sea, such as seals, sea lions, manatees, porpoises, dolphins, and whales.

Although all marine mammals have an aquatic existence, their ancestors were land animals. For example, a series of striking fossil discoveries of ancient whales in Pakistan, India, and Egypt provide strong evidence that whales evolved from mammals on land about 50 million years ago. Some whale ancestors had small, unusable hind legs, suggesting that the land mammal predecessor had no need for its hind legs when it developed a large paddle-shaped structure for a tail used to swim through water. Other fossils show a remarkable progression of skeletal adaptations for an increasingly aquatic existence, such as the migration of the blowhole (nostrils) toward the top of the head, upper vertebrae that become increasingly fused, shrinking hip and ankle structures, and jawbone and ear components designed for underwater hearing. Additional lines of evidence—including DNA analysis of modern whales and a host of anatomical similarities between land and marine mammals—confirm the evolution of whales from a hippopotamus-like land-dwelling ancestor.

The geologic record shows that life on land evolved from marine organisms millions of years ago. Why would a land mammal migrate back to the sea? One hypothesis suggests that they may have returned to the sea because of more abundant food sources. Another is that the extinction of many large marine predators that occurred at the same time as the demise of the dinosaurs allowed mammals to expand into a new environment: the sea.

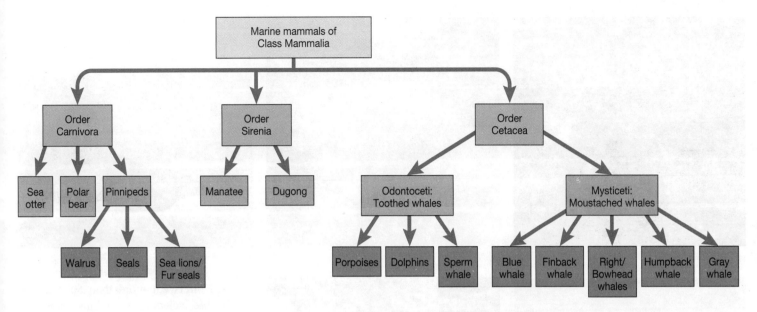

FIGURE 14.16 Major groups of marine mammals.
Organizational chart showing the taxonomic relationships of the various groups of marine mammals, including representative examples.

Mammalian Characteristics

All organisms in class Mammalia (including marine mammals) share the following characteristics:

- They are warm-blooded.
- They breathe air.
- They have hair (or fur) during at least some stage of their development.
- They bear live young.[7]
- The females of each species have mammary glands that produce milk for their young.

Marine mammals include at least 117 species within the orders Carnivora, Sirenia, and Cetacea. The major groups of marine mammals are shown in Figure 14.16 and described below.

Order Carnivora

All animals within order **Carnivora** (*carni* = meat, *vora* = eat)—such as the familiar cat and dog families on land—have prominent canine teeth. Marine representatives of order Carnivora include sea otters, polar bears, and the **pinnipeds** (*pinna* = feather, *ped* = a foot), which include walruses, seals, sea lions, and fur seals. The name *pinniped* describes these organisms' prominent skin-covered flippers, which are well adapted for propelling them through water.

Sea otters (Figure 14.17a) inhabit kelp beds in coastal waters of the eastern North Pacific Ocean. They are some of the smallest marine mammals, with adults reaching lengths up to 1.2 meters (4 feet). Sea otters lack an insulating layer of blubber but have extremely dense fur, which is extremely luxurious and was highly sought for pelts; as a result, they were hunted to the brink of extinction in the late 1800s. Fortunately, they have made a remarkable comeback and now inhabit most areas where they were formerly hunted. Sea otters seem particularly playful because of their habit of continually scratching themselves, which serves to clean their fur and adds an insulating layer of air. Because they lack the insulative benefit of blubber, they have high caloric requirements and are voracious eaters.

---

[7]This is true except for a few egg-laying monotreme mammals of Australia from the subclass Prototheria, which includes the duck-billed platypus and the spiny anteater (echidna).

(a)

(b)

(c)

(d)

(e)

FIGURE 14.17 Marine mammals of order Carnivora.
(a) Sea otter. **(b)** Polar bear. Pinnipeds include **(c)** walrus,
(d) harbor seals, and **(e)** California sea lions.

Sea otters eat more than 50 kinds of marine life, including sea urchins, crabs, lobsters, sea stars, abalone, clams, mussels, octopuses, and fish. They are one of the few types of animals known to use tools. During dives for prey items, they keep a tool—usually a rock—tucked under one arm while they use their dexterous hands to obtain food. When they return to the surface, they use the tool to break open the shells of their food while floating on their backs.

Polar bears (Figure 14.17b) are a type of marine mammal with massive webbed paws that make them excellent swimmers. The polar bear's fur is thick, and each hair is hollow for better insulation. Polar bears also have large teeth and sharp claws, which they use for prying and killing. Their diet consists mainly of seals, which they often capture at holes in the Arctic ice when the seals come up for a breath of air. The topic of shrinking Arctic sea ice and its affect on polar bear populations is discussed in Chapter 16, "The Oceans and Climate Change."

Walruses have large bodies and adults—both male and female—have ivory tusks up to 1 meter (3 feet) long (Figure 14.17c). Their tusks are used for territorial fighting, for hauling themselves onto icebergs, and sometimes for stabbing their prey.

Seals—also called the *earless seals* or *true seals*—differ from the **sea lions** and **fur seals**—also called the *eared seals*—in the following ways:

- Seals lack prominent ear flaps that are specific to sea lions and fur seals (look closely and compare Figures 14.17d and 14.17e).
- Seals have smaller and less-prominent front flippers (called *fore flippers*) than sea lions and fur seals.
- Seals have prominent claws that extend from their fore flippers that sea lions and fur seals lack (Figure 14.18).
- Seals have a different hip structure than sea lions and fur seals. Thus, seals cannot move their rear flippers underneath their bodies as sea lions and fur seals can (Figure 14.18).
- Seals, with their smaller front flippers and different hip structure, do not move around on land very well and can only slither along like caterpillars. Sea lions and fur seals, on the other hand, use their large front flippers and their rear flippers, which they can turn under their bodies, to walk easily on land and can even ascend steep slopes, climb stairs, and do other acrobatic tricks.

• Seals propel themselves through the water using a back-and-forth motion of their rear flippers (similar to a wagging tail), whereas sea lions and fur seals flap their large front flippers.

Order Sirenia

Animals of order **Sirenia** (*siren* = a mythical mermaidlike creature with an enticing voice) include the *manatees* and *dugongs*, collectively known as "sea cows."[8] Manatees are concentrated in coastal areas of the tropical Atlantic Ocean, while the dugongs populate the tropical regions of the Indian and Western Pacific Oceans.

Skeleton of a typical seal, genus *Phoca*

Skeleton of the Steller sea lion

Both manatees and dugongs have a paddlelike tail and rounded front flippers (Figure 14.19). They have sparse hairs covering their bodies, which are concentrated around the mouth. They are large animals that can reach lengths of up to 4.3 meters (14 feet) and weigh more than 1360 kilograms (3000 pounds). The land-dwelling ancestors of sirenians were elephant like; in fact, modern-day manatees have nails on their front flippers that resemble those of elephants.

Fore flippers

Elephant seal

Sea lion

Sirenians eat only shallow-water coastal grasses and are thus the only vegetarian marine mammals. They spend most of their lives in coastal waters that are heavily used by humans for commerce, recreation, development, and waste disposal, and so a major concern for sirenian survival is habitat destruction. A recent worldwide study of biologically sensitive seagrass habitat—which is vital for sirenians—indicates that it is being destroyed so rapidly that it is one of the most threatened ecosystems on Earth. The rate of seagrass loss, in fact, is similar to that of other endangered ecosystems, such as mangroves, coral reefs, and rainforests.

FIGURE 14.18 Skeletal and morphological differences between seals and sea lions. The most significant differences between seals and sea lions are that seals have smaller fore flippers with visible nails; the hip structure of sea lions allows them to bend their rear flippers underneath their bodies, which allows them good mobility on land; and sea lions have an external ear flap (not shown).

FIGURE 14.19 Marine mammals of order Sirenia. (a) West Indian manatees, which have a rounded tail fin and nails on their front flippers. **(b)** Indian Ocean dugong, which has a fluked tail fin similar to that of a whale and has no visible nails on its front flippers.

(a)

(b)

[8]Sea cows also include the cold-water Steller's sea cow (*Hydrodamalis gigas*), which was driven to extinction in 1768 by early whalers only 27 years after its discovery.

NORTHERN RIGHT WHALE (*Eubalaena glacialis*)
Northern right whale baleen can reach 2.8 m (9 ft) in length and is used to strain copepods and krill from surface waters. A similar species, the southern right whale, exists in high southern latitudes. Length is to 18 m (60 ft).

SPERM WHALE (*Physeter macrocephalus*)
Found mostly in tropical waters, these deep-diving toothed whales have a huge snout that contains a large amount of oil. Length of male is to 18 m (59 ft); length of female is to 10.5 m (35 ft).

FIGURE 14.20 Marine mammals of order Cetacea.
A composite drawing of representatives of the two whale suborders, drawn to relative scale. The toothed whales (Odontoceti) form complex social communities and include the bottlenose dolphin, killer whale, narwhal, and sperm whale. The baleen whales (Mysticeti) are the largest of all whales and include the right whale, gray whale, humpback whale, and blue whale.

In addition, there have been many accidents with motorboats that run over these slow-moving animals. In 2002, for example, the Florida Fish and Wildlife Commission reported the deaths of 305 Florida manatees, of which 31% were attributed to boat collisions. Scientists have recently developed a forward-looking sonar system called a "manatee finder" to help boaters locate and avoid the animals. The continuing decline in populations of manatees and dugongs, however, has led to them being classified as endangered species.

BOTTLENOSE DOLPHIN (*Tursiops truncatus*)
Found in all oceans, this is one of the many species of oceanic dolphins. Length is to 3 m (10 ft).

KILLER WHALE (*Orcinus orca*)
Cosmopolitan in distribution, this whale is unique in that it not only feeds on fish but also on seals, birds, and other whales. The male has a larger dorsal fin than the female. Length is to 9 m (31 ft).

NARWHAL (*Monodon monoceros*)
The scientific name, which means "one tooth, one horn" is accurate for the male of this Arctic whale. Length is to 6 m (20 ft).

GRAY WHALE (*Eschrichtius robustus*)
This bottom-feeding baleen whale has a small head and very reduced dorsal fin. It stays close to shore, and even enters the surf zone. Length is to 14 m (45 ft).

HUMPBACK WHALE (*Megaptera novaeangliae*)
These baleen whales produce some of the most complex songs of any marine mammal and are known for their energetic and athletic behaviors, such as breaching. The genus name is derived from their extraordinary large wing-like flippers. Length is to 16 m (52 ft).

BLUE WHALE (*Balaenoptera musculus*)
Probably the largest animal to ever inhabit the Earth, these baleen whales weigh up to 150 tons and can consume over 5 tons of krill per day. Length is to 30 m (100 ft).

FIGURE 14.20 (*CONTINUED*)

Order Cetacea

The order **Cetacea** (*cetus* = a whale) includes the whales, dolphins, and porpoises (Figure 14.20). The cetacean body is more or less cigar shaped and insulated with a thick layer of blubber. Cetacean forelimbs are modified into flippers that move only at the "shoulder" joint. The hind limbs are vestigial (rudimentary), not attached to the rest of the skeleton, and are usually not visible externally. All cetaceans share the following characteristics:

- An elongated (telescoped) skull
- Blowholes on top of the skull
- Very few hairs
- A horizontal tail fin called a *fluke* that is used for propulsion by vertical movements

These characteristics make cetaceans' bodies very streamlined, allowing them to be excellent swimmers.

MODIFICATIONS TO INCREASE SWIMMING SPEED Cetaceans' muscles are not a great deal more powerful than those of other mammals, so their ability to swim fast must result from modifications that reduce frictional drag. The muscles of a small dolphin, for example, would need to be five times stronger than they are to swim at 40 kilometers (25 miles) per hour in turbulent flow.

In addition to a streamlined body, cetaceans improve the flow of water around their bodies with a specialized skin structure. Their skin consists of a soft outer layer that is 80% water and has narrow canals filled with spongy material, and a stiffer inner layer composed mostly of tough connective tissue. The soft layer decreases the pressure differences at the skin–water interface by compressing when pressure is high and expanding when pressure is low, reducing turbulence and drag.

MODIFICATIONS TO ALLOW DEEP DIVING Humans can free-dive to a maximum depth of 130 meters (428 feet) and hold their breath in rare instances for up to six minutes. In contrast, sperm whales (*Physeter macrocephalus*) dive deeper than 2800 meters (9200 feet), and northern bottlenose whales (*Hyperoodon ampullatus*) can stay submerged for up to two hours. These remarkable feats require unique adaptations, such as special structures that allow them to use oxygen efficiently, muscular adaptations, and an ability to resist nitrogen narcosis.

Oxygen Usage Figure 14.21 shows the internal structures that allow cetaceans to remain submerged for extended periods. Inhaled air finds its way to tiny terminal chambers, the *alveoli* (*alveus* = a small hollow). Alveoli are lined with a thin alveolar membrane that is in contact with a dense bed of capillaries. The exchange of gases between the inhaled air and the blood (oxygen in, carbon dioxide out) occurs across the alveolar membrane. Some cetaceans have an exceptionally large concentration of capillaries surrounding the alveoli (Figure 14.21b), which have muscles that move air against the membrane by repeatedly contracting and expanding.

Cetaceans take from one to three breaths per minute while resting, compared with about 15 in humans. Because they hold the inhaled breath much longer, and because of the large capillary mass in contact with the alveolar membrane and the circulation of the air by muscular action, cetaceans can extract almost 90% of the oxygen in each breath, whereas terrestrial mammals extract only 4 to 20%.

To use oxygen efficiently during long dives, cetaceans store it and limit its use. The storage of so much oxygen is possible because prolonged divers have such a large blood volume per unit of body mass.

Some cetaceans have twice as many red blood cells per unit of blood volume and up to nine times as much myoglobin in their muscle tissue as terrestrial animals. As a result, large supplies of oxygen can be stored chemically in **hemoglobin** (*hemo* = blood, *globus* = sphere) within red blood cells and in myoglobin within muscles.

Muscular Adaptations Cetaceans' muscles are also adapted for deep dives. One adaptation is that their muscle tissue is relatively insensitive to high levels of carbon dioxide, which builds up in the body through respiration, especially during deep dives. Another adaptation is that their muscles can continue to function through anaerobic respiration when oxygen becomes depleted.

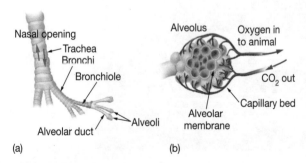

(a) (b)

FIGURE 14.21 Cetacean modifications to allow prolonged submergence. (a) Basic lung design. Air enters the lung through the trachea, and oxygen is absorbed into the blood through the walls of the alveoli. **(b)** Oxygen exchange in the alveolus. A dense mat of capillaries receives oxygen through the alveolar membrane, allowing whales to extract as much as 90% of oxygen from each breath.

In addition, research has shown that cetaceans' swimming muscles can still function during a dive even in the absence of oxygen. This suggests that these muscles and other organs, such as the digestive tract and kidneys, may be sealed off from the circulatory system by constriction of key arteries. The circulatory system would then service only essential components, such as the heart and brain. Because of the decreased circulatory requirements, the heart rate can be reduced by 20 to 50% of normal. Other research has shown, however, that no such reduction in heart rate occurs during dives by the common dolphin (*Delphinus delphis*), the white whale (*Delphinapterus leucas*), or the bottlenose dolphin (*Tursiops truncatus*).

Do Cetaceans Suffer from the Effects of Deep Diving? One difficulty with deep and prolonged dives is the absorption of compressed gases into the blood. When humans dive using compressed air—which includes nitrogen and oxygen—the higher pressure at depth causes more nitrogen to be dissolved in a diver's body and can cause divers to experience **nitrogen narcosis**, which is also called *rapture of the deep*. The effect of nitrogen narcosis is similar to drunkenness and can occur when a diver either goes too deep or stays too long at depths greater than 30 meters (100 feet) (see Box 12.2).

Another difficulty can occur when divers return to the surface too rapidly, in which case they may experience **decompression sickness**, which is also called the *bends*. During a rapid ascent, the lungs cannot remove excess gases from the bloodstream fast enough and the reduced pressure causes small bubbles of nitrogen to form in a diver's blood and tissue. This process is analogous to the bubbles that form in a carbonated beverage when the container is opened. The bubbles interfere with blood circulation and can cause bone damage, excruciating pain, severe physical debilitation, or even death.

Until recently, it was believed that cetaceans and other marine mammals had adaptations that prevented them from suffering from the effects of deep diving. However, research involving a rigorous examination of sperm whale skeletons reveals that sperm whales acquire progressive bone damage caused by recurring decompression sickness. The researchers conclude that sperm whales are neither anatomically nor physiologically immune to the effects of deep diving.

Still, the debilitating effects of deep diving are minimized in cetaceans because they have collapsible rib cages. By the time a cetacean has reached a depth of 70 meters (230 feet), its rib cage has collapsed under the 8 kilograms per square centimeter (8 atmospheres, or 118 pounds per square inch) of pressure. The lungs within the rib cage also collapse, removing all air from the alveoli. This, in turn, prevents the blood from absorbing additional gases across the alveolar membrane, minimizing nitrogen narcosis.

In addition, cetaceans may be naturally resilient to the buildup of nitrogen gas in their bodies. In a study where enough nitrogen was put into the tissue of a dolphin to give a human a severe case of the bends, for instance, the dolphin appeared to suffer no ill effects. This suggests that dolphins (as well as other marine mammals) may have simply evolved an insensitivity to the buildup of excess nitrogen gas.

SUBORDER ODONTOCETI Members of order Cetacea can be divided into two suborders: Odontoceti (the *toothed whales*) and Mysticeti (the *baleen whales*). Suborder **Odontoceti** (*odonto* = a tooth, *cetus* = a whale) includes the dolphins, porpoises, killer whales, and sperm whales.[9]

Characteristics of Toothed Whales All toothed whales have prominent teeth that are used to hold and orient fish and squid, although the killer whale is known to feed on a variety of larger animals, including other whales. The toothed whales form complex and long-lived social groups. Toothed whales have one external nasal

---

[9]Recent genetic analyses suggest that sperm whales are more closely related to baleen whales than to other toothed whales.

FIGURE 14.22 Jawbone of a killer whale. The lower jawbone of a killer whale (*Orcinus orca*), showing large teeth that end in points. Thus, killer whales are in the dolphin family.

opening (blowhole), while baleen whales have two. Although both toothed and baleen whales can emit and receive sounds, the ability to use sound is best developed in toothed whales (particularly sperm whales, which are the most vocal cetaceans).

Differences Between Dolphins and Porpoises Dolphins and porpoises are small toothed whales of suborder Odontoceti. They have similarities in appearance, behavior, and range and so are easily confused. For instance, both dolphins and porpoises (as well as seals, sea lions, and fur seals) can exhibit a behavior known as "porpoising," which is leaping out of the water while swimming. However, there are several morphological differences between dolphins and porpoises.

Porpoises are somewhat smaller and have a more stout (bulky and robust) body shape compared to the more elongated and streamlined dolphins. Generally, porpoises have a blunt snout (rostrum), while dolphins have a longer rostrum. Porpoises have a smaller and more triangular (or, on one species, no) dorsal fin, whereas a dolphin's dorsal fin is sickle-shaped, or **falcate** (*falcatus* = sickle) and appears hooked and curved backward in profile view.

They also have differences in the shape of their teeth, although it is often difficult to get close enough to see them. The teeth of dolphins end in points, while the teeth of porpoises are blunt or flat (shovel shaped) and resemble our incisors (front teeth). Killer whales have teeth that end in points (Figure 14.22) and thus are members of the dolphin family.

Echolocation and Hearing in Toothed Whales Despite their lack of vocal cords, toothed whales can produce a variety of sounds—some of which are within the range of human hearing. Sounds are emitted from the blowhole or, in sperm whales, near a special structure called the *museau du singe* ("monkey's muzzle") (Figure 14.23). Contractions of muscles in these structures produce sound that reflects off the front of the skull, which is bowl shaped and resembles a radar dish. The sound is concentrated as it passes through an organ called the **melon** (or the **spermaceti organ** in sperm whales). This organ can form various shapes and sizes of lenses (Figure 14.23a) and acts as an acoustical lens, focusing the sound. Speculations about the sounds' purpose range from **echolocation**—using sound to determine the direction and distance of objects—(clearly true) to a highly developed language (doubtful). In fact, what marine biologists know about cetaceans' use of sound is limited.

All marine mammals have good vision, but ocean conditions often limit its effectiveness. In coastal waters (where suspended sediment and dense plankton blooms make the water turbid) and in deeper waters (where light is limited or absent), echolocation surely assists the pursuit of prey or location of objects.

Using lower-frequency clicks at great distance and higher

FIGURE 14.23 Generation of echolocation clicks in small toothed and sperm whales. **(a)** In small toothed whales, clicks are generated within the blowhole, reflected off the frontal surface of the skull, and then focused by the melon, which can form lenses to focus the sound. **(b)** In the sperm whale, air passes from the trachea through the right nasal passage across the *museau du singe* ("monkey's muzzle"), where clicks are generated. The air passes along the distal air sac, past the closed blowhole, and returns to the lungs along the left nasal passage. The sounds are reflected off the frontal surface of the skull and are focused by the spermaceti organ before leaving the whale.

(a)
1. Blowhole—sound generated here
Lenses focus sound
2. Frontal surface of skull—sound reflected off this surface
3. Melon—sound focused here
4. Sound exits
Rostrum

(b)
2. Sound reflected off skull
3. Sound focused in spermaceti organ
Blowhole
Spermaceti
Frontal air sac
Left nasal passage
Organ
Right nasal passage
Frontal skull
Distal air sac
4. Sound exits
Rostrum
Trachea
Air flow
1. *Museau du singe* ("monkey's muzzle")—clicks generated here

frequency at closer range, the bottlenose dolphin (*Tursiops truncatus*) can detect a school of fish at distances exceeding 100 meters (330 feet). It can pick out an individual fish 13.5 centimeters (5.3 inches) long at a distance of 9 meters (30 feet). Sperm whales, moreover, can detect their main prey—squid—from distances of up to 400 meters (1300 feet).

To locate an object and determine its distance, toothed whales send sound signals through the water, some of which are reflected from various objects and are returned to the animal and interpreted (Figure 14.24). Because sound penetrates objects, echolocation can produce a three-dimensional image of the object's internal structure and density (which is more than eyesight alone can do). Recent research indicates that the cetaceans may also use a sharp burst of sound to stun their prey before they close in for the kill.

How the reflected sound is received back by toothed whales is not yet fully understood. In most mammals, the bony housing of the inner ear is fused to the skull. When submerged, sounds transmitted through the water are picked up by the skull and travel to the hearing structure from many directions, which makes it impossible to accurately locate the source of the sounds. This kind of hearing structure would not work for an animal that depends on echolocation to find objects in water.

All cetaceans have evolved structures that insulate the inner ear housing from the rest of the skull. In toothed whales, the inner ear is separated from the rest of the skull and surrounded by an extensive system of air sinuses (cavities). The sinuses are filled with an insulating emulsion of oil, mucus, and air and are surrounded by fibrous connective tissue and venous networks. In many toothed whales, it is believed that sound is picked up by the thin, flaring jawbone and passed to the inner ear via the connecting, oil-filled body.[10]

There is growing concern that noise pollution in the ocean is affecting cetaceans. This increased noise comes from the greater number of ships plying the world's oceans as well as the larger size, higher speeds, and enhanced propulsion power of individual ships. In fact, low-frequency ambient marine noise has increased tenfold during the past 50 years and is increasing at a rate of 3 decibels per decade. The impact of this increased underwater noise on cetacean hearing, behavior, and communication is unknown.

How Intelligent Are Toothed Whales? The question of cetacean intelligence is a topic of much debate. Although there may not be a definitive answer, the following facts about toothed whales imply a certain level of intelligence:

- They can communicate with each other by using sound.
- They have large brains relative to their body size.[11]
- Their brains are highly convoluted—a characteristic shared by many organisms that are considered to have highly developed intelligence (such as humans and other primates).
- Some wild dolphins have been reported to assist drowning humans in the ocean.
- Some dolphins have been trained to respond to hand signals and do tricks on command (such as retrieve objects).

Although toothed whales have remarkable abilities, this does not necessarily imply intelligence. Pigeons, for instance, which are not known for being highly intelligent, have also been trained to retrieve objects by using hand signals. Perhaps many of us would like to think that whales and dolphins are more intelligent than

FIGURE 14.24 Echolocation. Sounds are generated by toothed whales and bounced off objects in the ocean to determine their size, shape, distance, movement, density—and even internal structure.

Sonar and Echolocation

WEB VIDEO

Whale Vocalizations

---

[10]To simulate this, try pushing the end of a vibrating tuning fork into your chin. The sound is transmitted through your jaw directly to your ear.

[11]In fact, sperm whales have the largest brain of any animal on the planet—it has been reported to weigh up to 9 kilograms (20 pounds), which is over six times the weight of a typical human brain.

KILLER WHALES: A REPUTATION DESERVED?

Killer whales (*Orcinus orca*) are sleek and powerful predatory animals that inhabit all oceans of the world. Once considered ferocious man-eaters, it turns out they are social animals that don't harm people. Why, then, are they called *killer* whales?

Killer whales prey mainly on fish. When fish are not plentiful, some feed on other dolphins, large whales, penguins, birds, squid, turtles, seals, or sea lions (Figure 14B). Killer whales often hunt in groups, employing various strategies, including deception, to trap their prey. Their distinctive black-and-white coloration—a type of *disruptive coloration*—and white eye patch often confuse their prey as they close in for the kill. Killer whales have often been called "wolves of the sea" because of their group hunting tactics.

Killer whales often play with their food before killing it. Similar to the way a cat plays with a mouse, killer whales have been known to hone their hunting skills by repeatedly releasing their prey and then catching it again. Sometimes, they throw their prey completely out of the water. These behaviors appear cruel, so they may have contributed to the whale's common name.

Killer whales have rammed and sunk boats many times and have even been known to tug on divers' fins, but there is only one documented case of a killer whale killing a human. This occurred in 1991, when trainer Keltie Byrne of the marine park Sealand of the Pacific in Victoria, Canada, accidentally slipped into the killer whale pool. As she attempted to climb out, a killer whale pulled her back into the water, where she was tossed about by killer whales in the pool for 10 minutes. Finally, one whale carried her underwater in its mouth for longer than she could hold her breath, causing her to drown. Evidently, the killer whales saw her as a new play object and inadvertently killed her. In the wild, however, there has never been a documented case in which killer whales have maliciously attacked and killed a human being.

FIGURE 14B Killer whale (*Orcinus orca*) hunting sea lions near Valdes, Argentina.

WEB VIDEO

Killer Whales
Feeding on Sea Lions
in South America

they really are because humans feel an attachment to these charismatic, seemingly ever-smiling, air-breathing creatures. It is interesting to note that even experts in the field of animal intelligence disagree on how to assess *human* intelligence accurately, let alone that of a marine mammal.

If the large brain that toothed whales possess is not an indication of intelligence, then why is their brain so large? Leading whale researchers don't exactly know, but it might be because toothed whales need a large brain to process the wealth of information they receive from the sound echoes they transmit. Because intelligence is difficult to measure, perhaps it is best to say that animals of suborder Odontoceti are tremendously well adapted to the marine environment.

SUBORDER MYSTICETI Suborder **Mysticeti** (*mystic* = a moustache, *cetus* = a whale)—also known as the *baleen whales*—includes the world's largest whales (the blue whale, finback whale, and humpback whale) and the gray whale (a bottom feeder).

Baleen whales are generally much larger than toothed whales because of differences in food sources. Baleen whales eat lower on the food web (including zooplankton such as krill and small nektonic organisms), which are relatively abundant in the marine environment. How are the largest whales in the world able to survive on eating such small prey, especially when these smaller organisms are widely dispersed in the marine environment?

Use of Baleen To concentrate small prey items and separate them from seawater, baleen whales have parallel rows of **baleen** (*balaena* = whale) plates in their mouths instead of teeth (Figure 14.25a). These baleen plates hang from the whale's upper jaw and, when the whale opens its mouth, the baleen resembles

FIGURE 14.25 Baleen. **(a)** A diagrammatic cross section through the head of a typical baleen whale. The baleen plates, hanging from the upper jaw, form a sieve that allows these whales to concentrate and eat large quantities of smaller organisms. **(b)** How a baleen whale feeds. **(c)** A rack of baleen from a bottom-feeding gray whale. **(d)** Individual slat of baleen from a surface-skimming northern right whale.

FIGURE 14.26 A pair of humpback whales bubblenet feeding in Antarctic waters. Humpback whales (*Megaptera novaeangliae*) often feed by swimming in a circle underwater and emitting a curtain of bubbles to corral prey. Then each whale swims through the concentrated prey with their mouth open and surfaces in a vertical lunge. Baleen plates are used to filter prey items from the water and occur as parallel rows on the upper jaw that are separated by the roof of the mouth (*pink*). Also visible on the head are round bumps, which are called nodules or tubercules and hold a single long hair. Whalers called these bumps stove bolts because they looked like the stove bolts that hold a ship together.

WEB VIDEO

Humpback Whales
Bubblenet Feeding

KEY CONCEPT

Marine mammals include orders Carnivora (sea otters, polar bears, and pinnipeds—walrus, seals, sea lions, and fur seals), Sirenia (manatees and dugongs), and Cetacea (whales, dolphins, and porpoises).

a moustache (except that it is on the *inside* of their mouths), which is why these whales are sometimes called the moustached whales (Figures 14.25c, 14.26). Baleen is made of flexible keratin—the same as human nails and hair—and can be up to 4.3 meters (14 feet) long (Figure 14.25d).[12]

To feed, baleen whales fill their mouths with water that contains their prey items, (Figure 14.25b) allowing their pleated lower jaw to balloon in size. The whales force the water out between the fibrous plates of baleen, trapping small fish, krill, and other plankton inside their mouths. Mostly, baleen whales feed at or near the surface, sometimes working together in large groups and surfacing in vertical lunges (Figure 14.26). The gray whale, however, has short baleen slats and feeds by straining benthic organisms such as amphipods and shellfish from bottom sediment.

Baleen Whale Families Baleen whales can be grouped into one of the following three families:

1. The **gray whale**, which has short, coarse baleen, no dorsal fin, and only two to five ventral grooves on its lower jaw.

2. The **rorqual**[13] **whales**, which have short baleen, many ventral grooves, and are divided into two subfamilies:

   a) The *balaenopterids*, which have long, slender bodies, small sickle-shaped dorsal fins, and flukes with smooth edges (minke, Bryde's, sei, fin, and blue whales).

   b) The *megapterids*, or humpback whales, which have a more robust body, long flippers, flukes with uneven trailing edges, tiny dorsal fins, and nodules or tubercles (bumps that hold a single long hair) on the head.

3. The **right whales**,[14] which have long, fine baleen, broad triangular flukes, no dorsal fin, and no ventral grooves. The northern right whale is most threatened with extinction. The other members of this family are the Southern Hemisphere's southern right whale and the bowhead whale, which remains near the edge of the Arctic pack ice.

Baleen Whales and Sounds Baleen whales produce sound too, but at much lower frequencies than toothed whales. For example, gray whales produce pulses (possibly for echolocation) and moans that may help them maintain contact with other gray whales. Rorqual whales produce moans that last from one to many seconds. These sounds are extremely low in frequency and are probably used to communicate over distances of up to 50 kilometers (31 miles). Blue whales have been documented to produce sounds that may travel along the SOFAR channel across entire ocean basins.[15] Songs of humpback whales are thought to be a form of sexual display, but it is unclear whether their main purpose is to repel other males or to attract females.

---

[12]Baleen (also called whalebone) was used for such items as buggy whips and corset stays before synthetic materials—mostly plastics—were substituted.

[13]The term *rorqual* refers to the longitudinal grooves on the lower jaw called rorqual folds; *rorqual* means "furrow whale" in Norwegian.

[14]The right whales are so named because they swim slowly, live close to shore, float when dead, and yield plenty of oil, meat, and whalebone, so, from a 19th century whaler's point of view, they were the "right" whale to take.

[15]For more details about the SOFAR channel, see Box 16.1.

14.5 An Example of Migration: Why Do Gray Whales Migrate?

Many marine organisms—such as fish, squid, sea turtles, and marine mammals—undertake seasonal migrations. Some of the longest migrations known in the open ocean are those of baleen whales, and one of the best-studied is that of the gray whale (*Eschrichtius robustus*, often called the Pacific gray whale, or California gray whale). Gray whales, which are a medium-sized, slow-moving coastal whale with a mottled gray appearance, can live 60 years, grow to 15 meters (50 feet) in length, and weigh up to 32 metric tons (35 short tons).

Migration Route

The migratory routes of commercially important baleen whales (including gray whales) have been well known since the mid-1800s. Marine mammals are relatively easy to track because they must surface periodically for air. Gray whales are particularly easy to track because they spend their entire lives in nearshore areas. Radio tracking of individual gray whales has delineated the route and timing of their migration.

Gray whales undertake a 22,000-kilometer (13,700-mile) round-trip journey every year, the longest known migration of any mammal. Gray whales feed primarily on sea floor organisms in cold high-latitude waters in the coastal Arctic Ocean and the far northern Pacific Ocean near Alaska; they breed and give birth in warm tropical lagoons along the west coast of Baja California and mainland Mexico (Figure 14.27). Feeding occurs during the highly productive summer, when long hours of sunlight produce an abundant feast of crustaceans, clams, and other bottom-dwelling organisms in the shallow portions of the Bering, Chukchi, and Beaufort Seas. Without this bountiful food, the whales could not sustain themselves during the long migrations and the mating and calving season, when feeding is minimal.

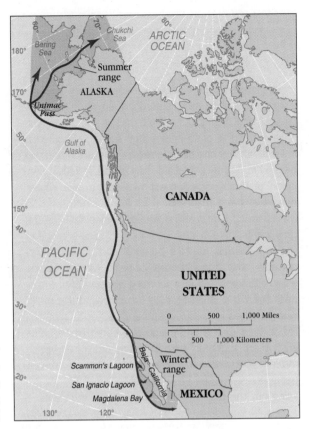

FIGURE 14.27 Gray whale migration route. Gray whales (*Eschrichtius robustus*) undertake as much as a 22,000 kilometers (13,700 miles) annual migration, the longest of any mammal. They migrate from Arctic summer feeding areas in the Bering and Chukchi Seas to warmer winter breeding and calving lagoons offshore Mexico.

Reasons for Migration

Initially, gray whales were thought to migrate so far because the physical environment of their cold-water feeding grounds did not meet the needs of young gray whales. Recent research on the physiology of newborn gray whales indicates, however, that gray whale calves can survive in much colder water. So why do they migrate? One hypothesis is that the migration is a relic from the Ice Age, when sea level was lower. During that time, the feeding grounds that are so productive today were above sea level. Hence, gray whales could not feast on the abundant food and probably gave birth to smaller calves that could not survive in the cold water. This necessitated the migration to warmer water regions, which continues to this day despite the abundant food supply.

Alternatively, gray whales may have left the colder waters to avoid killer whales, which are more numerous there and are a major threat to young whales. This may also explain why only those lagoons in Mexico with shallow entrances are used for calving. Killer whales have been seen near the lagoons, however, and have also been observed to feed in extremely shallow water (see Figure 14B).

Timing of Migration

The timing of the gray whale migration is closely linked to physical oceanographic conditions. The migration usually begins in September, after the high-latitude summer bloom in productivity has peaked. By this time, the whales have

How do whales, you know, DO IT?!

Whale sex is truly an incredible achievement. Imagine trying to copulate as whales do when you have nothing with which to grasp a mate and, in the ocean, you have nothing to push against for support! Copulation in large whales has been infrequently studied and witnessed in only a remarkably few cases. In fact, copulation of the world's largest whale, the blue whale, has never been observed.

From coastal-dwelling whale species such as the gray whale, here's what is known: Whales are one of the few animals besides humans and bonobo chimpanzees that copulate belly-to-belly. Mating begins when the female is in a forward position horizontally near the water surface. She turns toward the male, who emerges from below and enters her as they spiral on their long axis through the water, which helps push them together. As with many other mammals, mating takes only a few seconds. Both a whale's penis and its testes are internal to enhance streamlining but the tapered fibro-elastic tip of the penis is especially suited for the tricky act of copulation with no limbs. Once it is extruded outside the body for mating, it is dexterous enough to maneuver itself into a female's genital slit to deposit sperm.

KEY CONCEPT
Gray whales undertake the longest migration of any mammal, traveling from high-latitude Arctic summer feeding areas to low-latitude winter birthing and breeding lagoons in Mexico.

stored enough fat to last them until they return to high-latitude waters. Gray whales have been observed to feed during their migration, however, when the opportunity presents itself. When pack ice begins to form over their feeding grounds along the continental shelf, the whales begin to move south.

Pregnant females are the first to leave. They are followed by the nonpregnant mature females, immature females, mature males, and then immature males. After navigating through passages between the Aleutian Islands, they follow the coast throughout their southern journey. Traveling about 200 kilometers (125 miles) per day, most reach the lagoons of Baja California by the end of January.

In these warm-water lagoons, the pregnant females give birth to calves that are about 4.6 meters (15 feet) long and weigh about 1 metric ton (1.1 short tons). The calves nurse on milk that is almost half butterfat and has the consistency of cheese, allowing the calves to put on weight quickly during the next two months. While the calves are nursing, the mature males breed with the mature females that did not bear calves. Producing large offspring (the gestation period is up to one year) and providing them with fat-rich milk for several months requires enormous amounts of energy, so it is not uncommon for females to mate only once every two or three years.

Beginning in late February, they return north in reverse order (beginning, that is, with the immature males). Most of the whales are back in their high-latitude feeding grounds by the end of June, which coincides with the beginning of the summer bloom in productivity. The whales are able to feed once again on the prodigious quantities of bottom-dwelling organisms found here to replenish their depleted stores of fat and blubber before their next yearly trip south.

Gray Whales as Endangered Species

Although many other whales exist in smaller populations than before whaling (Figure 14.28) and are endangered species, the North Pacific gray whale was removed from the endangered species list in 1993 when their numbers exceeded 20,000, which surpassed the estimated size of their population before whaling. Out of nearly 1400 species listed as endangered since 1973, gray whales have become one of only 13 species to be removed from the endangered species list. Other populations of gray whales were not so fortunate. For instance, the gray whales that used to inhabit the North Atlantic Ocean were hunted to extinction several centuries ago, and the gray whales that live in the waters near Japan may also have recently become extinct.

These slow-moving whales of suborder Mysticeti spend most of their lives in coastal waters, which made them easy targets for whalers. In the mid-1800s, they were traced to their birthing and breeding lagoons and were hunted to the brink of extinction. A common strategy was to harpoon a calf, which then lured its vigilant mother to the whalers, too. During this time, gray whales were known as "devilfish" because the adults would often capsize small whaling boats when they came to the aid of their young. By the late 1800s, the number of gray whales had diminished to the point that they were difficult to find during their annual migration. Fortunately, these low numbers also made it difficult for whalers to hunt them successfully.

In 1938, the International Whaling Treaty banned the taking of gray whales, which were thought to be nearly extinct. This protection has allowed them to steadily increase in number to this day and to become the first marine creature to be removed from endangered status. Their repopulation is truly one of the most impressive success stories of how protecting animals can ensure their continued survival. What is perhaps most surprising is how friendly they are now toward people in boats (Figure 14.29) in the same lagoons where they were hunted to near extinction over 150 years ago. Devilfish, indeed!

Whaling and the International Whaling Commission

From the mid-1800s to the mid-1900s, many stocks of large whales in the world were overhunted and their numbers severely depleted (see Figure 14.28). The **International Whaling Commission (IWC)** was established in 1946 to manage the subsistence and commercial hunting of large whales. In 1986, the 72 nations that are members of the IWC passed a ban on commercial whaling in order to allow whales to recover from overhunting and to give researchers time to develop methods for assessing whale populations. Today, the ban on whaling is still in effect, although there has been a push by some nations to end the whaling moratorium and establish annual whale quotas. The ban can only be reversed by a three-quarters majority vote of member nations.

According to the IWC, there are three ways to engage in legal hunting of whales:

1. **Whaling by objection.** Countries can continue to hunt whales legally under an objection to the IWC ban on commercial whaling. (Notable countries doing this: Norway.)

2. **Scientific whaling.** Countries may decide to kill whales for scientific research. Under the IWC convention, meat from whales hunted for this research may be sold commercially. (Notable countries doing this: Japan.[16])

3. **Aboriginal subsistence whaling.** Subsistence whaling by native cultures is allowed by the IWC in special cases where there is a long-standing cultural tradition of whaling and where whale meat satisfies the nutritional needs of the community. (Notable countries doing this: Greenland, Russia, the United States, and Saint Vincent and the Grenadines in the Caribbean).

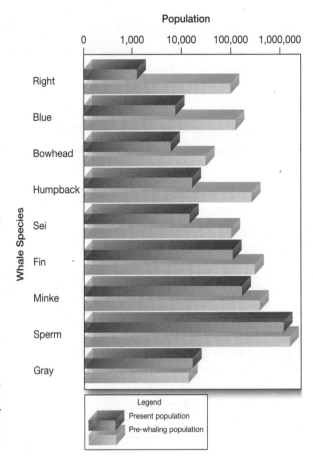

FIGURE 14.28 World whale populations (present and prewhaling). Bar graph showing present world whale populations (*red*) compared to prewhaling populations (*green*) for various species. Note that population size is shown as a logarithmic scale. Full-scale commercial whaling was suspended in 1986, when the plunging numbers of many whale species moved the International Whaling Commission to declare a moratorium. Today, however, certain countries are permitted to catch designated species for research or cultural reasons.

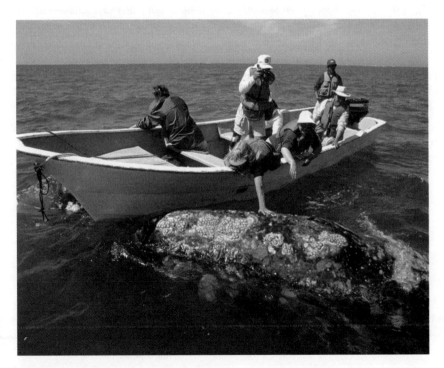

FIGURE 14.29 Gray whale friendly behavior. Gray whales (*Eschrichtius robustus*) exhibit friendly behavior by approaching a boat and initiating contact in Scammon's Lagoon, Baja California, Mexico.

[16]In 2007, Japan had planned to kill nearly 1000 humpback, fin, and minke whales in South Pacific waters for scientific purposes, but international pressure reduced the take to about 550 minkes.

Chapter in Review

• *Pelagic animals that comprise the majority of the ocean's biomass remain mostly within the upper surface waters of the ocean*, where their primary food source exists. Those animals that are not planktonic (floating forms such as microscopic zooplankton) depend on *buoyancy* or their *ability to swim* to help them remain in food-rich surface waters.

• *The rigid gas containers in some cephalopods and the expandable swim bladders in some fish help increase buoyancy.* Other organisms maintain their positions near the surface with *gas-filled floats* (such as those of the Portuguese man-of-war) and *soft bodies that lack high-density hard parts* (such as the jellyfish).

• *Nekton—squid, fish, and marine mammals—are strong swimmers* that depend on their swimming ability to avoid predators and obtain food. Squid swim by trapping water in their body cavities and forcing it out through a siphon. Most fish swim by creating a wave of body curvature that passes from the front of the fish to the back and provides a forward thrust.

• *The caudal (rear) fin provides the most thrust, while the paired pelvic and pectoral (chest) fins are used for maneuvering. The dorsal (back) and anal fins serve primarily as stabilizers.* A rounded caudal fin is flexible and can be used for maneuvering at slow speeds. The lunate fin is rigid and is of little use in maneuvering but produces thrust efficiently for fast swimmers such as tuna.

• *Fish can be categorized as lungers* (such as groupers) or *cruisers* (such as tuna). Lungers sit motionless and lunge at passing prey. They have mostly white muscle tissue, which fatigues more quickly than red muscle tissue. Cruisers swim constantly in search of prey and possess mostly red, myoglobin-rich muscle tissue.

• *Fish swim slowly when cruising, fast when hunting for prey, and fastest when trying to escape from predators.* Although *most fish are cold-blooded*, the fast-swimming tuna, *Thunnus*, is homeothermic, meaning that it maintains its body temperature well above water temperature.

• *Deep-water nekton have special adaptations—*such as *good sensory devices* and *bioluminescence*—that allow them to survive in this still and completely dark environment. *Bioluminescence—the ability to organically produce light—has many uses in the deep ocean.*

• *Many marine organisms such as fish, squid, and crustaceans exhibit schooling*, probably because it increases their chances of avoiding predation compared to swimming alone and serves to preserve the species. Some organisms live closely together in *symbiotic relationships*.

• *Good fossil evidence shows that marine mammals evolved from land-dwelling animals* about 50 million years ago. *Marine mammals are warm-blooded; breathe air; have hair or fur; bear live young; and the females have mammary glands.* Marine mammals belong to orders *Carnivora, Sirenia*, and *Cetacea*.

• *Marine mammals within order Carnivora have prominent canine teeth* and include *sea otters, polar bears*, and the *pinnipeds* (*walruses, seals, sea lions*, and *fur seals*). *Marine mammals of order Sirenia*, which include *manatees* and *dugongs* ("sea cows"), have toenails (manatees only), sparse hairs covering their bodies, and are vegetarians.

• The mammals best adapted to life in the open ocean are those of the *order Cetacea*, which includes *whales, dolphins*, and *porpoises*. Cetaceans have *highly streamlined bodies* so that they are fast swimmers. Other adaptations—such as being able to absorb 90% of the oxygen they inhale, storing large quantities of oxygen, reducing the use of oxygen by noncritical organs, and having collapsible ribs and lungs—*allow them to dive deeply* and minimize the effects of nitrogen narcosis and decompression sickness, although recent research indicates that they are not immune to it.

• *Cetaceans are divided into suborder Odontoceti (the toothed whales) and suborder Mysticeti (the baleen whales). Odontocetes use echolocation* to find their way through the ocean and locate prey. They emit clicking sounds, and can determine the size, shape, internal structure, and distance of the objects from the nature of the returning signals and the time elapsed.

• *Mysticetes*, which include the largest whales in the world, *separate their small prey from seawater using their baleen plates as a strainer.* Baleen whales include the *gray whale*, the *rorqual whales*, and the *right whales*.

• *Gray whales migrate from their cold-water summer feeding grounds in the Arctic to warm, low-latitude lagoons in Mexico during winter for breeding and birthing purposes.* This behavior may have evolved to allow their young to be born into warm water during the last ice age, when lower sea level eliminated today's highly productive Arctic feeding areas.

• *The International Whaling Commission (IWC) was established in 1946 to manage the subsistence and commercial hunting of large whales*, which had experienced severe population decreases. *Commercial whaling was banned* in 1986, although *whaling can still be done under objection to the ban, for scientific research, or by native cultures.*

Key Terms

Baleen (p. 429)	Cruiser (p. 413)	Homeothermic (p. 414)	Nitrogen narcosis (p. 425)
Bioluminesce (p. 414)	Decompression sickness (p. 425)	Hydrozoan (p. 409)	Odontoceti (p. 425)
Biomass (p. 405)	Deep-sea fish (p. 414)	International Whaling Commission (IWC) (p. 433)	Parasitism (p. 418)
Carnivora (p. 419)	Detritus (p. 414)		Photophore (p. 414)
Cetacea (p. 423)	Echolocation (p. 426)	Krill (p. 408)	Pinniped (p. 419)
Cnidarian (p. 409)	Falcate (p. 426)	Lunger (p. 411)	Poikilothermic (p. 414)
Cold-blooded (p. 414)	Foraminifer (p. 407)	Melon (p. 426)	Polar bear (p. 420)
Commensalism (p. 417)	Fur seal (p. 420)	Mutualism (p. 418)	Radiolarian (p. 407)
Copepod (p. 407)	Gray whale (p. 430)	Myoglobin (p. 413)	Right whale (p. 430)
Counterillumination (p. 415)	Hemoglobin (p. 424)	Mysticeti (p. 428)	Rorqual whale (p. 430)

Review Questions

1. Discuss why the rigid gas chamber in cephalopods limits the depth to which they can descend. Why do fish with a swim bladder not have this limitation?

2. Draw and describe several different types of microscopic and macroscopic zooplankton.

3. Name and describe the different types of fins that fish exhibit. What are the five basic shapes of caudal fins, and what are their uses?

4. Are most fast-swimming fish cold-blooded or warm-blooded? What advantage does this provide?

5. What are the two food sources of deep-water nekton? List several adaptations of deep-water nekton that allow them to survive in their environment.

6. Describe the mechanism by which bioluminescence is accomplished in deep-sea organisms. What is bioluminescence useful for in the marine environment?

7. What are several benefits of schooling? What other adaptations do pelagic animals possess to avoid being prey?

8. What are the three types of symbiosis, and how do they differ?

9. What common characteristics do all organisms in class Mammalia share?

10. Describe marine mammals within the order Carnivora, including their adaptations for living in the marine environment.

11. How can true seals be differentiated from the eared seals (sea lions and fur seals)?

12. Describe the marine mammals within the order Sirenia, including their distinguishing characteristics.

13. How can dolphins be differentiated from porpoises?

14. Describe differences between cetaceans of the suborder Odontoceti (toothed whales) with those of the suborder Mysticeti (baleen whales). Be sure to include examples from each suborder.

15. Describe the process by which the sperm whale produces echolocation clicks.

16. Discuss how sound reaches the inner ear of toothed whales.

17. Describe the mechanism by which baleen whales feed.

18. Discuss reasons why gray whales leave their cold-water feeding grounds during the winter season.

19. Why did the International Whaling Commission (IWC) invoke a ban on commercial whaling? What three ways exist to legally hunt whales? Which countries are doing each?

Critical Thinking Exercises

1. What are the major structural and physiological differences between the fast-swimming cruisers and lungers that patiently lie in wait for their prey?

2. List the modifications that are thought to give some cetaceans the ability to (a) increase their swimming speed, (b) dive to great depths without suffering the bends, and (c) stay submerged for long periods.

Oceanography on the Web

Visit the *Essentials of Oceanography* Online Study Guide for Internet resources, including chapter-specific quizzes to test your understanding and Web links to further your exploration of the topics in this chapter.

The *Essentials of Oceanography* Online Study Guide is at http://www.mygeoscienceplace.com/.

A sea kayaker explores tide pools teeming with life.
A sea kayaker explores shallow tide pools along the coast of Moresby Island, Queen Charlotte Islands, British Columbia, Canada. Many types of bottom-dwelling marine life can often be found in great abundance in tide pools.

"The deep sea is like a continent not yet discovered."

— *Thomas Dahlgren,*
marine ecologist (2006)

15 ANIMALS OF THE BENTHIC ENVIRONMENT

Of the 250,000 known species that inhabit the marine environment, more than 98% (about 245,000) live in or on the ocean floor. Ranging from the rocky, sandy, and muddy intertidal zone to the muddy deposits of the deepest ocean trenches, the ocean floor provides a tremendously varied environment that is home to a diverse group of specially adapted organisms.

Living at or near the interface of the ocean floor and seawater, an organism's success is closely related to its ability to cope with the physical conditions of the water, the ocean floor, and the other organisms that inhabit its environment. In this chapter, we'll examine a variety of benthic communities and the animals that inhabit them.

15.1 How Are Benthic Organisms Distributed?

The distribution of benthic **biomass**[1] shown in Figure 15.1 closely matches the distribution of chlorophyll in surface waters (which is an approximation of primary productivity; compare Figures 15.1 and 13.5). Mostly, life on the ocean floor depends on the productivity of the ocean's surface waters; as a result, great abundances of benthic life are found beneath areas of high primary productivity.

The vast majority of known benthic species live on the continental shelf, where the water is often shallow enough to allow sunlight to penetrate to the ocean bottom and support photosynthesis. Recent expeditions to the deep-ocean floor, however, suggest that there are a huge number of undescribed species that live there.

The number of benthic species found at similar latitudes on opposite sides of an ocean basin depends on how ocean surface currents affect coastal water temperature—one of the most important variables affecting species diversity. The Gulf Stream, for example, warms the European coast from Spain to the northern tip of Norway, giving rise to more than three times the number of benthic species than are found in similar latitudes along the Atlantic coast of North America, where the Labrador Current cools the water as far south as Cape Cod, Massachusetts.

15.2 What Communities Exist Along Rocky Shores?

Rocky shorelines teem with organisms that live on the surface of the ocean floor. These organisms, called **epifauna** (*epi* = upon, *fauna* = animal) are either permanently attached to the bottom (for example, marine algae) or move over it (for example, crabs). Table 15.1 lists some of the special adaptations these organisms have to withstand the rigors of life on rocky shores.

---

[1]Remember that *biomass* is the mass of living organisms.

FIGURE 15.1 Oceanic benthic biomass. The distribution of oceanic benthic biomass (in grams per square meter) shows that the ocean's lowest biomass is beneath the centers of subtropical gyres and the highest values are in high-latitude continental shelf areas. Note the similarity in distribution to that of surface chlorophyll (see Figure 13.5), which suggests that most of the benthic community receives its food from surface waters.

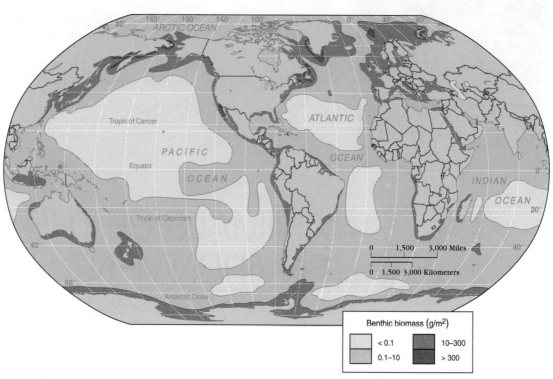

Diversity of species that inhabit rocky shores varies widely. Overall, rocky intertidal ecosystems have a moderate diversity of species compared to other benthic environments. The greatest animal diversity is in the lower (tropical) latitudes, while the diversity of algae is greater in the middle latitudes, probably because of better availability of nutrients.[2]

Intertidal Zonation

A typical rocky shore (Figure 15.2a) can be divided into a **spray zone**, which is above the spring high tide line and is covered by water only during storms, and an **intertidal zone**, which lies between the high and low tidal extremes. Along most shores, the intertidal zone can clearly be separated into the following subzones (Figure 15.2a):

- The **high tide zone**, which is relatively dry and is covered only by the highest high tides
- The **middle tide zone**, which is alternately covered by all high tides and exposed during all low tides
- The **low tide zone**, which is usually wet but is exposed during the lowest low tides

The subzones of the intertidal zone can also be delineated based on the populations of organisms that attach themselves to the bottom. Each centimeter of the rocky shore has a significantly different character than the centimeter above and below it, so organisms have evolved to withstand very specific degrees of exposure to the atmosphere. Consequently, the most finely delineated biozones in the marine environment can be found along rocky shores.

---

[2]As discussed in Chapter 13, this increased nutrient supply is a result of the lack of a permanent thermocline in the middle latitudes.

TABLE 15.1	ADVERSE CONDITIONS OF ROCKY INTERTIDAL ZONES AND ORGANISM ADAPTATIONS	
Adverse conditions of rocky intertidal zones	**Organism adaptations**	**Examples of organisms**
Drying out during low tide	• Ability to seek shelter or withdraw into shells • Thick exterior or exoskeleton to prevent water loss • External surfaces covered with rock or shell fragments to prevent water loss • Adapted to periodic drying out without dying	Sea slugs, snails, crabs, kelp
Strong wave activity	• In algae: Strong holdfasts to prevent being washed away • In animals: Seeking shelter or employing strong attachment threads, biological adhesives, a muscular foot, multiple legs, or hundreds of tube feet to allow them to attach firmly to the bottom • In both: Hard structures adapted to withstand wave energy; clustering closely together	Kelp, snails, sea stars, mussels, sea urchins
Predators occupy area during low tide/high tide	• Firm attachment of body parts, including a hard shell • Stinging cells • Camouflage • Inking response • Ability to break off body parts and regrow them later (regenerative capability)	Mussels, sea anemones, sea slugs, octopi, sea stars
Difficulty finding mates for attached species	• Release of large numbers of eggs/sperm into the water column during reproduction • Long organs to reach others for sexual reproduction	Abalones, sea urchins, barnacles
Rapid changes in temperature, salinity, pH, and oxygen content	• Ability to withdraw into shells to minimize exposure to rapid changes in environment • Ability to exist in varied temperature, salinity, pH, and low-oxygen environments for extended periods	Snails, limpets, mussels, barnacles
Lack of space or attachment sites	• Overtake another organism's space • Attach to other organisms • Planktonic larval forms that inhabit new areas, which limits parental and offspring competition for the same space	Bryozoans, coral, barnacles, limpets

The Spray (Supratidal) Zone: Organisms and Their Adaptations

Organisms that live within the spray zone, which is also known as the **supratidal** (*supra* = above, *tidal* = the tides) **zone**, must avoid drying out during the long periods when they are above water level. Consequently, many animals, such as the periwinkle snail (genus *Littorina*; Figure 15.2b), have shells, and few species of marine algae are found.

Found among the cobbles and boulders that typically cover the floors of sea caves well above the high tide line are rock lice or sea roaches (isopods of the genus *Ligia*). These scavengers reach lengths of 3 centimeters (1.2 inches) and

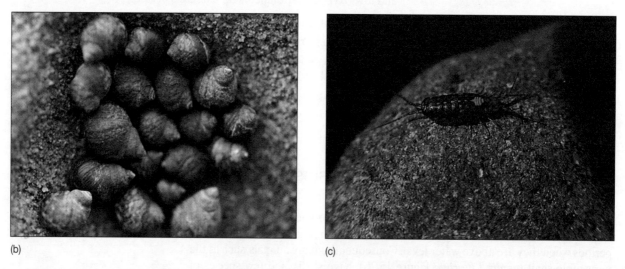

(b)

(c)

FIGURE 15.2 Rocky shore zonation and common organisms. **(a)** Diagrammatic view of tide zones (*left*) and common organisms (*right*) of a rocky shore (not to scale). **(b)** Periwinkles (*Littorina*), spray zone to upper high tide zone. **(c)** Rock louse (*Ligia*), spray zone. **(d)** Limpets (*Acmaea*), high tide zone. **(e)** Buckshot barnacles (*Chthamalus*), high tide zone. **(f)** Rock weed (*Fucus*), middle tide zone. **(g)** Acorn barnacles (*Balanus*), middle tide zone. **(h)** Blue mussel bed (*Mytilus*), including gooseneck barnacles (*Pollicipes*) and acorn barnacles (*Balanus*), middle tide zone. **(i)** Sea anemone (*Anthopleura*), low tide zone.

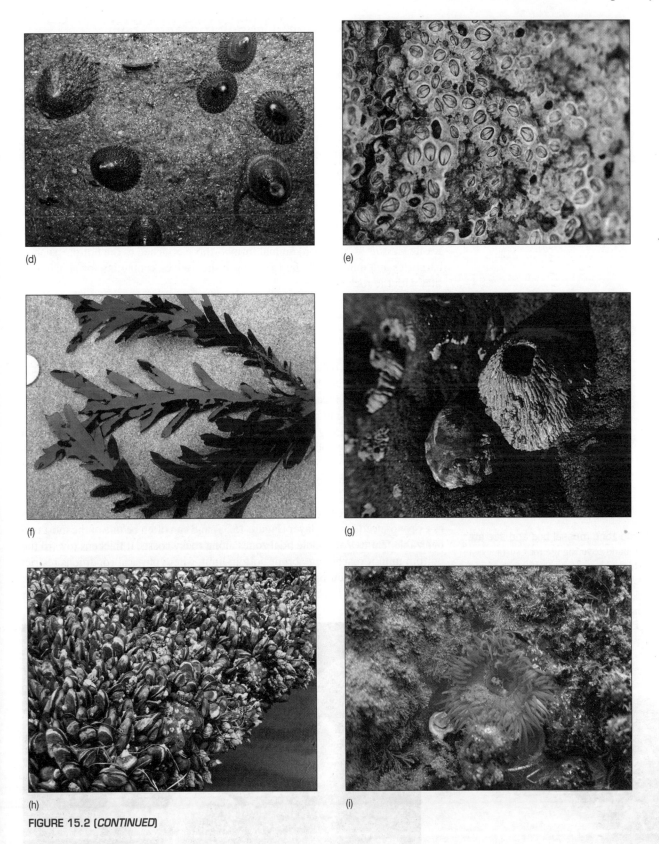

(d)

(e)

(f)

(g)

(h)

(i)

FIGURE 15.2 (*CONTINUED*)

scurry about at night feeding on organic debris (Figure 15.2c). During the day, they hide in crevices.

A distant relative of the periwinkle snail, the limpet is also found in the spray zone (genus *Acmaea;* Figure 15.2d). Both limpets and periwinkle snails feed on marine algae. The limpet has a flattened conical shell and a muscular foot with which it clings tightly to rocks.

The High Tide Zone: Organisms and Their Adaptations

Like animals within the spray zone, most animals that inhabit the high tide zone have a protective covering to prevent them from drying out. Periwinkles, for example, have a protective shell and can move between the spray zone and the high tide zone. Buckshot barnacles (Figure 15.2e) have a protective shell, too, but they cannot live above the high tide shoreline because they filter-feed from seawater, and their larval form is planktonic.

The most conspicuous algae in the high tide zone are rock weeds, members of the genus *Fucus* that live in colder latitudes (Figure 15.2f) and *Pelvetia* that live in warmer latitudes. Both have thick cell walls to reduce water loss during periods of low tide.

Rock weeds are among the first organisms to colonize a rocky shore. Later, **sessile** (*sessilis* = sitting on) animal forms—those attached to the bottom, such as barnacles and mussels—begin to establish themselves, competing for attachment sites with the rock weeds.

The Middle Tide Zone: Organisms and Their Adaptations

Seawater constantly bathes the middle tide zone, so more types of marine algae and soft-bodied animals can live there. The total biomass is much greater than in the high tide zone, so there is much greater competition for rock space among sessile forms.

Shelled organisms inhabiting the middle tide zone include acorn barnacles (*Balanus*) (Figure 15.2g); gooseneck barnacles (*Pollicipes*) (Figure 15.2h), which attach themselves to rocks with a long, muscular neck; and various mussels (genera *Mytilus* and *Modiolus*) (Figure 15.2h). Mussels attach to bare rock, algae, or barnacles during their planktonic stage and remain in place by means of strong *byssus* threads.

Mussels are often grouped together into a distinctive *mussel bed* that appears as a pronounced band or layer (Figure 15.3a) and can often be one of the most recognizable features of middle tidal zones along rocky coasts. It thickens toward the bottom until it reaches an abrupt bottom limit, where physical conditions restrict mussel growth. Often protruding from the mussel bed are numerous gooseneck barnacles; crowded in with the mussels are less-conspicuous species such as acorn

FIGURE 15.3 Middle tide zone mussel bed and sea star.
(a) The distinctive black band covering the rock surface is a bed of mussels (*Mytilus*), which is a common feature of middle tide zones along rocky shores such as this one along the Southern California coast. Also shown are acorn barnacles (*attached to mussels*) and gooseneck barnacles (*white*).
(b) An ochre sea star (*Pisaster*) feeds on a mussel by first enveloping a mussel with its tube feet and prying apart the mussel's shell. The star can then digest the mussel's soft tissues with its own everted stomach.

(a)

(b)

barnacles, crustaceans, marine worms, rock-boring clams, sea stars, and algae.

Carnivorous snails and sea stars (such as genera *Pisaster* and *Asterias*) feed upon mussels in the mussel beds. To pry open the mussel shell, sea stars pull on either side with hundreds of tubelike feet. The mussel eventually becomes fatigued and can no longer hold its shell halves closed. When the shell opens ever so slightly, the sea star turns its stomach inside out, slips it through the crack in the mussel shell, and digests the edible tissue inside (Figure 15.3b).

Where the rock surface flattens out within the middle tidal zone, tide pools trap water as the tide ebbs. These pools support microecosystems containing a wide variety of organisms. The most conspicuous member of this community is often the sea anemone (see Figure 15.2i), which is a relative of the jellyfish.

Sea anemone
(polyp body form)

FIGURE 15.4 Sea anemone structure and operation of its stinging cells. Sea anemone morphology (*left*) with detail of its stinging nematocysts (*inset*), which are used to sting and incapacitate prey. An internal view of the basic sea anemone body form is shown at right.

Shaped like a sack, anemones have a flat foot disk that provides a suction attachment to the rock surface. Directed upward, the open end of the sack is the mouth, which leads directly to the gut cavity and is surrounded by rows of tentacles (Figure 15.4). The tentacles are covered with stinging needlelike cells called **nematocysts** (*nemato* = thread, *cystis* = bladder) (Figure 15.4, *inset*), which inject the victim with a potent neurotoxin. When an organism brushes against a sea anemone's tentacles, the nematocysts are automatically released (except for certain organisms such as clownfish that live in a symbiotic relationship with a sea anemone).

Hermit crabs (*Pagurus*) inhabit tide pools, too. They have a well-armored pair of claws and upper body but a soft, unprotected abdomen, which they protect by inhabiting an abandoned snail shell (Figure 15.5a). They can often be seen scurrying around the tide pool area or fighting with other hermit crabs for new shells. Their abdomen has even evolved a curl to the right to make it fit properly into snail shells. Once in the snail shell, the crab can protect itself by closing off the shell's opening with its large claws.

In tide pools near the lower limit of the middle tide zone, sea urchins may be found feeding on algae (Figure 15.5b). Sea urchins have a five-toothed mouth centered on the bottom side of their hard spherical shell, consisting of fused calcium carbonate plates perforated to allow tube feet and water to pass through. Resembling a pincushion, the shell of a sea urchin has numerous spines for protection and to scrape out protective holes in rocks.

The Low Tide Zone: Organisms and Their Adaptations

The low tide zone is almost always submerged, so an abundance of algae is typically present. A diverse community of animals exists, too, but they are hidden by the great variety of marine algae and surf grass (*Phyllospadix*)

STUDENTS SOMETIMES ASK...

I've been at a tide pool and seen sea anemones. When I put my finger on one, it tends to gently grab my finger. Why does it do that?

The sea anemone is trying to kill you and wants to eat you (seriously!). Disguised as a harmless flower, the sea anemone is actually a vicious predator that will attack any unsuspecting animal (even a human) that its stinging tentacles entrap. Fortunately, the skin on your hands is thick enough to resist the stinging nematocyst and its neurotoxin. A couple of unsuspecting people, however, were interested in finding out if the sea anemone grabbed other things with its tentacles, so they put their *tongues* into a sea anemone. After a short time, their throats swelled almost completely closed, and they had to be rushed to a hospital. They lived, but the moral of this story is: *NEVER* put your tongue into a sea anemone!

(a)

(b)

FIGURE 15.5 Hermit crab and sea urchins. (a) Hermit crab (*Pagurus*) that has taken up residence in a *Maxwellia gemma* shell. **(b)** Purple sea urchins (*Echinus*) that have burrowed into the bottom of a rocky tide pool within the middle tide zone.

KEY CONCEPT

Rocky shores are divided into the spray zone and high, middle, and low tide (intertidal) zones. Many shelled organisms inhabit the upper zones, while more soft-bodied organisms and algae inhabit the lower zones.

FIGURE 15.6 Surf grass. Green surf grass (*Phyllospadix*) and various species of brown algae are exposed during an extremely low tide in this California tide pool. When the tide rises, the anchored surf grass floats and provides a protective hiding place for many low tide zone organisms.

(Figure 15.6). Various types of encrusting red algae (such as *Lithophyllum* and *Lithothamnium*), which are also seen in middle-zone tide pools, become very abundant in lower tide pools. In temperate latitudes, moderate-sized red and brown algae provide a drooping canopy beneath which much of the animal life can hide during low tide.

Scampering from crevice to crevice and in and out of tide pools across the full range of the intertidal zone are various species of shore crabs (Figure 15.7). These scavengers help keep the shore clean. Shore crabs spend most of the day hiding in cracks or beneath overhangs. At night, they eat algae as rapidly as they can tear them from the rock surface with their large front claws, called *chelae* (*khele* = claw). Their hard exoskeleton prevents them from drying out too quickly so they can spend long periods of time out of water.

15.3 What Communities Exist Along Sediment-Covered Shores?

Even though most sediment-covered shores have intertidal zones similar to rocky shores, life on and in sediment-covered shores requires very different adaptations than on rocky shores. Sediment-covered shores, for example, are composed of unconsolidated materials that often change shape and so require specific adaptations for organisms. In addition, there is much less species diversity in sediment-covered shores, but the organisms are usually found in great numbers. In the low tide zone of some beaches and on mud flats, for example, as many as 5000 to 8000 burrowing clams have been counted in only 1 square meter (10.8 square feet).

Nearly all large organisms that inhabit sediment-covered shores are called **infauna** (*in* = inside, *fauna* = animal) because they can burrow into the sediment. Sediment-covered shores also contain large numbers of microbial communities, particularly in quiet environments such as salt marshes and mud flats that tend to accumulate organic matter.

(a)

(b)

FIGURE 15.7 Shore crabs. (a) Sally lightfoot crab, *Grapsus grapsus*, which is a brightly colored and speedy crab found in tropical regions. **(b)** Shore crab, *Pachygrapsus crassipes*. This female is carrying eggs (dark oval structure curled under her abdomen).

Physical Environment of the Sediment

Sediment-covered shores include *coarse boulder beaches, sand beaches, salt marshes,* and *mud flats,* which represent progressively lower energy environments and are consequently composed of progressively finer sediment. The energy level that a shore experiences is related to the strength of waves and longshore currents. Along shores that experience low-energy levels, particle size becomes smaller, the sediment slope decreases, and overall sediment stability increases. Thus, the sediment in a fine-grained mud flat is more stable than that of a high-energy sandy beach.

A large quantity of water from breaking waves rapidly sinks into the sand and brings a continual supply of nutrients and oxygen-rich water for the animals that live there. This supply of oxygen also enhances bacterial decomposition of dead tissue. The sediment in salt marshes and mud flats is not nearly as rich in oxygen, however, so decomposition occurs more slowly.

Intertidal Zonation

The intertidal zone of the sediment-covered shore consists of supratidal, high tide, middle tide, and low tide zones, as shown in Figure 15.8. These zones are best developed on steeply sloping, coarse-sand beaches and are less distinct on the more gentle sloping, fine-sand beaches. On mud flats, the tiny, clay-sized particles

FIGURE 15.8 Intertidal zonation and common organisms of sediment-covered shores. Profile view of a coarse sand-covered shore showing intertidal zones, which are related to the amount of exposure during low tide, and common organisms, which usually occur only in specific tide zones. Beaches composed of finer sediment have more gentle slopes and show less distinct intertidal zonation.

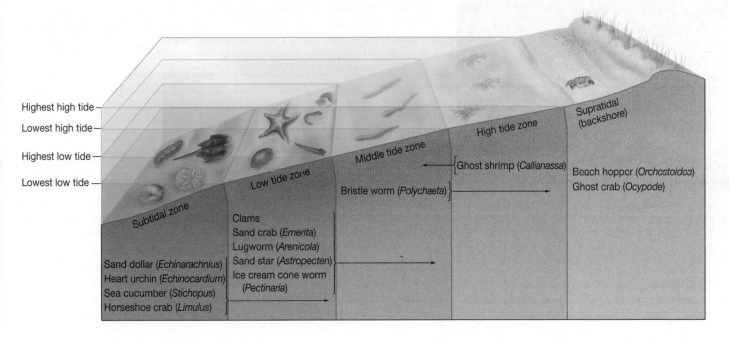

Highest high tide —
Lowest high tide —
Highest low tide —
Lowest low tide —

Supratidal (backshore)

High tide zone

Middle tide zone

Low tide zone

Subtidal zone

Ghost shrimp (*Callianassa*)

Bristle worm (*Polychaeta*)

Beach hopper (*Orchestoidea*)
Ghost crab (*Ocypode*)

Clams
Sand crab (*Emerita*)
Lugworm (*Arenicola*)
Sand star (*Astropecten*)
Ice cream cone worm (*Pectinaria*)

Sand dollar (*Echinarachnius*)
Heart urchin (*Echinocardium*)
Sea cucumber (*Stichopus*)
Horseshoe crab (*Limulus*)

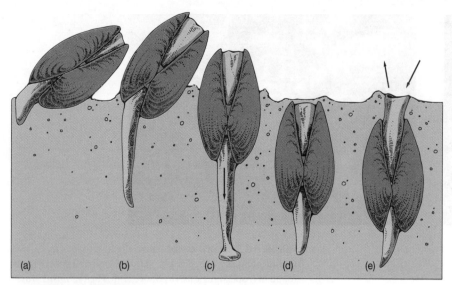

FIGURE 15.9 How a clam burrows. A clam burrows into sediment by **(a)** extending its pointed foot into the sediment and **(b)** forcing its foot deeper into the sediment and using this increasing leverage to bring the exposed, shell-clad body toward vertical. When the foot has penetrated deeply enough, a bulbous anchor forms at the bottom **(c)**, and a quick muscular contraction pulls the entire animal into the sediment **(d)**. The siphons are then pushed up above the sediment to pump in water **(e)**, from which the clam extracts food and oxygen.

form a deposit with essentially no slope, so zonation is not possible in this protected, low-energy environment.

The species of animals differ from zone to zone. As in intertidal rocky shores, however, the maximum *number* of species and the greatest *biomass* in intertidal sediment-covered shores are found near the low tide shoreline, and both diversity and biomass decrease toward the high tide shoreline.

Sandy Beaches: Organisms and Their Adaptations

Most animals at the beach burrow into the sand because there is no stable, fixed surface (as on rocky shores) to which they can attach. As a result, organisms are much less obvious than in other environments. By burrowing only a few centimeters beneath the surface, they encounter a much more stable environment where they are not bothered by fluctuations of temperature and salinity or the threat of drying out.

BIVALVE MOLLUSKS   A **bivalve** (*bi* = two, *valva* = a valve) is an animal having two hinged shells, such as a clam or a mussel. A **mollusk** is a member of the phylum Mollusca (*molluscus* = soft), characterized by a soft body and either an internal or external hard calcium carbonate shell.

Bivalve mollusks are well adapted to living within sediment. A single foot digs into the sediment to pull the creature down into the sand. The method by which clams bury themselves is shown in Figure 15.9. How deeply a bivalve can bury itself depends on the length of its siphons, which must reach above the sediment surface to pull in water for food (plankton) and oxygen. Indigestible matter is forced back out the siphon periodically by quick muscular contractions.

The greatest biomass of clams is burrowed into the low tide region of sandy beaches and decreases where the sediment becomes muddier.

ANNELID WORMS   A variety of **annelids** (*annelus* = a ring)—worms—are also well adapted to life in the sediment. The lugworm (*Arenicola*), for example, constructs a vertical, U-shaped burrow, the walls of which are strengthened with mucus. The worm moves forward to feed and extends its proboscis (snout) up into the head shaft of the burrow to loosen sand with quick, pulsing movements. A cone-shaped depression forms at the surface over the head end of the burrow as sand continually slides into the burrow and is ingested by the worm. As the sand passes through its digestive tract, the sand's *biofilm* (coating of organic matter) is digested, and the processed sand is deposited back at the surface.

CRUSTACEANS   **Crustaceans** (*crusta* = shell)—such as crabs, lobsters, shrimps, and barnacles—include predominately aquatic animals that are characterized by a segmented body, a hard exoskeleton, and paired, jointed limbs. On most sandy beaches, numerous crustaceans called *beach hoppers* feed on kelp cast up by storm waves or high tides. A common genus is *Orchestoidea*, which is only 2 to 3 centimeters (0.8 to 1.2 inches) long but can jump more than 2 meters (6.6 feet) high. Laterally flattened, beach hoppers usually spend the day buried in the sand or hidden in kelp. They become particularly active at night, when large groups may hop at the same time and form clouds above the piles of kelp on which they feed.

Sand crabs (*Emerita*) (Figure 15.10) are a type of crustacean common to many sandy beaches. Ranging in length from 2.5 to 8 centimeters (1 to 3 inches),

FIGURE 15.10 Sand crab. A sand crab (*Emerita*) emerges from the sand. They can often be found just beneath the surface of sandy beaches within the lower intertidal zone.

they move up and down the beach near the shoreline. They bury their bodies in the sand and leave their long, curved, V-shaped antennae pointing up the beach slope. These little crabs filter food particles from the water, and can be located by looking in the lower intertidal zone for a V-shaped pattern in the swash as it runs down the beach face.

ECHINODERMS   Echinoderms (*echino* = spiny, *derma* = skin) that live in beach deposits include the sand star (*Astropecten*) and heart urchin (*Echinocardium*). Sand stars prey on invertebrates that burrow into the low tide region of sandy beaches. The sand star is well designed for moving through sediment, with five tapered legs with spines and a smooth back.

More flattened and elongated than the sea urchins of the rocky shore, heart urchins live buried in the sand near the low tide line (Figure 15.11). They gather sand grains into their mouths, where the biofilm of organic matter that coats sand grains is scraped off and ingested.

MEIOFAUNA   Meiofauna (*meio* = lesser, *fauna* = animal) are small organisms that live in the spaces between sediment particles. These organisms, generally only 0.1 to 2 millimeters (0.004 to 0.08 inch) long, feed primarily on bacteria removed from the surface of sediment particles. Meiofauna include polychaetes, mollusks, arthropods, and nematodes (Figure 15.12) and live in sediment from the intertidal zone to deep-ocean trenches.

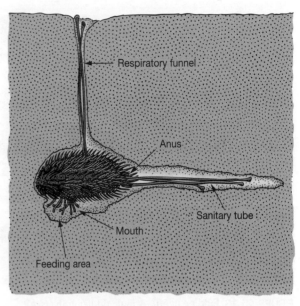

FIGURE 15.11 Heart urchin.   Feeding and respiratory structures of a heart urchin (*Echinocardium*), which feeds on the biofilm of organic matter that covers sand grains.

Mud Flats: Organisms and Their Adaptations

Eelgrass (*Zostera*) and turtle grass (*Thalassia*) are widely distributed in the low tide zone of mud flats and the adjacent shallow coastal regions. Numerous openings at the surface of mud flats attest to a large population of bivalve mollusks and other invertebrates.

Fiddler crabs (*Uca*) live in burrows that may exceed 1 meter (3 feet) deep in mud flats. Relatives of the shore crabs, they usually measure no more than 2 centimeters (0.8 inch) in width. Male fiddler crabs have one small claw and one oversized claw, which is up to 4 centimeters (1.6 inches) long (Figure 15.13). Fiddler crabs get their name because this large claw is waved around as if they were playing an imaginary fiddle. The females have two normal-sized claws. The large claw of the male is used to court females and to fight competing males.

> **KEY CONCEPT**
> Sediment-covered shores—including sandy beaches and mud flats—have an intertidal zonation similar to that of rocky shores but contain many organisms that live within the sediment (infauna).

(a)   (b)   (c)

FIGURE 15.12 Scanning electron micrographs of meiofauna.   **(a)** Head of a nematode, magnified 804 times. The pit on its left side and numerous projections are sensory structures. **(b)** Amphipod, which has a length of 3 millimeters (0.1 inch) and is related to crustaceans such as lobsters, crabs, and krill. **(c)** Polychaete worm, which has a length of 1 millimeter (0.04 inch) and is shown with its proboscis (mouth) extended (*left*).

FIGURE 15.13 Fiddler crab. A male fiddler crab (*Uca*) among eelgrass (*Zostera*) at Cape Hatteras, North Carolina. The fiddler crab uses its large claw for protection and for attracting mates.

15.4 What Communities Exist on the Shallow Offshore Ocean Floor?

The shallow offshore ocean floor extends from the spring low tide shoreline to the seaward edge of the continental shelf. It is mainly sediment covered, but rocky exposures may occur locally near shore. On rocky exposures, many types of marine algae exist, which have adaptations (such as gas-filled floats) for reaching from the shallow sea floor to near the sunlit surface waters.

The sediment-covered shelf has moderate to low species diversity. Surprisingly, the diversity of benthic organisms is *lowest* beneath upwelling regions. This is because upwelling waters that are rich in nutrients produce high pelagic production, so large amounts of dead organic matter are produced. When this matter rains down on the bottom and decomposes, it consumes oxygen, so the oxygen supply can be locally depleted, thereby limiting benthic populations. However, kelp beds associated with rocky bottoms are a specialized shallow-water community with higher diversity.

Rocky Bottoms (Subtidal): Organisms and Their Adaptations

A rocky bottom within the shallow inner **subtidal** (*sub* = under, *tidal* = the tides) **zone** is usually covered with various types of marine macro algae.

KELP AND KELP FORESTS Along the North American Pacific coast, the giant brown bladder **kelp** (*Macrocystis*) attaches to rocks as deep as 30 meters (100 feet) and is attached to rocky bottoms with a rootlike anchor called a *holdfast* (Figure 15.14a), which is so strong that only large storm waves can break the algae free. The *stipes* and *blades* of the algae are supported by gas-filled floats called *pneumatocysts* (*pneumato* = breath, *cystis* = bladder), which allow the algae to grow upward and extend for another 30 meters (100 feet) along the surface to allow for good exposure to sunlight. Under ideal conditions, *Macrocystis* can grow up to 0.6 meter (2 feet) per day, making it the fastest-growing algae in the world.

The giant brown bladder kelp and bull kelp (*Nereocystis*), another fast-growing kelp, often form beds called **kelp forests** along the Pacific coast (Figure 15.14b). Smaller tufts of red and brown algae are found on the bottom and also live on the kelp blades.

Kelp forests are highly productive ecosystems that provide shelter for a wide variety of organisms living within or directly upon the kelp as epifauna. These organisms are an important food source for many of the animals living in and near the kelp forest, including mollusks, sea stars, fishes, octopuses, lobsters, and marine mammals. Surprisingly, very few animals feed directly on the living kelp. Among those that do are sea urchins and a large sea slug called the sea hare (*Aplysia*). The distribution of kelp forests is shown in Figure 15.14c.

LOBSTERS Large crustaceans—including lobsters and crabs—are common along rocky bottoms. The spiny lobsters are named for their spiny covering and have two very large, spiny antennae (Figure 15.15a). These antennae serve as feelers and are equipped with noise-making devices near their base that are used in protection. The genus *Panulirus*, which reaches lengths to 50 centimeters (20 inches), is considered a delicacy and lives in water deeper than 20 meters (65 feet) along the European coast. The Caribbean lobster (*Panulirus argus*) sometimes

---

STUDENTS SOMETIMES ASK...

What is an urchin barren?

An urchin barren is created when the population of sea urchins goes unchecked and the urchins devour entire areas of giant brown bladder kelp (*Macrocystis*), one of the main types of algae in kelp forests. The urchins chew through the holdfast structure that holds the kelp in place and set it adrift. In California, the severe reduction of animals that prey on urchins (such as the wolf eel and sea otter) has upset the natural balance of ocean food webs. Consequently, sea urchins have proliferated and urchin barrens now exist where there were once lush kelp beds.

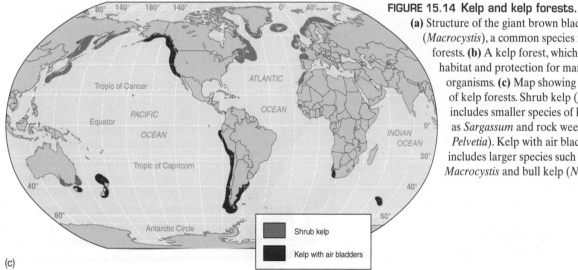

FIGURE 15.14 Kelp and kelp forests.
(a) Structure of the giant brown bladder kelp (*Macrocystis*), a common species in kelp forests. (b) A kelp forest, which provides habitat and protection for many marine organisms. (c) Map showing distribution of kelp forests. Shrub kelp (*green*) includes smaller species of kelp such as *Sargassum* and rock weed (*Fucus*, *Pelvetia*). Kelp with air bladders (*red*) includes larger species such as *Macrocystis* and bull kelp (*Nereocystis*).

exhibits a remarkable behavior when it migrates single file across the sea floor in lines that are several kilometers long.

Panulirus interruptus is the spiny lobster of the American West Coast. All spiny lobsters are taken for food, but none are as highly regarded as the so-called true lobsters (genus *Homarus*), which include the American (Maine) lobster, *Homarus americanus* (Figure 15.15b). Although they are scavengers like their

FIGURE 15.15 Spiny and American lobsters. (a) Spiny lobster (*Panulirus interruptus*), which is found along rocky bottoms in the Caribbean and the West Coast of North America. **(b)** American or Maine lobster (*Homarus americanus*), which has large claws that are used for feeding and for defense. It is found along the East Coast of North America from Labrador, Canada to North Carolina in the United States.

(a)

(b)

spiny relatives, the true lobsters also feed on live animals, including mollusks, crustaceans, and other lobsters.

OYSTERS Oysters are thick-shelled sessile (anchored) bivalve mollusks found in estuaries. They grow best where there is a steady flow of clean water to provide plankton and oxygen.

Oysters are food for sea stars, fishes, crabs, and snails that bore through the shell and rasp away the soft tissue inside (Figure 15.16). In fact, this may be one of the main reasons that oysters have such a thick shell.[3] Oysters also have great commercial importance to humans throughout the world as a food source.

Oyster beds are composed of empty shells of many previous generations that are cemented to a hard substrate or to one another, with the living generation on top. Each female produces many millions of eggs each year, which become planktonic larvae when fertilized. After a few weeks as plankton, the larvae attach themselves to the bottom. As a material upon which to anchor, oyster larvae prefer (in order): live oyster shells, dead oyster shells, and rock.

Coral Reefs: Organisms and Their Adaptations

Individual corals—called **polyps** (*poly* = many, *pous* = foot)—small benthic marine animals that feed with stinging tentacles and are related to jellyfish. Most species of corals are about the size of an ant, live in large colonies, and construct hard calcium carbonate structures for protection. Coral species are found throughout the ocean (and even in cold, deep water), but coral accumulations that are classified as **coral reefs**, which are wave-resistant structures produced by corals and other organisms,

Oyster drill

Shell

Pierced shell

Body

Oyster body

Mouth/ Rasp

FIGURE 15.16 An oyster-drill snail feeding on an oyster. An oyster-drill snail uses its rasplike mouthpiece (*inset*) to drill through an oyster's shell and feed on the oyster's soft body.

---

[3]This is an example of *co-evolution*, where a weapon possessed by one species creates evolutionary pressure in another species for a defense to defeat it. This, in turn, causes other evolutionary traits for new weapons, creating a co-evolutionary "arms race."

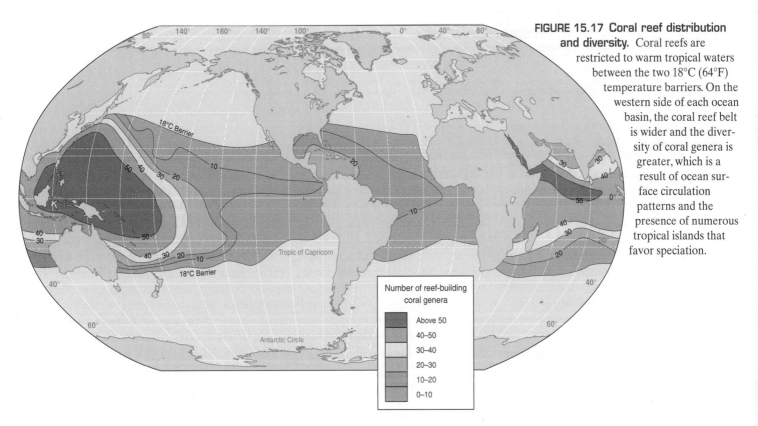

FIGURE 15.17 Coral reef distribution and diversity. Coral reefs are restricted to warm tropical waters between the two 18°C (64°F) temperature barriers. On the western side of each ocean basin, the coral reef belt is wider and the diversity of coral genera is greater, which is a result of ocean surface circulation patterns and the presence of numerous tropical islands that favor speciation.

are restricted to shallow warmer water regions. See Chapter 2 for a description of the stages of development in coral reefs.

CONDITIONS NECESSARY FOR CORAL REEF DEVELOPMENT Corals are very temperature sensitive and require warm water to survive. in fact, corals need water where the average monthly temperature exceeds 18°C (64°F) throughout the year (Figure 15.17). Furthermore, water that is too warm can kill corals: They cannot survive for long when the water temperature exceeds 30°C (86°F). That's why warmer-than-normal sea surface temperatures—such as those experienced during severe El Niños or other warming episodes—tend to stress corals and are linked to outbreaks of coral bleaching and other diseases (Box 15.1).

Water warm enough to support coral growth is found primarily within the tropics. Reefs also grow as far north and south as 35 degrees latitude on the western margins of ocean basins, however, where warm-water currents raise average sea surface temperatures (Figure 15.17).

The map in Figure 15.17 also shows the greater diversity of reef-building corals on the western side of ocean basins. More than 50 genera of corals thrive in a broad area of the western Pacific Ocean and a narrow belt of the western Indian Ocean. Fewer than 30 genera, however, occur in the Atlantic Ocean, with the greatest diversity occurring in the Caribbean Sea. This pattern is related to the positions of the continents prior to about 30 million years ago, when the warm equatorial Tethys Sea connected the world's tropical oceans and provided a highway for the worldwide distribution of coral species and reef-associated organisms. With time, tectonic changes in landmass position closed the Tethys Sea and were accompanied by changes in ocean currents and climate, which reduced coral reef biodiversity in areas such as the Atlantic. Further, the presence of numerous tropical islands in the western Pacific provides a variety of habitats that favors coral speciation.

STUDENTS SOMETIMES ASK...

I've heard about the recent discovery of deep-water corals. How are they different from shallow-water corals?

Although coral reefs are generally associated with shallow tropical seas, recent deep-ocean exploration using advanced acoustics and submersibles has revealed unexpectedly widespread and diverse coral ecosystems in deep, cold waters. These corals are found below sunlit surface waters—at a record depth of 6,328 meters (20,800 feet)—on continental shelves, continental slopes, seamounts, and mid-ocean ridge systems around the world. Since the corals don't live in particularly deep water, the term *cold-water coral* is more appropriate. They lack the symbiotic zooxanthellae algae that their shallow-water cousins have but can be brightly colored and use their stinging tentacles to capture tiny plankton or detritus concentrated by ocean currents. They build their skeletons of calcium carbonate as shallow corals do and create large reef structures or coral mounds that provide a habitat for many other species. Some species of deep-water coral may be thousands of years old. What is remarkable about them is that they have remained unnoticed for so long. New cold-water coral species, in fact, have recently been discovered in waters off highly populated Southern California!

15.1   FOCUS ON THE ENVIRONMENT

HOW WHITE I AM: CORAL BLEACHING AND OTHER DISEASES

Coral bleaching describes the loss of color in corals that causes them to turn white as if bleach has been poured on the reef (Figure 15A). Coral bleaching often occurs in response to elevated water temperatures and causes the coral's colorful symbiotic partner—zooxanthellae algae—to be killed outright, leave, or become toxic to their hosts, in which case they are expelled. Once bleached, the coral no longer receives nourishment from the algae, and if the coral does not regain its symbiotic algae within a matter of weeks it will die. Bleaching often occurs in surface waters—the top 2 to 3 meters (7 to 10 feet)—but has also been observed at depths of 30 meters (100 feet) and can occur as quickly as overnight.

Florida's coral reefs have experienced at least eight widespread bleachings since the early 1900s, and at least 70% of the corals along the Pacific Central American coast died due to bleaching associated with the severe El Niño event of 1982–1983. For example, coral reefs around the Galápagos Islands thrive in ocean water at or below 27°C (81°F). If the water is even 1 or 2°C (2 or 4°F) warmer for an extended period, however, the coral may expel the algae, in effect "bleaching" itself. The warming during the 1982–1983 El Niño was so severe and long-lived that two species of Panamanian coral became extinct. The bleaching episode of 1987 affected coral reefs worldwide, especially those in Florida and throughout the Caribbean. Since then, widespread bleachings have occurred with increasing frequency and intensity. For instance, the El Niño event of 1997–1998 raised water temperatures several degrees higher than normal and has been blamed for the most geographically widespread bleaching ever recorded, including the equatorial eastern Pacific Ocean, the Yucatán coast, the Florida Keys, and the Netherlands Antilles. In addition, a severe bleaching event in 2002 along Australia's Great Barrier Reef was associated with exceptionally high sea surface temperatures.

Besides abnormally high surface water temperatures (such as El Niño events), the algae may leave their hosts or be expelled due to elevated ultraviolet radiation levels, a decrease in sunlight-blocking particles high in the atmosphere, pollution, salinity changes, invasion of disease, or a combination of factors. Some researchers suggest that reactive oxygen builds up in the coral's tissues and becomes toxic when temperatures are excessively warm. Then the algae are expelled or, perhaps, the algae leave with dead tissue. The strong correlation between coral bleaching and elevated water temperature concerns marine scientists because sea surface temperatures are becoming warmer as a result of human-induced climate change. Whatever the cause, coral bleaching indicates that corals are experiencing severe environmental stress.

James Porter, a coral reef ecologist at the University of Georgia, and his colleagues study diseases that affect corals. They have been monitoring the health of corals in the Florida Keys since 1995 and have discovered the reappearance of *white plague disease* as well as a dozen new diseases, such as *white band disease*, *white pox*, *black band disease*, *yellow band (yellow blotch) disease*, *patchy necrosis*, and *rapid wasting disease*.

The cause of most of these diseases is still being investigated, and it is not known if the new diseases are from the invasion of microorganisms—bacteria, viruses, or fungi—or related to environmental stress as coral bleaching is. As human population has increased along the Florida Keys, the coral reefs of the Keys have begun to show signs of stress, thus making them more susceptible to a host of diseases. The increased nutrient levels and water turbidity resulting from soil runoff and improper sewage disposal in the Keys may contribute to the problem, too.

Easter Island

March 1999

March 2000

FIGURE 15A Normal and bleached coral. Normal coral (*Pocillopora verrucosa*) near Easter Island (*left*) and bleached coral one year later (*right*) after exceptionally high sea surface temperatures.

Besides warm water, other environmental conditions necessary for coral growth include the following:

- Strong sunlight (not for the corals themselves, which are animals and can exist in deeper water, but for the symbiotic photosynthetic microscopic dinoflagellate algae called **zooxanthellae** that live within the coral's tissues[4]).

- Strong wave or current action (to bring nutrients and oxygen).

- Lack of turbidity (suspended particles in the water tend to absorb radiant energy, interfere with the coral's filter-feeding capability, and can even bury corals, so corals are not usually found close to areas where major rivers drain into the sea).

- Salt water (corals die if the water is too fresh, which is another reason coral reefs do not form near the mouths of freshwater rivers).

- A hard substrate for attachment (corals cannot attach to a muddy bottom, so they often build upon the hard skeletons of their ancestors, creating coral reefs that are several kilometers thick).

SYMBIOSIS OF CORAL AND ALGAE "Coral reefs" are more than just coral. Algae, mollusks, and foraminifers contribute to the reef structure, too. Individual reef-building corals are **hermatypic** (*herma* = pillar, *typi* = type) because they have a *mutualistic relationship*[5] with microscopic algae (zooxanthellae) that live within the tissue of the coral polyp. The algae provide their coral hosts with a continual supply of food, and the corals provide the zooxanthellae with nutrients. Although coral polyps capture tiny planktonic food with their stinging tentacles, most reef-building corals receive up to 90% of their nutrition from symbiotic zooxanthellae algae. In this way, corals are able to survive in the nutrient-poor waters that are characteristic of tropical oceans.

Other reef animals also have a symbiotic relationship with various types of marine algae. Those that derive part of their nutrition from their algae partners are called **mixotrophs** (*mixo* = mix, *tropho* = nourishment) and include coral, foraminifers, sponges, and mollusks (Figure 15.18). The algae not only nourish the coral but may also contribute to its calcification by extracting carbon dioxide from the coral's body fluids.

WEB VIDEO
Coral and Coral Bleaching

KEY CONCEPT
Coral are small colonial animals with stinging cells that are found primarily in shallow tropical waters and need strong sunlight, wave or current action, lack of turbidity, normal salinity seawater, and a hard substrate for attachment.

FIGURE 15.18 Coral reef inhabitants that rely on symbiotic algae. (a) Coral polyps, which are nourished by internal zooxanthellae algae and also by extending their tentacles to capture tiny planktonic organisms from the surrounding water. **(b)** The blue-gray sponge *Niphates digitalis* (*left*) and the brown sponge *Agelas* (*right*), which contains symbiotic algae or bacteria. **(c)** A giant clam (*Tridacna gigas*), which depends on symbiotic algae living within its mantle tissue.

(a)

(b)

(c)

[4]It is zooxanthellae (*zoo* = animal, *xanthos* = yellow, *ella* = small) algae that give corals their distinctive bright coloration (which can be many colors besides yellow).

[5]See Chapter 14 for a discussion of the types of symbiosis, including mutualism.

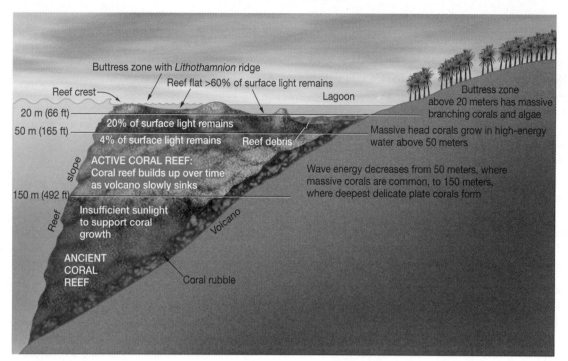

Buttress zone with *Lithothamnion* ridge
Reef flat >60% of surface light remains
Reef crest
Lagoon
Buttress zone above 20 meters has massive branching corals and algae
20 m (66 ft)
50 m (165 ft)
20% of surface light remains
4% of surface light remains
Reef debris
Massive head corals grow in high-energy water above 50 meters
slope
ACTIVE CORAL REEF: Coral reef builds up over time as volcano slowly sinks
Wave energy decreases from 50 meters, where massive corals are common, to 150 meters, where deepest delicate plate corals form
150 m (492 ft)
Insufficient sunlight to support coral growth
Reef
Volcano
ANCIENT CORAL REEF
Coral rubble

FIGURE 15.19 Coral reef zonation. Coral reefs exhibit zonation because of the decrease in both wave energy and sunlight intensity with increasing ocean depth. As a result, massive branching corals occur above 20 meters (66 feet), where wave energy is great; corals become more delicate with increasing depth, until a depth of around 150 meters (500 feet), where too little solar radiation is available to allow the survival of their symbiotic zooxanthellae algae.

FIGURE 15.20 Non-reef-building inhabitants.
(a) Coral reefs supply habitat and protection for many fishes, including this Guineafowl (spotted) puffer (*Arothron meleagris*). Puffers usually aren't quick enough to escape a predator, but they can expand their bodies into a large, spherical, spiny ball that is not easily eaten. **(b)** Unlike reef-building corals, some corals do not secrete a hard calcium carbonate structure, such as this soft gorgonian coral (*Nicella schmitti*), which has feeding polyps (*light purple*) extending from its branches. Each polyp is about 1 centimeter (0.4 inch) across.

(a)

(b)

Coral reefs actually contain up to three times as much algal biomass as animal biomass. Zooxanthellae, for example, account for up to 75% of the biomass of reef-building coral. Nevertheless, zooxanthellae account for less than 5% of the reef's overall algal mass (most of the rest is filamentous green algae).

CORAL REEF ZONATION On many large coral reefs, there is a well-developed vertical and horizontal zonation of the reef slope (Figure 15.19), which is caused by changes in sunlight, wave energy, salinity, water depth, temperature, and other factors. These zones can readily be identified by the types of coral present and the assemblages of other organisms found in and near the reef.

Because algae need sunlight for photosynthesis, the greatest depth to which active coral growth can occur is about 150 meters (500 feet). Water motion is less at these depths, so relatively delicate plate corals can live on the outer slope of the reef from 150 meters (500 feet) up to about 50 meters (165 feet), where light intensity is as low as 4% of the surface intensity (Figure 15.19).

From 50 meters (164 feet) to about 20 meters (66 feet), water motion from breaking waves increases on the side of the reef facing into the prevailing current flow. Correspondingly, the mass of coral growth and the strength of the coral structure supporting it increase toward the top of this zone, where light intensity is as low as 20% of the surface value.

The reef flat may have a water depth of a few centimeters to a few meters at low tide, so it has at least 60% of the surface light intensity. Many species of colorful reef fish inhabit this shallow water, as well as sea cucumbers, worms, and mollusks. In the protected water of the reef lagoon live gorgonian coral, anemones, crustaceans, mollusks, and echinoderms (Figure 15.20).

THE IMPORTANCE OF CORAL REEFS Coral reefs are some of the largest structures created by living creatures on Earth (Australia's Great Barrier Reef, for example, is more than 2000 kilometers [1250 miles] long). Although coral reefs cover less than half a percent of the ocean's surface area, they are home to 25% of all marine species, including almost a third of the world's estimated 20,000 species of marine fish. Coral reefs provide shelter, food, and breeding grounds that attract numerous other species including sea anemones, sea stars, crabs, sea slugs, clams, sponges, sea turtles, marine mammals, and sharks. In fact, coral reefs foster a diversity of species that surpasses even that of tropical rain forests, making coral reefs the most diverse communities in the marine environment.

Coral reefs provide many benefits to people. Some 100 million people worldwide depend upon healthy reef systems, which provide a multi-billion-dollar tourist industry. In fact, many tropical countries that have coral reefs receive more than 50% of their gross national product as tourism related to reefs. Fisheries associated with reefs supply more than one-sixth of all fish from the sea. Recently, pharmacologists and marine chemists have discovered a storehouse of new medical compounds from coral reef inhabitants that fight maladies such as cancer and infections. In addition, reefs help prevent shoreline erosion and protect coastal communities from storm waves and tsunami. The hard calcium carbonate skeletons of coral have even been used in some human bone grafts.

CORAL REEFS AND NUTRIENT LEVELS   When human populations increase on land adjacent to coral reefs, the reefs deteriorate. Fishing, trampling, boat collisions with the reef, sediment increase due to development, and removal of reef inhabitants by visitors all damage the reef. One of the more subtle effects is the inevitable increase in the nutrient levels of the reef waters from sewage discharge and farm fertilizers.

As nutrient levels increase in reef waters, the dominant benthic community changes in the following ways:

- At low nutrient levels, hermatypic corals and other reef animals that contain algal symbiotic partners thrive.
- Moderate nutrient levels favor fleshy benthic plants and algae, and high nutrient levels favor suspension feeders such as clams.
- At high nutrient levels, the phytoplankton mass exceeds the benthic algal mass, so benthic populations tied to the phytoplankton food web dominate.

Increased phytoplankton biomass reduces the clarity of the water, too, which interferes with the coral's filter-feeding capability. The fast-growing members of the phytoplankton-based ecosystem destroy the reef structure by overgrowing the slow-growing coral and through *bioerosion,* which is erosion of the reef by organisms. Bioerosion by sea urchins and sponges is particularly damaging to many coral reefs.

THE CROWN-OF-THORNS PHENOMENON   The crown-of-thorns (*Acanthaster planci*) is a sea star (Figure 15.21) that has greatly proliferated and destroyed living coral on many reefs throughout the western Pacific Ocean since 1962 and more recently in the Indian Ocean and Red Sea. The sea star moves across reefs and eats the coral polyps, devouring as much as 13 square meters (140 square feet) of coral in a single year. Normally, however, the coral can grow back if it has enough time to do so.

Though a natural part of reef ecosystems, the sea stars can cause extensive damage because, for reasons not fully understood, a small group can suddenly multiply to millions. For example, vast numbers of crown-of-thorns sea stars have recently decimated many coral communities, particularly on the Great Barrier Reef. Initially, divers were employed to smash the crown-of-thorns, but sea stars (which have tremendous regenerating capabilities) can easily produce new individuals from various body parts, so it only made the problem worse.

Some investigators suggest the proliferation of the crown-of-thorns sea star is a modern phenomenon brought about by the activities of humans, although there

FIGURE 15.21 Crown-of-thorns sea star. Crown-of-thorns sea stars (*Acanthaster planci*) have plagued Australia's Great Barrier Reef.

is little supporting evidence. There is, however, speculation that the crown-of-thorns sea star has multiplied because large reef fish that prey on them have been removed by overfishing. Other studies show that during the last 80,000 years, the crown-of-thorns sea star has been even more abundant than it is today. Thus, the sea star may be an integral part of the reef ecology in this region, and their increase may be part of a long-term natural cycle rather than a destructive event triggered by human actions.

CORAL REEFS IN DECLINE Studies concerning the health of coral reefs worldwide show that they are in rapid decline due to various human and environmental factors. A recent survey of coral reef ecosystems, for example, shows that only 30% are healthy now, down from 41% in 2000. Another study estimated that more than one-third of the major reef-building coral species are currently at high risk of extinction, with severe consequences for entire reef ecosystems. In the Caribbean, the area of sea floor covered by live hard coral has decreased 80% in the past 30 years. Even the Great Barrier Reef, widely regarded as one of the world's most pristine coral reefs, has lost over half of its coral cover during the past 40 years.

The most serious threat to coral reefs—overshadowing natural cataclysms such as hurricanes, floods, and tsunami—is human activity. Overfishing, for example, has depleted the populations of many of the fishes that graze on algae and keep it from smothering the reefs. Runoff laden with sediment and pollutants further fuels the growth of algae and spreads harmful bacteria. Even more threatening to coral reefs are increased levels of human-caused atmospheric carbon dioxide, which is absorbed into the ocean and increases ocean acidity, making it more difficult for corals to create their calcium carbonate skeletons.[6] In addition, global warming as a result of human activities has been shown to have increased ocean surface temperatures, affecting temperature-sensitive corals worldwide and making them more prone to disease and bleaching episodes (see Box 15.1). And, the predicted rise in sea level as a result of global warming may wreak havoc on corals by submerging them more deeply, in effect reducing the amount of sunlight they receive. The future for healthy coral reefs looks bleak unless immediate and dramatic conservation measures are enacted to preserve them.

> **KEY CONCEPT**
> Corals are able to survive in nutrient-depleted warm water by living symbiotically with zooxanthellae algae, which live within the coral's tissues, provide it with food, and give the coral its color.

15.5 What Communities Exist on the Deep-Ocean Floor?

The vast majority of the ocean floor lies submerged below several kilometers of water. Less is known about life in the deep ocean than about life in any of the shallower nearshore environments because it is difficult and expensive to investigate the deep sea. Just to obtain samples from the deep-ocean floor requires a specially designed submersible or a properly equipped research vessel that has a spool of high-strength cable at least 12 kilometers (7.5 miles) long. In the past, the inaccessibility of ocean depths fueled much debate about the existence of life in the deep ocean (see Web Box 15.1).

Even today, collecting samples by submersible or with a biological dredge is a time-consuming process. Because the supply of oxygen is limited, manned submersibles can stay down for only 12 hours, and it may take 8 of those hours to descend and ascend. To send a dredge to the deep-ocean floor and retrieve it from the depths takes about 24 hours.

Robotics and remotely operated vehicles (ROVs) are making it possible to observe and sample even the deepest reaches of the ocean more easily. Because

---

[6]For more information on the recent increase in ocean acidity and other climate change issues, see Chapter 16, "The Oceans and Climate Change."

they are unmanned, ROVs are cheaper to operate and can stay beneath the surface for months if necessary. These developments should lead to further discoveries in one of Earth's least known habitats.

The Physical Environment

The deep-ocean floor includes bathyal, abyssal, and hadal zones.[7] Here, the physical environment is much different than at the surface; it is quite stable and uniform. Light is present in only the lowest concentrations down to a maximum of 1000 meters (3300 feet) and absent below this depth. Everywhere the temperature rarely exceeds 3°C (37°F) and falls as low as −1.8°C (28.8°F) in the high latitudes. Salinity remains at slightly less than 35‰.[8] Oxygen content is constant and relatively high. Pressure exceeds 200 kilograms per square centimeter (200 atmospheres, or 2940 pounds per square inch) on the oceanic ridges, exceeds 300 to 500 kilograms per square centimeter (300 to 500 atmospheres, or 4410 to 7350 pounds per square inch) on the deep-ocean abyssal plains, and exceeds 1000 kilograms per square centimeter (1000 atmospheres, or 14,700 pounds per square inch) in the deepest trenches.[9] Bottom currents are generally slow but more variable than once believed. For example, **abyssal storms** created by warm- and cold-core eddies of surface currents affect certain areas, lasting several weeks and causing bottom currents to reverse and/or increase in speed.

A thin layer of sediment covers much of the deep-ocean floor. On abyssal plains and in deep trenches, sediment is composed of mudlike abyssal clay deposits. The accumulation of oozes—composed of dead planktonic organisms that have sunk through the water column—occurs on the flanks of oceanic ridges and rises. On the continental rise, there may be some coarse sediment from nearby land sources. Sediment may be absent on steep areas of the continental slope. It may also be absent near the crest of the mid-ocean ridge and along the slopes of seamounts and oceanic islands, where it had not had enough time to accumulate on newly formed ocean floor.

Food Sources and Species Diversity

Because of the lack of light, photosynthetic primary production cannot occur. Except for the chemosynthetic productivity that occurs around hydrothermal vents, all benthic organisms receive their food from the surface waters above. Only about 1 to 3% of the food produced in the euphotic (sunlit) zone reaches the deep-ocean floor, so the scarcity of food that drifts down from the sunlit surface waters—not low temperature or high pressure—limits deep-sea benthic biomass. However, some variability in the supply of food is caused by seasonal phytoplankton blooms at the surface. Figure 15.22 shows the food sources for deep-sea organisms.

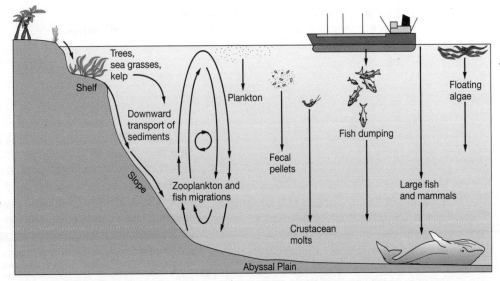

FIGURE 15.22 Food sources for deep-sea organisms. Most deep-sea organisms obtain their food from surface water after it slowly settles through the water column to the sea floor. The food supply is usually limited, except when large fish or mammals (such as whales) sink to the bottom.

[7]The bathyal, abyssal, and hadal zones are described in Chapter 12.

[8]Recall that average surface seawater salinity is 35 parts per thousand (‰).

[9]The pressure is 1 atmosphere (1 kilogram per square centimeter) at the ocean surface and increases by 1 atmosphere for each 10 meters (33 feet) of depth. Thus, a pressure of 1000 atmospheres is 1000 times that at the ocean's surface.

15.2   RESEARCH METHODS IN OCEANOGRAPHY

HOW LONG WOULD YOUR REMAINS REMAIN ON THE SEA FLOOR?

What happens to people who are buried at sea? How long do their remains remain on the sea floor? How long do the remains of a large organism such as a whale remain on the sea bottom? Oceanographers who study deep-sea bio-communities have conducted experiments in the deep sea to help answer these questions.

One experiment was conducted along the sea floor in the Philippine Trench, at a depth of 9600 meters (31,500 feet), in 1975. Several whole fish were placed on the sea floor, and an underwater camera positioned above them took a picture every few minutes to observe how long the bait remained there (Figure 15B). *Hirondellea gigas*, a scavenging benthic shrimplike amphipod, discovered the bait after only a few hours. The bait was swarming with amphipods after 9 hours, and it was stripped of flesh in 16 hours! Other studies obtained similar results, suggesting that organisms the size of humans would have their soft tissue devoured within a day on the deep-ocean floor.

For deep-sea organisms, large food falls represent an unpredictable but intense nutrient supply, instantaneously depositing as much food as would be delivered to the deep sea by the normal rain of detritus in about 2000 years. Deep-sea scavengers such as amphipods, hagfish, and sleeper sharks use special chemoreceptive sensory devices to identify and quickly locate food on the sea floor. In addition, whale carcasses can support a thriving ecosystem of benthic organisms—including some species normally associated with hydrothermal vents—that arrive as larvae drift on deep-ocean currents.

To test how long a whale's remains lasted on the sea floor, researchers used two dead juvenile gray whales that washed up on the beach in Southern California in 1996 and 1997. With permission from the National Marine Fisheries Service, the 5000-kilogram (5.5-ton) whales were intentionally weighted and sunk in the San Diego Trough. Researchers in a deep-diving submersible visited the carcasses at regular intervals and found that the gray whales were completely stripped of flesh in four months! Other studies indicate that even blue whales, which can weigh 25 times more than a gray whale, are stripped of their flesh in as little as six months.

0:00 hours   2:00 hours

4:05 hours   9:00 hours

12:10 hours   16:10 hours

FIGURE 15B Time-sequence photography of fish remains on the deep-ocean floor.

Many of the organisms that inhabit the deep sea have special adaptations to help them detect food using chemical clues. Once food is found, these organisms are efficient at consuming it (Box 15.2).

For many years, it was believed that the species diversity of the deep-ocean floor was quite low compared with shallow-water communities. Researchers studying sediment-dwelling animals in the North Atlantic, however, discovered an unexpectedly large diversity of species. An area of 21 square meters (225 square feet) contained 898 species, of which 460 were new to science. After analyzing 200 samples, new species were being discovered at a rate that suggested millions of deep-sea species!

It turns out that deep-sea species diversity—especially for small infaunal deposit feeders—rivals tropical rain forests. It also appears, however, that the distribution of deep-sea life is patchy and depends to a large degree on the presence of certain microenvironments.

KEY CONCEPT

The deep-ocean floor is a stable environment of darkness, cold water, and high pressure but still supports life. The food source for most deep-sea organisms is from sunlit surface waters.

Deep-Sea Hydrothermal Vent Biocommunities: Organisms and Their Adaptations

The surprising discovery of deep-sea hydrothermal (*hydro* = water, *thermo* = heat) vents and their biocommunities has been one of the most important finds in the modern history of ocean discovery. Life at hydrothermal vents may in fact provide insights into both the origin of life on Earth and its possible existence elsewhere in the solar system.

DISCOVERY OF HYDROTHERMAL VENT BIOCOMMUNITIES   An active hydrothermal vent field on the ocean floor was visited for the first time in 1977 during a dive of the submersible *Alvin*. The field exists in complete darkness in water below 2500 meters (8200 feet) in the Galápagos Rift, near the equator in the eastern Pacific Ocean (Figures 15.23 and 15.24). Hot water was observed spewing from cracks in the sea floor and from tall chimneys. Water temperature near the vents was 8 to 12°C (46 to 54°F), whereas normal water temperature at these depths is about 2°C (36°F).

These vents supported the first known **hydrothermal vent biocommunities**, consisting of organisms that were unknown to science and unusually large for those depths. The most prominent species include giant tubeworms up to 1.8 meters (6 feet) long (Figure 15.25a), clams as large as 25 centimeters (10 inches) across, large mussels, two varieties of white crabs, and extensive microbial mats. These biocommunities had up to 1000 times more biomass than the rest of the deep-ocean floor. In a region of scarce nutrients and small populations of organisms, these hydrothermal vents are truly the oases of the deep ocean.

FIGURE 15.23 *Alvin* **approaches a hydrothermal vent biocommunity.** Schematic view of a hydrothermal vent area, showing lava pillows and a black smoker that spews hot (350°C [662°F]), sulfide-rich water from a chimney. Organisms (counterclockwise from *Alvin*) include the grenadier fish (or rattail fish), octacoras, a sea anemone, white brachyuran crabs, large clams (*Calypotogena*), and tubeworms (*Riftia*).

FIGURE 15.24 Vents and seeps known to support deep-sea biocommunities. Location map of major hydrothermal vents (*red dots*), cold seeps (*blue dots*), and hydrocarbon seeps (*black dots*). Colored lines indicate plate boundaries.

FIGURE 15.25 Chemosynthetic life. (a) Tubeworms up to 1 meter (3.3 feet) long are found at the Galápagos Rift and other deep-sea hydrothermal vents. **(b)** Sulfur-oxidizing archaea (enlarged 20,000 times; white bar at top is 1 micron long) that live symbiotically within the tissue of tubeworms, clams, and mussels found at hydrothermal vents. **(c)** A hydrothermal vent biocommunity from the Mariana Back-Arc Basin, which included a new genus and species of sea anemone (*Marianactis bythios*); the gastropod *Alviniconcha hessleri,* which is the first known conch to contain chemosynthetic bacteria; and the galatheid crab (*Munidopsis marianica*).

In 1979, south of the tip of Baja California at 21 degrees north latitude on the East Pacific Rise, tall underwater chimneys were discovered belching hot vent water (350°C or 662°F) so rich in metal sulfides that it colored the water black. These chimney vents, which are composed primarily of sulfides of copper, zinc, and silver, came to be called **black smokers** because of their resemblance to factory smokestacks.

A typical hydrothermal vent may emit fluids that are not only hot (upwards of 350°C or 662°F), but also acidic (pH = 3−4) and extremely toxic, with high concentrations of dissolved hydrogen sulfide and heavy metals such as cadmium, arsenic, and lead. Yet the dark water venting from black smokers has been found to be rich in microbes.

CHEMOSYNTHESIS The most important members of these hydrothermal vent biocommunities are microscopic **archaea** (*archaeo* = ancient), which are primitive single-celled organisms that resemble bacteria but have chemical similarities to multicelled organisms. Archaea thrive on sea floor chemicals—most notably hydrogen sulfide—and perform **chemosynthesis** (*chemo* = chemistry, *syn* = with, *thesis* = an arranging), manufacturing carbohydrates (sugar) from water, carbon dioxide, and dissolved oxygen; sulfuric acid is produced as a byproduct (Figure 15.26). By chemosynthesizing, archaea form the base of the food web for vent ecosystems. Although some animals feed directly on archaea and larger prey,

Chemosynthesis	Hydrogen Sulfide	+	Water	+	Carbon dioxide	+	Oxygen	→	Sugar	+	Sulfuric acid

Representative reaction, viewed chemically	$6H_2S$	+	$6H_2O$	+	$6CO_2$	+	$6O_2$	$\xrightarrow{\text{Chemosynthesis}}$	$C_6H_{12}O_6$	+	$6H_2SO_4$

FIGURE 15.26 Chemosynthesis (*top*) and representative reaction viewed chemically (*bottom*). The process of chemosynthesis, which is accomplished by archaea, is represented in the top panel and is shown chemically in the bottom panel. Compare this figure with photosynthesis (Figure 13.1).

many of them depend primarily on a symbiotic relationship with archaea. Tubeworms and giant clams, for instance, depend entirely on sulfur-oxidizing archaea that live symbiotically within their tissues (Figure 15.25b). The microbes inside the tubeworms are provided habitat and bathed in hydrogen sulfide, which they chemosynthesize into sugars. The tubeworms, in return, get a steady supply of food and grow prolifically, sometimes gaining 80 centimeters (31 inches) in a year.

Recent analysis of the genome of the symbiotic archaea that lives inside tubeworms reveals that the microbe is remarkably versatile. For example, researchers found that it can use two different methods to metabolize carbon dioxide and can switch back and forth to accommodate fast-changing environmental conditions. Such metabolic flexibility is a valuable asset in deep-sea vent habitats characterized by fluctuating flows of hot fluids.

DISCOVERY OF OTHER HYDROTHERMAL VENT FIELDS   In 1981, humans in a submersible first visited the Juan de Fuca Ridge biocommunity offshore of Oregon. Although vent fauna at this site are less abundant than at the Galápagos Rift and on the East Pacific Rise, the metallic sulfide deposits from the vents aroused much interest because they are the only active hydrothermal vent deposits in U.S. waters.

In 1982, the first hydrothermal vents beneath a thick layer of sediment were discovered during a submersible dive in the Guaymas Basin of the Gulf of California. In this region, a spreading center is actively working to rift apart the sea floor as it is being covered with sediment. Sediment samples recovered in this region were high in sulfide and saturated with hydrocarbons, which may have entered the food chain through bacteria. The abundance and diversity of life discovered here may exceed those of the Galápagos Rift and along the East Pacific Rise.

Like the Guaymas Basin, the Mariana Basin of the western Pacific has a small spreading center beneath a sediment-filled basin. A research dive via submersible in 1987 revealed many new species of hydrothermal vent organisms (Figure 15.25c). Subsequent exploration has revealed numerous hydrothermal vent biocommunities in other parts of the Pacific Ocean (see Figure 15.24) and additional new species. In fact, more than 400 new species have been found so far at vent sites worldwide.

In 1985, the first active hydrothermal vents with associated biocommunities in the Atlantic Ocean were discovered at depths below 3600 meters (11,800 feet) near the axis of the Mid-Atlantic Ridge between 23 and 26 degrees north latitude. The predominant fauna of these vents consists of shrimp that have no eye lens but can detect levels of light emitted by the black smoker chimneys that are invisible to the human eye (Figure 15.27).

In 1993, a hydrothermal vent community was discovered on a flat-topped volcano rising to 1525 meters (5000 feet)—well above the walls of the Mid-Atlantic Ridge rift valley. Called the "Lucky Strike" vent field, it is about 1000 meters (3300 feet) shallower than most other sites. It is the only Mid-Atlantic Ridge site known to possess the mussels that are common at many other vent sites and is the only location where a new species of pink sea urchin has been found.

In August 2000, Japanese investigators discovered the Indian Ocean's first hydrothermal vent biocommunity, which is associated with black smokers spewing

FIGURE 15.27 Atlantic Ocean hydrothermal vent organisms. Swarm of particulate-feeding shrimp, the predominant animals observed at hydrothermal vents near 26 degrees north latitude on the Mid-Atlantic Ridge. Most shrimp are about 5 centimeters (2 inches) long.

water up to 365°C (689°F). The vents are covered by shrimp similar to those found in Atlantic fields, while sea anemones mark the ambient temperature boundaries beyond. In between are clusters of animals similar to those found at other hydrothermal vents.

Vents often differ dramatically from each other in chemical and geological characteristics. However, even vents that are physically similar can host distinctly different communities of organisms. For example, giant tubeworms are found only in Pacific vents. In the North Atlantic, meanwhile, shrimp and mussels dominate. Researchers are currently studying dispersal patterns and determining biogeographic relationships between vent sites to help explain this phenomenon.

Today, researchers continue to use submersibles to study deep-sea hydrothermal vents. Although there is direct evidence of about 300 hydrothermal vents worldwide, researchers suspect that another 700 or so await discovery. Every visit to a vent site—even a repeat visit—reveals new information about how vents work and the uniquely-adapted microbes and other organisms that live there. In fact, the research effort is so intense at some sites that researchers have recently adopted a self-enforced code of conduct to ensure that humans do not alter vent ecosystems.

LIFE SPAN OF HYDROTHERMAL VENTS Because the hot-water plumbing of the sea floor is controlled by sporadic volcanic activity associated with mid-ocean ridge spreading centers, a vent may remain active for only limited periods—years or sometimes decades. For instance, a hydrothermal vent field called the Coaxial Site along the Juan de Fuca Ridge offshore of Washington that had been active was revisited a few years later and found to be inactive. Inactive sites such as this one are identified by an accumulation of large numbers of dead hydrothermal vent organisms. When the vent becomes inactive and the hydrogen sulfide that serves as the source of energy for the community is no longer available, organisms of the community die if they cannot move elsewhere.

Other sites indicate an increase in volcanic activity. For example, at a site along the East Pacific Rise known as Nine-Degrees North, a large number of tubeworms were cooked by lava flowing into their midst in what has been described as a "tubeworm barbecue." The discovery of newly formed and ancient vent areas along spreading centers indicates that hydrothermal vents can suddenly appear or cease to operate. Moreover, areas of active venting may lie hundreds of kilometers apart.

Hydrothermal vent organisms are well adapted to the temporary nature of hydrothermal vents. Most have high metabolic rates, for example, which cause them to mature rapidly so they can reproduce while the vent is still active.

Studies of several hydrothermal vent sites suggest that species diversity is low. In fact, only about 300 animal species have been identified to date. Many species, however, are common to widely separated hydrothermal vent fields. Although hydrothermal vent animals typically release drifting larvae into the water, it is not clear how the larvae are able to survive the journey to hydrothermal vents that lie at such great distances from one another.

One idea, called the *dead whale hypothesis*, suggests that when large animals die they may sink to the deep-ocean floor, decompose, and provide an energy source in stepping stone fashion for the larvae of hydrothermal vent organisms. The organisms settle and grow here, then breed and release their own larvae, some of which make it to the next hydrothermal vent field. Other researchers believe that deep-ocean currents are strong enough to transport drifting larvae to new sites. Still others have suggested that the rift valleys of mid-ocean ridges act as passageways along which drifting larvae traverse to inhabit new vent fields. By whatever means they travel, they colonize new hydrothermal vents soon after the vents are created. In 1989, for example, a newly formed hydrothermal vent along the Juan de Fuca Ridge had no life forms. By 1993, however, tubeworms and other life forms had already established themselves.

STUDENTS SOMETIMES ASK...

Are the mussels found at hydrothermal vents edible?

Not for humans. The microbes that form the base of the food web use hydrogen sulfide gas (which has a characteristic "rotten egg" odor) as a source of energy. Sulfide, which is deadly poisonous at low levels to most organisms, tends to concentrate in the tissues of these organisms. Although organisms within the hydrothermal biocommunities can ingest sulfide and have mechanisms of getting rid of it, hydrothermal vent organisms would be toxic to humans. Even if they were edible, they would be expensive to harvest because they live at such great depths.

HYDROTHERMAL VENTS AND THE ORIGIN OF LIFE   Life is thought to have begun in the oceans, and environments similar to those of the hydrothermal vents must have been present in the early history of the planet. The uniformity of conditions and abundant energy of the vents, therefore, have led some scientists to propose that hydrothermal vents would have provided an ideal habitat for the origin of life. In fact, hydrothermal vents may represent one of the oldest life-sustaining environments because hydrothermal activity occurs wherever there are both volcanoes and water. The presence of bacteria-like archaea, which have ancient genetic makeup, helps support this idea.

The ancient status of deep-sea life was strengthened by the recent discovery of deep-sea microbes with identical genes to those of microbes found in the human body. Researchers isolated two previously unknown bacterial species from hydrothermal vents near Japan and compared the new species' genomes to the genomes of two common gut pathogens, one that causes ulcers and another that causes diarrhea. The comparison shows that despite eons of evolutionary change, the deep-sea species and the pathogens share genes that enable them to colonize animal hosts. According to the researchers, genes that likely help deep-sea bacteria maintain symbiotic relationships with other vent-dwelling organisms assist their gut-dwelling relatives in evading immune systems. The researchers suggest that the human-harming microbes evolved from deep-sea ancestors and later acquired more virulence factors while living in symbiosis with animals.

Low-Temperature Seep Biocommunities: Organisms and Their Adaptations

Three additional submarine seep environments—locations where water trickles out of the sea floor—have been found that chemosynthetically support biocommunities similar to hydrothermal vent communities.

HYPERSALINE SEEPS   In 1984, a hypersaline seep was studied in water depths below 3000 meters (9800 feet) at the base of the Florida Escarpment in the Gulf of Mexico (Figure 15.28a). The water from this seep had a salinity of 46.2‰, but its temperature was not warmer than normal. Researchers had discovered a **hypersaline seep biocommunity** similar in many respects to a hydrothermal vent biocommunity. The seeping water appears to flow from fractures at the base of a limestone escarpment (Figure 15.28b) and move out across the clay deposits of the abyssal plain at a depth of about 3200 meters (10,500 feet).

The hydrogen sulfide-rich waters support a number of white microbial growths called mats, which conduct chemosynthesis in a fashion similar to archaea at hydrothermal vents. These and other chemosynthetic microbes may provide most of the sustenance for a diverse community of animals that includes sea stars, shrimp, snails, limpets, brittle stars, anemones, tubeworms, crabs, clams, mussels, and a few species of fish (Figure 15.28c).

HYDROCARBON SEEPS   Also observed in 1984 were dense biological communities associated with oil and gas seeps on the Gulf of Mexico continental slope (Figure 15.29). Trawls at depths of between 600 and 700 meters (2000 and 2300 feet) recovered fauna similar to those observed at hydrothermal vents and

(a)

(b)

(c)

FIGURE 15.28 Hypersaline Seep Biocommunity at the base of the Florida Escarpment. (**a**) Map showing location of hypersaline seep. (**b**) Seismic reflection profile of Florida Escarpment and abyssal sediments at its base. Arrow marks location of seep. (**c**) Florida Escarpment seep biocommunity of dense mussel beds. White dots are small gastropods on mussel shells. Tubeworms (*lower right*) are covered with hydrozoans and galatheid crabs.

(a)

(b)

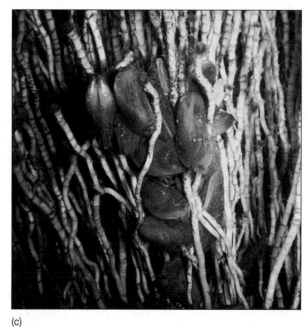

(c)

FIGURE 15.29 Hydrocarbon seeps on the continental slope in the Gulf of Mexico. (a) Map showing locations of known hydrocarbon seeps that contain biocommunities in the Gulf of Mexico. **(b)** Abundant mussels and tubeworms at Neptune's Gardens (Alaminos Canyon site). **(c)** Close-up of chemosynthetic mussels and tubeworms from the Bush Hill seep.

at the hypersaline seep in the Gulf of Mexico. Subsequent investigations have identified nearly 100 seeps on the continental slope with potential chemosynthetic biocommunities; 10 of these have been visited with submersibles to depths of 2775 meters (9100 feet) where chemosynthetic bacteria and a host of other organisms were discovered.

Carbon-isotope analysis indicates that these **hydrocarbon seep biocommunities** are based on chemosynthesis that derives its energy from hydrogen sulfide and/or methane. Microbial oxidation of methane produces calcium carbonate slabs found here and at other hydrocarbon seeps (see Figure 15.24).

SUBDUCTION ZONE SEEPS In 1984, a **subduction zone seep biocommunity** was discovered during one of *Alvin*'s dives to study folding of the sea floor in a subduction zone. The seep is located near the Cascadia subduction zone of the Juan de Fuca Plate at the base of the continental slope off the coast of Oregon (Figure 15.30a). The trench is filled with sediments, which are folded into a ridge at the seaward edge of the slope. At the crest of this ridge, water slowly flows from the 2-million-year-old folded sedimentary rocks into a thin overlying layer of soft sediment on the sea floor. Eventually, the water is released from the sediment through seeps on the ocean floor.

At a depth of 2036 meters (6678 feet), the seeps produce water that is only about 0.3°C (0.5°F) warmer than seawater at that depth. The vent water contains methane that is probably produced by decomposition of organic material in the sedimentary rocks. Microbes oxidize the methane, chemosynthetically producing food for themselves and the rest of the community, which contains many of the same genera found at other vent and seep sites (Figure 15.30b).

Since the detection of subduction zone seeps, similar communities have been discovered in other subduction zones, including the Japan Trench and the Peru–Chile Trench. All these subduction zone seeps are located on the landward side of the trenches at depths from 1300 to 5640 meters (4300 to 18,500 feet).

The Deep Biosphere: A New Frontier

The discovery of the rich microbe communities at hydrothermal vents has resulted in the exploration of the **deep biosphere**, an environment that exists within the sea floor itself. Only recently have scientists even considered that microbial life might exist deep within Earth, and in 2002 researchers made the first expedition to study life in this environment. Cores were drilled up to 420 meters (1380 feet) deep into the sea floor off Peru in water depths between 150 and 5300 meters (490 and 17,400 feet). At these depths, researchers discovered a host of diverse and active microbial communities living within circulating fluids that pass through the porous sea floor. Other subsequent research confirms the abundance and diversity of microbes in deep sea floor rocks and associated sediments that rivals the rich microbial ecosystems found in soil.

These studies suggest that as much as two-thirds of Earth's entire bacterial biomass might exist in the deep biosphere. Moreover, deep biosphere microbes fuel their metabolisms by taking advantage of the chemical energy stored in various minerals. In addition, the findings raise new questions about the role of the deep sea floor in the evolution of life on Earth. Intriguingly, other bodies in the solar system have similar subsurface conditions, so they might harbor microbes, too. Earth's deep biosphere will therefore continue to be an area of active research.

> **KEY CONCEPT**
>
> Hydrothermal vent biocommunities occur near black smokers and rely on chemosynthetic archaea for food. Other deep-sea biocommunities that depend on chemosynthesis exist around hypersaline, hydrocarbon, and subduction zone seeps.

FIGURE 15.30 Subduction zone seep biocommunities. **(a)** Map showing sea floor features and the location of vent biocommunities off the coast of Oregon. These communities are associated with the Cascadia subduction zone, where sediment filling the trench is folded into a ridge with vents at its crest. **(b)** Giant white clams (*Calyptogena soyoae*) half buried in methane-rich mud at 1100 meters (3600 feet) near the Japan Trench. The clams host sulfide-oxidizing microorganisms, which oxidize methane and supply the clams with food.

Chapter in Review

- *More than 98% of the 250,000 known marine species live in diverse environments within or on the ocean floor. Species diversity* of these benthic organisms *depends on their ability to adapt to the conditions of their environment,* particularly temperature. With few exceptions, the *biomass of benthic organisms closely matches that of photosynthetic productivity in surface waters above.*

- *Many adverse conditions exist in the intertidal zone of rocky shores, but organisms have adapted* so they can densely populate these environments. Influenced by the tides, rocky shores can be divided into a *high tide zone* (mostly dry), a *middle tide zone* (equally wet and dry), and a *low tide zone* (mostly wet). The *intertidal zone* is bounded by the *supratidal zone,* which is covered only by storm waves, and the *subtidal zone,* which extends below the low tide shoreline.

- *Each of these zones contains characteristic types of marine life.* Periwinkle snails, rock louses, and limpets can be found in the subtidal zone. Sessile organisms can be found in the high tide zone, especially buckshot barnacles. *Algae become more abundant in the middle tide zone, and the diversity and abundance of the flora and fauna increase toward the lower intertidal zone.* Acorn barnacles, gooseneck barnacles, mussels, and sea stars are commonly found in the middle tide zone, as well as sea anemones, fishes, hermit crabs, and sea urchins. The low tide zone in temperate latitudes has a variety of moderately sized red and brown algae that provide a drooping canopy for animal life.

- *Many varieties of burrowing infauna are common along sediment-covered shores* (that is, beaches, salt marshes, and mud flats). Compared with rocky shores, however, *the diversity of species in sediment-covered shores is less.* As with the rocky shore, *the diversity of species and abundance of life on the sediment-covered shore increase toward the low tide shoreline.*

- In more protected segments of the shore, wave energy is lower, so sand and mud are deposited. Sand deposits are usually well oxygenated compared to mud deposits. *The intertidal region of sediment-covered shores has high, middle, and low tide zones, similar to rocky shores.* Organisms characteristic of *sandy beaches* include bivalve (two-shelled) mollusks, lugworms, beach hoppers, sand crabs, sand stars, and heart urchins. Organisms characteristic of *mud flats* include eelgrass, turtle grass, bivalve mollusks, and fiddler crabs.

- *Attached to the rocky subtidal bottom just beyond the shoreline is a band of algae that often creates kelp forests.* Kelp forests are the home of many organisms, including other varieties of algae, mollusks, sea stars, fishes, octopus, lobsters, marine mammals, sea hares, and sea urchins.

- *Spiny lobsters* are common to rocky bottoms in the Caribbean and along the West Coast, and the *American (Maine) lobster* is found from Labrador to Cape Hatteras. Oyster beds found in estuarine environments consist of individuals that attach themselves to the bottom or to the empty shells of previous generations.

- *Coral reefs consist of large colonies of coral polyps and many other species that need warm water and strong sunlight to live.* Coral reefs are usually *found in nutrient-poor tropical waters.* Reef-building corals and other mixotrophs are *hermatypic,* containing *symbiotic algae (zooxanthellae)* in their tissues. Delicate varieties are found at 150 meters, and they become more massive near the surface, where wave energy is higher. *The potentially lethal "bleaching" of coral reefs is caused by the removal or expulsion of symbiotic algae,* probably under stress of elevated sea surface temperatures.

- *The physical conditions of the deep-ocean floor* are much different from those of shallow water. There is *no light* and the *water is uniformly cold. The primary food source is from the surface waters above, which limits biomass.* Species diversity in the deep ocean, however, is much higher than was previously thought.

- *Primary production in hydrothermal vent communities near black smokers is due to chemosynthesis.* Some evidence suggests that *hydrothermal vents may have been some of the first regions where life became established on Earth,* despite the short life span of individual vents. Chemosynthesis has also been identified in low-temperature seep biocommunities near *hypersaline, hydrocarbon,* and *subduction zone seeps.* Studies of the *deep biosphere* below the ocean floor *reveal a host of microbes.*

Key Terms

Abyssal storm (p. 457)

Annelid (p. 446)

Archaea (p. 460)

Biomass (p. 437)

Bivalve (p. 446)

Black smoker (p. 460)

Chemosynthesis (p. 460)

Coral bleaching (p. 452)

Coral reef (p. 450)

Crustacean (p. 446)

Deep biosphere (p. 465)

Echinoderm (p. 447)

Epifauna (p. 437)

Hermatypic (p. 453)

High tide zone (p. 438)

Hydrocarbon seep biocommunity (p. 464)

Hydrothermal vent biocommunity (p. 459)

Hypersaline seep biocommunity (p. 463)

Infauna (p. 444)

Intertidal zone (p. 438)

Kelp (p. 448)

Kelp forest (p. 448)

Low tide zone (p. 438)

Meiofauna (p. 447)

Middle tide zone (p. 438)

Mixotroph (p. 453)

Mollusk (p. 446)

Nematocyst (p. 443)

Polyp (p. 450)

Sessile (p. 442)

Spray zone (p. 438)

Subduction zone seep biocommunity (p. 464)

Subtidal zone (p. 448)

Supratidal zone (p. 439)

Zooxanthellae (p. 453)

Review Questions

1. What are some adverse conditions of rocky intertidal zones? What are some organisms' adaptations for those adverse conditions? Which conditions seem to be most important in controlling the distribution of life?

2. One of the most noticeable features of the middle tide zone along rocky coasts is a mussel bed. Describe general characteristics of mussels, and include a discussion of other organisms that are associated with mussels.

3. Describe how sandy and muddy shores differ in terms of energy level, particle size, sediment stability, and oxygen content.

4. How does the diversity of species on sediment-covered shores compare with that of the rocky shore? Suggest at least one reason why this occurs.

5. In which intertidal zone of a steeply sloping, coarse sand beach would you find each of the following organisms: clams, beach hoppers, ghost shrimp, sand crabs, and heart urchins?

6. Discuss the dominant species of kelp, their epifauna, and animals that feed on kelp in Pacific coast kelp forests.

7. Describe the environmental conditions required for development of coral reefs.

8. Describe the zones of the reef slope, the characteristic coral types, and the physical factors related to its zonation.

9. What is coral bleaching? How does it occur? What other diseases affect corals?

10. Where does the food come from to supply organisms living on the deep-ocean floor? How does this affect benthic biomass?

11. Describe the characteristics of hydrothermal vents. What evidence suggests that hydrothermal vents have short life spans?

12. What is the "dead whale hypothesis"? What other ideas have been suggested to help explain how organisms from hydrothermal vent biocommunities populate new vent sites?

13. What are the major differences between the conditions and biocommunities of the hydrothermal vents and the cold seeps? How are they similar?

Critical Thinking Exercises

1. Draw a diagram of the zones within the rocky-shore intertidal region and list characteristic organisms of each zone.

2. As one moves from the shoreline to the deep-ocean floor, what changes in the physical environment are experienced?

Oceanography on the Web

Visit the *Essentials of Oceanography* Online Study Guide for Internet resources, including chapter-specific quizzes to test your understanding and Web links to further your exploration of the topics in this chapter.

The *Essentials of Oceanography* Online Study Guide is at http://www.mygeoscienceplace.com/.

Smokestacks spew human-caused emissions into the atmosphere.
Emissions from the combustion of fossil fuels by power plants, cars, and factories are released into the atmosphere. These human-caused emissions are affecting all parts of the environment and especially the oceans.

"Human-induced climate change is a reality, not only in remote polar regions and in small tropical islands, but everyplace around the country, in our own backyards. It's happening. It's happening now. It's not just a problem for the future. We are beginning to see its impacts in our daily lives. More than that, humans are responsible for the changes that we are seeing, and our actions now will determine the extent of future change and the severity of the impacts."

—*Jane Lubchenco,*
marine ecologist and NOAA Chief Administrator (2009)

16 THE OCEANS AND CLIMATE CHANGE

CHAPTER AT A GLANCE

- Humans are adding vast amounts of greenhouse gases to the atmosphere, which is causing Earth's climate to change.

- As a result of climate change, there will be many unintended and severe changes in the ocean, including ocean warming, more intense hurricanes, increasing ocean acidity, changes in deep-water circulation, melting of polar ice, and rising sea level.

- Action must be taken to reduce human-caused greenhouse gases.

Climate change and global warming are topics that have received much media attention recently. These topics are often in public opinion polls and in newspaper headlines; as such, they have spurred intense debate on whether climate change is natural or human caused and what climate changes are likely to occur in the future. These topics have also become the subject of numerous international conferences and of complicated discussions among scientists. The urgent challenge of human-induced climate disruption continues to be one of the most studied aspects of climate change.

From a broad perspective, the geologic record has shown that Earth's climate is variable. Evidence from fossils in sea floor sediments and rocks on land suggest that practically everyplace on Earth has experienced dramatic swings in climate over geologic time. Some examples of this are stable continental regions that have remained at high latitudes yet display low-latitude fossils and coal deposits, sea floor sediments that represent much warmer or colder conditions than at present, and ice age deposits on the sea floor.

Recent research on human activities and their impact on the environment has demonstrated that people are inadvertently changing Earth's climate. Unlike changes in the past, modern climate change is dominated by human influences so large that they exceed the bounds of natural variability. Moreover, these changes are likely to continue for thousands of years. Climate changes can be very disruptive not only to humans but to many other life forms as well, especially if they occur as rapidly as some scientists predict.

In this chapter, we will examine Earth's climate system, the science that indicates Earth's recent and dramatic climate change, how the greenhouse effect works, how the oceans are being affected, and what can be done about this problem.

16.1 What Comprises Earth's Climate System?

Climate is defined as the conditions of Earth's atmosphere—including temperature, precipitation, and wind—that characteristically prevail in a particular region over extended time spans.

Obtaining a full understanding of Earth's climate involves studying more than just the atmosphere. Earth's climate is a complex and interacting system that includes the atmosphere, hydrosphere, geosphere, biosphere, and cryosphere.[1] Earth's **climate system** involves the exchanges of energy and moisture that occur among the five spheres. These exchanges link the atmosphere to the other spheres so that the entire system functions as an interactive unit. Changes to the climate system do not occur in isolation. Rather, when one part of it changes, the other components also react.

---

[1]The cryosphere (*kruos* = icy cold, *sphere* = a globe) refers to the ice and snow that exists at Earth's surface.

The major components of Earth's climate system are shown in Figure 16.1. Notice that the oceans are the most massive part of Earth's climate system.

Planetary atmospheric processes are large scale and include many **feedback loops**, which are processes that modify the end result. For example, warmer surface temperatures increase evaporation rates. This in turn increases water vapor in the atmosphere, which absorbs heat emitted from Earth's surface before it gets released into space. Therefore, the more water vapor in the air, the less heat escapes and the warmer the planet becomes. This type of feedback loop is called a *positive-feedback loop* because it reinforces the initial change.

Alternatively, *negative-feedback loops* tend to counteract or mitigate an initial change. One such example is the formation of clouds. A probable result of a global temperature rise is an accompanying increase in cloud cover due to the higher moisture content of the atmosphere. Most clouds are good reflectors of incoming solar energy, thus diminishing the amount of solar energy available to heat Earth's surface and warm the atmosphere. In this way, clouds can cause a decrease in overall air temperature.

These two examples of increased water vapor in the atmosphere show that it can be both a positive-feedback loop and a negative-feedback loop. Which effect, if either, is stronger? Recent studies show that the negative effect of higher reflectivity is dominant. Therefore, the net result of an increase in atmospheric moisture should be a decrease in air temperature. The magnitude of this negative-feedback loop, however, is not likely to be as great as the feedback caused by other positive feedback loops between other parts of Earth's climate system. Thus, although increases in atmospheric moisture and cloud cover may partly offset a global temperature increase, climate models show that the overall effect will still be a temperature increase. In fact, the scientific consensus is that the increasing levels of

FIGURE 16.1 Major components of Earth's climate system. Schematic view showing major components of Earth's climate system and the interactions that occur between various components.

human-caused[2] emissions will lead to a warmer planet with a different distribution of climate patterns than what currently exist on Earth.

The global climate system contains many feedback loops, such as the role of clouds at different altitudes, the presence of fine atmospheric particles called *aerosols*, the shading effect from air pollution, heat uptake by the oceans, and the addition of water vapor in the atmosphere. Many of these feedback loops influence other feedbacks. For example, some computer models of climate show that if Earth's climate does warm as anticipated, there will be more evaporation of seawater, thus using up much of the excess heat and generating more cloud cover, which will block the Sun's rays and significantly reduce the warming effect. As such, the successful modeling of Earth's climate and its feedback loops is one of the biggest scientific challenges today—even using some of the world's most powerful computers.

> **KEY CONCEPT**
>
> Earth's climate system consists of exchanges of energy and moisture between the atmosphere, hydrosphere, geosphere, biosphere, and cryosphere. The global climate system contains many complex feedback loops.

16.2 Earth's Recent Climate Change: Is It Natural or Caused By Human Influence?

Records of past climate change reveal that natural events have influenced climate throughout Earth's history. Skeptics of global climate change point out that because Earth's climate has fluctuated in the past, the recent climate change observed on Earth could be a natural event. How can scientists tell whether this is true?

Determining Earth's Past Climate: Proxy Data and Paleoclimatology

Climate scientists use three closely connected methods to understand changes in Earth's climate: They look at records of Earth's past climates to see how and why climate changed in the past; they build computer models that allow them to see how the climate works; and they closely monitor Earth's current vital signs with an array of instruments ranging from space-based satellites to deep-sea thermometers. These monitoring tools, however, have been available for only a few decades. To understand the behavior of the atmosphere and to anticipate future climate change, scientists must be able to discern how climate has changed in the past.

Instrumental records go back only a couple of centuries at best, and the further back we go, the less complete and more unreliable the data become. To overcome the lack of direct measurements in the past, scientists must decipher and reconstruct Earth's previous climates using indirect evidence. Such **proxy** (*proxum* = nearest) data come from natural recorders of climate variability such as sea floor sediments (see Chapter 4), coral deposits, annual layers of snow packed in glacial ice (Figure 16.2), fossil

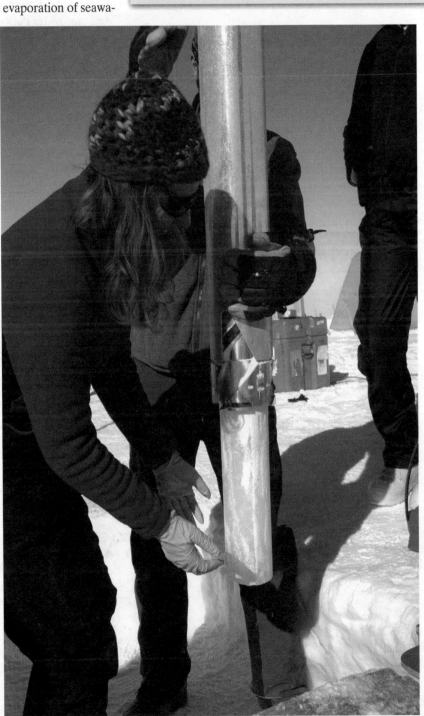

FIGURE 16.2 Researchers extract an ice core from its drilling tube. To reconstruct past temperatures and atmospheric conditions, scientists use natural records of climate change such as this ice core that was recently collected in Antarctica. The annual layers of snow packed in glacial ice preserve a record of climate that stretches back hundreds of thousands of years.

---

[2]Human-caused influence is also known by the term *anthropogenic* (*anthro* = human, *generare* = to produce).

pollen, tree-growth rings, and even historical documents. The data is cross-checked between the various methods and also matched with recent instrumental measurements (where overlap exists) to ensure accuracy. Scientists who analyze proxy data and reconstruct past climates are engaged in the study of **paleoclimatology** (*paleo* = ancient, *climate* = climate, *ology* = the study of). The main goal of such work is to understand Earth's past climate in order to gain insight into Earth's current and future climate. For example, climatologists have identified both warmer and cooler periods in Earth's recent past, such as the Medieval Warm Period (approximately 950–1250 A.D.) and the Little Ice Age (approximately 1400–1700 A.D.). As we will see, climatologists have used proxy data to construct a detailed history of Earth's climate that extends back in time over the past several hundred thousand years.

Natural Causes of Climate Change

Natural factors that affect Earth's climate include changes in solar energy, variations in Earth's orbit, volcanic eruptions, and even the movement of Earth's tectonic plates. Let's examine how each of these factors affects global climate.

CHANGES IN SOLAR ENERGY Among the most persistent hypotheses of climate change have been those based on the idea that the Sun is a variable star, and its output of energy varies through time. In essence, increases in solar output cause global warming, while reductions in solar energy result in global cooling. This notion is appealing because it can be used to explain climate change of any length or intensity. However, an increase in solar output also falls short of explaining recent warming. Earth-orbiting satellites have been making precise measurements of the Sun's output since the 1980s, and while the Sun's luminosity has increased by a small amount (0.04%), the observed changes were not large enough to account for the warming recorded during the same period. Even proxy data of solar brightness over the past 1000 years does not show a correlation with changes in climate.

Several proposals for climate change are based on solar variability related to **sunspots**, which are dark blemishes that occur periodically on the Sun's surface (Figure 16.3). Sunspots are huge magnetic storms that extend from the Sun's interior to its surface and are associated with the Sun's ejection of particles. These particles can disrupt satellite communications but also produce the *aurora* (*Aurora* = Roman goddess of dawn), which is a phenomenon caused by charged solar particles that interact with Earth's magnetic field and produce lights in the sky. In the Northern Hemisphere, these lights are known as the *aurora borealis*, or *northern lights*, and they have a matching component in the Southern Hemisphere, called the *aurora australis*, or *southern lights*.

FIGURE 16.3 Sunspots. The dark blemishes on this image of the Sun are called sunspots, which are actually huge magnetic storms. The occurrence of sunspots varies in an 11-year cycle, which does not correlate with recent climate changes on Earth.

Along with other solar activity, the numbers of sunspots seems to increase and decrease in a regular way, creating a cycle of about 11 years that has been observed since the 1700s. The last solar maximum occurred in 2001; the magnetically active sunspots at that time produced powerful solar flares that caused large geomagnetic disturbances and disrupted some space-based technology on Earth. In spite of efforts to correlate this cycle of sunspot activity to temperature and precipitation changes on Earth, there is no clear evidence to support it. In fact, many studies have shown that there is no significant correlation between solar activity and climate on such short timescales.

VARIATIONS IN EARTH'S ORBIT Another natural mechanism of climate change involves changes in Earth's orbit. Changes in the shape of the orbit (*eccentricity*), variations in the angle that Earth's axis makes with the plane of its orbit (*obliquity*), and the wobbling of the axis (*precession*) cause fluctuations in the seasonal and latitudinal distribution of solar radiation reaching Earth (Figure 16.4). These variations have cycles of about 100,000 years, 41,000 years, and 26,000 years, respectively; when they coincide with one another, they tend to amplify each other and cause climate variations on Earth. This idea, first developed by Serbian astrophysicist Milutin Milankovitch, is called a *Milankovitch cycle*. It is now well established that these variations have contributed to the alternating glacial and interglacial episodes that characterize the most recent ice age, which occurred during the past few million years.

Although it is well established that Milankovitch cycles are responsible for long-term climate change associated with the most recent ice age on Earth, these changes take many thousands of years to manifest themselves. In contrast, the dramatic and rapid climate change that is occurring on our planet cannot be explained by these long-term variations in Earth's orbit.

VOLCANIC ERUPTIONS Explosive volcanic eruptions emit huge quantities of gases and fine-grained debris into the atmosphere (Figure 16.5). The largest eruptions are sufficiently powerful to inject material high into the atmosphere, where it spreads around the globe and remains aloft for many months or even years. As was seen with historic eruptions such as Mount Tambora in Indonesia (1815), Krakatoa in Indonesia (1883), El Chichón in Mexico (1982), and Mount Pinatubo in the Philippines (1991), volcanic material ejected into the atmosphere filters out a portion of the incoming solar radiation, which in turn cools the planet. For example, the year after the 1815 eruption of Mount Tambora became widely known as the Year without Summer because of its effect on North American and European weather. However, the gases emitted during a volcanic eruption react with other components of the climate system and the volcanic dust eventually settles out. Thus, the cooling effect of a single eruption, no matter how large, is relatively small and short-lived.

If volcanism is to have a pronounced impact over an extended period, many great eruptions closely spaced in time would need to occur. If this happened, the upper atmosphere would be loaded with enough gases to alter the composition of the atmosphere and enough volcanic dust to seriously diminish the amount of solar radiation reaching the surface. Because no such period of explosive volcanism is known to have occurred in historic times, it is unlikely to be responsible for the recent observable climate changes. In the distant past, however, it may have been influential in contributing to climate shifts.

MOVEMENT OF EARTH'S TECTONIC PLATES As described in Chapter 2, Earth's tectonic plates have moved great distances. During the geologic past, plate movements have accounted for many dramatic climate changes as landmasses shifted in relation to one another and moved to different latitudinal positions. As land masses have moved, they have changed ocean circulation,

(a)

(b)

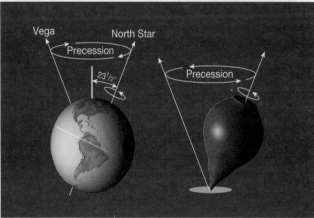
(c)

FIGURE 16.4 Variations in Earth's orbit. (a) The shape of Earth's orbit (*eccentricity*) gradually changes from nearly circular to one that is more elliptical and then back again during a cycle of about 100,000 years (note that Earth's elliptical orbit is greatly exaggerated in this figure). **(b)** The tilt of Earth's axis of rotation with respect to the plane of Earth's orbit (*obliquity*) varies from 21.5° to 24.5° during a cycle of about 41,000 years (currently, Earth's tilt is 23.5°). **(c)** Earth's axis wobbles like that of a spinning top (*precession*); as a result, the axis points to different spots in the sky during a cycle of about 26,000 years.

FIGURE 16.5 Volcanic eruptions spew volcanic debris and gases into the atmosphere. This 1991 eruption of Mount Pinatubo in the Philippines shows that volcanoes have the ability to inject into the atmosphere large quantities of volcanic dust and gases, which can circle the globe and block incoming solar radiation, thereby cooling the planet.

altering the transport of heat and moisture and consequently the climate. For example, the opening of Drake Passage between South America and Antarctica about 41 million years ago caused a fundamental reorganization of ocean currents in the Southern Hemisphere, leading to the isolation of Antarctica, which caused it to become much cooler and develop a permanent ice cap. However, the rate of plate movement is very slow—only a few centimeters per year—and so appreciable changes in the positions of continents occur only over great spans of geologic time. Thus, climate changes triggered by shifting plates are extremely gradual and happen on a scale of millions of years.

CAN NATURAL CLIMATE CHANGE FACTORS EXPLAIN RECENTLY OBSERVED CLIMATE CHANGES? It is clear that natural factors have changed Earth's climate in the past and that they will undoubtedly change it in the future. For example, natural climate change has been definitively linked to global climate shifts such as the Pleistocene Ice Age, the Medieval Warm Period, and the Little Ice Age. However, an examination of natural climate change factors reveals that the recently observed climate changes such as the rate of warming in recent decades is greater than can be explained by any natural factors. In fact, several recent studies based on paleoclimate data reveal that the warming in the past three decades is unprecedented on Earth during the past 1000 years. The only viable explanation for these recent climate changes including warming of Earth's surface is the well-documented increase in human-caused emissions.

The IPCC: Documenting Human-Caused Climate Change

In 1988, the United Nations Environment Programme and the World Meteorological Organization sponsored the **Intergovernmental Panel on Climate Change (IPCC)**, a worldwide group of atmospheric and climate scientists that began studying the human effects on climate change and global warming. The IPCC utilizes peer-reviewed literature to analyze all aspects of climate change—including science, impacts, adaptation, and mitigation—to provide independent scientific advice about climate change. Since 1990, the group has published a series of assessment reports (Figure 16.6) that are highly regarded by both scientists and policymakers and have sparked international movement on climate change.

The IPCC's first assessment report, released in 1990, became the basis for the United Nations Framework Convention on Climate Change, an international treaty in which signatories agreed to the idea of reducing concentrations of greenhouse gases in the atmosphere. The IPCC's second assessment report, published in 1995, states that "the balance of evidence suggests a discernable human influence on global climate" and that global warming "is unlikely to be entirely due to natural causes."

In 2001, a third IPCC assessment report was published under the guidance of 426 scientists and was unanimously accepted by more than 160 delegates from 100 countries. The report states: "There is new and stronger evidence that most of the warming observed over the past 50 years is attributable to human activities." The report notes that recent regional climate changes already have affected many physical and biological systems on Earth and that projected climate change—as well as changes in climate extremes—could have major consequences. The report also revised the estimate of the world's expected temperature increase for the period between 1990 and 2100. Previously, the amount of predicted warming had been 1.0 to 3.5°C (1.8 to 6.3°F); the new report revised it upward at 1.4 to 5.8°C (2.5 to 10.4°F), based on new climate models.

CLIMATE CHANGE 2007
SYNTHESIS REPORT

A Report of the Intergovernmental Panel on Climate Change

FIGURE 16.6 Cover of the IPCC Climate Change 2007 Synthesis Report. The Intergovernmental Panel on Climate Change (IPCC) has published four assessment reports since 1990 confirming that human-induced emissions are altering Earth's climate.

In 2005, an international consortium of science academies, including the U.S. National Academy of Sciences, issued this statement: "The scientific understanding of climate change is now sufficiently clear to justify nations taking prompt action . . . . As the United Nations Framework Convention on Climate Change (UNFCCC) recognizes, a lack of full scientific certainty about some aspects of climate change is not a reason for delaying an immediate response that will, at a reasonable cost, prevent dangerous [human-induced] interference with the climate system."

In 2007, a fourth IPCC assessment report—created by more than 600 authors from 40 countries and reviewed by more than 600 individuals—was published. The report was accepted and approved by representatives from 113 countries. The fourth IPCC report confirmed what many scientists had long suspected: Human-caused climate change is already altering Earth. In fact, *climate change models can mimic present-day conditions only if human emissions are taken into account.* Some of the documented changes specifically mentioned in the report include the warming of oceans and land, temperature extremes, melting of snow and ice, changing wind patterns, changing water patterns, and a variety of changes to a large assortment of organisms. The report also states that the temperature increases observed since the mid-20th century are very likely due to human-caused emissions, with the probability of human influence upgraded to greater than 90% certainty. This IPCC report clearly documents the fact that by adding emissions to the atmosphere, humans are altering global climate and are producing significant impacts on physical and biological systems worldwide. A fifth IPCC assessment report is expected to be published in 2014.

The IPCC assessment reports provide strong documentation of the planet's human-induced climate changes, such as global warming. In recognition of that fact, the IPCC was named a co-recipient of the 2007 Nobel Peace Prize, along with former U.S. Vice President Al Gore, Jr., for his work on the documentary film *An Inconvenient Truth.* When it bestowed the award, the Nobel Committee noted, "Through the scientific reports it has issued over the past two decades, the IPCC has created an ever-broader informed consensus about the connection between human activities and global warming."

Other subsequent reports confirm the findings of the IPCC. In 2009, for example, the U.S. Global Change Research Program issued a 190-page interagency report entitled "Global Climate Change Impacts in the United States." The report states that "global warming is unequivocal and primarily human-induced." The report also notes that "global average temperature has risen by about 1.5°F [0.8°C] since 1900. By 2100, it is projected to rise another 2 to 11.5°F [1.1 to 6.4°C]. Increases at the lower end of this range are more likely if global heat-trapping gas emissions are cut substantially. If emissions continue to rise at or near current rates, temperature increases are more likely to be near the upper end of the range." The report warns that climate change will have numerous impacts on water resources, ecosystems, agriculture, coastal areas, human health, and other sectors.

16.3 What Causes the Atmosphere's Greenhouse Effect?

There is ample documentation that human-caused emissions are responsible for the recent and dramatic climate changes experienced on Earth. One such change is the increase in average worldwide temperature, which is called **global warming**. Although the warming of Earth's surface and atmosphere is a natural process controlled by the greenhouse effect, it is also being altered by human emissions, a phenomenon that is often referred to as the *anthropogenic greenhouse load* or the *enhanced greenhouse effect.*

The **greenhouse effect** gets its name because it keeps Earth's surface and lower atmosphere warm in a way similar to a greenhouse that keeps plants warm

STUDENTS SOMETIMES ASK...

Why was this winter so cold when there's supposed to be global warming?

One of the documented changes of a warmer world is increased variation in temperature extremes. This means that while the climate is warming, there will be a wider range of temperatures, including both warmer and colder temperature extremes. In essence, global warming increases the chances of such extreme events occurring. Also, remember that climate is the long-term average of weather, so although it might be colder during one season, the climate can still be warming. What matters is not what happens on any given day or season but what the trend is over a period of years. On this, the data are clear: Earth is experiencing long-term global warming.

KEY CONCEPT
Earth's climate has changed in the past due to natural causes such as changes in the Sun's output, variations in Earth's orbit, volcanic activity, or the movement of tectonic plates. Multiple lines of evidence show that the current climate changes are due primarily to human activities that release heat-trapping emissions into the atmosphere.

enough to grow regardless of outside conditions (Figure 16.7). Energy radiated by the Sun covers the full electromagnetic spectrum, but most of the energy that reaches Earth's surface is short wavelengths, in and near the visible portion of the spectrum. In a greenhouse, shortwave sunlight passes through the glass or plastic covering, where it strikes the plants, the floor, and other objects inside and is converted into longer-wavelength infrared radiation (heat). Some of this heat energy escapes from the greenhouse and some is trapped for a while by the glass or plastic covering, which keeps the greenhouse nice and snug—much like what happens in Earth's atmosphere.[3]

Earth's Heat Budget and Changes in Wavelength

Figure 16.8 diagrams the various components of Earth's **heat budget**, which describes all the ways in which heat is added to and subtracted from Earth. In the upper atmosphere, most solar radiation within the visible spectrum penetrates the atmosphere to Earth's surface, like sunlight coming through greenhouse glass. After scattering by atmospheric molecules and reflection off clouds, about 47% of the solar radiation that is directed towards Earth is absorbed by the oceans and continents. About 23% is absorbed by the atmosphere and clouds, and about 30% is reflected into space by atmospheric backscatter, clouds, and Earth's surface.

Figure 16.9 shows that most of the energy coming to Earth from the Sun is within the visible spectrum and peaks at a wavelength of 0.48 micrometer[4] (0.0002 inch). The atmosphere is transparent to much of this radiation, but it is absorbed by materials such as water and rocks at Earth's surface. These surface materials absorb and then emit radiation away from Earth's surface toward space as longer wavelength infrared (heat) radiation, with a peak at a wavelength of 10 micrometers (0.004 inch). Molecules of atmospheric gases such as water vapor, carbon dioxide, and other gases intercept the heat radiation that attempts to leave the planet, thus heating the atmosphere. This heating of the atmosphere is known as the greenhouse effect. Because Earth has maintained a relatively constant average temperature over long periods of time, the rates of energy absorption and reradiation back into space must be equal.

In summary, most of the solar radiation that is not reflected back to space passes through the atmosphere and is absorbed at Earth's surface. Earth's surface, in turn, emits longer wavelength infrared radiation (heat). A portion of this energy is absorbed by certain heat-trapping gases in the atmosphere, thus producing the greenhouse effect. Thus, *the change of wavelengths from visible to infrared is the key to understanding how the greenhouse effect works.*

Some of the infrared energy absorbed in the atmosphere becomes reabsorbed by Earth to continue the process; the rest is lost to space. The solar radiation received at the surface is therefore retained for a time within our atmosphere, where it moderates temperature fluctuations between night and day and also between seasons.

Which Gases Contribute to the Greenhouse Effect?

Earth's greenhouse effect is caused by an array of atmospheric gases, many of which have both natural and human-caused sources. Take, for example, water vapor, which contributes more to the greenhouse effect than any other gas. In

FIGURE 16.7 **How a greenhouse works.** The glass of a greenhouse allows incoming sunlight to pass through but traps heat. Similarly, gases like water, carbon dioxide, and methane in Earth's atmosphere act just like the glass of a greenhouse by allowing sunlight to pass through but trapping heat.

web animation

Global Warming

STUDENTS SOMETIMES ASK...

What would Earth's temperature be like if there was no natural greenhouse effect?

In a word: *freezing*! The worldwide average temperature of Earth and the lowermost atmosphere (troposphere) is about 15°C (59°F). If the atmosphere contained no heat-trapping greenhouse gases, the average worldwide temperature would be about −18°C (0°F). At this temperature, our planet would very likely have a frozen surface akin to that of Mars. Instead, the atmosphere's greenhouse gases help create and sustain the moderate temperatures that make Earth habitable.

[3]Recent studies have indicated that an additional factor in keeping a greenhouse warm is that the greenhouse covering prevents mixing of air inside with cooler air outside. Although this is different from how the atmosphere works, the term *greenhouse effect* is still commonly used to describe the atmosphere's warming process.

[4]A micrometer (μm), or micron, is one-millionth of a meter.

fact, water vapor is the single most important absorber of heat—its contribution to the greenhouse effect is between 36% and 66% of the greenhouse effect—and together with clouds comprises between 66% and 85% of the greenhouse effect. Mostly, though, water vapor enters the atmosphere through evaporation and by other natural processes. Although atmospheric water vapor concentrations fluctuate regionally, studies suggest that human activity does not significantly affect water vapor concentrations except at local scales, such as near irrigated fields. And even then, the water vapor does not stay in the atmosphere for very long. In essence, human activities do not directly affect the amount of water vapor in the atmosphere on a global scale.

Table 16.1 shows the concentration of **greenhouse gases**—so called because of their heat-trapping capacity—that have been increasing as a result of human activities. Remarkably, these gases exist in very small amounts in the atmosphere, yet they have a profound effect on heating. Some of these greenhouse gases are released by both human and natural sources (such as carbon dioxide, which has been a component of the atmosphere long before human activities). Others, however, have no natural source and thus are clearly human induced (such as the chemicals known as chlorofluorocarbons).

Of all the human-caused gases, carbon dioxide makes the greatest relative contribution to increasing the greenhouse effect (Table 16.1). Carbon dioxide enters the atmosphere as the result of combustion of carbon compounds with oxygen and is a colorless and odorless gas that is the same one we exhale from our lungs. The conversion of **fossil fuels** (oil and natural gas) into energy by cars, factories, and power plants accounts for the majority of the annual human contribution to carbon dioxide emissions, with industrialized nations contributing the most. As a result of human activities, therefore, atmospheric concentration of carbon dioxide has increased nearly 40% over the past 250 years (Figure 16.10). What concerns scientists is that over the past 250 years—and especially in the past 50 years—human activities have been responsible for raising the concentration of greenhouse gases in the atmosphere at an ever-increasing rate. The concentration of atmospheric carbon dioxide is currently 387 parts per million and is increasing by about 2 parts per million each year; this rate of increase is double that from only 50 years ago. In terms of sheer numbers, humans are now pumping into the atmosphere more than 8 billion metric tons (8.8 billion short tons) of carbon dioxide each year.[5]

Methane is the second most abundant human-caused greenhouse gas (Table 16.1). It is produced by leakage from decomposing trash in landfills, by methane-belching domestic cattle, and by agriculture (particularly the cultivation of rice). Even though methane has a lower concentration in the atmosphere than carbon dioxide, it has a greater ability to produce warming on a per-molecule basis. Since the industrial revolution began in about 1750, the concentration of methane in the atmosphere has increased by 250%.

In 2005, researchers recovered a nearly 3.2-kilometer (2-mile) continuous ice core from Antarctica that contains a record of past atmospheric concentrations of

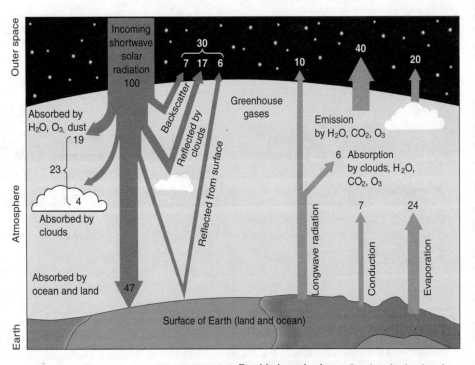

FIGURE 16.8 Earth's heat budget. One hundred units of shortwave solar radiation from the Sun (mostly visible light) are reflected, scattered, and absorbed by various components of the Earth–atmosphere system. The absorbed energy is radiated back into space from Earth as longwave infrared radiation (heat). If this infrared radiation does not leave Earth, global warming will occur.

Atmospheric Energy Balance

FIGURE 16.9 Energy radiated by the Sun and Earth. The intensity of energy radiated by the Sun peaks at a wavelength of 0.48 micrometer (0.0002 inch), which is in the visible part of the spectrum. Some of this energy is absorbed or reflected while some reradiates from Earth in the infrared (heat) range at a wavelength of 10 micrometers (0.004 inch).

---

[5]On average, each person on Earth emits more than 1 metric ton (1.1 short tons) of carbon dioxide per year. Of course, this number is several times greater for those living in industrial nations than for those living in developing countries.

TABLE 16.1 HUMAN-CAUSED GREENHOUSE GASES AND THEIR CONTRIBUTION TO INCREASING THE GREENHOUSE EFFECT

Atmospheric gas	Human-caused sources of gas	Pre-industrial (circa 1750) concentration (ppbv[a])	Present concentration (ppbv[a])	Current rate of increase or decrease (% per year)	Relative contribution to increasing the greenhouse effect (%)	Infrared radiation absorption per molecule (number of times greater than CO_2)
Carbon dioxide (CO_2)	Combustion of fossil fuels	280,000	387,0000	+0.5	60	1
Methane (CH_4)	Leakage, domestic cattle, rice agriculture	700	1750	+1.0	15	25
Nitrous oxide (N_2O)	Combustion of fossil fuels, industrial processes	270	315	+0.2	5	200
Tropospheric ozone (O_3)	Byproduct of combustion	0	10–80	+0.5	8	2000
Chlorofluorocarbon (CFC-11)	Refrigerants, industrial uses	0	0.26	−1.0	4	12,000
Chlorofluorocarbon (CFC-12)	Refrigerants, industrial uses	0	0.54	0.0	8	15,000
Total					100	

[a]ppbv = parts per billion by volume (not by weight).

STUDENTS SOMETIMES ASK...

Isn't carbon dioxide causing the hole in the ozone layer?

Here's the short answer: Definitely not! The ozone layer occurs within the atmosphere's stratosphere and is composed of ozone molecules (O_3) that absorb most of the Sun's ultraviolet radiation. Without it, unhealthy levels of ultraviolet radiation would reach Earth's surface, making the planet largely uninhabitable. The main ozone hole (actually, a seasonal thinning of the ozone layer) occurs above the South Pole, with a smaller one above the North Pole. Both are caused by chemical reactions with natural and human-generated compounds, particularly the now-banned chemicals CFC-11 and CFC-12, but not carbon dioxide. CFCs are also strong greenhouse gases (see Table 16.1), so CFCs are thus double threats to the environment: Their buildup in the atmosphere leads to the destruction of the ozone layer, and at the same time, contributes to global warming. Notice also from Table 16.1 that tropospheric (lower atmosphere) ozone, which is a byproduct of combustion, is a potent greenhouse gas. With the ban of CFCs firmly in place, scientists predict that the ozone layer will achieve its normal thickness by mid-century. However, new research reports that human-generated nitrous oxide, which destroys ozone, is now the single greatest ozone-depleting substance.

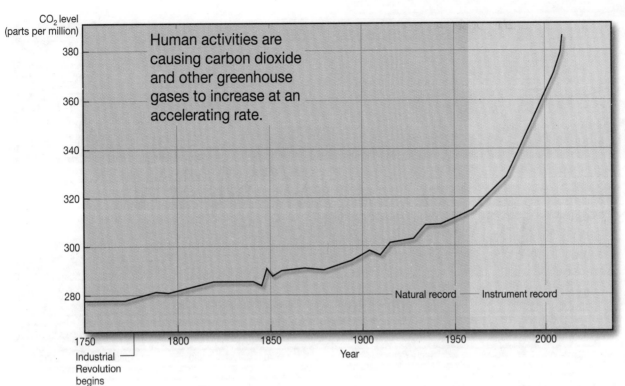

CO₂ level
(parts per million)

Human activities are causing carbon dioxide and other greenhouse gases to increase at an accelerating rate.

Natural record — Instrument record

Year

Industrial Revolution begins

FIGURE 16.10 Amount of carbon dioxide in the atmosphere since 1750. There has been a dramatic increase of average worldwide atmospheric carbon dioxide since the Industrial Revolution began in the late 1700s. Values for 1958 to the present are from instrumental measurement of carbon dioxide at Mauna Loa Observatory in Hawaii; natural record values prior to 1958 are estimated from air bubbles in polar ice cores.

carbon dioxide and methane—two important greenhouse gases—that get trapped as the ice accumulates. Analysis of the core shows that current atmospheric concentrations of carbon dioxide and methane are at their highest levels in at least the past 800,000 years (Figure 16.11). In addition, the chemical make-up of the ice provides a proxy of the past average temperature on Earth, which shows a strong correlation with atmospheric methane and carbon dioxide.

The other trace gases shown in Table 16.1—nitrous oxide, tropospheric ozone, and chlorofluorocarbons—are present in far lower concentrations. Yet they are still very important because they absorb many times more infrared radiation per molecule than carbon dioxide or methane (Table 16.1, *last column*), thus making them very potent contributors to warming. Still, these gases have a smaller overall contribution to increasing the greenhouse effect because their concentrations are so low. Nevertheless, all of these gases must be taken into account when considering the total amount of greenhouse warming.

KEY CONCEPT
The greenhouse effect is caused by gases that allow sunlight to pass through but trap heat energy before it is radiated back to space. Carbon dioxide is foremost in an array of gases from human activity that increase the atmosphere's ability to trap heat.

FIGURE 16.11 Ice core data of atmospheric composition and global temperature. Antarctic ice core data for the past 800,000 years showing atmospheric carbon dioxide (*red curve*), methane (*green curve*), and average global temperature (*black curve*). Atmospheric composition is from analysis of trapped air bubbles in ice; temperature reconstruction is derived from the chemical make-up of the ice. The enlargement (*right*) shows the most recent 2000 years.

(a)

(b)

FIGURE 16.12 Instrumental temperature record since 1865. The record of global average surface air temperature from thermometer readings indicates a global warming of at least 0.8°C (1.4° F) over the past 140 years. The peaks and troughs indicate the natural year-to-year variability of climate.

What Changes Are Occurring Because of Global Warming?

Melting glaciers and ice caps, shorter winters, shifts in species distribution, and a steady rise in average global and sea surface temperatures are just some of the indications that additional human-induced greenhouse warming is occurring. Take, for example, these observations about Earth's temperature, which are based on weather stations on land, satellite data, and, for earlier measurements, proxy data or data from ships:

- Earth's average surface temperature has risen 0.6°C (1.1°F) over the past 30 years and 0.8°C (1.4°F) over the past 140 years (Figure 16.12).
- The rate of warming in the past 50 years was double the rate observed over the past 100 years.
- Worldwide, the 8 warmest years have all occurred since 1998, and the 14 warmest years on record have all occurred since 1990.
- Over the past century, the planet has experienced the largest increase in surface temperature in 1300 years.

Today, there is a scientific consensus that human-induced emissions are responsible for this observed warming. In fact, the warming trends observed since 1950 cannot be explained without accounting for human-caused greenhouse gases.

As global temperatures continue to increase, researchers use sophisticated climate models to forecast what changes will occur on Earth. Because of the complexity of the climate system and its feedback loops, not all models agree as to what or how severe those changes will be. However, there are points on which the models do agree: a strong warming of high northern latitudes, a moderate warming of middle latitudes, and relatively little warming in low latitudes. Other predicted changes—many of which are already happening—include the following:

- Earlier summertime seasons, with higher summer temperatures, including longer and more intense heat waves.
- More extreme precipitation events, such as severe droughts in certain areas and increased chances of flooding in other areas.
- The worldwide retreat of mountain glaciers, which is already being observed.

STUDENTS SOMETIMES ASK...

I've heard that scientists were predicting an oncoming ice age only a few decades ago. What's changed?

Skeptics of global warming have pointed out that in the 1970s, climate scientists were warning of an imminent ice age. In reality, the idea lacked scientific consensus, although the media popularized the notion with sometimes quite alarmist accounts. It is true that from the 1950s through the 1970s, there was an observed global cooling trend. This fact, coupled with the idea that ice ages are cyclical and that our planet was poised for millennia of global cooling based on variations in Earth's orbit, led to speculation that Earth may return to an ice age. However, it is now known that the recent cooling was probably due to a substantial increase in aerosols, which at the time masked the telltale signature of global warming. Looking at a longer view of global temperature since that time, Earth's recent warming trend can be clearly discerned.

- Water contamination issues that lead to larger outbreaks of waterborne infectious diseases such as malaria, yellow fever, and dengue fever.
- Shifts in the distribution of plant and animal communities that affect entire ecosystems and may drive certain species to extinction.

Note that not all predicted changes have negative consequences. For instance, increased warming is expected to provide a longer growing season for some crops, and increased atmospheric carbon dioxide should help promote productivity in plants. However, a number of uncertainties remain in understanding regional effects of climate change, and various components of the climate system may respond to these changes in unanticipated and surprising ways.

16.4 What Changes Are Occurring in the Oceans?

The oceans are a key component in the global climate system that is currently experiencing dramatic changes. Let's examine some of the observed and predicted effects of global warming in the oceans.

Increasing Ocean Temperatures

Studies have revealed that the oceans have absorbed the majority of the increased heat in the atmosphere. Indeed, millions of ocean temperature observations at various depths reveal that there has been an increase in surface temperature (Figure 16.13). These measurements indicate that global sea surface temperatures have risen by about 0.6°C (1°F) from global warming, mainly since about 1970. However, this warming has not been uniform throughout the ocean. The greatest temperature increases have been experienced in the Arctic Ocean, near the Antarctic Peninsula, and in tropical waters. Even deep waters are showing signs of warming: In some places, warming has been documented to a depth of 0.8 kilometer (0.5 mile) or more. To determine the extent of warming experienced in the oceans, scientists have initiated global monitoring of ocean temperature (Box 16.1).

FIGURE 16.13 Global temperature change. Map showing the change in land and ocean surface temperature in 2008 compared to the 1950–1980 baseline period. Most of the globe is anomalously warm (*red areas*) as a result of greenhouse warming, with the greatest temperature increases in the Arctic Ocean, Siberia, the Antarctic Peninsula, and tropical regions. A persistent cool-water La Niña event (*blue area*) is affecting the values in the tropical Pacific Ocean. Gray areas represent no data.

2008 Surface Temperature Change (°C)

-3.5 -2.5 -1.5 -1 -0.6 -0.2 0.2 0.6 1 1.5 2.5 3.5

THE ATOC EXPERIMENT: SOFAR SO GOOD?

Worldwide, a layer exists in the ocean at a depth of about 1000 meters (3300 feet) formed by temperature and pressure conditions that cause sound originating above and below it to become refracted, or bent, into the layer (Figure 16A, *lower inset*). Once in this layer, called the *SOFAR channel* (an acronym for *sound fixing and ranging*), or *deep sound channel*, sound is efficiently trapped and transmitted long distances. For instance, certain whales may use the SOFAR channel to send sounds across entire ocean basins.

The idea of sending sounds through the SOFAR channel in an effort to detect the amount of ocean warming as a result of the greenhouse effect was initiated by Walter Munk of the Scripps Institute of Oceanography (Figure 16A, *upper inset*). His experiment, named **Acoustic Thermometry of Ocean Climate (ATOC)**, is designed to accurately measure the travel time of similar low-frequency sound signals through the SOFAR channel now and in the future. The speed of sound in seawater increases as temperature increases, so sound should take less time to travel the same distance in the future if, in fact, the oceans are warming.

In 1991, Munk's group successfully tested ATOC at Heard Island in the southern Indian Ocean, from which sound can reach many different receiving sites along straight-line paths (Figure 16A). The researchers deployed an underwater array similar to a series of loudspeakers that sent *acoustical* (*akouein* = to hear) signals for six days. These signals refracted into the ocean's SOFAR channel and were transmitted throughout the oceans. After traveling for many hours and as far as 19,000 kilometers (11,800 miles), the signals were received at shipboard recording stations.

The success of ship-based testing at Heard Island led to the establishment of a fixed sound source near Pioneer Seamount off California and an array of fixed receivers throughout the Pacific Ocean. In 1995, ATOC sound signals were sent again. Even though many precautions were taken to avoid any unwanted effects on marine mammals, three humpback whales were found dead in the area a few days after the sound transmissions had begun. The sounds were halted while the U.S. National Marine Fisheries Service (NMFS) conducted research to determine whether the sounds affected the hearing of nearby whales and contributed to their deaths. After extensive scientific study, their results indicated that marine mammals are unaffected by the transmissions and that the dead whales were an unfortunate coincidence. The long-term effect of ATOC signals on marine mammals—including marine mammal communication through the SOFAR channel—is poorly understood but is also likely to be minimal. The NMFS approved the project and transmissions from offshore California and Hawaii have been conducted without incident, producing a wealth of data that indicates a warming trend in the Pacific and establishing an important baseline for comparison with future measurements.

FIGURE 16A The ATOC experiment. Map showing Heard Island sound travel paths, photograph of oceanographer Walter Munk (*upper inset*), and diagram of the SOFAR channel (*lower inset*). Temperature and pressure conditions in the ocean combine to produce the SOFAR channel (*layer B*), which traps and transmits sound energy. Sound waves created in layers A and C are bent into the SOFAR channel and remain within it, allowing the sound to be transmitted across entire ocean basins.

The impacts of a warmer ocean are far-reaching and will persist for several centuries. For example, increased seawater temperatures are likely to affect temperature-sensitive organisms such as corals. As discussed in Chapter 15, warmer sea surface temperatures have been implicated in widespread coral bleaching events (see Box 15.1). In addition, increased seawater temperatures are likely to affect the distribution of sea ice, the ocean's deep-water circulation pattern, El Niño/La Niña events, and the development of hurricanes.

Increasing Hurricane Activity

Many scientists have suggested that warmer oceans would most certainly cause an increase in the general level of storminess because additional heat accelerates evaporation, which fuels hurricanes. In fact, the frequency and severity of recent hurricanes—especially those in the Atlantic Ocean (see Box 6.2)—have kindled a debate on the effect that global warming may have on the formation of hurricanes. Although the recent landfall of several large Atlantic hurricanes leads to a general impression that hurricanes have increased, there have been conflicting reports on the topic in the scientific literature. Some articles have attributed increases in hurricane intensity, numbers, and wind speeds to warmer sea surface temperatures, while others have claimed that changes in data-gathering methods and instrumentation are responsible for the trends. Other studies suggest that the apparent increase in hurricanes can be considered within the statistical limits of normal.

Although the number of tropical storms has not increased worldwide, the scientific consensus is that global warming has led to more intense hurricanes. In the most comprehensive study of recent hurricane activity to date, researchers demonstrate that there have been significant increases in tropical storm intensity and duration around the world since 1970 and that these trends are strongly related to rising sea surface temperatures. Another study of historical Atlantic hurricanes over the past 1500 years suggests that times of peak hurricane activity are related to increased sea surface temperatures and the reinforcing effects of La Niña–like climate conditions. Other research explicitly shows that the most energetic storm levels—those with Category 4 and 5 designations—have increased significantly, particularly in the North Atlantic and northern Indian Oceans. And, experts warn that as climate continues to warm as expected, there will likely be additional increases in peak hurricane wind speed and rainfall.

Changes in Deep-Water Circulation

Evidence from deep-sea sediments and computer models indicates that changes in the global deep-water circulation pattern can dramatically and abruptly affect climate. Circulation in the North Atlantic Ocean, which provides an important source of deep water (Figure 16.14), is particularly sensitive to these changes.

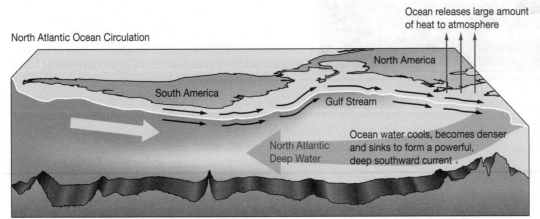

FIGURE 16.14 North Atlantic Ocean circulation. Perspective view of circulation in the North Atlantic Ocean, showing that the Gulf Stream carries a tremendous amount of heat northward that warms the North Atlantic region. As this water cools, it generates a huge volume of cold, salty, dense water called North Atlantic Deep Water that sinks into the deep-ocean basin and flows southward. Disruption of this circulation pattern could have severe effects on global climate.

The movie The Day After Tomorrow *depicts rapid climate change as a result of alterations in deep-water circulation. Could this really happen?*

Although Hollywood movies are well known for dramatization, what is interesting about this blockbuster 2004 film is that its story line is based on recent scientific findings: The ocean's deep-water circulation helps drive ocean currents around the globe and is important to world climate. In fact, strong evidence suggests that the North Atlantic deep-water circulation has already weakened and may further weaken during this century, resulting in unpleasant effects on our climate—but certainly not as rapid or as cataclysmic as the situation portrayed in the film. Computer models suggest that the continued weakening of the North Atlantic deep-water circulation will result in some long-term cooling, particularly over parts of northern Europe.

What drives deep-water circulation is the sinking of cold, dense surface waters at high latitudes, particularly in the North Atlantic. If surface waters stopped sinking because they are too warm and thus low in density, then the oceans would absorb and redistribute heat from solar radiation much less efficiently. This would likely cause even warmer surface water temperatures and much higher land temperatures than are experienced now.

Many scientific studies suggest that the buildup of greenhouse gases in the atmosphere will change ocean circulation. One way in which this could happen is that warmer air temperatures will increase the rate at which glaciers in Greenland melt, forming a pool of fresh, low-density surface water in the North Atlantic Ocean. This freshwater could inhibit the downwelling that generates North Atlantic Deep Water, reorganizing global circulation patterns and causing a corresponding change in climate. Many climate experts warn that a large outflow of freshwater from Greenland could take the North Atlantic system of currents to a tipping point, causing rapid reorganization of deep-water currents and related changes in climate. Indeed, evidence suggests that an outburst from a North American ice-dammed lake flooded the North Atlantic with freshwater about 8000 years ago, causing rapid global climate change. This event may be the type of scenario that the North Atlantic could experience again because of increased precipitation and melting of ice.

Melting of Polar Ice

Computer models have predicted that global warming will affect Earth's polar regions in a very dramatic way. One fundamental difference between the two polar regions is that in the Northern Hemisphere, the polar region is dominated by the Arctic Ocean and its cover of drifting sea ice (an ocean surrounded by land), whereas the South Pole is dominated by the continent of Antarctica and its thick ice cap, including shelf ice that extends into the ocean (land surrounded by an ocean).

The Arctic is one of the locations where the effects of global warming are being most keenly felt (see Figure 16.13) and likely will experience quite dramatic changes in the future; this phenomenon is called *Arctic amplification*. Since 1978, satellite analysis of the extent of Arctic Ocean sea ice indicates that it is dramatically shrinking and thinning at an accelerating rate (Figure 16.15). In the past decade alone, there has been a loss of over 2 million square kilometers (800,000 square miles) of Arctic sea ice. In fact, measurements of the ice cap in 2007 revealed that it had shrunk to its smallest size since researchers began keeping records; its extent fell below the previous record low in 2005 by an area roughly the size of Texas and California combined. In addition, the interior ice is now unusually thin and spread out, which has resulted in wide patches of ice-free ocean during the summer—even at the North Pole.

Climate models are in general agreement that one of the strongest signals of greenhouse warming will be a loss of Arctic sea ice. Indeed, during the past 15 years, the decline in Arctic sea ice has occurred much faster than models had predicted. Cycles of natural variability are known to play a role in Arctic sea ice extent, but the sharp decline observed in the past two decades cannot be explained by natural variability alone. The accelerated Arctic sea ice melting appears to be linked to shifts in Northern Hemisphere atmospheric circulation patterns that have caused the region to experience unusually rapid warming. As a result, ocean temperatures in the Arctic Ocean have also

FIGURE 16.15 Arctic sea ice decline.
Perspective view of satellite data, showing the extent of Arctic sea ice in September 2007 compared with the average extent of sea ice from 1979–2000 (*red line*). Note the opening of an ice-free Northwest Passage. The substantial decrease in amount and thickness of Arctic Ocean sea ice is due to human-induced warming of the Arctic.

increased, causing sea ice to melt from below. Disappearance of sea ice is likely to enhance future warming in the region because lower amounts of sea ice will reflect less of the Sun's radiation back into space, creating a positive-feedback loop and exacerbating the problem as heat is absorbed by the newly uncovered ocean. Researchers fear that the Arctic may be on the verge of a fundamental transition or "tipping point" that will lead to the Arctic having only seasonal ice cover. Some models, for example, suggest that the Arctic could experience the complete disappearance of summer sea ice as early as 2030.

The decrease of sea ice in the Arctic has already had profound effects on Arctic ecosystems. Polar bears (*Ursus maritimus*; Figure 16.16), for example, are excellent swimmers but do not hunt in the water. Instead, they require a platform of floating sea ice to capture their prey items, which are mainly seals. As the Arctic Ocean becomes more ice-free and the ice habitat shrinks, polar bears will have more difficulty finding adequate food and making dens. As a result, polar bear breeding and survival rates may decline below the point needed to maintain the population. Their habitat destruction has been so severe that polar bears were listed as Threatened Species in 2008, according to the U.S. Endangered Species Act. Studies reveal that polar bears are likely to lose nearly half of their summer sea ice habitat by mid-century, which would in turn reduce the world's polar bear population—currently estimated at 25,000—by two-thirds.

In addition, human inhabitants of the Arctic are also being affected by the lack of sea ice, as some of their food sources become scarcer because marine species have migrated further from shore to be near the ice edge. Arctic residents have complained that their weather is changing, and a recent study supports their claim. The study determined that the years with the least amount of Arctic sea ice had significantly stronger Arctic storms. One new opportunity that now exists, however, involves the creation of a new "Northwest Passage" shipping lane linking the North Pacific and North Atlantic Oceans through the largely ice-free portions of the Arctic Ocean (Figure 16.15).

While all these changes are taking place in the Arctic, different but equally dramatic ones are taking place in Antarctica, particularly in the western part of Antarctica that includes the Antarctic Peninsula. As discussed in Chapter 6, Antarctica produces many icebergs from glaciers on land. The rate at which Antarctica is producing icebergs—especially large icebergs—has increased in recent years. For example, the Antarctic Peninsula's Larsen Ice Shelf has decreased by more than 40% over the past decade, including a huge release of 3250 square kilometers (1250 square miles) of ice during two months in 2002 (see Figure 6.24d). In 2006, Antarctica lost nearly 200 billion metric tons (220 short tons) of ice; during 10 days in 2008, the Wilkins Ice Shelf lost over 400 square kilometers (160 square miles) of ice. The rate of thinning of the Pine Island Glacier—the largest stream of fast-moving ice on the West Antarctic Ice Sheet—quadrupled from 1995 to 2006. And, in the past 30 years, there have been 10 major Antarctic ice shelf collapses—including the disappearance of the ice shelves knows as Jones, Larsen A, Muller, and Wordie—after some 400 years of relative stability. Scientists attribute this catastrophic retreat to warming in Antarctica; the Antarctic Peninsula has experienced some of the greatest amount of warming worldwide (see Figure 16.13). In fact, Antarctica has warmed at a rate of about 0.12°C (0.22°F) per decade since 1957, for a total average temperature rise of 0.5°C (1°F) (Figure 16.17).

FIGURE 16.16 Habitat destruction threatens polar bears. Polar bears (*Ursus maritimus*) are reliant on floating sea ice as a feeding platform and for building dens. As a result of habitat destruction caused by shrinking Arctic sea ice, polar bears were designated a Threatened Species in 2008.

Recent Increase in Ocean Acidity

The human-induced increase in the amount of carbon dioxide in the atmosphere has some severe implications for ocean chemistry and for marine life. Recent studies show that a little less than half of the carbon dioxide released by the burning of fossil fuels stays in the atmosphere and about a third currently ends up in

Temperature change per decade (degrees Celsius)

| 0 | 0.05 | 0.10 | 0.15 | 0.20 | 0.25 |

FIGURE 16.17 Antarctic warming trends. This satellite image shows the amount of warming that Antarctica has experienced since 1957. The data are from satellites and weather station measurements. Notice that western Antarctica has experienced the greatest temperature change.

the oceans, dissolving into seawater at the ocean surface. Evidence is mounting that this additional carbon dioxide overwhelms the ocean's natural ability to buffer itself.[6] The absorbed carbon dioxide forms carbonic acid in seawater, lowering the ocean's pH (increasing its acidity in a process called **ocean acidification**) and changing the balance of carbonate and bicarbonate ions. In fact, the oceans have already absorbed enough carbon dioxide for surface waters to have experienced a pH decrease of 0.1 pH unit since preindustrial times; a recent study has confirmed a 0.04 pH unit decrease in the North Pacific Ocean during just the past two decades. Other studies suggest an additional pH decrease will be likely in the future.

Moreover, this shift toward increased acidity and the changes in ocean chemistry that ensue makes it more difficult for certain marine creatures to build and maintain hard parts out of easily dissolved calcium carbonate. The decline in pH thus threatens a diverse assortment of calcifying organisms—creatures that grow calcium carbonate skeletons or shells—such as coccolithophores, foraminifers, pteropods, calcareous algae, sea urchins, mollusks, and corals (Figure 16.18). These organisms provide essential food and habitat to many other species, so their demise could affect entire ocean ecosystems. Recent studies have shown that in the past 20 years, ocean acidification has already caused a 15% decrease in the growth rate of corals in Australia's Great Barrier Reef.

The graph in Figure 16.19 shows the projected increase of carbon dioxide in the ocean and the resulting decrease in ocean pH (rise in acidity). The graph shows that if the current trend of human-induced carbon dioxide emissions

[6]For a discussion of the ocean's buffering system and pH, see Chapter 5.

(a) Coccolithophores (diameter of each = 20 microns, or 0.0008 in.)

(b) Pteropod (diameter = 2 mm, or 0.08 in.)

(c) Sea urchins

(d) Corals

FIGURE 16.18 Examples of marine organisms that are affected by increased ocean acidity. Organisms that make their skeletons or shells out of easily dissolved calcium carbonate include **(a)** coccolithophores, which are type of phytoplankton; **(b)** a pteropod, which is a zooplankton that is a small swimming snail with a shell; **(c)** sea urchins; and **(d)** corals. As ocean acidity increases, these and many other types of organisms will have a more difficult time building and maintaining hard parts.

continues, by 2100 the ocean will experience a pH decrease of at least 0.3 pH unit; some studies indicate that pH could decrease by as much as 0.5 pH unit. Even at the lower value, this reduction of pH represents a change in ocean chemistry that has not occurred for millions of years. An additional concern is that this increase in acidity will eventually be transmitted to the deep-ocean floor by the initiation of deep currents from cold, dense surface waters. This is particularly worrisome because the organisms that inhabit deep-ocean habitats are adapted to its stable, unchanging environment.

Several factors influence the amount of carbon dioxide absorbed by the oceans. Processes involved in distributing carbon dioxide within the ocean–atmosphere system cause it to be divided unequally between the two reservoirs. For example, carbon dioxide gas is readily absorbed by the ocean and, as a result, the ocean contains a much larger amount of carbon dioxide than the atmosphere.[7] The amount of

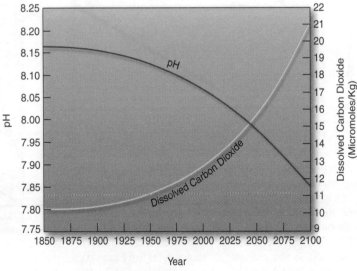

FIGURE 16.19 Historical and projected dissolved carbon dioxide and ocean pH. As the concentration of carbon dioxide in the ocean increases, so does ocean acidity (causing pH to decline).

---

[7]Of the three places where carbon dioxide resides—atmosphere, ocean, and land biosphere—approximately 93% is found in the ocean. The atmosphere, in contrast, contains the smallest amount.

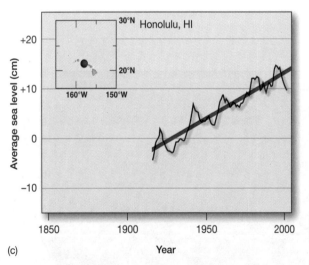

FIGURE 16.20 Measured relative sea level rise from tide gauges. Sea level data from **(a)** New York City, New York, shows an increase of 40 centimeters (16 inches) since 1850. Similar increases are shown in **(b)** San Francisco, California, and **(c)** Honolulu, Hawaii. While some of the documented rise is due to local effects (for example, New York is experiencing isostatic uplift after glaciation), the majority is likely caused by the addition of water from the melting of continental ice caps and glaciers as well as from thermal expansion of warmer ocean water.

carbon dioxide dissolved in the ocean varies with the chemistry of seawater but also has certain limits. Once the ocean approaches saturation of carbon dioxide, it will absorb less of the gas, which means that more will remain in the atmosphere. As the ocean warms, it will further reduce the amount of carbon dioxide that goes into the oceans because warmer water can't hold as much dissolved gas. Another factor is how rapidly deep waters mix with surface waters: The more rapid the mixing, the more it facilitates the uptake of carbon dioxide from the atmosphere. If deep-water circulation slows as predicted, this will also slow the uptake of carbon dioxide from the atmosphere. In essence, more of the carbon dioxide being released now will stay in the atmosphere, where it will create additional human-caused warming.

Rising Sea Level

Analysis of worldwide tide records indicates that there has been a rise in global sea level of between 10 and 25 centimeters (4 and 10 inches) over the past 100 years. At certain tide-recording stations where data go back well into the 19th century, there has been an increase in relative sea level of as much as 40 centimeters (16 inches) over the past 150 years (Figure 16.20). More recently, satellite altimeter data since 1993 indicate a global increase in sea level of about 3 millimeters (0.1 inch) per year (Figure 16.21).

Clearly, sea level is rising. Two main factors contribute to this global rise in sea level: (1) thermal expansion of ocean water as it warms and (2) an increase in the amount of water in the ocean from the melting of ice on land. Note that melting of floating sea ice (such as in the Arctic Ocean) or floating ice shelves (such as those that fringe Antarctica) does not contribute to sea level rise because that ice/water is already in the ocean. More specifically, in order of their overall contribution to the observed global rise in sea level (Figure 16.22), the main contributors are:

1. The melting of Antarctic and Greenland ice sheets
2. The thermal expansion of ocean surface waters
3. The melting of land glaciers and small ice caps
4. The thermal expansion of deep-ocean waters

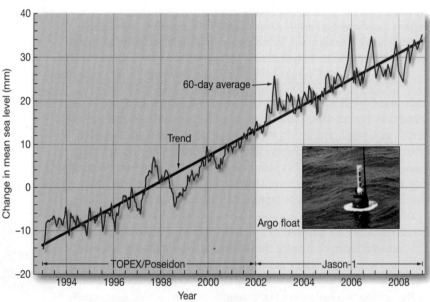

FIGURE 16.21 Sea level rise determined by satellites. Radar altimeter data from TOPEX/Poseidon and Jason-1 satellites combined with Argo drifting floats (*inset*; see also Chapter 7) reveal that sea level rose 3 millimeters (0.1 inch) per year since 1993. Researchers attribute about half of that increase to melting ice and the other half to thermal expansion as the ocean absorbs excess heat from the atmosphere.

An additional factor that affects global sea level is the storage of water on land in reservoirs. A recent study indicates that the amount of this storage has varied but generally increased since 1900 and suggests that without reservoirs, sea level would have risen even more.

Although the current rate of sea level rise might seem inconsequential, even a small amount of sea level rise can severely affect regions that have a gently sloping shoreline, such as the U.S. Atlantic and Gulf Coasts. Hazards associated with sea level rise include drowning of beaches, accelerated coastal erosion, permanent inland flooding, alteration of coastal ecosystems, loss of protective coastal wetlands, and increased damage from destructive storms. Moreover, if global warming increases the intensity of hurricanes, as discussed above, damage to coastal regions will be even greater.

The current rate of global sea level rise, though small, is likely to increase as Greenland and Antarctic ice sheets experience additional warming and make a greater contribution to sea level rise. In fact, detailed studies of Antarctic ice thickness reveal that the rate at which the ice is thinning near the coast has doubled since the 1990s. Neither the Greenland or Antarctic ice sheets are likely to disappear before 2100, but there is the danger that global warming could trigger massive and catastrophic discharges of ice from these ice sheets. A recent study determined that if the West Antarctic Ice Sheet were to collapse, it would raise global sea level by about 3.2 meters (10.5 feet).

According to recent models, the rate of sea level rise will increase with increased global warming. Studies of sea level rise that include both thermal expansion and ice-sheet contributions project a rise in sea level by 2100 of between 0.5 and 1.4 meters (1.6 and 4.6 feet), which is particularly worrisome for low-lying coastal regions. In addition, increased amounts of human settlement and development in coastal regions compound the problem. And, projections suggest that sea level may well rise by several meters in the next few hundred years.

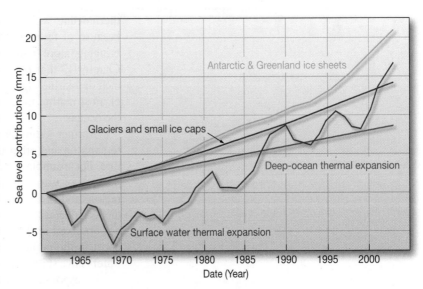

FIGURE 16.22 Main components that contribute to global sea level rise. Each line on this graph shows how much each of the four main components contributes to overall sea level rise. The four components are (1) Antarctic and Greenland ice sheets, (2) glaciers and small ice caps, (3) deep-ocean thermal expansion, and (4) surface water thermal expansion.

Other Predicted Changes

Several other ocean changes are predicted to result from global warming. One is the transmission of sound in the sea (see Box 16.1). A recent study indicates that the increasing amount of carbon dioxide dissolved in seawater makes it more efficient at transmitting sound waves. Researchers predict that by 2050, ocean sounds such as whale calls may travel 70% farther than today; the effect on marine animals is unknown.

Another ocean effect is lower dissolved oxygen in seawater. As discussed in Chapter 12, dissolved oxygen in seawater is vital for most marine animals, which extract dissolved oxygen directly from seawater. As the ocean warms, its ability to hold and carry dissolved oxygen is diminished, while at the same time the metabolic rate of marine organisms increases, which means they need higher levels of dissolved oxygen. In addition, warmer surface waters will limit the overturning process that brings oxygen to deep waters. At current rates of carbon dioxide emissions, studies predict severe oxygen-depleted zones both at the surface and into deeper waters for thousands of years. Reduced oxygen levels will likely have dramatic consequences for marine ecosystems and coastal regions that already experience oxygen-depleted "dead" zones (see Box 13.2).

Still another effect of ocean warming is the alteration of oceanic productivity, which has implications for the distribution of essentially all marine organisms. As ocean surface waters warm, ocean stratification will increase and a stronger

thermocline will develop.[8] As a result, productivity is expected to decrease because of fewer nutrients caused by diminished upwelling and by upwelling bringing more nutrient-depleted warmer waters to the surface. Recall from Chapter 13 that **phytoplankton** (*phyto* = plant, *planktos* = wandering)—which include marine algae such as *diatoms* and *coccolithophores*—comprise the base of most marine food webs and thus support the rest of the larger organisms in the oceans.

Warmer waters can also affect marine organisms directly. Many types of phytoplankton and other organisms are very sensitive to changes in water temperature. For example, a large study of phytoplankton in the North Atlantic shows that ocean warming has increased the abundance of phytoplankton in cooler regions and decreased them in warmer waters. A recent study off California documents a decrease in cool-water organisms caused by a deep, penetrative warming not observed in the past 1400 years. In these organisms' place, there has been a boost in the population of 25 fish groups that prefer warmer waters as surface waters have shifted from cold to warm temperatures over recent decades.

In response to rising ocean temperatures, marine organisms have also begun to migrate into deeper waters and toward the poles. As verification of this trend, a recent study of fish species in the North Sea suggests that many commercially important fish, such as cod, whiting, and anglerfish, have shifted northward as much as 800 kilometers (500 miles). The report notes that if these climate trends continue, some species of fish may withdraw completely from the North Sea by 2050. Changes such as these have severe implications for the health of marine ecosystems and the sustainability of marine fisheries.

Finally, there is great concern amongst the scientific community that the human-induced greenhouse effect may bring unpleasant surprises such as abrupt changes in Earth systems that could not have been predicted.

> **KEY CONCEPT**
> Changes occurring in the ocean due to increased global warming include increased ocean temperatures, more intense hurricane activity, changes in deep-water circulation, melting of polar ice, increased ocean acidity, and rising sea level.

16.5 What Should Be Done to Reduce Greenhouse Gases?

The consensus of scientific studies suggest that the planet has warmed due to human-caused greenhouse gas emissions. Moreover, scenarios for future warming look bleak. For example, if human-caused emissions remain at or near their current rate of increase, atmospheric carbon dioxide is expected to exceed 500 parts per million sometime between 2050 and 2100, causing global temperatures to increase by at least 2°C (3.6°F) and more likely by about 5°C (9°F). Based on paleoclimate data, these values of atmospheric carbon dioxide and global temperature significantly exceed those of at least the past 420,000 years.

Recently, there have been serious discussions about deliberately manipulating Earth's climate system to counteract human-caused global warming and its unwanted effects. These manipulations—called **global engineering**, or *geoengineering*—are very controversial. Some of the concerns about any type of global engineering include the justification for intentionally altering any of Earth's systems on a global scale, the possibility of harmful side effects, who should pay for its implementation, and whether it would have to be constantly maintained. In addition, skeptics of global engineering point out that it distracts from perhaps the most immediate way of limiting human-caused climate change: reducing the amount of greenhouse gases that are spewed into the atmosphere.

Most global engineering proposals fall into two general types: (1) reducing the amount of sunlight reaching Earth or (2) removing human-caused greenhouse gases from the atmosphere and disposing of them somewhere else. Examples of the first type include spraying sulfate aerosols into the atmosphere

---

[8]For more details on the thermocline (layer of rapidly changing temperature), see Chapter 5.

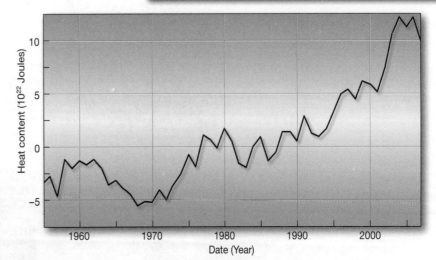

to mimic the cooling effect of a major volcanic eruption or installing thousands of reflective sunshades in orbit to block incoming sunlight. Examples of the second type include removing atmospheric carbon dioxide and placing it into subsurface layers within Earth or into the deep ocean.

In this section, we'll examine how the oceans naturally counteract global warming, how the ocean system reduces greenhouse gases, and what potential solutions exist.

The Ocean's Role in Reducing Global Warming

Because the oceans naturally absorb vast amounts of carbon dioxide from the atmosphere, the oceans therefore play a vital role in reducing the greenhouse effect. In fact, the vast majority of carbon dioxide in the ocean–atmosphere system is found in the ocean because carbon dioxide is approximately 30 times more soluble in water than are other common gases. Currently, a little less than half of the carbon dioxide humankind releases into the atmosphere stays there; about a third enters the oceans with the rest absorbed by land plants.

THE OCEAN'S BIOLOGICAL PUMP   What happens to the carbon dioxide that enters the ocean? Most of it is incorporated into organisms through photosynthesis and through their secretion of carbonate shells. Moreover, carbon dioxide is cycled very effectively from the atmosphere to the ocean. In fact, more than 99% of the carbon dioxide added to the atmosphere in the geologic past by volcanic activity has been removed by the ocean and deposited in marine sediments as biogenous calcium carbonate and fossil fuels. Thus, the ocean acts as a *repository* (or *sink*) for carbon dioxide, soaking it up and removing it from the environment as sea floor deposits. This process of removing material from sunlit surface waters to the sea floor is called a **biological pump** because it "pumps" carbon dioxide and nutrients from the upper ocean and concentrates them in deep-sea waters and sea floor sediments (Figure 16.23).

THE OCEAN AS A THERMAL SPONGE   Due to its unique thermal properties,[9] water can absorb large quantities of heat without much change in temperature. Thus, the thermal properties of the ocean make it ideal for minimizing the increase in global temperature. Further, the oceans serve as the planet's biggest single reservoir for surplus energy. If not for the oceans, the planet would be experiencing a much greater increase in temperature. In essence, the oceans act as a "thermal sponge," absorbing heat but not increasing much in temperature and so minimize the amount of warming experienced. Even so, recent studies have documented that the heat content of the oceans has been increasing (Figure 16.24).

FIGURE 16.23 The ocean's biological pump. Schematic view of the ocean's biological pump, which removes carbon dioxide from the atmosphere.

> KEY CONCEPT
> The ocean plays a key role in reducing atmospheric greenhouse gases through its biological pump; it also minimizes global warming by acting as a thermal sponge.

FIGURE 16.24 Heat content of the oceans. Graph showing how the heat content of the oceans has increased since the 1950s. The short-term variability of the curve shows the natural variation of the ocean's heat content and is influenced by factors such as El Niño/La Niña events.

---

[9]For a discussion of water's unique thermal properties, such as latent heat, see Chapter 5.

Possibilities for Reducing Greenhouse Gases

There is much debate about what to do about the increasing human-caused emissions in the atmosphere. One idea is to eliminate human emissions before they even get into the atmosphere. Other proposals involve using the oceans to reduce the amount of human-caused emissions in the atmosphere. Let's examine two of these proposals.

THE IRON HYPOTHESIS Stimulating productivity in the ocean has been proven to remove carbon dioxide from the atmosphere. Through photosynthesis, phytoplankton such as diatoms convert carbon dioxide dissolved in the ocean to carbohydrate and oxygen gas. By capturing and removing additional amounts of carbon dioxide from the ocean, the ocean can, in turn, absorb more heat-trapping carbon dioxide from the atmosphere, thus cooling the planet.

Areas of the ocean that have relatively low productivity, such as in the tropics, are a good place to stimulate productivity and thus increase the amount of carbon dioxide removed from the atmosphere. In 1987, oceanographer John Martin determined that the absence of the essential nutrient iron limited productivity in tropical oceans, so he proposed fertilizing the ocean with iron to increase its productivity. "Give me a half a tanker of iron and I'll give you the next ice age," Martin once famously quipped. Subsequently, this idea became known as the **iron hypothesis** (Figure 16.25). In 1993, Martin's associates tested the idea by adding a soluble solution of finely ground iron to a small patch of ocean near the Galápagos Islands in the Pacific Ocean. Their results, combined with the results of about a dozen other open-ocean experiments worldwide since 1993, confirmed that adding iron to the ocean increased phytoplankton productivity up to 30 times. In fact, some of the patches of iron-enriched high productivity were visible to Earth-orbiting satellites.

FIGURE 16.25 The iron hypothesis. Seeding the ocean with the essential nutrient iron stimulates productivity and draws in heat-trapping carbon dioxide from the atmosphere that is used by phytoplankton. Some of this carbon dioxide, tied up as tissue or in fecal pellets, sinks toward the sea floor, thereby removing it from the environment. Photo (*inset*) shows a view from a research vessel involved in applying finely-ground iron to the ocean near Antarctica.

Carbon dioxide in atmosphere

Iron added to ocean

Although the results from these small-scale open-ocean experiments proved that the iron hypothesis did indeed draw carbon dioxide out of the atmosphere, the scientists had to overcome problems grinding the iron fine enough, dispersing the iron, and keeping it in solution for long periods of time. A more serious problem, however, is the long-term global environmental effects of increasing the amount of carbon dioxide in the ocean and stimulating biological productivity. For example, there is concern that severe oxygen depletion of seawater could occur in areas where iron fertilization is conducted because the large population of algae that is produced eventually dies and decomposes, thus consuming dissolved oxygen. In addition, decomposition releases byproducts such as carbon dioxide and nitrous oxide—both important greenhouse gases. As discussed previously, higher amounts of carbon dioxide in the ocean lead to increased ocean acidity, which is a problem for marine life and marine ecosystems. Another problem is from interference with the natural ecology of large oceanic regions—and its unforeseeable consequences. Nevertheless, even larger open-ocean experiments have been proposed and several private companies have filed patents for ocean-fertilization technologies to enable ocean fertilization to occur on a commercial scale.

SEQUESTERING EXCESS CARBON DIOXIDE IN THE OCEANS Successful experiments have involved capturing emissions either before they are released into the atmosphere or directly from the atmosphere and then pumping the gas into the deep ocean or underground reservoirs. This process—called **sequestering** (*sequester* = depository) carbon dioxide—thereby removes carbon dioxide from the atmosphere and, as a result, reduces global warming. If the deep ocean is used as a disposal site for carbon dioxide, however, there are concerns about how it would impact deep-sea chemistry and, as a result, marine ecosystems. In addition, it is unclear how long the sequestered carbon dioxide will stay in the deep ocean because of deep-water circulation patterns. However, the capture of carbon dioxide emissions and their subsequent disposal into deep reservoirs beneath the sea floor is already occurring at a handful of test sites worldwide.

The Kyoto Protocol: Limiting Greenhouse Gas Emissions

The mounting scientific evidence that global warming and some of its side effects are occurring has led to international efforts to address the human contribution to the greenhouse effect. A number of international conferences have resulted in an agreement among 60 nations to voluntarily limit greenhouse gas emissions. This agreement, which is called the **Kyoto Protocol** (because it was created at an international conference held in 1997 in Kyoto, Japan), sets target reductions for each country. For example, industrialized countries (such as the United States, which constitutes only about 5% of world population but is responsible for about 20% of worldwide carbon dioxide emissions[10]) are to reduce their collective emission of six greenhouse gases by at least 5% by 2012 compared to 1990 levels. Although 122 nations (representing 44% of the total worldwide carbon dioxide emissions) have ratified the treaty, the U.S. government has withdrawn its support for the protocol, citing potential harm to the world economy.

In late 2009, an international agreement reached at a meeting of delegates from both industrialized nations and major emerging economies at the United Nations Climate Change Conference in Copenhagen, Denmark, formally recognized a mandate to curb human-induced greenhouse gas emissions. The accord cites a goal of holding the global rise in average global temperatures to 2°C (3.6°F) but does not specify a long-term method for reducing emissions.

---

[10]China, which is a highly populated and rapidly industrializing country, recently surpassed the United States as the leading carbon dioxide emitter worldwide. The United States is currently second, with India and Russia next.

STUDENTS SOMETIMES ASK...

What can I do to help with the problem of global warming?

Even though global warming is a worldwide problem, there are many things concerned individuals can do to help curb greenhouse gas emissions:

1. *Drive smart:* Tune up your car and drive with properly inflated tires.
2. *Write your politicians:* Urge them to raise fuel economy standards for vehicles.
3. *Go green:* Support clean, renewable, non-fossil-fuel energy sources.
4. *Switch lights:* Replace incandescent light bulbs with energy-efficient compact fluorescent bulbs.
5. *Check your house:* Insulate and weather-strip; ask your utility company for a free energy audit.
6. *Become a smart water consumer:* Turn your water heater down and use low-flow faucets.
7. *Buy energy-efficient electronics and appliances:* Replace older, inefficient refrigerators and air conditioners.
8. *Plant a tree, protect a forest:* Preserve plant communities, which absorb carbon dioxide.
9. *Reduce, reuse, and recycle:* Support recycling efforts by choosing recycled products.
10. *Educate and vote:* Educate others and support measures that encourage energy conservation.

Note that these measures are all sound practices for preserving the environment that make sense no matter what the future levels of global warming might be.

Even if greenhouse gas concentrations stabilized today, with no additional increases, the planet would continue to warm by about 0.6°C (1°F) over the next century because it takes years for Earth's climate system to fully react to increases in greenhouse gases. This future warming is often referred to as Earth's *commitment to warming*. Based on plausible emissions scenarios, the IPCC estimates that average surface temperatures could rise between 2°C and 6°C (3.6°F and 10.8°F) by the end of the 21st century. Scenarios that assume that people will burn even larger amounts of fossil fuels than we do today give warming estimates in the top end of this temperature range, while the scenarios that assume that greenhouse gas emissions will grow slowly or not increase at all suggest a much smaller amount of warming. Not since the end of the last ice age 10,000 years ago, when Earth warmed by about 5°C (9°F), has the average temperature changed as dramatically as the change that scientists are predicting in less than 100 years.

At this point, it is very clear that human activities—such as burning fossil fuels, releasing emissions, and land use changes—are altering the environment on a global scale. Although the changes cannot be completely eliminated, many human impacts can be reduced. For instance, activities that affect the environment most severely—such as the high rate of consumption of fossil fuels and their subsequent harmful emissions—need to be decreased. In addition, plant communities must be preserved and much of what has already been removed by deforestation must be replaced in order to halt further damage. Finally, a high priority must be placed on research that improves our understanding of how Earth's climate system works.

> ### KEY CONCEPT
> Possibilities for reducing greenhouse gases include adding iron to the ocean to stimulate productivity and absorbing carbon dioxide from the atmosphere; sequestering excess carbon dioxide in the deep ocean; and limiting greenhouse gas emissions.

Chapter in Review

- *Earth's climate system includes the atmosphere, hydrosphere, geosphere, biosphere, and cryosphere (the ice and snow that exists at Earth's surface). This system involves exchanges of energy and moisture that occur among the five spheres. Both positive-feedback loops that reinforce changes and negative-feedback loops that counteract changes* modify Earth's climate.

- *Paleoclimatology*, the study of Earth's past climate, uses *proxy data*, which consist of *natural recorders of past climate*, including *sea floor sediments, glacial ice, fossil pollen, tree-growth rings*, and information contained in *historical documents*.

- *Several explanations have been formulated to explain Earth's climate change.* Current hypotheses for *natural factors* (causes unrelated to human activities) of climate change include *changes in the Sun's output associated with sunspots, variations in Earth's orbit, volcanic activity, and movement of Earth's tectonic plates*. Although natural mechanisms have altered climate in the past, *recent climate change is greater than can be explained by any natural factors*.

- Assessment reports published by the *Intergovernmental Panel on Climate Change (IPCC)* clearly document that the *current climate changes observed on Earth are due primarily to human activities that release heat-trapping greenhouse gas emissions to the atmosphere*.

- *The increase in average worldwide temperature is called global warming.* Although the warming of Earth's surface and atmosphere is a natural process controlled by the *greenhouse effect*, it is also being *altered by human greenhouse gas emissions*, a phenomenon that is often referred to as the *enhanced greenhouse effect*.

- *The greenhouse effect is produced by incoming sunlight that changes in wavelength, thus heating Earth. Energy reaching Earth from the Sun is mostly in the ultraviolet and visible regions* of the electromagnetic spectrum, whereas *energy radiated back to space from Earth is primarily in the*

infrared (heat) region. Water vapor, carbon dioxide, methane, and other trace gases absorb infrared radiation and thus heat the atmosphere.

- *Earth's average surface temperature has warmed over the past century* and there is strong evidence that it is due primarily to human-caused increases of certain *heat-trapping gases such as carbon dioxide and methane*. Models predict that there will be a *strong warming of high northern latitudes*, a moderate warming of middle latitudes, and relatively little warming in low latitudes. Other predicted changes caused by global warming include *changes in the length of seasons, more intense heat waves, changes in both average and extreme temperature and precipitation, retreat of mountain glaciers, alteration of the range of infectious diseases, and shifts in the distribution of plants and animals*.

- *Changes that have been observed in the oceans due to global warming include increased ocean temperatures, more intense hurricane activity, changes in deep-water circulation, melting of polar ice, increase in ocean acidity, and rising sea level. These changes in the ocean will continue for centuries*.

- *The ocean removes carbon dioxide from the atmosphere by its biological pump, which pumps carbon dioxide into sea floor deposits. The ocean also acts as a thermal sponge by soaking up excess heat from the atmosphere*, thereby minimizing the amount of warming experienced.

- *The ocean can be used as a repository for some of society's carbon dioxide emissions* through either the *iron hypothesis, which stimulates phytoplankton productivity with the addition of finely ground iron*, or through *sequestering excess carbon dioxide by pumping it directly into the deep ocean*. However, the *effect* that these proposals might cause in the ocean is largely *unknown*.

- *The Kyoto Protocol establishes limits on greenhouse gas emissions*, but the *United States has not agreed to support it* because of potential harm to the economy. Nevertheless, there is already a *commitment to warming* and various *scenarios can be used to predict the amount of future warming*.

Key Terms

Acoustic Thermometry of Ocean Climate (ATOC) (p. 482)

Biological pump (p. 491)

Climate (p. 469)

Climate system (p. 469)

Feedback loop (p. 470)

Fossil fuel (p. 477)

Global engineering (p. 490)

Global warming (p. 475)

Greenhouse effect (p. 475)

Greenhouse gases (p. 477)

Heat budget (p. 476)

Intergovernmental Panel on Climate Change (IPCC) (p. 474)

Iron hypothesis (p. 492)

Kyoto Protocol (p. 493)

Ocean acidification (p. 486)

Paleoclimatology (p. 472)

Phytoplankton (p. 490)

Proxy (p. 471)

Sequester (p. 493)

Sunspots (p. 472)

Thermocline (p. 490)

Review Questions

1. List the five parts of Earth's climate system.

2. What are climate feedback loops? Give some examples of both types.

3. What are proxy data? List several examples. Why are such data necessary for paleoclimatology studies?

4. List several examples of natural climate change. Do natural climate change mechanisms account for the recent climate changes that Earth is experiencing?

5. Describe the fundamental difference between solar radiation absorbed at Earth's surface and the radiation that is primarily responsible for heating Earth's atmosphere.

6. Discuss the greenhouse gases in terms of their relative concentrations in the atmosphere and their relative contributions to global warming.

7. Why has the carbon dioxide level of the atmosphere been rising for more than 150 years?

8. How are atmospheric temperatures likely to change as carbon dioxide levels continue to increase?

9. Describe several changes that are already occurring in the oceans because of global warming.

10. What physical conditions produce a SOFAR channel, or sound channel, below the ocean's surface? How is the SOFAR channel being used to detect warming in the oceans?

11. How does the ocean's biological pump work to help reduce global warming?

12. How does the ocean act as a thermal sponge, thereby helping minimize the amount of global warming experienced?

13. What is the Kyoto Protocol? Why has the United States not agreed to support it?

14. What commitment to warming will Earth experience in the future? What strategies exist to reduce future warming?

Critical Thinking Exercises

1. What is the difference between weather and climate? If it rains in a particular area during a day, does that mean that the area has a wet climate? Explain.

2. Some friends tell you that they've heard that the recent climate change Earth is experiencing is just part of a natural cycle. What would you explain to them—including using any figures from this chapter—to help convince them otherwise?

3. Sketch a labeled diagram that shows how Earth's greenhouse effect works.

4. Describe the iron hypothesis, and discuss the relative merits and dangers of undertaking such a "global engineering" project that could cause dramatic changes in the environment worldwide.

Oceanography on the Web

Visit the *Essentials of Oceanography* Online Study Guide for Internet resources, including chapter-specific quizzes to test your understanding and Web links to further your exploration of the topics in this chapter.

The *Essentials of Oceanography* Online Study Guide is at http://www.mygeoscienceplace.com/.

AFTERWORD

"In the end, we will conserve only what we love. We love only what we understand. We will understand only what we are taught."
— BABA DIOUM,
Senegalese conservationist (1968)

At the end of our journey through this book together, it seems fitting to examine people's perceptions of the ocean. Many people describe the ocean as "powerful," "awe inspiring," "moving," "serene," "abundant," and "majestic." Others call it "vast," "infinite," or "boundless." These are all appropriate descriptions, because even though humans have been exploring and studying the ocean for centuries, the ocean still holds many secrets. The oceans are constantly surprising researchers with unusual features, newly discovered species, and geologic wonders that exist within its watery world.

Despite the ocean's impressive size, it is beginning to feel the effects of human activities. For instance, every ocean contains large areas of floating plastic and even remote beaches are littered with trash. Organisms living in the ocean also feel the effect of humankind's use of the ocean. Whaling in the 19th and 20th centuries, for example, pushed many great whale populations to near extinction. Restrictions on whaling and the development of substitutes for whale products helped whales survive this threat, but now they face destruction of their feeding and breeding grounds. Overfishing, however, more than any other human activity, has altered the marine ecosystem, suggesting that the ocean is not quite as "vast," "infinite," or "boundless" as most people believe.

Humans have become one of the most important agents of change on the planet. This is largely due to our rapidly expanding human population (Figure Aft.1). Today, nearly 7 billion people occupy the planet, and births now exceed deaths by about two and a half times. At the present rate of population increase—which sounds small enough, at about 1.1%, but produces truly staggering numbers—there are more than 2 new people on the planet each second, or about 9000 more people each hour. Each year there are about 77 million more of us, a total equal to the combined populations of the six largest cities in the world (Mumbai, Shanghai, Karachi, Delhi, Istanbul, and São Paulo). The number of people has quadrupled since 1900 and is expected to peak at about 9.2 billion around 2050. Clearly, our burgeoning human population is the greatest environmental threat of all.

Human-induced changes in the marine environment are broad and far-reaching. Examples include pollution, shoreline development, overfishing, introduction of non-native species, biodiversity decline, ecosystem degradation, and perhaps most serious of all, climate change. In 2008, a study of the cumulative impact of 17 of

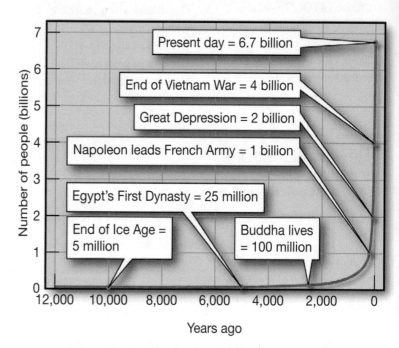

FIGURE AFT.1 Human population growth. Graph showing world population, which has experienced a rapid growth in recent decades. It took 4 million years for humanity to reach the 2 billion mark but only 50 years to double that amount. The current world population is nearly 7 billion people and is increasing at a rate of over 1% per year.

the most urgent land- and ocean-based threats to worldwide marine ecosystems shows that no areas of the ocean are untouched by human activities. The study revealed that fully one-third of the oceans are strongly affected by multiple factors and that the most heavily impacted ecosystems are continental shelves, rocky reefs, coral reefs, seagrass beds, and deep-sea seamounts. However, the report notes that large areas of relatively little human impact remain, particularly near the poles.

Several U.S. commissions have suggested ways to protect the marine environment. In 2003, for example, the Pew Oceans Commission recommended significant changes aimed at guiding the way in which the federal government should manage American's marine environment. In 2004, the U.S. Commission on the Oceans submitted 212 recommendations for a coordinated and comprehensive national ocean policy. In 2008, the Joint Ocean Commission issued a report card assessing the nations' collective progress in ocean policy during 2007 (its overall grade: a "C," with some categories receiving a "D"). These commissions urge an integrated research and education ecosystem-based management approach to support ocean environmental health and resource sustainability. Another recommendation is the establishment of marine protected areas.

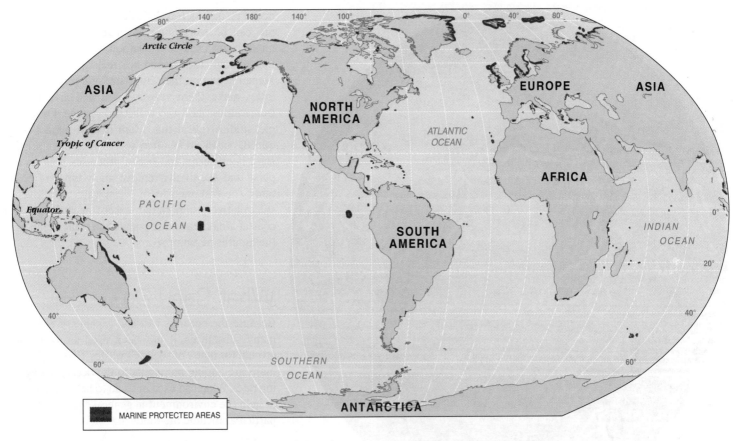

FIGURE AFT.2 Marine protected areas. Worldwide, over 4000 marine protected areas (MPAs) have been established, offering various levels of protection to living, nonliving, cultural, and/or historic resources. MPAs cover less than 1% of the world ocean.

What Are Marine Protected Areas?

Concerns about the health and longevity of the oceans have led to the establishment of **marine protected areas (MPAs)**, which cover a wide range of marine areas with some level of restriction to protect living, nonliving, cultural, and/or historic resources (Figure Aft.2). MPAs can be established for a multitude of reasons: to protect a certain species, to benefit fisheries management, or to protect full ecosystems, rare habitat, or nursing grounds for fish. MPAs are also established to protect historical sites such as shipwrecks and important cultural sites such as aboriginal fishing grounds. MPAs can be very large (for example, Australia's 2000-kilometer [1200-mile] Great Barrier Reef) or very small (for example, Italy's tiny coastal Marina Protetta Capo Rizzuto). Because the term *MPA* has been used widely around the globe, its meaning in any one region may be quite different than in another. MPAs offer various levels of protection that include areas designated as marine sanctuaries, marine reserves, special protected areas, marine parks, no-take refuges, and areas of special conservation, all of which have specific types of restrictions associated with them as defined by the laws of the governing body.

Studies have shown that MPAs can help increase biodiversity, protect habitats, and aid in the recovery of fish populations when placed and managed effectively. While MPAs may not solve all of the issues that threaten various parts of the ocean, they have been shown to help restore marine ecosystems on a local scale and act as buffers to larger-scale impacts.

In 1972, the U.S. Congress began establishing a type of MPA called a **national marine sanctuary** to protect vital pockets of the ocean from further degradation. Today, 14 national marine sanctuaries cover more than 47,000 square kilometers (18,000 square miles) in areas such as the Florida Keys, the Stellwagen Bank off Massachusetts, the Channel Islands off Southern California, the Flower Garden Banks in the Gulf of Mexico, and the Hawaiian Islands (Figure Aft.3). Many activities that degrade the marine environment, however, are still allowed in marine sanctuaries, such as fishing, recreational boating, and even mining of some resources.

Many scientists who recognize the importance of preserving vital marine habitats are calling for governments to more fully protect marine areas by establishing large no-take refuges called **marine reserves** in which fishing and other activities are prohibited. Such action would allow the recovery of heavily overfished

Northwest Hawaiian Islands
(Papahānaumokuākea)
Marine National Monument

Olympic Coast

Cordell Bank

Gulf of the Farallones

Monterey Bay

Channel Islands

Exclusive Economic Zone

Hawaiian Islands
Humpback Whale

Fagatele Bay

Stellwagen Bank

Thunder Bay

Monitor

Gray's Reef

Florida Keys

Flower Garden Banks

U.S. National Marine Sanctuaries

FIGURE AFT.3 U.S. national marine sanctuaries. The United States has established 14 U.S. national marine sanctuaries, which protect natural and/or cultural resources. Also shown is the boundary of the 200-nautical-mile (370-kilometer) Exclusive Economic Zone (*yellow lines*).

ocean resources, too. A healthy coral reef, for example, can be worth more as a tourist draw than it might be as a source of seafood.

Although the oceans are feeling the effects of human activities, their huge size and physical properties make them very resilient and give them a tremendous ability to withstand change. For example, studies reveal that when human impact is reduced, ocean areas often return to a near pristine state because natural ocean processes tend to disperse and eventually remove many types of pollutants. The vast majority of ocean water, moreover, is still relatively unpolluted, except in shallow-water coastal areas near large population centers and near the mouths of major rivers.

What Can I Do?

Because the ocean is vast and capable of absorbing many substances, it has been used as a dumping ground for many of society's wastes. Even today, humans are adding pollutants to the ocean at staggering rates. What can each of us do to help? Some ways to help the environment in general and the ocean in particular include the following:

- **Minimize your impact on the environment.** Reduce the amount of waste you generate by making wise consumer choices. Avoid products with excessive packaging and support companies that have good environmental records. Use non-toxic or less hazardous products around the house. Conserve resources. Reuse and recycle items, then help close the recycling loop by buying goods made of recycled materials. Do simple things that make a positive impact on the environment (Box Aft.1).

- **Become politically aware.** Many ocean-related issues come before the public and require a majority of voters to approve a proposal before they are enacted into law. This "majority rules" is true for local as well as national and international issues. Within our lifetimes, for instance, we may very well decide whether to spend large amounts of money to add finely ground iron to the ocean to reduce the amount of carbon dioxide in the atmosphere. Many political issues in the future will involve the ocean.

- **Educate yourself about how the ocean works.** A recent poll indicates that more than 90% of the American public consider themselves scientifically illiterate. With our society becoming more scientifically advanced, people need to understand how science operates. Science is not meant to be comprehended by an elite few. Rather, science is for everyone. By studying oceanography, you have begun to understand how the ocean works. It is our hope that you will be a lifelong student of the ocean. And if you are considering participating in the scientific study of the oceans, more details on working in marine science can be found in Appendix V, "Careers in Oceanography."

stocks and protect sea floor communities decimated by trawling the sea floor with nets. In 2006, for example, the United States established the 360,000-square-kilometer (139,000-square-mile) Northwest Hawaiian Islands Marine National Monument, creating the world's largest marine reserve at the time. The reserve, which has been renamed the Papahānaumokuākea Marine National Monument, was eclipsed in size by the Phoenix Islands Protected Area, which was established in 2008 and is the size of California.

Worldwide, more than 4000 marine reserves exist, but they still cover less than 1% of the world ocean. And, proper enforcement within these "no-take" reserves remains an issue. Although the commercial and recreational fishing industries have historically opposed creating marine reserves, research indicates that marine reserves "spill over" and provide benefits to surrounding regions by boosting certain populations of commercially important fish outside their borders. Marine preserves also protect large fish and so help restore the natural predator-prey relationships of healthy, self-sustaining ecosystems. Other countries are beginning to realize the economic benefit of fully protecting

AFT.1   FOCUS ON THE ENVIRONMENT

TEN SIMPLE THINGS YOU CAN DO TO HELP PREVENT MARINE POLLUTION

Nobody made a greater mistake than he who did nothing because he could only do a little.
— EDMUND BURKE (circa 1790)

There are many simple things you can do every day to help prevent marine pollution, such as the following:

1. **Snip plastic six-pack rings.** Plastic six-pack rings entangle many marine organisms, so snip each circle with scissors before you toss them into the garbage—or, better yet, recycle them along with the cans or bottles to which they are attached. If you find any at a beach, pick them up, snip them, and recycle them, too.

2. **Use lawn fertilizers, yard chemicals, and laundry detergent sparingly.** Lawn fertilizers contain nitrates and phosphates, which cause harmful algal blooms when runoff from land enters the ocean through storm drains. Detergents also contain phosphates, so read the detergent label to find one that is phosphate free and use a smaller amount than recommended. Use yard chemicals such as pesticides and weed killers only when absolutely necessary.

3. **Clean up after your pet.** Dog and cat feces have high bacteria levels. When they wash into a stream or storm drain and eventually to the ocean, they also provide nitrates and phosphates, which create harmful algal blooms.

4. **Make sure your car doesn't leak oil.** Oil that leaks from automobiles is responsible for a large percentage of the oil that gets into the ocean. Annually, the amount of oil that enters the ocean as runoff from road sources (non-point-source pollution) through storm drains is greater than a major oil spill. If you change your car's oil yourself, be sure to recycle the used oil at an appropriate recycling center.

5. **Drive less and carpool more.** Reducing the amount of gasoline you use reduces the amount of oil that must be transported across the ocean, which minimizes the potential for oil spills.

6. **Take your own bags to the grocery store.** Although paper bags are biodegradable, plastic bags are not and are becoming an increasing problem in the ocean, especially for animals like sea turtles that eat plastic bags when they mistake them for jellyfish. That's why plastic bags—as well as Styrofoam containers—have been banned in certain countries and coastal communities.

7. **Don't release balloons.** Balloons that are released far from the ocean can still wind up there, where they deflate, quickly lose their color, and resemble drifting jellyfish that marine animals can ingest.

8. **Don't litter.** Any material that is carelessly discarded on land can become non-point-source pollution when it washes down a storm drain, into a stream, and eventually into the ocean.

9. **Pick up trash at the beach or volunteer for an organized beach cleanup.** It is important to remove trash that washes up at the beach so it can't endanger marine organisms. Trash arrives at the beach from non-point-source pollution, ships, recreational boaters, beachgoers, and other sources. It is truly surprising (and somewhat horrifying) to discover what ends up at the beach.

10. **Inform and educate others.** Many people are unaware that their actions have a negative influence on the environment—especially the marine environment.

FIGURE AFT.4 Sunset at the ocean.

APPENDIX I
METRIC AND ENGLISH UNITS COMPARED

How many inches are there in a mile? How many cups in a gallon? How many pounds in a ton? In our daily lives, we often need to convert between units. Worldwide, the metric system of measurement is the most widely used system. Besides the United States, only *two other countries in the world*—Liberia and Myanmar (formerly Burma)—still use English units as their primary system of measurement. The metric system has many advantages over the English system. It is simple, logical, and makes conversion between units easy. For those of us in the United States, it is only a matter of time before the change to the metric system occurs.

Benjamin Franklin was one of the first to propose that the United States adopt the sensible metric system. Interestingly, the United States was officially declared a metric nation by the Secretary of the Treasury in 1893, but the idea was never embraced by Americans.

On December 23, 1975, U.S. President Gerald R. Ford signed the Metric Conversion Act of 1975. It defined the metric system as the International System of Units (officially called the *Système International d'Unités*, [SI]) as interpreted in the United States by the Secretary of Commerce. The Trade Act of 1988 and other legislation declared the metric system the preferred system of weights and measures for U.S. trade and commerce, called for the federal government to adopt metric specifications, and mandated the Commerce Department to oversee the program.

Although the metric system has not become the system of choice for most Americans' daily use, and there is great resistance to using it, the United States must change over to remain competitive in world markets. Many of the sciences are leading the way in this changeover. In fact, oceanographers all over the world have been using the metric system for years.

The English System

The English system actually consists of two related systems—the U.S. Customary System[1] (used in the United States and its dependencies) and the British Imperial System (used throughout Great Britain). Ironically, Great Britain has now largely converted to the metric system. The basic unit of length in the English system is the *yard*; the basic unit of weight (not mass) is the *pound*.[2]

In the English system, the units of length were initially based arbitrarily on dimensions of the body. The yard as a measure of length, for example, can be traced to the early Saxon kings. They wore a sash around their waists that could be used as a convenient measuring device. Thus, the word *yard* comes from the Saxon word *gird* (like a girdle), in reference to the circumference of a person's waist. The circumference of a person's waist varies from person to person, however, and even varies from time to time on the *same* person, so it is of limited use. It had to be standardized to be useful, so King Henry I of England decreed that the yard should be the distance from the tip of his nose to the end of his thumb!

Romans initially defined the mile (*mille passuum* = 1000 paces) as an even 5000 feet. The early Tudor rulers in England, however, defined a *furlong* ("furrow-long") as 220 yards, based on the length of agricultural fields. To facilitate the conversion between miles and furlongs, Queen Elizabeth I declared in the 16th century that the traditional Roman mile of 5000 feet would be forever replaced by one of 5280 feet, making the mile exactly 8 furlongs. Today, a furlong is an archaic unit of measurement (although still used in horse races), but a mile is still 5280 feet.

The Metric System

The metric system of weights and measures was devised in France and adopted there in 1799. It is based on a unit of length called the *meter* and a unit of mass called the *kilogram*. Originally defined as one ten-millionth the distance from the North Pole to the equator, the meter is now defined as the distance light travels through a vacuum in $1/299{,}792{,}458$ second. The kilogram was originally related to the volume of one cubic meter of water. It is now defined as the mass of the International Prototype Kilogram, a precision-fabricated cylinder of platinum–iridium alloy about the size of a plum that is kept at Sèvres (near Paris), France, but work is currently under way to base the kilogram on a fundamental property of nature. Other metric units can be defined in terms of the meter and the kilogram.

Fractions and multiples of the metric units are related to each other by powers of 10, allowing conversion from one unit to a multiple of it simply by shifting the decimal point. The lengthy arithmetical operations required with English units can be avoided. Even the names of the metric units indicate how many are in a larger unit. For instance, how many cents are there in a dollar? It is the same as the number of *centi*grams in a gram. The prefixes listed in Table A1.1 have been accepted for designating multiples and fractions of the meter, the gram (which equals $1/1000$ of a kilogram), and other units.

Despite many fears that changing to the metric system will be an economic burden on businesses in the United States, the conversion has already begun. Examples include 35-millimeter film,

---

[1]The names of the units and the relationships between them are generally the same in the U.S. Customary System and the British Imperial System, but the sizes of the units differ, sometimes considerably.

[2]"Mass" is commonly equated with "weight," but technically the "mass" of an object refers to the amount of matter in it, whereas its "weight" is caused by the gravitational attraction between the object and Earth. Furthermore, the basic unit of mass in the English system is the *slug,* although it is rarely used.

TABLE A1.1 — SOME COMMON PREFIXES FOR BASIC METRIC UNITS

Factor	Name	Prefix name
10^{12} = 1,000,000,000,000	trillion	tera
10^{9} = 1,000,000,000	billion	giga
10^{6} = 1,000,000	million	mega
10^{3} = 1000	thousand	kilo
10^{2} = 100	hundred	hecto
10^{1} = 10	ten	deka
10^{-1} = 0.1	tenth	deci
10^{-2} = 0.01	hundredth	centi
10^{-3} = 0.001	thousandth	milli
10^{-6} = 0.000001	millionth	micro
10^{-9} = 0.000000001	billionth	nano
10^{-12} = 0.000000000001	trillionth	pico

2-liter soft drink bottles, 750-milliliter wine bottles, computers with gigabytes of memory, and 10-kilometer runs. Cars are now manufactured metrically in order to compete with other countries. Most people in the United States will experience the increasing use of the metric system in their daily lives. Some ways to ease yourself into this unfamiliar (yet sensible) system of units include noticing distances on road signs in kilometers, using a meterstick instead of a yardstick, and charting your weight in kilograms.

Temperature Scales

The Celsius (centigrade) temperature scale was invented in 1742 by a Swedish astronomer named Anders Celsius. The scale was designed so that the freezing point of pure water—the temperature at which it changes state from a liquid to a solid—is set as 0 degrees. Similarly, the boiling point of pure water—the temperature at which it changes state from a liquid to a gas—is set at 100 degrees. Doing so made the liquid range of water—0 degrees to 100 degrees—an even 100 units, giving the scale its name: centigrade (*centi* = 100, *grade* = graduations).

The Fahrenheit temperature scale, on the other hand, sets water's freezing and boiling points at 32 degrees and 212 degrees, respectively, for a spread of 180 units. This scale was devised by a German-born physicist named Gabriel Daniel Fahrenheit, who invented the mercury thermometer in 1714. He initially designed the scale so that normal body temperature was set at 100°F. However, because of inaccuracies in early thermometers or how the scale was initially devised, normal human body temperature is now known to be 98.6°F (37°C).

Conversion Tables

The following tables show conversions between various units:

LENGTH

1 micrometer	0.001 millimeter / 0.0000394 inch
1 millimeter (mm)	1000 micrometers / 0.1 centimeter / 0.001 meter / 0.0394 inch
1 centimeter (cm)	10 millimeters / 0.01 meter / 0.394 inch
1 meter (m)	100 centimeters / 39.4 inches / 3.28 feet / 1.09 yards / 0.547 fathom
1 kilometer (km)	1000 meters / 1093 yards / 3280 feet / 0.62 statute mile / 0.54 nautical mile
1 inch (in)	25.4 millimeters / 2.54 centimeters
1 foot (ft)	12 inches / 30.5 centimeters / 0.305 meter
1 yard (yd)	3 feet / 0.91 meter
1 fathom (fm)	6 feet / 2 yards / 1.83 meters
1 statute mile (mi)	5280 feet / 1760 yards / 1609 meters / 1.609 kilometers / 0.87 nautical mile
1 nautical mile (nm)	1 minute of latitude / 6076 feet / 2025 yards / 1852 meters / 1.15 statute miles
1 league (lea)	5280 yards / 15,840 feet / 4805 meters / 3 statute miles / 2.61 nautical miles

AREA

1 square centimeter (cm²)	0.155 square inch
	100 square millimeters
1 square meter (m²)	10,000 square centimeters
	10.8 square feet
1 square kilometer (km²)	100 hectares
	247.1 acres
	0.386 square mile
	0.292 square nautical mile
1 square inch (in²)	6.45 square centimeters
1 square foot (ft²)	144 square inches
	929 square centimeters

VOLUME

1 cubic centimeter (cc; cm³)	1 milliliter
	0.061 cubic inch
1 liter (l)	1000 cubic centimeters
	61 cubic inches
	1.06 quarts
	0.264 gallon
1 cubic meter (m³)	1,000,000 cubic centimeters
	1000 liters
	264.2 gallons
	35.3 cubic feet
1 cubic kilometer (km³)	0.24 cubic mile
	0.157 cubic nautical mile
1 cubic inch (in³)	16.4 cubic centimeters
1 cubic foot (ft³)	1728 cubic inches
	28.32 liters
	7.48 gallons

MASS

1 gram (g)	0.035 ounce
1 kilogram (kg)	2.2 pounds†
	1000 grams

† The pound is a weight unit, not a mass unit, but it is often used as such.

MASS (continued)

1 metric ton (mt)	2205 pounds
	1000 kilograms
	1.1 U.S. short tons
1 pound† (lb)	16 ounces
	454 grams
	0.454 kilogram
1 U.S. short ton (ton; t)	2000 pounds
	907.2 kilograms
	0.91 metric ton

† The pound is a weight unit, not a mass unit, but it is often used as such.

PRESSURE

1 kilogram per square centimeter (at sea level)	1 atmosphere (atm)
	760 millimeters of mercury
	101,300 Pascal
	1013 millibars
	14.7 pounds per square inch
	29.9 inches of mercury
	33.9 feet of freshwater
	33 feet of seawater

SPEED

1 centimeter per second (cm/s)	0.0328 foot per second
1 meter per second (m/s)	2.24 statute miles per hour
	1.94 knots
	3.28 feet per second
	3.60 kilometers per hour
1 kilometer per hour (kph)	27.8 centimeters per second
	0.62 mile per hour
	0.909 foot per second
	0.55 knot
1 statute mile per hour (mph)	1.61 kilometers per hour
	0.87 knot
1 knot (kt)	1 nautical mile per hour
	51.5 centimeters per second
	1.15 miles per hour
	1.85 kilometers per hour

OCEANOGRAPHIC DATA

Velocity of sound in 34.85‰ seawater	4945 feet per second
	1507 meters per second
	824 fathoms per second

Seawater with 35 grams of dissolved substances per kilogram of seawater	3.5 percent (%)
	35 parts per thousand (‰)
	35,000 parts per million (ppm)
	35,000,000 parts per billion (ppb)

TEMPERATURE

Exact formula

$$°C = \frac{(°F - 32)}{1.8}$$

$$°F = (1.8 \times °C) + 32$$

Approximation (easy way)

$$°C = \frac{(°F - 30)}{2}$$

$$°F = (2 \times °C) + 30$$

Some useful equivalent temperatures

100°C = 212°F   (boiling point of pure water)
40°C = 104°F   (heat wave conditions)
37°C = 98.6°F   (normal body temperature)
30°C = 86°F   (very warm—almost hot)
20°C = 68°F   (room temperature)
10°C = 50°F   (a warm winter day)
3°C = 37°F   (average temperature of deep water)
0°C = 32°F   (freezing point of pure water)

In degrees centigrade
Thirty is hot, twenty is pleasing;
Ten is not, and zero is freezing.

APPENDIX III
LATITUDE AND LONGITUDE ON EARTH

Suppose that you find a great fishing spot or a shipwreck on the sea floor. How would you remember where it is—far from any sight of land—so that you might return? How do sailors navigate a ship when they are at sea? Even using sophisticated equipment such as the Global Positioning System (GPS), which uses satellites to determine location, how is this information reported?

To solve problems like these, a navigational grid—a series of intersecting lines across a globe—is used. Once starting places are fixed for a grid, a location can be identified based on its position within the grid. Some cities, for example, use the regular numbering of streets as a grid. Even if you have never been to the intersection of 5th Avenue and 42nd Street in New York City, you would be able to locate it on a map, or know which way to travel if you were at 10th Avenue and 42nd Street. Although many grid (or coordinate) systems are used today, the one most universally accepted uses *latitude* and *longitude*.

A series of north–south and east–west lines that together comprise a grid system can be used to locate points on Earth's surface whether at sea or on land. The north–south lines of the grid are called *meridians* and extend from pole to pole (Figure A3.1). The meridian lines converge at the poles and are spaced farthest apart at the equator. The east–west lines of the grid are called *parallels* because they are parallel to one another. The longest parallel is the *equator* (so called because it divides the globe into two equal hemispheres), and the parallels at the poles are a single point (Figure A3.1).

Latitude and Longitude

Latitude is the angular distance (in degrees of arc) measured north or south of the starting line (the equator) from the center of Earth. All points that lie along the same parallel are an identical distance from the equator, so they all have the same latitude. The latitude of the equator is 0 degrees, and the North and South Poles lie at 90 degrees north and 90 degrees south, respectively. Figure A3.2 shows that the latitude of New Orleans is an angular distance of 30 degrees north from the equator.

Longitude is the angular distance (in degrees of arc) measured east or west of the starting line from the center of Earth. All meridians are identical (none is longer or shorter than the others, and they all pass through both poles), so the starting line of longitude has been chosen arbitrarily. Before it was agreed upon by all nations, different countries used different starting points for 0 degrees longitude. Examples include the Canary Islands, the Azores, Rome, Copenhagen, Jerusalem, St. Petersburg, Pisa, Paris, and

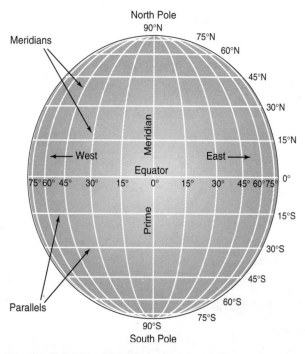

FIGURE A3.1 Earth's grid system. Earth's grid system is composed of parallels (which extend east–west and are measured north or south of the equator) and meridians (which extend north–south and are measured west or east of the Prime Meridian). Parallels are lines of latitude while meridians are lines of longitude. Note that while all meridians are the same length, the parallels are not (the longest parallel is the equator).

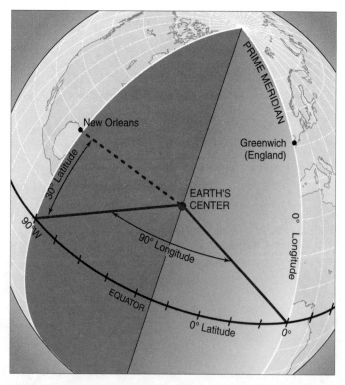

FIGURE A3.2 Location of New Orleans. New Orleans is located at 30 degrees north latitude and 90 degrees west longitude. Note the angles of each relative to the center of Earth.

Philadelphia. At the 1884 International Meridian Conference, it was agreed that the meridian that passes through the Royal Observatory at Greenwich, England, would be used as the zero or starting point of longitude. This zero degree line of longitude is also called the *Prime Meridian*, and the longitude for any place on Earth is measured east or west from this line. Longitude can vary from 0 degrees along the Prime Meridian to 180 degrees (either east or west), which is halfway around the globe and is known as the *International Date Line*. As shown in Figure A3.2, New Orleans is 90 degrees west of the Prime Meridian.

A particular latitude and longitude defines a unique location on Earth, provided the direction from the starting point is given, too. For instance, 42 degrees north and 120 degrees west defines a unique spot on Earth because it is different from 42 degrees south and 120 degrees west and from 42 degrees north and 120 degrees east.

A degree of latitude or longitude can be divided into smaller units. One degree (°) of arc (angular distance) is equal to 60 minutes (') of arc. One minute of arc is equal to 60 seconds (") of arc. When using a small-scale map or a globe, it may be difficult to estimate latitude and longitude to the nearest degree or two. When using a large-scale map, however, it is often possible to determine the latitude and longitude to the nearest fraction of a minute.

Determination of Latitude and Longitude

Today, latitude and longitude can be determined very precisely by using satellites that remain in orbit around Earth in fixed positions. How did navigators determine their position before this technology was available?

Latitude was determined from the positions of particular stars. Initially, navigators in the Northern Hemisphere measured the angle between the horizon and the North Star (Polaris), which is directly above the North Pole. The latitude north of the equator is the angle between the two sightings (Figure A3.3). In the Southern Hemisphere, the angle between the horizon and the Southern Cross was used because the Southern Cross is directly overhead at the South Pole. Later, the angle of the Sun above the horizon, corrected for the date, was also used.

There was no method of determining longitude until one based on time was developed at the end of the 18th century. As Earth turns on its rotational axis, it moves through 360 degrees of arc every 24 hours (one complete rotation on its axis) (Figure A3.4a). Earth, therefore, rotates through 15 degrees of longitude per hour (360 degrees ÷ 24 hours = 15 degrees per hour). As a result, a navigator needed only to know the time at the prime or Greenwich meridian (Figure A3.4b) at the exact same time the Sun was at its highest point (local noon) at the ship's location. In this way, a navigator aboard a ship could calculate the ship's longitude each day at noon. That's why the development of John Harrison's chronometer (see Box 1.2 in Chapter 1) was so crucial for navigation.

Suppose a ship sets sail west across the Atlantic Ocean from Europe, checking its longitude each day at noon local time. One day when the Sun is at the noon position (noon local time), the

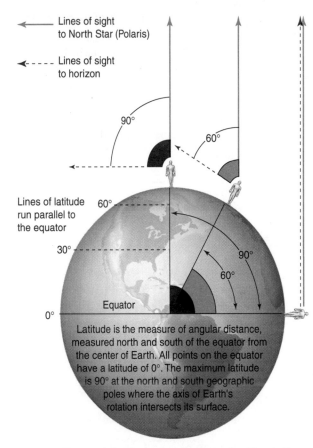

FIGURE A3.3 Determining latitude based on the North Star Latitude can be determined by noting the angular difference between the horizon and the North Star, which is directly over the North Pole of Earth.

FIGURE A3.4 Determining longitude based on time. View of Earth as seen from above the North Pole. **(a)** Earth rotates 360 degrees of arc every 24 hours. **(b)** The Greenwich Meridian is set as 0 degree longitude, which divides the globe into Eastern and Western Hemispheres. The International Date Line is 180 degrees from the Greenwich Meridian. **(c)** An example of how a ship at sea can determine its longitude using time.

chronometer reads 16:18 hours (0:00 is midnight and 12:00 is noon). What is the ship's longitude (Figure A3.4c)?

If the clock is keeping good time (which Harrison's chronometer did), then we know that the ship is 4 hours and 18 minutes behind (west of) Greenwich time. To determine the longitude, we must convert time into longitude. Each hour represents 15 degrees of longitude based on the rotation of Earth. Thus, the four hours represents 60 degrees of longitude (4 hours × 15 degrees of longitude = 60 degrees). One degree is divided into 60 minutes of arc, so Earth rotates through $1/4$ degree (15′) of arc per minute of time. Thus, 18 minutes of time multiplied by 15 minutes of arc per minute of time equals 270 minutes of arc. To convert 270 minutes of arc into degrees, it must be divided by 60 minutes per degree, which gives 4.5 degrees of longitude. Therefore, the answer is 60 degrees plus 4.5 degrees, or 64.5 degrees west longitude.

APPENDIX IV
A CHEMICAL BACKGROUND: WHY WATER HAS 2 H's AND 1 O

An element (*elementum* = a first principle) is a substance comprised entirely of like particles that cannot be broken into smaller particles by chemical means. The atom (*a* = not, *tomos* = cut) is the smallest particle of an element that can combine with similar particles of other elements to produce compounds. The periodic table of elements shown in Figure A4.1 lists the elements and describes their atoms. A compound (*compondre* = to put together) is a substance containing two or more elements combined in fixed proportions. A molecule (*molecula* = a mass) is the smallest particle of an element or compound that, in the free state, retains the characteristics of the substance.

As an illustration of these terms, consider Sir Humphrey Davey's use of electrical dissociation to break the compound water into its component elements, hydrogen and oxygen. Atoms of the elements hydrogen (H) and oxygen (O) combine in the proportion 2 to 1, respectively, to produce molecules of water (H_2O). As an electric current is passed through the water, the molecules dissociate into hydrogen atoms that collect near the cathode (negatively charged electrode) and oxygen atoms that collect near the anode (positively charged electrode). Here they combine to form the diatomic gaseous molecules of the elements hydrogen (H_2) and oxygen (O_2). Because there are twice as many hydrogen atoms as oxygen atoms in a given volume of water, twice as many molecules of hydrogen gas (H_2) as oxygen gas (O_2) are formed. Further, the volume of gas under identical conditions of temperature and pressure is proportional to the number of gas particles (molecules) present, so two volumes of hydrogen gas are produced for each volume of oxygen gas.

A Look at the Atom

Building on earlier discoveries, the Danish physicist Niels Bohr (1884–1962) developed his model of the atom as a small solar system in which a positively charged nucleus takes the place of the Sun and the planets that orbit around it are represented by negatively charged electrons. Although this model has since been diagrammatically altered, it is still commonly used to demonstrate the arrangement of electrons and nuclear particles in the atom.

Bohr's earliest concern was with the atom of hydrogen, which he considered to consist of a single positively charged proton (*protos* = first) in its nucleus orbited by a single negatively charged electron (*electro* = electricity). Since the mass of the electron is only about $1/1840$ the mass of the proton, it will be considered negligible in our discussion of atomic masses.

According to the Bohr model, the number of protons—or units of positive charge in the nucleus—coincides with the atomic number of the element. Thus hydrogen, with an atomic number of 1, has a nucleus (*nucleos* = a little nut) containing a single proton. Helium, the next heavier element, having an atomic number of 2, contains two nuclear protons, and so forth. The atomic number

also indicates the number of electrons in a normal atom of any element, because this number is equal to the number of protons in the nucleus (Figure A4.2).

An isotope (*isos* = equal, *topos* = place) is an atom of an element that has a different atomic mass than other atoms of the same element. As we will see, chemical properties of atoms are determined by the electron arrangement that surrounds the nucleus. This arrangement, in turn, is determined by the number of protons in the nucleus. Because some isotopes have different atomic masses but identical chemical characteristics, there must be a nuclear particle in the nucleus other than the proton that can influence the atomic mass of an atom but does not affect the electron structure surrounding the nucleus (Figure A4.3).

Nuclear research has discovered the additional particle, the neutron (*neutr* = neutral) which was postulated by Ernest Rutherford in 1920 and was first detected by his associate James Chadwick in 1932. It has a mass very similar to that of the proton but no electrical charge. This characteristic of being electrically neutral has made it one of the particles most utilized by nuclear physicists, who continue to explore the atomic nucleus and to make new discoveries of nuclear particles. We will not consider these particles, as knowledge of them is not necessary for our understanding of the chemical nature of atoms.

An atom of a given element can be changed to an ion of that element by adding or taking away one or more electrons, and it is changed to an isotope of the element by adding or taking away one or more neutrons. Adding or taking away one or more protons will change the atom to an atom of a different element.

The atom can be divided into two parts—the nucleus, which contains neutrons and protons, and the electron cloud surrounding the nucleus that is involved in chemical reactions. The random motion of electrons makes it impossible to determine the precise location of electrons in this cloud at any instant, but it is possible to estimate the most probable position of an electron in this cloud. The regions in which there would more likely be particular electrons can be viewed as concentric spheres—or shells—that surround the nucleus (see Figure A4.2).

Chemical Bonds

In considering the chemical reactions in which atoms are involved, we will be concerned primarily with the distribution of electrons in the outer shell. When atoms combine to form compounds, they usually do so by forming one of two bonds:

1. **Ionic** (*ienai* = to go) **bonds**, where electrons are either gained or lost
2. **Covalent** (*co* = with, *valere* = to be strong) **bonds**, where electrons are shared between atoms

Ionic bonding produces an ion, an electrically charged atom that no longer has the properties of a neutral atom of the

Periodic Table of the Elements

Atomic number
Symbol of element
Atomic weight
Name of element

1
H
1.0080
Hydrogen

Legend:
- Inert Gas
- Gas
- Liquid

Light Metals

Transitional Elements

Heavy Metals

Nonmetals

	I A	II A	III B	IV B	V B	VI B	VII B		VIII B		I B	II B	III A	IV A	V A	VI A	VII A	VIII A
1	1 **H** 1.0080 Hydrogen																	2 **He** 4.003 Helium
2	3 **Li** 6.939 Lithium	4 **Be** 9.012 Beryllium											5 **B** 10.81 Boron	6 **C** 12.011 Carbon	7 **N** 14.007 Nitrogen	8 **O** 15.994 Oxygen	9 **F** 18.998 Fluorine	10 **Ne** 20.1863 Neon
3	11 **Na** 22.990 Sodium	12 **Mg** 24.31 Magnesium											13 **Al** 26.98 Aluminum	14 **Si** 28.09 Silicon	15 **P** 30.974 Phosphorus	16 **S** 32.064 Sulphur	17 **Cl** 35.453 Chlorine	18 **Ar** 39.948 Argon
4	19 **K** 39.102 Potassium	20 **Ca** 40.08 Calcium	21 **Sc** 44.96 Scandium	22 **Ti** 47.90 Titanium	23 **V** 50.94 Vanadium	24 **Cr** 52.00 Chromium	25 **Mn** 54.94 Manganese	26 **Fe** 55.85 Iron	27 **Co** 58.93 Cobalt	28 **Ni** 58.71 Nickel	29 **Cu** 63.54 Copper	30 **Zn** 65.37 Zinc	31 **Ga** 69.72 Gallium	32 **Ge** 72.59 Germanium	33 **As** 74.92 Arsenic	34 **Se** 78.96 Selenium	35 **Br** 79.909 Bromine	36 **Kr** 83.80 Krypton
5	37 **Rb** 85.47 Rubidium	38 **Sr** 87.62 Strontium	39 **Y** 88.91 Yttrium	40 **Zr** 91.22 Zirconium	41 **Nb** 92.91 Niobium	42 **Mo** 95.94 Molybdenum	43 **Tc** (99) Technetium	44 **Ru** 101.1 Ruthenium	45 **Rh** 102.90 Rhodium	46 **Pd** 106.4 Palladium	47 **Ag** 107.870 Silver	48 **Cd** 112.40 Cadmium	49 **In** 114.82 Indium	50 **Sn** 118.69 Tin	51 **Sb** 121.75 Antimony	52 **Te** 127.60 Tellurium	53 **I** 126.90 Iodine	54 **Xe** 131.30 Xenon
6	55 **Cs** 132.91 Cesium	56 **Ba** 137.34 Barium	57 TO 71	72 **Hf** 178.49 Hafnium	73 **Ta** 180.95 Tantalum	74 **W** 183.85 Tungsten	75 **Re** 186.2 Rhenium	76 **Os** 190.2 Osmium	77 **Ir** 192.2 Iridium	78 **Pt** 195.09 Platinum	79 **Au** 197.0 Gold	80 **Hg** 200.59 Mercury	81 **Tl** 204.37 Thallium	82 **Pb** 207.19 Lead	83 **Bi** 208.98 Bismuth	84 **Po** (210) Polonium	85 **At** (210) Astatine	86 **Ra** (222) Radon
7	87 **Fr** (223) Francium	88 **Ra** 226.05 Radium	89 TO 103															

Lanthanide series

57 **LA** 138.91 Lanthanum	58 **Ce** 140.12 Cerium	59 **Pr** 140.91 Praseodymium	60 **Nd** 144.24 Neodymium	61 **Pm** (147) Promethium	62 **Sm** 150.35 Samarium	63 **Eu** 157.25 Europium	64 **Gd** 158.92 Gadolinium	65 **Tb** 158.92 Terbium	66 **Dy** 162.50 Dysprosium	67 **Ho** 164.93 Holmium	68 **Er** 167.26 Erbium	69 **Tm** 168.93 Thullium	70 **Yb** 173.04 Ytterbium	71 **Lu** 174.97 Lutetium

Actinide series

89 **Ac** (227) Actinium	90 **Th** 232.04 Thorium	91 **Pa** (231) Protactinium	92 **U** 238.03 Uranium	93 **Np** (237) Neptunium	94 **Pu** (242) Plutonium	95 **Am** (243) Americium	96 **Cm** (247) Curium	97 **Bk** (249) Berkelium	98 **Cf** (251) Californium	99 **Es** (254) Einsteinium	100 **Fm** (253) Fermium	101 **Md** (256) Mendelevium	102 **No** (256) Nobelium	103 **Lw** (257) Lawrencium

FIGURE A4.1 The periodic table of the elements.

FIGURE A4.2 Bohr-Stoner orbital models for atoms. Each atom is composed of a positively charged nucleus with negatively charged electrons around it. The nucleus, which occupies very little space, contains most of the mass of the atom. The atomic number is equal to the number of protons (positively charged nuclear particles) in the nucleus. Note that the first shell holds only two electrons and other shells can hold eight (or more) electrons.

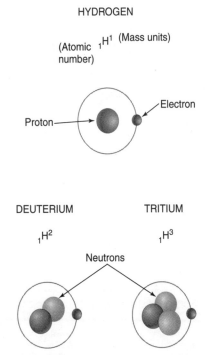

FIGURE A4.3 Hydrogen isotopes. Isotopes are atoms of an element that have different atomic masses. The hydrogen atom ($_1H^1$) accounts for 99.98% of the hydrogen atoms on Earth and has a nucleus that contains only one proton. Deuterium ($_1H^2$) contains one neutron and one proton in its nucleus and combines with oxygen to form "heavy water" with a molecular mass of 20. Tritium ($_1H^3$) is a very rare radioactive isotope of hydrogen that has a nucleus containing one proton and two neutrons.

element it represents. A positively charged ion, a cation (*kation* = something going down) is produced by the loss of electrons from the outer shell, the positive charge being equal to the number of electrons lost. A negatively charged ion, an anion (*anienai* = to go up), is produced by the gain of electrons in the outer shell of an atom, and its charge is equal to the number of electrons gained.

An example of a compound formed by ionic bonding is common table salt, which is sodium chloride (Figure A4.4). In the formation of this compound, the sodium atom, which has one electron in its outer shell, loses this electron and forms a sodium ion with a positive electrical charge of one. The chlorine atom, which contains seven electrons in its outer shell, completes its shell by gaining an electron and becoming a chloride ion with a negative charge of one. These two ions are held in close proximity by an electrostatic attraction between the two ions of equal and opposite charge.

Moreover, it is the tendency of an individual atom to assume the outer-shell electron content of the inert gases such as helium (2), neon (8), and argon (8) that make it chemically reactive (see Figure A4.2). Normally, if an atom can assume this configuration by either sharing one or two electrons with an atom of another element or by losing or gaining one or two electrons, the elements are highly reactive. By contrast, the elements are less reactive if three or four electrons must be shared, gained, or lost to achieve the desired configuration.

Valence (*valentia* = capacity) is the number of hydrogen atoms with which an atom of a given element can combine with either ionic or covalent bonds. Elements with lower valences of one or two, for example, combine chemically in a more highly reactive manner than do those with higher valences of three or four or, in

FIGURE A4.4 Ionic bonds in sodium chloride (table salt). Ions of sodium (left) and chlorine (right) combine to form sodium chloride, producing common table salt. Notice the contrast in the outer shells of the ions of sodium (Na^+) and chlorine (Cl^-) with the atoms of these elements shown in Figure A4.2.

WATER (covalent bond)

FIGURE A4.5 Covalent bonds in water. Water (H_2O) is composed of 2 atoms of hydrogen and 1 atom of oxygen, held together by covalent bonds.

certain instances, more than four. Although those elements with higher valences do not react as violently as low-valence elements, they have a greater combining power and can gather about them larger numbers of atoms of other elements than can the atoms with lower valence values.

An example of a covalent bond is the sharing of electrons by hydrogen and oxygen atoms in the water molecule (Figure A4.5). In the formation of this molecule, both hydrogen atoms and the oxygen atom assume the inert gas configuration they seek by sharing electrons.

APPENDIX V
CAREERS IN OCEANOGRAPHY

Many people think a career in oceanography consists of swimming with marine animals at a marine life park or snorkeling in crystal-clear tropical waters studying coral reefs. In reality, these kinds of jobs are extremely rare and there is intense competition for them. Most oceanographers use science to answer questions about the ocean, such as the following:

- What is the role of the ocean in limiting the climate change?
- What kinds of pharmaceuticals can be found naturally in marine organisms?
- How does sea floor spreading relate to the movement of tectonic plates?
- What economic deposits are there on the sea floor?
- Can rogue waves be predicted?
- What is the role of longshore transport in the distribution of sand on the beach?
- How does a particular pollutant affect organisms in the marine environment?

Preparation for a Career in Oceanography

Preparing yourself for a career in oceanography is an interesting and rewarding, yet difficult, path to travel. The study of oceanography is typically divided into four different academic disciplines (or subfields) of study:

- *Geological oceanography* is the study of the structure of the sea floor and how the sea floor has changed through time; the creation of sea floor features; and the history of sediments deposited on it.
- *Chemical oceanography* is the study of the chemical composition and properties of seawater; how to extract certain chemicals from seawater; and the effects of pollutants.
- *Physical oceanography* is the study of waves, tides, and currents; the ocean–atmosphere relationship that influences weather and climate; and the transmission of light and sound in the oceans.
- *Biological oceanography* is the study of oceanic life forms and their relationships to one another; adaptations to the marine environment; and developing ecologically sound methods of harvesting seafood.

Other disciplines include ocean engineering, marine archaeology, and marine policy. Oceanography is an *interdisciplinary* science because it utilizes all the disciplines of science as they apply to the oceans. Some of the most exciting work and best employment opportunities combine two or more of these disciplines.

Individuals working in oceanography and marine-related fields need a strong background (typically an undergraduate degree) in at least one area of basic science (for example, geology, physics, chemistry, or biology) or engineering. In almost all cases, mathematics is required as well. Marine archaeology requires a background in archaeology or anthropology; marine policy studies require a background in at least one of the social sciences (such as law, economics, or political science).

The ability to speak and write clearly—as well as critical thinking skills—are prerequisites for any career. Fluency in computers—preferably PC systems, not Macintosh—is rapidly becoming a necessity. Because many job opportunities in oceanography require trips on research vessels (Figure A5.1), any shipboard experience is also desirable. Mechanical ability (the ability to fix equipment while on board a vessel without having to return to port) is a plus. Depending on the type of work that is required,

FIGURE A5.1 Oceanographers at work on a research vessel.
Oceanographers deploy a sonar device on a cable using the A-frame on Scripps Institute of Oceanography's R/V *Melville*.

other traits that may be desirable include the ability to speak one or more foreign languages; certification as a scuba diver; the ability to work for long periods of time in cramped conditions; physical stamina; physical strength; and a high tolerance to motion sickness.

Oceanography is a relatively new science (with much room left for discovery), so most people enter the field with an advanced degree (master's or doctorate). Work as a marine technician, however, usually requires only a bachelor's degree or applicable experience. It does take a large commitment to achieve an advanced degree but, in the end, the journey itself is what makes all the hard work worthwhile.

Job Duties of Oceanographers

There has been and will continue to be enormous expansion in the number of ocean-related jobs. Job opportunities for oceanographers exist with scientific research institutions (universities), various government agencies, and private companies that are engaged in searching for economic sea floor deposits, investigating areas for sea farming, and evaluating natural energy production from waves, currents, and tides. The duties of oceanographers vary from job to job but generally can be described as follows:

- *Geological oceanographers and geophysicists* explore the ocean floor and map submarine geological structures. Studies of the physical and chemical properties of rocks and sediments give us valuable information about Earth's history. The results of their work help us understand the processes that created the ocean basins and the interactions between the ocean and the sea floor.

- *Chemical oceanographers and marine geochemists* investigate the chemical composition of seawater and its interaction with the atmosphere and the sea floor. Their work may include analysis of seawater components, desalination of seawater, and studying the effects of pollutants. They also examine chemical processes operating within the marine environment and work with biological oceanographers to study living systems. Their study of trace chemicals in seawater helps us understand how ocean currents move seawater around the globe, and how the ocean affects climate.

- *Physical oceanographers* investigate ocean properties such as temperature, density, wave motions, tides, and currents. They study ocean–atmosphere relationships that influence weather and climate, the transmission of light and sound through water, and the ocean's interactions with its boundaries at the sea floor and the coast.

- *Biological oceanographers, marine biologists, and fisheries scientists* study marine plants and animals. They want to understand how marine organisms develop, relate to one another, adapt to their environment, and interact with their environment. They develop ecologically sound methods of harvesting seafood and study biological responses to pollution. New fields associated with biological oceanography include marine biotechnology (the use of natural marine resources in the development of new industrial and biomedical products) and molecular biology (the study of the structure and function of bioinformational molecules—such as DNA, RNA, and proteins—and the regulation of cellular processes at the molecular level). Because marine biology is the best known field of oceanography (and because the larger marine animals have such wide appeal), it is currently the most competitive, too.

- *Marine and ocean engineers* apply scientific and technical knowledge to practical uses. Their work ranges from designing sensitive instruments for measuring ocean processes to building marine structures that can withstand ocean currents, waves, tides, and severe storms. Subfields include acoustics; robotics; electrical, mechanical, civil, and chemical engineering; as well as naval architecture. They often use highly specialized computer techniques.

- *Marine archaeologists* systematically recover and study material evidence, such as shipwrecks, graves, buildings, tools, and pottery remaining from past human life and culture that is now covered by the sea. Marine archaeologists use state-of-the-art technology to locate underwater archaeological sites.

- *Marine policy experts* combine their knowledge of oceanography and social sciences, law, or business to develop guidelines and policies for the wise use of the ocean and coastal resources.

Other job opportunities for oceanographers include work as science journalists specializing in marine science, teachers at various grade levels, and aquarium and museum curators.

Sources of Career Information

For sources of career information, consult the catalog of any college or university that offers a curriculum in oceanography or marine science. Pamphlets that feature oceanography career information include:

- *Marine Science Careers: A Sea Grant Guide to Ocean Opportunities* by NOAA's Sea Grant College; available online at http://marinecareers.net.
- *Careers in Oceanography and Marine-Related Fields* by The Oceanography Society; available online at http://www.onr.navy.mil/careers/ocean_marine/.
- *Preparing for a Career in Oceanography* by the Scripps Institute of Oceanography at the University of California, San Diego; available online at http://www.siommg.ucsd.edu/slices/.
- *The SeaWorld/Bush Gardens Guide to Zoological Park Careers* by SeaWorld's Education Department; available online at http://www.seaworld.org/infobooks/zoocareers/home.html.
- *Careers in Science and Engineering: A Student Planning Guide to Graduate School and Beyond* by the National Academies Press; available online at http://www.nap.edu/openbook.php?record_id=5129.

Other online sources of oceanography career information include the following:

- The U.S. Navy's Website on careers in oceanography, at http://www.oc.nps.edu/careers.html.

REPORT FROM A STUDENT/OCEANOGRAPHER

One of the true pleasures of teaching is that some of your students become so interested in the subject matter you teach that they pursue a career in it. One of Al Trujillo's former students, Joseph Fell-McDonald (Figure A5A), works as a ranger and interpretive specialist on Maui for the State of Hawaii's Department of Land and Natural Resources, Division of Forestry and Wildlife, Natural Area Reserve System. Joe writes,

Aloha:

My career in oceanography-related work has followed a long and sinuous path. After high school I attended a trade school for mechanical engineering, where I learned how to fix cars and build houses. With this background, I worked in industry for many years yet I had a yearning for something satisfying, enjoyable, and well-paid. I bounced from place to place and job to job not really settling on a career but beginning to realize that I enjoyed a lifestyle near the world's oceans where I could surf, swim, lounge, and play. Living in various coastal areas nearly my whole life, I was always amazed at the interaction of the oceans. I decided fixing and building things was not for me. So I looked into colleges and attended nearby Palomar Community College in California, where I took many courses in geography, geology, and biology. I also enrolled in an oceanography course and realized how important the oceans are to life in general. It was during this time that it hit me: I longed for a career in ocean science!

Because I was formally trained in mechanical engineering and construction, I knew I could get a job just about anywhere. I decided to give the island of Maui a try just after finishing my courses in oceanography. There was no formal work in oceanography here so I applied for a job as a vessel mechanic at a local eco-tour company. The company offered volunteer opportunities, including photo identification and public interpretation of the seasonal humpback whales that migrate to Maui each year. The one thing I realized on Maui was that not one organization—be it a government branch, non-profit organization, or company—could control, regulate, or even understand the broad basis of the world's oceans. I became fascinated with my surroundings and volunteered at many places, realizing my best attribute was an understanding of Earth's terrain and oceanic interactions. I volunteered and studied native coastal restoration projects and got hired by a local botanical garden to promote native Hawaiian plants and Hawaiian plant restoration.

FIGURE A5A Former oceanography student Joseph Fell-McDonald (*at far right on vessel and inset*) at work in the Hawaiian Islands Humpback Whale National Marine Sanctuary, Maui, Hawaii.

I was then recruited to help restore a high erosion area at a National Marine Sanctuary. The National Oceanic and Atmospheric Administration (NOAA) Hawaiian Islands Humpback Whale National Marine Sanctuary (sister sanctuary to Monterey Bay) hired me to do building maintenance, coastal dune restoration, vessel repair for scientific exploration, and general public liaison. I was asked to assist with the National Marine Fisheries Service in helping stranded marine life—particularly the green sea turtle (*Chelonia mydas*), which often strands itself when it succumbs to disease—and habitat restoration and monitoring of the critically endangered hawksbill turtle (*Eretmochelys imbricata*). I also became involved with rescuing stranded Hawaiian monk seals (*Monachus schauinslandi*) and entangled humpback whales (*Megaptera novaeangliae*). I credit my success to a full-rounded education, being open to new opportunities, volunteering, and lots of hard work.

I currently work as a ranger for the State of Hawaii's Department of Land and Natural Resources, Division of Forestry and Wildlife, Natural Area Reserve System (NARS). The NARS program is the highest level of protection that Hawaii can offer its lands. I work on Maui at the Ahihi-Kinau Natural Area Reserve and Surrounding State Protected Lands Kenioio and Makena. We follow recommendations by residents and local native Hawaiian kapuna (elders) to bring conservation back to Ahihi-Kinau. Much of my work is enforcement of protection laws, although I do a fair amount of public education,

restoration, cultural inventory, biologic surveying, and other protection of natural resources. The reserve is approximately 2000 land acres and about 800 marine protected acres out to a water depth of 100 fathoms. I patrol the area via four-wheel drive vehicle, jet ski, ATV, and even on horseback.

The most common question I get asked is, "How does someone get a job like yours?" Truthfully, I wake up with a smile on my face every day and enjoy the location, pay, and benefits. Sometimes it can be a tough and demanding job but I actually enjoy it. For many people, it is hard to believe that studying a broad range of sciences can lead to an enjoyable and fulfilling career. I also met my wife and companion here, who was working as a marine biologist with the U.S. Fish and Wildlife Service. Due to my compassion and deep understanding of a broad range of sciences, I was able to apply my education, experience, and curiosity into the career of my dreams. I encourage anyone who wants to learn more about natural resources or careers on Maui to contact me.

Joseph Fell-McDonald, Ahihi-Kinau Ranger
State of Hawaii Department of Land
and Natural Resources
Division of Forestry and Wildlife
54 High Street, Room 101
Wailuku, Maui, HI 96793
e-mail: joseph.c.fell-mcdonald@hawaii.gov

- The Website of Peter Brueggeman of the Scripps Institute of Oceanography, which offers a comprehensive list of information about careers in oceanography, marine science, and marine biology, including many links, at http://ocean.peterbrueggeman.com/career.html.

- The Palomar College Oceanography Program Careers in Oceanography Website, which includes this appendix, at http://www.palomar.edu/oceanography/links/Careers.html.

- The SUNY Stony Brook Biological Sciences Department offers a listing of worldwide marine laboratories and institutions, at http://life.bio.sunysb.edu/marinebio/mblabs.html.

- Woods Hole Oceanographic Institution's Website devoted to the achievements of women oceanographers, including biographies and unique perspectives of women scientists, at http://www.womenoceanographers.org.

GLOSSARY

A

Abiotic environment The nonliving components of an ecosystem.

Abyssal clay Deep-ocean (oceanic) deposits containing less than 30% biogenous sediment. Often oxidized and red in color, thus commonly termed red clay.

Abyssal hill A volcanic peak rising less than 1 kilometer (0.6 mile) above the ocean floor.

Abyssal hill province A deep-ocean region, particularly in the Pacific Ocean, where oceanic sedimentation rates are so low that abyssal plains do not form and the ocean floor is covered with abyssal hills.

Abyssal plain A flat depositional surface extending seaward from the continental rise or oceanic trenches.

Abyssal storm Stormlike occurrences of rapid current movement affecting the deep ocean floor. They are believed to be caused by warm- and cold-core eddies of surface currents.

Abyssal zone The benthic environment between 4000 and 6000 meters (13,000 and 20,000 feet).

Abyssopelagic The open-ocean (oceanic) environment below 4000 meters (13,000 feet) in depth.

Acid A substance that releases hydrogen ions (H^+) in solution.

Acoustic Thermometry of Ocean Climate (ATOC) The measurement of oceanwide changes in water properties such as temperature by transmitting and receiving low-frequency sound signals.

Active margin A continental margin marked by a high degree of tectonic activity, such as those typical of the Pacific Rim. Types of active margins include convergent active margins (marked by plate convergence) and transform active margins (marked by transform faulting).

Adiabatic Pertaining to a change in the temperature of a mass resulting from compression or expansion. It requires no addition of heat to or loss of heat from the substance.

Age of Discovery The 30-year period from 1492 to 1522 when Europeans explored the continents of North and South America and the globe was circumnavigated for the first time.

Agulhas Current A warm current that carries Indian Ocean water around the southern tip of Africa and into the Atlantic Ocean.

Air mass A large area of air that has a definite area of origin and distinctive characteristics.

Albedo The fraction of incident electromagnetic radiation reflected by a surface.

Algae Primarily aquatic, eukaryotic, photosynthetic organisms that have no root, stem, or leaf systems. Can be microscopic or macroscopic.

Alkaline A substance that releases hydroxide ions (OH^-) in solution. Also called basic.

Alveoli A tiny, thin-walled, capillary-rich sac in the lungs where the exchange of oxygen and carbon dioxide takes place.

Amino acid One of more than 20 naturally occurring compounds that contain NH_2 and COOH groups. They combine to form proteins.

Amnesic shellfish poisoning Partial or total loss of memory resulting from poisoning caused by eating shellfish with high levels of domoic acid, a toxin produced by a diatom.

Amphidromic point A nodal, or "no-tide," point in the ocean or sea around which the crest of the tide wave rotates during one tidal period.

Amphipoda A crustacean order containing laterally compressed members such as the "beach hoppers."

Anadromous Pertaining to a species of fish that spawns in freshwater and then migrates into the ocean to grow to maturity.

Anaerobic respiration Respiration carried on in the absence of free oxygen (O_2). Some bacteria and protozoans carry on respiration this way.

Anchovy (anchoveta) A small silvery fish (*Engraulis ringens*) that swims through the water with its mouth open to catch its food.

Andesite A gray, fine-grained volcanic rock composed chiefly of plagioclase feldspar.

Anhydrite A colorless, white, gray, blue, or lilac evaporite mineral (anhydrous calcium sulfate, $CaSO_4$) that usually occurs as layers associated with gypsum deposits.

Animalia A kingdom of many-celled animals.

Anion An atom that has gained one or more electrons and has an electrical negative charge.

Annelida A phylum of elongated segmented worms.

Anomalistic month The time required for the Moon to go from perigee to perigee, 27.5 days.

Anoxic Without oxygen.

Antarctic Bottom Water A water mass that forms in the Weddell Sea, sinks to the ocean floor, and spreads across the bottom of all oceans.

Antarctic Circle The latitude 66.5° south.

Antarctic Circumpolar Current The eastward-flowing current that encircles Antarctica and extends from the surface to the deep-ocean floor. The largest volume current in the oceans. Also called the West Wind Drift.

Antarctic Convergence The zone of convergence along the northern boundary of the Antarctic Circumpolar Current where the southward-flowing boundary currents of the subtropical gyres converge on the cold Antarctic waters.

Antarctic Divergence The zone of divergence separating the westward-flowing East Wind Drift and the eastward-flowing Antarctic Circumpolar Current.

Antarctic Intermediate Water Antarctic zone surface water that sinks at the Antarctic convergence and flows north at a depth of about 900 meters (2950 feet) beneath the warmer upper-water mass of the South Atlantic Subtropical Gyre.

Anthophyta Seed-bearing plants.

Anticyclone An atmospheric system characterized by the rapid, outward circulation of air masses about a high-pressure center that is associated with sinking air. Anticyclones circulate clockwise in the Northern Hemisphere and counterclockwise in the Southern Hemisphere and are usually accompanied by dry, clear, fair weather.

Anticyclonic flow The flow of air around a region of high pressure clockwise in the Northern Hemisphere.

Antilles Current A warm current that flows north seaward of the Lesser Antilles from the North Equatorial Current of the Atlantic Ocean to join the Florida Current.

Antinode A zone of maximum vertical particle movement in standing waves where crest and trough formation alternate.

Aphelion The point in the orbit of a planet or comet where it is farthest from the Sun.

Aphotic zone A zone without light. The ocean is generally in this state below 1000 meters (3280 feet).

Apogee The point in the orbit of the Moon or an artificial satellite that is farthest from Earth.

Aragonite A form of $CaCO_3$ that is less common and less stable than calcite. Pteropod shells are usually composed of aragonite.

Archaea One of the three major domains of life. The domain consists of simple microscopic bacteria-like creatures (including methane producers and sulfur oxidizers that inhabit deep-sea vents and seeps) and other microscopic life forms that prefer environments of extreme conditions of temperature and/or pressure.

Archipelago A large group of islands.

Arctic Circle The latitude 66.5° north.

Arctic Convergence A zone of converging currents similar to the Antarctic Convergence but located in the Arctic.

Argo A global array of free-drifting profiling floats that move vertically and measure the temperature, salinity, and other water characteristics of the upper 2000 meters (6600 feet) of the ocean.

Aspect ratio The index of propulsive efficiency obtained by dividing the square of fin height by fin area.

Asthenosphere A plastic layer in the upper mantle 80 to 200 kilometers (50 to 124 miles) deep that may allow lateral movement of lithospheric plates and isostatic adjustments.

Atlantic-type margin See *passive margin*.

Atoll A ring-shaped coral reef growing upward from a submerged volcanic peak. It may have low-lying islands composed of coral debris.

Atom A unit of matter, the smallest unit of an element, having all the characteristics of that element and consisting of a dense, central, positively charged nucleus surrounded by a system of electrons.

Atomic mass The mass of an atom, usually expressed in atomic mass units.

Atomic number   The number of protons in an atomic nucleus.

Autotroph   Algae, plants, and bacteria that can synthesize organic compounds from inorganic nutrients.

Autumnal equinox   The passage of the Sun across the equator as it moves from the Northern Hemisphere into the Southern Hemisphere, approximately September 23. During this time, all places in the world experience equal lengths of night and day. Also called fall equinox.

B

Backshore   The inner portion of the shore, lying landward of the mean spring tide high water line. Acted upon by the ocean only during exceptionally high tides and storms.

Backwash   The flow of water down the beach face toward the ocean from a previously broken wave.

Bacteria   One of the three major domains of life. The domain includes unicellular, prokaryotic microorganisms that vary in terms of morphology, oxygen and nutritional requirements, and motility.

Bacterioplankton   Bacteria that live as plankton.

Bacteriovore   An organism that feeds on bacteria.

Bar-built estuary   A shallow estuary (lagoon) separated from the open ocean by a bar deposit such as a barrier island. The water in these estuaries usually exhibits vertical mixing.

Barrier flat   An area that lies between the salt marsh and dunes of a barrier island and that is usually covered with grasses or forests if protected from overwash for a sufficient length of time.

Barrier island   A long, narrow, wave-built island separated from the mainland by a lagoon.

Barrier reef   A coral reef separated from the nearby landmass by open water.

Barycenter   The center of mass of a system.

Basalt   A dark-colored volcanic rock characteristic of the ocean crust. Contains minerals with relatively high iron and magnesium content.

Base   See *alkaline*.

Bathyal zone   The benthic environment between the depths of 200 and 4000 meters (660 and 13,000 feet). It includes mainly the continental slope and the oceanic ridges and rises.

Bathymetry   The measurement of ocean depth.

Bathypelagic zone   The pelagic environment between the depths of 1000 and 4000 meters (3300 and 13,000 feet).

Bathyscaphe   A specially designed deep-diving submersible.

Bathysphere   A specially designed deep-diving submersible that resembles a sphere.

Bay barrier   A marine deposit attached to the mainland at both ends and extending entirely across the mouth of a bay, separating the bay from the open water. Also known as a bay-mouth bar.

Beach   Sediment seaward of the coastline through the surf zone that is in transport along the shore and within the surf zone.

Beach compartment   A series of rivers, beaches, and submarine canyons involved in the movement of sediment to the coast, along the coast, and down one or more submarine canyons.

Beach face   The wet, sloping surface that extends from the berm to the shoreline. Also known as the low tide terrace.

Beach replenishment   The addition of beach sediment to replace lost or missing material. Also called beach nourishment.

Beach starvation   The interruption of sediment supply and resulting narrowing of beaches.

Beaufort Wind Scale   A standardized wind scale that describes the appearance of the sea surface from dead calm conditions to hurricane-force winds.

Benguela Current   The cold eastern boundary current of the South Atlantic Subtropical Gyre.

Benthic   Pertaining to the ocean bottom.

Benthos   The forms of marine life that live on the ocean bottom.

Berm   The dry, gently sloping region on the backshore of a beach at the foot of the coastal cliffs or dunes.

Berm crest   The area of a beach that separates the berm from the beach face. The berm crest is often the highest portion of a berm.

Bicarbonate ion (HCO_3^-)   An ion that contains the radical group HCO_3^-.

Bioaccumulation   The accumulation of a substance, such as a toxic chemical, in various tissues of a living organism.

Bioerosion   Erosion of reef or other solid bottom material by the activities of organisms.

Biofilm   Coating of organic matter such as that found on sand grains.

Biogenous sediment   Sediment containing material produced by plants or animals, such as coral reefs, shell fragments, and housings of diatoms, radiolarians, foraminifers, and coccolithophores.

Biogeochemical cycle   The natural cycling of compounds among the living and nonliving components of an ecosystem.

Biological pump   The movement of CO_2 that enters the ocean from the atmosphere through the water column to the sediment on the ocean floor by biological processes—photosynthesis, secretion of shells, feeding, and dying.

Bioluminescence   Light organically produced by a chemical reaction. Found in bacteria, phytoplankton, and various fishes (especially deep-sea fish).

Biomagnification   Concentration of impurities as animals are eaten and the impurity is passed through food chains.

Biomass   The total mass of a defined organism or group of organisms in a particular community or in the ocean as a whole.

Biomass pyramid   A representation of trophic levels that illustrates the progressive decrease in total biomass at successive higher levels of the pyramid.

Bioremediation   The technique of using microbes to assist in cleaning toxic spills.

Biotic community   The living organisms that inhabit an ecosystem.

Biozone   A region of the environment that has distinctive biological characteristics.

Bivalve   A mollusk, such as an oyster or a clam, that has a shell consisting of two hinged valves.

Black smoker   A hydrothermal vent on the ocean floor that emits a black cloud of hot water filled with dissolved metal particles.

Body wave   A longitudinal or transverse wave that transmits energy through a body of matter.

Boiling point   The temperature at which a substance changes state from a liquid to a gas at a given pressure.

Bore   A steep-fronted tide crest that moves up a river in association with an incoming high tide.

Boundary current   The northward- or southward-flowing currents that form the western and eastern boundaries of the subtropical current gyres.

Brackish   Low-salinity water caused by the mixing of freshwater and saltwater.

Brazil Current   The warm western boundary current of the South Atlantic Subtropical Gyre.

Breaker zone   A region where waves break at the seaward margin of the surf zone.

Breakwater   An artificial structure constructed roughly parallel to shore and designed to protect a coastal region from the force of ocean waves.

Brittle   Descriptive term for a substance that is likely to fracture when force is applied to it.

Bryozoa   A phylum of colonial animals that often share one coelomic cavity. Encrusting and branching forms secrete a protective housing (zooccium) of calcium carbonate or chitinous material.

Buffering   The process by which a substance minimizes a change in the acidity of a solution when an acid or base is added to the solution.

Buoyancy   The ability or tendency to float or rise in a liquid.

Bycatch   Marine organisms that are caught incidentally by fishers seeking commercial species.

C

Calcareous   Containing calcium carbonate.

Calcite   A mineral with the chemical formula $CaCO_3$.

Calcite compensation depth (CCD)   The depth at which the amount of calcite ($CaCO_3$) produced by the organisms in the overlying water column is equal to the amount of calcite the water column can dissolve. No calcite deposition occurs below this depth, which, in most parts of the ocean, is at a depth of 4500 meters (15,000 feet).

Calcium carbonate ($CaCO_3$)   A chalklike substance secreted by many organisms in the form of coverings or skeletal structures.

California Current   The cold eastern boundary current of the North Pacific Subtropical Gyre.

Calorie   A unit of heat, defined as the amount of heat required to raise the temperature of 1 gram of water 1°C.

Calving   The process by which a glacier breaks at an edge, so that a portion of the ice separates and falls from the glacier.

Canary Current   The cold eastern boundary current of the North Atlantic Subtropical Gyre.

Capillarity   The action by which a fluid, such as water, is drawn up in small tubes as a result of surface tension.

Capillary wave   An ocean wave whose wavelength is less than 1.74 centimeters (0.7 inch). The dominant restoring force for such waves is surface tension.

Carapace (1) A chitinous or calcareous shield that covers the cephalothorax of some crustaceans. (2) The dorsal portion of a turtle shell.

Carbohydrate An organic compound containing the elements carbon, hydrogen, and oxygen with the general formula $(CH_2O)_n$.

Carbonate ion (CO_3^{-2}) An ion that contains the radical group CO_3^{-2}.

Caribbean Current The warm current that carries equatorial water across the Caribbean Sea into the Gulf of Mexico.

Carnivora The order of marine mammals that includes the sea otter, polar bear, and pinnipeds.

Carnivore An animal that depends on other animals solely or chiefly for its food supply.

Carotin An orange-yellow pigment found in plants.

Cation An atom that has lost one or more electrons and has an electrical positive charge.

Caulerpa taxifolia A tropical seaweed; a cold-water clone was introduced into the aquarium industry and found its way into coastal waters of the Mediterranean and Southern California. It continues to spread in the Mediterranean, but has been eradicated in Southern California.

Centigrade temperature scale A temperature scale based on the freezing point ($0°C = 32°F$) and boiling point ($100°C = 212°F$) of pure water. Also known as the Celsius scale after its founder.

Centripetal force A center-seeking force that tends to make rotating bodies move toward the center of rotation.

Cephalopoda A class of the phylum Mollusca whose members have a well-developed pair of eyes and a ring of tentacles surrounding the mouth. The shell is absent or internal on most members. The class includes the squid, octopus, and nautilus.

Cetacea An order of marine mammals that includes the whales, dolphins, and porpoises.

Chalk A soft, compact form of calcite, generally gray-white or yellow-white in color and derived chiefly from microscopic fossils.

Chemical energy A form of potential energy stored in the chemical bonds of compounds.

Chemosynthesis A process by which bacteria or archaea synthesize organic molecules from inorganic nutrients using chemical energy released from the bonds of a chemical compound (such as hydrogen sulfide) by oxidation.

Chloride ion (Cl^-) A chlorine atom that has become negatively charged by gaining one electron.

Chlorinity The amount of chloride ion and ions of other halogens in ocean water expressed in parts per thousand (‰) by weight.

Chlorophyll A group of green pigments that make it possible for plants to carry on photosynthesis.

Chlorophyta Green algae. Characterized by the presence of chlorophyll and other pigments.

Chondrite A stony meteorite composed primarily of silicate rock material and containing chondrules (spheroidal granules). They are the most commonly found meteorites.

Chronometer An exceptionally precise timepiece.

Chrysophyta An important phylum of planktonic algae that includes the diatoms. The presence of chlorophyll is masked by the pigment carotin that gives the plants a golden color.

Ciguatera A type of seafood poisoning caused by ingestion of certain tropical reef fish (most notably barracuda, red snapper, and grouper) that have high levels of naturally occurring dinoflagellate toxins.

Cilium A short, hairlike structure common on lower animals. Beating in unison, cilia may create water currents that carry food toward the mouth of an animal or may be used for locomotion.

Circadian rhythm Behavioral and physiological rhythms of organisms related to the 24-hour day. Sleeping and waking patterns are an example.

Circular orbital motion The motion of water particles caused by a wave as the wave is transmitted through water.

Circumpolar Current An eastward-flowing current that extends from the surface to the ocean floor and encircles Antarctica.

Clay (1) A particle size between silt and colloid. (2) Any of various hydrous aluminum silicate minerals that are plastic, expansive, and have ion exchange capabilities.

Climate The meteorological conditions, including temperature, precipitation, and wind that characteristically prevail in a particular region; the long-term average of weather.

Cnidaria A phylum that contains some 10,000 species of predominantly marine animals with a sack-like body and stinging cells on tentacles that surround the single opening to the gut cavity. There are two basic body forms. The medusa is a pelagic form represented by the jellyfish. The polyp is a predominantly benthic form found in sea anemones and corals. Previously named Coelenterata.

Cnidoblast A stinging cell of phylum Cnidaria that contains the stinging mechanism (nematocyst) used in defense and capturing prey.

Coast A strip of land that extends inland from the coastline as far as marine influence is evidenced in the landforms.

Coastal geostrophic current See *geostrophic current*.

Coastal plain estuary An estuary formed by rising sea level flooding a coastal river valley.

Coastal upwelling The movement of deeper nutrient-rich water into the surface water mass as a result of windblown surface water moving offshore.

Coastal waters The relatively shallow water areas that adjoin continents or islands.

Coastal wetland A biologically productive region bordering estuaries and other protected coastal areas; typically as salt marshes in latitudes greater than 30° and as mangrove swamps in lower latitudes.

Coastline The landward limit of the effect of the highest storm waves on the shore.

Coccolith Tiny calcareous discs averaging about 3 micrometers (0.00012 inch) in diameter that form the cell wall of coccolithophores.

Coccolithophore A microscopic planktonic form of algae encased by a covering composed of calcareous discs (coccoliths).

Coelenterata A phylum of radially symmetrical animals that includes two basic body forms, the medusa and the polyp. Includes jellyfish (medusoid) and sea anemones (polypoid). Preferred name is now Cnidaria.

Cohesion The intermolecular attraction by which the elements of a body are held together.

Cold core ring A circular eddy of a surface current that contains cold water in its center and rotates counterclockwise in the Northern Hemisphere.

Cold front A weather front in which a cold air mass moves into and under a warm air mass. It creates a narrow band of intense precipitation.

Cold-blooded See *poikilothermic* and *ectothermic*.

Colonial animal An animal that lives in groups of attached or separate individuals. Groups of individuals may serve special functions.

Columbia River estuary An estuary at the border between the states of Washington and Oregon that has been most adversely affected by the construction of hydroelectric dams.

Comb jelly Common name for members of the phylum Ctenophora. See also *ctenophore*.

Commensalism A symbiotic relationship in which one party benefits and the other is unaffected.

Compensation depth for photosynthesis The depth at which net photosynthesis becomes zero; below this depth, photosynthetic organisms can no longer survive. This depth is greater in the open ocean (up to 100 meters or 330 feet) than near the shore due to increased turbidity that limits light penetration in coastal regions.

Compound A substance containing two or more elements combined in fixed proportions.

Condensation The conversion of water from the vapor to the liquid state. When it occurs, the energy required to vaporize the water is released into the atmosphere. This is about 585 calories per gram of water at 20°C.

Conduction The transmission of heat by the passage of energy from particle to particle.

Conjunction The apparent closeness of two heavenly bodies. During the new moon phase, Earth and the Moon are in conjunction on the same side of the Sun.

Constant proportions, principle of A principle which states that the major constituents of ocean-water salinity are found in the same relative proportions throughout the ocean, independent of salinity.

Constructive interference A form of wave interference in which two waves come together in phase, for example, crest to crest, to produce a greater displacement from the still-water line than that produced by either of the waves alone.

Consumer An animal within an ecosystem that consumes the organic mass produced by the producers.

Continent About one-third of Earth's surface that rises above the deep-ocean floor to be exposed above sea level. Continents are composed primarily of granite, an igneous rock of lower density than the basaltic oceanic crust.

Continental accretion Growth or increase in size of a continent by gradual external addition of crustal material.

Continental arc An arc-shaped row of active volcanoes produced by subduction that occurs along convergent active continental margins.

Continental borderland A highly irregular portion of the continental margin that is submerged beneath the ocean and is characterized by depths greater than those characteristic of the continental shelf.

Continental drift A term applied to early theories supporting the possibility the continents are in motion over Earth's surface.

Continental effect Describes areas that are less affected by the sea and therefore having a greater range of temperature differences (both daily and yearly).

Continental margin The submerged area next to a continent comprising the continental shelf, continental slope, and continental rise.

Continental rise A gently sloping depositional surface at the base of the continental slope.

Continental shelf A gently sloping depositional surface extending from the low water line to the depth of a marked increase in slope around the margin of a continent or island.

Continental slope A relatively steeply sloping surface lying seaward of the continental shelf.

Convection Heat transfer in a gas or liquid by the circulation of currents from one region to another.

Convection cell A circular-moving loop of matter involved in convective movement.

Convergence The act of coming together from different directions. There are polar, tropical, and subtropical regions of the oceans where water masses with different characteristics come together. Along these lines of convergence, the denser masses will sink beneath the others.

Convergent plate boundary A lithospheric plate boundary where adjacent plates converge, producing ocean trench–island arc systems, ocean trench–continental volcanic arcs, or folded mountain ranges.

Copepoda An order of microscopic to nearly microscopic crustaceans that are important members of zooplankton in temperate and subpolar waters.

Coral A group of benthic anthozoans that exist as individuals or in colonies and secrete $CaCO_3$ external skeletons. Under the proper conditions, corals may produce reefs composed of their external skeletons and the $CaCO_3$ material secreted by varieties of algae associated with the reefs.

Coral bleaching The loss of color in coral reef organisms that causes them to turn white. Coral bleaching is caused by the removal or expulsion of the coral's symbiotic zooxanthellae algae in response to high water temperatures or other adverse conditions.

Coral reef A calcareous organic reef composed significantly of solid coral and coral sand. Algae may be responsible for more than half of the $CaCO_3$ reef material. Found in waters where the minimum average monthly temperature is 18°C or higher.

Core (1) The deep, central layer of Earth, composed primarily of iron and nickel. It has a liquid outer portion 2270 kilometers (1410 miles) thick and a solid inner core with a radius of 1216 kilometers (756 miles). (2) A cylinder of sediment and/or rock material usually obtained by drilling.

Coriolis effect An apparent force resulting from Earth's rotation causes particles in motion to be deflected to the right in the Northern Hemisphere and to the left in the Southern Hemisphere.

Cosmogenous sediment Sediment derived from outer space.

Cotidal line A line connecting points where high tide occurs simultaneously.

Counterillumination Camouflaging by using bioluminescence to match the color and intensity of dim filtered sunlight from above and obliterate a telltale shadow.

Countershading Protective coloration in an animal or insect, characterized by darker coloring of areas exposed to light and lighter coloring of areas that are normally shaded.

Covalent bond A chemical bond formed by the sharing of one or more electrons, especially pairs of electrons, between atoms.

Crest (wave) The portion of an ocean wave that is displaced above the still-water level.

Cruiser Fish (such as the bluefin tuna) that constantly cruise pelagic waters in search of food.

Crust (1) The uppermost outer layer of Earth's structure that is composed of basaltic oceanic crust and granitic continental crust. The average thickness of the crust ranges from 8 kilometers (5 miles) beneath the ocean to 35 kilometers (22 miles) beneath the continents. (2) A hard covering or surface layer of hydrogenous sediment.

Crustacea A class of subphylum Arthropoda that includes barnacles, copepods, lobsters, crabs, and shrimp.

Crystalline rock Igneous or metamorphic rocks. These rocks are made up of crystalline particles with orderly molecular structures.

Ctenophore A member of the phylum of gelatinous organisms that are more or less spheroidal with biradial symmetry. These exclusively marine animals have eight rows of ciliated combs for locomotion, and most have two tentacles for capturing prey.

Current A physical movement of water.

Cyclone An atmospheric system characterized by the rapid, inward circulation of air masses about a low-pressure center that is associated with rising air. Cyclones circulate counterclockwise in the Northern Hemisphere and clockwise in the Southern Hemisphere and are usually accompanied by stormy, often destructive, weather.

Cyclonic flow The flow of air around a region of low pressure counterclockwise in the Northern Hemisphere.

D

Davidson Current A northward-flowing current along the Washington–Oregon coast that is driven by geostrophic effects on a large freshwater runoff.

DDT An insecticide (dichlorodiphenyltrichloroethane) that caused damage to marine bird populations in the 1950s and 1960s. Its use is now banned throughout most of the world.

Dead zone A region of hypoxic conditions that kills off most marine organisms that cannot escape. It is usually the result of eutrophication caused by runoff from land-based fertilizer applications.

Decay distance The distance over which waves change from a choppy "sea" to uniform swell.

Declination The angular distance of the Sun or Moon above or below the plane of Earth's equator.

Decomposer Primarily bacteria that break down nonliving organic material, extract some of the products of decomposition for their own needs, and make available the compounds needed for primary production.

Decompression sickness A serious condition that occurs in divers when they ascend too rapidly, causing nitrogen bubbles to form in the blood and tissue, resulting in great pain and sometimes death. Also known as the bends.

Deep biosphere The microbe-rich region beneath the sea floor.

Deep boundary current A relatively strong deep current flowing across the continental rise along the western margin of ocean basins.

Deep current A density-driven circulation that is initiated at the ocean surface by temperature and salinity conditions that produce a high-density water mass, which sinks and spreads slowly beneath surface waters.

Deep-ocean Assessment and Reporting of Tsunamis (DART) A system that utilizes sea floor sensors capable of picking up the small yet distinctive pressure pulse from a tsunami at the surface.

Deep-ocean basin Areas of the ocean floor that have deep water, are far from land, and are underlain by basaltic crust.

Deep scattering layer (DSL) A layer of marine organisms in the open ocean that scatter signals from an echo sounder. It migrates daily from depths of slightly over 100 meters (330 feet) at night to more than 800 meters (2600 feet) during the day.

Deep-sea fan A large fan-shaped deposit commonly found on the continental rise seaward of such sediment-laden rivers as the Amazon, Indus, or Ganges-Brahmaputra. Also known as a submarine fan.

Deep-sea fish Any of a large group of fishes that lives within the aphotic zone and has special adaptations for finding food and avoiding predators in darkness.

Deep-sea system The bathyal, abyssal, and hadal benthic environments.

Deep water The water beneath the permanent thermocline (and resulting pycnocline) that has a uniformly low temperature.

Deep-water wave An ocean wave traveling in water that has a depth greater than one-half the average wavelength. Its speed is independent of water depth.

Delta A low-lying deposit at the mouth of a river, usually having a triangular shape as viewed from above.

Density The mass per unit volume of a substance. Usually expressed as grams per cubic centimeter (g/cm^3). For ocean water with a salinity of 35‰ at 0°C, the density is 1.028 g/cm^3.

Density stratification A layering based on density, where the highest density material occupies the lowest space.

Deposit feeder An organism that feeds on food items that occur as deposits, including detritus and various detritus-coated sediment.

Depositional-type shore A shoreline dominated by processes that form deposits (such as sand bars and barrier islands) along the shore.

Desalination   The removal of salt ions from ocean water to produce pure water.

Destructive interference   A form of wave interference in which two waves come together out of phase, for example, crest to trough, and produce a wave with less displacement than the larger of the two waves would have produced alone.

Detritus   (1) Any loose material produced directly from rock disintegration. (2) Material resulting from the disintegration of dead organic remains.

Diatom   A member of the class Bacillariophyceae of algae that possesses a wall of overlapping silica valves.

Diatomaceous earth   A deposit composed primarily of the tests of diatoms mixed with clay. Also called diatomite.

Diffraction   A change in the direction or intensity of a wave after passing an obstacle that cannot be interpreted as refraction or reflection.

Diffusion   A process by which fluids move through other fluids by random molecular movement from areas of high concentration to areas in which they are in lower concentrations.

Dinoflagellate   A single-celled microscopic planktonic organism that may possess chlorophyll and belong to the phylum Pyrrophyta (autotrophic) or may ingest food and belong to the class Mastigophora of the phylum Protozoa (heterotrophic).

Dipolar   Having two poles. The water molecule possesses a polarity of electrical charge with one pole being more positive and the other more negative in electrical charge.

Discontinuity   An abrupt change in a property such as temperature or salinity at a line or surface.

Disphotic zone   The dimly lit zone, corresponding approximately to the mesopelagic, in which there is not enough light to support photosynthetic organisms; sometimes called the twilight zone.

Disruptive coloration   A marking or color pattern that confuses prey.

Dissolved oxygen   Oxygen that is dissolved in ocean water.

Distillation   A method of purifying liquids by heating them to their boiling point and condensing the vapor.

Distributary   A small stream flowing away from a main stream. Such streams are characteristic of deltas.

Disturbing force   The energy that causes waves to form.

Diurnal inequality   The difference in the heights of two successive high tides or two successive low tides during a lunar (tidal) day.

Diurnal tidal pattern   A tidal pattern exhibiting one high tide and one low tide during a tidal day; a daily tide.

Divergence   A horizontal flow of water from a central region, as occurs in upwelling.

Divergent plate boundary   A lithospheric plate boundary where adjacent plates diverge, producing an oceanic ridge or rise (spreading center).

Doldrums   A global belt of light, variable winds near the equator, resulting from the vertical flow of low-density air masses upward within this equatorial belt. Associated with much precipitation.

Dolphin   (1) A brilliantly colored fish of the genus *Coryphaena*. (2) The name applied to the small, beaked members of the cetacean family Delphinidae.

Dorsal   Pertaining to the back or upper surface of most animals.

Downwelling   In the open or coastal ocean, where Ekman transport causes surface waters to converge or impinge on the coast, surface water that moves down beneath the surface.

Drift bottle   Equipment used to study ocean current movement by drifting with currents.

Driftnet   A fishing net made of monofilament fishing line that catches organisms by entanglement.

Drifts   Thick sediment deposits on the continental rise produced where the deep boundary current slows and loses sediment when it changes direction to follow the base of the continental slope.

Drowned beach   An ancient beach now beneath the coastal ocean because of rising sea level or subsidence of the coast.

Drowned river valley   The lower part of a river valley that has been submerged by rising sea level or subsidence of the coast.

Dune (coastal)   A coastal deposit of sand lying landward of the beach and deriving its sand from onshore winds that transport beach sand inland.

Dynamic topography   A surface configuration resulting from the geopotential difference between a given surface and a reference surface of no motion. A contour map of this surface is useful in estimating the nature of geostrophic currents.

E

Earthquake   A sudden motion or trembling in Earth, caused by the sudden release of slowly accumulated strain by faulting (movement along a fracture in Earth's crust) or volcanic activity.

East Australian Current   The warm western boundary current of the South Pacific Subtropical Gyre.

East Pacific Rise   A fast-spreading divergent plate boundary extending southward from the Gulf of California through the eastern South Pacific Ocean.

East Wind Drift   The coastal current driven in a westerly direction by the polar easterly winds blowing off Antarctica.

Eastern boundary current   Equatorward-flowing cold drifts of water on the eastern side of all subtropical gyres.

Eastern Pacific Garbage Patch   An area in the eastern part of the North Pacific (Turtle) Gyre that serves as an accumulation area for floating plastic and other trash; it is about twice the size of Texas.

Ebb current   The flow of water seaward during a decrease in the height of the tide.

Echinodermata   A phylum of animals that have bilateral symmetry in larval forms and usually a five-sided radial symmetry as adults. Benthic and possessing rigid or articulating exoskeletons of calcium carbonate with spines, this phylum includes sea stars, brittle stars, sea urchins, sand dollars, sea cucumbers, and sea lilies.

Echo sounder   A device that transmits sound from a ship's hull to the ocean floor where it is reflected back to receivers. The speed of sound in the water is known, so the depth can be determined from the travel time of the sound signal.

Echolocation   A sensory system in odontocete cetaceans in which usually high-pitched sounds are emitted and their echoes interpreted to determine the direction and distance of objects.

Ecliptic   The plane of the center of the Earth–Moon system as it orbits around the Sun.

Ecosystem   All the organisms in a biotic community and the abiotic environmental factors with which they interact.

Ectothermic   Of or relating to an organism that regulates its body temperature largely by exchanging heat with its surroundings; cold-blooded.

Eddy   A current of any fluid forming on the side of a main current. It usually moves in a circular path and develops where currents encounter obstacles or flow past one another.

Ekman spiral   A theoretical consideration of the effect of a steady wind blowing over an ocean of unlimited depth and breadth and of uniform viscosity. The result is a surface flow at 45° to the right of the wind in the Northern Hemisphere. Water at increasing depth below the surface will drift in directions increasingly more slowly and to the right until at about 100 meters (330 feet) depth it may move in a direction opposite to that of the wind.

Ekman transport   The net transport of surface water set in motion by wind. Due to the Ekman spiral phenomenon, it is theoretically in a direction 90° to the right and 90° to the left of the wind direction in the Northern Hemisphere and Southern Hemisphere, respectively.

El Niño   A southerly flowing warm current that generally develops off the coast of Ecuador around Christmastime. Occasionally it will move farther south into Peruvian coastal waters and cause the widespread death of plankton, fish, and other organisms such as marine mammals that depend on fish for food.

El Niño–Southern Oscillation (ENSO)   The correlation of El Niño events with an oscillatory pattern of pressure change in a persistent high-pressure cell in the southeastern Pacific Ocean and a persistent low-pressure cell over the East Indies.

Electrical conductivity   The ability or power to conduct or transmit electricity.

Electrolysis   A separation process by which salt ions are removed from saltwater through water-impermeable membranes toward oppositely charged electrodes.

Electromagnetic energy   Energy that travels as waves or particles with the speed of light. Different kinds possess different properties based on wavelength. The longest wavelengths belong to radio waves, up to 100 kilometers (60 miles) in length. At the other end of the spectrum are cosmic rays with greater penetrating power and wavelengths of less than 0.000001 micrometer.

Electromagnetic spectrum   The spectrum of radiant energy emitted from stars and ranging between cosmic rays with wavelengths of less than 10 to 11 centimeters (4 to 4.3 inches) and very long waves with wavelengths in excess of 100 kilometers (60 miles).

Electron   A subatomic particle that orbits the nucleus of an atom and has a negative electric charge.

Electron cloud   The diffuse area surrounding the nucleus of an atom where electrons are found.

Electrostatic force   A force caused by electric charges at rest.

Element   One of a number of substances, each of which is composed entirely of like particles—atoms—that cannot be broken into smaller particles by chemical means.

Emerging shoreline   A shoreline resulting from the emergence of the ocean floor relative to the ocean surface. It is usually rather straight and characterized by marine features usually found at some depth.

ENSO   See *El Niño–Southern Oscillation (ENSO)*.

ENSO index   An index showing the relative strength of El Niño and La Niña conditions.

Environment   The sum of all physical, chemical, and biological factors to which an organism or community is subjected.

Environmental bioassay   An environmental assessment technique that determines the concentration of a pollutant that causes 50% mortality among a specific group of test organisms.

Epicenter   The point on Earth's surface that is directly above the focus of an earthquake.

Epifauna   Animals that live on the ocean bottom, either attached or moving freely over it.

Epipelagic zone   A subdivision of the oceanic province that extends from the surface to a depth of 200 meters (660 feet).

Equator   The imaginary great circle around Earth's surface, equidistant from the poles and perpendicular to Earth's axis of rotation. It divides Earth into the Northern Hemisphere and the Southern Hemisphere.

Equatorial   Pertaining to the equatorial region.

Equatorial countercurrent   Eastward-flowing currents found between the North and South Equatorial Currents in all oceans but particularly well developed in the Pacific Ocean.

Equatorial current   Westward-flowing currents that travel along the equator in all ocean basins, caused by the trade winds. They are called North or South Equatorial Currents, depending on their position north or south of the equator.

Equatorial low   A band of low atmospheric pressure that encircles the globe along the equator.

Equatorial upwelling   The movement of deeper nutrient-rich water into the surface water mass as a result of divergence of currents along the equator.

Erosion   The group of natural processes, including weathering, dissolution, abrasion, corrosion, and transportation, by which material is worn away from Earth's surface.

Erosional-type shore   A shoreline dominated by processes that form erosional features (such as cliffs and sea stacks) along the shore.

Estuarine circulation pattern   A flow pattern in an estuary characterized by a net surface flow of low-salinity water toward the ocean and an opposite net subsurface flow of seawater toward the head of the estuary.

Estuary   A partially enclosed coastal body of water in which salty ocean water is significantly diluted by freshwater from land runoff. Examples of estuaries include river mouths, bays, inlets, gulfs, and sounds.

Eukarya   One of the three major domains of life. The domain includes single-celled or multicellular organisms whose cells usually contain a distinct membrane-bound nucleus.

Euphotic zone   A layer that extends from the surface of the ocean to a depth where enough light exists to support photosynthesis, rarely deeper than 100 meters (330 feet).

Euryhaline   A descriptive term for organisms with a high tolerance for a wide range of salinity conditions.

Eurythermal   A descriptive term for organisms with a high tolerance for a wide range of temperature conditions.

Eustatic sea level change   A worldwide raising or lowering of sea level.

Eutrophic   A region of high productivity.

Eutrophication   The enrichment of waters by a previously scarce nutrient.

Evaporation   The process of changing from the liquid to the vapor state at a temperature below the boiling point of a substance.

Evaporite   A sedimentary deposit that is left behind when water evaporates. Evaporite minerals include gypsum, calcite, and halite.

Evolution   The change of groups of organisms with the passage of time, mainly as a result of natural selection, so that descendants differ morphologically and physiologically from their ancestors.

Exclusive Economic Zone (EEZ)   A coastal zone that generally extends 200 nautical miles (370 kilometers) from shore and establishes coastal nation jurisdiction including mineral resources, fish stocks, and pollution. If the continental shelf extends beyond the 200-mile EEZ, the EEZ is extended to 350 nautical miles (648 kilometers) from shore.

Extrusive rock   Igneous rock that flows out onto Earth's surface before cooling and solidifying (lava).

Eye   (1) An organ of vision or of light sensitivity. (2) The circular low-pressure area of relative calm at the center of a hurricane.

F

Fact   Something having real, demonstrable existence. A scientific fact is an occurrence that has been repeatedly confirmed.

Fahrenheit temperature scale (°F)   A temperature scale whereby the freezing point of water is 32° and the boiling point of water is 212°.

Falcate   Curved and tapering to a point; sickle-shaped.

Falkland Current   A northward-flowing cold current found off the southeastern coast of South America.

Fall bloom   A middle-latitude bloom of phytoplankton that occurs during the fall and is limited by the availability of sunlight.

Fall equinox   See *autumnal equinox*.

Fan   A gently sloping, fan-shaped feature normally located near the lower end of a canyon. Also known as a submarine fan.

Fat   An organic compound formed from alcohol, glycerol, and one or more fatty acids; a lipid, it is a solid at atmospheric temperatures.

Fathom (fm)   A unit of depth in the ocean, commonly used in countries using the English system of units. It is equal to 1.83 meters (6 feet).

Fault   A fracture or fracture zone in Earth's crust along which displacement has occurred.

Fault block   A crustal block bounded on at least two sides by faults. Usually elongate; if it is down-dropped, it produces a graben; if uplifted, it is a horst.

Fauna   The animal life of any particular area or of any particular time.

Fecal pellet   The excrement of planktonic crustaceans that assist in speeding up the descent rate of sedimentary particles by combining them into larger packages.

Ferrel cell   The large atmospheric circulation cell that occurs between 30° and 60° latitude in each hemisphere.

Ferromagnesium   Minerals rich in iron and magnesium.

Fetch   (1) Pertaining to the area of the open ocean over which the wind blows with constant speed and direction, thereby creating a wave system. (2) The distance across the fetch (wave-generating area) measured in a direction parallel to the direction of the wind.

Filter feeder   An organism that obtains its food by filtering seawater for other organisms. Also known as suspension feeder.

Fishery   Fish caught from the ocean by commercial fishers.

Fishery management   The organized effort directed at regulating fishing activity with the goal of maintaining a long-term fishery.

Fissure   A long, narrow opening; a crack or cleft.

Fjord   A long, narrow, deep, U-shaped inlet that usually represents the seaward end of a glacial valley that has become partially submerged after the melting of the glacier.

Flagellum   A whiplike living structure used by some cells for locomotion.

Floe   A piece of floating ice other than fast ice or icebergs. May range in maximum horizontal dimension from about 20 centimeters (8 inches) to more than 1 kilometer (0.6 mile).

Flood current   A tidal current associated with increasing height of the tide, generally moving toward the shore.

Flood tide   A rising tide.

Flora   The plant life of any particular area or of any particular time.

Florida Current   A warm current flowing north along the coast of Florida that merges into the Gulf Stream.

Folded mountain range   A mountain range formed as a result of the convergence of lithospheric plates. Folded mountain ranges are characterized by masses of folded sedimentary rocks that formed from sediments deposited in the ocean basin that was destroyed by the convergence.

Food chain   The passage of energy materials from producers through a sequence of a herbivore and a number of carnivores.

Food web   A group of interrelated food chains.

Foraminifer   An order of planktonic and benthic protozoans that possess protective coverings, usually composed of calcium carbonate.

Forced wave   A wave that is generated and maintained by a continuous force such as the gravitational attraction of the Moon.

Foreshore The portion of the shore lying between the normal high and low water marks; the intertidal zone.

Fossil Any remains, print, or trace of an organism that has been preserved in Earth's crust.

Fracture zone An extensive linear zone of unusually irregular topography of the ocean floor, characterized by large seamounts, steep-sided or asymmetrical ridges, troughs, or long, steep slopes. Usually represents ancient, inactive transform fault zones.

Free wave A wave created by a sudden rather than a continuous impulse that continues to exist after the generating force is gone.

Freeze separation The desalination of seawater by multiple episodes of freezing, rinsing, and thawing.

Freezing The process by which a liquid is converted to a solid at its freezing point.

Freezing point The temperature at which a liquid becomes a solid under any given set of conditions. The freezing point of water is 0°C at one atmosphere pressure.

Fringing reef A reef that is directly attached to the shore of an island or continent. It may extend more than 1 kilometer (0.6 mile) from shore. The outer margin is submerged and often consists of algal limestone, coral rock, and living coral.

Fucoxanthin The reddish-brown pigment that gives brown algae its characteristic color.

Full moon The phase of the Moon that occurs when the Sun and Moon are in opposition; that is, they are on opposite sides of Earth. During this time, the lit side of the Moon faces Earth.

Fully developed sea The maximum average size of waves that can be developed for a given wind speed when it has blown in the same direction for a minimum duration over a minimum fetch.

Fungi Any of numerous eukaryotic organisms of the kingdom Fungi, which lack chlorophyll and vascular tissue and range in form from a single cell to a body mass of branched filamentous structures that often produce specialized fruiting bodies. The kingdom includes the yeasts, molds, lichens, and mushrooms.

Fur seal Any of several eared seals of the genera *Callorhinus* or *Arctocephalus*, having thick, soft underfur.

Fusion reaction A type of nuclear reaction where hydrogen atoms are converted to helium atoms, thereby releasing large amounts of energy.

G

Galápagos Rift A divergent plate boundary extending eastward from the Galápagos Islands toward South America. The first deep-sea hydrothermal vent biocommunity was discovered here in 1977.

Galaxy One of the billions of large systems of stars that make up the universe.

Gas hydrate A latticelike compound composed of water and natural gas (usually methane) formed in high-pressure and low-temperature environments such as those found in deep ocean sediments. Also known as clathrates because of their cagelike chemical structure.

Gaseous state A state of matter in which molecules move by translation and only interact through chance collisions.

Gastropoda A class of mollusks, most of which possess an asymmetrical, spiral one-piece shell and a well-developed flattened foot. A well-developed head will usually have two eyes and one or two pairs of tentacles. Includes snails, limpets, abalone, cowries, sea hares, and sea slugs.

Geostrophic current A current that grows out of Earth's rotation and is the result of a near balance between gravitational force and the Coriolis effect.

Gill A thin-walled projection from some part of the external body or the digestive tract used for respiration in a water environment.

Gill net See *driftnet*.

Glacial deposit A sedimentary deposit formed by a glacier and characterized by poor sorting.

Glacier A large mass of ice formed on land by the recrystallization of old, compacted snow. It flows from an area of accumulation to an area of wasting where ice is removed from the glacier by melting.

Glauconite A group of green hydrogenous minerals consisting of hydrous silicates of potassium and iron.

Global engineering Deliberately manipulating one or more of Earth's systems for the benefit of humankind. Also called geoengineering.

Global Positioning System (GPS) A system of satellites that transmit microwave signals to Earth, allowing people at the surface to accurately locate themselves.

Globigerina ooze An ooze that contains a large percentage of the calcareous tests of the foraminifer *Globigerina*.

Goiter An enlargement of the human thyroid gland, visible as a swelling at the front of the neck, often associated with iodine deficiency.

Gondwanaland A hypothetical protocontinent of the Southern Hemisphere named for the Gondwana region of India. It included the present continental masses Africa, Antarctica, Australia, India, and South America.

Graded bedding Stratification in which each layer displays a decrease in grain size from bottom to top.

Gradient The rate of increase or decrease of one quantity or characteristic relative to a unit change in another. For example, the slope of the ocean floor is a change in elevation (a vertical linear measurement) per unit of horizontal distance covered. Commonly measured in meters per kilometer.

Grain size The average size of the grains of material in a sample. Also known as fragment or particle size.

Granite A light-colored igneous rock characteristic of the continental crust. Rich in nonferromagnesian minerals such as feldspar and quartz.

Gravitational force The force of attraction that exists between any two bodies in the universe that is proportional to the product of their masses and inversely proportional to the square of the distance between the centers of their masses.

Gravity wave A wave for which the dominant restoring force is gravity. Such waves have a wavelength of more than 1.74 centimeters (0.7 inch), and their speed of propagation is controlled mainly by gravity.

Gray whale A slow-moving, coastal-dwelling baleen whale (*Eschrichtius robustus*) of northern Pacific waters, having grayish-black coloring with white blotches. It undertakes the longest yearly migration of any mammal.

Greenhouse effect The heating of Earth's atmosphere that results from the absorption by components of the atmosphere such as water vapor and carbon dioxide of infrared radiation from Earth's surface.

Groin A low artificial structure built perpendicular to the shore and designed to interfere with longshore transportation of sediment so that it traps sand and widens the beach on its upstream side.

Groin field A series of closely spaced groins.

Gross ecological efficiency The amount of energy passed on from a trophic level to the one above it divided by the amount it received from the one below it.

Gross primary production The total carbon fixed into organic molecules through photosynthesis or chemosynthesis by a discrete autotrophic community.

Grunion A small fish (*Leuresthes tenuis*) of coastal waters of California and Mexico that spawns at night along beaches during the high tides of spring and summer. Grunion time their reproductive activities to coincide with tidal phenomena and are the only fish that comes completely out of water to spawn.

Gulf Stream The high-intensity western boundary current of the North Atlantic Subtropical Gyre that flows north off the East Coast of the United States.

Guyot See *tablemount*.

Gypsum A colorless, white, or yellowish evaporite mineral, $CaSO_4 \cdot 2H_2O$.

Gyre A large, horizontal, circular-moving loop of water. Used mainly in reference to the circular motion of water in each of the major ocean basins centered in subtropical high-pressure regions.

H

Habitat A place where a particular plant or animal lives. Generally refers to a smaller area than environment.

Hadal Pertaining to the deepest ocean environment, specifically that of ocean trenches deeper than 6 kilometers (3.7 miles).

Hadal zone Pertaining to the deepest ocean benthic environment, specifically that of ocean trenches deeper than 6 kilometers (3.7 miles).

Hadley cell The large atmospheric circulation cell that occurs between the equator and 30° latitude in each hemisphere.

Half-life The time required for half the atoms of a sample of a radioactive isotope to decay to an atom of another element.

Halite A colorless or white evaporite mineral, NaCl, which occurs as cubic crystals and is used as table salt.

Halocline A layer of water in which a high rate of change in salinity in the vertical dimension is present.

Hard stabilization Any form of artificial structure built to protect a coast or to prevent the movement of sand along a beach. Examples include groins, breakwaters, and seawalls.

Harmful algal bloom (HAB) See *red tide*.

Headland A steep-faced irregularity of the coast that extends out into the ocean.

Heat Energy moving from a high temperature system to a lower temperature system. The heat gained by the one system may be used to raise its temperature or to do work.

Heat budget (global)   The equilibrium that exists on the average between the amounts of heat absorbed by Earth and that returned to space.

Heat capacity   The amount of heat energy required to raise the temperature of a substance by 1°C. See also *specific heat.*

Heat energy   Energy of molecular motion. The conversion of higher forms of energy such as radiant or mechanical energy to heat energy within a system increases the heat energy within the system and the temperature of the system.

Heat flow (flux)   The quantity of heat flow to Earth's surface per unit of time.

Hemoglobin   A red pigment found in red blood corpuscles that carries oxygen from the lungs to tissue and carbon dioxide from tissue to lungs.

Herbivore   An animal that relies chiefly or solely on plants for its food.

Hermatypic coral   Reef-building corals that have symbiotic algae in their ectodermal tissue. They cannot produce a reef structure below the euphotic zone.

Heterotroph   Animals and bacteria that depend on the organic compounds produced by other organisms as food. Organisms not capable of producing their own food by photosynthesis.

High slack water   The period of time associated with the peak of high tide when there is no visible flow of water into or out of bays and rivers.

High tide zone   The portion of the intertidal zone that lies between the lowest high tides and highest high tides that occur in an area. It is, on average, exposed to desiccation for longer periods each day than it is covered by water.

High water (HW)   The highest level reached by the rising tide before it begins to recede.

Higher high water (HHW)   The higher of two high waters occurring during a tidal day where tides exhibit a mixed tidal pattern.

Higher low water (HLW)   The higher of two low waters occurring during a tidal day where tides exhibit a mixed tidal pattern.

Highly stratified estuary   A relatively deep estuary in which a significant volume of marine water enters as a subsurface flow. A large volume of freshwater stream input produces a widespread low surface–salinity condition that produces a well-developed halocline throughout most of the estuary.

Holoplankton   Organisms that spend their entire life as members of the plankton.

Homeothermic   Of or relating to an animal that maintains a precisely controlled internal body temperature using its own internal heating and cooling mechanisms; warm-blooded.

Horse latitudes   The global belts between about 30° and 35° north and south latitude where winds are light and variable as a result of the vertical movement of air masses downward at these latitudes, causing a hot, dry climate. These belts are associated with the major continental and maritime deserts of the world.

Hotspot   The relatively stationary surface expression of a persistent column of molten mantle material rising to the surface.

Hurricane   A tropical cyclone in which winds reach speeds in excess of 120 kilometers (74 miles) per hour.

Generally applied to such storms in the North Atlantic Ocean, eastern North Pacific Ocean, Caribbean Sea, and Gulf of Mexico. Such storms in the western Pacific Ocean are called typhoons and those in the Indian Ocean are known as cyclones.

Hydration   The condition of being surrounded by water molecules, as when sodium chloride dissolves in water.

Hydrocarbon   Any organic compound consisting only of hydrogen and carbon. Crude oil is a mixture of hydrocarbons.

Hydrocarbon seep biocommunity   A deep bottom-dwelling community of organisms associated with a hydrocarbon seep from the ocean floor. The community depends on methane and sulfur-oxidizing bacteria as producers. The bacteria may live free in the water, on the bottom, or symbiotically in the tissues of some of the animals.

Hydrogen bond   An intermolecular bond that forms within water because of the dipolar nature of water molecules.

Hydrogenous sediment   Sediment that forms from precipitation from ocean water or ion exchange between existing sediment and ocean water. Examples are manganese nodules, metal sulfides, and evaporites.

Hydrologic cycle   The cycle of water exchange among the atmosphere, land, and ocean through the processes of evaporation, precipitation, runoff, and subsurface percolation. Also called the water cycle.

Hydrothermal spring   Vents of hot water found primarily along the spreading axes of oceanic ridges and rises.

Hydrothermal vent   Ocean water that percolates down through fractures in recently formed ocean floor is heated by underlying magma and surfaces again through these vents. They are usually located near the axis of spreading along the mid-ocean ridge.

Hydrothermal vent biocommunity   A deep bottom-dwelling community of organisms associated with a hydrothermal vent. The hot water vent is usually associated with the axis of a spreading center, and the community is dependent on sulfur-oxidizing bacteria that may live free in the water, on the bottom, or symbiotically in the tissue of some of the animals of the community.

Hydrozoa   A class of cnidarians that characteristically exhibit alternation of generations, with a sessile polypoid colony giving rise to a pelagic medusoid form by asexual budding.

Hypersaline   Waters that are highly or excessively saline.

Hypersaline lagoon   A shallow lagoon that may reach high salinity levels due to little tidal flushing, high evaporation rates, and low freshwater input.

Hypersaline seep   A seep of high-salinity water that trickles out of the sea floor.

Hypersaline seep biocommunity   A bottom-dwelling community of organisms associated with a hypersaline seep that depend on methane and sulfur-oxidizing bacteria as producers. The bacteria may live free in the water, on the bottom, or symbiotically in the tissue of some of the animals within the biocommunity.

Hypertonic   Pertaining to the property of an aqueous solution having a higher osmotic pressure (salinity) than another aqueous solution from which it is separated by a semipermeable membrane that will allow

osmosis to occur. The hypertonic fluid will gain water molecules through the membrane from the other fluid.

Hypothesis   A tentative, testable statement about the general nature of the phenomenon observed.

Hypotonic   Pertaining to the property of an aqueous solution having a lower osmotic pressure (salinity) than another aqueous solution from which it is separated by a semipermeable membrane that will allow osmosis to occur. The hypotonic fluid will lose water molecules through the membrane to the other fluid.

Hypsographic curve   A curve that displays the relative elevations of the land surface and depths of the ocean.

Ice Age   The most recent glacial period, which occurred during the Pleistocene Epoch.

Iceberg   A massive piece of glacier ice that has broken from the front of the glacier (calved) into a body of water. It floats with its tip at least 5 meters (16 feet) above the water's surface and at least four-fifths of its mass submerged.

Ice floe   See *floe.*

Ice rafting   (1) The movement of trapped sediment within or on top of ice by flotation. (2) The forcing of some ice flows on top of others as a result of expanding floes running out of open water on which to float as they grow.

Ice sheet   An extensive, relatively flat accumulation of ice.

Igneous rock   One of the three main classes into which all rocks are divided (igneous, metamorphic, and sedimentary). Rock that forms from the solidification of molten or partly molten material (magma).

In situ   In place; *in situ* density of a sample of water is its density at its original depth.

Incidental catch   See *bycatch.*

Indian Ocean Subtropical Gyre   The large, counter-clockwise-flowing subtropical gyre that exists in the Indian Ocean. Also called the *Majid Gyre.*

Inertia   Newton's first law of motion. It states that a body at rest will stay at rest and a body in motion will remain in uniform motion in a straight line unless acted on by some external force.

Infauna   Animals that live buried in the soft substrate (sand or mud).

Infrared radiation   Electromagnetic radiation lying between the wavelengths of 0.8 micrometers (0.000003 inch) and about 1000 micrometers (0.04 inch). It is bounded on the shorter wavelength side by the visible spectrum and on the long side by microwave radiation.

Inner sublittoral zone   The zone on the inner continental shelf, above the intersection with the euphotic zone, where attached plants grow.

Insolation   The rate at which solar radiation is received per unit of surface area at any point at or above Earth's surface.

Integrated Ocean Drilling Program (IODP)   A drilling program that replaced the Ocean Drilling Program in 2003 with a new drill ship that has riser technology, enabling cores to be collected from deep within Earth's interior.

Interface   A surface separating two substances of different properties, such as density, salinity, or temperature. In oceanography, it usually refers to a separation of two layers of water with different densities caused by significant differences in temperature and/or salinity.

Interface wave   An orbital wave that moves along an interface between fluids of different density. An example is ocean surface waves moving along the interface between the atmosphere and the ocean, which is about one thousand times more dense than air.

Interference (wave)   The overlapping of different wave groups, either in phase (constructive interference, which results in larger waves), out of phase (destructive interference, which results in smaller waves), or some combination of the two (mixed interference).

Intermolecular bond   A relatively weak bond that forms between molecules of a given substance. The hydrogen bond and the van der Waals bonds are intermolecular bonds.

Internal wave   A wave that develops below the surface of a fluid, the density of which changes with increased depth. This change may be gradual or occur abruptly at an interface.

International Whaling Commission (IWC)   An international body that was established in 1946 to manage the subsistence and commercial hunting of large whales. In 1986, the IWC passed a ban on commercial whaling in order to allow whales to recover from overhunting and to give researchers time to develop methods for assessing whale populations.

Intertidal zone   The ocean floor within the foreshore region that is covered by the highest normal tides and exposed by the lowest normal tides, including the water environment of tide pools within this region.

Intertropical Convergence Zone (ITCZ)   The global zone where northeast trade winds and southeast trade winds converge. It occurs close to the equator but averages about 5° north latitude in the Pacific and Atlantic Oceans and 7° south latitude in the Indian Ocean.

Intraplate feature   Any feature that occurs within a tectonic plate and not along a plate boundary.

Intrusive rock   An igneous rock such as granite that cools slowly beneath Earth's surface.

Invertebrate   An animal without a backbone.

Ion   An atom that becomes electrically charged by gaining or losing one or more electrons. The loss of electrons produces a positively charged cation, and the gain of electrons produces a negatively charged anion.

Ionic bond   A chemical bond formed as a result of the electrical attraction.

Irminger Current   A warm current that branches off from the Gulf Stream and moves up along the west coast of Iceland.

Iron hypothesis   A hypothesis that states that an effective way of increasing productivity in the ocean is to fertilize the ocean by adding the only nutrient that appears to be lacking—iron. Adding iron to the ocean also increases the amount of carbon dioxide removed from the atmosphere.

Irons   A meteorite consisting essentially of iron, but it may also contain up to 30% nickel.

Island arc   A linear arrangement of islands, many of which are volcanic, usually curved so that the concave side faces a sea separating the islands from a continent. The convex side faces the open ocean and is bounded by a deep-ocean trench.

Island mass effect   An effect that occurs as surface current flows past an island and causes surface water to be carried away from the island on the downcurrent side. This water is replaced in part by upwelling of water on the downcurrent side of the island.

Isohaline   Of the same salinity.

Isopoda   An order of dorsoventrally flattened crustaceans that are mostly scavengers or parasites on other crustaceans or fish.

Isopycnal   Of the same density.

Isostasy   A condition of equilibrium, comparable to buoyancy, by which Earth's brittle crust floats on the plastic mantle.

Isostatic adjustment   The adjustment of crustal material due to isostasy.

Isostatic rebound   The upward movement of crustal material due to isostasy.

Isotherm   A line connecting points of equal temperature.

Isothermal   Of the same temperature.

Isotonic   Pertaining to the property of having equal osmotic pressure. If two such fluids were separated by a semipermeable membrane that will allow osmosis to occur, there would be no net transfer of water molecules across the membrane.

Isotope   One of several atoms of an element that has a different number of neutrons, and therefore a different atomic mass, than the other atoms, or isotopes, of the element.

J

Jellyfish   (1) Free-swimming, umbrella-shaped medusoid members of the cnidarian class Scyphozoa. (2) Also frequently applied to the medusoid forms of other cnidarians.

Jet stream   An easterly moving air mass at an elevation of about 10 kilometers (6 miles). Moving at speeds that can exceed 300 kilometers (185 miles) per hour, the jet stream follows a wavy path in the middle latitudes and influences how far polar air masses may extend into the lower latitudes.

Jetty   A structure built from the shore into a body of water to protect a harbor or a navigable passage from being closed off by the deposition of longshore drift material.

Juan de Fuca Ridge   A divergent plate boundary off the Oregon–Washington coast.

K

K–T event   An extinction event marked by the disappearance of the dinosaurs that occurred 65 million years ago at the boundary between the Cretaceous (K) and Tertiary (T) Periods of geologic time.

Kelp   Large varieties of Phaeophyta (brown algae).

Kelp forest   A extensive bed of various species of macroscopic brown algae that provides a habitat for many other types of marine organisms.

Key   A low, flat island composed of sand or coral debris that accumulates on a reef flat.

Kinetic energy   Energy of motion, which increases as the mass or speed of the object in motion increases.

Knot (kt)   A unit of speed equal to 1 nautical mile per hour, approximately 1.15 statute (land) miles per hour.

Krill   A common name frequently applied to members of crustacean order Euphausiacea (euphausids).

Kuroshio Current   The warm western boundary current of the North Pacific Subtropical Gyre.

Kyoto Protocol   An agreement among 60 nations to voluntarily limit greenhouse gas emissions, signed in 1997 in Kyoto, Japan.

L

La Niña   An event where the surface temperature in the waters of the eastern South Pacific falls below average values. It often follows an El Niño event.

Labrador Current   A cold current flowing south along the coast of Labrador in the northwest Atlantic Ocean.

Lagoon   A shallow stretch of seawater partly or completely separated from the open ocean by an elongate narrow strip of land such as a reef or barrier island.

Laguna Madre   A hypersaline lagoon located landward of Padre Island along the south Texas coast.

Laminar flow   The manner in which a fluid flows in parallel layers or sheets such that the direction of flow at any point does not change with time. Also known as nonturbulent flow.

Land breeze   The seaward flow of air from the land caused by differential cooling of Earth's surface.

Langmuir circulation   A cellular circulation set up by winds that blow consistently in one direction with speeds in excess of 12 kilometers (7.5 miles) per hour. Helical spirals running parallel to the wind direction are alternately clockwise and counterclockwise.

Larva   An embryo that has a different form before it assumes the characteristics of the adult of the species.

Latent heat   The quantity of heat gained or lost per unit of mass as a substance undergoes a change of state (such as liquid to solid) at a given temperature and pressure.

Latent heat of condensation   The heat energy that must be removed from one gram of a substance to convert it from a vapor at a given temperature below its boiling point. For water, it is 585 calories at 20°C.

Latent heat of evaporation   The heat energy that must be added to one gram of a liquid substance to convert it to a vapor at a given temperature below its boiling point. For water, it is 585 calories at 20°C.

Latent heat of freezing   The heat energy that must be removed from one gram of a substance at its melting point to convert it to a solid. For water, it is 80 calories.

Latent heat of melting   The heat energy that must be added to one gram of a substance at its melting point to convert it to a liquid. For water, it is 80 calories.

Latent heat of vaporization   The heat energy that must be added to one gram of a substance at its boiling point to convert it to a vapor. For water, it is 540 calories.

Lateral line system   A sensory system running down both sides of fishes to sense subsonic pressure waves transmitted through ocean water.

Latitude   Location on Earth's surface based on angular distance north or south of the equator. Equator = 0°; North Pole = 90° north; South Pole = 90° south.

Laurasia   An ancient landmass of the Northern Hemisphere. The name is derived from Laurentia, pertaining to the Canadian Shield of North America, and Eurasia, of which it was composed.

Lava   Fluid magma coming from an opening in Earth's surface, or the same material after it solidifies.

Law of gravitation   See *gravitational force*.

Leeuwin Current   A warm current that flows south out of the East Indies along the western coast of Australia.

Leeward   The direction toward which the wind is blowing or waves are moving.

Levee   (1) Natural low ridges on either side of river channels that result from deposition during flooding. (2) Artificial ridges built by humans to control water flow.

Light   Electromagnetic radiation that has a wavelength in the range from about 4000 (violet) to about 7700 (red) angstroms and may be perceived by the normal unaided human eye.

Light-year   The distance traveled by light during one year at a speed of 300,000 kilometers (186,000 miles) per second. It equals 9.8 trillion kilometers (6.2 trillion miles).

Limestone   A class of sedimentary rocks composed of at least 80% carbonates of calcium or magnesium. Limestones may be either biogenous or hydrogenous.

Limpet   A mollusk of the class Gastropoda that possesses a low conical shell that exhibits no spiraling in the adult form.

LIMPET 500   The world's first commercial wave power plant that can generate up to 500 kilowatts of power. It is located on Islay, a small island off the west coast of Scotland, and began generating electricity in November 2000.

Linnaeus, Carolus   Latinized name of Swedish botanist Carl von Linné, the father of taxonomic classification and binomial nomenclature.

Liquid state   A state of matter in which a substance has a fixed volume but no fixed shape.

Lithify   A process by which sediment becomes hardened into sedimentary rock.

Lithogenous sediment   Sediment composed of mineral grains derived from the weathering of rock material and transported to the ocean by various mechanisms of transport, including running water, gravity, the movement of ice, and wind.

Lithosphere   The outer layer of Earth's structure, including the crust and the upper mantle to a depth of about 200 kilometers (124 miles). Lithospheric plates are the major components involved in plate tectonic movement.

Lithothamnion **ridge**   A feature common to the windward edge of a reef structure, characterized by the presence of the red algae *Lithothamnion*.

Littoral zone   The benthic zone between the highest and lowest spring tide shorelines; also known as the intertidal zone.

Lobster   A large marine crustacean considered a delicacy. *Homarus americanus* (American or Maine lobster) possesses two large chelae (pincers) and is found offshore from Labrador to North Carolina. Various species of *Panulirus* (spiny lobsters or rock lobsters) have no chelae but possess long, spiny antennae effective in warding off predators. *P. argus* is found off the coast of Florida and in the West Indies, whereas *P. interruptus* is common along the coast of Southern California.

Longitude   Location on Earth's surface based on angular distance east or west of the Prime (Greenwich) Meridian (0° longitude). 180° longitude is the International Date Line.

Longitudinal wave   A wave phenomenon when particle vibration is parallel to the direction of energy propagation.

Longshore bar   A deposit of sediment that forms parallel to the coast within or just beyond the surf zone.

Longshore current   A current located in the surf zone and running parallel to the shore as a result of waves breaking at an angle to the shore.

Longshore drift   The load of sediment transported along the beach from the breaker zone to the top of the swash line in association with the longshore current. Also called longshore transport or littoral drift.

Longshore trough   A low area of the beach that separates the beach face from the longshore bar.

Lophophore   A horseshoe-shaped feeding structure bearing ciliated tentacles characteristic of the phyla Bryozoa, Brachiopoda, and Phoronidea.

Low slack water   The period of time associated with the peak of low tide when there is no visible flow of water into or out of bays and rivers.

Low tide terrace   See *beach face*.

Low tide zone   The portion of the intertidal zone that lies between the lowest low tide shoreline and the highest low tide shoreline.

Low water (LW)   The lowest level reached by the water surface at low tide before the rise toward high tide begins.

Lower high water (LHW)   The lower of two high waters occurring during a tidal day where tides exhibit a mixed tidal pattern.

Lower low water (LLW)   The lower of two low waters occurring during a tidal day where tides exhibit a mixed tidal pattern.

Lunar day   The time interval between two successive transits of the Moon over a meridian, approximately 24 hours and 50 minutes of solar time. Also called a tidal day.

Lunar month   The time it takes for one orbit of the Moon around Earth; 29½ days Also known as the lunar cycle or synodic month.

Lunar tide   The part of the tide caused solely by the tide-producing force of the Moon.

Lunger   Fish that sit motionless on the ocean floor waiting for prey to appear (for example, grouper). A quick burst of speed over a short distance is used to capture prey.

Lysocline   The level in the ocean at which calcium carbonate begins to dissolve, typically at a depth of about 4000 meters (13,100 feet). Below the lysocline, calcium carbonate dissolves at an increasing rate with increasing depth until the calcite compensation depth (CCD) is reached.

M

Macroplankton   Plankton larger than 2 centimeters (0.8 inch) in their smallest dimension.

Magma   Fluid rock material from which igneous rock is derived through solidification.

Magnetic anomaly   A distortion of the regular pattern of Earth's magnetic field resulting from the various magnetic properties of local concentrations of ferromagnetic minerals in Earth's crust.

Magnetic dip   The dip of magnetite particles in rock units of Earth's crust relative to sea level. It is approximately equivalent to latitude. Also called magnetic inclination.

Magnetic field   A condition found in the region around a magnet or an electric current, characterized by the existence of a detectable magnetic force at every point in the region and by the existence of magnetic poles.

Magnetic inclination   See *magnetic dip*.

Magnetite   The mineral form of black iron oxide, Fe_3O_4, that often occurs with magnesium, zinc, and manganese and is an important ore of iron.

Magnetometer   A device used for measuring the magnetic field of Earth.

Manganese nodule   A concretionary lump containing oxides of manganese, iron, copper, cobalt, and nickel found scattered over the ocean floor.

Mangrove swamp   A marshlike environment dominated by mangrove trees. They are restricted to latitudes below 30°.

Mantle   (1) The zone between the core and crust of Earth; rich in ferromagnesian minerals. (2) In pelecypods, the portion of the body that secretes shell material.

Mantle plume   A rising column of molten magma from Earth's mantle.

Marginal sea   A semi-enclosed body of water adjacent to a continent and floored by submerged continental crust.

Mariculture   The application of the principles of agriculture to the production of marine organisms.

Marine effect   Describes locations that experience the moderating influences of the ocean, usually along coastlines or islands.

Marine Mammals Protection Act   An act by U.S. Congress in 1972 that specifies rules to protect marine mammals in U.S. waters.

Marine Protected Area (MPA)   An area in which there is some level of restriction to protect living, nonliving, cultural, and/or historic resources.

Marine reserve   A type of MPA in which all species and their habitat are fully protected.

Marine sanctuary   A type of MPA in which biologic or cultural resources are protected. In some marine sanctuaries, fishing, recreational boating, and mining are allowed.

Marine terrace   A wave-cut bench that has been exposed above sea level.

MARPOL (Marine Pollution)   An international treaty that banned the disposal of all plastics and regulated the dumping of most other garbage at sea.

Marsh   An area of soft, wet, flat land that is periodically flooded by salt water and common in portions of lagoons.

Maximum sustainable yield (MSY)   The maximum fishery biomass that can be removed yearly and still be sustained by the fishery ecosystem.

Mean high water (MHW)   The average height of all the high waters occurring over a 19-year period.

Mean higher high water (MHHW)   The average height of the daily higher of the high waters occurring over a 19-year period where tides exhibit a mixed tidal pattern.

Mean low water (MLW) The average height of all the low waters occurring over a 19-year period.

Mean lower low water (MLLW) The average height of the daily lower of the low waters occurring over a 19-year period where tides exhibit a mixed tidal pattern.

Mean sea level (MSL) The mean surface water level determined by averaging all stages of the tide over a 19-year period, usually determined from hourly height observations along an open coast.

Mean tidal range The difference between mean high water and mean low water.

Meander A sinuous curve, bend, or turn in the course of a current.

Mechanical energy Energy manifested as work being done; the movement of a mass some distance.

Mediterranean circulation Circulation characteristic of bodies of water with restricted circulation with the ocean that results from an excess of evaporation as compared to precipitation and runoff similar to the Mediterranean Sea. Surface flow is into the restricted body of water with a subsurface counterflow as exists between the Mediterranean Sea and the Atlantic Ocean.

Medusa A free-swimming, bell-shaped cnidaria body form with a mouth at the end of a central projection and tentacles around the periphery.

Meiofauna Small species of animals that live in the spaces among particles in a marine sediment.

Melon A fatty organ located forward of the blowhole on certain odontocete cetaceans that is used to focus echolocation sounds.

Melting point The temperature at which a solid substance changes to the liquid state.

Mercury A silvery white poisonous metallic element, liquid at room temperature and used in thermometers, barometers, vapor lamps, and batteries and in the preparation of chemical pesticides.

Meridian of longitude Great circles running through the North and South Poles.

Meroplankton Planktonic larval forms of organisms that are members of the benthos or nekton as adults.

Mesopelagic zone That portion of the oceanic province 200 to 1000 meters (660 to 3300 feet) deep. Corresponds approximately with the disphotic (twilight) zone.

Mesosaurus An extinct, presumably aquatic, reptile that lived about 250 million years ago. The distribution of its fossil remains helps support plate tectonic theory.

Mesosphere The middle region of Earth below the asthenosphere and above the core.

Metal sulfide A compound containing one or more metals and sulfur.

Metamorphic rock Rock that has undergone recrystallization while in the solid state in response to changes of temperature, pressure, and chemical environment.

Meteor A bright trail or streak that appears in the sky when a meteoroid is heated to incandescence by friction with Earth's atmosphere. Also called a falling or shooting star.

Meteorite A stony or metallic mass of matter that has fallen to Earth's surface from outer space.

Methane hydrate A white compact icy solid made of water and methane. The most common type of gas hydrate.

Microplankton Net plankton. Plankton not easily seen by the unaided eye, but easily recovered from the ocean with the aid of a silk-mesh plankton net.

Mid-Atlantic Ridge A slow-spreading divergent plate boundary running north–south and bisecting the Atlantic Ocean.

Mid-ocean ridge A linear, volcanic mountain range that extends through all the major oceans, rising 1 to 3 kilometers (0.6 to 2 miles) above the deep-ocean basins. Averaging 1500 kilometers (930 miles) in width, rift valleys are common along the central axis. Source of new oceanic crustal material.

Middle tide zone The portion of the intertidal zone that lies between the highest low tide shoreline and the lowest high tide shoreline.

Migration Long journeys undertaken by many marine species for the purpose of successful feeding and reproduction.

Minamata Bay, Japan The site of the occurrence of human poisoning in the 1950s by mercury contained in marine organisms that were consumed by victims.

Minamata disease A degenerative neurological disorder caused by poisoning with a mercury compound found in seafood obtained from waters contaminated with mercury-containing industrial waste.

Mineral An inorganic substance occurring naturally on Earth and having distinctive physical properties and a chemical composition that can be expressed by a chemical formula. The term is also sometimes applied to organic substances such as coal and petroleum.

Mixed interference A pattern of wave interference in which there is a combination of constructive and destructive interference.

Mixed surface layer The surface layer of the ocean water mixed by wave and tide motions to produce relatively isothermal and isohaline conditions.

Mixed tidal pattern A tidal pattern exhibiting two high tides and two low tides per tidal day with a marked diurnal inequality. Coastal locations that experience such a tidal pattern may also show alternating periods of diurnal and semidiurnal patterns. Also called mixed semidiurnal.

Mixotroph An organism that depends on a combination of autotrophic and heterotrophic behavior to meet its energy requirements. Many coral reef species exhibit such behavior.

Mohorovicíc discontinuity (Moho) A sharp compositional discontinuity between the crust and mantle of Earth. It may be as shallow as 5 kilometers (3 miles) below the ocean floor or as deep as 60 kilometers (37 miles) beneath some continental mountain ranges.

Molecular motion Molecules move in three ways: vibration, rotation, and translation.

Molecule A group of two or more atoms bound together by ionic or covalent bonds.

Mollusca A phylum of soft, unsegmented animals usually protected by a calcareous shell and having a muscular foot for locomotion. Includes snails, clams, chitons, and octopi.

Monera A kingdom of organisms that do not have nuclear material confined within a sheath but spread throughout the cell. Includes bacteria, blue-green algae, and Archaea.

Mononodal Pertaining to a standing wave with only one nodal point or nodal line.

Monsoon A name for seasonal winds derived from the Arabic word for season, mausim. The term was originally applied to winds over the Arabian Sea that blow from the southwest during summer and the northeast during winter.

Moraine A deposit of unsorted material deposited at the margins of glaciers. Many such deposits have become important economically as fishing banks after being submerged by the rising level of the ocean.

Mud Sediment consisting primarily of silt and clay-sized particles smaller than 0.06 millimeters (0.002 inch).

Mutualism A symbiotic relationship in which both participants benefit.

Myoglobin A red, oxygen-storing pigment found in muscle tissue.

Mysticeti The baleen whales.

N

Nadir The point on the celestial sphere directly opposite the zenith and directly beneath the observer.

Nannoplankton Plankton less than 50 micrometers (0.002 inch) in length that cannot be captured in a plankton net and must be removed from the water by centrifuge or special microfilters.

Nansen bottle A device used by oceanographers to obtain samples of ocean water from beneath the surface.

National Flood Insurance Program (NFIP) A program financed by the U.S. government that was intended to prevent costly federal aid after a natural disaster but instead encourages building in risk-prone areas.

Natural selection The process in nature by which only the organisms best adapted to their environment tend to survive and transmit their genetic characters in increasing numbers to succeeding generations while those less adapted tend to be eliminated.

Nauplius A microscopic, free-swimming larval stage of crustaceans such as copepods, ostracodes, and decapods. Typically has three pairs of appendages.

Neap tide Tides of minimal range occurring about every two weeks when the Moon is in either first- or third-quarter moon phase.

Nearshore The zone of a beach that extends from the low tide shoreline seaward to where breakers begin forming.

Nebula A diffuse mass of interstellar dust and/or gas.

Nebular hypothesis A model that describes the formation of the solar system by contraction of a nebula.

Nektobenthos Those members of the benthos that can actively swim and spend much time off the bottom.

Nekton Pelagic animals such as adult squids, fish, and mammals that are active swimmers to the extent that they can determine their position in the ocean by swimming.

Nematath   A linear chain of islands and/or seamounts that are progressively older in one direction. It is created by the passage of a lithospheric plate over a hotspot.

Nematocyst   The stinging mechanism found within the cnidoblast of members of the phylum Cnidaria.

Neritic province   That portion of the pelagic environment from the shoreline to where the depth reaches 200 meters (660 feet).

Neritic sediment   That sediment composed primarily of lithogenous particles and deposited relatively rapidly on the continental shelf, continental slope, and continental rise.

Net primary production   The primary production of producers after they have removed what is needed for their metabolism.

Neutral   A state in which there is no excess of either the hydrogen or the hydroxide ion.

Neutron   An electrically neutral subatomic particle found in the nucleus of atoms that has a mass approximately equivalent to that of a proton.

New moon   The phase of the Moon that occurs when the Sun and the Moon are in conjunction; that is, they are both on the same side of Earth. During this time, the dark side of the Moon faces Earth.

New production   Primary production supported by nutrients supplied from outside the immediate ecosystem by upwelling or other physical transport.

Newton's law of universal gravitation   An equation that quantifies gravitational force between two bodies; it states that the gravitational force is directly proportional to the product of the masses of the two bodies and is inversely proportional to the square of the distance between the two masses.

Niche   The ecological role of an organism and its position in the ecosystem.

Niigata, Japan   The site of mercury poisoning of humans in the 1960s by ingestion of contaminated seafood.

Nitrogen narcosis   A sickness that affects divers. It results from too much nitrogen gas being dissolved in the blood and reducing the flow of oxygen to tissues. The threat of this problem increases with increasing pressure (depth).

Node   The point on a standing wave where vertical motion is lacking or minimal. If this condition extends across the surface of an oscillating body of water, the line of no vertical motion is a nodal line.

Non-native species   Species that are introduced into waters in which they are alien and often cause severe problems by displacing native species. Also called exotic, alien, or invasive species.

Non-point-source pollution   Any type of pollution entering the ocean from multiple sources rather than from a single discrete source, point, or location. Examples include urban runoff, trash, pet waste, lawn fertilizer, or other types of pollution generated by a multitude of sources. Also called poison runoff.

North Atlantic Current   The northernmost current of the North Atlantic Subtropical Gyre.

North Atlantic Deep Water   A deep-water mass that forms primarily at the surface of the Norwegian Sea and moves south along the floor of the North Atlantic Ocean.

North Atlantic Subtropical Gyre   The large, clockwise-flowing subtropical gyre that exists in the North Atlantic Ocean. Also called the *Columbus Gyre*.

North-East Pacific Time-series Undersea Networked Experiments (NEPTUNE)   A cutting-edge sea floor observatory system designed to monitor tectonic activity along the Juan de Fuca tectonic plate in the northeast Pacific Ocean.

North Pacific Current   The northernmost current of the North Pacific Subtropical Gyre.

North Pacific Subtropical Gyre   The large, clockwise-flowing subtropical gyre that exists in the North Pacific Ocean. Also called the *Turtle Gyre*.

Northern boundary current   The northern boundary current of Northern Hemisphere subtropical gyres.

Northeast Monsoon   A northeast wind that blows off the Asian mainland onto the Indian Ocean during the winter season.

Norwegian Current   A warm current that branches off from the Gulf Stream and flows into the Norwegian Sea between Iceland and the British Isles.

Nucleus   The positively charged central region of an atom, composed of protons and neutrons and containing almost all of the mass of the atom.

Nudibranch   A sea slug. A member of the mollusk class Gastropoda that has no protective covering as an adult. Respiration is carried on by gills or other projections on the dorsal surface.

Nutrient   Any of a number of organic or inorganic compounds used by primary producers. Nitrogen and phosphorus compounds are important examples.

O

Observation   An occurrence that can be measured with one's senses.

Ocean   The entire body of salt water that covers more than 71% of Earth's surface.

Ocean acidification   The process by which the ocean's pH is lowered, which increases its acidity.

Ocean acoustical tomography   A method by which changes in water temperature may be determined by changes in the speed of transmission of sound. It has the potential to help map ocean circulation patterns over large ocean areas.

Ocean beach   The beach on the open-ocean side of a barrier island.

Ocean Drilling Program (ODP)   A program that replaced the Deep Sea Drilling Project in 1983, focusing on drilling the continental margins using the drill ship *JOIDES Resolution*.

Ocean thermal energy conversion (OTEC)   A technique that involves generating energy by using the difference in temperature between surface waters and deep waters in low latitude regions.

Oceanic Common Water   Deep water found in Pacific and Indian Oceans as a result of mixing of Antarctic Bottom Water and North Atlantic Deep Water.

Oceanic crust   A mass of rock with a basaltic composition that is about 5 kilometers (3 miles) thick.

Oceanic province   The division of the pelagic environment where the water depth is greater than 200 meters (660 feet).

Oceanic ridge   A portion of the global mid-ocean ridge system that is characterized by slow spreading and steep slopes.

Oceanic rise   A portion of the global mid-ocean ridge system that is characterized by fast spreading and gentle slopes.

Oceanic sediment   The inorganic abyssal clays and the organic oozes that accumulate slowly on the deep-ocean floor.

Ocelli   A light-sensitive organ around the base of many medusoid bells.

Odontoceti   The toothed whales.

Offset   Separation that occurs due to movement along a fault.

Offshore   The comparatively flat submerged zone of variable width extending from the breaker line to the edge of the continental shelf.

Oligotrophic   Exhibiting low levels of biological production, such as the centers of subtropical gyres.

Omnivore   An animal that feeds on both plants and animals.

Oolite   A deposit formed of small spheres from 0.25 to 2 millimeters (0.01 to 0.08 inch) in diameter. They are usually composed of concentric layers of calcite.

Ooze   A pelagic sediment containing at least 30% skeletal remains of pelagic organisms, the balance being clay minerals. Oozes are further defined by the chemical composition of the organic remains (siliceous or calcareous) and by their characteristic organisms (e.g., diatomaceous ooze, foraminifer ooze).

Opal   An amorphous form of silica ($SiO_2 \cdot nH_2O$) that usually contains from 3 to 9% water. It forms the shells of radiolarians and diatoms.

Opposition   The separation of two heavenly bodies by 180° relative to Earth. The Sun and Moon are in opposition during the full moon phase.

Orbital wave   A wave phenomenon in which energy is moved along the interface between fluids of different densities. The wave form is propagated by the movement of fluid particles in orbital paths.

Orthogonal line   A line constructed perpendicular to a wave front and spaced so that the energy between lines is equal at all times. Orthogonals are used to help determine how energy is distributed along the shoreline by breaking waves.

Osmosis   Passage of water molecules through a semipermeable membrane separating two aqueous solutions of different solute concentration. The water molecules pass from the solution of lower solute concentration into the other.

Osmotic pressure   A measure of the tendency for osmosis to occur. It is the pressure that must be applied to the more concentrated solution to prevent the passage of water molecules into it from the less concentrated solution.

Osmotic regulation   Physical and biological processes used by organisms to counteract the osmotic effects of differences in osmotic pressures of their body fluids and the water in which they live.

Ostracoda   An order of crustaceans that are minute and compressed within a bivalve shell.

Otocyst   Gravity-sensitive organs around the bell of a medusa.

Outer sublittoral zone   The continental shelf below the intersection with the euphotic zone where no plants grow attached to the bottom.

Outgassing The process by which gases are removed from within Earth's interior.

Overfishing A situation that occurs when adult fish in a population are harvested faster than their natural rate of reproduction.

Oxygen compensation depth The depth in the ocean at which marine plants receive just enough solar radiation to meet their basic metabolic needs. It marks the base of the euphotic zone.

Oxygen minimum layer (OML) A zone of low dissolved oxygen concentration that occurs at a depth of about 700 to 1000 meters (2300 to 3280 feet).

P

Pacific Decadal Oscillation (PDO) A natural oscillation in the Pacific Ocean that lasts 20 to 30 years and appears to influence sea surface temperatures.

Pacific Ring of Fire An extensive zone of volcanic and seismic activity that coincides roughly with the borders of the Pacific Ocean.

Pacific-type margin See *active margin*.

Paleoceanography The study of how the ocean, atmosphere, and land have interacted to produce changes in ocean chemistry, circulation, biology, and climate.

Paleogeography The study of the historical changes of shapes and positions of the continents and oceans.

Paleomagnetism The study of Earth's ancient magnetic field.

Pancake ice Circular pieces of newly formed sea ice from 0.3 to 3 meters (1 to 10 feet) in diameter that form in the early fall in polar regions.

Pangaea An ancient supercontinent of the geologic past that contained all Earth's continents.

Panthalassa A large, ancient ocean that surrounded Pangaea.

Paralytic shellfish poisoning (PSP) Paralysis resulting from poisoning caused by eating shellfish contaminated with the toxic dinoflagellate *Gonyaulax*.

Parasitism A symbiotic relationship between two organisms in which one benefits at the expense of the other.

Parts per thousand (‰) A unit of measurement used in reporting salinity of water equal to the number of grams of dissolved substances in 1000 grams of water. For example, 1‰ is equivalent to 0.1%, or 1000 ppm.

Passive margin A continental margin that lacks a plate boundary and is marked by a low degree of tectonic activity, such as those typical of the Atlantic Ocean.

PCBs A group of industrial chemicals (polychlorinated biphenyls) used in a variety of products; responsible for several episodes of ecological damage in coastal waters.

Peat deposit Partially carbonized organic matter found in bogs and marshes that can be used as fertilizer and fuel.

Pelagic environment The open ocean environment, which is divided into the neritic province (water depth 0 to 200 meters or 656 feet) and the oceanic province (water depth greater than 200 meters or 656 feet).

Pelecypoda A class of mollusks characterized by two more or less symmetrical lateral valves with a dorsal hinge. These filter feeders pump water through the filter system and over gills through posterior siphons. Many possess a hatchet-shaped foot used for locomotion and burrowing. Includes clams, oysters, mussels, and scallops.

Perigee The point on the orbit of an Earth satellite (Moon) that is nearest Earth.

Perihelion That point on the orbit of a planet or comet around the Sun that is closest to the Sun.

Permeability Capacity of a porous rock or sediment for transmitting fluid.

Peru Current The cold eastern boundary current of the South Pacific Subtropical Gyre.

Petroleum A naturally occurring liquid hydrocarbon.

Pfiesteria piscicida A species of toxic dinoflagellate that has been known to cause fish kills.

pH scale A measure of the acidity or alkalinity of a solution, numerically equal to 7 for neutral solutions, increasing with increasing alkalinity and decreasing with increasing acidity. The pH scale commonly in use ranges from 0 to 14.

Phaeophyta Brown algae characterized by the carotenoid pigment fucoxanthin. Contains the largest members of the marine algal community.

Phosphate Any of a number of phosphorus-bearing compounds.

Phosphorite A sedimentary rock composed primarily of phosphate minerals.

Photic zone The upper ocean in which the presence of solar radiation is detectable. It includes the euphotic and disphotic zones.

Photophore One of several types of light-producing organs found primarily on fishes and squids inhabiting the mesopelagic and upper bathypelagic zones.

Photosynthesis The process by which plants and algae produce carbohydrates from carbon dioxide and water in the presence of chlorophyll, using light energy and releasing oxygen.

Phycoerythrin A red pigment characteristic of the Rhodophyta (red algae).

Phytoplankton Algal plankton. One of the most important communities of primary producers in the ocean.

Picoplankton Small plankton within the size range of 0.2 to 2.0 micrometers (0.000008 to 0.00008 inch) in size. Composed primarily of bacteria.

Pillow basalt A basalt exhibiting pillow structure. See *pillow lava*.

Pillow lava A general term for those lavas displaying discontinuous pillow-shaped masses (pillow structure) caused by the rapid cooling of lava as a result of underwater eruption of lava or lava flowing into water.

Ping A sharp, high-pitched sound made by the transmitting device of many sonar systems.

Pinniped A group of marine mammals that have prominent flippers; includes the sea lions/fur seals, seals, and walruses.

Planker Informal term for plankton.

Plankton Passively drifting or weakly swimming organisms that are not independent of currents. Includes mostly microscopic algae, protozoa, and larval forms of higher animals.

Plankton bloom A very high concentration of phytoplankton, resulting from a rapid rate of reproduction as conditions become optimal during the spring in high latitude areas. Less obvious causes produce blooms that may be destructive in other areas.

Plankton net A plankton-extracting device that is cone shaped and typically of a silk material. It is towed through the water or lifted vertically to extract plankton down to a size of 50 micrometers (0.0002 inch).

Plantae A kingdom of many-celled plants.

Plastic (1) Capable of being shaped or formed. (2) Composed of plastic or plastics.

Plate tectonics Global dynamics having to do with the movement of a small number of semirigid sections of Earth's crust, with seismic activity and volcanism occurring primarily at the margins of these sections. This movement has resulted in changes in the geographic positions of continents and the shape and size of ocean basins.

Plume A rising column of molten mantle material that is associated with a hotspot when it penetrates Earth's crust.

Plunging breaker Impressive curling breakers that form on moderately sloping beaches.

Pneumatic duct An opening into the swim bladder of some fishes that allows rapid release of air into the esophagus.

Poikilothermic An organism whose body temperature varies with and is largely controlled by its environment; cold-blooded.

Polar Pertaining to the polar regions.

Polar cell The large atmospheric circulation cell that occurs between 60° and 90° latitude in each hemisphere.

Polar easterly wind belt Global wind belt that moves away from the polar regions toward the polar front at about 60° north or south latitude in each hemisphere. They move from a northeasterly direction in the Northern Hemisphere and from a southeasterly direction in the Southern Hemisphere.

Polar front The boundary between the global wind belts' prevailing westerlies and polar easterlies that is centered at about 60° latitude in each hemisphere and is characterized by rising air and much precipitation.

Polar high The region of high atmospheric pressure that occurs at the poles in both hemispheres.

Polar wandering curve A curve that shows the change in the position of a pole through time.

Polarity Intrinsic polar separation, alignment, or orientation, especially of a physical property (such as magnetic or electrical polarity).

Pollution (marine) The introduction of substances that result in harm to the living resources of the ocean or humans who use these resources.

Polychaeta A class of annelid worms that includes most of the marine segmented worms.

Polyp A single individual of a colony or a solitary attached cnidarian.

Population A group of individuals of one species living in an area.

Porifera A phylum of sponges. Supporting structure composed of $CaCO_3$ or SiO_2 spicules or fibrous spongin. Water currents created by flagella-waving choanocytes enter tiny pores, pass through canals, and exit through a larger osculum.

Porosity The ratio of the volume of all the empty spaces in a material to the volume of the whole.

Potential energy The energy of a particle or system of particles derived from position, or condition, rather than motion.

Precession Describes the change in the attitude of the Moon's orbit around Earth as it slowly changes its direction. The cycle is completed every 18.6 years and is accompanied by a clockwise rotation of the plane of the Moon's orbit that is completed in the same time interval.

Precipitate To cause a solid substance to be separated from a solution, usually due to a change in physical or chemical conditions.

Precipitation In a meteorological sense, the discharge of water in the form of rain, snow, hail, or sleet from the atmosphere onto Earth's surface.

Prevailing westerly wind belt Global wind belt that moves from the subtropical high-pressure belts at about 30° north or south latitude toward the polar front at about 60° north or south latitude. They move from a southwesterly direction in the Northern Hemisphere and from a northwesterly direction in the Southern Hemisphere.

Primary productivity The rate at which energy is stored by organisms through the formation of organic matter (carbon-based compounds) using energy derived from solar radiation (photosynthesis) or chemical reactions (chemosynthesis).

Prime meridian The meridian of longitude 0° used as a reference for measuring longitude that passes through the Royal Observatory at Greenwich, England. Also known as the Greenwich Meridian.

Producer The autotrophic component of an ecosystem that produces the food that supports the biocommunity.

Productivity See *primary productivity*.

Progressive wave A wave in which the waveform progressively moves.

Propagation The transmission of energy through a medium.

Protein A very complex organic compound made up of large numbers of amino acids. Proteins make up a large percentage of the dry weight of all living organisms.

Protoctista A kingdom of organisms that includes any of the unicellular eukaryotic organisms and their descendant multicellular organisms. Includes single-celled and multicelled marine algae as well as single-celled animals called protozoa.

Protoearth The young, early developing Earth.

Proton A positively charged subatomic particle found in the nucleus of atoms that has a mass approximately equivalent to that of a neutron.

Protoplanet Any planet that is in its early stages of development.

Protoplasm The self-perpetuating living material making up all organisms, mostly consisting of the elements carbon, hydrogen, and oxygen combined into various chemical forms.

Protozoa A phylum of one-celled animals with nuclear material confined within a nuclear sheath.

Proxigean A tidal condition of extremely large tidal range that occurs when spring tides coincide with perigee. Also called "closest of the close moon" tides.

Pseudopodia An extension of protoplasm in a broad, flat, or long needlelike projection used for locomotion or feeding. Typical of amoeboid forms such as foraminifers and radiolarians.

Pteropoda An order of pelagic gastropods in which the foot is modified for swimming and the shell may be present or absent.

Purse seine net A style of large fishing net that resembles a purse. It is set around a grouping of organisms (such as tuna) and the bottom is drawn tight to capture the organisms.

Pycnocline A layer of water in which a high rate of change in density in the vertical dimension is present.

Pyrrophyta A phylum of dinoflagellates that possess flagella for locomotion.

Q

Quadrature The state of the Moon during the first- and third-quarter moon phases when the Sun and the Moon are at right angles relative to Earth.

Quarter moon First- and third-quarter moon phases, which occur when the Moon is in quadrature about one week after the new moon and full moon phases, respectively. The third-quarter moon phase is also known as the last quarter moon phase.

Quartz A very hard mineral composed of silica, SiO_2.

R

Radiata A grouping of phyla with primary radial symmetry—phyla Cnidarian and Ctenophora.

Radioactivity The spontaneous breakdown of the nucleus of an atom resulting in the emission of radiant energy in the form of particles or waves.

Radiolaria An order of planktonic and benthic protozoans that possess protective coverings usually made of silica.

Radiometric age dating A technique that involves the use of radioactive half-lives to determine the age of a rock.

Ray A cartilaginous fish in which the body is dorsoventrally flattened, eyes and spiracles are on the upper surface, and gill slits are on the bottom. The tail is reduced to a whiplike appendage. Includes electric rays, manta rays, and stingrays.

Recreational beach The area of a beach above shoreline, including the berm, berm crest, and the exposed part of the beach face.

Red clay See *abyssal clay*.

Red muscle fiber Fine muscle fibers rich in myoglobin that are abundant in cruiser-type fishes.

Red tide A reddish-brown discoloration of surface water, usually in coastal areas, caused by high concentrations of microscopic organisms, usually dinoflagellates. It probably results from increased availability of certain nutrients. Toxins produced by the dinoflagellates may kill fish directly; decaying plant and animal remains or large populations of animals that migrate to the area of abundant plants may also deplete the surface waters of oxygen and cause asphyxiation of many animals.

Reef A strip or ridge of rocks, sand, coral, or human-made objects that rises to or near the surface of the ocean and creates a navigational hazard.

Reef flat A platform of coral fragments and sand on the lagoonal side of a reef that is relatively exposed at low tide.

Reef front The upper seaward face of a reef from the reef edge (seaward margin of reef flat) to the depth at which living coral and coralline algae become rare, 16 to 30 meters (50 to 100 feet).

Reflection (wave) The process in which a wave has part of its energy returned seaward by a reflecting surface.

Refraction (wave) The process by which the part of a wave in shallow water is slowed down, causing the wave to bend and align itself nearly parallel to the shore.

Regenerated production The portion of gross primary production that is supported by nutrients recycled within an ecosystem.

Relict beach A beach deposit laid down and submerged by a rise in sea level. It is still identifiable on the continental shelf, indicating that no deposition is presently taking place at that location on the shelf.

Relict sediment A sediment deposited under a set of environmental conditions that still remains unchanged although the environment has changed, and it remains unburied by later sediment. An example is a beach deposited near the edge of the continental shelf when sea level was lower.

Relocation The strategy of moving a structure that is threatened by being claimed by the sea.

Residence time The average length of time a particle of any substance spends in the ocean. It is calculated by dividing the total amount of the substance in the ocean by the rate of its introduction into the ocean or the rate at which it leaves the ocean.

Respiration The process by which organisms use organic materials (food) as a source of energy. As the energy is released, oxygen is used and carbon dioxide and water are produced.

Restoring force A force such as surface tension or gravity that tends to restore the ocean surface displaced by a wave to that of a still water level.

Resultant force The difference between the provided gravitational force of various bodies and the required centripetal force on Earth. The horizontal component of the resultant force is the tide-producing force.

Reverse osmosis A method of desalinating ocean water that involves forcing water molecules through a water-permeable membrane under pressure.

Reversing current The tide current as it occurs at the margins of landmasses. The water flows in and out for approximately equal periods of time separated by slack water where the water is still at high and low tidal extremes.

Rhodophyta A phylum of algae composed primarily of small encrusting, branching, or filamentous plants that receive their characteristic red color from the presence of the pigment phycoerythrin. With a worldwide distribution, they are found at greater depths than other algae.

Rift valley A deep fracture or break, about 25 to 50 kilometers (15 to 30 miles) wide, extending along the crest of a mid-ocean ridge.

Rifting The movement of two plates in opposite directions such as along a divergent boundary.

Right whale A surface-feeding baleen whale of the family Balaenidae that were a favorite target of early whalers.

Rip current A strong narrow surface or near-surface current of short duration and high speed flowing seaward through the breaker zone at nearly right angles to the shore. It represents the return to the ocean of water that has been piled up on the shore by incoming waves.

Rip-rap Large blocky material used to armor coastal structures.

Rogue wave An unusually large wave that occurs unexpectedly amid other waves of smaller size. Also known as a superwave, monster wave, sleeper wave, or freak wave.

Rorqual whale A large baleen whale with prominent ventral groves (rorqual folds) of the family Balaenopteridae: the minke, Baird's, Bryde's, sei, fin, blue, and humpback whales.

Rotary current A tidal current that is observed in the open ocean and makes one complete rotation during a tidal period.

Rotary drilling Drilling involving the use of a long, hollow pipe with a drill bit on its end that is rotated to crush the rock around the outside and retain a cylinder of rock (a core sample) on the inside of the pipe.

S

Saffir-Simpson scale A scale of hurricane intensity that divides tropical cyclones into categories based on wind speed and damage.

Salinity A measure of the quantity of dissolved solids in ocean water. Formally, it is the total amount of dissolved solids in ocean water in parts per thousand (‰) by weight after all carbonate has been converted to oxide, the bromide and iodide to chloride, and all the organic matter oxidized. It is normally computed from conductivity, refractive index, or chlorinity.

Salinometer An instrument that is used to determine the salinity of seawater by measuring its electrical conductivity.

Salpa A genus of pelagic tunicates that are cylindrical, transparent, and found in all oceans.

Salt A substance that yields ions other than hydrogen or hydroxyl. Salts are produced from acids by replacing the hydrogen with a metal.

Salt marsh A relatively flat area of the shore where fine sediment is deposited and salt-tolerant grasses grow. One of the most biologically productive regions of Earth.

Salt wedge estuary A very deep river mouth with a very large volume of freshwater flow beneath which a wedge of saltwater from the ocean invades. The Mississippi River is an example.

San Andreas Fault A transform fault that cuts across the state of California from the northern end of the Gulf of California to Point Arena north of San Francisco.

Sand Particle size of 0.0625 to 2 millimeters (0.002 to 0.08 inch). It pertains to particles that lie between silt and granules on the Wentworth scale of grain size.

Sargasso Sea A region of convergence in the North Atlantic lying south and east of Bermuda where the water is a very clear, deep blue color, and contains large quantities of floating *Sargassum*.

Sargassum A brown alga characterized by a bushy form, substantial holdfast when attached, and a yellow-brown, green-yellow, or orange color. The two dominant species of macroscopic algae in the Sargasso Sea are *S. fluitans* and *S. natans*.

Scarp A linear steep slope on the ocean floor separating gently sloping or flat surfaces.

Scavenger An animal that feeds on dead organisms.

Schooling A well-defined large groups of fish, squid, and crustaceans that apparently aid them in survival.

Scientific method The principles and empirical processes of discovery and demonstration considered characteristic of or necessary for scientific investigation, generally involving the observation of phenomena, the formulation of a hypothesis concerning the phenomena, experimentation to demonstrate the truth or falseness of the hypothesis, and a conclusion that validates or modifies the hypothesis.

Scuba An acronym for *s*elf-*c*ontained *u*nderwater *b*reathing *a*pparatus, a portable device containing compressed air that is used for breathing underwater.

Scyphozoa A class of cnidarians that includes the true jellyfish in which the medusoid body form predominates and the polyp is reduced or absent.

Sea (1) A subdivision of an ocean, generally enclosed by land and usually composed of salt water. Two types of seas are identifiable and defined. They are the Mediterranean seas, where a number of seas are grouped together collectively as one sea, and adjacent seas, which are connected individually to the ocean. (2) A portion of the ocean where waves are being generated by wind.

Sea anemone A member of the class Anthozoa whose bright color, tentacles, and general appearance make it resemble flowers.

Sea arch An opening through a headland caused by wave erosion. Usually develops as sea caves are extended from one or both sides of the headland.

Sea breeze The landward flow of air from the sea caused by differential heating of Earth's surface.

Sea cave A cavity at the base of a sea cliff formed by wave erosion.

Sea cow See *Sirenia*.

Sea cucumber A common name given to members of the echinoderm class Holotheuroidea.

Sea floor spreading A process producing the lithosphere when convective upwelling of magma along the oceanic ridges moves the ocean floor away from the ridge axes at rates between 2 to 12 centimeters (0.8 to 5 inches) per year.

Sea ice A form of ice originating from the freezing of ocean water.

Sea lion Any of several eared seals with a relatively long neck and large front flippers, especially the California sea lion *Zalophus californianus* of the northern Pacific. Along with the fur seals, these marine mammals are known as eared seals.

Sea otter A seagoing otter that has recovered from near extinction along the North Pacific coasts. It feeds primarily on abalone, sea urchins, and crustaceans.

Sea snake A reptile belonging to the family Hydrophiidae with venom similar to that of cobras. They are found primarily in the coastal waters of the Indian Ocean and the western Pacific Ocean.

Sea stack An isolated, pillarlike rocky island that is detached from a headland by wave erosion.

Sea turtle Any of the reptilian order Testudinata found widely in warm water.

Sea urchin An echinoderm belonging to the class Echinoidea possessing a fused test (external covering) and well-developed spines.

Seaknoll See *abyssal hill*.

Seal (1) Any of several earless seals with a relatively short neck and small front flippers. Also known as true seals. (2) A general term that describes any of the various aquatic, carnivorous marine mammals of the families Phocidae and Otariidae (true seals and eared seals), found chiefly in the Northern Hemisphere and having a sleek, torpedo-shaped body and limbs that are modified into paddlelike flippers.

Seamount An individual volcanic peak extending over 1000 meters (3300 feet) above the surrounding ocean floor.

Seasonal thermocline A thermocline that develops due to surface heating of the oceans in middle to high latitudes. The base of the seasonal thermocline is usually above 200 meters (656 feet).

Seawall A wall built parallel to the shore to protect coastal property from the waves.

SeaWiFS An instrument aboard the SeaStar satellite launched in 1997 that measures the color of the ocean with a radiometer and provides global coverage of ocean chlorophyll levels as well as land productivities every two days.

Secchi disk A light-colored disk-shaped device that is lowered into water in order to measure the water's ability to transmit light.

Sediment Particles of organic or inorganic origin that accumulate in loose form.

Sediment maturity A condition in which the roundness and degree of sorting increase and clay content decreases within a sedimentary deposit.

Sedimentary rock Rock resulting from the consolidation of loose sediment, or rock resulting from chemical precipitation, such as sandstone and limestone.

Seep An area where water of various temperature trickles out of the sea floor.

Seiche A standing wave of an enclosed or semienclosed body of water that may have a period ranging from a few minutes to a few hours, depending on the dimensions of the basin. The wave motion continues after the initiating force has ceased.

Seismic Pertaining to an earthquake or Earth vibration, including those that are artificially induced.

Seismic moment magnitude (M_w) A scale used for measuring earthquake intensity based on energy released in creating very long-period seismic waves.

Seismic sea wave See *tsunami*.

Seismic surveying The use of sound-generating techniques to identify features on or beneath the ocean floor.

Semidiurnal tidal pattern A tidal pattern exhibiting two high tides and two low tides per tidal day with small inequalities between successive highs and successive lows; a semidaily tide.

Sessile Permanently attached to the substrate and not free to move about.

Sewage sludge The semisolid material precipitated by sewage treatment.

Shallow-water wave A wave on the surface having a wavelength of at least 20 times water depth. The bottom affects the orbit of water particles and speed is determined by water depth.

Shelf break The depth at which the gentle slope of the continental shelf steepens appreciably. It marks the boundary between the continental shelf and continental rise.

Shelf ice Thick shelves of glacial ice that push out into Antarctic seas from Antarctica. Large tabular icebergs calve at the edge of these vast shelves.

Shoaling To become shallow.

Shore The area seaward of the coast, which extends from the highest level of wave action during storms to the low water line.

Shoreline The line marking the intersection of water surface with the shore. Migrates up and down as the tide rises and falls.

Side-scan sonar A method of mapping the topography of the ocean floor along a strip up to 60 kilometers (37 miles) wide using computers and sonar signals that are directed away from both sides of the survey ship.

Silica Silicon dioxide (SiO_2).

Silicate A mineral whose crystal structure contains SiO_4 tetrahedra.

Siliceous A condition of containing abundant silica (SiO_2).

Sill A submarine ridge partially separating bodies of water such as fjords and seas from one another or from the open ocean.

Silt A particle size of 0.008 to 0.0625 millimeter (0.0003 to 0.002 inch). It is intermediate in size between sand and clay.

Siphonophora An order of hydrozoan cnidarians that form pelagic colonies containing both polyps and medusae. An example is *Physalia*.

Sirenia An order of large, vegetarian marine mammals that includes dugongs and manatees, which are also known as sea cows.

Slack water A situation that occurs when a reversing tidal current changes direction at high tide (high slack water) or low tide (low slack water). During slack water, the current speed is zero.

Slick A smooth patch on an otherwise rippled surface caused by a monomolecular film of organic material that reduces surface tension.

Slightly stratified estuary An estuary of moderate depth in which marine water invades beneath the freshwater runoff. The two water masses mix so the bottom water is slightly saltier than the surface water at most places in the estuary.

SOFAR channel An acronym for the *sound fixing and ranging* channel, which is a low-velocity sound travel zone that coincides with the permanent thermocline in low and middle latitudes.

Solar day The 24-hour period during which Earth completes one rotation on its axis.

Solar distillation A process by which ocean water can be desalinated by evaporation and the condensation of the vapor on the cover of a container. The condensate then runs into a separate container and is collected as freshwater. Also called solar humidification.

Solar humidification See *solar distillation*.

Solar system The Sun and the celestial bodies, asteroids, planets, and comets that orbit around it.

Solar tide The partial tide caused by the tide-producing forces of the Sun.

Solid state A state of matter in which the substance has a fixed volume and shape. A crystalline state of matter.

Solstice The time during which the Sun is directly over one of the tropics. In the Northern Hemisphere the summer solstice occurs on June 21 or 22 as the Sun is over the Tropic of Cancer, and the winter solstice occurs on December 21 or 22 when the Sun is over the Tropic of Capricorn.

Solute A substance dissolved in a solution. Salts are the solute in saltwater.

Solution A state in which a solute is homogeneously mixed with a liquid solvent. Water is the solvent for the solution that is ocean water.

Solvent A liquid that has one or more solutes dissolved in it.

Somali Current A current that flows north along the Somali coast of Africa during the southwest monsoon season.

Sonar An acronym for *sound navigation and ranging*, a method using sound that allows the distance of objects to be determined in the ocean.

Sorting A texture of sediments, where a well-sorted sediment is characterized by having great uniformity of grain sizes.

Sounding A measured depth of water beneath a ship.

South Atlantic Subtropical Gyre The large, counterclockwise-flowing subtropical gyre that exists in the South Atlantic Ocean. Also called the *Navigator Gyre*.

South Pacific Subtropical Gyre The large, counterclockwise-flowing subtropical gyre that exists in the South Pacific Ocean. Also called the *Heyerdahl Gyre*.

Southern boundary current The southern boundary current of Southern Hemisphere subtropical gyres.

Southern Oscillation The periodic change in the pressure differential between the Southeastern Pacific high pressure and the Western Pacific equatorial low pressure that occurs in concert with El Niño–Southern Oscillation events.

Southwest Monsoon A southwest wind that develops during the summer season. It blows off the Indian Ocean onto the Asian mainland.

Southwest Monsoon Current During the southwest monsoon season, an eastward-flowing current that replaces the west-flowing North Equatorial Current in the Indian Ocean.

Space dust Micrometeoroid space debris.

Species A fundamental category of taxonomic classification, ranking below a genus or subgenus and consisting of related organisms capable of interbreeding.

Species diversity The number or variety of species found in a subdivision of the marine environment.

Specific gravity The ratio of density of a given substance to that of pure water at 4°C and at one atmosphere pressure.

Specific heat The amount of heat energy required to raise the temperature of 1 gram of a substance by 1°C. Also known as specific heat capacity.

Spermaceti organ A large fatty organ located within the head region of sperm whales (*Physeter macrocephalus*) that is used to focus echolocation sounds.

Spermatophyta See *Anthophyta*.

Spherule A cosmogenous microscopic globular mass composed of silicate rock material (tektites) or of iron and nickel.

Spicule A minute, needlelike calcareous or siliceous projection found in sponges, radiolarians, chitons, and echinoderms that acts to support the tissue or provide a protective covering.

Spilling breaker A type of breaking wave that forms on a gently sloping beach, which gradually extracts the energy from the wave to produce a turbulent mass of air and water that runs down the front slope of the wave.

Spit A small point, low tongue, or narrow embankment of land commonly consisting of sand deposited by longshore currents and having one end attached to the mainland and the other terminating in open water.

Splash wave A long-wavelength wave created by a massive object or series of objects falling into water; a type of tsunami.

Sponge See *Porifera*.

Spray zone The shore zone lying between the high tide shoreline and the coastline. It is covered by water only during storms.

Spreading center A divergent plate boundary.

Spreading rate The rate of divergence of plates at a spreading center.

Spring bloom A middle-latitude bloom of phytoplankton that occurs during the spring and is limited by the availability of nutrients.

Spring equinox See *vernal equinox*.

Spring tide A tide of maximum range occurring about every two weeks when the Moon is in either new or full moon phase.

Stack An isolated mass of rock projecting from the ocean off the end of a headland from which it has been separated by wave erosion.

Standard seawater Ampules of ocean water for which the chlorinity has been determined by the Institute of Oceanographic Services in Wormly, England. The ampules are sent to laboratories all over the world so that equipment and reagents used to determine the salinity of ocean water samples can be calibrated by adjustment until they give the same chlorinity as is shown on the ampule label.

Standing stock (crop) The mass of fishery organisms present in an ecosystem at a given time.

Standing wave A wave, the form of which oscillates vertically without progressive movement. The region of maximum vertical motion is an antinode. On either side are nodes, where there is no vertical motion but maximum horizontal motion.

Stenohaline Pertaining to organisms that can withstand only a small range of salinity change.

Stenothermal Pertaining to organisms that can withstand only a small range of temperature change.

Stick chart A device made of sticks or pieces of bamboo that was used by early navigators at sea.

Still water level The horizontal surface halfway between crest and trough of a wave. If there were no waves, the water surface would exist at this level. Also known as zero energy level.

Storm An atmospheric disturbance characterized by strong winds accompanied by precipitation and often by thunder and lightning.

Storm surge A rise above normal water level resulting from wind stress and reduced atmospheric pressure during storms. Consequences can be more severe if it occurs in association with high tide.

Strait of Gibraltar The narrow opening between Europe and Africa through which the waters of the Atlantic Ocean and Mediterranean Sea mix.

Stranded beach An ancient beach deposit found above present sea level because of a lowering of sea level.

Streamlining The shaping of an object so it produces the minimum of turbulence while moving through a fluid medium. The teardrop shape displays a high degree of streamlining.

Stromatolite A calcium carbonate sedimentary structure in which algal assemblages trap sediment and bind it into forms that are often dome shaped. They are known to form only in shallow-water environments.

Subduction The process by which one lithospheric plate descends beneath another as they converge.

Subduction zone A long, narrow region beneath Earth's surface in which subduction takes place.

Subduction zone seep biocommunity Animals that live in association with seeps of pore water squeezed out of deeper sediments. They depend on sulfur-oxidizing bacteria that act as producers for the ecosystem.

Submarine canyon A steep, V-shaped canyon cut into the continental shelf or slope.

Submarine fan See *deep-sea fan*.

Submerged dune topography Ancient coastal dune deposits found submerged beneath the present shoreline because of a rise in sea level or submergence of the coast.

Submerging shoreline A shoreline formed by the relative submergence of a landmass in which the shoreline is on landforms developed under subaerial processes. It is characterized by bays and promontories and is more irregular than a shoreline of emergence.

Subneritic province The benthic environment extending from the shoreline across the continental shelf to the shelf break. It underlies the neritic province of the pelagic environment.

Suboceanic province The benthic environments seaward of the continental shelf.

Subpolar Pertaining to the oceanic region that is covered by sea ice in winter. The ice melts away in summer.

Subpolar gyre A small, circular-moving loop of water that is centered at about 60° latitude in both hemispheres. Subpolar gyres rotate in a counterclockwise orientation in the Northern Hemisphere and clockwise in the Southern Hemisphere.

Subpolar low A global belt of low atmospheric pressure located at about 60° north or south latitude that is associated with vertical flow of low-density air upward and much precipitation.

Substrate The base on which an organism lives and grows.

Subsurface current A current usually flowing below the pycnocline, generally at slower speed and in a different direction from the surface current.

Subtidal zone That portion of the benthic environment extending from low tide to a depth of 200 meters (660 feet); considered by some to be the surface of the continental shelf.

Subtropical Pertaining to the oceanic region poleward of the tropics (about 30° latitude).

Subtropical Convergence The zone of convergence that occurs within all subtropical gyres as a result of Ekman transport driving water toward the interior of the gyres.

Subtropical gyre A large, circular-moving loop of water that is centered at about 30° latitude and is initiated by the trade winds and the prevailing westerlies. A total of five subtropical gyres exist, with rotation clockwise in the Northern Hemisphere and counterclockwise in the Southern Hemisphere.

Subtropical high A region of high atmospheric pressure located at about 30° latitude.

Sulfur A yellow mineral composed of the element sulfur. It is commonly found in association with hydrocarbons and salt deposits.

Sulfur-oxidizing bacteria Bacteria that support many deep-sea hydrothermal vents and cold-water seep biocommunities by using energy released by oxidation to synthesize organic matter chemosynthetically.

Summer solstice In the Northern Hemisphere, it is the instant when the Sun moves north to the Tropic of Cancer before changing direction and moving southward toward the equator approximately June 21.

Summertime beach A beach that is characteristic during summer months. It typically has a wide sandy berm and a steep beach face.

Superwave See *rogue wave*.

Supratidal zone The splash or spray zone above the spring high tide shoreline.

Surf beat An irregular wave pattern caused by mixed interference that results in a varied sequence of larger and smaller waves.

Surf zone The nearshore zone of breaking waves.

Surface tension The tendency for the surface of a liquid to contract owing to intermolecular bond attraction.

Surfing The sport of riding on the crest or along the tunnel of a wave, especially while standing or lying on a surfboard.

Surging breaker A compressed breaking wave that builds up over a short distance and surges forward as it breaks. It is characteristic of abrupt beach slopes.

Suspension feeder See *filter feeder*.

Suspension settling The process by which fine-grained material that is being suspended in the water column slowly accumulates on the sea floor.

Sverdrup (Sv) A unit of flow rate equal to 1 million cubic meters per second. Named after Norwegian oceanographer Harald Sverdrup.

Swash A thin layer of water that washes up over exposed beach as waves break at the shore.

Swell A free ocean wave by which energy put into ocean waves by wind in the sea is transported with little energy loss across great stretches of ocean to the margins of continents where the energy is released in the surf zone.

Swim bladder A gas-containing, flexible, cigar-shaped organ that aids many fishes in attaining neutral buoyancy.

Symbiosis A relationship between two species in which one or both benefit or neither or one is harmed. Examples are commensalism, mutualism, and parasitism.

Syzygy Either of two points in the orbit of the Moon (full or new moon phase) when the Moon lies in a straight line with the Sun and Earth.

T

Tablemount A conical volcanic feature on the ocean floor resembling a seamount except that it has had its top truncated to a relatively flat surface.

Taxonomy The classification of organisms in an ordered system that indicates natural relationships.

Tectonic estuary An estuary, the origin of which is related to tectonic deformation of the coastal region.

Tectonics Deformation of Earth's surface by forces generated by heat flow from Earth's interior.

Tektite See *spherule*.

Temperate Pertaining to the oceanic region where pronounced seasonal change occurs (about 40° to 60° latitude). Also known as the middle latitudes.

Temperature A direct measure of the average kinetic energy of the molecules of a substance.

Temperature of maximum density The temperature at which a substance reaches its highest density. For water, it is 4°C.

Temperature–salinity (T–S) diagram A diagram with axes representing water temperature and salinity, whereby the density of the water can be determined.

Terrigenous sediment Sediment produced from or of the Earth. Also called lithogenous sediment.

Territorial sea A strip of ocean, 12 nautical miles wide, adjacent to land over which the coastal nation has control over the passage of ships.

Test The supporting skeleton or shell (usually microscopic) of many invertebrates.

Tethys Sea An ancient body of water that separated Laurasia to the north and Gondwanaland to the south. Its location was approximately that of the present Alpine–Himalayan mountain system.

Texture The general physical appearance of an object.

Theory A well-substantiated explanation of some aspect of the natural world that can incorporate facts, laws (descriptive generalizations about the behavior of an aspect of the natural world), logical inferences, and tested hypotheses.

Thermal contraction The reduction in size as a result of lowering of temperature.

Thermocline A layer of water beneath the mixed layer in which a rapid change in temperature can be measured in the vertical dimension.

Thermohaline circulation The vertical movement of ocean water driven by density differences resulting from the combined effects of variations in temperature and salinity; produces deep currents.

Tidal bore A steep-fronted wave that moves up some rivers when the tide rises in the coastal ocean.

Tidal bulge The theoretical mound of water found on both sides of Earth caused by the relative positions of the Moon (lunar tidal bulges) and the Sun (solar tidal bulges).

Tidal day See *lunar day*.

Tidal period The time that elapses between successive high tides. In most parts of the world, it is 12 hours and 25 minutes.

Tidal range The difference between high tide and low tide water levels over any designated time interval, usually one lunar day.

Tide The periodic rise and fall of the surface of the ocean and connected bodies of water resulting from the gravitational attraction of the Moon and Sun acting unequally on different parts of Earth.

Tide-generating force The magnitude of the centripetal force required to keep all particles of Earth having identical mass moving in identical circular paths required by the movements of the Earth–Moon system is identical. This required force is provided by the gravitational attraction between the particles and the Moon. This gravitational force is identical to the required centripetal force only at the center of Earth. For ocean tides, the horizontal component of the small force that results from the difference between the required and provided forces is the tide-generating force on that individual particle. These forces are such that they tend to push the ocean water into bulges toward the tide-generating body on one side of Earth and away from the tide-generating body on the opposite side of Earth.

Tide wave The long-period gravity wave generated by tide-generating forces and manifested in the rise and fall of the tides.

Tissue An aggregate of cells and their products developed by organisms for the performance of a particular function.

Tombolo A sand or gravel bar that connects an island with another island or the mainland.

Topography The configuration of a surface. In oceanography it refers to the ocean bottom or the surface of a mass of water with given characteristics.

Toxic compound A poisonous substance capable of causing injury or death, especially by chemical means.

Trade winds Global wind belt that moves from the subtropical high-pressure belts at about 30° north or south latitude toward the equatorial region. They move from a northeasterly direction in the Northern Hemisphere and from a southeasterly direction in the Southern Hemisphere.

Transform fault A fault with side-to-side motion that offsets segments of a mid-ocean ridge. Oceanic transform faults occur wholly on the ocean floor, while continental transform faults occur on land.

Transform plate boundary The boundary between two lithospheric plates formed by a transform fault.

Transitional wave A wave moving from deep water to shallow water that has a wavelength more than twice the water depth but less than 20 times the water depth. Particle orbits are beginning to be influenced by the bottom.

Transverse wave A wave in which particle motion is at right angles to energy propagation.

Trench A long, narrow, and deep depression on the ocean floor with relatively steep sides that is caused by plate convergence.

Trophic level A nourishment level in a food chain. Plant producers constitute the lowest level, followed by herbivores and a series of carnivores at the higher levels.

Tropic of Cancer The latitude 23.5° north, which is the furthest location north that receives vertical rays of the Sun.

Tropic of Capricorn The latitude 23.5° south, which is the furthest location south that receives vertical rays of the Sun.

Tropical Pertaining to, characteristic of, occurring in, or inhabiting the tropics.

Tropical cyclone See *hurricane*.

Tropical tide A tide that occurs twice monthly when the Moon is at its maximum declination near the Tropic of Cancer or the Tropic of Capricorn.

Tropics The region of Earth's surface lying between the Tropic of Cancer and the Tropic of Capricorn. Also known as the Torrid Zone.

Troposphere The lowermost portion of the atmosphere, which extends from Earth's surface to 12 kilometer (7 miles). It is where all weather is produced.

Trough (wave) The part of an ocean wave that is displaced below the still-water level.

Tsunami A seismic sea wave. A long-period gravity wave generated by a submarine earthquake or volcanic event. Not noticeable on the open ocean but builds up to great heights in shallow water.

Turbidite deposit A sediment or rock formed from sediment deposited by turbidity currents characterized by both horizontally and vertically graded bedding.

Turbidity A state of reduced clarity in a fluid caused by the presence of suspended matter.

Turbidity current A gravity current resulting from a density increase brought about by increased water turbidity. Possibly initiated by some sudden force such as an earthquake, the turbid mass continues under the force of gravity down a submarine slope.

Turbulent flow Flow in which the flow lines are confused heterogeneously due to random velocity fluctuations.

Typhoon See *hurricane*.

U

Ultraplankton Plankton for which the greatest dimension is less than 5 micrometers (0.0002 inch). They are very difficult to separate from the water.

Ultrasonic Sound frequencies above those that can be heard by humans (above 20,000 cycles per second).

Ultraviolet (UV) radiation Electromagnetic radiation shorter than visible radiation and longer than X rays. The approximate range is 1 to 400 nanometers.

Upper water Area of the ocean near the surface that includes the mixed layer and the permanent thermocline. It is approximately the top 1000 meters (3300 feet) of the ocean.

Upwelling The process by which deep, cold, nutrient-laden water is brought to the surface, usually by diverging equatorial currents or coastal currents that pull water away from a coast.

V

Valence The combining capacity of an element measured by the number of hydrogen atoms with which it will combine.

van der Waals force A weak attractive force between molecules resulting from the interaction of one molecule and the electrons of another.

Vapor The gaseous state of a substance that is liquid or solid under ordinary conditions.

Vent An opening on the ocean floor that emits hot water and dissolved minerals.

Ventral Pertaining to the lower or under surface.

Vernal equinox The passage of the Sun across the equator as it moves from the Southern Hemisphere into the Northern Hemisphere, approximately March 21. During this time, all places in the world experience equal lengths of night and day. Also known as the spring equinox.

Vertebrata The subphylum of chordates that includes those animals with a well-developed brain and a skeleton of bone or cartilage; includes fish, amphibians, reptiles, birds, and land animals.

Vertically mixed estuary Very shallow estuaries such as lagoons in which freshwater and marine water are totally mixed from top to bottom so that the salinity at the surface and the bottom is the same at most places within the estuary.

Virioplankton Viruses that live as plankton.

Viscosity A property of a substance to offer resistance to flow caused by internal friction.

Volcanic arc An arc-shaped row of active volcanoes directly above a subduction zone. Can occur as a row of islands (island arc) or mountains on land (continental arc).

W

Walker Circulation Cell The pattern of atmospheric circulation that involves the rising of warm air over the East Indies low-pressure cell and its descent over the high-pressure cell in the southeastern Pacific Ocean off the coast of Chile. It is the weakening of this circulation that accompanies an El Niño event, which has led to the development of the term El Niño–Southern Oscillation event.

Walrus A large marine mammal (*Odobenus rosmarus*) of Arctic regions belonging to the order Pinnipedia and having two long tusks, tough wrinkled skin, and four flippers.

Waning crescent The Moon when it is between third-quarter and new moon phases.

Waning gibbous The Moon when it is between full moon and third-quarter phases.

Warm-blooded See *homeothermic*.

Warm front A weather front in which a warm air mass moves into and over a cold air mass producing a broad band of gentle precipitation.

Water mass A body of water identifiable from its temperature, salinity, or chemical content.

Wave A disturbance that moves over the surface or through a medium with a speed determined by the properties of the medium.

Wave base   The depth at which circular orbital motion becomes negligible. It exists at a depth of one-half wavelength, measured vertically from still water level.

Wave-cut beach   A gently sloping surface produced by wave erosion and extending from the base of the wave-cut cliff out under the offshore region.

Wave-cut cliff   A cliff produced by landward cutting by wave erosion.

Wave dispersion   The separation of waves as they leave the sea area by wave size. Larger waves travel faster than smaller waves and thus leave the sea area first, to be followed by progressively smaller waves.

Wave frequency (f)   The number of waves that pass a fixed point in a unit of time (usually one second). A wave's frequency is the inverse of its period.

Wave height (H)   The vertical distance between a crest and the adjoining trough.

Wave period (T)   The elapsed time between the passage of two successive wave crests (or troughs) past a fixed point. A wave's period is the inverse of its frequency.

Wave speed (S)   The rate at which a wave travels. It can be calculated by dividing a wave's wavelength (L) by its period (T).

Wave steepness   Ratio of wave height (H) to wavelength (L). If a 1:7 ratio is ever exceeded by the wave, then the wave breaks.

Wave train   A series of waves from the same direction. Informally known as a wave set.

Wavelength (L)   The horizontal distance between two corresponding points on successive waves, such as from crest to crest.

Waxing crescent   The Moon when it is between new moon and first-quarter phases.

Waxing gibbous   The Moon when it is between first-quarter and full moon phases.

Weather   The state of the atmosphere at a given time and place, with respect to variables such as temperature, moisture, wind velocity, and barometric pressure.

Weathering   A process by which rocks are broken down by chemical and mechanical means.

Wentworth scale of grain size   A logarithmic scale for size classification of sediment particles.

West Australian Current   A cold current that forms the eastern boundary current of the Indian Ocean Subtropical Gyre. It is separated from the coast by the warm Leeuwin Current except during El Niño–Southern Oscillation events when the Leeuwin Current weakens.

West Wind Drift   See *Antarctic Circumpolar Current*.

Western boundary current   Poleward-flowing warm currents on the western side of all subtropical gyres.

Western boundary undercurrent (WBUC)   A bottom current that flows along the base of the continental slope eroding sediment from it and redepositing the sediment on the continental rise. It is confined to the western boundary of deep-ocean basins.

Western intensification   Pertaining to the intensification of warm western boundary currents of each subtropical gyre that are faster, narrower, and deeper than their corresponding eastern boundary currents.

Wetland   See *coastal wetland*.

Whirlpool   A rapidly rotating current of water; a vortex.

White muscle fiber   Thick muscle fibers with relatively low concentrations of myoglobin that make up a large percentage of the muscle fiber in lunger-type fishes.

White smoker   A smoker similar to a black smoker but emits water of a lower temperature that is white in color.

Wilson cycle   A model that uses plate tectonic processes to show the distinctive life cycle of ocean basins during their formation, growth, and destruction.

Wind-driven circulation   A movement of ocean water that is driven by winds. This includes most horizontal movements in the surface waters of the world's oceans.

Windward   The direction from which the wind is blowing.

Winter solstice   The instant the southward-moving Sun reaches the Tropic of Cancer before changing direction and moving north back toward the equator, approximately December 21.

Wintertime beach   A beach that is characteristic during winter months. It typically has a narrow rocky berm and a flat beach face.

Z

Zebra mussel   A non-native species released into U.S. and Canadian waters of the Great Lakes region.

Zenith   The point on the celestial sphere directly over the observer.

Zooplankton   Animal plankton.

Zooxanthellae   A form of algae that lives as a symbiont in the tissue of corals and other coral reef animals and provides varying amounts of their required food supply.

CREDITS AND ACKNOWLEDGMENTS

Cover Photo
estockphoto/Egypt, Red Sea, Manta Ray.

Frontispiece
© Bruce C. Heezen & Marie Tharp.

About the Authors
Trujillo © APT Photos. **Thurman** Photo by Hal Thurman.

Table of Contents
viii © APT Photos. **ix** Walter H. F. Smith and David T. Sandwell, *Science*, 1997/National Geophysical Data Center/NOAA. "Primary Funding from the National Science Foundation." **x** Image courtesy Quade Paul. **xi** Image courtesy of NASA's Earth Observatory. **xii** Richard Bouhet/AFP/Getty Images. **xiii** Georgette Douwma/Getty Images.

Introduction
Opener Ian Cartwright/Getty Images. **Figure I.2** NASA/Photo Researchers. **Figure I.3** NASA/Courtesy of nasaimages.org.

Chapter 1
Opener Courtesy of NASA's Earth Observatory/Reto Stöckli. **Figure 1A** Photo courtesy David Knudsen/National Geographic Society. **Figure 1B** Courtesy of Woods Hole Oceanographic Institution. **Figure 1C** © APT Photos; Polynesian stick chart courtesy of Glen Foss. **Figure 1D** © APT Photos. **Figure 1E** John Harrison (1693–1776) 1767 (oil on canvas) by Thomas King (d.1769). Science Museum, London, UK/The Bridgeman Art Library. **Figure 1F left** Smithsonian Institution Libraries © 2001 Smithsonian Institution. **Figure 1F right** David Parry/PA Photos/Landov. **Figure 1.1** From the *Challenger* Report, Great Britain, 1895. **Figure 1.3** Data from Kennish, M. J. (1994) and the National Geographic Society. **Figure 1.4** Official photograph U.S. Navy. **Figure 1.8 inset** U.S. Naval Historical Center Photography. **Figure 1.10** Reprinted by permission from Tarbuck, E. J. and Lutgens, F. K., *Earth Science*, 6th ed. (Figs. 19.1 and 19.2), Macmillan Publishing Company, 1991. **Figure 1.11** Courtesy of NASA and the Space Telescope Science Institute. **Figure 1.12** After Tarbuck, E. J. and Lutgens, F. K., *The Earth: An Introduction to Physical Geology*, 5th ed. (Fig. 1.10), Prentice Hall, 1996. **Figure 1.13** Steve Munsinger/Photo Researchers. **Figure 1.19b** Jim Sugar/Corbis. **Figure 1.23** After Zimmer, C., 2001, How old is it? *National Geographic* 200:3, 92. **Figure 1.24** After Tarbuck, E. J. and Lutgens, F. K., *The Earth: An Introduction to Physical Geology*, 7th ed. (Fig. 8.15), Prentice Hall, 2002. Data from the Geological Society of America, the U.S. Geological Survey, and the International Commission on Stratigraphy.

Chapter 2
Opener © APT Photos. **Figure 2A** Photo courtesy Deeanne Edwards, marinelifephoto.com. **Figure 2B** Image provided courtesy of the NEPTUNE Project (http://www.neptune.washington.edu) and the Center of Environmental Visualization (CEV). **Figure 2.1** Courtesy of Bildarchiv Preussischer Kulturbesitz, West Berlin. **Figure 2.2** After Dietz, R. S. and Holden, J. C., 1970, Reconstruction of Pangaea: Breakup and dispersion of continents, Permian to present, *Journal of Geophysical Research* 75:26, 4939–4956. **Figure 2.3** From *Continental Drift* by Don and Maureen Tarling, © 1971 by G. Bell&Sons, Ltd. Reprinted by permission of Doubleday & Co., Inc. **Figure 2.4** After Tarbuck, E. J. and Lutgens, F. K., *Earth Science*, 8th ed. (Fig. 7.6), Prentice Hall, 1997. **Figure 2.5** After Tarbuck, E. J. and Lutgens, F. K., *Earth Science*, 8th ed. (Fig. 7.7), Prentice Hall, 1997. **Figure 2.6** After Tarbuck, E. J. and Lutgens, F. K., *Earth Science*, 8th ed. (Fig. 7.4), Prentice Hall, 1997. **Figure 2.7a** Reprinted by permission from Tarbuck, E. J. and Lutgens, F. K., *The Earth: An Introduction to Physical Geology*, 3d ed. (Fig. 18.8), Merrill Publishing Company, 1990. **Figure 2.7b** Reprinted by permission from Tarbuck, E. J. and Lutgens, F. K., *The Earth: An Introduction to Physical Geology*, 3d ed. (Fig. 18.9), Merrill Publishing Company, 1990. **Figure 2.8** After Tarbuck, E. J. and Lutgens, F. K., *Earth Science*, 8th ed. (Fig. 7.17), Prentice Hall, 1997. **Figure 2.9** After Tarbuck, E. J. and Lutgens, F. K., *Earth Science*, 8th ed. (Fig. 7.18), Prentice Hall, 1997. **Figure 2.10** Reprinted by permission from Tarbuck, E. J. and Lutgens, F. K., *The Earth: An Introduction to Physical Geology*, 3d ed. (Fig. 18.11), Merrill Publishing Company, 1990. **Figure 2.11** After Tarbuck, E. J. and Lutgens, F. K., *Earth Science*, 8th ed. (Fig. 7.20), Prentice Hall, 1997. **Figure 2.12** After Tarbuck, E. J. and Lutgens, F. K., *The Earth: An Introduction to Physical Geology*, 3d ed. (Fig. 19.16), Merrill Publishing Company, 1990. After *The Bedrock Geology of the World*, by R. L. Larson et al., Copyright © 1985 by W. H. Freeman. **Figure 2.13a** After Tarbuck, E. J. and Lutgens, F. K., *The Earth: An Introduction to Physical Geology*, 3d ed. (Fig. 5.11), Merrill Publishing Company, 1990. Data from National Geophysical Data Center/NOAA. **Figure 2.13b** After Tarbuck, E. J. and Lutgens, F. K., *The Earth: An Introduction to Physical Geology*, 3d ed. (Fig. 5.11), Merrill Publishing Company, 1990; modified with data from W. B. Hamilton, U.S. Geological Survey. **Figure 2.14** Reprinted by permission from Tarbuck, E. J. and Lutgens, F. K., *The Earth: An Introduction to Physical Geology*, 3d ed. (Fig. 6.7), Merrill Publishing Company, 1990. **Figure 2.15** After Tarbuck, E. J. and Lutgens, F. K., *Earth Science*, 8th ed. (Fig. 7.10), Prentice Hall, 1997. **Figure 2.16** Courtesy Patricia Deen, Palomar College. **Figure 2.17** After Tarbuck, E. J. and Lutgens, F. K., *Earth Science*, 8th ed. (Fig. 7.12), Prentice Hall, 1997. **Figure 2.18a** After Tarbuck, E. J. and Lutgens, F. K., *Earth Science*, 8th ed. (Fig. 7.11), Prentice Hall, 1997. **Figure 2.18b** Courtesy of NASA's Earth Observatory. **Figure 2.18c** Photo courtesy Anthony Philpotts; from A. Philpotts and J. Ague, *Principles of Igneous and Metamorphic Petrology*, 2nd Edition (2009), Cambridge University Press. **Figure 2.19** Scripps Institution of Oceanography Geological Collections, University of California at San Diego. **Figure 2.20** Reprinted by permission from Tarbuck, E. J. and Lutgens, F. K., *Earth Science*, 5th ed. (Fig. 6.11), Merrill Publishing Company, 1988. **Figure 2.21c** Roger Werth/Woodfin Camp/Getty Images. **Figure 2.22a and b** After Tarbuck, E. J. and Lutgens, F. K., *Earth Science*, 8th ed. (Fig. 7.15),

Chapter 3

Chapter 4

University of California at San Diego. **Figure 4.16** © APT Photos. **Figure 4.17** Reprinted by permission of The Open University Course Team, *Ocean chemistry and deep-sea sediments*, 1989, Fig. 1.6. **Figure 4.18** With thanks to Joseph Holliday, El Camino College. **Figure 4.19** After Sverdrup, H. U., et al., 1942. **Figure 4.20** Modified after Sverdrup, H. U., et al., 1942. **Figure 4.21** Courtesy Susumu Honjo, Woods Hole Oceanographic Institution. **Figure 4.22** Divins, D. L., NGDC Total Sediment Thickness of the World's Oceans & Marginal Seas, Retrieved date 4/10/2006, http://www.ngdc.noaa.gov/mgg/sedthick/sedthick.html. **Figure 4.23** Scott Gibson/Corbis. **Figure 4.24** Courtesy of GEOMAR Research Center, Kiel, Germany. **Figure 4.26** Courtesy Patricia Deen, Palomar College. **Figure 4.27** Courtesy of Deep Sea Ventures, Inc. **Figure 4.28** After Cronan, D. S., 1977, Deep sea nodules: Distribution and geochemistry, in Glasby, G. P., ed., *Marine Manganese Deposits*, Elsevier Scientific Publishing Co. **Table 4.1** With thanks to Patricia Deen, Palomar College. **Table 4.2** Source: Wentworth, 1922; After Udden, 1898.

Chapter 5

Opener Image courtesy Quade Paul. **Figure 5A** John Paul Kay/Peter Arnold, Inc. **Figure 5B inset** From C. W. Thompson and Sir John Murray, *Report on the Scientific Results of the Voyage of H.M.S.* Challenger, Vol. 1. Great Britain: *Challenger* Office, 1895, Plate 1. **Figure 5.1** After Tarbuck, E. J. and Lutgens, F. K., *The Earth: An Introduction to Physical Geology*, 5th ed. (Fig. 2.4), Prentice Hall, 1996. **Figure 5.3** Used with permission from R. W. Christopherson, *Geosystems*, 2d ed. (Fig. 7.7, p. 186), Macmillan Publishing Company, 1994. **Figure 5.11** After data from Jet Propulsion Laboratory, NASA. **Figure 5.13** Electron Microscopy Laboratory, Agricultural Research Service, USDA. **Figure 5.14** Martyn F. Chillmaid/Photo Researchers. **Figure 5.17** Peter Guttman/Corbis. **Figure 5.18** After Tarbuck, E. J. and Lutgens, F. K., *The Earth: An Introduction to Physical Geology*, 4th ed. (Fig. 10.2), Macmillan Publishing Company, 1993. **Figure 5.22** After Pickard, G. L., *Descriptive Physical Oceanography*, Pergamon Press Ltd., 1963. **Figure 5.23** After Sverdrup, H. U., et al., 1942. **Figure 5.25** After Pickard, G. L., *Descriptive Physical Oceanography*, Pergamon Press Ltd., 1963.

Chapter 6

Opener Image Ralph A. Clevenger/CORBIS. **Figure 6A** Photo courtesy Morgan P. Sanger, The Columbus Foundation. **Figure 6B left** Photo courtesy NOAA. **Figure 6B right** AP/Wide World Photos. **Figure 6.5** After Gross, M. G., *Oceanography*, 6th ed. (Fig. 5.2), Prentice Hall, 1993. **Figure 6.14** After Gross, M. G., *Oceanography*, 6th ed. (Fig. 5.17), Prentice Hall, 1993. **Figure 6.15** Reprinted by permission from Lutgens, F. K. and Tarbuck, E. J., *The Atmosphere*, 6th ed. (Fig. 8.2), Prentice Hall, 1995. **Figure 6.17** Courtesy of NASA's Earth Observatory. **Figure 6.19 inset** Bob Stovall, Bruce Coleman/Photoshot. **Figure 6.20** Photo courtesy of The Rosenberg Library, Galveston, Texas. **Figure 6.21** Smiley N. Pool-Pool/Getty Images. **Figure 6.23a** Photo courtesy Stephen J. Krasemann/Photo Researchers. **Figure 6.23b** Courtesy of NASA. **Figure 6.24a** William W. Bacon/Rapho/Photo Researchers. **Figure 6.24c** Photo courtesy Josh Landis/National Science Foundation. **Figure 6.24d** Courtesy

of NASA's Earth Observatory. **Figure 6.25** Courtesy of NASA's Earth Observatory. **Figure 6.26** Photo courtesy Michel Brigaud/La Mediatheque EDF, Boulogne, France.

Chapter 7

Opener NASA Earth Observatory. **Figure 7A map** Courtesy of *Eos Transactions AGU* 73:34, 361 (1992). Copyright by the American Geophysical Union. **Figure 7A left inset** Photo © Dave Ingraham, provided by Curtis C. Ebbesmeyer (www.flotsa-metrics.com). **Figure 7A right inset** Courtesy of *Eos Transactions AGU* 75:37, 425 (1994). Copyright by the American Geophysical Union. **Figure 7B map** Courtesy of the U.S. Navy. **Figure 7B photo** Corbis. **Figure 7.1a** Douglas Alden, Scripps Institution of Oceanography, University of California at San Diego. **Figure 7.1b** Aanderaa Instruments A/S, Bergen, Norway. **Figure 7.2** NASA. **Figure 7.3a** Data courtesy Argo Information Center at www.argo.ucsd.edu. **Figure 7.3b** Photo courtesy of the Japan Coast Guard. **Figure 7.9** After data from NASA and NOAA. **Figure 7.17 top** Courtesy O. Brown, R. Evans, and M. Carle, University of Miami Rosenstiel School of Marine and Atmospheric Science, Miami, Florida. **Figure 7.19** NASA. **Figure 7.22** Maps courtesy of the International Research Institute for Climate and Society (IRI), Lamont-Doherty Earth Observatory, Columbia University. Data from Reynolds, R.W., N.A. Rayner, T.M. Smith, D.C. Stokes, and W. Wang, 2002: An Improved In Situ and Satellite SST Analysis for Climate. *J. Climate*, 15, 1609–1625. **Figure 7.23** NOAA-CIRES Climate Diagnostics Center, University of Colorado at Boulder. **Figure 7.25** Maps courtesy of the International Research Institute for Climate and Society (IRI), Lamont-Doherty Earth Observatory, Columbia University. Data from Reynolds, R.W., N.A. Rayner, T.M. Smith, D.C. Stokes, and W. Wang, 2002: An Improved In Situ and Satellite SST Analysis for Climate. *J. Climate*, 15, 1609–1625. **Figure 7.28** Courtesy of Woods Hole Oceanographic Institution and modified from *Science* 305:5686, 953 (2004). **Figure 7.29** Copyright © Verdant Power, Inc. 2006. Illustration by John Wuilliez, Ripe Studios. **Table 7.3** With thanks to Holly Dodson, Sierra College.

Chapter 8

Opener AP Photo/Ben Margot. **Figure 8A** Courtesy of 1st Officer Claudio Suttora/www.michelangelo-raffaello.com. **Figure 8C** Images acquired and processed by CRISP, National University of Singapore. IKONOS image © CRISP 2004. **Figure 8D** NASA's Earth Observatory. **Figure 8.1b** NASA's Earth Observatory and Jacques Descloitres, MODIS Land Rapid Response Team at NASA GSFC. **Figure 8.2** After Kinsman, B., 1965. **Figure 8.4a** Modified from *The Tasa Collection: Shorelines*. Published by Macmillan Publishing Co., New York. Copyright © 1986 by Tasa Graphic Arts, Inc. **Figure 8.6** AP Photo/Kyodo News. **Figure 8.11** NASA. **Figure 8.13** Official photograph U.S. Navy. **Figure 8.16** After Gross, M. G., *Oceanography*, 6th ed. (Fig. 8.4), Prentice Hall, 1993. **Figure 8.17** From *The Tasa Collection: Shorelines*. Published by Macmillan Publishing, New York. Copyright © 1986 by Tasa Graphic Arts, Inc. All rights reserved. **Figure 8.18a** GigglePix/Veer. **Figure 8.18b** Corbis/SuperStock. **Figure 8.18c** blickwinkel/Alamy. **Figure 8.19b** Adapted from Tarbuck, E. J. and Lutgens, F. K., *Earth Science*, 6th ed. (Fig. 6.14) Macmillan

Publishing Company, 1991. **Figure 8.19c** Woody Woodworth/ Creation Captured. **Figure 8.20** Gene Blevins/LA Daily News/ Corbis. **Figure 8.22b** Joanne Davis/AFP/Newscom. **Figure 8.23** Corbis/Bettmann. **Figure 8.24** After González, F. I., 1999, Tsunami! *Scientific American* 280:5, 59. Modified 2009. **Figure 8.25** Courtesy of NOAA Center for Tsunami Research. **Figure 8.26** Courtesy of Oregon Department of Geology. **Figure 8.27** Courtesy of Wavegen. **Figure 8.28** Courtesy of Pelamis Wave Power. **Figure 8.29** Map constructed from data in U.S. Navy Summary of Synoptic Meteorological Observations (SSMO). Adapted from Sea Secrets, *Sea Frontiers* 33:4, 260–261, International Oceanographic Foundation, 1987. **Table 8.1** Source: After Bowditch, N., 1958.

Chapter 9

Opener Laxzlo Podor/Alamy Images. **Figure 9A** Photo courtesy of New Brunswick Department of Tourism. **Figure 9B** © Juergen Skarwan/Reuters/CORBIS. **Figure 9C** Eda Rogers/Sea Images. **Figure 9.10** Modified from *The Tasa Collection: Shorelines*. Published by Macmillan Publishing Co., New York. Copyright © 1986 by Tasa Graphic Arts, Inc. **Figure 9.15** After von Arx, W. S., 1962; original by H. Poincaré 1910, Leçons de Mécanique Céleste, a Gauther-Crofts, Vol. 3. **Figure 9.16** After Hauge, C., Tides, currents, and waves, *California Geology*, July 1972. **Figure 9.18** Nova Scotia Department of Tourism. **Figure 9.20** Peter McBride/Aurora & Quanta Productions. **Figure 9.21** Courtesy Michel Brigaud/La Mediatheque EDF, Boulogne, France.

Chapter 10

Opener Richard Bouhet/AFP/Getty Images. **Figure 10A** © APT Photos. **Figure 10B** Photo courtesy Drew Wilson, *Virginian-Pilot* © 1999. **Figure 10.2** APT Photos. **Figure 10.3a** University of Washington Libraries, Special Collections, John Shelton Collection, 14461. **Figure 10.5** PCL/Alamy. **Figure 10.6** University of Washington Libraries, Special Collections, John Shelton Collection, 5902. **Figure 10.8a** USDA-ASCS. **Figure 10.8b** Photo © 2003 Andrew Alden; geology.about.com/. **Figure 10.9a and b** After Tarbuck, E. J. and Lutgens, F. K., *The Earth: An Introduction to Physical Geology*, 4th ed. (Fig. 14.12), Macmillan Publishing Company, 1993. **Figure 10.9c** USDA-ASCS. **Figure 10.11a** NASA's Earth Observatory. **Figure 10.11b** NASA. **Figure 10.15** Data courtesy U.S. Geological Survey. **Figure 10.16** Image courtesy Earth Satellite Corporation. **Figure 10.17** University of Washington Libraries, Special Collections, John Shelton Collection, 8974. **Figure 10.19** University of Washington Libraries, Special Collections, John Shelton Collection, S2–31. **Figure 10.20** After Tarbuck, E. J. and Lutgens, F. K., *Earth Science*, 5th ed., Merrill Publishing Company, 1988. **Figure 10.21** Courtesy U.S. Army Corps of Engineers. **Figure 10.23a** The Fairchild Aerial Photography Collection at Whittier College, Flight C-1670, Frame 4. **Figure 10.23b** The Fairchild Aerial Photography Collection at Whittier College, Flight C-14180, Frame 3:61. **Figure 10.25** APT Photos. **Figure 10.26** APT Photos.

Chapter 11

Opener AP Photo/Noah Berger. **Figure 11A upper** Natalie Forbes/ NGS Image Collection. **Figure 11A lower** NOAA. **Figure 11B**

Bob Jordan/AP Wide World Photos. **Figure 11C** Tony Freeman/ Photo Edit. **Figure 11D** APT Photos. **Figure 11.6a** Canopy Photography/Veer. **Figure 11.6b** M-SAT Ltd./SPL/Photo Researchers. **Figure 11.9** After Officer, C. B., et al., 1984. **Figure 11.12a** Adapted from *Encyclopedia of Oceanography*, edited by Rhodes Fairbridge, © 1966. Reprinted by permission of Dowden, Hutchinson, & Ross, Inc., Stroudsburg, PA. **Figure 11.12b** After Judson, S., et al., *Physical Geology*, 7th ed, Prentice Hall, 1987. **Figure 11.13b** © tbkmedia.de/Alamy. **Figure 11.13c** APT Photos. **Figure 11.15** NOAA. **Figure 11.16** After Mitchell, J. G., 1999, In the wake of the spill: Ten years after the *Exxon Valdez*. *National Geographic* 195:3, 96–117. **Figure 11.17** Gary Braasch/Corbis. **Figure 11.20** © 1994 John Trever, *Albuquerque Journal*. Reprinted by permission. **Figure 11.21** AP Wide World Photos. **Figure 11.23a** Courtesy of Massachusetts Water Resources Authority. **Figure 11.24** age fotostock/SuperStock. **Figure 11.25** Minamata, Tokomo is bathed by her mother, ca. 1972. Photograph by W. Eugene Smith. Collection, Center for Creative Photography, The University of Arizona. Aileen M. Smith, Courtesy Black Star, Inc., New York. **Figure 11.27** APT Photos. **Figure 11.28** Reprinted with permission of the Ocean Conservancy (formerly the Center for Marine Conservation). **Figure 11.29a** Photo by Wayne Perryman, National Marine Fisheries Service. **Figure 11.29b** Joe McDonald/Bruce Coleman/Photoshot. **Figure 11.29c** Susan Middleton & David Liittschwager. **Figure 11.31** © APT Photos. **Table 11A** Data from The Oil Spill Intelligence Report at http:// www.iosc.org/papers/01480.pdf.

Chapter 12

Opener Jeffrey L. Rotman/Corbis. **Figure 12B** Courtesy of Scripps Institution of Oceanography Photographic Archives, University of California at San Diego. **Figure 12.9** After Sverdrup, H. U., et al., 1942. **Figure 12.11** Reprinted by permission of Brill Academic Publishers, Leiden, Netherlands, from Gustaaf M. Hallegraeff, *Plankton: A Microscopic World*, 1988, p. 21. **Figure 12.17 photo** Minden Pictures/Masterfile. **Figure 12.18** Mircea Bezergheanu/Shutterstock. **Figure 12.19a** Deeanne Edwards, marinelifephoto.com. **Figure 12.19b** © APT Photos. **Figure 12.20** Photo © Jeffrey Jeffords. **Figure 12.23** © David Shale/npl/Minden Pictures. **Figure 12.24** Courtesy of Scripps Institution of Oceanography, University of California at San Diego.

Chapter 13

Opener Mike Kelly/Getty Images. **Figure 13A** Carleton Ray/Photo Researchers. **Figure 13C** John Springer Collection/Corbis. **Figure 13D** Courtesy of the American Geophysical Union. **Figure 13E top, middle** Photos courtesy Charles Anderson and the Monroe County Public Library, Key West, Florida. **Figure 13E bottom** Photo © 2007 Loren McClenachan, Scripps Institution of Oceanography, University of California at San Diego. **Figure 13.2** Scripps Institution of Oceanography Explorations, Scripps Institution of Oceanography, University of California at San Diego. Photo by Elizabeth L. Venrick. **Figure 13.4** Patricia Deen, Palomar College. **Figure 13.5** NASA Earth Observatory. **Figure 13.6c** SeaWiFS Project, NASA/Goddard Space Flight Center and ORBIMAGE. **Figure 13.7** APT Photos. **Figure 13.8a, b, and d** APT Photos.

Figure 13.8c Photo by Hal Thurman. **Figure 13.9a** Reprinted by permission of Brill Academic Publishers, Leiden, Netherlands, from Gustaaf M. Hallegraeff, *Plankton: A Microscopic World*, 1988, p. 43. **Figure 13.9b** Courtesy Wuchang Wei, Scripps Institution of Oceanography, University of California at San Diego. **Figure 13.9c** Reprinted by permission of Brill Academic Publishers, Leiden, Netherlands, from Gustaaf M. Hallegraeff, *Plankton: A Microscopic World*, 1988, p. 91. **Figure 13.9d** Reprinted by permission of Brill Academic Publishers, Leiden, Netherlands, from Gustaaf M. Hallegraeff, *Plankton: A Microscopic World*, 1988, p. 81. **Figure 13.10** Claire Ting/SPL/Photo Researchers. **Figure 13.11d** Photo courtesy of Scripps Institution of Oceanography, University of California at San Diego. **Figure 13.23** After Pauley, D. and Christensen, V., 1995, Primary production required to sustain global fisheries. *Nature* 374:5656, 255–257. **Figure 13.23** Data from the United Nations Food and Agriculture Organization. **Figure 13.24** Data from the United Nations Food and Agriculture Organization. **Figure 13.25** Photo by W. High, courtesy of National Marine Fisheries Service. **Figure 13.26** With kind thanks to Pete Pederson. **Figure 13.27** Data from the United Nations Food and Agriculture Organization. **Figure 13.28** Data from Mora, C., et al., 2009, Management Effectiveness of the World's Marine Fisheries. *PLoS Biol* 7(6): e1000131. doi:10.1371/journal.pbio. 1000131. **Figure 13.29** Courtesy Monterey Bay Aquarium. **Table 13.1** Data after Strahler, A. H. and Strahler, A. N., *Modern Physical Geography*, 4th ed. (Table 25.1), Wiley, 1992.

Chapter 14

Opener Georgette Douwma/Getty Images. **Figure 14A** Kelvin Aitken/Peter Arnold. **Figure 14B** Francois Gohier/Photo Researchers. **Figure 14.3** Kozo Takahashi, Kyushu University, Fukuoka, Japan. **Figure 14.4** © APT Photos. **Figure 14.5** From Giesbrecht, W., *Fauna und Flora des Golfes von Neapel und der Angrenzenden Meeres-Abschnitte*, 1892, Berlin, Verlag Von R. Friedländer and Sohn. Courtesy of Scripps Institution of Oceanography Explorations, Scripps Institution of Oceanography, University of California at San Diego. **Figure 14.6 main** Courtesy of Scripps Institution of Oceanography, University of California at San Diego. Photographer: Paige Jennings. **Figure 14.6 inset** Peter Parks/imagequestmarine.com. **Figure 14.7b** WaterFrame/Alamy. **Figure 14.10a** © Dave Fleetham/Photolibrary. **Figure 14.10b** Photo © Wayne A. and Karen D. Brown. **Figure 14.10c** © Kerstin Layer/Photolibrary. **Figure 14.10d** Richard Herrmann/Getty Images. **Figure 14.10e** © Dave Fleetham/Photolibrary. **Figure 14.11a** Fred Bavendam/ Minden Pictures. **Figure 14.11b** Photo courtesy of National Marine Fisheries Service. **Figure 14.12a-g** After Lalli, C. M. and Parsons, T. R., *Biological Oceanography: An Introduction* (Fig. 6.5), Pergamon Press, 1993. **Figure 14.12h** Photo courtesy Philip A. Hastings, Curator of Marine Vertebrates, Scripps Institution of Oceanography, University of California at San Diego. **Figure 14.13** After Lalli, C. M. and Parsons, T. R., *Biological Oceanography: An Introduction* (Figs. 6.6b and 6.7a), Pergamon Press, 1993. **Figure 14.14** Fred McConnaughey/ Photo Researchers. **Figure 14.15a** Peter Arnold, Inc./Alamy. **Figure 14.15b** Georgie Holland/Photolibrary. **Figure 14.15c** Roger Steene/imagequestmarine.com. **Figure 14.17a** Jeff Foott/Bruce Coleman/Photoshot. **Figure 14.17b** Elvele Images Ltd./Alamy. **Figure 14.17c** © Photoshot Holdings Ltd./Alamy. **Figure 14.17d** Arco Images GmbH/Alamy. **Figure 14.17e** © APT Photos. **Figure 14.19a** Fred Bavendam/Minden Pictures. **Figure 14.19b** D. Fleetham/Oxford Scientific Films/Animals Animals/Earth Scenes. **Figure 14.22** © APT Photos, with thanks to SeaWorld of California. **Figure 14.25c and d** © APT Photos, with thanks to SeaWorld of California. **Figure 14.26** © Steven J. Kazlowski/ Alamy. **Figure 14.28** Data from National Marine Fisheries Service. **Figure 14.29** NHPA/Photoshot. **Table 14A** Adapted from the International Shark Attack File at http://www.flmnh.ufl.edu/ fish/Sharks/isaf/isaf.htm; fatality data from U.S. Center for Disease Control and Prevention.

Chapter 15

Opener Joel W. Rogers/Corbis. **Figure 15A** Photos courtesy Jerry Wellington, University of Houston. **Figure 15B** Reprinted from R.R. Hessler, et al., Scavenging amphipods from the floor of the Philippine Trench, *Deep-Sea Research* 25:1029–1047, Fig. 1. © 1978, with permission from Elsevier Science. Photos supplied by Robert R. Hessler. **Figure 15.1** After Zenkevitch, L. A., et al., 1971. **Figures 15.2b, c, e, and g** Photos by Hal Thurman. **Figures 15.2d, f, h, and i** © APT Photos. **Figure 15.3a** © APT Photos. **Figure 15.3b** Jay Spurr/Bruce Coleman, Inc./Photoshot. **Figure 15.5a** Photo by James McCullagh. **Figure 15.5b** Photo by Hal Thurman. **Figure 15.6** © APT Photos. **Figure 15.7a** Fred Bavendam/ Minden Pictures. **Figure 15.7b** Eda Rogers/Eda Rogers/Sea Images. **Figure 15.10** Walter Dawn/National Audubon Society/Photo Researchers. **Figure 15.12** Howard J. Spero, University of California at Davis. **Figure 15.13** Stephen J. Krasemann/Peter Arnold. **Figure 15.14b** David Hall/Photo Researchers. **Figure 15.15a** Photo by B. Kiwala. **Figure 15.15b** Andrew J. Martinez/Photo Researchers. **Figure 15.17** After Stehli, F. G. and Wells, J. H., Diversity and Age Patterns in Hermatypic Corals, *Systematic Zoology* 20, 115–126, 1971. **Figure 15.18a** Christopher Newbert. **Figure 15.18b** Clive R. Wilkinson, Australian Institute of Marine Science. **Figure 15.18c** Comstock Images/Getty Images. **Figure 15.20a** Kerry L. Werry/ Shutterstock. **Figure 15.20b** Charles Stirling (Diving)/Alamy. **Figure 15.21** Photo courtesy Deeanne Edwards, marinelifephoto.com. **Figure 15.22** After Lalli, C. M. and Parsons, T. R., *Biological Oceanography: An Introduction* (Fig. 8.16), Pergamon Press, 1993. **Figure 15.25a** J. Frederick Grassle, Institute of Marine and Coastal Sciences, Rutgers University. **Figure 15.25b** SEM photomicrograph courtesy of Woods Hole Oceanographic Institution. **Figure 15.25c** Photo courtesy Robert Hessler, Scripps Institution of Oceanography, University of California at San Diego. **Figure 15.26** With thanks to Ron Johnson, Old Dominion University. **Figure 15.27** Photo courtesy Peter A. Rona, NOAA. **Figure 15.28c** Courtesy C. K. Paull, Scripps Institution of Oceanography, University of California at San Diego. **Figure 15.29b and c** Courtesy Charles R. Fisher, Pennsylvania State University. **Figure 15.30b** Y. Fujiwara/JAMSTEC/Japan Marine Science and Technology Center.

Chapter 16

Opener Corbis Premium RF/Alamy. **Figure 16A inset** Photo courtesy Walter Munk, Scripps Institution of Oceanography, University of California at San Diego. **Figure 16.1** Reprinted with the kind permission of Dennis Tasa; modified from Tarbuck, E. J. ed. and Lutgens, F. K., *Earth: An Introduction to Physical Geology*, 9th (Fig. 21.2), Pearson Prentice Hall, 2008. **Figure 16.2** Photo courtesy of Reto Stöckli. **Figure 16.3** Solar & Heliospheric Observatory consortium (ESA & NASA)/Photo Researchers. **Figure 16.4** Reprinted with the kind permission of Dennis Tasa; from Tarbuck, E. J. and Lutgens, F. K., *Earth: An Introduction to Physical Geology*, 9th ed. (Fig. 18.33), Pearson Prentice Hall, 2008. **Figure 16.5** Stock-Trek/Getty Images. **Figure 16.6** Intergovernmental Panel on Climate Change. **Figure 16.10** Data for 1958 to recent from laboratory of Charles Keeling, Scripps Institution of Oceanography, University of California at San Diego. Carbon dioxide concentrations prior to 1958 estimated from air bubbles in polar ice cores. Adapted from *Our Changing Climate,* Reports to the Nation on Our Changing Planet, Fall 1997, No. 4, University Corporation for Atmospheric Research. **Figure 16.11** From Brock, E., 2008, Palaeoclimate: Windows on the greenhouse, *Nature* 453, 291-292 (15 May 2008) | doi:10.1038/453291a. **Figure 16.12** Adapted from *Our Changing Climate,* Reports to the Nation on Our Changing Planet, Fall 1997, No. 4, University Corporation for Atmospheric Research. Updated with data to 2009 from NASA Earth Observatory. **Figure 16.13** NASA Earth Observatory. **Figure 16.14** Adapted from an illustration in *Oceanus* (11/16/2006) by E. Paul Oberlander, Woods Hole Oceanographic Institution. **Figure 16.15** NASA Earth Observatory. **Figure 16.16** © Elvele Images Ltd./Alamy. **Figure 16.17** NASA Earth Observatory. **Figure 16.18a** Reprinted by permission of Brill Academic Publishers, Leiden, Netherlands, from Gustaaf M. Hallegraeff, *Plankton: A Microscopic World*, 1988, p. 8. **Figure 16.18b** Sinclair Stammers/Photo Researchers, Inc. **Figure 16.18c** Jeff Rotman/Alamy. **Figure 16.18d** Elvele Images Ltd./Alamy. **Figure 16.19** After Doney, S. C., 2006, The dangers of ocean acidification. *Scientific American* 294:3, 62. **Figure 16.20a** After Neumann, J. E., et al., *Sea-level rise and global climate change: A review of impacts to U.S. coasts*, PEW Center on Global Climate Change, 2000. **Figure 16.20b and c** After Miller, L. and Douglas, B. C., 2004, Mass and volume contributions to twentieth-century global sea level rise. *Nature* 428:5656, 407. **Figure 16.21** NASA Earth Observatory; modified to include recent data. **Figure 16.22** NASA Earth Observatory. **Figure 16.24** NASA Earth Observatory. **Figure 16.25 photo** Courtesy Ken Buesseler, Woods Hole Oceanographic Institution. **Table 16.1** Modified after Rodhe, H., 1990.

Afterword

Figure Aft.2 Data from MPA Global at http://www.mpaglobal.org/index.php?action=aboutus. **Figure Aft.3** After NOAA/National Ocean Service at http://mpa.gov/ mpaservices/atlas/fig1_nmsmap.html. **Figure Aft.4** © APT Photos.

Appendices

AII Reproduced by permission of Hubbard Scientific, Inc./American Educational Products, Inc. © Hubbard Scientific, Inc. **Figure A5A** Photos courtesy Joe Fell-McDonald. **Figure A5.1** © APT Photos.

INDEX

Note: Page numbers followed by f or t refer to Figures or Tables

Z